*Abstract*

*Algebra*

A series of advanced mathematics texts under the editorship of CARL B. ALLENDOERFER

MEASURE AND INTEGRATION by Sterling K. Berberian

TOPICS IN HIGHER ANALYSIS by Harold K. Crowder and S. W. McCuskey

ABSTRACT ALGEBRA by W. E. Deskins

THEORY AND SOLUTION OF ORDINARY DIFFERENTIAL EQUATIONS by Donald Greenspan

RETRACING ELEMENTARY MATHEMATICS by Leon Henkin, W. Norman Smith, Verne J. Varineau, and Michael J. Walsh

INTRODUCTION TO MATHEMATICAL STATISTICS by Robert V. Hogg and Allen T. Craig.

ELEMENTARY MATRIX ALGEBRA, Second Edition, by Franz E. Hohn

METHODS IN ANALYSIS by Jack Indritz.

PROJECTIVE AND RELATED GEOMETRIES by Harry Levy

STATISTICAL THEORY by B. W. Lindgren

INTRODUCTION TO PROBABILITY THEORY by James R. McCord, III, and Richard M. Moroney, Jr.

ELEMENTS OF ABSTRACT ALGEBRA by John T. Moore

# ABSTRACT ALGEBRA

W. E. DESKINS
*Professor of Mathematics*
*Michigan State University*

*THE MACMILLAN COMPANY, NEW YORK*
*COLLIER-MACMILLAN LIMITED, LONDON*

*First Printing*

Library of Congress catalog card number: 64–12167

THE MACMILLAN COMPANY, NEW YORK
COLLIER-MACMILLAN CANADA, LTD., TORONTO, ONTARIO

*Printed in the United States of America*

To the memory of CYRUS COLTON MacDUFFEE

# Contents

PREFACE xi

1. A COMMON LANGUAGE 1
   - *1.1. Sets* 1
   - *1.2. Ordered pairs, products, and relations* 9
   - *1.3. Functions and mappings* 15
   - *1.4. Binary operations* 21
   - *1.5. Abstract systems* 24
   - *1.6. Suggested reading* 30

2. THE BASIC NUMBER SYSTEMS 32
   - *2.1. The natural number system* 32
   - *2.2. Order and cancellation* 39
   - *2.3. Well-ordering* 43
   - *2.4. Counting and finite sets* 45
   - *2.5. The integers defined* 50
   - *2.6. Ordering the integers* 58
   - *2.7. Isomorphic systems and extensions* 63
   - *2.8. Another extension* 66
   - *2.9. Order and density* 71
   - *2.10. * The real number system* 74
   - *2.11. Power of the abstract approach* 77
   - *2.12. Remarks* 80
   - *2.13. Suggested reading* 81

3. DECOMPOSITIONS OF INTEGERS 82
   - *3.1. Divisor theorem* 82
   - *3.2. Congruence and factors* 88
   - *3.3. Primes* 92
   - *3.4. Greatest common factor* 96
   - *3.5. Unique factorization again* 104

An asterisk (*) indicates sections or chapters containing material which is not essential to the understanding of the principal ideas in subsequent chapters.

3.6. *Euler's totient* 111
3.7. *Suggested reading* 119

4. * DIOPHANTINE PROBLEMS 121
4.1. *Linear Diophantine equations* 121
4.2. *More linear Diophantine equations* 128
4.3. *Linear congruences* 134
4.4. *Pythagorean triples* 143
4.5. *Method of descent* 149
4.6. *Sum of two squares* 152
4.7. *Suggested reading* 161

5. ANOTHER LOOK AT CONGRUENCES 162
5.1. *The system of congruence classes modulo m* 162
5.2. *Homomorphisms* 167
5.3. *Subsystems and quotient systems* 174
5.4. * *System of ideals* 182
5.5. * *Remarks* 190
5.6. *Suggested reading* 190

6. GROUPS 191
6.1. *Definitions and examples* 191
6.2. *Elementary properties* 199
6.3. *Subgroups and cyclic groups* 207
6.4. *Cosets* 215
6.5. *Abelian groups* 221
6.6. * *Finite Abelian groups* 227
6.7. * *Normal subgroups* 232
6.8. * *Sylow's theorem* 240
6.9. * *Additional remarks* 246
6.10. *Suggested reading* 248

7. RINGS, DOMAINS, AND FIELDS 249
7.1. *Definitions and examples* 249
7.2. *Elementary properties* 256
7.3. *Exponentiation and scalar product* 261
7.4. *Subsystems and characteristic* 267
7.5. *Isomorphisms and extensions* 272

*7.6. Homomorphisms and ideals* 280
*7.7. Ring of functions* 288
*7.8. Suggested reading* 297

8. POLYNOMIAL RINGS 298
*8.1. Polynomial rings* 298
*8.2. Polynomial domains* 306
*8.3. Reducibility in the domain of a field* 313
*8.4. Reducibility over the rational field* 321
*8.5. Ideals and extensions* 327
*8.6. Root fields and splitting fields* 334
*8.7. * Automorphisms and Galois groups* 339
*8.8. * An application to geometry* 347
*8.9. * Transcendental extensions and partial fractions* 351
*8.10. Suggested reading* 359

9. * QUADRATIC DOMAINS 360
*9.1. Quadratic fields and integers* 360
*9.2. Factorization in quadratic domains* 368
*9.3. Gaussian integers* 373
*9.4. Ideals and integral bases* 379
*9.5. The semigroup of ideals* 387
*9.6. Factorization of ideals* 393
*9.7. Unique factorization and primes* 397
*9.8. Quadratic residues* 403
*9.9. Principal ideal domains* 409
*9.10. Remarks* 413
*9.11. Suggested reading* 414

10. * MODULAR SYSTEMS 415
*10.1. The polynomial ring of J/(m)* 415
*10.2. Zeros modulo a prime* 421
*10.3. Zeros modulo a prime power* 424
*10.4. Zeros modulo a composite* 430
*10.5. Galois fields* 437
*10.6. Automorphisms of a Galois field* 439
*10.7. Suggested reading* 445

11. MODULES AND VECTOR SPACES 446
*11.1. Definitions and examples* 446

*11.2. Subspaces* 454
*11.3. Linear independence and bases* 459
*11.4. Dimension and isomorphism* 467
*11.5. Row echelon form* 473
*11.6. Uniqueness* 480
*11.7. Systems of linear equations* 484
*11.8. Column rank* 488
*11.9. Suggested reading* 492

12. LINEAR TRANSFORMATIONS AND MATRICES 493
*12.1. Homomorphisms and linear transformations* 494
*12.2. Bases and matrices* 498
*12.3. Addition* 504
*12.4. Multiplication* 511
*12.5. Rings of linear transformations and of matrices* 518
*12.6. Nonsingular matrices* 525
*12.7. Change of basis* 530
*12.8. * Ideals and algebras* 536
*12.9. Suggested reading* 542

13. ELEMENTARY THEORY OF MATRICES 543
*13.1. Special types of matrices* 544
*13.2. A factorization* 549
*13.3. On the right side* 556
*13.4. Over a polynomial domain* 563
*13.5. Determinants* 568
*13.6. Determinant of a product* 575
*13.7. Characteristic polynomial* 582
*13.8. Triangularization and diagonalization* 588
*13.9. Nilpotent matrices and transformations* 596
*13.10. Jordan form* 602
*13.11. Remarks* 611
*13.12. Suggested reading* 611

GENERAL REFERENCES 613

INDEX 615

# Preface

The purpose of this book is to provide college and university students of mathematics with an accessible yet nontrivial introduction to those concepts which are basic to abstract algebra or the analysis of abstract algebraic systems. These systems, which consist of sets of elements, operations on and relations among the elements, and descriptive axioms, are abstractions and generalizations of various models which evolved from efforts to explain or discuss physical phenomena and as such occupy a prominent position in modern mathematics and science.

After a discussion of the essential ingredients of a mathematical system in the first chapter, we proceed with a development and investigation of the familiar number systems in the next four chapters. This number theoretic approach to modern algebra is particularly advantageous since it enables us to demonstrate the axiomatic development of a system and to illustrate important methods, constructions, proofs, and ideas while dealing with one of the beautiful and fascinating portions of classical mathematics. (In Chapters 9 and 10 additional topics in number theory are treated.) The resulting theory provides us with examples and guidelines which are used in the analysis of such important systems as groups, rings, fields, integral domains, polynomial rings, vector spaces, rings of linear transformations, and matric rings, and this enables us to point out and emphasize the role of analogy in the extension and development of mathematics.

Moreover, from number theoretic considerations comes one of the basic unifying concepts of abstract algebra, namely, the idea of factorization and decomposition. From the study of the factorization and decomposition of the ordinary integers we progress, via the notion of congruence, to the study of the decomposition of a system relative to a subsystem or collection of subsystems. Thus the concept of factorization and decomposition provides the central, unifying theme for our investigations of algebraic systems in this book. The resulting accentuation of the uses of subsystems and quotient systems (or homomorphic images) in the analysis of mathematical systems is very important to the development of the student's appreciation of present-day research in pure and applied mathematics.

The program adopted here of dealing initially with familiar systems in a careful, although somewhat sophisticated, fashion allows the student to assimilate the basic language and ideas of abstract algebra while maintaining contact with his previous mathematical experience. As more complex and abstract systems and concepts are presented for study and as the analysis becomes more difficult, numerous examples and heuristic discussions are included to assist the student to an understanding of the material. Problems follow each section in considerable quantity and provide additional material for classroom discussion as well as a challenge to the student (who is not expected to do all of the problems, which range from routine to difficult). Also, a list of several short articles and books that should prove helpful to the student in his studies and to the instructor is given at the end of each chapter. All in all, this book represents an effort to make accessible to the interested student a considerable body of significant results, methods, ideas, and questions from abstract algebra.

The inclusion of many examples and exercises and the treatment of a number of interrelated and important topics have naturally resulted in a book of some size. Therefore it is inevitable that a person or class using this book will have to omit certain sections or chapters. For this reason a diagram is included (opposite page) to indicate the interdependence of the chapters. For example, the solid line leading down from Chapter 3 to Chapter 4 in the diagram means that a thorough study of the material in Chapter 3 is recommended before any work is started on Chapter 4. The broken line leading down from Chapter 2 to Chapter 3 means that a student should be able to understand the material in Chapter 3 even though he has only skimmed through Chapter 2. And, of course, Chapters 4 and 5 are quite independent of each other since there is no line leading down from Chapter 4 to Chapter 5 in the diagram. (The remainder of the diagram should be easily interpreted from this.) In addition to this schematic aid, I have marked with an asterisk in the Table of Contents those chapters and sections treating of material which is not particularly utilized in subsequent chapters.

Experience in teaching senior students at Michigan State University from a preliminary version of this work indicates that there is enough material here for a one-year course, plus special assignments for superior and interested students. Certainly Chapters 3, 5, 6 (selected topics), 7, 8, 11, 12, and 13 present to the student the basic features of the theory of numbers, the theory of rings, and the theory of vectors and matrices. Chapters 1 and 2 serve to ease the uninitiated into the stream of modern axiomatic mathematics, and Chapters 4, 6, 9, and 10 provide enrichment and interesting diversions and supplements.

I should like to express here my gratitude to the many students who worked through the barely legible preliminary version of this book and offered interesting and helpful criticisms, suggestions, and encouragements; to my excellent typist, Frau Jetter of Tübingen, Germany; to my friend and colleague Professor J. Adney, for his many helpful discussions and suggestions; and to Professor James H. Bennett of The University of Michigan for his critical reading of the first two chapters.

W. E. Deskins

East Lansing, Michigan.

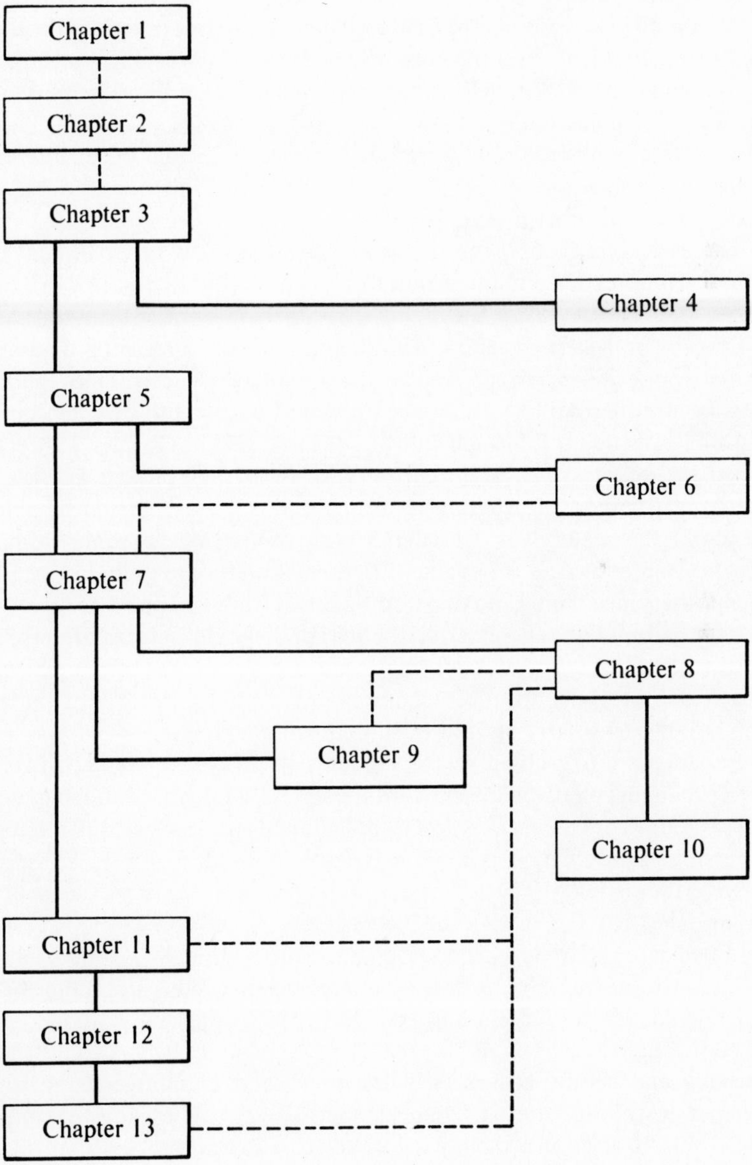

Chapter 1
Chapter 2
Chapter 3
Chapter 4
Chapter 5
Chapter 6
Chapter 7
Chapter 8
Chapter 9
Chapter 10
Chapter 11
Chapter 12
Chapter 13

# 1

# A Common Language

Our aim in this book is basically a very simple one: to show how the familiar methods and ideas used in the analysis of the system of "whole numbers" have been and are being extended and generalized to enable more diverse mathematical systems to be analyzed. In particular the concept of factorization or decomposition into "simpler" pieces underlies essentially all of our efforts. However, before we can proceed with this program of study we must try to establish a common starting point and path of approach. Even before doing this we must agree upon some basic assumptions, terms, and notations, and these are set down in this chapter.

Since the student will have encountered most of this material previously in one form or another he should strive to maintain contact between the various formulations by constructing examples, doing problems, asking questions of his instructors and fellow students, and reading other accounts of the material. (A collection of problems is included in each section, and a suggested reading list is included at the end of each chapter.)

Apart from the assumptions and agreements which are discussed in the following sections, we shall assume that there is a general understanding of the logical reasoning involved in proceeding from hypotheses to conclusions. Although we shall at times discuss the various forms in which a theorem can be stated and will always try to set forth the important features of each proof, neither a formal treatment of logic nor the use of formal logic appears in this book.

## 1.1 Sets

Any discussion must involve words and ideas which either have been agreed upon as undefined and undefinable or have been defined by using such primitives. These undefined terms, which can be somewhat arbitrarily selected, take on meaning from the assumptions or axioms which describe the undefined objects by stating relations between them. The axioms naturally are used to prove conclusions or theorems concerning the undefined terms and the objects which have been defined by using the undefined terms. In this manner a theory is developed.

We begin with the undefined notions of *set* and of *set membership*. Various words such as *class*, *family*, *collection*, and *aggregate*, are used interchangeably with the word *set*, and the *members* of a set are generally referred to as the *elements* of the set.

Intuitively a set is a collection of objects called the elements of the set. This sentence does not define the concepts, however; they are undefined terms in the common language we assume throughout this book.

Whenever feasible a set is denoted by a capital letter and an element of a set by a small letter. Since a set can consist of a collection of other sets it is apparent that this convention cannot always be observed. The notation

$$a \in A$$

indicates that the element $a$ is a member of the set $A$ and is sometimes read as "$a$ belongs to $A$." The notation

$$a \notin A$$

indicates that the element $a$ is *not* a member of the set $A$.

Particular sets are usually specified in one of two ways. Either the elements of the set are listed within a set of braces, or a property is stated which the elements of the set and *only* the elements of the set satisfy. The only word of explanation needed for the first method is that the order in which the elements are listed is of no importance. This independence from order of listing is due to a very basic assumption.

*Axiom of Extent.* The set $A$ equals the set $B$, written $A = B$, if every element of $A$ is an element of $B$ and every element of $B$ is an element of $A$.

Thus a set is completely known if its elements are known, and the two methods of specifying a set are merely statements that the elements of a set are known if they can be listed or if a characterizing property can be found. The notation for listing the elements (i.e., braces) has already been mentioned. A slightly more elaborate notation is frequently used for the second, namely,

$$\{x\colon (\text{condition or conditions which } x \text{ must satisfy})\},$$

which is read "the set of all elements $x$ which satisfy the condition or conditions."

*Note.* An element $x$ and the set $\{x\}$ consisting of the element $x$ should not be confused with one another.

*Example* 1. Let $A$ be the set $A = \{a, b, c, d, e\}$. Then the set $B = \{a, e\}$ can also be described using the second method; viz.,

$$B = \{x\colon x \in A \text{ and } x \text{ is a vowel}\}.$$

Thus, "$B$ is the set of all elements from $A$ which are also vowels."

Now let $C$ be the set $\{b, c, d\}$. What is meant by

$$D = \{x: x \in C \text{ and } x \text{ is a vowel}\}?$$

Clearly in adopting this notation we implicitly accept the axiom that for each collection of conditions there is a set whose elements are just the objects meeting those conditions. So we are led to accept the existence of a set containing no elements, the *empty* or *void set*. We use the symbol $\varnothing$ to denote this convenient set. Then the above statement means that $D = \varnothing$.

In Example 1 the elements of the set $B$ are also elements of the set $A$, suggesting that the set $B$ is "contained in" $A$. We formalize this as a definition.

DEFINITION 1.1. A set $T$ is a *subset* of a set $S$ if and only if every element of $T$ is also an element of $S$. A set $T$ is a *proper subset* of a set $S$ if and only if $T$ is a subset of $S$ but $S$ is *not* a subset of $T$.

If $T$ is a subset of $S$ we write

$$T \subseteq S \quad \text{or} \quad S \supseteq T,$$

and if $T$ is a proper subset of $S$ we write

$$T \subset S \quad \text{or} \quad S \supset T.$$

This is completely analogous to the familiar notation for inequality.

Suppose we list the subsets of the set $A = \{x, y\}$. They are $\{x\}$, $\{y\}$, $\{x, y\}$, and $\varnothing$, and if the student is surprised that $A$ and $\varnothing$ are subsets of $A$, he need only check the definition to see that this is indeed the case. Certainly every element of $A$ and every element of $\varnothing$ (which contains no elements) are in $A$.

An important use of the concept of subset stems from the following elementary theorem. In our subsequent work we shall often want to prove that two sets are equal, and we will generally use a two-pronged attack based on this result.

THEOREM 1.1. *The set $S$ equals the set $T$ if and only if $S$ is a subset of $T$ and $T$ is a subset of $S$.*

First we remark that there are actually *two* theorems here, or there would be if the results were written in the conventional "If . . ., then . . ." form. Recasting the material in this form yields

THEOREM 1.1*a*. *If $S \subseteq T$ and $T \subseteq S$, then $S = T$.*

THEOREM 1.1*b*. *If $S = T$, then $S \subseteq T$ and $T \subseteq S$.*

The first statement is the one frequently used, and the proof is quite easy. We are given that $S \subseteq T$ and $T \subseteq S$, statements which were defined to mean, respectively, that every element of $S$ is an element of $T$ and every element of $T$ is an element of $S$ (undefined terms). Then from the Axiom of Extent we conclude that $S = T$.

The second statement is proved similarly.

The notion of a subset provides us with a means of comparing sets, or ranking sets. There are also various ways of combining sets to form other

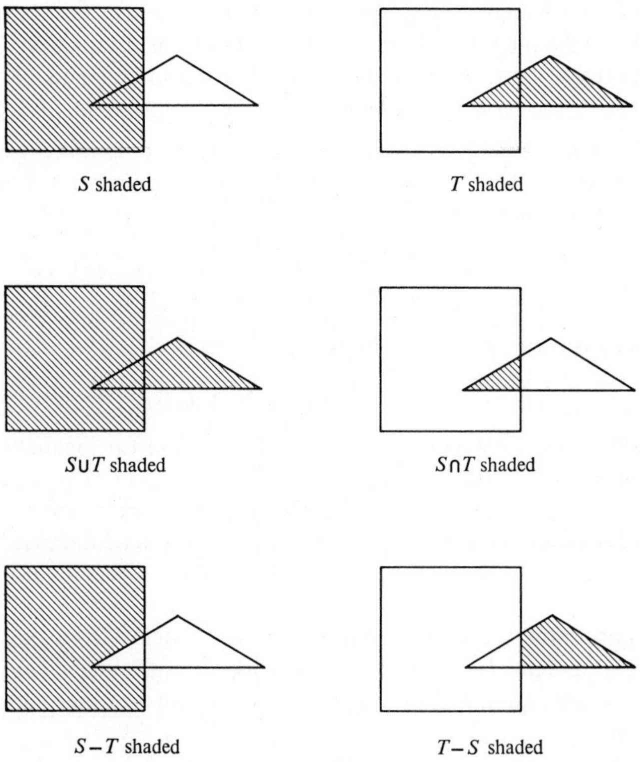


**Figure 1.1**

sets, and by defining these in terms of our undefined concepts and studying them we build our (intuitive) theory of sets.

DEFINITION 1.2.

| | |
|---|---|
| *Union:* | $S \cup T = \{a\colon a \in S \text{ or } a \in T\}$. |
| *Intersection:* | $S \cap T = \{a\colon a \in S \text{ and } a \in T\}$. |
| *Difference:* | $S - T = \{a\colon a \in S \text{ and } a \notin T\}$. |

In other words, the set $S \cup T$ (read "$S$ union $T$") is the collection of those elements which belong to either or both $S$ and $T$; the set $S \cap T$ (read "$S$ intersection $T$") consists of just those elements which lie in both $S$ and $T$;

and the set $S - T$ (read "$S$ minus $T$") is the collection of elements of $S$ which are not in $T$. We can illustrate these with the diagrams in Fig. 1.1, in which it is understood that the set $S$ consists of the points inside the square and the set $T$ the points inside the triangle.

Such diagrams, often called *Venn diagrams*, are useful visual aids to understanding relations between sets. Although they cannot be used to prove statements, the appropriate diagram can sometimes help one discern just what must be or has been proved. The diagrams sometimes suggest theorems, too. The diagrams in Fig. 1.1 make *plausible* the following theorems:

Theorem 1.2. $(S \cap T) \cup (S - T) = S.$
Theorem 1.3. $(S - T) \cup T = S \cup T.$
Theorem 1.4. $S \subseteq S \cup T.$
Theorem 1.5. $(S - T) \cap T = \varnothing.$
Theorem 1.6. $S - T = S - (S \cap T).$
Theorem 1.7. $S - T$ and $T - S$ are in general different sets.
And there are others, too.

In proving, or in attempting to prove, the validity of such statements we can use the axioms which have been assumed, the definitions which have been made, and the theorems which have already been proved. (At the moment this collection is a small one.) As an example we shall prove Theorem 1.2.

THEOREM 1.2. *If $S$ and $T$ are sets, then*

$$(S \cap T) \cup (S - T) = S.$$

In proving this we first use the definitions of intersection, union, and difference to establish the two conclusions

$$(S \cap T) \cup (S - T) \subseteq S, \tag{1.1}$$

$$(S \cap T) \cup (S - T) \supseteq S. \tag{1.2}$$

Then the conclusion of Theorem 1.2 follows from Theorem 1.1. For conclusion (1.1) we need only note that the sets $S \cap T$ and $S - T$ are both subsets of $S$. To establish conclusion (1.2) we observe that an element $s$ of $S$ is either an element of $T$ or it is not an element of $T$. If $s \in T$, then

$$s \in S \cap T;$$

if $s \notin T$, then

$$s \in S - T.$$

In any case $s \in S$ implies

$$s \in S \cap T \ \textit{or} \ s \in S - T,$$

and we conclude that

$$(S \cap T) \cup (S - T) \supseteq S.$$

Then by Theorem 1.1 we conclude from (1) and (2) that

$$(S \cap T) \cup (S - T) = S.$$

There are many other theorems about sets which involve only the ideas which we have already discussed. Some of these are quite trivial to prove, e.g.,

$$S \cup T = T \cup S; \qquad S \cap T = T \cap S; \qquad S \subseteq S \cup T,$$

but others require careful thought. We now consider a theorem which illustrates another type of statement and its method of proof.

THEOREM 1.7. *If $S$ and $T$ are sets, then $S - T$ and $T - S$ differ in general.*

The meaning of this statement is that the two sets $S - T$ and $T - S$ are *not always* equal. In other words there are *some* sets $S$ and $T$ such that $S - T$ and $T - S$ are not equal. Certainly, then, one way to verify the statement is to find particular sets $S$ and $T$ for which $S - T \neq T - S$, and for this purpose we select $S = \varnothing$ and $T = \{\varnothing\}$. That is, we take as $S$ the empty set and as $T$ the set whose *element* is the empty set. Since

$$S - T = S, \qquad T - S = T, \qquad \text{and} \quad S \neq T,$$

we have proved the theorem.

Many other choices for $S$ and $T$ serve equally well; certainly any two nonempty sets which are *disjoint* (i.e., have an empty intersection) can be used in the proof.

We close our brief development of the elementary theory of sets with diagrams and a theorem concerning three sets.

THEOREM 1.8 (DE MORGAN'S THEOREM). *If $C$, $S$, and $T$ are sets, then*

$$(C - S) \cap (C - T) = C - (S \cup T).$$

In the diagrams in Fig. 1.2 we take $C$, $S$, and $T$ as the points inside the circle, square, and triangle, respectively.

We prove first that

$$(C - S) \cap (C - T) \supseteq C - (S \cup T). \tag{1.3}$$

Let $x$ lie in $C - (S \cup T)$. Then

$$x \in C \qquad \text{and} \qquad x \notin (S \cup T),$$

and $x \notin (S \cup T)$ implies that

$$x \notin S \qquad \textit{and} \qquad x \notin T.$$

Therefore

$$x \in (C - S) \qquad \textit{and} \qquad x \in (C - T),$$

so that

$$x \in (C - S) \cap (C - T),$$

implying that conclusion (1.3) is valid.

Now we take an element $y$ in $(C - S) \cap (C - T)$. By definition of intersection,

$$y \in (C - S) \quad \text{and} \quad y \in (C - T).$$

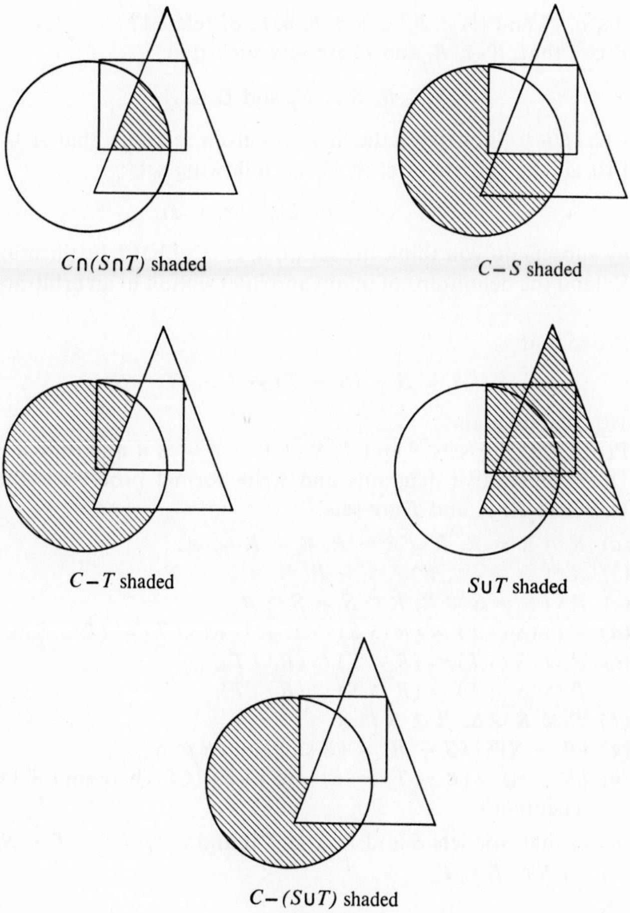


**Figure 1.2**

Therefore $y$ belongs to $C$ but to neither $S$ nor $T$. Thus

$$y \notin (S \cup T),$$

and we conclude that

$$(C - S) \cap (C - T) \subseteq C - (S \cup T).$$

The desired conclusion follows from Theorem 1.1.

## Exercise 1.1

**1.** Can there be unequal empty sets? Explain your answer.

**2.** Use the Axiom of Extent to prove that

$$\{a, b, c\} = \{b, a, c, b\}.$$

How are $\{a, b, c\}$ and $\{b, a, b, a, b, a, b, a, b, a\}$ related?

**3.** Prove that, if $A$, $B$, and $C$ are sets such that

$$A \subseteq B,\ B \subseteq C, \text{ and } C \subseteq A,$$

then $A = C$. (*Hint:* Show from the first two given relations that $A \subseteq C$.)

**4.** List all the subsets of each of the following sets:

$$\varnothing;\quad \{x\};\quad \{a, b\};\quad \{x, y, z\}.$$

How many subsets do you think the set $\{a, b, c, d, e\}$ has? Justification?

**5.** Extend the definitions of union and intersection to an arbitrary collection of sets.

**6.** Prove that

$$S \cap T = S - (S - T) = T - (T - S).$$

Draw illustrative diagrams.

**7.** Prove that, for sets $S$ and $T$, $S - T = T - S$ if and only if $S = T$.

**8.** Draw illustrative diagrams and write formal proofs for the following statements, where $R$, $S$, and $T$ are sets:

(*a*) $R \cap R = R$, $R \cup R = R$, $R - R = \varnothing$.
(*b*) $R \cap \varnothing = \varnothing$, $R \cup \varnothing = R$, $R - \varnothing = R$.
(*c*) $R \cup S = S \cup R$, $R \cap S = S \cap R$.
(*d*) $R \cap (S \cap T) = (R \cap S) \cap T$, $R \cup (S \cup T) = (R \cup S) \cup T$.
(*e*) $R \cup (S \cap T) = (R \cup S) \cap (R \cup T)$,
$R \cap (S \cup T) = (R \cap S) \cup (R \cap T)$.
(*f*) $R \subseteq R \cup S$, $R \supseteq R \cap S$.
(*g*) $(R - S) \cup (S - R) = (R \cup S) - (R \cap S)$.
(*h*) $(R - S) \cup (R - T) = R - (S \cap T)$. (Cf. Theorem 1.8, De Morgan's Theorem.)

**9.** Prove that, for sets $S$ and $T$, $S \supseteq T$ if and only if $S \cup T = S$ and if and only if $S \cap T = T$.

**10.** Let

$R$ = set of all Ruritanians,
$S$ = set of all socialists,
$M$ = set of all monarchists,
$C$ = set of all cattle raisers,
$W$ = set of all whisky drinkers,
$T$ = set of all tea drinkers,
$P$ = set of all pipe smokers,
$A$ = set of all argumentative people,

and rewrite the following not-to-be-debated statements in symbolic form:

(*a*) Ruritanian socialists always drink tea ($T \supseteq R \cap S$).
(*b*) An argumentative Ruritanian is never a monarchist.

(*c*) Some monarchists in Ruritania who do not drink whisky do not smoke a pipe or drink tea.

(*d*) No cattle are raised in Ruritania.

(*e*) All cattle raisers who do not smoke a pipe drink either whisky or tea.

(*f*) Those people in Ruritania who are neither socialist nor monarchist are very argumentative.

**11.** Draw diagrams for the statements in Problem 10.

**12.** Show that, if $a$, $b$, $c$, and $d$ are arbitrary elements, then the set equations

$$\{a, b\} = \{a, c\} \quad \text{and} \quad \{\{a\}, \{a, b\}\} = \{\{c\}, \{c, d\}\}$$

imply, respectively, that $b = c$ and that $a = c$ and $b = d$.

**13.** Write out proofs for Theorem 1.3, 1.4, 1.5, and 1.6.

## 1.2 Ordered Pairs, Products, and Relations

A more elaborate but more rewarding concept for constructing new sets is that of *ordered pair*. Intuitively an ordered pair $(a, b)$ is a set *with* an orientation or *order*, i.e., not a set but more than a set. Consequently we shall take *ordered pair* as an undefined concept and, necessarily, extend the Axiom of Extent to cover this extended idea of set.

*Axiom of Pair Equality.* The ordered pair $(a, b)$ equals the ordered pair $(c, d)$, written $(a, b) = (c, d)$, if and only if $a = c$ and $b = d$.

Perhaps a word is in order concerning the symbol $=$. This is commonly used to denote *logical identity*, and with our Axiom of Extent and Axiom of Pair Equality, we are, by assumption, extending this concept.

Although we could take ordered triple as an undefined term, this is quite unnecessary since such a notion can be defined in terms of ordered pairs in a manner which agrees with our intuitive concept.

DEFINITION 1.3. The *ordered triple* $(a, b, c)$ of elements $a$, $b$, and $c$ is the ordered pair $\big(a, (b, c)\big)$.

Nor is it necessary to assume an axiom of triple equality. Instead we prove the following result.

THEOREM 1.9. $(a, b, c) = (d, e, f)$ *if and only if* $a = d$, $b = e$, *and* $c = f$.

To prove these statements we use the above definition of triple and the Axiom of Pair Equality. If

$$(a, b, c) = (d, e, f),$$

then

$$\big(a, (b, c)\big) = \big(d, (e, f)\big)$$

so that

$$a = d \qquad \text{and} \qquad (b, c) = (e, f)$$

by the Axiom of Pair Equality, which also implies that $b = e$ and $c = f$.

If $a = d$, $b = e$, and $c = f$, then this argument can be reversed, yielding the other half of the theorem.

Although the concepts of ordered pair, ordered triples, and ordered sets in general are not of modern origin (the student knows of course that the idea of ordered pair is basic in analytic geometry), their usefulness for describing and constructing mathematical systems has been widely recognized only in recent years. Modern abstract algebra began with this recognition. We shall use these and related concepts continually throughout this book.

In reality it is not the ordered pairs themselves which are so useful but rather various sets of ordered pairs. We start with the largest such set associated with two sets $R$ and $S$.

DEFINITION 1.4. The *Cartesian product* of two sets $R$ and $S$ is the set

$$R \times S = \{(r, s) : r \in R, s \in S\}.$$

For example, if $R = \{a, b, c\}$ and $S = \{x, y\}$, then

$$R \times S = \{(a, x), (a, y), (b, x), (b, y), (c, x), (c, y)\}$$

and

$$S \times R = \{(x, a), (x, b), (x, c), (y, a), (y, b), (y, c)\}.$$

(This example shows that $R \times S$ and $S \times R$ are in general *unequal* sets.) The coordinate systems familiar to the student from analytic geometry provide additional examples.

Of considerable importance in the development of our language for abstract mathematics are various subsets of Cartesian products. We note that the Cartesian product $S \times S$ of a set $S$ with itself consists of all possible pairings of elements, so that a subset of $S \times S$ describes a way of pairing off or relating certain elements of $S$.

DEFINITION 1.5. A subset $\mathbf{R}$ of $S \times S$ is a *binary relation* on $S$, and if $(a, b)$ is in $\mathbf{R}$ we write $a\mathbf{R}b$ (read "$a$ is related to $b$ by $\mathbf{R}$"). $\mathbf{R}$ is an *equivalence relation* on $S$ if and only if it is:

*Reflexive:* $a\mathbf{R}a$ for every $a$ in $S$.
*Symmetric:* If $a\mathbf{R}b$, then $b\mathbf{R}a$.
*Transitive:* If $a\mathbf{R}b$ and $b\mathbf{R}c$, then $a\mathbf{R}c$.

The concept of binary relation, since the set $S \times S$ has so many subsets, is too general for us to work with, but the idea of equivalence relation or generalized equality is basic to the classification systems of all sciences, as well as mathematics. There are, however, very important binary relations which are *not* equivalence relations, although these generally have some of the properties of equivalence relations. The following examples illustrate what is meant by this statement.

*Example* 1. Let $T$ be a set of triangles in a plane, and define $\mathbf{R}$ as the set

$$\mathbf{R} = \{(a, b) : a \in T, b \in T, a \text{ and } b \text{ are congruent}\}.$$

Then $a\mathbf{R}b$ if and only if $a$ and $b$ are congruent triangles from $T$, or, using the usual notation employed in plane geometry, $a \cong b$. This is clearly an equivalence relation on $T$, and much of the material in plane geometry deals with this generalized equality.

*Example* 2. Let $L$ be a set of lines in a plane and define $\mathbf{R}$ as the set

$$\mathbf{R} = \{(a, b): a \in L,\ b \in L,\ a \text{ is perpendicular to } b\}.$$

This binary relation on $L$ is not an equivalence relation since it is neither reflexive (a line is not perpendicular to itself) nor transitive (if $a$ is perpendicular to $b$ and $b$ is perpendicular to $c$, then $a$ and $c$ are parallel or coincident) but it is symmetric.

*Example* 3. Let $P$ be a set of people, and define $\mathbf{R}$ as the set

$$\mathbf{R} = \{(a, b): a \in P,\ b \in P,\ a \text{ is the same sex as } b\}.$$

This is a binary relation on $P$ which is also an equivalence relation.

*Example* 4. Let $P(S)$ be the set of all subsets of $S$ ($P(S)$ is called the *power set* of $S$), and define $\mathbf{R}$ as the set

$$\mathbf{R} = \{(A, B): A \text{ and } B \text{ are subsets of } S, \text{ and } A \subseteq B\}.$$

The binary relation $\mathbf{R}$, or, as we usually say, the relation $\subseteq$, is reflexive (since a set is a subset of itself) and transitive but it is not symmetric.

The word *classification* was mentioned above in the discussion of equivalence relation, but the connection was not explained. The classifying of objects is the separating of the set of objects into subsets according to some criterion. The classification of people by sex is the separation of the set of people into two subsets, the set of males and the set of females, which are disjoint. Since hierarchical classifications are also quite common we exclude these by formalizing the concept we wish to discuss here.

DEFINITION 1.6. A *partition* $\mathbf{C}$ of a set $S$ is a collection of nonempty subsets of $S$ which has the properties:

(*a*) All distinct pairs of elements of $\mathbf{C}$ are disjoint.

(*b*) Each element of $S$ belongs to some element of $\mathbf{C}$.

We see, therefore, that the set of men in $P$ and the set of women in $P$ provide a partition of $P$, a set of people. A deck of playing cards used in bridge is partitioned through the notion of suit, a concept important to the game. Such partitions are very common.

The connection between equivalence relations and partitions is a key to the understanding of the ideas. Let $\mathbf{E}$ be an equivalence relation on a set $S$, and for each element $a$ in $S$ define

$$S_a = \{b: b \in S \text{ and } (a, b) \in \mathbf{E}\},$$

the *equivalence class* of $a$. Then the set $\mathbf{E}'$ of all such sets $S_a$ is a partition of $S$. To prove this we must show that $\mathbf{E}'$ has the required two properties.

First, let $S_a$ and $S_b$ be two elements of $\mathbf{E}'$ and suppose that they have the element $c$ in common. By definition of the sets $S_a$ and $S_b$, this means that

$a\mathbf{E}c$ and $b\mathbf{E}c$. Since $\mathbf{E}$ is an equivalence relation, from $a\mathbf{E}c$ and $b\mathbf{E}c$ we conclude that

(1.4) $a\mathbf{E}c$ and $c\mathbf{E}b$ by symmetry,

(1.5) $a\mathbf{E}b$ by transitivity,

(1.6) $c\mathbf{E}a$ and $b\mathbf{E}c$ by symmetry,

(1.7) $b\mathbf{E}a$ by transitivity.

Conclusion (1.5) implies that $S_a \supseteq S_b$, and conclusion (1.7) implies that $S_a \subseteq S_b$. Therefore

$$S_a = S_b \quad \text{if} \quad S_a \cap S_b \neq \varnothing,$$

which means that distinct (i.e., unequal) elements of $\mathbf{E}'$ are disjoint. Thus $\mathbf{E}'$ has property (*a*) of Definition 1.6.

Now let $x$ be an arbitrary element of $S$. By definition $\mathbf{E}'$ contains $S_x$, and $x$ is an element of $S_x$ since $x\mathbf{E}x$ by the reflexivity of $\mathbf{E}$. Therefore $\mathbf{E}'$ has property (*b*) of Definition 1.6, and we have proved Theorem 1.10.

THEOREM 1.10. *If* $\mathbf{E}$ *is an equivalence relation on the set* $S$, *then* $\mathbf{E}'$, *the collection of all equivalence classes* $S_a$, *is a partition of* $S$.

The converse of this result is also true. That is, if $\mathbf{C}$ is a partition of the set $S$, then the set

$$\mathbf{C}'' = \{(a, b)\colon a \text{ and } b \text{ belong to the same element of } \mathbf{C}\}$$

is an equivalence relation on $S$. First we see that $(a, a)$ is in $\mathbf{C}''$ for every $a$ in $S$, since every $a$ of $S$ lies in some element of $\mathbf{C}$. Then, if $a$ and $b$ belong to the same element of $\mathbf{C}$ (so that $(a, b) \in \mathbf{C}''$), certainly $b$ and $a$ belong to the same element of $\mathbf{C}$. Finally, if $a$ and $b$ belong to the element $C_a$ of $\mathbf{C}$ and if $b$ and $c$ belong to the element $C_c$ of $\mathbf{C}$, then $C_a = C_c$ since distinct elements of $\mathbf{C}$ are disjoint. Therefore $a$ and $c$ belong to the same element of $\mathbf{C}$.

Since this last part of the proof (the transitivity) is a bit involved we will rewrite it in a different form.

Given: $(a, b)$ and $(b, c)$ are in $\mathbf{C}''$.
To prove: $(a, c)$ is in $\mathbf{C}''$.

| | |
|---|---|
| 1. $(a, b)$ and $(a, c)$ are in $\mathbf{C}''$. | Given. |
| 2. $a$ and $b$ lie in the same element $C_a$ of $\mathbf{C}$, and $b$ and $c$ lie in the same element $C_c$ of $\mathbf{C}$. | Definition of $\mathbf{C}''$. |
| 3. $\mathbf{C}_a \cap \mathbf{C}_c \neq \varnothing$. | $b \in C_a$ and $b \in C_c$. |
| 4. $C_a = C_c$. | Distinct elements of $\mathbf{C}$ are disjoint. |
| 5. $a$ and $c$ lie in $C_a = C_c$, so that $(a, c) \in \mathbf{C}''$. | Definition of $\mathbf{C}''$. |

Such an outline form for a proof should be utilized by the student whenever he has difficulty with a proof.

The partition $\mathbf{E}'$ defined above for the equivalence relation $\mathbf{E}$ is said to be the partition *induced* on $S$ by $\mathbf{E}$. Similarly the equivalence relation $\mathbf{C}''$ is said to be induced on $S$ by the partition $\mathbf{C}$. We summarize the connections between the two as follows.

THEOREM 1.11. *An equivalence relation* $\mathbf{E}$ *on a set* $S$ *induces a partition* $\mathbf{E}'$ *on* $S$, *and a partition* $\mathbf{C}$ *of* $S$ *induces an equivalence relation* $\mathbf{C}''$ *on* $S$. *Furthermore*

$$(\mathbf{E}')'' = \mathbf{E} \text{ and } (\mathbf{C}'')' = \mathbf{C}'.$$

*Example* 5. Let $T$ be the set of all people in Texas, and define

$$T_m = \{x: x \in T, \text{ and } x \text{ was born in the month } m\}.$$

Then the twelve subsets of $T$ so described form a partition of $T$. Equivalently we say that $x$ and $y$ of $T$ are birth-month-related if their birthdays fall in the same month. The variations between these sets $T_m$ as measured in total numbers, average size, average intelligence, etc., can be of considerable interest to sociologists, scientists, and merchants in their study of the whole set $T$.

We conclude this section by introducing two abstractions of the familiar concept of order. These again involve the three properties used in defining an equivalence relation, so a brief discussion of these seems in order here.

**Figure 1.3**

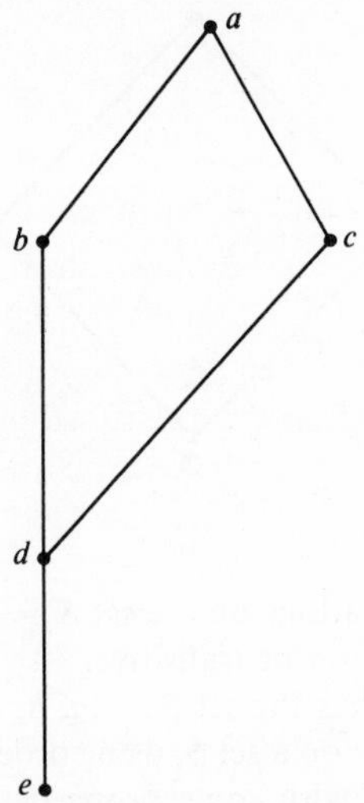


DEFINITION 1.7. Let $\mathbf{R}$ be a binary relation on the set $S$.

(*a*) $\mathbf{R}$ is a *linear order* on $S$ if and only if (1) either $a\mathbf{R}b$ or $b\mathbf{R}a$ for any two distinct elements $a$ and $b$ of $S$, (2) $a\mathbf{R}a$ for no $a \in S$ (i.e., $(a, a)$ never lies in $\mathbf{R}$), and (3) $a\mathbf{R}c$ when $a\mathbf{R}b$ and $b\mathbf{R}c$.

(*b*) $\mathbf{R}$ is a *partial order* on $S$ if and only if (1) $a\mathbf{R}a$ for every $a \in S$, (2) both $a\mathbf{R}b$ and $b\mathbf{R}a$ cannot hold when $a \neq b$, and (3) $a\mathbf{R}c$ when $a\mathbf{R}b$ and $b\mathbf{R}c$.

The most familiar mathematical examples of these are provided by inequality of integers (linear order) and set inclusion (partial order). The student should recognize that the main distinction between a linear order and a partial order on $S$ lies in the comparableness of the elements of $S$. Under a linear ordering any two distinct elements of $S$ are comparable; this is generally not true of a partial ordering.

Nodal diagrams are sometimes used to indicate the ordering in a finite set.

*Example* 6. Let $S = \{a, b, c, d, e\}$. Then the nodes of the following diagram represent the elements of $S$, and two elements are comparable if one lies above the other *and* if they are connected, as shown in Fig. 1.3, by line segments that descend *only*. Formally Fig. 1.3 illustrates the relation **R** where

$$\mathbf{R} = \{(a, b), (a, d), (a, e), (b, d), (b, e), (a, c), (c, d), (c, e), (d, e)\},$$

and when the five pairs $(a, a)$, $(b, b)$, $(c, c)$, $(d, d)$, and $(e, e)$ are included the result is easily verified to be a partial order on $S$.

*Example* 7. Let $S$ be the set of all subsets of the set $A = \{a, b\}$, and let set inclusion be the order relation on $S$. Denoting the subsets as

$$A, \quad B = \{a\}, \quad C = \{b\}, \quad \text{and} \quad \varnothing,$$

we can represent the set and the relation by the diagram in Fig. 1.4.

**Figure 1.4**

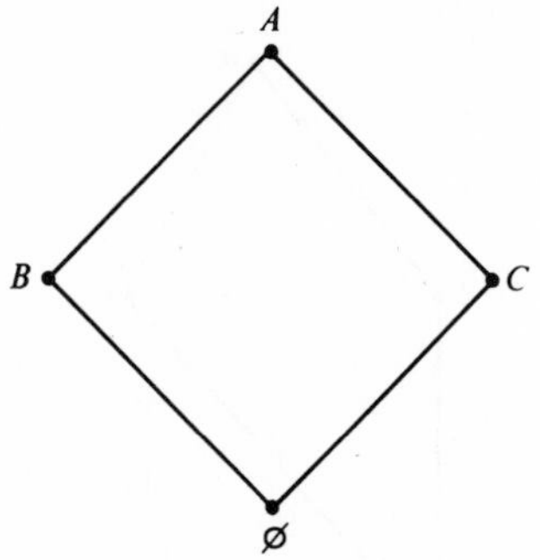


## Exercise 1.2

**1.** List three different relations on the set $S = \{a, b, c\}$, and decide whether they are reflexive, symmetric, and/or transitive.

**2.** How many relations has the set $S = \{a, b, c, d\}$?

**3.** Define *ternary* relation on a set $S$, using ordered triples. Give a geometric example of a ternary relation with some properties analogous to symmetry or transitivity.

**4.** Prove that set equality is an equivalence relation on the collection of subsets of a set $S$.

**5.** Find examples of sets and relations on the sets which are

(*a*) Reflexive but not symmetric or transitive.
(*b*) Symmetric but not reflexive or transitive.
(*c*) Transitive but not reflexive or symmetric.

(*d*) Reflexive and symmetric but not transitive.
(*e*) Reflexive and transitive but not symmetric.
(*f*) Symmetric and transitive but not reflexive.

**6.** With reference to Problem 5(*f*) what do you think of the following argument? "The reflexive property for a relation **R** is a consequence of the symmetric and transitive properties of **R**. For the statements '$a\mathbf{R}b$ implies $b\mathbf{R}a$' and '$a\mathbf{R}b$ and $b\mathbf{R}c$ imply $a\mathbf{R}c$' together yield '$a\mathbf{R}a$' by merely replacing $c$ by $b$."

**7.** What are the properties of the relations defined on the set $A$ of living Americans by the following:

(*a*) Is married to.
(*b*) Has been married to.
(*c*) Is a (blood) relative of.
(*d*) Lives within a mile of.
(*e*) Born in the same town as.
(*f*) Is an acquaintance of an acquaintance of an . . . .

**8.** List several partitions of the set $A$ of living Americans.

**9.** Is it possible to have a relation on a set of relations? Illustrate by considering the subsets of $S \times S$ under set inclusion.

**10.** Let $S$ be the set of all subsets of the set $A = \{a, b, c\}$, and let set inclusion be a relation on $S$. Draw a nodal diagram for the set and its relation.

**11.** Draw a nodal diagram illustrating a finite set with a linear order. What conclusions can you reach concerning the word linear?

**12.** Using Problem 12 of Exercise 1.1, *define* ordered pair and *prove* that two ordered pairs are equal if and only if corresponding components are equal.

**13.** Let $R$, $S$, and $T$ be sets. Are the two sets $R \times (S \times T)$ and $(R \times S) \times T$ equal? Explain your answer.

## 1.3 Functions and Mappings

In his previous mathematics courses the student has certainly devoted much of his time and effort to the study of "functions." This work has undoubtedly convinced the student of the importance of the concept of function (perhaps because of its usefulness in applying mathematics to obtain solutions of physical problems) but has probably left him somewhat uncertain of the meaning of the term. In order to establish this notion firmly in our common language we shall now give a formal definition of function.

Intuitively a function describes some sort of correspondence between the elements of two (not necessarily different) sets whereby to each element of one set is assigned some element from the other set. Thus a function seems to be a type of pairing not unlike that involved in a relation on a set. Consequently it is quite natural that we can use the previously discussed concepts of Cartesian product and ordered pairs to define a function.

DEFINITION 1.8. A *function* $F$ of a set $S$ to a set $T$ is a subset of $S \times T$ with the properties:

(*a*) For each $s \in S$ there is a $t \in T$ such that $(s, t) \in F$.
(*b*) If $(s, t)$ and $(s, r)$ are in $F$, then $t = r$.

Informally stated, properties (*a*) and (*b*) require that each element of $S$ appear exactly once as a first element in a pair of $\boldsymbol{F}$.

This definition is a formal and precise way of stating that a function $\boldsymbol{F}$ of the set $S$ to the set $T$ associates with *each* element of $S$ *some* element of $T$, where we understand that $t$ is associated with $s$ if and only if

$$(s, t) \in \boldsymbol{F}.$$

We frequently indicate that $\boldsymbol{F}$ associates $t$ with $s$, i.e., that

$$(s, t) \in \boldsymbol{F},$$

by writing

$$t = \boldsymbol{F}(s),$$

which should be read as "$t$ is the *image* of $s$ under $\boldsymbol{F}$." The set $S$ is the *domain* of $\boldsymbol{F}$ and the set $\boldsymbol{F}(S)$, defined as

$$\boldsymbol{F}(S) = \{t\colon t \in T \text{ and } (s, t) \in \boldsymbol{F}\},$$

is the *range* of $\boldsymbol{F}$ or the *image* of $S$ under $\boldsymbol{F}$. Note that $\boldsymbol{F}(S)$ can be a proper subset of $T$.

Since the idea of function has been so widely studied various other terminology is often employed. Functions are frequently called *mappings* or *maps*, and the statement "$\boldsymbol{F}$ is a mapping of the set $S$ to the set $T$" lends itself admirably to geometric representations of abstract functions (see Fig. 1.5).

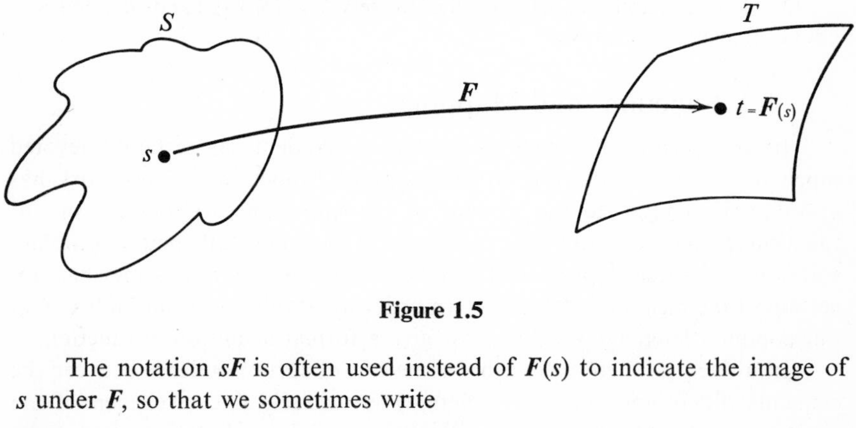


**Figure 1.5**

The notation $s\boldsymbol{F}$ is often used instead of $\boldsymbol{F}(s)$ to indicate the image of $s$ under $\boldsymbol{F}$, so that we sometimes write

$$t = s\boldsymbol{F}$$

instead of

$$t = \boldsymbol{F}(s).$$

The notation

$$\boldsymbol{F}\colon s \to s\boldsymbol{F}$$

is also used to indicate that the function $\boldsymbol{F}$ maps the elements $s$ onto the image $s\boldsymbol{F}$.

A basic difficulty that many students have in assimilating the abstract concept of function stems from confusing a formula *describing* a function with the function itself. This is probably due to the fact that the functions studied in elementary courses are usually described by formulas. The formula

$$F(x) = x^2 + x + 2, \qquad x \text{ an integer},$$

is *not* a function, but it does *describe* a function $F$ from the integers to the integers. We recall that there are two methods of describing a set: (1) itemizing the set, and (2) characterizing the set by a collection of properties. But the characterizing properties are not to be confused with the set itself.

Now for some illustrative examples.

*Example* 1. Let $S$ and $T$ be the sets $\{a, b, c\}$ and $\{x, y\}$, respectively. Then the set

$$\{(a, x), (b, x), (c, x)\}$$

is a function $F$ from $S$ to $T$ which can be represented geometrically as in Fig. 1.6.

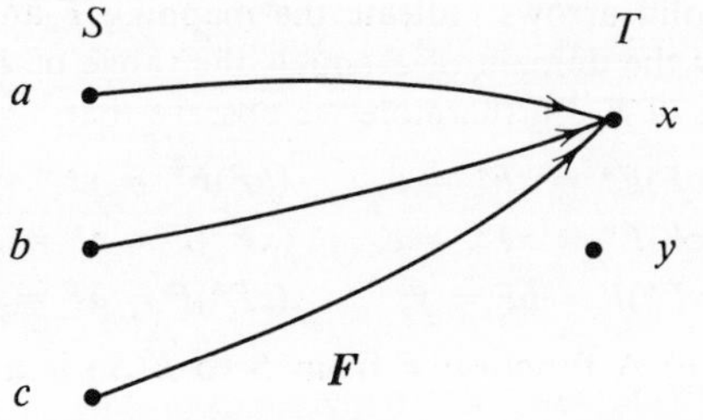


**Figure 1.6**

The arrows indicate that $F$ maps $a$ onto $x$, $b$ onto $x$, and $c$ onto $x$. In this case $F(S)$ is the set $\{x\}$ since $y$ is the image of no element under $F$.

*Example* 2. Let $S$ be the set $\{a, b, c\}$. Then the sets

$$\{(a, b), (a, c), (b, c), (c, a)\} \text{ and } \{(a, b), (b, c)\}$$

both fail to satisfy the necessary requirements to be functions from $S$ to $S$. In the first case the element $a$ appears twice as a first element, and in the second case the element $c$ fails to appear as a first element.

*Example* 3. Let $S$ be the set of all Europeans who have living mothers, and let $T$ be the set of all women in the world. Then the set

$$F = \{(s, t) : s \in S,\ t \in T, \text{ and } t \text{ is the mother of } s\}$$

is a function from $S$ to $T$. This function can also be described by the formula

$$sF \text{ (or } F(s)) \text{ is the mother of } s.$$

*Example* 4. Let $S = \{a, b, c\}$ and $T = \{x, y, z\}$. Then the two sets

$$F = \{(a, z), (b, y), (c, x)\}$$

and

$$F^* = \{(z, a), (y, b), (x, c)\}$$

are both functions, $F$ from $S$ to $T$ and $F^*$ from $T$ to $S$, as can be seen in Fig. 1.7.

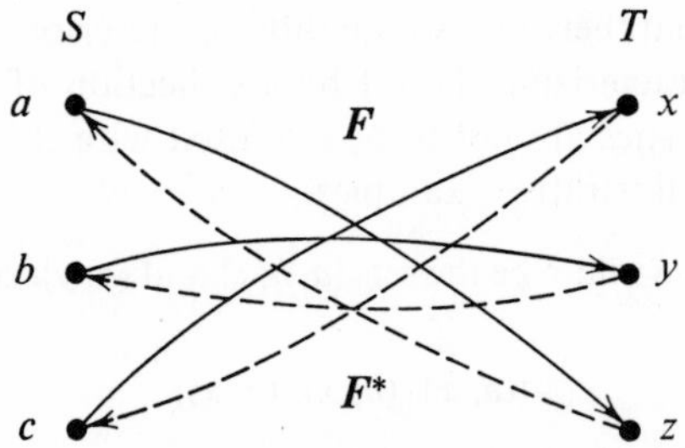


**Figure 1.7**

In this figure the solid arrows indicate the mapping $F$ and the dashed arrows indicate $F^*$. Clearly the domain of $F$ equals the range of $F^*$ and the domain of $F^*$ equals the range of $F$. Furthermore we observe that

$$\begin{aligned} (aF)F^* &= zF^* = a, & (bF)F^* &= yF^* = b, \\ (cF)F^* &= xF^* = c, & (xF^*)F &= cF = x, \\ (yF^*)F &= bF = y, & (zF^*)F &= aF = z. \end{aligned}$$

DEFINITION 1.9. (*a*) A function $F$ from $S$ to $F(S)$ is a *one-to-one mapping* if the set

$$F^* = \{(t, s): (s, t) \in F\}$$

is a function from $F(S)$ to $S$. If $F^*$ is a function it is called the *inverse mapping* of $F$.

(*b*) A function $F$ from $S$ to $T$ is a mapping of $S$ *into* $T$ if $T \neq F(S)$ and *onto* $T$ if $T = F(S)$.

(*c*) Two sets $S$ and $T$ are *equivalent* sets if there is a one-to-one mapping from $S$ onto $T$.

Clearly, then, in Example 4, $F$ is a one-to-one mapping, $F$ is a mapping of $S$ onto $T$, and $S$ and $T$ are equivalent sets.

Since functions are sets, being subsets of a Cartesian product, the equality of functions has already been defined. A useful criterion for the equality of functions is provided by Theorem 1.12.

THEOREM 1.12. *If $F$ and $G$ are functions, if*

$$\{\textit{domain of } F\} = \{\textit{domain of } G\} = S,$$

*and if $sF = sG$ for every $s \in S$, then $F = G$.*

Let $(s, t) \in \boldsymbol{F}$. Then $s \in S$ and so lies in the domain of $\boldsymbol{G}$. This means that there is an element $r$ in the range of $\boldsymbol{G}$ such that

$$(s, r) \in \boldsymbol{G}.$$

Furthermore $r = t$ since we are given that $s\boldsymbol{F} = s\boldsymbol{G}$, and this means that $(s, r) = (s, t)$ by the Axiom of Pair Equality. Consequently

$$(s, t) \in \boldsymbol{G},$$

and we conclude that $\boldsymbol{F} \subseteq \boldsymbol{G}$. The same argument with $\boldsymbol{F}$ and $\boldsymbol{G}$ interchanged shows that $\boldsymbol{G} \subseteq \boldsymbol{F}$, and so, by Theorem 1.11, $\boldsymbol{F} = \boldsymbol{G}$.

This result explains why it is permissible in many cases to work with the formula for the image, $s\boldsymbol{F}$ or $\boldsymbol{F}(s)$, when such a formula exists, rather than work with the function itself. It is, however, no excuse for confusing the two.

We conclude with the discussion of a familiar example from analytic geometry, using intuitive concepts the student has encountered before.

*Example* 5. Let $\boldsymbol{F}$ be the function from the real numbers to the real numbers defined by $\boldsymbol{F}(x) = x^2$. This function can be written

$$\boldsymbol{F} = \{(x, y)\colon x \text{ is a real number, and } y = x^2\}.$$

The graph of this function, shown in Fig. 1.8, provides a geometrical presentation of the elements of $\boldsymbol{F}$, viz., the ordered pairs $(x, y)$, as points in the plane.

**Figure 1.8**

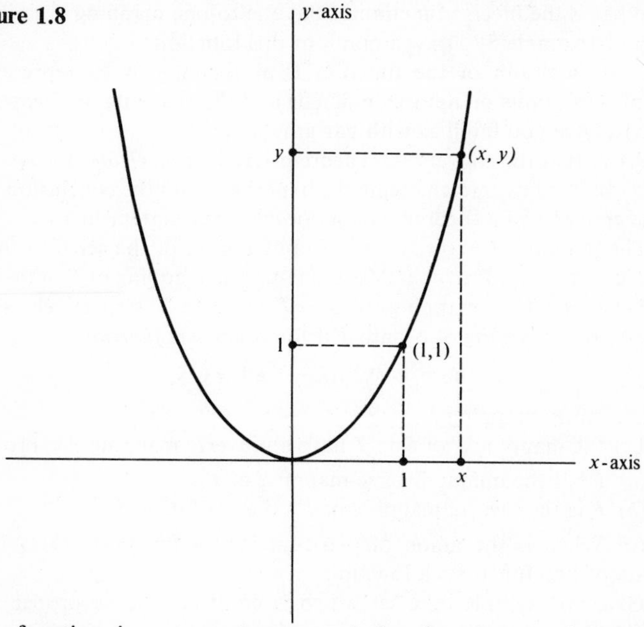


This function is *not* one-to-one and therefore has no inverse function. However, if the domain of $\boldsymbol{F}$ is restricted to positive numbers, then $\boldsymbol{F}$ is a one-to-one mapping.

## Exercise 1.3

**1.** Let $S$ and $T$ be the sets $\{a, b, c\}$ and $\{x, y\}$, respectively. How many functions are there from $S$ to $T$? How many one-to-one functions? How many functions of $S$ onto $T$?

**2.** Describe some functions familiar to you from your science studies.

**3.** What can you say about the following sets?

(*a*) $F = \{(x, y): x$ is an integer, and $y = 2x\}$.
(*b*) $F = \{(x, y): x$ is a man, and $y$ is his wife$\}$.
(*c*) $F = \{(x, y): x$ is a woman, and $y$ is a son of $x\}$.

**4.** Let $F$ be a function from $S$ to $T$ and $G$ be a function from $R$ to $M$. Show that, if $R$ contains the range of $F$, then the set

$$K = \{(x, y): x \in S \text{ and } (xF, y) \in G\}$$

is a function from $S$ to $M$. $K$ is the *composite* of $F$ and $G$, and we write

$$xK = (xF)G \quad \text{or} \quad K(x) = G(F(x)).$$

This is the "function of a function" concept which the student has encountered in his calculus course.

**5.** How many one-to-one mappings has $S = \{a, b, c\}$ onto itself? (Such mappings are called *permutations* of $S$.) Show that the composite (Problem 4) of two of these permutations is again a permutation.

**6.** Make a mapping diagram illustrating the idea of composite function.

**7.** What is the inverse function of the one-to-one mapping described in the discussion of Example 5? Draw a graph of this function.

**8.** Draw a graph of the function $F$ of Example 4 by representing the elements of $S$ as points on a horizontal axis and the elements of $T$ as points on a vertical axis. (Are you familiar with bar graphs?)

**9.** Prove that the converse of Theorem 1.12 is true. (*Note:* the *converse* of a theorem is obtained by interchanging the hypothesis and the conclusion. Needless to say, the converse of a theorem is not *always* a true statement.)

**10.** The mapping $I = \{(x, y): x \in S$, and $x = y\}$ of the set $S$ to the set $S$ is called the *identity* map. Prove that $I$ is a one-to-one mapping of $S$ onto $S$.

**11.** Let $F$ and $G$ be mappings of $S$ to $T$ and $T$ to $S$, respectively. Prove that $F$ is a one-to-one mapping of $S$ onto $T$ if the *composite function*

$$K: x \to (xF)G, \qquad \text{all } x \in S,$$

equals the identity mapping $I$.

**12.** Let the mapping $F$ of $S$ to $T$ have an inverse mapping $F^*$. Prove that

(*a*) $F^*$ is the unique inverse mapping of $F$.
(*b*) $F$ is the inverse mapping of $F^*$ (i.e., $(F^*)^* = F$).

**13.** (*a*) When is the union of two functions a function? (*b*) When is the intersection of two functions a function?

**14.** Give an example of a set which is equivalent to a proper subset of itself.

**15.** What is meant by the statement "A function is determined uniquely by the images of the elements in its domain"?

## 1.4 Binary Operations

In the preceding sections we studied pairings within a set (relations) and pairings of elements in one set with elements in another set (functions). These pairings produced other elements, the ordered pairs which made up the relations and functions. Now we shall consider a more fertile type of pairing of elements of a set, a type of pairing which will "produce" an element of the same set. This concept of combining elements of a set $S$ to obtain other elements of $S$ is an abstraction of the familiar ideas of addition and multiplication.

DEFINITION 1.10. A *binary operation* on the set $S$ is a function $\mathbf{O}$ from the set $S \times S$ to the set $S$.

Using the notation of the previous section we would write

$$c = (a, b)\mathbf{O} \qquad \text{or} \qquad c = \mathbf{O}((a, b))$$

when the element $((a, b), c)$ lies in $\mathbf{O}$. However we usually write

$$c = a\mathbf{O}b$$

when $((a, b), c)$ lies in $\mathbf{O}$, or, since we are dealing with a generalization of addition and multiplication, we use some variation of the ordinary symbolism for these operations. Thus $((a, b), c) \in \mathbf{O}$ is sometimes written as

$$c = a * b, \; c = a \odot b, \; c = a \bigcirc b, \; c = a \boxplus b, \text{ etc.}$$

Since an operation is a function we know that an operation $\mathbf{O}$ on the set $S$ is uniquely determined by the images of the elements of $S \times S$. Thus, if a formula or rule describes one and only one image for each $(a, b) \in S \times S$, then a binary operation on $S$ is determined. In this sense the formula and the operation are equivalent ideas, but they should not be confused.

Several examples of binary operations were introduced earlier in this chapter without being so designated.

*Example* 1. Let $S$ be the set of all subsets of a set $U$. Then the rule,

$$x\mathbf{O}y = x \cup y$$

for each $x$ and each $y$ in $S$, describes an operation $\mathbf{O}$ on $S$ since it assigns one and only one element of $S$ to each pair $(x, y)$ of $S \times S$.

*Example* 2. Let $S$ be the set of all subsets of a set $U$. Then the rule,

$$x\mathbf{Q}y = x \cap y$$

for each $x$ and each $y$ in $S$, describes an operation $\mathbf{Q}$ on $S$ since it assigns one and only one element of $S$ to each pair $(x, y)$ of $S \times S$.

These examples illustrate that the same set can have many different binary operations, for it is evident that $\mathbf{O}$ and $\mathbf{Q}$ are in general different. Set difference can be used to define another binary operation on this set $S$, and there are still others.

What properties does a particular operation **O** have? We attempt to deal with this question by analogy. That is, we list the properties of the well-known operations of well-known sets and then try to determine whether or not **O** possesses these properties. (So a person must have a certain amount of knowledge before he can obtain more!) Some of the simpler properties of ordinary addition and multiplication have been singled out and abstracted for this purpose.

DEFINITION 1.11. An operation **O** on the set $S$ is

(*a*) *Commutative* if $a\mathbf{O}b = b\mathbf{O}a$ for each $a$ and each $b$ in $S$.

(*b*) *Associative* if $(a\mathbf{O}b)\mathbf{O}c = a\mathbf{O}(b\mathbf{O}c)$ for each $a$, each $b$, and each $c$ in $S$.

From Problems 8(*c*) and 8(*d*) of Section 1.1 we know that the operations of Examples 1 and 2 possess both of these properties.

*Example* 3. Let $F$ be the set of all functions of a set $S$ to itself. Then the concept of *composite function* describes an operation **O** on $F$:

$$\mathbf{G}\mathbf{O}\mathbf{H} = \{(s, t): s \in S \text{ and } (s\mathbf{G}, y) \in \mathbf{H}\},$$

for each $\mathbf{G}$ and each $\mathbf{H}$ in $F$ (cf. Problem 4, Exercise 1.3). This rule assigns a particular function to each pair $(\mathbf{G}, \mathbf{H})$ of $F \times F$.

This operation on the set $F$ of functions is a useful one, as the student will remember from his study of calculus, but it does not in general possess both of the properties listed above, as we will now show.

*Example* 4. Let $S$ be the set $\{a, b\}$. Then the set $F$ of all functions of $S$ to $S$ is the set

$$F = \{\{(a, a), (b, a)\}, \{(a, b), (b, b)\}, \{(a, a), (b, b)\}, \{(a, b), (b, a)\}\}.$$

Label these four functions as $\mathbf{G}$, $\mathbf{H}$, $\mathbf{I}$, and $\mathbf{K}$, from left to right respectively. Then we see that, for the composite operation **O**, the elements of **O** are described by

$$\begin{array}{llll} \mathbf{GOG} = \mathbf{G}, & \mathbf{GOH} = \mathbf{H}, & \mathbf{GOI} = \mathbf{G}, & \mathbf{GOK} = \mathbf{H} \\ \mathbf{HOG} = \mathbf{G}, & \mathbf{HOH} = \mathbf{H}, & \mathbf{HOI} = \mathbf{H}, & \mathbf{HOK} = \mathbf{G} \\ \mathbf{IOG} = \mathbf{G}, & \mathbf{IOH} = \mathbf{H}, & \mathbf{IOI} = \mathbf{I}, & \mathbf{IOK} = \mathbf{K} \\ \mathbf{KOG} = \mathbf{G}, & \mathbf{KOH} = \mathbf{H}, & \mathbf{KOI} = \mathbf{K}, & \mathbf{KOK} = \mathbf{I}. \end{array}$$

Clearly **O** is not a commutative operation since

$$\mathbf{GOH} \neq \mathbf{HOG}, \qquad \mathbf{GOK} \neq \mathbf{KOG}, \qquad \mathbf{HOK} \neq \mathbf{KOH}.$$

Frequently when an operation is written down it is displayed as a *multiplication* (or *operation*) *table*, which is basically a variation on the idea of a graph.

The multiplication table for the operation **O** of Example 4 is written in the following way.

| **O** | *G* | *H* | *I* | *K* |
|---|---|---|---|---|
| *G* | *G* | *H* | *G* | *H* |
| *H* | *G* | *H* | *H* | *G* |
| *I* | *G* | *H* | *I* | *K* |
| *K* | *G* | *H* | *K* | *I* |

To find what $GOH$ is, locate the row labeled $G$ on the left and the column headed by $H$. They intersect in the letter $H$, so we conclude from the table that

$$GOH = H.$$

The table states that $HOG = G$ since the letter $G$ lies at the intersection of row $H$ with column $G$.

## Exercise 1.4

**1.** Write out the operation tables for all of the binary operations on the set $S = \{x, y\}$, and determine which are commutative and which are associative.

**2.** How many binary operations has the set $S = \{a, b, c, d\}$? Explain.

**3.** What sort of symmetry (if any) does the operation table of a commutative binary operation possess?

**4.** Define *ternary operation* on a set $S$. Give an example of a ternary operation on the points of a plane.

**5.** Prove that the operation of Example 3 is associative.

**6.** Let **O** and **Q** be two operations on a set $S$. **O** is said to be *distributive* over **Q** from the left if

$$x\mathbf{O}(y\mathbf{Q}z) = (x\mathbf{O}y)\mathbf{Q}(x\mathbf{O}z).$$

Determine whether the operations of Examples 1 and 2 possess any such property.

**7.** Extend the concept of a binary operation on a set $S$ to the case where the "product" lies in a set $T$. Illustrate.

**8.** Is the Cartesian product of $S$ with itself a binary operation on $S$? Explain.

**9.** Let $S$ be a set with an operation **O**. An element $e$ of $S$ is called a *left identity element* if $e\mathbf{O}s = s$ for every $s$ in $S$, and a *right identity element* if $s\mathbf{O}e = s$ for every $s$ in $S$. Find the left and right identity elements (if any) of the examples of this section. Find the identities for Problem 1 above.

**10.** Let $S$ be a set with an operation **O**. An element $z$ of $S$ is called a *left zero* if $z\mathbf{O}s = z$ for every $s$ in $S$, and a *right zero* if $s\mathbf{O}z = z$ for every $s$ in $S$. Find the zeros of Examples 1–4 of this section.

**11.** An operation **O** on a set $S$ is said to have the *left cancellation property* if, for arbitrary elements $a$, $b$, and $c$ of $S$, the equation

$$a\mathbf{O}b = a\mathbf{O}c$$

implies that $b = c$. Determine whether the operations in Examples 1–4 of this section have this property.

**12.** Let $S$ be a set with an operation **O**. An element $s$ of $S$ is called *idempotent* if $s\mathbf{O}s = s$. Determine the indempotent elements in Examples 1, 2, and 4 of this section.

**13.** Prove that, if a set $S$ with operation **O** has a left identity element $e$ and a right identity element $f$, then $e = f$. (*Hint:* Consider $e\mathbf{O}f$.)

**14.** An operation **O** on a set $S$ is said to be *invertible* if for any two elements $a$ and $b$ of $S$ there exist elements $r$ and $s$ in $S$ such that $a\mathbf{O}r = s\mathbf{O}a = b$. Find an invertible operation **O** on the set

$$S = \{a, b, c, d\}.$$

What special property does the operation table of an invertible operation have?

## 1.5 Abstract Systems

Thus far in this chapter we have assembled a sizable collection of concepts (undefined and defined), terms, and notations, and we have illustrated these with examples which were sometimes intuitive, sometimes elementary (even trivial), and often rather sophisticated. Our stated objective was to develop a common language, a dictionary, we might say. Now we shall indicate our purpose in doing this by describing in a very general way the remaining contents of the book.

Not very many years ago algebra was considered to be merely symbolic arithmetic (a view which is still not uncommon). In arithmetic calculations specific numbers were used while letters representing numbers were used in algebraic calculations. Eventually mathematicians became aware that some of the symbolic statements from this generalized arithmetic, which were true when the symbols were replaced by numbers (such as the integers or fractions), were also true when the symbols were replaced by various other "objects." Thus algebra evolved into the study of mathematical systems which have many of the properties of the "ordinary" number system.

What is a mathematical system? Using the terms from our dictionary (and relying heavily upon our intuition) we define the term as it is used in this book.

DEFINITION 1.12. A *mathematical system* $S$ is a set $S = \{E, O, A\}$ where $E$ is a nonempty set of elements, $O$ is a set of relations and operations on $E$, and $A$ is a set of axioms concerning the elements of $E$ and $O$. The elements of $E$ are called the elements of the system.

Inasmuch as certain concepts have been assumed or defined for the sets $E$ and $O$, they are also taken to be part of $S$. We shall take equality of elements in $E$ as the basic equivalence relation of every mathematical system.

A mathematical system is analyzed by introducing definitions, new relations, new operations, etc., into the system (if possible and if needed) and proving theorems concerning the various elements of components of the system. The resulting body is usually designated the *theory* of the system.

A system $S = \{E, O, A\}$ is classified as *abstract* if the elements of the sets $E$ and $O$ are undefined except as their properties, which are set forth by $A$, define them. Otherwise it is thought of as a *concrete system*, a special case of an abstract system.

Finally we note that systems which possess many of the properties of the systems of integers (frequently because they were created by abstracting from certain properties of the integers) are called *algebraic systems*. (There are also geometrical systems, topological systems, etc.)

Thus a brief description of the remaining chapters of this book is given by the phrase, "A study of the elementary properties of certain concrete and abstract algebraic systems." The table of contents provides information on *which* elementary properties and *what* concrete and abstract algebraic systems, but further amplification is due.

In the next chapter we will initiate a careful study of the system of integers (the ordinary whole numbers) which is designed to mesh the student's knowledge of arithmetic with the material of this first chapter. In other words we plan to develop a portion of the Theory of Numbers in such a way that the student will reinforce and clarify his understanding of the material in this chapter and also add to his knowledge of the integers.

Then we shall study some abstract algebraic systems, which, being algebraic, have some features in common with the system of integers. These common features enable us, *sometimes*, to extend or generalize concepts of the number system to the abstract systems. The success, and sometimes the failure, of these efforts to generalize, by analogy, numerical properties to an abstract algebraic system $S$ leads to increased understanding of $S$. Knowledge of $S$ of course applies also to any mathematical system, concrete or abstract, which satisfies the axiom set of $S$. This accounts for the power of the abstract approach.

Other concrete algebraic systems are also studied, but there is no need to mention them here except to say that they involve physical and mathematical concepts which are generally known to some extent by college and university students as well as many high school students. These concrete systems serve as spawning and testing grounds for conjectures about the abstract systems, provide illustrations of abstract results, and in general prevent the study of abstract algebra from being just a game with words.

Now we shall illustrate the terms introduced in this section. Let $E$ be a set of elements denoted by $a, b, c, \cdots$, let $\mathbf{O}$ and $\mathbf{Q}$ be two binary operations on $E$, and let $A$ consist of the following axioms:

*Axiom* 1. The operations $\mathbf{O}$ and $\mathbf{Q}$ are commutative.

*Axiom* 2. There exist unequal elements $e$ and $z$ in $E$ such that, for each $x \in E$,

$$z\mathbf{O}x = x\mathbf{O}z = x \quad \text{and} \quad e\mathbf{Q}x = x\mathbf{Q}e = x.$$

*Axiom* 3. Each operation is distributive over the other:

$$a\mathbf{O}(b\mathbf{Q}c) = (a\mathbf{O}b)\mathbf{Q}(a\mathbf{O}c) \quad \text{and} \quad a\mathbf{Q}(b\mathbf{O}c) = (a\mathbf{Q}b)\mathbf{O}(a\mathbf{Q}c).$$

*Axiom* 4. For each $a \in E$ there is an element $a' \in E$ such that

$$a\mathbf{O}a' = e \quad \text{and} \quad a\mathbf{Q}a' = z.$$

The set $S = \{E, O, A\}$, where $O = \{\mathbf{O}, \mathbf{Q}\}$, is an abstract algebraic system called a *Boolean ring*.

Several questions can and should be considered. Are there examples of such a system (i.e., do concrete systems whose components can be interpreted in the above manner exist)? How is the abstract system to be analyzed (i.e., how does one formulate propositions which are apt to be true in this system)? Why should we attempt to analyze this system?

To answer the first question, let $R$ be an arbitrary nonempty set and let $E$ be the set of all subsets of $R$. Then the set

$$S' = \{E, O, A\},$$

where $O$ is the empty set and $A$ is the set of axioms for sets discussed in Section 1.1 (i.e., the assumption of the understanding of the meaning of membership and the Axiom of Extent), is a concrete system. In this system we *defined* two binary operations by defining two rules of combination, union and intersection, and we *proved* (with the student's help) that these two operations are commutative and that each is distributive over the other. Also we know that the subsets $R$ and $\varnothing$, which are elements of $E$, are elements such that, for each $x \in E$,

$$\varnothing \cup x = x \cup \varnothing = x \quad \text{and} \quad R \cap x = x \cap R = x,$$

and $R \neq \varnothing$ since $R$ is nonempty. Finally we can prove easily that, if $x \in E$, then $R - x$ is an element of $E$ and has the property that

$$x \cup (R - x) = R \quad \text{and} \quad x \cap (R - x) = \varnothing.$$

Therefore, since a theorem proved in a system has all the validity of an axiom of the system, we conclude that this concrete system is a Boolean ring (i.e., an example of the abstract concept of a Boolean ring).

The second question is, in a sense, unanswerable since it is unlikely that any system can be "completely" known. However, conjectures which result in theorems are usually the result of reasoning by analogy, abstracting from examples, and/or manipulation of a formal symbolism. Considerable ingenuity is often required and displayed in the formulating of conjectures as well as in proving theorems.

If we consider the operations **O** and **Q** of an abstract Boolean ring as abstract addition and abstract multiplication, respectively, and adopt the usual symbolism of $+$ and $\cdot$, then the equations of Axiom 2 can be written as

$$z + x = x + z = x \quad \text{and} \quad e \cdot x = x \cdot e = x.$$

This formulation suggests that $z$ is rather like the number zero and that $e$ resembles the number one. These numbers are known to have some remarkable properties. They are, for example, the only two integers which are idempotent relative to multiplication. So we conjecture that $e$ and $z$ are idempotent relative to **Q**, the abstract multiplication of a Boolean ring, and that they are the only elements of $E$ with this property. Testing this conjecture on our concrete example of a Boolean ring we decide that all elements of $E$ must be idempotent relative to each of the two operations. This is indeed the case.

THEOREM 1.13. *If $x$ is an element of $E$, then*

$$x + x = x \quad \textit{and} \quad x \cdot x = x.$$

*Proof.*

$$x = x \cdot e \quad \text{by Axiom 2,}$$
$$x \cdot e = x \cdot (x + x') \quad \text{by Axiom 4,}$$
$$x \cdot (x + x') = (x \cdot x) + (x \cdot x') \quad \text{by Axiom 3,}$$
$$(x \cdot x) + (x \cdot x') = (x \cdot x) + z \quad \text{by Axiom 4,}$$
$$(x \cdot x) + z = x \cdot x \quad \text{by Axiom 2,}$$

and

$$x = x \cdot x \quad \text{by transitivity.}$$

Instead of proving directly that $x + x = x$ we note that a curious duality exists in the axioms of a Boolean ring. If the symbols **O** and **Q** (or $+$ and $\cdot$) and $e$ and $z$ are interchanged, **O** with **Q** and $e$ with $z$, there is *no* resulting change in the statements. This formal manipulation suggests and essentially proves a very basic theorem in Boolean rings.

THEOREM 1.14. *A theorem in a Boolean ring remains valid if the operations* **O** *and* **Q** *and the identity elements e and z are interchanged throughout the statement.*

This is the Principle of Duality of Boolean rings. Thus the other part of Theorem 1.13 follows from the proved part by duality.

Another well-known property of the number zero suggests the next result.

THEOREM 1.15. *For any element a of E,* $a \cdot z = z$.

*Proof.*

$$a \cdot z = (a \cdot z) + z \quad \text{by Axiom 2,}$$
$$(a \cdot z) + z = (a \cdot z) + (a \cdot a') \quad \text{by Axiom 4,}$$
$$(a \cdot z) + (a \cdot a') = a \cdot (z + a') \quad \text{by Axiom 3,}$$
$$a \cdot (z + a') = a \cdot a' \quad \text{by Axiom 2,}$$
$$a \cdot a' = z \quad \text{by Axiom 4,}$$

and

$$a \cdot z = z \quad \text{by transitivity.}$$

The dual of this result shows that analogies often are imperfect.

THEOREM 1.15*b*. *For any element a of E,* $a + e = e$.

We suggested above that $e$ in Boolean rings resembled the number one. Clearly this analogy is not exact.

Abstracting from the properties of set union and intersection we conclude that the operations **O** and **Q** should be associative, and we can prove this as follows.

THEOREM 1.16. *If a, b, and c are elements of E, then*

$$a + (b + c) = (a + b) + c \quad \textit{and} \quad a \cdot (b \cdot c) = (a \cdot b) \cdot c.$$

Before proving this we prove a result which is needed several times in the proof of the theorem.

*Lemma* 1.1. If $a$ and $b$ are elements of $E$, then

$$a \cdot (a + b) = a \quad \text{and} \quad a + (a \cdot b) = a.$$

*Proof of Lemma.*

$$\begin{aligned} a \cdot (a + b) &= (a + z) \cdot (a + b) && \text{by Axiom 2,} \\ (a + z) \cdot (a + b) &= a + (z \cdot b) && \text{by Axiom 3,} \\ a + (z \cdot b) &= a + z && \text{by Theorem 1.15,} \\ a + z &= a && \text{by Axiom 2,} \end{aligned}$$

and

$$a + (a \cdot b) = a \quad \text{by transitivity.}$$

The other statement follows by duality.

*Proof of Theorem.* Denote the elements $a + (b + c)$ and $(a + b) + c$ as $x$ and $y$, respectively. Then

$$\begin{aligned} a \cdot x &= (a \cdot a) + \big(a \cdot (b + c)\big) && \text{by Axiom 3,} \\ (a \cdot a) + \big(a \cdot (b + c)\big) &= a + \big(a \cdot (b + c)\big) && \text{by Theorem 1.13,} \\ a + \big(a \cdot (b + c)\big) &= a && \text{by Lemma 1.1,} \end{aligned}$$

and

$$a \cdot x = a \quad \text{by transitivity.}$$

Similarly

$$a \cdot y = a,$$

so that we have

$$a \cdot x = a \cdot y.$$

Now we show that $a' \cdot x = a' \cdot y$.

$$\begin{aligned} a' \cdot x &= (a' \cdot a) + \big(a' \cdot (b + c)\big) && \text{by Axiom 3,} \\ a' \cdot a + \big(a' \cdot (b + c)\big) &= a' \cdot (b + c) && \text{by Axioms 4 and 2,} \end{aligned}$$

and

$$\begin{aligned} a' \cdot x &= a' \cdot (b + c). \\ a' \cdot y &= \big(a' \cdot (a + b)\big) + (a' \cdot c) && \text{by Axiom 3,} \\ \big(a' \cdot (a + b)\big) + (a' \cdot c) &= \big((a' \cdot a) + (a' \cdot b)\big) + (a' \cdot c) && \text{by Axiom 3,} \\ \big((a' \cdot a) + (a' \cdot b)\big) + (a' \cdot c) &= (a' \cdot b) + (a' \cdot c) && \text{since } a' \cdot a = z, \\ (a' \cdot b) + (a' \cdot c) &= a' \cdot (b + c) && \text{by Axiom 3,} \end{aligned}$$

so that

$$a' \cdot x = a' \cdot y = a' \cdot (b + c).$$

Now an operation is a function, and a function we know maps equal elements onto equal elements. Therefore

$$(a \cdot x) + (a' \cdot x) = (a \cdot y) + (a' \cdot y).$$

Distributivity reduces this equation to the simpler equation

$$(a + a') \cdot x = (a + a') \cdot y,$$

and since $a + a' = e$ we conclude that $x = y$. Therefore

$$a + (b + c) = (a + b) + c.$$

The other half of the theorem follows from the Principle of Duality.

We recall that the subsets of a set are partially ordered by set inclusion, so we ask if it is possible to define a partial order in a Boolean ring. One of our set theoretic theorems stated that, for two subsets $A$ and $B$ of a set $W$,

$$A \cap B = B \qquad \text{if and only if } A \supseteq B.$$

Abstracting from this we define a relation **R** in a Boolean ring with the rule

$$a\mathbf{R}b \qquad \text{means} \qquad a \cdot b = b.$$

Whether **R** is a partial order on $E$ is left for the student to determine.

Many other theorems on Boolean rings are easily discovered and proved although the subject is by no means a trivial one. We shall not, however, develop the subject any further since we introduced the concept only to illustrate our general discussion of systems.

Finally, why should we attempt to analyze this (or any other) abstract system? This is a very subjective question which each person must answer for himself. Some people claim to study abstract algebra for its "beauty" and "purity"; other people find their curiosity aroused. Then, too, many systems, such as Boolean rings, have their useful applications. We note that Boolean ring theory has considerable importance in the analysis and design of electrical networks. (See the article by F. Hohn mentioned in the suggested reading list at the end of the chapter.)

## Exercise 1.5

**1.** Prove the following theorems about Boolean rings:

(*a*) To each elements $a \in E$ there corresponds exactly one element $a'$ such that

$$a + a' = e \qquad \text{and} \qquad a \cdot a' = z.$$

(*b*) The relation **R**, defined by $a\mathbf{R}b$ if and only if $a \cdot b = b$, is a partial order in a Boolean ring.

(*c*) For any $a \in E$, $e\mathbf{R}a$ and $a\mathbf{R}z$.

**2.** If **O** is a binary operation on a set $S$, if $a, b, c$ are elements, and if $a = b$, then

$$a\mathbf{O}c = b\mathbf{O}c.$$

This is sometimes referred to as "true by substitution," but, using the definition of operation, state the real justification.

**3.** Give an example of an abstract geometric system.

**4.** Prove in Boolean rings that, if

$$a + b = a + c \qquad \textit{and} \qquad a \cdot b = a \cdot c,$$

then $b = c$.

**5.** Show that the set $E = \{e, z\}$ and the binary operations defined by the following operation tables constitute an example of a Boolean ring:

| O | e | z |
|---|---|---|
| e | e | e |
| z | e | z |

| Q | e | z |
|---|---|---|
| e | e | z |
| z | z | z |

Compare this with the Boolean ring of all subsets of the set $W = \{w\}$.

**6.** Write out the operation tables for the Boolean ring of all subsets of the set

$$T = \{s, t\}.$$

(The operations are given by set union and intersection.)

**7.** Abstracting from known properties of set difference, define difference of two elements in a Boolean ring. (*Hint:* Consider $a - b = (a' + b)'$.)

**8.** Let $E$ be a nonempty set of whole numbers, and let two binary operations on $E$ be defined by the rules:

$$a * b = \text{smaller of } a \text{ and } b$$

(or either if $a = b$),

$$a \bigcirc b = \text{larger of } a \text{ and } b$$

(or either if $a = b$).

When is the resulting mathematical system a Boolean ring? Compare with Problem 5 when $E = \{0, 1\}$.

## 1.6 Suggested Reading

*Articles*

Denbow, C. H., "Postulates and mathematics," *Amer. Math. Monthly*, **62** (1955), 233–236.

Guy, W. T., Jr., "On equivalence relations," *Amer. Math. Monthly*, **62** (1955), 179.

Hohn, F., "Some mathematical aspects of switching," *Amer. Math. Monthly*, **62** (1955), 75–90.

McShane, E. J., "Operating with sets," *Twenty-Third Yearbook, National Council of Teachers of Mathematics* (1957), 36–64.

Rosenbaum, R. A. "Remark on equivalence relations," *Amer. Math. Monthly*, **62** (1955), 650.

Stabler, E. R., "Boolean algebra as an introduction to postulational methods," *Amer. Math. Monthly*, **51** (1944), 106–110.

Thielman, H. P., "On definition of functions," *Amer. Math. Monthly*, **60** (1953), 259–262.

*Books*

Christian, R. R., *Introduction to Logic and Sets*, Ginn & Company, Boston, 1958.

Eves, H., and C. V. Newsom, *Introduction to the Foundations and Fundamental Concepts of Mathematics*, Rinehart & Company, New York, 1958.

Halmos, P., *Naive Set Theory*, D. Van Nostrand Company, Princeton, N.J., 1960.

Henkin, L., W. N. Smith, V. J. Varineau, and M. J. Walsh, *Retracing Elementary Mathematics*, The Macmillan Company, New York, 1962.

Hohn, F., *Applied Boolean Algebra*, 2nd ed., The Macmillan Company, New York, 1964.

Kelley, J. L., *Introduction to Modern Algebra*, D. Van Nostrand Company, Princeton, N.J., 1960.

Kershner, R., and L. Wilcox, *The Anatomy of Mathematics*, Ronald Press, New York, 1950.

Northrop, E. P. (and staff), *Fundamental Mathematics*, vol. 1, University of Chicago Press, Chicago, 1948.

Wilder, R. L., *Introduction to the Foundations of Mathematics*, John Wiley & Sons, New York, 1952.

# 2

# The Basic Number Systems

IN THIS CHAPTER, the system of natural numbers, the system of integers, and the rational number system are introduced in a fashion consistent with the discussion in the preceding chapter. The natural number system is treated axiomatically, the system of integers is developed as a particular system based on the natural number system (and thereby requiring no additional axioms), and the rational numbers are obtained from the integers in the same manner. This development does not reveal any new "facts" about the numbers discussed, but it does establish a reasonably clearly defined basis from which to proceed in our study of algebraic systems.

Certainly every educated person is familiar (to some degree) with the axiomatic development of plane geometry by Euclid. However, not so many people know that numbers can be introduced in a similar fashion since this treatment is of modern origin, stemming from the work of such late nineteenth-century mathematicians as R. Dedekind and G. Peano. Thus the ideas and methods of this chapter can properly be called both classical and modern.

## 2.1 The Natural Number System

There are many different sets of axioms which can be used in discussing the natural numbers, or any other system, since any theorem which can be proved in a system can also be incorporated into the axiom set of the system. (Such a process naturally requires knowledge of at least one set of axioms.) A small set of axioms can be useful in deciding the question of consistency (i.e., the existence or nonexistence of contradictions in the system) but since this thorny problem is dodged in this book such a criterion is of no consequence. A large set of axioms, on the other hand, is often selected by authors or teachers in order to avoid certain difficulties of presentation. A compromise approach is attempted here.

DEFINITION 2.1. The *system of natural numbers* consists of a set $N$, two binary operations on $N$ which are called *addition* and *multiplication* and are symbolized by $+$ and $\cdot$, and the following axioms:

*Axiom* A. $N$ contains exactly one element, denoted by 1, with the property that

$$a \cdot 1 = 1 \cdot a = a$$

for each $a \in N$.

*Axiom* B. For each $a$ and each $b$ of $N$,

$$a \cdot (b + 1) = (a \cdot b) + a.$$

*Axiom* C. For each $a$ and each $b$ of $N$,

$$a + (b + 1) = (a + b) + 1.$$

*Axiom* D. For each $a \neq 1$ in $N$ there is a unique element $b$ of $N$ such that $a = b + 1$.

*Axiom* E. For given elements $a$ and $b$ of $N$ exactly one of the three equations,

$$a = b, \qquad a + x = b, \qquad a = b + y,$$

where $x$ and $y$ are in $N$, is valid.

*Axiom* F. If $M$ is a subset of $N$ with the properties

(i) $$1 \in M,$$

and

(ii) $k + 1$ is in $M$ whenever the element $k$ (of $N$) is in $M$,

then $M = N$.

The elements of $N$ are referred to as the *natural numbers*, and the system of natural numbers is denoted by

$$\{N, +, \cdot\}$$

or, more usually, by the letter $N$. The familiar symbolism for the elements of $N$ is used.

A little thought should convince almost anyone that these axioms indeed embody properties that natural numbers should intuitively be expected to have. But how about all of the other properties we believe the natural number to possess? Certainly the most familiar of these must be proved in order to justify our labeling of the mathematical system above the natural number system.

In carrying out this program we will not only show what can be developed from this rather limited set of axioms but also demonstrate a type of proof, called *mathematical induction*, which is basic to all of mathematics. This method of proof is a consequence of Axiom F which is sometimes called the

Axiom of Induction. (Do *not* confuse "mathematical induction" with "inductive reasoning"!)

THEOREM 2.1 (PRINCIPLE OF MATHEMATICAL INDUCTION). *Let $P(n)$ be a proposition defined for each natural number $n$. Then $P(n)$ is true for every natural number $n$ if ($a$) $P(1)$ is true, and ($b$) $P(k + 1)$ is true whenever $P(k)$ is true.*

A *proposition* $P(n)$ is understood here to be a statement involving the natural number $n$ which is either true or false for each particular value of $n$.

To prove the theorem we take $M$ to be the set of exactly those natural numbers for which the proposition is true. By part ($a$) of the hypothesis $1 \in M$ and by part ($b$) of the hypothesis $k + 1$ belongs to $M$ whenever the natural number $k$ belongs to $M$. Therefore from Axiom F we conclude that $M = N$, which means that $P(n)$ is true for every natural number.

The student should observe that since there are two parts to the hypothesis of this theorem a proof based on the Principle of Mathematical Induction should be given in two parts, the first being a verification of the validity of $P(1)$.

THEOREM 2.2 (ASSOCIATIVITY OF ADDITION). *The proposition*

$$P(n)\colon a + (b + n) = (a + b) + n$$

*for any natural numbers $a$ and $b$, is true for every natural number $n$.*

$P(1)$ is certainly true in our system since it is precisely Axiom C. So now we try to show that, *when* $P(k)$ is true, then $P(k + 1)$ is true also. If this can be done, then the theorem is itself a true statement by the Principle of Mathematical Induction (and we say the theorem has been proved by mathematical induction).

We wish to prove that, if $P(k)$ is true, where $k$ is an arbitrary but fixed natural number, then $P(k + 1)$ is true. This means that the truth of $P(k)$ is our hypothesis, usually referred to as the *induction hypothesis*, and we must conclude from it, *and* the axioms, definitions, and theorems valid in the system, that $P(k + 1)$ is true.

In this particular case we must prove that

$$a + \big(b + (k + 1)\big) = (a + b) + (k + 1)$$

for each $a$ and each $b$ in $N$ if

$$a + (b + k) = (a + b) + k$$

for each $a$ and each $b$ in $N$. Now

$$b + (k + 1) = (b + k) + 1$$

by Axiom C, so that, by the definition of binary operation,

$$a + \big(b + (k + 1)\big) = a + \big((b + k) + 1\big).$$

Since $(b + k)$ is an element of $N$ we conclude from Axiom C that

$$a + \big((b + k) + 1\big) = \big(a + (b + k)\big) + 1.$$

Now we use the induction hypothesis and conclude that

$$\big(a + (b + k)\big) + 1 = \big((a + b) + k\big) + 1.$$

Again since $(a + b)$ is an element of $N$ we see from Axiom C that

$$\big((a + b) + k\big) + 1 = (a + b) + (k + 1).$$

Then by the transitivity of equality we have from these equations the desired result,

$$a + \big(b + (k + 1)\big) = (a + b) + (k + 1)$$

for each $a$ and each $b$ in $N$. This completes the proof of Theorem 2.2 by mathematical induction.

Theorem 2.2, referred to as the *Associative Law* for Addition of natural numbers, establishes a key property of the binary operation of addition. (Operations which are not associative seem quite difficult to study; see the article by T. Evans listed in Suggested Reading.) Another fundamental property of addition in $N$ is the *Commutative Law.*

THEOREM 2.3 (COMMUTATIVITY OF ADDITION). *The proposition*

$$P(n)\colon a + n = n + a$$

*for each a in N, is true for every natural number n.*

First we must show that $a + 1 = 1 + a$ for each $a$ in $N$, and this is done by using mathematical induction to prove the proposition

$$P_1(n)\colon n + 1 = 1 + n.$$

To prove this proposition we note first that, by the reflexive property of equality,

$$1 + 1 = 1 + 1$$

so that $P_1(1)$ is true. Then we ask whether

$$(k + 1) + 1 = 1 + (k + 1)$$

whenever

$$k + 1 = 1 + k.$$

Consider the quantity $1 + (k + 1)$; by Axiom C we can write

$$1 + (k + 1) = (1 + k) + 1,$$

and this combined with the induction hypothesis

$$k + 1 = 1 + k$$

yields the desired result

$$1 + (k + 1) = (1 + k) + 1 = (k + 1) + 1.$$

Hence the proposition $P_1(n)$ is true for all $n \in N$ by Theorem 2.1, and we know that $a + 1 = 1 + a$ for each $a$ in $N$.

Now suppose $a + k = k + a$ for any $a \in N$ and some $k \in N$ (the induction hypothesis). Consider the element $a + (k + 1)$; by Theorem 2.2,

$$a + (k + 1) = (a + k) + 1,$$

and since $a + k = k + a$ by hypothesis, we have

$$(a + k) + 1 = (k + a) + 1.$$

Associativity implies that

$$(k + a) + 1 = k + (a + 1),$$

and since

$$a + 1 = 1 + a,$$

this means that

$$k + (a + 1) = k + (1 + a).$$

Applying the associative law again yields

$$k + (1 + a) + (k + 1) + a.$$

Thus we see that

$$a + (k + 1) = (k + 1) + a \qquad \text{for any } a \in N,$$

and the proof by mathematical induction is complete.

What about the Associative and Commutative Laws for Multiplication? How are they proved from the axioms? First we "tie" multiplication to addition by proving a distributive law; by doing this we arrange matters so that our results on addition can be used to study multiplication.

THEOREM 2.4. *If a, b, and c are any elements of N, then*

$$a \cdot (b + c) = (a \cdot b) + (a \cdot c).$$

Although this theorem is not stated in the propositional form of the previous theorems it can be recast in that form. With an eye on Axiom B, we select the form,

$$a \cdot (b + n) = (a \cdot b) + (a \cdot n)$$

for each $a$ and each $b$ in $N$, for $P(n)$. Then $P(1)$ is true by Axioms B and A.

Now our induction hypothesis states that, for any $a$ and $b$ and for some $k$ in $N$,

$$a \cdot (b + k) = (a \cdot b) + (a \cdot k).$$

Considering the element $a \cdot (b + (k + 1))$, we conclude

$$\begin{aligned} a \cdot (b + (k + 1)) &= a \cdot ((b + k) + 1) && \text{by Axiom C,} \\ a \cdot ((b + k) + 1) &= (a \cdot (b + k)) + a && \text{by Axiom B,} \\ (a \cdot (b + k)) + a &= ((a \cdot b) + (a \cdot k)) + a && \text{by induction hypothesis,} \\ ((a \cdot b) + (a \cdot k)) + a &= (a \cdot b) + ((a \cdot k) + a) && \text{by Theorem 2.2,} \\ (a \cdot b) + ((a \cdot k) + a) &= (a \cdot b) + (a \cdot (k + 1)) && \text{by Axiom B,} \end{aligned}$$

so that

$$a \cdot (b + (k + 1)) = (a \cdot b) + (a \cdot (k + 1)).$$

This completes the proof by mathematical induction of the *Left Distributive Law* for Multiplication relative to addition.

There is a Right Distributive Law for Multiplication also, and we shall state it without proof since the proof is not very different from the above.

THEOREM 2.5. *If a, b, and c are any natural numbers then*

$$(a + b) \cdot c = (a \cdot c) + (b \cdot c).$$

Theorems 2.5 and 2.6 are referred to as the *Distributive Laws for Multiplication* in $N$.

Now we can prove the *Commutative Law for Multiplication.*

THEOREM 2.6 (COMMUTATIVITY OF MULTIPLICATION). *For any natural numbers a and b,* $a \cdot b = b \cdot a$.

We proceed by induction on $b$, i.e., we use mathematical induction to establish the proposition

$$P(n)\colon a \cdot n = n \cdot a$$

for each $a$ in $N$. $P(1)$ is true by an axiom. Our induction hypothesis states that $a \cdot k = k \cdot a$ for each $a$ and some $k$ in $N$, and we examine the elements

$$a \cdot (k + 1) \quad \text{and} \quad (k + 1) \cdot a.$$

Using the Distributive Law for Multiplication we see that

$$a \cdot (k + 1) = (a \cdot k) + (a \cdot 1) \quad \text{and} \quad (k + 1) \cdot a = (k \cdot a) + (1 \cdot a).$$

Since $a \cdot 1 = 1 \cdot a = a$ by Axiom A and since the induction hypothesis has $a \cdot k = k \cdot a$, we conclude that

$$a \cdot (k + 1) = (k + 1) \cdot a.$$

The *Associative Law for Multiplication* is stated but not proved since the proof contributes nothing new.

THEOREM 2.7 (ASSOCIATIVITY OF MULTIPLICATION). *If a, b, and c are natural numbers then*

$$a \cdot (b \cdot c) = (a \cdot b) \cdot c.$$

The student should observe that in the proof of each theorem use is made of the previously proved theorem. Thus the order of presentation of the theorems is quite important.

The common symbols 1, 2, 3, 4, $\cdots$ are used hereafter for the elements of $N$ with the understanding that these just constitute a convenient way to denote the objects

$$1,\ 1 + 1,\ (1 + 1) + 1,\ ((1 + 1) + 1) + 1, \text{ etc.}$$

## Exercise 2.1

**1.** Restate Theorem 2.5 in propositional forms. Which form seems more promising?

**2.** How does one conclude from the definition of binary operation that $b = c$ implies $a \cdot b = a \cdot c$?

**3.** Prove Theorem 2.5.

**4.** Prove that addition is *not* distributive over multiplication. (When does $a + (b \cdot c) = (a + b) \cdot (a + c)$?)

**5.** In discussing mathematical induction it was emphasized that the proof falls into two parts. Show that it is sometimes possible to complete one part of the argument even though the proposition is *not* true, by considering the following:

(*a*) $P(1)$ is true for the proposition $P(n)$: $n = 1$.

(*b*) Prove that, for the proposition $P(n)$: $n = n + 1$, the truth of $P(k)$ implies the truth of $P(k + 1)$.

**6.** Prove the proposition

$$P(n)\colon 3 \cdot ((1 \cdot ) + (2 \cdot 3) + \cdots + (n \cdot (n \cdot (n + 1)))) = n \cdot (n + 1) \cdot (n + 2).$$

**7.** Prove the proposition $P(n)$: $n \neq n + 1$ by mathematical induction. (*Hint:* Use Axiom E.)

**8.** Prove that $a + b \neq a$ for any natural numbers $a$ and $b$. (*Hint:* Use mathematical induction on $a$, and apply Axiom E.)

**9.** Prove the following geometrical theorem by mathematical induction: The sum of the interior angles of an $(n + 2)$ sided plane polygon is $n(180°)$.

**10.** Find the error in the follow "proof" of the proposition $P(n)$: any $n$ objects are equal to one another.

(*a*) $P(1)$ is certainly true.

(*b*) Suppose $P(k)$ is true and consider the $k + 1$ objects

$$a_1, a_2, \cdots, a_k, a_{k+1}.$$

By the induction hypothesis the $k$ objects

$$a_1, a_2, \cdots, a_k$$

are equal to each other as are the $k$ objects

$$a_2, \cdots, a_k, a_{k+1}.$$

So $a_1 = a_2 = \cdots = a_k$ and $a_2 = \cdots = a_k = a_{k+1}$. Then, by transitivity,

$$a_1 = a_2 = \cdots = a_k = a_{k+1}.$$

Thus $P(n)$ is true for all natural numbers $n$.

**11.** Use the Associative Law to prove that, for $a$, $b$, $c$, and $d$ in $N$,

$$(a + b) + (c + d) = a + ((b + c) + d).$$

How would you generalize this?

**12.** If $L$ is a proper subset of $N$, then in view of the Axiom of Induction what must be true of $L$?

## 2.2 Order and Cancellation

Now we introduce a binary relation on $N$, the familar "greater than" relation, and prove that it is a linear order on $N$. This relation is one of the principal examples of a linear order.

DEFINITION 2.2. $\mathbf{R} = \{(a, b): a \text{ and } b \in N \text{ and } a = b + c \text{ for some natural number } c\}$. If $a\mathbf{R}b$, then we write $a > b$ or $b < a$ (read "$a$ is *larger than* $b$" and "$b$ is *smaller than* $a$", respectively).

Thus $2 > 1$ since $2 = 1 + 1$ and $3 < 5$ since $5 = 3 + 2$.

THEOREM 2.8 (TRICHOTOMY). *If $a$ and $b$ are natural numbers, then exactly one of the following is true:*

(i) $a = b$,
(ii) $a > b$,
(iii) $a < b$.

This is of course just a restatement of Axiom E in the terminology introduced above.

THEOREM 2.9. *The relation on $N$ symbolized by $>$ is transitive.*

To prove this we must show that, if $a > b$ and $b > c$, then $a > c$. By definition $a > b$ means that there is a natural number $x$ such that

$$a = b + x,$$

and $b > c$ means that

$$b = c + y \qquad \text{for some } y \in N.$$

Therefore

$$a = (c + y) + x$$

by the definition of binary operation, so that from associativity we conclude

$$a = c + (x + y).$$

Since $x + y$ is a natural number this equation means

$$a > c.$$

Thus the binary relation $>$ is transitive.

We recall Definition 1.7 which states that a *linear order* on a set is a relation $\mathbf{R}$ which has the properties (1) $a\mathbf{R}b$ or $b\mathbf{R}a$ if $a \neq b$, (2) $a \not\mathbf{R} a$, and (3) $\mathbf{R}$ is transitive.

THEOREM 2.10. *The binary relation $>$ is a linear order on the natural numbers.*

This is an immediate consequence of Theorems 2.8 and 2.9.

There is a geometric interpretation of this linear order which is basic to analytic geometry. If two distinct points and a direction, called "right", along a line are selected arbitrarily, then the natural numbers can be represented by equispaced points as indicated in Fig. 2.1. Then $a > b$ means that the point corresponding to $a$ lies to the right of the point corresponding to $b$.

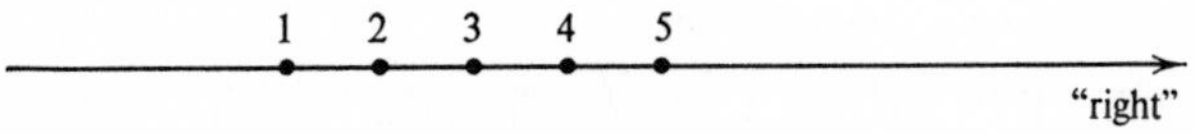


**Figure 2.1**

Since the relation "greater than" is defined by using the operation of addition we should expect it to have further associations with the binary operations of $N$.

THEOREM 2.11. *If $a$ and $b$ are natural numbers such that $a > b$, then, for each $n \in N$,*

(i) $$a + n > b + n,$$
(ii) $$a \cdot n > b \cdot n.$$

The statement $a > b$ means that $a = b + c$ for some natural number $c$. Then

$$a + n = (b + c) + n = b + (c + n) = b + (n + c) = (b + n) + c,$$

so that

$$a + n > b + n$$

for each $n \in N$.
Similarly, equations

$$a \cdot n = (b + c) \cdot n = (b \cdot n) + (c \cdot n)$$

mean that

$$a \cdot n > b \cdot n.$$

This theorem and the Trichotomy Law for the natural numbers enable us to prove the "Cancellation Laws" for Addition and Multiplication. (These the student will recognize as versions of the intuitive concepts of "subtraction" and "division.")

THEOREM 2.12 (CANCELLATION LAW FOR ADDITION). *If $a$, $b$, and $c$ are natural numbers such that $a + c = b + c$, then $a = b$.*

Consider the natural numbers $a$ and $b$. By the Trichotomy Law exactly one of the following is valid:

$$a = b, \qquad a > b, \qquad b > a.$$

If we can show that the hypothesis excludes the two possibilities $a > b$ and $b > a$ (or $a < b$), then we have proved the theorem. So suppose $a > b$; then by Theorem 2.11,

$$a + c > b + c.$$

But this is impossible since we are given that

$$a + c = b + c.$$

Therefore the possibility $a > b$ leads to a contradiction of the hypothesis. Similarly $b > a$ is ruled out by the hypothesis since

$$b + c > a + c$$

is incompatible with the given equation $b + c = a + c$.

Thus the theorem is proved.

In the same manner the Cancellation Law for Multiplication of natural numbers is proved.

THEOREM 2.13 (CANCELLATION LAW FOR MULTIPLICATION). *If $a$, $b$, and $c$ are natural numbers such that*

$$a \cdot c = b \cdot c,$$

*then $a = b$.*

This method of proof is called *proof by contradiction*. In this type of proof we assume that the desired conclusion is indeed false and deduce from this assumption a statement which contradicts a statement known or given to be true. In the above proof we assume that $a$ is *not* equal to $b$ and conclude from that assumption, using trichotomy and Theorem 2.11, that either

$$a + c > b + c \quad \text{or} \quad b + c > a + c,$$

a statement which contradicts the given condition, $a + c = b + c$.

The Cancellation Laws can also be extended to cover inequalities.

THEOREM 2.14. *Let $a$, $b$, and $c$ be natural numbers.*

(i) *If $(a + c) > (b + c)$, then $a > b$.*
(ii) *If $a \cdot c > b \cdot c$, then $a > b$.*

This is the converse of Theorem 2.11 and is proved by using Theorem 2.11 and the Trichotomy Law.

A basic property of the natural numbers is illustrated by the "equi-spacing" of the geometric representation mentioned above.

THEOREM 2.15. *If $a$ is a natural number, then there is no natural number $n$ such that $a < n < a + 1$.*

Suppose there is such an $n$. Then by definition of $<$ there are natural numbers $x$ and $y$ such that

$$a + x = n \qquad \text{and} \qquad n + y = a + 1.$$

Therefore

$$(a + x) + y = a + 1,$$
$$a + (x + y) = a + 1,$$

and

$$x + y = 1 \qquad \text{by cancellation.}$$

Now by Axiom D either $y = 1$ or $y = t + 1$ for some natural number $t$. Then either

$$x + 1 = 1, \quad \text{when } y = 1,$$

or

$$x + (t + 1) = (x + t) + 1 = 1, \quad \text{when } y = t + 1.$$

Since both of these conclusions violate Axiom E (see Problem 7 of Exercise 2.1), our assumption that such an $n$ exists in $N$ leads to a contradiction, and the theorem is proved.

## Exercise 2.2

**1.** Let $a$, $b$, and $c$ be natural numbers such that $a = b$ and $b > c$. Prove that $a > c$. (*Hint:* Use Axiom of Pair Equality.)

**2.** Define the relation symbolized by $\leqslant$. Is it a linear order on $N$? Explain.

**3.** Prove Theorem 2.13.

**4.** Prove Theorem 2.14.

**5.** Prove that, if $a$, $b$, $c$, and $d$ are natural numbers such that

$$a > b \qquad \text{and} \qquad c > d,$$

then

$$a \cdot c > b \cdot d \qquad \text{and} \qquad a + c > b + d.$$

**6.** Prove that, if $a$, $b$, and $c$ are natural numbers such that

$$a = b \cdot c \qquad \text{and} \qquad c > 1,$$

then $a > b$. (*Hint:* Use Axiom D.)

**7.** Prove the proposition $P(n)$: $1 \leqslant n$ for all natural numbers $n$.

**8.** Replace Axiom E by Axiom E′: There is no natural number $c$ such that $1 = c + 1$. Now prove Axiom E as a theorem by mathematical induction.

**9.** Prove that, if $a$ and $b$ are natural numbers such that $a < b + 1$, then $a \leqslant b$.

**10.** The symbols $<$ and $>$ can stand for two *different* dual relations where (1, 2) belongs to one but not the other. Examine the definition of relation and explain.

## 2.3 Well-Ordering

The geometric representation of the linear order on $N$ which was mentioned in the previous section is based on the intuitive idea of ordering points on a line through the use of the concept of direction. Thus the set of points on a line serves as a model of a linearly ordered set. Yet this example does *not* have one of the basic order properties possessed by the natural numbers. This is one reason only some of the points are used in the geometric representation.

DEFINITION 2.3. A set $S$ is said to be *well-ordered* by a linear order $\mathbf{R}$ if each nonempty subset $T$ of $S$ contains an element $m$ with the property that if

$$t \in T \quad \text{and} \quad t \neq m$$

then $t\mathbf{R}m$. The element $m$ is called a *smallest element* of $T$.

It is a simple matter to show that a nonempty subset $T$ of a set with a linear order $\mathbf{R}$ can have at most one smallest element. For $a\mathbf{R}b$ and $b\mathbf{R}a$ cannot *both* hold in a linearly ordered set. Thus we may speak of *the* smallest element in discussing well-ordering.

THEOREM 2.16 (WELL-ORDERING THEOREM). *The natural numbers are well ordered* by $>$.

To prove this we must show that a nonempty set of natural numbers possesses a smallest element. Let $S$ be such a set. Certainly if $1 \in S$, then 1 is the smallest element of $S$ since by Axiom D 1 is smaller than any natural number $a \neq 1$. So we need only consider the case where $1 \notin S$. In this case we deal with the set $S'$ consisting of those natural numbers which are smaller than *every* element of $S$. By the above remark about 1 we see that $1 \in S'$. What else can we say about $S'$? In particular $S' \neq N$ since $S'$ is a subset of $N - S$ which must be a proper subset of $N$ due to the condition, $S \neq \varnothing$.

Now we regard the Axiom of Induction, Axiom F. This says that a set $M$ of natural numbers with the two properties

(i) $$1 \in M,$$

(ii) $$k + 1 \text{ is in } M \text{ whenever } k \text{ is in } M,$$

is in fact the set $N$. Since

$$1 \in S' \quad \text{but} \quad S' \neq N$$

we conclude that $S'$ cannot have property (ii). This means that there is at least one natural number $k$ in $S'$ for which $k + 1$ is *not* in $S'$.

Let $k$ be such a natural number (i.e., $k \in S'$, $k + 1 \notin S'$). Then we claim that $k + 1$ is a smallest (and by the above discussion, *the* smallest) element of $S$. Since $k + 1$ is not in $S'$ it must, by trichotomy, be greater than or equal to some element of $S$. But if $k + 1$ is greater than some element $s$ of $S$, then we have a natural number $s$ such that

$$k < s < k + 1.$$

Since this is impossible by Theorem 2.15, we conclude that $k + 1$ is an element of $S$ which is not greater than any other element of $S$. Thus $S$ has a smallest element in all cases.

(Loosely speaking, we have "counted through" the elements of $S'$ to get to the first, or smallest, number in $S$.)

This result is such a basic one that it is frequently taken as an axiom instead of Axiom F. We can show that this is a reasonable approach to the natural numbers by proving Axiom F as a theorem when the Well-Ordering Theorem is assumed as an axiom in its place.

THEOREM 2.17. *If Theorem* 2.16 *is taken as an axiom, Axiom F*, then Axiom F can be proved true.*

Let $M$ be a set of natural numbers such that

(i) $$1 \in M,$$

(ii) $$k + 1 \text{ is in } M \text{ whenever } k \text{ is in } M.$$

Using Axiom F* we wish to prove that $M = N$. We do this by proving that $N - M = \varnothing$. For if $N - M$, which we denote by $S$, is *not* empty it contains a smallest element $s$ by Axiom F*. Since $1 \in M$, $1 \notin S$ and so $s \neq 1$. Then by Axiom D there is a natural number $t$ such that $s = t + 1$. Since $s$ is the smallest element of $S$ and since $t < s$ we conclude that $t \in M$. But we are given that $k + 1$ is in $M$ whenever $k$ is, so $t \in M$ implies $t + 1 = s$ is in $M$. Since $M \cap S = \varnothing$, an element cannot belong to both $M$ and $S$, and so the assumption $S \neq \varnothing$ has led to a contradiction, thereby proving that $M = N$.

Since mathematical induction is based on Axiom F we could also base it on Theorem 2.17. We can also use the Well-Ordering Theorem to obtain a slightly different method of proof which is very helpful.

THEOREM 2.18 (SECOND PRINCIPLE OF INDUCTION). *If a proposition $P(n)$ is true for $n = k + 1$ whenever it is true for* all *values of $n \leqslant k$, and if $P(1)$ is true, then $P(n)$ is true for all natural numbers $n$.*

Consider the set $S$ of natural numbers for which $P(n)$ is *not* true. If $S$ is not empty, then it contains a smallest element $s$. As $s \neq 1$ there is a natural $k$ such that $k + 1 = s$. This means that $P(n)$ is true for all natural numbers less than $k + 1$ since no such natural number can be in $S$. But our hypothesis says that $P(k + 1)$ is true whenever $P(n)$ is true for all $n \leqslant k$. This contradiction (i.e., that $P(k + 1)$ is both true and not true) proves the theorem.

We recognize that the Second Principle of Induction provides us with more working material than the previously used Principle of Mathematical Induction since the induction hypothesis in the second method is the assumption that $P(n)$ is true for all $n \leqslant k$.

## Exercise 2.3

1. Give three examples of linearly ordered sets which are not well-ordered.
2. Let $S$ be the set $S = \{a, b, c, d\}$ and $T$ be the set

$$T = \{S, \{a, b, c\}, \{a, b\}, \{b, c, d\}, \{b, c\}, \{c, d\}\}.$$

Show that $T$, relative to the partial ordering of set inclusion, has several "minimal" elements. Illustrate with a nodal diagram.

3. Write out a proof of the statement that each nonempty subset of a well-ordered set has a unique minimal or smallest element.

4. A subset $T \neq \varnothing$ of a set $S$ with a linear order $\mathbf{R}$ which is read as "less than" is said to have an *upper bound* if there is an element $s$ in $S$ such that $t\mathbf{R}s$ for each $t \neq s$, $t \in T$. Prove that, if a set of natural numbers has an upper bound (which is not necessarily in the set), then it contains a largest element. (*Hint:* Consider the set of all upper bounds.)

5. Prove the Third Principle of Induction: If $P(n)$ is true for all $n \leqslant d$, where $d$ is a fixed natural number, and if, for each natural number $m$, $P(m + d)$ is true whenever $P(k)$ is true for all natural numbers $k$ such that $m \leqslant k < m + d$, then $P(n)$ is true for all natural numbers $n$.

6. Show that the Principle of Mathematical Induction is a special case of the Third Principle of Induction.

7. Use the Well-Ordering Theorem to prove that the statements

$$a^1 = a \quad \text{and} \quad a^{k+1} = a^k \cdot a,$$

where $a$ is a natural number, define $a^n$ for every natural number $n$. (*Hint:* Let $S$ be the set of all $n$ for which $a^n$ is not defined and prove $S$ empty.)

## 2.4 Counting and Finite Sets

Undoubtedly the concept of natural number was developed because of man's desire to compare and/or measure sets of various objects. A basket contains 10 apples; a farmer owns 10 bulls; a man has \$10 in his pocket; etc. In each of these the natural number 10 is used to measure the set of objects involved, and if one asks how the number 10 is arrived at in each case, he should expect to receive the answer, "By counting."

How can these intuitive and familiar concepts be formulated in the system we've defined? A look at an example may indicate a way. Let $S$ be the set $\{a, b, c\}$. Any child in the first grade can tell us that this set contains three elements, and he can explain why by pointing his finger at the letters and intoning the words "one, two, three." In our language, a one-to-one mapping from the set $S$ onto the set $\{1, 2, 3\}$ is established, and since 3 (or three) is the unique maximal element of this set of natural numbers, the mapping identifies this natural number with $S$.

DEFINITION 2.4. A nonempty set $S$ of distinct objects has the *count* $n$, $n$ a natural number, if and only if there exists a one-to-one mapping $\boldsymbol{F}$ of the set $S$ onto the set $M_n$ of the natural numbers $m \leqslant n$. Such a mapping $\boldsymbol{F}$ is a *counting* of the set $S$.

This certainly agrees with the example above. For

$$\boldsymbol{F} = \{(a, 1), (b, 2), (c, 3)\}$$

is a one-to-one mapping of $\{a, b, c\}$ onto $\{1, 2, 3\}$, and so $\{a, b, c\}$ has the count 3. (We usually say that a set having count $n$ *contains* $n$ elements or has the *cardinal* $n$.)

There are in fact several other countings of the set $S = \{a, b, c\}$. Each of the following functions is a counting of $S$:

$$\begin{aligned} \boldsymbol{G} &= \{(a, 2), (b, 1), (c, 3)\}, \\ \boldsymbol{H} &= \{(a, 1), (b, 3), (c, 2)\}, \\ \boldsymbol{K} &= \{(a, 3), (b, 2), (c, 1)\}. \end{aligned}$$

This abundance of countings raises a very critical question: Since a set can have several countings, can it also have more than one count? If a set is counted in different ways will the count always be the same (theoretically, anyway)? The answer is provided by the next theorem.

THEOREM 2.19. *The proposition $P(n)$: $M_n$, the set of natural numbers $m \leqslant n$, is equivalent to no proper subset of itself, is true for every natural number $n$.*

We use the Second Principle of Induction. First we recall that set $A$ is *equivalent* to set $B$ if and only if there is a one-to-one mapping of $A$ onto $B$. Then we note that $P(1)$ is certainly true since the only proper subset of $\{1\}$ is $\varnothing$ and there is no mapping, one-to-one or otherwise, of $\{1\}$ onto $\varnothing$.

Now suppose $P(n)$ is true for all $n \leqslant k$; we wish to prove from this assumption that $P(k + 1)$ is true. If $P(k + 1)$ is *not* true then there exists a one-to-one mapping $\boldsymbol{F}$ of the set

$$\{1, 2, \cdots, k, k + 1\} = S$$

onto a proper subset $T \subset S$. We wish to deduce from the existence of $\boldsymbol{F}$ a contradiction to the induction hypothesis, and we consider two cases.

*Case* 1. $T \subseteq M_k$, the set of $m \in N$ with $m \leqslant k$. Then the composite function $\boldsymbol{F} * \boldsymbol{F}$ defined by

$$\boldsymbol{F} * \boldsymbol{F} : m \to \boldsymbol{F}(\boldsymbol{F}(m)) = (m\boldsymbol{F})\boldsymbol{F}, \qquad \text{all } m \in S,$$

is a one-to-one mapping of $S$ onto a proper subset $U$ of $T$. That $\boldsymbol{F} * \boldsymbol{F}$ is one-to-one was proved in the first chapter. We now show that $U$, the image of $S$ under $\boldsymbol{F} * \boldsymbol{F}$, is a proper subset of $T$.

If

$$\boldsymbol{F}(\boldsymbol{F}(m)) = \boldsymbol{F}(t), \qquad m \text{ and } t \text{ in } S,$$

then, since $\boldsymbol{F}$ is one-to-one,

$$\boldsymbol{F}(m) = t.$$

So select $x$ as an element in $S - T$ (which is not empty since $T \neq S$). Then $\boldsymbol{F}(x)$, an element of $T$, is not in $U$. For

$$\boldsymbol{F}(x) \in U$$

implies that there is an $m \in S$ such that

$$\boldsymbol{F}(\boldsymbol{F}(m)) = \boldsymbol{F}(x),$$

an equation which implies that

$$x = \boldsymbol{F}(m)$$

and so lies in $T$. Since $T \cap (S - T) = \varnothing$ this is impossible so we conclude that $\boldsymbol{F} * \boldsymbol{F}$ is a mapping of $S$ onto a proper subset $U$ of $T$.

Now by means of $\boldsymbol{F} * \boldsymbol{F}$ we define a one-to-one mapping $\boldsymbol{G}$ of the set $M_k$ on to a proper subset of itself (and thereby obtain a contradictory situation). $\boldsymbol{G}$ is defined by the rules:

$$\boldsymbol{G}: \begin{cases} a \to a & \text{if } a \notin T = \boldsymbol{F}(S), \\ a \to \boldsymbol{F}(a) & \text{if } a \in T. \end{cases}$$

To show that $\boldsymbol{G}$ is one-to-one we must prove that

$$\boldsymbol{G}(a) = \boldsymbol{G}(b)$$

implies $a = b$. Either $\boldsymbol{G}(a) = \boldsymbol{G}(b)$ is an element of $M_k - T$, in which case

$$\boldsymbol{G}(a) = a = \boldsymbol{G}(b) = b,$$

or $\boldsymbol{G}(a) = \boldsymbol{G}(b)$ is an element of $T$, so that

$$\boldsymbol{G}(a) = \boldsymbol{F}(a) = \boldsymbol{G}(b) = \boldsymbol{F}(b),$$

which means that $a = b$ since $\boldsymbol{F}$ is one-to-one.

Finally $\boldsymbol{G}(M_k) = M_k - (T - U)$, so that $\boldsymbol{G}$ is a one-to-one mapping of $M_k$ onto a proper subset of itself. This contradicts the induction hypothesis.

*Case* 2. $T \nsubseteq M_k$. This means that the natural number $k + 1$ is in $T$. We reduce this case to the one already considered by altering the function $\boldsymbol{F}$. Now there is a natural number

$$x \in S = \{\text{set of all natural numbers } m \leqslant k + 1\}$$

such that $\boldsymbol{F}(x) = k + 1$, since this is what is meant by the statement $\boldsymbol{F}$ is a mapping of $S$ *onto* $T$. Further, there is a natural number $y$ in $S - T$ since $T \neq S$. We define the function $\boldsymbol{F}'$ by the rules

$$\boldsymbol{F}': \begin{cases} a \to \boldsymbol{F}(a) & \text{if } a \in S,\ a \neq x, \\ x \to y. \end{cases}$$

Clearly $\boldsymbol{F}'$ is a one-to-one mapping from $S$ onto $T'$ which is the set

$$(T - \{k + 1\}) \cup \{y\}.$$

Now we proceed as in Case 1 to obtain a contradiction of the induction hypothesis.

So by the method of contradiction we prove that the truth of all $P(n)$ for $n \leqslant k$ implies the truth of $P(k + 1)$. Proving this completes the proof of the theorem by the Second Principle of Induction.

The above proof is not easy, so we shall make two attempts to clarify the proceedings (at the risk of causing more confusion). First the geometric diagrams in Fig. 2.2 may help keep the mappings in mind. In this diagramed

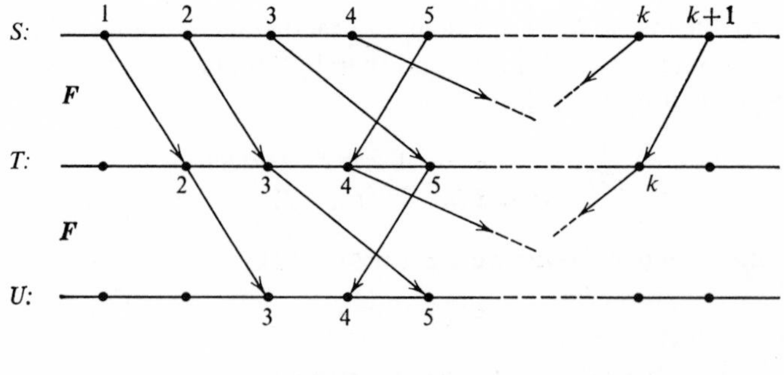


**Figure 2.2**

situation the composite function $\boldsymbol{F} * \boldsymbol{F}$ maps 1 onto 3, 2 onto 5, 3 onto 4, etc.; $1 \notin T$; and 1 and 2 are not in $U$. For this situation the function $\boldsymbol{G}$ would have the diagram shown in Fig. 2.3. This indicates that the image set is a proper subset of $M_k$.

The difficulty one has in following the proof of Theorem 2.19 probably stems from the fact that we are in effect constructing and dealing with functions that do not exist. Let us look at an example of the above constructions where the functions do exist.

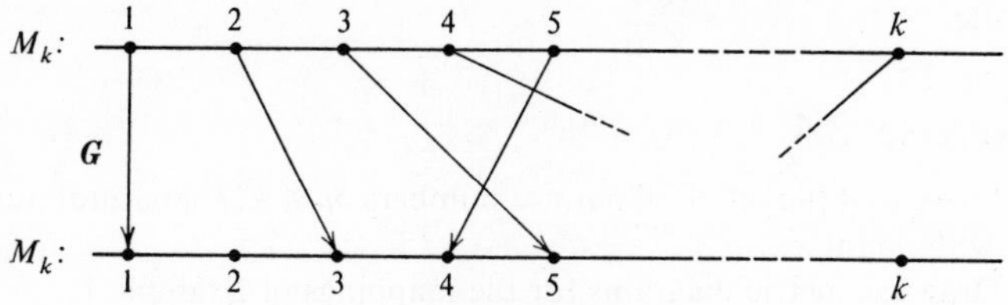


**Figure 2.3**

*Example* 1. Let $N$ denote the set of natural numbers and $F$ the function

$$F = \{(x, y): x \in N \text{ and } y = x + 1\}.$$

This function is called the *successor mapping*. The set $T$ of images of $N$ under $F$ is the set

$$N - \{1\}.$$

Then $F * F$ is the function

$$\{(x, y): x \in N \text{ and } y = x + 2\},$$

and $U$, the set of images of $N$ under $F * F$, is the set

$$N - \{1, 2\}.$$

And the construction for $G$ yields the following one-to-one mapping $G$ of the set

$$T = N - \{1\}$$

*into* itself:

$$G: \begin{cases} x \to 2 & \text{when } x = 2 \\ x \to x + 1 & \text{when } x > 2. \end{cases}$$

Now how does Theorem 2.19 prove that a set has at most one count? Well, suppose a set $S$ has two counts $m$ and $n$. This means there is a one-to-one correspondence between the elements of $S$ and the first $m$ natural numbers, and also a one-to-one correspondence between the elements of $S$ and the first $n$ natural numbers. These two mappings combine to furnish a one-to-one correspondence between the first $m$ and the first $n$ natural numbers. By Theorem 2.19 such a correspondence implies that $n = m$.

*Corollary* 2.19.1. The count of a set is unique.

DEFINITION 2.5. A *finite set* is a set with a count. An *infinite set* is a set $\neq \varnothing$ without a count.

Example 1 indicates that the set $N$ of natural integers is an infinite set. For, if $N$ were finite and had count $n$, then the mappings of the example would provide a mapping of

$$M_n = \{\text{set of all natural numbers } m \leqslant n\}$$

onto a proper subset of itself in a one-to-one fashion. Since this violates Theorem 2.19, $N$ is an infinite set.

Note that according to Definition 2.5 the empty set $\varnothing$ is neither finite nor infinite.

## Exercise 2.4

**1.** Prove that the set of all natural numbers $m \leqslant k$, $k$ a natural number, is a finite set with count $k$.

**2.** Draw geometric diagrams for the mappings of Example 1.

**3.** Prove that a set is infinite if it possesses a one-to-one mapping onto a proper subset of itself.

**4.** Prove that a subset $\neq \varnothing$ of a finite set $S$ is itself finite. (*Hint:* Use induction on the count of $S$.)

**5.** Prove that, if the set $S$ has count $n$, then any subset $T \neq \varnothing$ of $S$ has count $m \leqslant n$. (See Problem 4.)

**6.** Show that the sets of points on any two line segments of a plane are equivalent. What does this indicate about such sets?

**7.** Prove that sets with equal counts are equivalent sets.

**8.** What can you say about a one-to-one mapping $F$ of the set $M_n$ of the first $n$ natural numbers onto itself if $F$ preserves the ordering of the numbers (i.e., $a > b$ implies $F(a) > F(b)$)?

**9.** Counting a set is sometimes called "ordering" a set. What do you think this means?

**10.** A set which is equivalent to the set $N$ of all natural numbers is called a *denumerable* set. Give an example, other than $N$, of such a set.

**11.** Prove that the composite function $F * F$ is one-to-one when $F$ is one-to-one.

**12.** Use mathematical induction to prove that a finite set $T$ of elements from a set $S$ with a linear order $\mathbf{R}$ has a "largest" and a "smallest" element. ($m$ is the largest element of $T$ if $m\mathbf{R}a$ for every $a$ in $T$ not equal to $m$, and $s$ is the smallest element if $a\mathbf{R}s$ for every $a \in S$, $a \neq s$. Induction is on the number of elements in $T$.)

## 2.5 The Integers Defined

One of the problems which mathematicians must study is the *preimage problem*: If $F$ is a function from the set $S$ to the set $T$ and if $t \in T$, what elements of $S$ (if any) have $t$ as an image under $F$? This is usually stated in the form, "Solve the equation

$$F(x) = t$$

for $x$." If the function $F$ is a function defined by a certain type of rule, then we frequently attempt to obtain another rule or formula which will indicate the preimage $x$ for each $t \in T$. Such efforts often lead to the invention of new operations and often to construction of an extension of the mathematical systems involved. This procedure is an important one, and we apply it frequently.

A very simple function $F$ from $N$ to $N$ is defined by the rule

$$F: x \to x + k,$$

where $k$ is an arbitrary but fixed natural number. This type of function is based on addition, so to "solve" the equation,

$$x + k = t,$$

we need a rule for "undoing" addition. To establish this reversal of addition as a binary operation we must "extend" the system of natural numbers to a larger system. For in the system $N$ such equations as

$$x + 1 = 1$$

do not possess "solutions," i.e., there is *no* natural number $x$ such that $x + 1 = 1$. The "extension" which we shall invent is the system of integers and the new operation that of subtraction.

(The system of integers can be developed from a set of axioms exactly as the system $N$ was developed. However, such an approach would tend to obscure the relations between the integers and the natural numbers.)

The explanation given above to justify the introduction of a new system involves a *pair* of natural numbers. That is, for the two natural numbers $k$ and $t$ we have the problem of finding an $x$ such that $x + k = t$. However, in the system of natural numbers the same $x$ can work for many different $k$ and $t$:

$$\begin{aligned} 2 + 1 &= 3 \\ 2 + 2 &= 4 \\ 2 + 3 &= 5 \\ &\vdots \end{aligned}$$

Thus different pairs correspond to the same $x$. This suggests that we should use a "condensed" version of $N \times N$ in defining our new system. This condensing is done by means of an equivalence relation.

DEFINITION 2.6. The relation symbolized by $\sim$ is defined on the set $N \times N$ by

$$(a, b) \sim (c, d)$$

if and only if $a + d = b + c$.

For example,

$$(3, 1) \sim (4, 2)$$

since

$$3 + 2 = 1 + 4,$$

and similarly

$$(3, 1) \sim (5, 3) \qquad \text{and} \qquad (4, 2) \sim (5, 3).$$

Clearly this is a formal device for stating that these pairs are related to the same $x$ that we indicated above.

THEOREM 2.20. *The relation $\sim$ is an equivalence relation on $N \times N$.*

(i) $(a, b) \sim (a, b)$ since $a + b = b + a$.

(ii) If $(a, b) \sim (c, d)$, then $(c, d) \sim (a, b)$. For the equation $a + d = b + c$ can be rewritten as $c + b = d + a$ by using the properties of natural numbers.

(iii) Suppose $(a, b) \sim (c, d)$ and $(c, d) \sim (e, f)$. Then by definition of the relation,

$$a + d = b + c \quad \text{and} \quad c + f = d + e.$$

Therefore

$$(a + d) + (c + f) = (b + c) + (d + e),$$

which, using the Associative Law and Commutative Law, can be written

$$(a + f) + (c + d) = (b + e) + (c + d).$$

By the Cancellation Law for addition in $N$ this yields

$$a + f = b + e,$$

so that

$$(a, b) \sim (e, f).$$

**Figure 2.4**

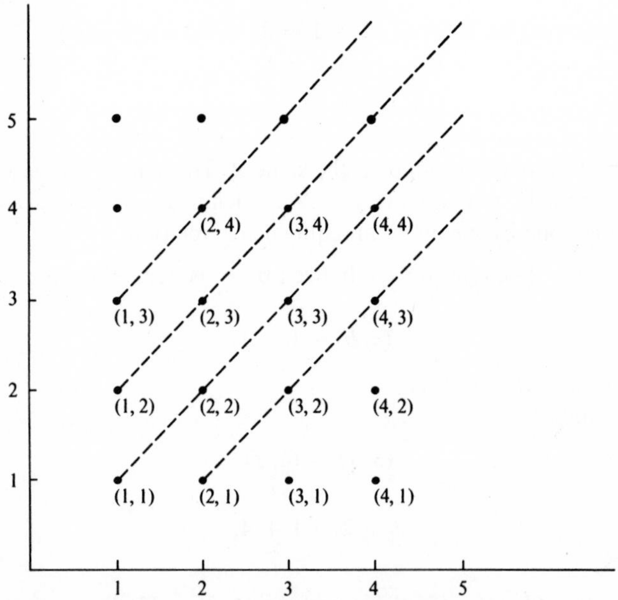


This equivalence relation on $N \times N$ can be illustrated geometrically as in the diagram in Fig. 2.4. In the diagram two pairs are equivalent if and only if their corresponding points lie on the same diagonal line.

As we know, an equivalence relation partitions a set into nonoverlapping, nonempty subsets. The elements of this partition of $N \times N$ will be our integers, so we introduce some notation for them.

DEFINITION 2.7. $[a, b] = \{(x, y): (x, y) \in N \times N \text{ and } (x, y) \sim (a, b)\}$. The set of all $[a, b]$ is denoted by $J$.

Since the elements of $J$ are precisely the elements of a partition they do not overlap. Relative to Fig. 2.4, $[a, b]$ consists of all the ordered pairs $(x, y)$ whose corresponding points lie on the diagonal through the point corresponding to $(a, b)$.

THEOREM 2.21. $[a, b] = [c, d]$ *if and only if* $(a, b) \sim (c, d)$.

This is a basic property of the elements of a partition.

Now the set $J$ is our set of integers, and we can think of $[a, b]$ as $a - b$. This and our experience suggest the binary operations for the system.

THEOREM 2.22. *The rules*

$$[a, b] \oplus [c, d] = [a + c, b + d]$$

and

$$[a, b] \odot [c, d] = [(a \cdot c) + (b \cdot d), (a \cdot d) + (b \cdot c)],$$

*define binary operations, referred to as* addition *and* multiplication, *respectively, on the set J.*

We must prove that addition and multiplication are *well-defined* by these rules. That is, we must show that the rule for combining $[a, b]$ and $[c, d]$ is independent of the particular representatives $(a, b)$ and $(c, d)$, respectively, of the *sets* $[a, b]$ and $[c, d]$. In short we have to prove that, if

$$[a, b] = [e, f] \quad \text{and} \quad [c, d] = [m, n],$$

then

$$[a + c, b + d] = [e + m, f + n]$$

and

$$[(a \cdot c) + (b \cdot d), (a \cdot d) + (b \cdot c)] = [(e \cdot m) + (f \cdot n), (e \cdot n) + (f \cdot m)].$$

This is a simple task when reduced to a problem concerning the natural numbers such as we will now indicate. From the equations $a + f = b + e$ and $c + n = d + m$ we obtain the eight equations

$$\begin{aligned} c \cdot (a + f) &= c \cdot (b + e), & d \cdot (a + f) &= d \cdot (b + e), \\ n \cdot (a + f) &= n \cdot (b + e), & m \cdot (a + f) &= m \cdot (b + e), \\ a \cdot (c + n) &= a \cdot (d + m), & b \cdot (c + n) &= b \cdot (d + m), \\ e \cdot (c + n) &= e \cdot (d + m), & f \cdot (c + n) &= f \cdot (d + m). \end{aligned}$$

When added, these yield

$$\begin{aligned} &2 \cdot \big(((a \cdot c) + (b \cdot d)) + ((e \cdot n) + (f \cdot m))\big) + \big((e \cdot d) + (f \cdot c) \\ &\qquad + (b \cdot n) + (a \cdot m) + (e \cdot c) + (f \cdot d) + (a \cdot n) \\ &\qquad + (b \cdot m)\big) \\ = {}&2 \cdot \big(((a \cdot d) + (b \cdot c)) + ((e \cdot m) + (f \cdot n))\big) + \big((e \cdot d) + (f \cdot c) \\ &\qquad + (b \cdot n) + (a \cdot m) + (e \cdot c) + (f \cdot d) + (a \cdot n) \\ &\qquad + (b \cdot m)\big), \end{aligned}$$

so that, by the Cancellation Laws,

$$\begin{aligned} &\big((a \cdot c) + (b \cdot d)\big) + \big((e \cdot n) + (f \cdot m)\big) \\ &\qquad = \big((a \cdot d) + (b \cdot c)\big) + \big((e \cdot m) + (f \cdot n)\big). \end{aligned}$$

This equation means that

$$[(a \cdot c) + (b \cdot d), (a \cdot d) + (b \cdot c)] = [(e \cdot m) + (f \cdot n), (e \cdot n) + (f \cdot m)],$$

and we see that multiplication is well-defined in $J$. The corresponding result for addition is proved in a similar fashion.

The set $J$ and the binary operations just defined make up the *system of integers*. The axioms of this system are those of set theory and the system of natural numbers. We denote the system by $J$.

How does this system compare with $N$, the system of natural numbers? More specifically, do the operations of $J$ have the nice properties that the operations of $N$ have?

THEOREM 2.23. *The operations of addition and multiplication in J have the following properties:*

(i) *They are commutative.*
(ii) *They are associative.*
(iii) *Multiplication is distributive over addition.*

The proofs of these are elementary exercises involving the properties of $N$, the definition of $J$, and Theorem 2.21. We illustrate by proving the Commutative Law of Addition. Consider elements $[a, b]$ and $[c, d]$ of $J$. Then

$$[a, b] \oplus [c, d] = [a + c, b + d]$$

by definition, and

$$[c, d] \oplus [a, b] = [c + a, d + b].$$

Now

$$(c + a) + (b + d) = (d + b) + (a + c)$$

because of the properties of the natural numbers. Therefore

$$(c + a, d + b) \sim (a + c, b + d),$$

so that, by Theorem 2.21,

$$[c + a, d + b] = [a + c, b + d].$$

Thus

$$[a, b] \oplus [c, d] = [c, d] \oplus [a, b].$$

Proofs of the remaining properties are left as exercises for the student.

This system also has properties *not* possessed by $N$.

THEOREM 2.24. *$J$ contains an additive identity as well as a multiplicative identity.*

The element $[a, a]$ is the additive identity element of $J$ since

$$[x, y] \oplus [a, a] = [x + a, y + a] = [a, a] \oplus [x, y].$$

But

$$(x, y) \sim (x + a, y + a)$$

since

$$x + (y + a) = y + (x + a)$$

in $N$. Therefore

$$[x + a, y + a] = [x, y]$$

and

$$[x, y] \oplus [a, a] = [x, y] = [a, a] \oplus [x, y].$$

Similarly the element $[a + 1, a]$ is the multiplicative identity element of $J$. For

$$[x, y] \odot [a + 1, a] = [x \cdot (a + 1) + y \cdot a, x \cdot a + y \cdot (a + 1)],$$

and since

$$(x + (x \cdot a + y \cdot a), y + (x \cdot a + y \cdot a)) \sim (x, y),$$

we conclude that

$$[x, y] \odot [a + 1, a] = [x, y].$$

Moreover, relative to the identity element $[a, a]$ each element $[x, y] \in J$ has an *additive inverse.*

THEOREM 2.25. *For each $[x, y] \in J$ there is an element $[m, n]$ in $J$ such that*

$$[x, y] \oplus [m, n] = [a, a].$$

For

$$[x, y] \oplus [y, x] = [x + y, y + x] = [a, a],$$

demonstrating the existence of an additive inverse for $[x, y]$.

*Corollary* 2.25.1 (*Cancellation for Addition*). If $[a, b]$, $[c, d]$, and $[e, f]$ are elements of $J$, then the equation

$$[a, b] \oplus [c, d] = [a, b] \oplus [e, f]$$

implies that

$$[c, d] = [e, f].$$

For, using the Associative Law (Theorem 2.23) of Addition,

$$[b, a] \oplus ([a, b] \oplus [c, d]) = [b, a] \oplus ([a, b] \oplus [e, f])$$

yields

$$[a, a] \oplus [c, d] = [a, a] \oplus [e, f],$$

so that

$$[c, d] = [e, f].$$

The existence of additive inverses for every element in $J$ enables us to introduce the binary operation of subtraction for $J$. This operation is useful in calculations involving integers.

THEOREM 2.26. *The rule*

$$[a, b] - [c, d] = [a, b] \oplus [d, c]$$

*defines a binary operation on J called* subtraction *and symbolized by the minus sign* $-$.

As in the proof of Theorem 2.22 we must prove that this rule is well-defined. This follows simply from the fact that addition is a binary operation, for, if

$$[a, b] = [e, f] \quad \text{and} \quad [c, d] = [m, n],$$

then

$$[d, c] = [n, m]$$

and

$$[a, b] \oplus [d, c] = [e, f] \oplus [n, m].$$

Thus

$$[a, b] - [c, d] = [e, f] - [m, n].$$

Now consider the function $\boldsymbol{F}$ from $J$ to $J$ defined for a fixed $[m, n]$ in $J$ by

$$\boldsymbol{F}: [x, y] \to [x, y] + [m, n], \qquad \text{each } [x, y] \in J.$$

What integers are mapped onto $[a, b]$ by this function? In other words, what are the solutions of the equation

$$[x, y] \oplus [m, n] = [a, b]?$$

By subtracting $[m, n]$ from both sides we conclude that

$$[x, y] = [a + n, b + m].$$

Furthermore, this is the only solution, for suppose $[x', y']$ and $[x'', y'']$ are both mapped onto $[a, b]$ by $F$. Then

$$[a, b] = [x', y'] \oplus [m, n] = [x'', y''] \oplus [m, n],$$

so that

$$[x', y'] = [x'', y'']$$

by the Cancellation Law.

## Exercise 2.5

**1.** Determine which of the following integers are equal: [7, 5], [3, 1], [1, 3], [1001, 999], [77, 79], [77, 99], [1, 1], [99, 99], $[a, a]$, $[b, b]$, $[b, b + 2]$, $[a + 2, a]$. Justify.

**2.** Prove Theorem 2.21 from Definitions 2.6 and 2.7.

**3.** Determine whether the following rules for "products" are well-defined:

(*a*) Let $P$ be a partition of a nonempty set $S$ of people according to birth month. (Thus two people from $S$ belong to the same element of $P$ if they were both born in February but possibly in different years.) Define the "product" of the class to which person $a$ belongs and the class to which $b$ belongs as the class to which the younger belongs (or both belong). In symbols,

$$[a] * [b] = [c],$$

where $c$ is the younger of $a$ and $b$.

(*b*) Let $[x, y], [u, v] \in J$, and define their "product" by

$$[x, y] \# [u, v] = [a, b],$$

where $a$ is the smaller of $x$ and $y$ whereas $b$ is the smaller of $u$ and $v$.

(*c*) Let $[x, y], [u, v] \in J$, and define their "product" by

$$[x, y] \bigcirc [u, v] = [a, b],$$

where $a$ is the larger of $x$ and $u$ whereas $b$ is the larger of $y$ and $v$.

**4.** Complete the proof of Theorem 2.22.

**5.** Complete the proof of Theorem 2.23.

**6.** Prove that the identity elements of Theorem 2.24 are unique.

**7.** Prove that $[a, a] \odot [c, d] = [a, a]$ in $J$.

**8.** Is the operation of subtraction commutative? Associative? Distributive? Explain.

**9.** Show that the function $F$, defined from $J$ to $J$ for the fixed integer $[m, n]$ by

$$F\colon [x, y] \to [x, y] \oplus [m, n],$$

is a one-to-one mapping from $J$ onto $J$.

**10.** Prove that the pair $(a, a + n)$ lies in $[x, y]$ if and only if $y = x + n$.

**11.** Prove that $[x, y] = [a, a]$ if and only if $x = y$.

## 2.6 Ordering the Integers

In Fig. 2.4, the geometric diagram used in Section 2.5 to illustrate the partition of $N \times N$, we effectively associated the elements of $J$ with certain diagonal lines. From that figure we see that [2, 1] is to the right of [1, 1], [4, 2] is to the right of [2, 1], etc., and this suggests the following relation on $J$.

DEFINITION 2.8. The relation on $J$ symbolized by $\circleddash\!\!>$ (read "larger than") is defined by the condition:

$$[a, b] \circledgtr [c, d]$$

if and only if $a + d > b + c$.

$[a, b] \circledgtr [c, d]$ is sometimes written as $[c, d] \circledless [a, b]$ ($\circledless$ is read "smaller than").

We see that $[2, 1] \circledgtr [1, 1]$, since $2 + 1 > 1 + 1$, and that $[4, 2] \circledgtr [2, 1]$, since $4 + 1 > 2 + 2$. So the formal definition seems to fit with our observation from the diagram.

Again we are faced with the problem of showing that the definition really defines a relation, that is, we must show that $\circledgtr$ is well-defined. Let

$$[a', b'] = [a, b] \qquad \text{and} \qquad [c', d'] = [c, d].$$

Then

$$a' + b = b' + a \qquad \text{and} \qquad c' + d = d' + c.$$

Now

$$a + d > b + c$$

and

$$b' + d' = b' + d'$$

together imply

$$(a + d) + (b' + d') > (b + c) + (b' + d'),$$

so that replacing $a + b'$ by $a' + b$ and $c + b'$ by $c' + b$ we obtain

$$(a' + d') + (b + d) > (b' + c') + (b + d).$$

Then, by Theorem 2.14,

$$a' + d' > (b' + c'),$$

so that

$$[a', b'] \circledgtr [c', d'].$$

To show that this relation is a linear order on $J$ we must prove the Trichotomy Law and transitivity.

THEOREM 2.27 (TRICHOTOMY). *If* $[a, b]$ *and* $[c, d]$ *lie in* $J$, *then exactly one of the following is true:*

(i) $$[a, b] = [c, d],$$

(ii) $$[a, b] ⧁ [c, d],$$

(iii) $$[c, d] ⧁ [a, b].$$

This is a simple consequence of the Trichotomy Law for natural numbers, which states that for the two natural numbers $a + d$ and $b + c$ exactly one of the following is true:

(i) $$a + d = b + c,$$

(ii) $$a + d > b + c,$$

(iii) $$b + c > a + d.$$

Rewriting these in the notation of $J$ we have the theorem proved.

THEOREM 2.28 (TRANSITIVITY). *If* $[a, b] ⧁ [c, d]$ *and* $[c, d] ⧁ [e, f]$, *then* $[a, b] ⧁ [e, f]$.

Adding (in $N$) the inequalities

$$a + d > b + c \quad \text{and} \quad c + f > d + e$$

yields

$$(a + f) + (c + d) > (b + e) + (c + d),$$

so that, by Theorem 2.14,

$$a + f > b + e.$$

Thus $[a, b] ⧁ [e, f]$.

The arithmetic of inequalities in $J$ is rather similar to that in $N$, with one very important difference centering around the integer $[a, a]$.

THEOREM 2.29. *In* $J$: (i) $[a, b] \oplus [c, d] ⧁ [a, b] \oplus [e, f]$ *if and only if* $[c, d] ⧁ [e, f]$.

(ii) *If* $[x, y] ⧁ [a, a]$, *then* $[x, y] \odot [c, d] ⧁ [x, y] \odot [e, f]$ *if and only if* $[c, d] ⧁ [e, f]$.

(iii) *If* $[x, y] ⧀ [a, a]$, *then* $[x, y] \odot [c, d] ⧁ [x, y] \odot [e, f]$ *if and only if* $[c, d] ⧀ [e, f]$.

(This reversal of the inequality in (iii) is the difference alluded to above.)

We shall prove (iii) and leave the remainder of the theorem for the student to prove. If

$$[c, d] ⧀ [e, f] \quad \text{and} \quad [x, y] ⧀ [a, a]$$

then

$$x + a < y + a \quad \text{and} \quad c + f < d + e,$$

so that there are natural numbers $n$ and $m$ such that

$$y = x + n \qquad \text{and} \qquad d + e = (c + f) + m.$$

By adding the equations

$$y \cdot (d + e) = y \cdot (c + f) + m$$

and

$$(x + n) \cdot (c + f) + m = (x + n) \cdot (d + e),$$

and rearranging terms we obtain

$$\begin{aligned} &\big((x \cdot c) + (y \cdot d) + (x \cdot f) + (y \cdot e)\big) + \big((x \cdot m) + (n \cdot c) + (n \cdot f) + (n \cdot m)\big) \\ &= \big((x \cdot d) + (y \cdot c) + (x \cdot e) + (y \cdot f)\big) + (y \cdot m) + \big(n \cdot (d + e)\big). \end{aligned}$$

Since

$$y \cdot m = (x \cdot m) + (n \cdot m) \quad \text{and} \quad n \cdot (d + e) = (n \cdot c) + (n \cdot f) + (n \cdot m),$$

this equation becomes

$$\begin{aligned} &\big((x \cdot c) \, (+ y \cdot d) + (x \cdot f) + (y \cdot e)\big) + \big((x \cdot m) + (n \cdot c) + (n \cdot f) + (n \cdot m)\big) \\ &\qquad = \big((x \cdot d) + (y \cdot c) + (x \cdot e) + (y \cdot f)\big) + \big((x \cdot m) + (n \cdot c) \\ &\qquad\qquad + (n \cdot f) + (n \cdot m)\big) + n \cdot m. \end{aligned}$$

Therefore

$$\begin{aligned} &\big((x \cdot c) + (y \cdot d) + (x \cdot f) + (y \cdot e)\big) \\ &\qquad > \big((x \cdot d) + (y \cdot c) + (x \cdot e) + (y \cdot f)\big) \end{aligned}$$

so that

$$[x, y] \odot [c, d] ⧁ [x, y] \odot [e, f].$$

Conversely, suppose

$$[x, y] \odot [c, d] ⧁ [x, y] \odot [e, f]$$

and

$$[x, y] ⧀ [a, a],$$

and consider the two integers $[c, d]$ and $[e, f]$. By trichotomy either

$$[c, d] = [e, f], \ [c, d] ⧁ [e, f]$$

or

$$[c, d] ⧀ [e, f].$$

The above argument, with the integers $[c, d]$ and $[e, f]$ interchanged, shows that the relation

$$[c, d] ⧁ [e, f],$$

written

$$[e, f] ⧀ [c, d],$$

implies that

$$[x, y] \odot [e, f] \circledgt [x, y] \odot [c, d],$$

contradicting the hypothesis. Surely

$$[c, d] = [e, f]$$

implies that

$$[x, y] \odot [c, d] = [x, y] \odot [e, f],$$

which also contradicts the hypothesis. Thus the hypothesis

$$[x, y] \odot [c, d] \circledgt [x, y] \odot [e, f]$$

implies

$$[c, d] \circledlt [e, f]$$

when

$$[x, y] \circledlt [a, a].$$

The Cancellation Law for multiplication of integers is proved in this manner also; viz., by using the Trichotomy Law.

By the Trichotomy Law the additive identity element $[a, a]$ partitions the set $J$ into three subsets of elements which are so distinctive that we give them special names.

DEFINITION 2.9. An integer $[x, y]$ is

(i) *Positive:* if $[x, y] \circledgt [a, a]$,

(ii) *Zero:* if $[x, y] = [a, a]$,

(iii) *Negative:* if $[x, y] \circledlt [a, a]$.

Since

$$[x, y] \circledgt [a, a]$$

if and only if $x + a > y + a$, and since this latter condition is equivalent to $x > y$, we conclude that the integer $[x, y]$ is positive if and only if

$$x > y.$$

Similarly $[x, y]$ is zero if and only if

$$x = y,$$

and $[x, y]$ is negative if and only if

$$x < y.$$

Now we can prove the familiar rule dealing with the products of positive and/or negative integers.

THEOREM 2.30. *The product* $[a, b] \odot [c, d]$ *is:*

(i) *Positive if the two integers are both positive.*
(ii) *Positive if the two integers are both negative.*
(iii) *Negative if one integer is positive and the other is negative.*

Suppose $[a, b]$ and $[c, d]$ are both negative, i.e.,

$$[a, b] \olessthan [x, x] \qquad \text{and} \qquad [c, d] \olessthan [x, x].$$

Then by Theorem 2.29, part (iii),

$$[a, b] \odot [c, d] \ogreaterthan [a, b] \odot [x, x],$$

so that, since

$$[a \cdot b] \odot [x, x] = [x, x],$$

we conclude that the product of two negative integers is greater than zero, and hence positive.

The remainder of the theorem is left as an exercise.

Theorem 2.29 can also be used to prove that the sum of two positive integers is positive and that the sum of two negative integers is negative. For, if

$$[a, b] \ogreaterthan [x, x] \qquad \text{and} \qquad [c, d] \ogreaterthan [x, x],$$

then by Theorem 2.29, part (i),

$$[a, b] \oplus [c, d] \ogreaterthan [a, b] \oplus [x, x].$$

But

$$[a, b] \oplus [x, x] = [a, b],$$

so that, by the transitivity of the linear order,

$$[a, b] \oplus [c, d] \ogreaterthan [a, b] \ogreaterthan [x, x],$$

and the sum is positive.

## Exercise 2.6

**1.** Arrange the following integers by order: [11, 30], [1000, 1001], [1001, 1000], [1, 1000], [22, 20], $[a + 7, 7]$, $[n, n + 18]$.

**2.** Prove (i) of Theorem 2.29 by rewriting it as a problem concerning the natural numbers.

**3.** Prove (ii) of Theorem 2.29.

**4.** Prove that $[x, y]$ is positive if and only if there exists a natural number $n$ such that $x = y + n$.

**5.** Use the result of Problem 4 to prove that the sum and the product of two positive integers are positive integers.

**6.** Complete the proof of Theorem 2.30.

**7.** Describe the equivalence relation on $J$ defined by the partition of $J$ given by Definition 2.9.

**8.** Prove the Cancellation Law for Multiplication in $J$: if

$$[x, y] \neq [a, a],$$

then

$$[x, y] \odot [c, d] = [x, y] \odot [e, f]$$

implies that

$$[c, d] = [e, f].$$

Why is the condition $[x, y] \neq [a, a]$ essential?

**9.** Prove that the *negative function* $\boldsymbol{F}$ defined by $\boldsymbol{F}([x, y]) = [y, x]$ is a one-to-one mapping of $J$ onto $J$.

**10.** Prove that $[a, b] \otimes [c, d]$ if and only if there exists a *positive* integer $[e, f]$ such that

$$[a, b] = [c, d] \oplus [e, f].$$

(Use the result of Problem 4 above.)

**11.** Illustrate Theorems 2.29 and 2.30 with numerical examples.

**12.** Describe Definition 2.9 in terms of the geometric illustration of the elements of $J$.

## 2.7 Isomorphic Systems and Extensions

From the results of the preceding section we see that the set $P$ of positive integers and the binary operations of addition and multiplication form a mathematical system also. Technically speaking, the binary operations of this new system are *induced* on $P$ by the operations of $J$. For addition in $J$, as a function from $J \times J$ to $J$, is a subset $A$ of $(J \times J) \times J$, and so is multiplication a subset $M$ of $(J \times J) \times J$. We proved in Section 2.6, then, that

$$A \cap ((P \times P) \times J) \subseteq (P \times P) \times P$$

and

$$M \cap ((P \times P) \times J) \subseteq (P \times P) \times P.$$

Therefore these intersections are binary operations on $P$, the operations induced by those of $J$. The same symbolism will be used for these operations on $P$ that is used in the system $J$, and $\{P, \oplus, \odot\}$, the system of positive integers, is referred to as a *subsystem* of $\{J, \oplus, \odot\}$ for obvious reasons.

Another important fact is known about the elements of $P$: With each positive integer is associated exactly one natural number. In other words there is a one-to-one mapping $\boldsymbol{F}$ of $P$ onto $N$ given by

$$\boldsymbol{F}: [x + n, x] \rightarrow n,$$

for each $[x + n, x]$ in $P$.

This mapping is clearly suggested by our intuitive interpretation of the integer $[x, y]$ as "$x$ minus $y$," an interpretation which associates $n$ with $[x + n, x]$.

The function so defined not only establishes a one-to-one relationship between the elements of $P$ and the elements of $N$, but it does this in a way which is consistent with the nominal correspondence between the binary operations of the systems. That is,

$$\boldsymbol{F}([x + n, x] \oplus [y + m, y]) = n + m$$

and

$$\boldsymbol{F}([x + n, x] \odot [y + m, y]) = n \cdot m.$$

In other words, the image of the sum (in $P$) is the sum (in $N$) of the images, and the image of the product (in $P$) is the product (in $N$) of the images. This observation is quite easy to verify, for

$$[x + n, x] \oplus [y + m, y] = [(x + y) + (m + n), x + y]$$

and

$$\begin{aligned}[x + n, x] \odot [y + m, y] = [&((2 \cdot x \cdot y) + (n \cdot y) + (x \cdot m)) + (n \cdot m),\\ &((2 \cdot x \cdot y) + (n \cdot y) + (x \cdot m))].\end{aligned}$$

(The words addition and multiplication establish a correspondence between the relations symbolized by $+$ and $\oplus$ and those by $\cdot$ and $\odot$.)

DEFINITION 2.10. The system $\{S, O\}$ is *isomorphic* with the system $\{S', O'\}$ if and only if there exist one-to-one mappings from $S$ onto $S'$ and from $O$ onto $O'$ which are compatible.

These mappings, indicated by

$\boldsymbol{F}$ of $S$ onto $S'$:

$$s \leftrightarrow s' = \boldsymbol{F}(s)$$

$$t \leftrightarrow t' = \boldsymbol{F}(t)$$

and $\boldsymbol{G}$ of $O$ onto $O'$:

$$* \leftrightarrow \circ,$$

are *compatible if*

$$\boldsymbol{F}: s * t \leftrightarrow s' \circ t'.$$

In other symbols,

$$\boldsymbol{F}(s * t) = (\boldsymbol{F}(s)) \circ (\boldsymbol{F}(t)).$$

Since the mappings involved in establishing an isomorphism from one system onto another are one-to-one, onto mappings, we see easily that the concept of isomorphism is an equivalence relation on a collection of mathematical systems. It is in fact this type of equality which gives the abstract approach in mathematics its power, and once two systems have been identified as isomorphic systems it is customary even to adopt the same symbolism for both systems.

THEOREM 2.31. *The system of positive integers is isomorphic with the system of natural numbers.*

The correspondence discussed above clearly establishes the isomorphism.

Hereafter we will use the simpler notation of the natural number system for *both* the natural numbers and the positive integers. Thus the symbol 2 denotes both a natural number and the positive integer $[n + 2, n]$. And an equation such as

$$[a + 3, a] \oplus [b + 2, b] = [x + 5, x]$$

is written

$$3 + 2 = 5.$$

Since the negative function establishes a one-to-one correspondence between the positive integers and the negative integers,

$$[x, y] \leftrightarrow [y, x],$$

and since subtraction utilizes this idea, we denote the negative integer $[x, x + n]$ by $-n$ (read "minus $n$"). And the symbol 0 is used to denote the zero integer, $[a, a]$.

Thus $J$ consists of the positive integers $1, 2, 3, \cdots$, the zero integer 0, and the negative integers $-1, -2, -3, \cdots$.

So we have constructed a new system $J$ from the system $N$ of natural numbers which contains, in the sense of isomorphism, the original system $N$. This is emphasized by using the notation of $N$ for part of $J$.

DEFINITION 2.11. If a system is isomorphic with a subsystem of a second system, then the second system is said to be an *extension* of the first.

So the system of integers is an extension of the system of natural numbers, and this extension is invented in order to make addition into an invertible operation.

## Exercise 2.7

**1.** Show that the mathematical system $\{N, +\}$ is isomorphic with the system $\{E, +\}$, where $E$ is the set of even natural numbers.

**2.** Compare the order relation $>$ in $N$ with that of $\circledcirc$ in $P$. Should the same symbol be adopted for both? Why? (See Problem 10, Exercise 2.6.)

**3.** The axioms of a system $\{S, O\}$ relate and define the elements of $S$ and $O$. If $\{S, O\}$ and $\{S', O'\}$ are isomorphic, what can be said about the axioms of the two systems? Illustrate, using the systems $P$ and $N$.

**4.** Prove that isomorphism is an equivalence relation.

**5.** Show that the rule

$$F([x + n, x]) = n$$

defines a one-to-one mapping of $P$ onto $N$.

**6.** Is the negative function an isomorphism of the system $J$ with itself? That is, does the mapping described by $F(x) = -x$, each $x \in J$, define an isomorphism of $J$ with itself? (*Hint:* Consider $F(x + y)$ and $F(x \cdot y)$.)

**7.** Discuss the preimage problem for the function described by

$$F(x) = x + 7$$

(*a*) over the integers, (*b*) over the natural numbers.

**8.** The *absolute value* function is defined on $J$ by the rule,

$$x \to |x| = x \qquad \text{if } x \geqslant 0$$

and

$$|x| = 0 - x \text{ (or } -x) \qquad \text{if } x < 0.$$

Show that this function is neither one-to-one nor onto $J$.

**9.** Prove that $|x \cdot y| = |x| \cdot |y|$ for each $x$ and $y$ in $J$. Is

$$|x + y| = |x| + |y|?$$

**10.** How does the concept of isomorphism justify the word "the" in the name, the natural number system?

**11.** Is the system $J$ well-ordered by $\circledless$, now designated $<$ ?

**12.** Show that the set of negative integers forms a subsystem of $\{J, +\}$ which is isomorphic with $\{P, +\}$.

**13.** Prove that the product of two integers is zero if and only if at least one of the integers is zero.

**14.** Can the system of integers be extended again by *exactly* the same method used to obtain the integers from the natural numbers? Explain.

## 2.8 Another Extension

When we consider the preimage problem for such functions on $J$ as those given by

$$x \to (3 \cdot x) - 1$$

or

$$x \to (7 \cdot x) + 2,$$

we recognize that a further extension which would permit multiplication to be invertible would be very useful (if it existed).

As before pairs of numbers are involved. This is due to the fact that we are attempting to invent a "solution" of an "equation" such as

$$2 \cdot x = 3,$$

so that the "solution" is dependent on the pair (3, 2). But if $2 \cdot x = 3$, then

$$4 \cdot x = 6, \qquad 6 \cdot x = 9, \qquad 8 \cdot x = 12, \cdots,$$

so that the "solution" is also associated with the pairs

$$(6, 4), (9, 6), (12, 8), \cdots.$$

So we will again deal with pairs in extending the system $J$ in order to introduce division. However, not all of the elements of $J \times J$ are used, for since the zero integer has the property

$$0 \cdot n = 0, \qquad \text{all } n \in J,$$

it seems reasonable to expect zero to have the same property in the extended system (which will contain $J$ in the sense of isomorphism). Since there is no reason to expect

$$0 \cdot x = k, \qquad k \neq 0,$$

to have a "solution" then, we restrict our attention to $J \times J^*$, where

$$J^* = J - \{0\}.$$

Now we introduce an equivalence relation on $J \times J^*$ which will associate the pairs (3, 2), (6, 4), (9, 6), (12, 8) as was indicated to be desirable above.

DEFINITION 2.12. The relation on $J \times J^*$ symbolized by $\approx$ is defined by the rule

$$(a, b) \approx (c, d)$$

if and only if $a \cdot d = b \cdot c$.

Thus

$$(3, 2) \approx (6, 4),$$

since $3 \cdot 4 = 2 \cdot 6$, and

$$(9, 6) \approx (12, 8)$$

since $9 \cdot 8 = 6 \cdot 12$.

This relation can be shown to have the required properties quite easily. Transitivity is demonstrated as follows: From

$$(a, b) \approx (c, d) \qquad \text{and} \qquad (c, d) \approx (e, f)$$

we have the equations

$$a \cdot d = b \cdot c \qquad \text{and} \qquad c \cdot f = d \cdot e$$

in $J$. Then

$$(a \cdot d) \cdot f = (b \cdot c) \cdot f = b \cdot (c \cdot f) = b \cdot (d \cdot e),$$

and using the Cancellation Law of Multiplication in $J$ (note that $d \neq 0$) we conclude that

$$a \cdot f = b \cdot e.$$

Thus $(a, b) \approx (e, f)$. The other properties are proved similarly.

The set $R$ of equivalence classes in $J \times J^*$ defined by this equivalence relation and denoted by

$$a/b = \{(x, y)\colon (x, y) \in J \times J^* \text{ and } (a, b) \approx (x, y)\},$$

is the set of *rational numbers*. So a *rational number*, or *fraction*, is an equivalence class $a/b$, an element of the partition of $J \times J^*$ by the equivalence relation $\approx$.

How are the binary operations of addition and multiplication to be defined? The following *strictly formal manipulation* of symbols suggests our definitions:

$$\begin{aligned} b \cdot x &= a \qquad \text{and} \qquad d \cdot y = c, \\ d \cdot b \cdot x &= d \cdot a \qquad \text{and} \qquad b \cdot d \cdot y = b \cdot c, \\ (b \cdot d \cdot x) + (b \cdot d \cdot y) &= (a \cdot d) + (b \cdot c) \\ b \cdot d \cdot (x + y) &= (a \cdot d) + (b \cdot c). \end{aligned}$$

Thus, if $x$ is a "number" associated with the pair of integers $(a, b)$ and $y$ is associated with the pair $(c, d)$, then the "sum" should be associated with the pair $\big((a \cdot d) + (b \cdot c), b \cdot d\big)$. Similarly the "product" should be associated with the pair $(a \cdot c, b \cdot d)$.

THEOREM 2.32. *The rules*

$$a/b \boxplus c/d = \big((a \cdot d) + (b \cdot c)\big)/b \cdot d$$

*and*

$$a/b \boxdot c/d = a \cdot c/b \cdot d,$$

*define binary operations on R called* addition, *symbolized by* $\boxplus$. *and* multiplication, *symbolized by* $\boxdot$.

First we observe that, since $b$ and $d$ are nonzero integers, certainly $b \cdot d$ is different from zero. Thus the sum and the product are elements of $R$. Now suppose that $(a', b')$ lies in $a/b$ and $(c', d')$ lies in $c/d$. To prove $\boxdot$ well-defined we must show that $(a' \cdot c', b' \cdot d')$ lies in $a \cdot c/b \cdot d$. From

$$(a', b') \in a/b \qquad \text{and} \qquad (c', d') \in c/d$$

we know that

$$a' \cdot b = b' \cdot a \qquad \text{and} \qquad c' \cdot d = d' \cdot c.$$

Multiplying (in $J$, of course) we obtain

$$(a' \cdot b) \cdot (c' \cdot d) = (b' \cdot a) \cdot (d' \cdot c)$$

so that

$$(a' \cdot c') \cdot (b \cdot d) = (b' \cdot d') \cdot (a \cdot c).$$

This last equation proves that

$$(a' \cdot c', b' \cdot d') \approx (a \cdot c, b \cdot d)$$

and so

$$a' \cdot c'/b' \cdot d' = a \cdot c/b \cdot d.$$

The proof that addition is well-defined is similar to this.

DEFINITION 2.13. The system $\{R, \boxplus, \boxdot\}$ is the *rational number system.*

This mathematical system has all the properties of the system of integers and some additional ones. We now mention some of these.

THEOREM 2.33. *The rational number system has the following properties:*

(i) *Addition and multiplication are commutative and associative operations.*

(ii) *R possesses an additive identity and a multiplicative identity, viz.,* $0/1$ *and* $1/1$, *respectively.*

(iii) *Each element of R has an additive inverse element.*

(iv) *Each element of R except* $0/1$ *has a multiplicative inverse element.*

(v) *Multiplication is distributive over addition.*

First, what is meant by an "inverse element" for an element relative to an operation?

Roughly stated, an *inverse element* $y$ of the element $x$ relative to the binary operation $*$ is distinguished by the fact that $x * y = y * x$ is the identity element for $*$. Thus, in $J$, $-2$ is the additive inverse of 2 since $-2 + 2 = 0$.

The additive inverse of $a/b$ is the rational number $(-a)/b$, which is usually called the *negative* of $a/b$. The multiplicative inverse of $a/b \neq 0/1$ is the rational number $b/a$, which is usually called the *reciprocal* of $a/b$. Clearly the restriction $a/b \neq 0/1$ means that the integer $a$ is *not* zero. Thus $b/a$ is an integer. The equations

$$a/b \boxplus (-a)/b = ((a \cdot b) + (b \cdot (-a)))/b \cdot b = 0/b \cdot b$$

and

$$a/b \boxdot b/a = a \cdot b/b \cdot a$$

indicate that (iii) and (iv) are true since

$$0/b \cdot b = 0/1 \quad \text{and} \quad a \cdot b/b \cdot a = 1/1.$$

Since the proofs of the other properties are so much like the proofs of the properties of the integers we shall sketch only one and leave the remainder for the student to supply. We prove here that multiplication is associative. Let $a/b$, $c/d$, and $e/f$ be fractions; then

$$\begin{aligned}(a/b \boxdot c/d) \boxdot e/f &= (a \cdot c/b \cdot d) \boxdot e/f \\ &= (a \cdot c) \cdot e/(b \cdot d) \cdot f.\end{aligned}$$

But multiplication in $J$ is associative, so that

$$\begin{aligned}(a \cdot c) \cdot e/(b \cdot d) \cdot f &= a \cdot (c \cdot e)/b \cdot (d \cdot f) \\ &= a/b \boxdot (c/d \boxdot e/f).\end{aligned}$$

Now we observe that, because of the idempotency of the integer 1, the operations of addition and multiplication for $R$ induce binary operations on the set

$$W = \{a/b \colon a/b \in R \text{ and } b = 1\}.$$

That is, the sum of two elements of $W$ is in $W$,

$$a/1 \boxplus c/1 = (a + c)/1,$$

and the product of the two elements of $W$ is in $W$,

$$a/1 \boxdot c/1 = a \cdot c/1.$$

Thus the system $\{W, \boxplus, \boxdot\}$ is a subsystem of the rational number system. The elements of $W$ are called *rational integers* since the system is isomorphic with $\{J, +, \cdot\}$.

THEOREM 2.34. *The system of rational integers is isomorphic with the system of integers.*

To prove the theorem we must, of course, exhibit one-to-one correspondences between the components of the two systems. The name adopted for the operations and the two equations above concerning the elements of $W$ suggest the following:

$$a/1 \leftrightarrow a = F(a/1),$$
$$\boxplus \leftrightarrow +,$$
$$\boxdot \leftrightarrow \cdot.$$

Since

$$F(a/1 \boxplus b/1) = F\big((a + b)/1\big) = a + b$$

and

$$F(a/1 \boxdot b/1) = F(a \cdot b/1) = a \cdot b,$$

we see that the correspondences are compatible.

As a result of this theorem we adopt the notation of $J$ for the elements of $W$, the rational integers, and for the operations of addition and multiplication in $R$. Thus we write

$$1 + 1/2 = 3/2$$

instead of

$$1/1 \boxplus 1/2 = 3/2.$$

The inverse elements relative to addition and multiplication can be used to define the inverse operations of subtraction and division.

THEOREM 2.35. *The rules*

$$(a/b) - (c/d) = (a/b) + \big((-c)/d\big)$$

*and*

$$(a/b) \div (c/d) = (a/b) \cdot (d/c)$$

*whenever* $c \neq 0$, *define the binary operations of* subtraction *and* division, *denoted by* $-$ and $\div$, *respectively.*

Strictly speaking the rule for $\div$ defines a mapping from $R \times R^*$ onto $R$ since "division by zero" is excluded. However, this function is referred to as a binary operation.

The notation of subtraction in $J$ is used here since it can be shown that subtraction in $R$ induces an operation in $W$ which agrees with subtraction in $J$. That is,

$$(a/1) - (b/1) = a + (-b) = a - b.$$

The definition of division and the adoption of the notation of $J$ for $W$ enable us to write

$$a \div b = a/b, \qquad b \neq 0,$$

from

$$(a/1) \div (b/1) = a/1 \boxdot 1/b = a \cdot 1/b \cdot 1 = a/b, \qquad b/1 \neq 0/1.$$

In this sense a rational number can be thought of as the ratio of two integers.

## Exercise 2.8

**1.** Determine which of the following are related pairs of integers (by Definition 2.12): (7, 11), (1, 2), (3, 7), (9, 18), (−77, −121), (−88, −176), (−2, 4), (−6, −14).

**2.** Show that $a/b = c/d$ if and only if $(a, b) \approx (c, d)$. (*Hint:* Since $a/b$ and $c/d$ are sets, $a/b = c/d$ if and only if $a/b \subseteq c/d$ and $a/b \supseteq c/d$.)

**3.** Prove that addition in $R$ is well-defined.

**4.** Prove Theorem 2.33.

**5.** Prove that the additive and multiplicative identity elements are unique. (*Hint:* Suppose $(a/b) + (c/d) = a/b$.)

**6.** Why does 0 have no multiplicative inverse? (Consider $0 \cdot a/b = 1$ and multiply by $b/a$.)

**7.** Suppose $(a/b) \cdot (c/d) = 1$ and $(e/f) \cdot (a/b) = 1$. Apply the associative law to $((e/f) \cdot (a/b)) \cdot (c/d)$ and prove that $c/d = e/f$. What does this say about the multiplicative inverse of a rational number?

**8.** For elements $x$ and $y$ of $R$ illustrate and prove that:

(i) The negative of $x + y$ is (negative of $x$) + (negative of $y$).

(ii) The negative of the negative of $x$ is $x$.

(iii) The reciprocal of $x \cdot y$ is (reciprocal of $x$) $\cdot$ (reciprocal of $y$).

(iv) The reciprocal of the reciprocal of $x$, $x \neq 0$, is $x$.

**9.** Show that, for rational numbers $r$ and $s$, $r \neq 0$, there is one and only one rational number $x$ such that $r \cdot x = s$. How does this show that the precise method used to obtain to $R$ from $J$ *cannot* yield a further extension of $R$?

**10.** Prove Theorem 2.35.

**11.** Determine whether division is commutative, associative, and/or distributive.

**12.** Draw a diagram similar to Fig. 2.4 in Section 2.5 to illustrate the integers. Show that points corresponding to equivalent pairs of integers lie on a ray emanating from the origin.

## 2.9 Order and Density

Since the integers are contained in the system of rational numbers (in the sense of isomorphism) we have an order relation defined on part of the rational number system. Can we define an order on the whole system which reduces to this one on the subsystem? Before attempting a definition we look at the order on the subsystem of integers. We know (Problem 10 of Exercise 2.6) that, for integers $a$ and $b$,

$$a > b$$

if and only if there is a positive integer $c$ such that

$$a = b + c.$$

(We adopt this particular formulation since it does not involve the use of pairs of natural numbers in the notation.) If we expect to extend this formulation of the relation to cover the whole of $R$ we must first define the concept of positive rational number.

DEFINITION 2.14. A rational number $a/b$ is:

(i) *Positive:* If $a \cdot b > 0$,
(ii) *Zero:* If $a \cdot b = 0$,
(iii) *Negative:* If $a \cdot b < 0$.

This definition is consistent with the concepts and notations adopted for $R$ from $J$. The rational number $a/1$ is denoted by $a$ and clearly $a/1$ is positive, zero, or negative exactly as $a$ is. Furthermore, since $b \neq 0$ in any fraction $a/b$ we see that $a \cdot b = 0$ if and only if $a = 0$, so that $0/b = 0/1$, designated now as 0, is the only zero element of $R$.

Since the definition above is stated in terms of a particular pair $(a, b)$ of the class $a/b$ we must show that the concept is well-defined. Let $(c, d) \in a/b$; then $(c, d) \approx (a, b)$, so that $b \cdot c = a \cdot d$. Therefore, if $a \cdot b > 0$, the equation

$$(a \cdot b) \cdot (c \cdot d) = (a \cdot a) \cdot (d \cdot d),$$

obtained by multiplying by the product $a \cdot d$, implies that

$$c \cdot d > 0$$

since certainly $a \cdot a$ and $d \cdot d$ are positive. And, if $a \cdot b = 0$, then, since $b \neq 0$, we have $a = 0$. Then the equation

$$b \cdot c = a \cdot d$$

shows that $c$ must be zero, and so $a \cdot b = 0$ implies $c \cdot d = 0$. Similarly $a \cdot b < 0$ implies $c \cdot d < 0$, and so the concept is well-defined.

The so-called "law of signs" which was proved for $J$ can also be proved in $R$.

THEOREM 2.36. *The product of two rational numbers is:*

(*a*) *Positive if both numbers are positive or if both numbers are negative.*
(*b*) *Zero if either number is zero.*
(*c*) *Negative if one number is positive and one is negative.*

This result follows quite easily from the properties of $J$. If $a/b$ is positive and $c/d$ is negative, then

$$a \cdot b > 0 \quad \text{and} \quad c \cdot d < 0.$$

Consider the product

$$(a/b) \cdot (c/d) = (a \cdot c)/(b \cdot d).$$

Since

$$(a \cdot b) \cdot (c \cdot d) < 0,$$

we conclude that

$$(a \cdot c) \cdot (b \cdot d) < 0$$

and the product is negative. The rest of the theorem is proved similarly.

Now we define the order relation.

DEFINITION 2.15. The rational number $a/b$ is *greater than* the rational number $c/d$ if and only if there is a positive rational number $e/f$ such that $a/b = c/d + e/f$. The relation is symbolized as

$$a/b > c/d.$$

Alternatively we can define $a/b > c/d$ if and only if the difference $a/b - c/d$ is a positive rational number. For certainly

$$a/b = c/d + (a/b - c/d),$$

and

$$e/f = a/b - c/d.$$

Since subtraction is a well-defined operation this means that the above relation is well-defined.

To establish the transitivity of this relation we consider the inequalities

$$a/b > c/d \quad \text{and} \quad c/d > e/f.$$

Then there are positive rationals $g/h$ and $m/n$ such that

$$a/b = c/d + g/h \quad \text{and} \quad c/d = e/f + m/n.$$

So

$$a/b = e/f + (g/h + m/n),$$

and we need to show that the sum of two positive numbers is positive.

$$(g/h) + (m/n) = ((g \cdot n) + (h \cdot m))/(h \cdot n),$$

and this number is positive if the integer $q$,

$$q = (h \cdot n) \cdot ((g \cdot n) + (h \cdot m)),$$

is positive. Since

$$q = (h \cdot n) \cdot ((g \cdot n) + (h \cdot m)) = ((h \cdot g) \cdot (n \cdot n)) + ((h \cdot h) \cdot (m \cdot n))$$

and $h \cdot g$ and $m \cdot n$ are positive, we see that $q$ is positive. Thus we have proved the transitivity of "greater than" and the closure of the positive rationals under addition.

There are many other important properties of the order relation in $R$, but we shall end this brief study of the rationals with the mention of a property of order in $R$ which the corresponding order in $J$ does not possess. This is the *density property.*

THEOREM 2.37. *If $a/b$ and $c/d$ are rational numbers such that $a/b > c/d$, then there is a rational number $e/f$ such that*

$$a/b > e/f > c/d.$$

Certainly the rational number $1/2 \cdot (a/b + c/d)$, which is suggested by geometric considerations (e.g., midpoint), serves to prove the theorem. This can be extended to show that "between" any two rational numbers there is an infinite set of rational numbers.

## Exercise 2.9

**1.** Classify and order the following rational numbers: $1/2$, $-1/-2$, $-10$, $-10/-3$, $-1/3$, 0.

**2.** Prove that the product of two negative fractions is positive.

**3.** State the Trichotomy Law for $R$. Prove that it is a simple consequence of the corresponding law of $J$ when the alternative form of Definition 2.15 is used.

**4.** Show that the sum of two negative fractions is negative.

**5.** Show that $(1/2) \cdot ((a/b) + (c/d))$ lies between $a/b$ and $c/d$.

**6.** Is there a smallest positive integer? Is there a smallest positive rational number? Explain.

**7.** Describe a correspondence between the rational numbers and certain points on a line. Interpret order and density in this geometric representation.

**8.** Extend the concept of absolute value of integers to the rationals.

**9.** What can you say about the rational numbers $x$ and $y$ if

(*a*) $$(x + (1/2)) \cdot (y - 2) > 0,$$

(*b*) $$(x - y) \cdot (x + y) < 0,$$

(*c*) $$(x - (1/2)) \div (y + 1) > 1?$$

**10.** Show that, if $a/b > c/d$ and $m/n > 0$, then

$$(a/b) \cdot (m/n) > (c/d) \cdot (m/n).$$

What about the converse?

**11.** Does the formula,

$$a/b \boxed{>} c/d$$

if and only if $a \cdot d > b \cdot c$, define a relation on $R$? (Consider the case for $a/b = -1/2 = 1/-2$ and $c/d = 1/3$.)

**12.** Adjust the formula of Problem 11 to yield the order relation on $R$. (*Hint:* Choose class representatives with second element in pair a positive integer.)

## 2.10 The Real Number System

The two extensions we have studied thus far were introduced as methods for inventing "solutions" to the preimage problem for certain types of functions. In a later chapter we shall again use ordered sets (e.g., ordered pairs, ordered triples, etc.) to construct extensions of the rational number system, extensions which provide for "solutions" to the preimage problem for other functions. However, in this section we will discuss an extension of the rationals motivated by geometric considerations.

Certainly the selection of two distinct points and the labeling of one 0 and the other 1 establishes in a well-known manner a geometric representation of the rational numbers by points on a line (see Fig. 2.5). But not all of the

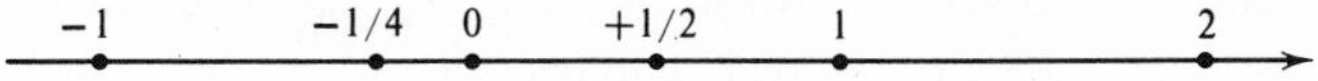


**Figure 2.5**

points on the line are used, in spite of the density of the rational numbers. This astonishing fact was discovered several thousands of years ago by Greek mathematicians, who could construct a line segment whose "length" was a "number" which, by the Pythagorean Theorem on right triangles, when multiplied by itself, produced the integer 2. But an ingenious argument (given in the next chapter) was developed which proved that no rational number had this property. (In other words the Greeks showed that $\sqrt{2}$ is not a rational number.) Thus to develop a number system for the Euclidean world one must "fill up the holes" in the rational number system, thereby producing the real number system.

Several methods for extending the rationals to the reals are known; here we shall mention the one which most resembles the methods already studied, a method due to the great nineteenth-century mathematician, R. Dedekind. Suppose the line in Fig. 2.5 is cut at a point $P$. This partitions the points of the line into three sets, the left set, the right set, and the set consisting of the point $P$. Corresponding to this geometric partition we have three subsets of $R$, and we reduce this collection to two by including the rational number, if any, which corresponds to the point $P$ in both of the other sets. The result is an ordered pair $(A, B)$ of subsets of $R$, where $A$ consists of the rational numbers corresponding to $P$ and to the points left of $P$, and $B$ consists of the rational numbers corresponding to the point $P$ and to the points right of $P$. This ordered pair is called a *cut* or a *Dedekind cut*, and this cut becomes the real number which corresponds to the point $P$. Abstracting from this essentially intuitive discussion produces the following formal definition.

DEFINITION 2.16. A *Dedekind cut* is an ordered pair $(A, B)$ of two nonempty subsets $A$ and $B$ of $R$ with the properties:

(i) $A \cup B = R$.
(ii) If $a \in A$, $b \in B$, then $a \leqslant b$.
(iii) $A \cap B$ is a set of at most one element.

The set $Re$ of all such pairs is made into the real number system by introducing addition, multiplication, and order. Consider the following rule:

*Addition.* $(A, B) \oplus (C, D)$ is the cut $(E, F)$, where $F = \{b + d: b \in B$ and $d \in D\}$ and $E = \{a + c: a \in A$ and $c \in C\}$. It is simple to prove that $(E, F)$ is a cut, and that the binary operation so defined is commutative and associative, possesses an identity, and is invertible.

However, since neither the real number system nor the method of Dedekind cuts is essential to the remaining portion of this book we shall not continue this development. Instead we will *assume* that the student is familiar with the system of real numbers as a mathematical system $\{Re, +, \cdot, <\}$ having these properties:

1. Addition $(+)$, and multiplication $(\cdot)$ are commutative and associative binary operations.
2. Multiplication is distributive over addition.
3. $Re$ contains elements 0 and 1 such that $0 \neq 1$, $a + 0 = 0 + a$, and $a \cdot 1 = 1 \cdot a = a$ for each $a \in Re$.
4. For each $a$ in $Re$ there is an element $-a$ in $Re$ such that $a + (-a) = 0$.
5. For each $a \neq 0$ in $Re$ there is an element $b$ in $Re$ such that $a \cdot b = 1$.
6. $<$ is a linear order on $Re$ with the properties of the linear order on the rationals.
7. If a nonempty subset of $Re$ has a lower bound in $Re$, then it has a greatest lower bound.

These properties, and especially property (7), should be well known to the student since they are basic to the study of calculus. Property (7) is often called the *continuity* property.

## Exercise 2.10

**1.** Show that the pair $(A, B)$, where $A = \{a: a \in R, a \leqslant 0\}$ and $B = \{b: b \in R, b \geqslant 0\}$ is a Dedekind cut.

**2.** Show that the pair $(A, B)$, where $B = \{b: b \in R, b > 0, b \cdot b > 2\}$ and $A = R - B$, is a cut.

**3.** Show that the cut of Problem 1 is an additive identity in the set of cuts.

**4.** Prove that addition of cuts is associative and commutative.

**5.** If $(A, B)$ is a cut such that $A \cap B \neq \varnothing$, it is called a *rational cut*. Show that the sum of two rational cuts is a rational cut. Construct an example.

**6.** Try to define multiplication of cuts so that the product of two rational cuts corresponds to the cut defined by the product in $R$ of the rationals.

**7.** Use set inclusion to define a linear order on the set of cuts.

**8.** Is property (iii) of Definition 2.16 essential to the definition?

**9.** Let $(A, B)$ be a Dedekind cut on $Re$ and show that as a result of Property (7) the set $A \cap B$ always consists of exactly one real number.

## 2.11 Power of the Abstract Approach

In this chapter we have encountered four different mathematical systems each of which has two binary operations which are associative. Other associative binary operations were discussed in Chapter 1. These operations all have a common property, and by proving that an "abstract" associative binary operation on a set has this property we can handle all of these operations and many others simultaneously.

Let $\{S, *\}$ be a mathematical system, where $*$ denotes an associative binary operation on $S$. (Such a system is called a *semigroup*.) Since the binary operation is associative we have by definition,

$$a * (b * c) = (a * b) * c$$

for any $a$, $b$, and $c$ in $S$. Repeated use of this associative law enables us to prove that, for any elements $a$, $b$, $c$, and $d$ in $S$,

$$a * \big(b * (c * d)\big) = (a * b) * (c * d).$$

In fact we can show that any ordered set of four elements from $S$ has exactly one "product" associated with it, viz., $a * \big(b * (c * d)\big)$, by using the associative law for $*$ to prove that all other associations of the four elements are equal to this one. Thus the elements

$$a * \big(b * (c * d)\big),\ a * \big((b * c) * d\big),\ \big(a * (b * c)\big) * d,$$
$$\big((a * b) * c\big) * d,\ (a * b) * (c * d)$$

are all equal, and the associative law for $*$ is extended to cover the case of four elements.

Since the *number* of elements, rather than the selection of elements, is vital here we see that the extension of this property can be phrased as a proposition involving the natural numbers.

THEOREM 2.38 (GENERALIZED ASSOCIATIVE LAW). *Let $a_1, a_2, \cdots, a_n$ be an ordered set of n not necessarily distinct elements of the semigroup $\{S, *\}$. Then each association of these elements relative to $*$ yields the element*

$$a_1 * \big(a_2 * (a_3 * \cdots * (a_{n-1} * a_n))\cdots\big).$$

(By an association of the elements $a_1, a_2, \cdots, a_n$ we mean pairings of elements, indicated by parentheses, in such a manner that $*$ can be applied successively to yield a product.)

This proposition is proved using the Second Principle of Induction. Now $P(1)$ is true vacuously since a single element has no associations, and $P(2)$ is true since a pair of elements has a single association. And $P(3)$ is true since the two associations, $a_1 * (a_2 * a_3)$ and $(a_1 * a_2) * a_3$, are equal by the associativity of $*$.

Then the induction hypothesis states that all the associations of any ordered set of $m$ elements of $S$

$$b_1, \cdots, b_m,$$

where $m$ is a natural number $\leqslant k$, yield products equal to

$$b_1 * (b_2 * \cdots * (b_{m-1} * b_m) \cdots).$$

Now consider an association of the ordered set of elements,

$$\{a_1, a_2, \cdots, a_{k+1}\}.$$

The $k$th and last step in an association of these $k + 1$ elements naturally involves just two elements of $S$ since the association is a successive pairing. For example we might have

$$\big((a_1 * a_2) * a_3\big) * \big((a_4 * (\cdots * a_{k+1})) \cdots\big).$$

Then the induction hypothesis can be applied, if necessary, to each of these two parts since each part involves an ordered set of no more than $k$ elements. Therefore the induction hypothesis reduces an association of the $k+1$ elements to the form

$$[a_1 * (a_2 * (a_3 * \cdots * (a_{r-1} * a_r) \cdots))] * [a_{r+1} * \cdots * (a_k * a_{k+1}) \cdots],$$

where $r$ is a natural number less than $k + 1$. Then the regular Associative Law, applied to the product of the three elements

$$a_1, \big(a_2 * (a_3 * \cdots * (a_{r-1} * a_r) \cdots)\big),$$

and

$$[a_{r+1} * \cdots * (a_k * a_{k+1}) \cdots]$$

reduces this association to

$$a_1 * [(a_2 * (a_3 * \cdots * (a_{r-1} * a_r) \cdots)) * [a_{r+1} * \cdots * (a_k * a_{k+1}) \cdots]],$$

and the induction hypothesis applied to the second factor reduces this to

$$a_1 * \big(a_2 * (a_3 * \cdots * (a_k * a_{k+1}) \cdots)\big),$$

completing the induction.

To illustrate the procedure we take $k + 1 = 6$. Then one association of the six elements $a_1, a_2, a_3, a_4, a_5, a_6$ yields

$$x = \big((a_1 * a_2) * a_3\big) * \big((a_4 * a_5) * a_6\big).$$

Now

$$(a_1 * a_2) * a_3 = a_1 * (a_2 * a_3),$$

and

$$(a_4 * a_5) * a_6 = a_4 * (a_5 * a_6),$$

so that

$$x = \big(a_1 * (a_2 * a_3)\big) * \big(a_4 * (a_5 * a_6)\big).$$

Then

$$x = a_1 * ((a_2 * a_3) * (a_4 * (a_5 * a_6)))$$

by the Associative Law, and since

$$(a_2 * a_3) * \big(a_4 * (a_5 * a_6)\big) = a_2 * \big(a_3 * (a_4 * (a_5 * a_6))\big)$$

by the induction hypothesis, we conclude that

$$x = a_1 * \big(a_2 * (a_3 * (a_4 * (a_5 * a_6)))\big).$$

Note that an *ordered set* of $n$ not necessarily distinct elements of $S$ is a mapping of the set $N_n$ of the first $n$ natural numbers to the set $S$. Instead of writing the pairs of elements which comprise this mapping as $(a, n)$ we have used the subscript notation $a_n$. Then $a_1$ is the first element (i.e., it corresponds to 1) of the ordered set, $a_2$ is the second, etc.

From this theorem we conclude that the Generalized Associative Law is valid for all the binary operations of this chapter. Of course the term "product" is replaced by "addition" in the appropriate places. Since the parentheses do not lead to different "products" through different associations they are frequently omitted. Thus in the arthimetic of integers we write

$$3 + 7 + (-1) + 5$$

instead of

$$(3 + (7 + ((-1) + 5)))$$

or

$$(3 + 7) + ((-1) + 5).$$

Back in the abstract semigroup $\{S, *\}$ as a consequence of the Generalized Associative Law we see that the rule

$$\boldsymbol{F}: (a, n) \rightarrow a * \cdots * a \qquad (n \text{ times})$$

defines a mapping $\boldsymbol{F}$ of the set $S \times N$ onto $S$. This function (sometimes called *exponentiation* or *scalar multiplication*) establishes a link between a nice, familiar system, $N$, and the abstract system $S$. We shall see in a later chapter how this bridge enables us to study the abstract system.

THEOREM 2.39. *For $a$ in $S$ and $n$ and $m$ in $N$,*

$$\boldsymbol{F}(a, n) * \boldsymbol{F}(a, m) = \boldsymbol{F}(a, m) * \boldsymbol{F}(a, n) = \boldsymbol{F}(a, n + m).$$

This is a corollary of the preceding theorem since the ordered set of $n + m$ $a$'s from the semigroup $S$ has a product which is independent of the association.

The usual notations for this function in the number systems of this chapter are, for multiplication, $a^n$, and, for addition, $a \cdot n$ (because of the Distributive Law). Thus

$$a^n \cdot a^m = a^{n+m}$$

for any real number $a$ and natural numbers $n$ and $m$. Here the function is indicated by the symbol $a^n$, which stands for the image of the pair $(a, n)$, and a result concerning the function is stated in terms of the images.

## Exercise 2.11

**1.** State the Generalized Associative Laws for the operations of the rational number system.

**2.** State the Generalized Commutative Law for a binary operation. Prove that, if the binary operation of the semigroup $\{S, *\}$ is commutative, then the Generalized Commutative Law holds.

**3.** What is the Generalized Distributive Law?

**4.** For the semigroup $\{S, *\}$ prove the "law of exponents":

$$F(F(a, m), n) = F(a, m \cdot n) \text{ for } a \in S \text{ and } m, n \text{ in } N.$$

(*Note:* For multiplication in $R$ this takes the more familiar form $(a^m)^n = a^{m \cdot n}$.)

**5.** How many pairs of parentheses appear in an association of the ordered set $\{a_1, a_2, \cdots, a_n\}$ for the binary operation $*$? Is this number the same for all associations?

**6.** How is exponentiation by the integers defined for the binary operations of $R$? Can this definition be extended to an abstract semigroup?

**7.** Show that the set $S = \{2^n: n \in N\}$ and ordinary multiplication form a semigroup isomorphic with the semigroups $\{N, +\}$ and $\{\{3^n: n \in N\}, \cdot\}$.

**8.** Relative to Problem 6, show that the set $S = \{3^n: n \in J\}$ and multiplication form a semigroup isomorphic with the semigroup $\{J, +\}$.

**9.** State a generalized "trichotomy" law for a linearly ordered set, and prove it, using the Second Principle of Induction.

## 2.12 Remarks

It was not our intention in this chapter to reveal new facts about the familiar number systems. Instead we attempted to develop these systems in a manner which would (1) demonstrate the axiomatic approach to the study of mathematics, (2) illustrate the concepts and terminology introduced in the previous chapter, and (3) introduce the concept of extending a system to obtain a new and more "flexible" system. Moreover, this development permitted the utilization in fairly simple situations of several very important methods of proof.

Many similar developments exist in other books, and we urge the student to study some of these.

## 2.13 Suggested Reading

*Articles*

Dedekind, R., *Essays on the Theory of Numbers* (trans. by W. W. Beman), Open Court Publishing Co., LaSalle, Ill., 1901.

Evans, T., "Nonassociative number theory," *Amer. Math. Monthly*, **64** (1957), 299–308.

Hahn, H., "Is there an infinity?" *Sci. American*, **187**, Nov. 1952, 76–84.

Huntington, E. V., "Postulational method in mathematics," *Amer. Math. Monthly*, **41** (1934), 84–92.

Lennes, N. J., "Foundation of arithmetic," *Amer. Math. Monthly*, **45** (1938), 70–75.

*Books*

Dantzig, T., *Number, the Language of Science*, 4th ed., The Macmillan Co., New York, 1954.

Dubisch, R., *The Nature of Number*, Ronald Press, New York, 1952.

Eves, H., and C. V. Newsom, *Introduction to the Foundations and Fundamental Concepts of Mathematics*, Rinehart & Company, New York, 1958.

Fraenkel, A., *Integers and the Theory of Numbers*, The Scripta Mathematica Studies 5, Scripta Mathematica, New York, 1955.

Henkin, L., W. N. Smith, V. J. Varineau, and M. J. Walsh, *Retracing Elementary Mathematics*, The Macmillan Company, New York, 1962.

Landau, E. G. H., *Foundations of Analysis: The Arithmetic of Whole, Rational, Irrational and Complex Numbers* (trans. by F. Steinhardt), Chelsea Publishing Co., New York, 1951.

Ringenberg, L., *A Portrait of 2*, National Council of Teachers of Mathematics, Washington, D.C., 1957.

# 3

# Decompositions of Integers

IF $a$ AND $b$ are elements of $J$, the system of integers, then we know by the Trichotomy Law that exactly one of the statements

$$a = b, \qquad a > b, \qquad a < b,$$

is true. This means that each integer $a$ splits the set of all integers into three nonoverlapping subsets. Such a partition provides a useful but rather rough classification of the integers.

In this chapter we introduce a different classification of the integers relative to a nonzero integer. This classification is essentially based on the concept of division, but since we are investigating decompositions of integers little use is made here of the rational numbers.

*Note:* In this and subsequent chapters the multiplication symbol $\cdot$ is generally omitted, and we write $ab$ instead of $a \cdot b$.

## 3.1 Divisor Theorem

In elementary school we learn a method for "dividing" one positive integer into another and obtaining a "quotient" and a "remainder." This method is basically one of subtracting multiples of the first from the second until the difference is nonnegative but less than the "divisor." This difference is called the "remainder" and the multiplier is called the "quotient." The basis for this algorithm or method is the Divisor Theorem.

THEOREM 3.1. *If $a$ and $b$ are integers and $a \neq 0$, then there exist unique integers $q$ and $r$ such that*

$$b = aq + r$$

*and*

$$0 \leqslant r < |a|.$$

The element $q$ is the *quotient* and $r$ is the *remainder.*

First we prove the existence of elements $q$ and $r$ when $a$ is a positive integer. Consider the set $S = \{b - am : m \in J, b - am \geqslant 0\}$. $S$ is not empty, for $a \geqslant 1$ and $|b| \geqslant 0$ imply that either $b \in S$ or $(b - ab) \in S$. Therefore $S$ has a smallest element $r$, and

$$r = b - aq$$

for some integer $q$. Furthermore, $r$ is smaller than $a$ since the relation $r \geqslant a$ implies that

$$0 \leqslant r - a = b - a(q + 1) < r$$

which contradicts the minimality of $r$. Thus for the positive integer $a$ and the integer $b$ there exist integers $q$ and $r$ such that

$$b = aq + r$$

and

$$0 \leqslant r < a.$$

If $a < 0$, then $-a > 0$ so that by the above argument there are integers $q'$ and $r$ such that

$$b = (-a)q' + r$$

and

$$0 \leqslant r < (-a).$$

This means that there are integers $q$ and $r$ such that

$$b = aq + r$$

and

$$0 \leqslant r < |a|.$$

To prove the uniqueness of the quotient and remainder we employ a very standard argument for showing uniqueness. Suppose $q''$ and $r''$ are integers with the same properties as $q$ and $r$, viz.,

$$b = aq'' + r''$$

and

$$0 \leqslant r'' < |a|.$$

Then

$$aq'' + r'' = aq + r,$$
$$aq'' - aq = r - r'',$$

and

$$a(q'' - q) = r - r''.$$

Using absolute values we obtain the equation

$$|a| \cdot |q'' - q| = |r - r''|.$$

By the definition of absolute value of an integer we know that

$$|r - r''| = r - r'' \qquad \text{or} \qquad r'' - r,$$

both of which are smaller than $|a|$, so that we have

$$|a| \cdot |q'' - q| = |r - r''| < |a|.$$

Now if $q'' \neq q$ we see that

$$|q'' - q| \geqslant 1,$$

and so

$$|a| \cdot |q'' - q| \geqslant |a|.$$

Since the integer $|a| \cdot |q'' - q|$ cannot be both smaller than $|a|$ and greater than or equal to $|a|$, we conclude that

$$q'' = q,$$

which implies that

$$r'' = r.$$

Thus the quotient and remainder are unique.

This simple existence theorem has many consequences as we shall see. One elementary corollary provides the basis for our decimal notation.

THEOREM 3.2. *Let $a$ and $b$ be positive integers, $a > 1$. Then $b$ is expressible uniquely in the radix form with base $a$ as*

$$b = a^n c_n + \cdots + ac_1 + c_0$$

*where $c_n$ is a positive integer and the $c_i$ are integers with $0 \leqslant c_i < a$ for $0 \leqslant i \leqslant n$.*

We use the Second Principle of Induction, applied to $b$. If $b = 1$ then it is already expressed in this form, with $n = 0$ and $c_0 = 1$. For our induction hypothesis we have the statement, "Each positive integer less than or equal to $k$ is expressible in radix form." Now consider the positive integer $k + 1$. By the Divisor Theorem,

$$k + 1 = qa + r, \qquad \text{where } 0 \leqslant r < a.$$

We wish to show that the induction hypothesis can be applied to $q$.

If $(k + 1) < a$, then

$$k + 1 = 0 \cdot a + (k + 1),$$

so that by the uniqueness of $q$ and $r$,

$$q = 0 \qquad \text{and} \qquad k + 1 = r.$$

If $(k + 1) \geqslant a$, then $(k + 1) > r$, and so

$$(k + 1) - r = qa$$

is positive, implying that $q$ is positive. Finally, if $q$ were greater than or equal to $k + 1$, then the inequalities

$$a > 1 \qquad \text{and} \qquad q \geqslant k + 1$$

imply

$$aq > k + 1,$$

which contradicts the equation

$$k + 1 = aq + r, \qquad r \geqslant 0.$$

Thus we conclude that

$$0 \leqslant q < k + 1.$$

If $q = 0$, then the equation

$$k + 1 = aq + r, \qquad 0 \leqslant r < a,$$

shows that $k + 1$ is already expressed in the desired form. If $q > 0$, then we can apply the induction hypothesis and conclude that

$$q = a^m c_m + \cdots + ac_1 + c_0$$

where $c_m > 0$ and the $c_i$ are integers with $0 \leqslant c_i < a$ for $0 \leqslant i \leqslant m$. Therefore

$$k + 1 = (a^m c_m + \cdots + ac_1 + c_0)a + r$$

so that

$$k + 1 = a^{m+1}c_m + \cdots + a^2 c_1 + ac_0 + r,$$

which is the desired form since $0 \leqslant r < a$.

Thus we have proved by induction that every positive integer can be expressed in radix form with base $a$.

Uniqueness is proved by the method used in the previous theorem. Suppose

$$b = a^n c_n + \cdots + ac_1 + c_0$$

and

$$b = a^r d_r + \cdots + ad_1 + d_0,$$

where $c_n$ and $d_r$ are positive and $c_i$ and $d_j$ are nonnegative integers less than $a$ for $0 \leqslant i \leqslant n$ and $0 \leqslant j \leqslant r$. Subtracting, we obtain an equation of the form

$$0 = a^m e_m + \cdots + ae_1 + c_0,$$

where $|e_i| < a$ since

$$e_i = c_i - d_i.$$

If the $e_i$ are not all equal to zero, then from the nonzero $e_i$ we choose the one with minimal subscript, say $e_s$, and by using the Cancellation Law for Multiplication, we obtain from

$$0 = a^m e_m + \cdots + a^s e_s,$$
$$0 = a^{m-s} e_m + \cdots + a e_{s+1} + e_s.$$

Therefore

$$-e_s = a(a^{m-s-1} e_m + \cdots + e_{s+1}),$$

and

$$|e_s| = a \cdot |a^{m-s-1} e_m + \cdots + e_{s+1}|$$

which we write as

$$|e_s| = at.$$

Now $t \neq 0$, since $e_s$ is by assumption different from zero, so that $t \geqslant 1$. But the inequalities

$$a > 1 \quad \text{and} \quad t \geqslant 1$$

imply

$$at \geqslant a,$$

which in turn implies that

$$|e_s| \geqslant a.$$

This contradiction means that all the $e_i = 0$, and so the radix representation of $b$, relative to the base $a$, is unique.

This result enables us to construct a system of symbols for the positive integers in the following way. For the finite set of nonnegative integers less than the base $a$ (i.e., the digits) arbitrary symbols are selected and the integer

$$b = c_n a^n + \cdots + c_1 a + c_0$$

is written as

$$b = (c_n \cdots c_1 c_0)_a.$$

Taking $a$ as 10 and using the customary symbols for the digits we write 2107 as an abbreviation for

$$2 \cdot (10)^3 + 1 \cdot (10)^2 + 0 \cdot (10)^1 + 7.$$

This is the familiar *position notation* for the positive integers. Of course other bases can be selected also.

If $a$ is taken as 6, then, since

$$2107 = (351) \cdot 6 + 1,$$
$$351 = (58) \cdot 6 + 3,$$
$$58 = 9 \cdot 6 + 4,$$
$$9 = 1 \cdot 6 + 3,$$

we have, after substituting and simplifying,

$$2107 = 1 \cdot 6^4 + 3 \cdot 6^3 + 4 \cdot 6^2 + 3 \cdot 6 + 1,$$

and

$$2107 = (13431)_6.$$

If $a$ is taken as 5, then, since

$$\begin{aligned} 2107 &= (421)5 + 2, \\ 421 &= (84)5 + 1, \\ 84 &= (16)5 + 4, \\ 16 &= 3 \cdot 5 + 1, \end{aligned}$$

after substituting and simplifying, we have

$$2107 = 3 \cdot 5^4 + 1 \cdot 5^3 + 4 \cdot 5^2 + 1 \cdot 5 + 2,$$

and so

$$2107 = (31412)_5.$$

The student should observe that the use of the Divisor Theorem in the above examples provides a simple method for converting a decimal representation of a positive integer to the radix representation for another base. Thus, to obtain the representation for the base 2 of the integer 13, we write

$$\begin{aligned} 13 &= 6 \cdot 2 + 1, \\ 6 &= 3 \cdot 2 + 0, \\ 3 &= 1 \cdot 2 + 1, \\ 1 &= 0 \cdot 2 + 1. \end{aligned}$$

Then writing the remainders in reverse order (i.e., the last remainder first, the next-to-last remainder second, etc.) yields the representation

$$13 = (1101)_2.$$

To convert $(1101)_2$ back to decimal notation we write

$$(1101)_2 = 1 \cdot 2^3 + 1 \cdot 2^2 + 0 \cdot 2 + 1$$

and using the addition and multiplication tables for the decimal digits (which we memorized long ago) we obtain

$$(1101)_2 = 8 + 4 + 1 = 13.$$

## Exercise 3.1

**1.** Express 1112 to the base 12 and to the base 2.

**2.** Construct the addition and multiplication tables for the octal digits (base 8) and use them to evaluate the product of $(1314)_8$ and $(707)_8$. Check in the decimal system.

**3.** Discuss the advantages and disadvantages of a representation system based on 2, 5, 10, 12, or 20.

**4.** If $n + 1$ weights are available, being $1, 2, 4, 8, \cdots$, and $2^n$ units, respectively, what measurements can be made with a balance scale?

**5.** Prove that, if $a$, $b$, and $c$ are integers such that

$$0 \leqslant b < |a| \quad \text{and} \quad 0 \leqslant c < |a|,$$

then $(b - c) < |a|$. (*Hint:* $|a| \geqslant |a| - c$.)

**6.** Can radix representation be extended to include the negative integers? Explain.

**7.** Discuss the extension of radix representation to the rationals.

**8.** Consider the following method for multiplying 23 and 17:

$$\begin{aligned} 23 &= (11)2 + 1;\ 17 \\ 11 &= 5 \cdot 2 + 1;\ \ 34 = 2(17) \\ 5 &= 2 \cdot 2 + 1;\ \ 68 = 2(34) \\ 2 &= 1 \cdot 2 + 0;\ 136 = 2(68) \\ 1 &= 0 \cdot 2 + 1;\ 272 = 2(136) \end{aligned}$$

Then $1 \cdot 17 + 1 \cdot 34 + 1 \cdot 68 + 0 \cdot 136 + 1 \cdot 272 = 391 = (23)(17)$. Explain and justify.

## 3.2 Congruence and Factors

From the Divisor Theorem we see that, if an arbitrary integer is divided by the positive integer $m$, then the remainder is just one of the $m$ integers $0, 1, \cdots, m - 1$. Thus the positive integer $m$ and the concept of remainder determine a partition of $J$ into $m$ subsets. We describe this partition by introducing an appropriate equivalence relation on $J$.

DEFINITION 3.1. If $a$, $b$, and $m$ are integers, $m > 0$, then $a$ is congruent with $b$ modulo $m$, written $a \equiv b \bmod m$, if and only if $a$ and $b$ have the same remainder when divided by $m$.

The *modulus* $m$ is used to "measure" the integers, and the remainders determine the classes to which integers belong.

*Example* 1. If $m = 7$, then, since $1 = 0 \cdot 7 + 1$ and $8 = 1 \cdot 7 + 1$, we see that $8 \equiv 1 \bmod 7$. If $m = 5$, then $-17 \equiv 8 \bmod 5$ since $-17 = (-4)5 + 3$ and $8 = 1 \cdot 5 + 3$. And any two integers are congruent mod 1.

It is almost obvious from the definition that congruence mod $m$ is an equals relation. Certainly $a$ and $a$ have the same remainder relative to $m$, and, if $a$ and $b$ have the same remainder relative to $m$, then so do $b$ and $a$. Finally, if $a$ and $b$ have the same remainder relative to $m$ and if $b$ and $c$ have the same remainder relative to $m$, then, because of the uniqueness of the remainders, $a$ and $c$ have the same remainder. Thus,

(i) $a \equiv a \bmod m$,

(ii) $a \equiv b \bmod m$ implies $b \equiv a \bmod m$,

and

(iii) $a \equiv b \bmod m$ and $b \equiv c \bmod m$ imply $a \equiv c \bmod m$.

THEOREM 3.3. *Congruence* mod $m$ *is an equivalence relation on* $J$.

Because of the unusual properties of the integer zero special attention is directed to the zero class.

DEFINITION 3.2. The integer $a \neq 0$ is a *factor* of the integer $b$ (and $b$ is a *multiple* of $a$) if and only if there is an integer $c$ such that $b = ac$. We indicate that $a$ is a factor of $b$ with the symbolism $a \mid b$.

THEOREM 3.4. *The positive integer* $m$ *is a factor of the integer* $a$ *if and only if* $a \equiv 0 \bmod m$.

If $m$ is a factor of $a$ then by definition there exists an integer $c$ such that

$$a = mc = mc + 0.$$

So $a \equiv 0 \bmod m$ since $0 = 0m + 0$. The converse is equally obvious.

The concept of factor permits another characterization of congruence.

THEOREM 3.5. *The integer* $a$ *is congruent with the integer* $b$ *modulo* $m$ *if and only if* $m$ *is a factor of* $a - b$. $a \equiv b \bmod m$ *if and only if* $a - b = km$ *for some integer* $k$.

If $a \equiv b \bmod m$, then, by definition of congruence,

$$a = mq_1 + r$$

and

$$b = mq_2 + r, \qquad 0 \leqslant r < m.$$

Then

$$r = a - mq_1 = b - mq_2$$

and

$$a - b = m(q_1 - q_2) = mk.$$

Conversely, if

$$a - b = mk,$$

then

$$a = b + mk.$$

Now by the Divisor Theorem,

$$b = qm + r, \qquad 0 \leqslant r < m,$$

so that

$$a = (qm + r) + mk.$$

Thus

$$a = (q + k)m + r, \qquad 0 \leqslant r < m,$$

so that by the uniqueness, $r$ is the remainder of both $a$ and $b$ relative to $m$. Consequently

$$a \equiv b \bmod m.$$

Now let $n$ be an arbitrary nonzero integer. Does $n$ have any factors, and if so what are they? Since we can restrict our attention to positive factors without sacrificing generality, this is equivalent to asking, "For what moduli, if any, does $n$ lie in the zero class"? It is a simple arithmetic problem to find the remainder (or *least residue*) of a given integer relative to a given modulus, but the problem of finding which moduli yield a given remainder for a given integer is somewhat more complex. We see that the problem of finding integers $m > 0$ such that, for a given $x$ and $r$,

$$x \equiv r \bmod m$$

is equivalent to finding the positive factors of the difference $x - r$ by Theorem 3.4.

Certainly the nonzero integer $n$ has two positive factors, namely 1 and $|n|$, since

$$n = 1 \cdot n = (-1)(-n).$$

On the other hand $n$ has only a finite number of distinct positive factors as we will now show.

THEOREM 3.6. *If $m$ is a positive factor of the integer $n \neq 0$, then $m \leqslant |n|$. Since there are just $|n|$ positive integers less than or equal to $|n|$, the integer $n$ has no more than $|n|$ distinct positive factors.*

Since $m$ is a factor of $n$ there is an integer $k > 0$ such that

$$|n| = mk.$$

By trichotomy, if $m$ is *not* less than or equal to $|n|$, then

$$m > |n|.$$

Therefore

$$|n| = mk > |n|k,$$

so that by the Cancellation Law

$$1 > k.$$

But this is impossible since $k$ is a positive integer and 1 is the smallest positive integer. This contradiction rules out the possibility $m > |n|$ and thereby proves the theorem.

Now in a sense our problem of finding the positive factors of the nonzero integer $n$ is solved since we have an algorithm or procedure which in $n$ steps determine all positive factors of $n$: Compute the least residue of $n$ modulo each of the $|n|$ numbers $1, 2, 3, \cdots, |n|$. Actually this can be improved upon by noting that factors come in pairs since

$$a = bc$$

implies that *both* $b$ and $c$ are factors. Thus to determine the positive factors of

$n$ it is only necessary to check the least residue modulo the numbers 1, 2, 3, $\cdots$, $s$ where $s$ is the smallest positive integer such that

$$(s + 1)^2 > |n|.$$

*Example* 2. Consider the integer $n = 171$. Since $(14)^2 = 196 > 171$ we check the least residues of 171 modulo the positive integers less than 14:

$$\begin{aligned} 171 &\equiv 1 \bmod 2 \\ &\equiv 0 \bmod 3 \\ &\equiv 3 \bmod 4 \\ &\equiv 1 \bmod 5 \\ &\equiv 3 \bmod 6 \\ &\equiv 3 \bmod 7 \end{aligned} \qquad \begin{aligned} 171 &\equiv 3 \bmod 8 \\ &\equiv 0 \bmod 9 \\ &\equiv 1 \bmod 10 \\ &\equiv 6 \bmod 11 \\ &\equiv 3 \bmod 12 \\ &\equiv 2 \bmod 13 \end{aligned}$$

Since $171 = 3(57)$ and $171 = 9 \cdot 19$, the numbers 1, 3, 9, 19, 57, and 171 are the only positive factors of 171.

We observe that, if $a$ is *not* a factor of $n$, then neither is any multiple of $a$, a factor of $n$. For $n = (ka)c$ implies $n = a(kc)$. Thus the procedure indicated above can be shortened even more by crossing out multiples of numbers which have already proved to be nonfactors of $n$. In the example above there is no need to check the numbers 4, 6, 8, 10, or 12 since 2 is not a factor of 171.

## Exercise 3.2

**1.** Describe the partition of $J$ modulo 5.

**2.** Show that addition and multiplication in $J$ induce binary operations in the set of all integers congruent with zero mod two.

**3.** Use Theorem 3.5 to show that $a \equiv b \bmod m$ and $c \equiv d \bmod m'$ imply $ac \equiv bd \bmod mm'$.

**4.** Prove that, if $a$, $b$, $c$, and $d$ are positive integers such that $a < b^2$, $a = cd$, and $c > b$, then $d < b$. (*Hint:* Assume $d \geqslant b$.)

**5.** Determine the positive factors of 391.

**6.** If the positive factors of $n$ are known, what are the other integral factors?

**7.** How many integral factors has zero?

**8.** Show that:

(i) $a \mid b$ implies $a \mid bc$.

(ii) $a \mid b$ and $b \mid c$ imply $a \mid c$.

(iii) $a \mid b$ and $b \mid a$ imply $a = b$ or $-b$.

**9.** Define the relation **R** on $J$ by $a\mathbf{R}b$ if and only if $a$ is a factor of $b$. What can you say about this relation?

**10.** Use the Associative and Distributive Laws to show that, if $a$ is a factor of $b$ and also of $c$, then $a$ is a factor of $(mb + nc)$ for any integers $m$ and $n$.

**11.** Show that $n \equiv 1 \bmod 2$ implies that $n^2 \equiv 1 \bmod 8$.

**12.** Show that 6 is a factor of three consecutive integers.

**13.** Show that, if $m \equiv 1 \bmod 2$ and $n \equiv 1 \bmod 2$, then $m^2 + n^2 \equiv 0 \bmod 2$ but $m^2 + n^2 \not\equiv 0 \bmod 4$.

**14.** Prove that 30 is a factor of $n^5 - n$ for each integer $n$.

**15.** Show that the square of no positive integer $n$ is congruent with 3 modulo 4.

## 3.3 Primes

In the previous section we considered the problem of finding the different positive factors of a nonzero integer. Now we restrict our attention to certain "minimal" factors, and the nature of this minimality is indicated as follows.

DEFINITION 3.3. A *prime integer* (or a prime) is an integer $p > 1$ whose only positive factors are 1 and $p$. An integer $m > 1$ is called a *composite* if it is not prime.

Thus 2, 3, 5, 7, 19, and 73 are primes whereas 4, 6, 15, and 1111 are composites.

The reason for the introduction of this minimality concept is based on the following simple observation: If $a = bc$ and $b = de$, then $a = dec$. Thus a factor of a factor of $n$ is also a factor of $n$. Then since we are dealing with positive factors only, it seems that each nonzero integer $n$ with $|n| > 1$ has at least one prime factor (which may be $|n|$). This reasoning leads us to expect that a composite can be written as a product of prime factors (as the word composite suggests).

THEOREM 3.7. *An integer $n > 1$ is either a prime or a product of primes.*

The proof is based on the Second Principle of Induction (adjusted slightly since we are dealing with integers $n \geqslant 2$). Certainly 2 is a prime since there is no integer between 1 and 2. So our induction hypothesis states that each integer $m$, $1 < m \leqslant k$, is either a prime or expressible as a product of primes. Now consider the integer $k + 1$. If $k + 1$ is a prime then we need say no more. If $k + 1$ is not a prime then it has a positive factor $f$ which is neither 1 nor $k + 1$. By definition of factor, there is an integer $g$ such that

$$k + 1 = fg,$$

and surely $1 < g < k + 1$ by Theorem 3.6 and the restrictions on $f$. Therefore the induction hypothesis states that $f$ and $g$ are each either primes or products of prime factors. Substitution yields an expression for $k + 1$ as a product of prime factors. Thus we can write $n$ as a product of primes, and since the primes are not necessarily all different, this product can be written in the form

$$n = p_1^{e_1} p_2^{e_2} \cdots p_r^{e_r}$$

where $p_1, p_2, \cdots, p_r$ are distinct primes and the $e_i$ are positive integers.

Such an expression is called a *factorization* of $n$ into prime factors, a representation of $n$ as a product of prime factors. For a given $n$ a factorization into primes may be obtainable in several different ways; for example,

$$100 = 4 \cdot 25 = (2 \cdot 2)(5 \cdot 5) = 2^2 \cdot 5^2,$$
$$100 = 2 \cdot 50 = 2(5(10)) = 2 \cdot 5 \cdot 5 \cdot 2 = 5^2 \cdot 2^2,$$
$$100 = 10 \cdot 10 = (2 \cdot 5)(2 \cdot 5) = 2^2 \cdot 5^2.$$

In each case the same factorization, except for a permutation of the factors, is obtained, and it may appear obvious to the student that this is always the case. Indeed we can and will prove that the factorization into primes is unique, but it is a fact which requires proof. There are, however, mathematical systems in which factorization into primes is *not* unique, and we shall discuss one of these now.

*Example* 1. Let $T$ be the set of all integral multiples of three. Since

$$3m + 3n = 3(m + n) \quad \text{and} \quad (3m)(3n) = 3(3mn)$$

for any integers $m$ and $n$, we see that $\{T, +, \cdot\}$ is a mathematical system with two binary operations. In this system the number 18 is "composite" since $18 = 3 \cdot 6$ and 3 and 6 are in $T$, but the numbers, 3, 6, 12, 15, 21, 24, 30, $\cdots$ are "primes" since they cannot be factored *within* the system. The "composites" of this system in general have many different factorizations into "primes":

$$36 = 3 \cdot 12 = 6 \cdot 6,$$
$$72 = 3 \cdot 24 = 6 \cdot 12,$$
$$144 = 3 \cdot 48 = 6 \cdot 24 = 12 \cdot 12.$$

Thus factorization is not unique in this system.

There are algebraic systems which are extensions of the system of integers in which factorization into primes is not unique. Since these are rather too complicated to describe briefly and since they are discussed in detail in Chapter 10, we shall only mention their existence at this time.

Now we return to the problem of showing that factorization into primes is unique in $J$.

THEOREM 3.8 (FUNDAMENTAL THEOREM OF ARITHMETIC). *The factorization of an integer $n > 1$ into primes is unique up to a permutation of the factors.*

If the theorem is not true, then, by the Well-Ordering Theorem, among the integers greater than 1 which possess more than one different factorization into primes there is a smallest which we shall label $s$. Certainly if $n$ is an integer such that $1 < n < s$, then $n$ is uniquely factorable. Consider two different factorizations of $s$ into primes,

$$s = p_1 p_2 \cdots p_m = q_1 q_2 \cdots q_r. \tag{3.1}$$

What can we say about the two sets of primes $\{p_1, \cdots, p_m\}$ and $\{q_1, q_2, \cdots, q_r\}$? First, neither $m$ nor $r$ is 1 since $s$ cannot be a prime (which obviously has only one factorization). Furthermore, the intersection of these two sets is empty, for, if $p_i$ is a common member, then since

$$1 < s/p_i < s$$

($s/p_i$ is a factor of $s$) we know by the minimality of $s$ that $s/p_i$ is uniquely factorable into primes. However, canceling $p_i$ out of equation (3.1) leaves two different factorizations of $s/p_i$. Thus we conclude that

$$\{p_1, \cdots, p_m\} \cap \{q_1, \cdots, q_r\} = \varnothing.$$

Now compare $p_1$ and $q_1$; since $p_1 \neq q_1$, one is larger than the other, and we label the larger $p_1$. Thus $q_1 < p_1$. Since $q_1$ is a prime it is larger than 1 so that

$$1 < p_1 - q_1 < p_1.$$

Therefore the integer

$$t = (p_1 - q_1)(p_2 \cdots p_m)$$

has the properties

$$t < p_1(p_2 \cdots p_m) = s$$

and

$$1(p_2 \cdots p_m) \leqslant t,$$

and so $t$ is an integer between 1 and $s$. By the minimality of $s$ the integer $t$ is uniquely factorable into primes. However,

$$\begin{aligned} t &= p_1(p_2 \cdots p_m) - q_1(p_2 \cdots p_m) \\ &= q_1 q_2 \cdots q_r - q_1 p_2 \cdots p_m \\ &= q_1(q_2 \cdots q_r - p_2 \cdots p_m), \end{aligned}$$

and this leads to two different factorizations of $t$, one containing $q_1$ and one without $q_1$. For consider the expression

$$t = (p_1 - q_1) p_2 \cdots p_m;$$

a factorization of $p_1 - q_1$ into primes leads to a factorization of $t$ into primes, so consider the prime factors of $p_1 - q_1$. We claim that $q_1$ is *not* a factor of $p_1 - q_1$ since

$$p_1 - q_1 = kq_1$$

implies

$$p_1 = kq_1 + q_1 = (k + 1)q_1,$$

which is impossible since $p_1$ and $q_1$ are distinct primes. Thus the expression

$$t = (p_1 - q_1) p_2 \cdots p_m$$

leads to a factorization of $t$ *without* the factor $q_1$, whereas the expression

$$t = q_1(q_2 \cdots q_r - p_2 \cdots p_m)$$

leads to a factorization of $t$ *with* the factor $q_1$. This contradiction proves the theorem.

We shall present another, perhaps simpler, proof of this very basic result in Section 3.5. The second proof requires some concepts which have not yet been introduced.

Now that we know the composites are constructed from the primes in a unique fashion we might ask how many primes exist. Is it possible that there are only finitely many multiplicative "building blocks" for the positive integers?

THEOREM 3.9 (EUCLID). *The set of primes is infinite.*

Suppose the set of primes is finite; then the set can be counted, $p_1, p_2, \cdots, p_n$. Form the integer

$$m = 1 + p_1 p_2 \cdots p_n.$$

Clearly $m$ is an integer greater than 1, so we know that $m$ is either a prime or a product of primes. However,

$$m \equiv 1 \bmod p_i, \qquad i = 1, 2, \cdots, n,$$

so that none of the primes $p_1, \cdots, p_n$ is a factor of $m$. Thus the assumption that the set of primes is finite leads to an impossible situation, and so the theorem is proved.

Not only are there infinitely many primes, but these primes are scattered rather irregularly among the positive integers.

THEOREM 3.10. *For each integer $n > 1$ there exists a set of $n$ consecutive composite integers.*

To prove this theorem we need only demonstrate the existence of one such set for each $n > 1$. Form the $n$ positive integers

$$(n + 1)! + 2, (n + 1)! + 3, \cdots, (n + 1)! + n + 1.$$

Since $(n + 1)!$ is a multiple of each positive integer $k \leqslant n + 1$, we see that $k$ is a factor of $(n + 1)! + k$ when $k \leqslant n + 1$.

For example, $5! + 2 = 122$ is divisible by 2, $5! + 3 = 123 = 3(41)$, $5! + 4 = 124 = 4(31)$, and $5! + 5 = 125 = 5(25)$, so that the four numbers 122, 123, 124, and 125 are consecutive composites. (There are other sets of four, such as 24, 25, 26, 27 and 32, 33, 34, 35.)

Even though arbitrarily large clusters of consecutive composites do occur, the following statement can be proved about the number of primes. If $\pi(n)$ denotes the number of primes less than or equal to the integer $n > 1$ then for large values of $n$ the number $\pi(n)$ is approximated by $n/\log n$. This is a rough statement of the Prime Number Theorem, which was proved in 1896 by J. Hadamard and C. de la Vallée Poussin.

A glance at a collection of primes reveals several pairs of primes which differ by two, e.g., 3 and 5, 5 and 7, 11 and 13, 17 and 19, 101 and 103, etc. Are there infinitely many of these pairs? This is the "twin prime" problem, one of many unsolved problems in number theory.

## Exercise 3.3

**1.** In the system $T$ of multiples of three find two examples, other than those of the example in the text, which have different factorizations.

**2.** Let $m$ be any integer $> 1$, and show that $M$, the set of all multiples of $m$, and ordinary addition and multiplication form a mathematical system. Show that, if $p$ is a prime of $J$ which is not a factor of $m$, then the number $k = m^2p^2$ has two different factorizations into "primes" in $M$.

**3.** Show that congruence mod 4 separates the set of primes into three non-overlapping classes. How many such classes does congruence mod 8 define?

**4.** Prove that there are infinitely many primes of the form $4k - 1$ (such as 3, 7, 11, 23, 31, $\cdots$). (*Hint:* Assume $p_1, \cdots, p_r$ are the only such primes and form the integer $n = 4p_1p_2\cdots p_r - 1$.)

**5.** Obtain a list of all primes less than 300 by the following method (sieve of Eratosthenes): First, write down 2, and then proceeding through the ordered integers write down only those which are not multiples of numbers that have already been listed. So we write 2, 3, 5, 7, 11, 13, 17, 19, 23, etc. (Or the numbers from 2 to 300 can all be written and then the multiples crossed out: 2, 3, ~~4~~, 5, ~~6~~, 7, ~~8~~, $\cdots$.)

**6.** Show that no formula of the type

$$f(n) = a_0 + a_1n + \cdots + a_rn^r, \qquad a_i \in J,$$

can represent a prime for every integer $n$. (Consider $f(a_0)$.)

**7.** What can you say about the factorization of an arbitrary integer?

**8.** Prove that, if $n$ is a positive integer such that $2^n - 1$ is a prime, then $n$ is a prime. (Note that $2^{5a} - 1 = (2^a)^5 - (2^a)^4 + (2^a)^4 - (2^a)^3 + (2^a)^3 - (2^a)^2 + (2^a)^2 - 2^a + 2^a - 1$.)

**9.** Show that each integer $n > 1$ is the product of a perfect square and a square-free integer, and that this representation is unique. (An integer is square-free if none of its factors greater than one is a perfect square.)

**10.** Use the Fundamental Theorem of Arithmetic to show that, if $p$ is a prime and $b$ is an integer such that $b \not\equiv 0 \bmod p$, then $ab \equiv 0 \bmod p$ implies $a \equiv 0 \bmod p$.

**11.** Find three different sets of five consecutive composite integers.

**12.** Draw a graph of $\pi(n)/n$ for $n$ between 1 and 30.

**13.** Prove that there is no prime $p$ such that $p^n = 2^m - 1$ where $n$ and $m$ are integers greater than 1.

**14.** Prove that there is no prime $p$ such that $p^n = 2^m + 1$ where $n$ and $m$ are integers greater than 2.

**15.** Prove that $n!$ is divisible by $1 + 2 + \cdots + n$ if and only if $n + 1$ is not an odd prime.

## 3.4 Greatest Common Factor

Up to now we have been concerned only with the factors of a single positive integer, but here we introduce the concept of common factor.

DEFINITION 3.4. A positive integer $t$ is a *common factor* of a nonempty set $S$ of positive integers if and only if $t$ is a factor of every element of $S$.

Clearly 2 and 3 are both common factors of the set $\{6, 12, 60\}$, and 2 is certainly a common factor of the set of all positive multiples of 10.

By Theorem 3.6 the collection of all common factors of a nonempty set $S$ of positive integers is a finite set $F_S$. For the set $S$ has a smallest element $s$

by the Well-Ordering Theorem, and since $s$ has at most $s$ distinct positive factors we see that $F_S$ cannot have more than $s$ elements. And since a finite set of integers (in this case $F_S$) naturally contains exactly one maximal element, we conclude that a nonempty set $S$ possesses a unique *greatest common factor* (or G.C.F.).

THEOREM 3.11. *A nonempty set of positive integers possesses a unique greatest common factor.*

If $S$ is a finite set denoted by $\{a_1, \cdots, a_n\}$, then the G.C.F. of $S$ is often symbolized by $(a_1, \cdots, a_n)$. Thus the G.C.F. of the set $\{9, 12\}$ is indicated by $(9, 12)$, and clearly

$$(9, 12) = 3.$$

(The context in which this symbolism is used will enable us to distinguish G.C.F. from ordered pair.)

The concept can be extended to sets of integers not all of which are zero by defining the G.C.F. of such a set to be the G.C.F. of the distinct absolute values. Then by the above argument the G.C.F. of such a set exists and is a unique positive integer.

Theorem 3.11 is an existence theorem which gives no indication of how to find the G.C.F. With this problem in mind we restrict our attention to finite sets of positive integers, and especially to sets of two positive integers.

THEOREM 3.12 (THE EUCLIDEAN ALGORITHM). *The minimal nonzero remainder $r_m$ in the following set of equations is the G.C.F. of the two positive integers $a$ and $b$:*

$$\begin{aligned}
b &= aq_1 + r_1, & 0 &< r_1 < a,\\
b &= r_1q_2 + r_2, & 0 &< r_2 < r_1,\\
r_1 &= r_2q_3 + r_3, & 0 &< r_3 < r_2,\\
&\vdots\\
r_{m-2} &= r_{m-1}q_m + r_m, & 0 &< r_m < r_{m-1},\\
r_{m-1} &= r_mq_{m+1}.
\end{aligned}$$

We see that the set of equations is obtained by repeated application of the Divisor Theorem, and the set is finite since the remainders are all positive integers less than $a$ and are all distinct.

First we note that the G.C.F., $(a, b) = d$, is a factor of both $a$ and $b$ since it is a common factor, so that by writing the first equation as

$$r_1 = b - aq_1$$

and applying the distributive law we conclude that $d$ is a factor of $r_1$. Writing the second equation as

$$r_2 = a - r_1q_2$$

we see also that $d$ is a factor of $r_2$. Continuing in this fashion we conclude finally that $d$ is a factor of $r_m$.

However, if we start at the bottom and work up we see that $r_m$ is a common factor of $a$ and $b$. The last equation

$$r_{m-1} = r_m q_{m+1}$$

shows that $r_m$ is a factor of $r_{m-1}$. Then the distributive law and the next-to-last equation

$$r_{m-2} = r_{m-1} q_m + r_m$$

show that $r_m$ is also a factor of $r_{m-2}$. Since each equation up from here involves the two preceding remainders we conclude that $r_m$ is a common factor of the $m + 2$ positive integers $r_m, r_{m-1}, \cdots, r_1, a, b$.

Now we mesh these two pieces of information, which imply that

$$d \leqslant r_m \tag{3.2}$$

and

$$r_m \leqslant d, \tag{3.3}$$

and conclude that

$$d = r_m.$$

Thus we have a straightforward routine for finding the G.C.F. of two positive integers. Certainly the number of steps is not greater than one plus the larger of the two integers.

Little use is made in the above discussion of the integers $q_i$. These integers are of considerable importance, however. If the set of $m + 1$ equations of the algorithm is collapsed into a single equation by eliminating the $m - 1$ remainders $r_1, r_2, \cdots, r_{m-1}$, then an expression for the G.C.F. as the sum of a multiple of $a$ and a multiple of $b$ is obtained. The following example illustrates this.

*Example* 1. Find $d = (382, 26)$.

$$\begin{aligned} 382 &= (14)(26) + 18, \qquad & 0 < 18 < 26,\\ 26 &= 1(18) + 8, & 0 < 8 < 18,\\ 18 &= 2(8) + 2, & 0 < 2 < 8,\\ 8 &= 4(2). \end{aligned}$$

Therefore $2 = (382, 26)$. Now we solve the first equation for 18 and substitute in the second equation:

$$\begin{aligned} 18 &= 1(382) - 14(26),\\ 26 &= 1(382 - 14(26)) + 8. \end{aligned}$$

Solving this for 8 yields

$$8 = 15(26) - 1(382),$$

and by substituting this and the expression for 18 in the third equation we get

$$1(382) - 14(26) = 2[15(26) - 1(382)] + 2.$$

Therefore

$$2 = 3(382) + (-44)(26),$$

and the G.C.F. of 26 and 382 is expressed as the sum of multiples of 26 and 382.

This example indicates, then, that the Euclidean algorithm can be used to find integers (not necessarily positive) $x$ and $y$ for the positive integers $a$ and $b$ such that

$$(a, b) = ac + by.$$

From this idea we can develop an interesting characterization of the G.C.F. of $a$ and $b$.

THEOREM 3.13. *The least positive integer $n$ of the form*

$$n = ax + by$$

*for integers $x$ and $y$ is the G.C.F. of the two positive integers $a$ and $b$.*

Consider the set $G$ of all the positive integers of the form $ax + by$, where $x$ and $y$ are integers (not necessarily positive). Since

$$a = a \cdot 1 + b \cdot 0$$

and

$$b = a \cdot 0 + b \cdot 1,$$

we see that $a$ and $b$ belong to $G$. Thus $G \neq \varnothing$ and so by the Well-Ordering Theorem $G$ contains a smallest element $n$ which by definition of $G$ is of the form

$$n = ax + by$$

for some integers $x$ and $y$. Therefore for any two positive integers $a$ and $b$, such a positive $n$ exists.

Now we must show that $n = (a, b)$. Denoting $(a, b)$ by $d$, we know that

$$a = dr \qquad \text{and} \qquad b = ds$$

for some integers $r$ and $s$ since $a$ and $b$ are multiples of $d$. Then by substituting we see that

$$n = ax + by = d(rx + sy)$$

and so $d$, as a factor of $n$, is no larger than $n$ by Theorem 3.6,

$$d \leqslant n.$$

On the other hand, $n$ is a common factor of $a$ and $b$ as we can see from the minimality of $n$. For, using the Divisor Theorem, we obtain

$$a = qn + r, \qquad 0 \leqslant r < n,$$

and, if $r \neq 0$, then $r$ is an element of $G$ since

$$r = a - qn = a - q(ax + by) = a(1 - qx) + b(-qy).$$

But this is impossible since $n$ is the smallest element of $G$. Therefore

$$a = qn,$$

and $n$ is a factor of $a$. In exactly the same way we can show that $n$ is a factor of $b$, for by the Divisor Theorem

$$b = q'n + r', \qquad 0 \leqslant r' < n,$$

and if $r' \neq 0$, then, since

$$r' = b - q'n = b - q'(ax + by) = a(-q'x) + b(1 - q'y),$$

$r'$ is an element of $G$. Since $n$ is the smallest element of $G$ this is impossible, so that $r'$ must be zero. So

$$b = q'n,$$

and we conclude that $n$ is a common factor of $a$ and $b$. This means that

$$n \leqslant d$$

since $d$ is the G.C.F. and, from the two inequalities,

$$d \leqslant n \qquad \text{and} \qquad n \leqslant d,$$

the only possible conclusion is

$$n = d.$$

Thus the theorem is proved.

Since the Euclidean algorithm provides us with a simple routine for finding $(a, b)$ and for finding integers $x$ and $y$ such that

$$(a, b) = ax + by,$$

the characterization provided by Theorem 3.13 is of no practical importance in dealing with the elements of $J$. However, alternative characterizations of concepts are often of great importance as aids in extending these concepts to other mathematical systems and in generalizing them. In a later chapter we shall see how Theorem 3.13 suggests a method for extending a system in which factorization is not unique to one in which factorization is unique.

Now we ask whether there exists a method for finding the G.C.F. of a finite set of positive integers, $\{a_1, a_2, \cdots, a_m\}$, where $m > 2$. Since the Euclidean algorithm provides a way for handling two integers, we might expect some repeated application of that algorithm to various pairs to yield the G.C.F., and that is the case. We prove a reduction theorem which indicates the procedure to be followed.

THEOREM 3.14. *If $\{a_1, a_2, \cdots, a_m\}$ is a set of $m > 2$ positive integers, then*

$$(a_1, a_2, \cdots, a_m) = \big((a_1, a_2), \cdots, a_m\big).$$

This theorem states that to find the G.C.F. of the integers 211, 991, and 772 we first find the G.C.F. $d$ of two of them, say

$$d = (991, 772),$$

and then find the G.C.F. of $d$ and the unused integer 211. More succinctly,

$$(991, 772, 211) = ((991, 772), 211).$$

In the proof of the theorem we use the notation

$$h = (a_1, a_2, \cdots, a_m), \qquad k = ((a_1, a_2), \cdots, a_m),$$

and

$$d = (a_1, a_2);$$

thus

$$k = (d, a_3, \cdots, a_m).$$

We shall prove that $h = k$ by obtaining the two inequalities, $h \leqslant k$ and $k \leqslant h$.

Since $k = (d, a_3, \cdots, a_m)$ surely $k$ is a common factor of each of the integers $d, a_3, \cdots, a_m$. But $d$ is a common factor of $a_1$ and $a_2$, so that we have

$$d = kd', \qquad a_1 = da'_1, \qquad \text{and} \qquad a_2 = da'_2.$$

Then substitution yields

$$a_1 = k(d'a'_1) \qquad \text{and} \qquad a_2 = k(d'a'_2),$$

so that $k$ is a common factor of the $m$ positive integers $a_1, a_2, \cdots, a_m$, and so

$$k \leqslant h,$$

since $h$ is the G.C.F. of $\{a_1, a_2, \cdots, a_m\}$.

On the other hand, $h$ is a common factor of $\{a_1, \cdots, a_m\}$ so that there are integers $b_i$ such that

$$a_i = hb_i, \qquad i = 1, 2, \cdots, m.$$

Since $d = (a_1, a_2)$ we know by Theorem 3.13 that there are integers $x$ and $y$ such that

$$d = a_1x + a_2y.$$

Then substitution yields

$$d = (hb_1)x + (hb_2)y = h(b_1x + b_2y),$$

and we see that $h$ is a factor of $d$. This means that $h$ is a common factor of the set $\{d, a_3, \cdots, a_m\}$ and so

$$h \leqslant k.$$

Consequently $h = k$, and the theorem is proved.

*Corollary* 3.14.1. If $\{a_1, a_2, \cdots, a_m\}$ is a set of positive integers, then there exist integers $x_1, x_2, \cdots, x_m$ such that

$$(a_1, a_2, \cdots, a_m) = a_1x_1 + a_2x_2 + \cdots + a_mx_m.$$

This is proved by induction, using the preceding two theorems. Certainly for $m = 3$ we have

$$d = a_1x_1 + a_2x_2$$

and

$$k = dy_1 + a_3x_3$$

for some integers $x_1$, $x_2$, $y_1$, and $x_3$ by the previous theorems. Then substitution yields

$$k = (a_1x_1 + a_2x_2)y_1 + a_3x_3,$$

and since $k = (a_1, a_2, a_3)$ this means that there exist integers $x_i'$, $i = 1, 2, 3$, such that

$$(a_1, a_2, a_3) = a_1x_1' + a_2x_2' + a_3x_3'.$$

The general statement is proved in exactly this way from the induction hypothesis.

•*Example* 2. Find (486, 288, 204), and express it linearly in terms of the three numbers 486, 288, and 204. We compute:

$$\begin{aligned} 486 &= 1(288) + 198, \\ 288 &= 1(198) + 90, \\ 198 &= 2(90) + 18, \\ 90 &= 5(18). \end{aligned}$$

Thus $18 = (486, 288)$, and we express 18 linearly in terms of 486 and 288 by collapsing the set of the first three equations:

$$\begin{aligned} r_1 &= 198 = 1(486) - 1(288), \\ r_2 &= 90 = 288 - 1(r_1) = 288 - 1(486 - 1(288)), \\ &= 2(288) - 1(486). \end{aligned}$$

So

$$18 = 198 - 2(90) = [1(486) - 1(288)] - 2[2(288) - 1(486)],$$

and

$$18 = (486, 288) = 3(486) + (-5)(288).$$

Then we compute (18, 204):

$$\begin{aligned} 204 &= 11(18) + 6, \\ 18 &= 3(6). \end{aligned}$$

Therefore

$$6 = (18,\ 204) = (486, 288, 204)$$

and

$$6 = 204 + (-11)18 = 204 + (-11)[3(486) + (-5)(288)]$$

so that

$$6 = (486, 288, 204) = (-33)(486) + (55)(288) + (1)(204).$$

We note again that the G.C.F. of a set $S$ of arbitrary integers not all zero is the G.C.F. of the set of absolute values of the elements of $S$. Thus the G.C.F. of $\{486, -288, -204\}$ is, by the above work, precisely 18. Moreover, we can write

$$18 = (-33)(486) + (-55)(-288) + (-1)(-204).$$

# Exercise 3.4

**1.** Use the Euclidean algorithm to compute (320, 144) and express it in the form $320x + 144y$.

**2.** Find integers $x$ and $y$ such that

$$(7469, 2387) = 7469x + 2387y.$$

**3.** Find (10672, −4147).

**4.** Show that a positive integer $n$ is the G.C.F. of the positive integers $a$ and $b$ if and only if (i) $n$ is a common factor of $a$ and $b$, and (ii) every common factor of $a$ and $b$ is a factor of $n$. (*Hint:* Use Theorem 3.13.)

**5.** Find (991, 772, 211).

**6.** If $a$, $b$, and $c$ are positive integers, does $((a, b), c) = (a, (b, c))$? Why?

**7.** Let $a$ and $b$ be integers (not both zero) and consider the set

$$T = \{ax + by: x, y \in J\}.$$

Show that:

(i) $T$ is closed under addition and subtraction (i.e., the sum and the difference of any two elements of $T$ are in $T$).

(ii) $T$ has a smallest positive element $t$.

(iii) $t = (a, b)$, the G.C.F. of $\{a, b\}$.

**8.** Show that a set of integers closed under subtraction is also closed under addition. (See Problem 7(i).)

**9.** Show that the number of steps in the Euclidean algorithm can be reduced (in general) by selecting the remainders $r_{i+1}$ so that $-r_i/2 < r_{i+1} < r_i/2$. Then we would write Example 2 of this section as:

$$486 = 2(288) + (-90), \quad -288/2 < -90 < 288/2,$$
$$288 = 3(1 - 901) + 18, \quad -90/2 < 18 < 90/2$$
$$90 = 1 - 901 = 5(18).$$

**10.** Show that, if $a$, $b$, $c$, and $d$ are integers such that $a = bc + d$ and $|a| + |b| \neq 0$, then $(a, b) = (b, d)$.

**11.** Show that the integers $x$ and $y$ in the expression

$$(a, b) = ax + by$$

are *not* unique by adding and subtracting $abn$, $n$ an arbitrary integer:

$$(a, b) = ax + by + abn - abn.$$

Find three different pairs of $x$ and $y$ for the $a$ and $b$ of Example 1.

**12.** Show that, if $x$ and $y$ are integers such that $(a, b) = ax + by$, then $(x, y) = 1$. (Use Theorem 3.13 and the Cancellation Law.)

**13.** Find an integer $x$ such that

$$26x \equiv 2 \bmod 382.$$

(See Example 1.)

**14.** Show that the smallest element $t$ of the set $T$ in Problem 7 is a factor of every integer in $T$. (*Hint:* If $t = ax + by$, $m = ax' + by'$, and $m = qt + r$, then $r \in T$.)

**15.** Show that $(a, bc) = (a, b)(b, c)$ if $(b, c) = 1$.

**16.** Prove that $(a, a + k)$ is a factor of $k$, where $a$ and $k$ are integers not both zero.

## 3.5 Unique Factorization Again

The theory of the common factor provides us with a theoretical device for checking through the primes in a factorization of an integer $n > 2$ and showing that, if $p$ is a prime factor of $n$, then it must be one of the primes in the factorization. The details follow.

DEFINITION 3.5. Two integers $a$ and $b$, not both zero, are *relatively prime* if and only if $(a, b) = 1$. A set of nonzero integers is a *relatively prime set* if and only if the G.C.F. of the set is 1.

The material of the last section provides criteria and methods for checking to see if two integers are relatively prime or not.

THEOREM 3.15. *Two nonzero integers $a$ and $b$ are relatively prime if and only if integers $x$ and $y$ exist such that $ax + by = 1$.*

This is a consequence of Theorem 3.13. We note that $(|a|, |b|) = (a, b)$ by definition.

THEOREM 3.16. *If $p$ and $q$ are primes, then either $p = q$ or $(p, q) = 1$.*

The positive factors of $p$ and of $q$ are, respectively, 1 and $p$ and 1 and $q$. If $p \neq q$, then 1 is the only common factor of $p$ and $q$ so that $(p, q) = 1$.

THEOREM 3.17. *If $a$, $b$, and $c$ are positive integers such that $(a, b) = 1$ and $a$ is a factor of $bc$, then $a$ is a factor of $c$.*

From $(a, b) = 1$ we know there are integers $x$ and $y$ such that

$$1 = ax + by,$$

and since $a \mid bc$ we know that

$$bc = ak$$

for some integer $k$. Therefore

$$c = c \cdot 1 = c(ax + by) = a(cx) + (bc)y = a(cx) + a(ky) = a(cx + ky),$$

and we conclude that $a$ is a factor of $c$.

We use these last two results to prove the key to another proof of the uniqueness of the factorization into primes.

*Lemma* 3.1. If $p$ is a prime factor of the positive integer $m$ which is expressible as

$$m = p_1 p_2 \cdots p_n,$$

where the $p_i$ are all primes, then $p$ equals one of the $p_i$.

This rather obvious-looking result is proved by mathematical induction on $n$, the number of prime factors $p_i$. If $n = 1$, then $m = p_1$ is a prime, and since $p$ is given to be both a prime and a factor of $m$, we must conclude $p = p_1$. Thus the proposition for $n = 1$ is proved.

Our induction hypothesis states that, if $p$ is a factor of an integer which is a product of $k$ primes, then $p$ is equal to one of these primes. So suppose $p \mid (p_1 p_2 \cdots p_k p_{k+1})$; then we must show that $p$ equals one of the $p_i$. Compare $p$ and $p_{k+1}$; if $p = p_{k+1}$ we are through. If $p \neq p_{k+1}$, then by Theorem 3.16 $(p, p_{k+1}) = 1$, and so by Theorem 3.17 we see that since

$$p \mid (p_1 \cdots p_k)p_{k+1} \qquad \text{and} \qquad (p, p_{k+1}) = 1,$$

we have

$$p \mid (p_1 \cdots p_k).$$

Then by the induction hypothesis we conclude that $p$ equals one of the primes $p_1, \cdots, p_k$. So in either case (the two cases are defined by $p = p_{k+1}$ and $p \neq p_{k+1}$) $p$ equals one of the $p_i$, $1 \leqslant i \leqslant k + 1$, and the induction is complete.

This is the lemma which is necessary for the formalization of the following *heuristic* argument for the uniqueness of prime factorizations. Suppose

$$p_1 p_2 \cdots p_m = q_1 q_2 \cdots q_r,$$

where the $p_i$ and $q_j$ are primes, $1 \leqslant i \leqslant m$ and $1 \leqslant j \leqslant r$. Compare $p_1$ and $q_1$; if $p_1 = q_1$, then we cancel it from both sides of the equation. If $p_1 \neq q_1$, then $p_1$ "must" be a factor of $q_2 \cdots q_r$, so we compare $p_1$ and $q_2$, etc. "Eventually" we see that $p_1$ equals one of the $q_j$ and we cancel from both sides. Then we repeat with $p_2$, etc. After a finite number of steps the left side equals 1 and so must the right.

We can now show an alternative proof of Theorem 3.8, discussed earlier.

*Second Proof of Theorem* 3.8. We use the Second Principle of Induction. Certainly 2 is uniquely factorable into primes since it is a prime. This begins our induction since 1 is not covered by the proposition. Now our induction hypothesis states that any integer greater than 1 and less than $s$ is uniquely factorable into primes. Consider the integer $s$, and suppose it has the factorizations

$$s = p_1 p_2 \cdots p_m = q_1 q_2 \cdots q_r,$$

where $p_i$ and $q_j$ are primes for $1 \leqslant i \leqslant m$ and $1 \leqslant j \leqslant r$. By the lemma above, $p_1$, as a factor of

$$s = q_1 q_2 \cdots q_r,$$

must equal one of the $q_j$, and because of the Commutative Law we can take

$$p_1 = q_1.$$

Then

$$s/p_1 = p_2\cdots p_m = q_2\cdots q_r$$

is an integer less than $s$ since $p_1 > 1$ (as all primes are) implies

$$s = (s/p_1)p_1 > s/p_1.$$

And we can take $s/p_1 > 1$, since $s/p_1 = 1$ implies

$$s = p_1 = q_1,$$

and no more needs to be said about that case. Thus the induction hypothesis can be applied to $s/p_1$, and we conclude that $m = r$ and

$$\{p_2, \cdots, p_m\} = \{q_2, \cdots, q_r\}.$$

Since $p_1 = q_1$ this means that the factorization of $s$ into primes is unique up to a permutation of the factors. This completes the induction.

The uniqueness of factorization into primes can be used to prove the nonexistence of rational numbers with certain properties. In particular we can show that there is no rational number whose square is a prime.

THEOREM 3.18. *There exist no positive integers $a$ and $b$ such that*

$$a^2 = pb^2,$$

*where $p$ is a prime.*

Suppose integers $a$ and $b$ exist such that

$$a^2 = pb^2.$$

If $d = (a, b)$, then $a = a_1d$ and $b = b_1d$, and so

$$(a_1d)^2 = p(b_1d)^2,$$

implying that

$$a_1{}^2 = pb_1{}^2.$$

Moreover, $(a_1, b_1) = 1$ since

$$d = ax + by = a_1dx + b_1dy$$

implies, after cancellation,

$$1 = a_1x + b_1y.$$

Now the equation

$$a_1{}^2 = pb_1{}^2$$

means that $p$ is a prime factor of $a_1{}^2$, and since the prime factors of $a_1{}^2$ are precisely the prime factors of $a_1$ written twice (this is where the Unique Factorization Theorem comes in) we conclude that $p$ is also a prime factor of $a_1$. But as noted in the previous sentence each prime factor of $a_1$ appears twice (at least) as a prime factor of $a_1^2$. In other words,

$$a_1 = c_1 p$$

implies

$$a_1^2 = (c_1 p)(c_1 p) = c_1^2 p^2.$$

Therefore substitution in $a_1^2 = pb_1^2$ yields

$$c_1^2 p^2 = pb_1^2.$$

By the Cancellation Law this means that

$$c_1^2 p = b_1^2.$$

From this equation we conclude in exactly the same manner that $p$ is a factor of $b_1^2$ and hence of $b_1$. Therefore from our assumption that integers $a$ and $b$ exist such that

$$a^2 = pb^2, \qquad p \text{ a prime},$$

we obtain the conclusions that

$$(a_1, b_1) = 1$$

and that $p$ is a common factor of $a_1$ and $b_1$.

This contradiction proves the theorem.

The connection with rational numbers is made by the observation that

$$(a/b)^2 = p$$

can be written as

$$(a/1)^2(1/b)^2 = p,$$

so that

$$(a/1)^2 = p(b/1)^2$$

or

$$a^2 = pb^2.$$

In dealing with rational numbers, incidentally, we often make use of a concept in $J$ closely related to that of G.C.F.

Definition 3.6. The *least common multiple* (L.C.M.) of a set $\{a_1, a_2, \cdots, a_m\}$ of nonzero integers is the smallest positive integer which is a multiple of each of the integers $a_1, a_2, \cdots, a_m$.

Since the integer

$$|a_1 a_2 \cdots a_m|$$

is both positive and a multiple of each $a_i$, the set $M$ of all positive *common multiples* of all the $a_i$ is certainly not empty. Therefore $M$ contains a unique minimal element, proving the following result.

THEOREM 3.19. *Each finite set of nonzero integers has a unique L.C.M.*

If the integers in the set are factored into primes, then the L.C.M. of the set is easily found by multiplying together the highest power of each prime which is a factor of one of the integers in the set. To find the L.C.M. of the set {9, 10, 12} we note that $2^2$ is the greatest power of 2 which is a factor of one of the elements, as is $3^2$ the greatest power of 3, and 5 the greatest power of 5, dividing elements of the set. Therefore

$$m = (2^2)(3^2)(5) = 180$$

is the L.C.M. of {9, 10, 12}.

THEOREM 3.20. *The L.C.M. of* $\{a_1, a_2, \cdots, a_n\}$ *is the product of the maximal powers of primes which occur as factors of the integers* $a_i$.

Denote the L.C.M. of $\{a_1, \cdots, a_n\}$ by $m$ and the product of the maximal prime power factors by $k$. First we will show that $m \leqslant k$ by showing that $k$ is a common multiple of all the $a_i$. Consider an integer of the set, say $a_1$. Now $a_1$ is factorable as

$$a_1 = p_1^{e_1} p_2^{e_2} \cdots p_r^{e_r}$$

where the $p_i$ are distinct primes and the $e_i$ are positive integers. Since $k$ is the product of the maximal powers of primes which divide some one of the $a_i$, certainly each $p_i$ appears as a factor of $k$, and to at least as great an exponent as $e_i$ by the maximality used to define $k$. Therefore $a_1$ is certainly a factor of $k$, and since the same argument is valid for the other $a_i$ we conclude that $k$ is a common multiple of the set. Thus $m \leqslant k$.

Now consider the prime factors of $m$ and $k$. If $p^s$ is the maximal power of $p$ which is a factor of $k$, then, by definition of $k$, $p^s$ is a factor of at least one element, say $a_1$, of the set. But $m$ is a multiple of $a_1$, so we see that $p^s$ is a factor of $m$,

$$m = p^s m_1.$$

By the same argument, if $q^t$, $q \neq p$, is the maximal power of the prime $q$ which is a factor of $k$, then

$$m = q^t m_2.$$

Now $(q^t, p^s) = 1$ by the uniqueness of prime factorization, so from Theorem 3.17 we see that $q^t$ is a factor of $m_1$, and

$$m = p^s q^t m_3.$$

Clearly continuation of this argument shows that $k$ is a factor of $m$, and so

$$k \leqslant m.$$

Then from these two inequalities we conclude that $k = m$, and the theorem is proved.

Of course it is possible that the L.C.M. of a set of integers which are not factored (or not easily factored) may be desired, and this raises the question of whether the Euclidean algorithm or some other routine can be used to find the L.C.M. Such a procedure should, if possible, replace the process of factorization by a combination of arithmetic processes. First we consider the situation for sets of two elements.

THEOREM 3.21. *If a and b are positive integers, then $ab/(a, b)$ is the L.C.M. of $\{a, b\}$.*

Denote $(a, b)$ by $d$. Since $d$ is a factor of $a$ and $b$,

$$a = da_1, \qquad b = db_1,$$

we see that

$$x = ab/d = ab_1 = ba_1,$$

and so $x$ is a common multiple of $a$ and $b$. Thus $x$ is at least as large as $m$, the L.C.M. of $\{a, b\}$.

Now let $p^s$ be the maximal power of the prime $p$ which divides $x$. Since $x = ab_1$ we know by the uniqueness of factorization that, if $p$ is a factor of $x$, then $p$ is a factor of $a$ and/or $b_1$. Similarly, since $x = ba_1$, then $p$ is a factor of $b$ and/or $a_1$. Now $(a_1, b_1) = 1$ surely, so that $a_1$ and $b_1$ cannot both have $p$ as a factor, and we will take $(b_1, p) = 1$. This means that $p^s$, as a factor of $x = ab_1$, is necessarily a factor of $a$, and since $m$ is a multiple of $a$ we see that $p^s$ is a factor of $m$. Continuing in this manner we show that all the maximal powers of primes dividing $x$ are also factors of $m$. So $x$ is a factor of $m$, and hence $x \leqslant m$. This combines with $m \leqslant x$ to show that $x = m$.

This result means that we have two ways of finding the L.C.M. of $\{486, 288\}$. From the factorizations into prime powers,

$$486 = 2 \cdot 3^5 \qquad \text{and} \qquad 288 = 2^5 \cdot 3^2,$$

we conclude that the L.C.M. is $2^5 \cdot 3^5$. However, since we know that $(486, 288) = 18$ from Example 2 of the previous section, we can find the L.C.M. by evaluating $(486)(288)/18$.

The method based on the G.C.F. can be extended to sets of more than two positive integers by the following reduction theorem.

THEOREM 3.22. *If $\{a_1, a_2, \cdots, a_n\}$ is a set of positive integers with $n \geqslant 3$, then its L.C.M. equals the L.C.M. of $\{m, a_3, \cdots, a_n\}$, where $m$ is the L.C.M. of $\{a_1, a_2\}$.*

This is a consequence of Theorem 3.20, for surely a prime power factor of some one of the $n$ integers $a_1, a_2, \cdots, a_n$ is also a factor of one of the $n - 1$ integers $m, a_3, \cdots, a_n$ since $m$ is a common multiple of $a_1$ and $a_2$. The argument also reverses, since a maximal prime power factor of $m$ is by Theorem 3.20 a factor of $a_1$ and/or $a_2$.

*Example* 1. Find the L.C.M. of {486, 288, 204}. From the above work we see that the L.C.M. of {486, 288} is 7776, so consider the set {204, 7776}. By one method or another we find that

$$(7776, 204) = 12.$$

Thus the L.C.M. of {7776, 204} is (7776)(204)/12 = (7776)(17). So the L.C.M. of {486, 288, 204} is 132, 192.

## Exercise 3.5

**1.** Find the positive integers less than 20 which are relatively prime to 20. (*Note:* We say that $a$ is *relatively prime to b* if $(a, b) = 1$.)

**2.** Define a relation on the set of positive integers by the rule: $a\mathbf{R}b$ if and only if $(a, b) = 1$. Is this relation reflexive, symmetric, or transitive? Explain.

**3.** Find integers $x$ and $y$ such that

$$21x + 17y = 1.$$

Is there an integer $m$ such that $21\ m \equiv 1 \bmod 17$? Explain.

**4.** Show that, if $p$ and $q$ are prime factors of the integer $m$, $p \neq q$, then $pq$ is a factor of $m$.

**5.** Use the argument of Theorem 3.18 to show that there is no rational number whose third power is 2.

**6.** Show that $\sqrt{6}$ is not rational. Can you generalize this?

**7.** For a fixed prime $p$ let $B$ be the set $\{b: b \in R, b > 0, \text{ and } b^2 > p\}$ and $A$ be the set $R - B$. Show that the pair $(A, B)$ is a Dedekind cut of $R$.

**8.** What is meant by, "Reduce the fraction $a/b$ to lowest terms"? Is this based on a reasonable criterion for selecting a representative of $a/b$?

**9.** How is the L.C.M. used in dealing with the arithmetic of $R$? Why? (See Problem 8.)

**10.** Show that all of the factors of $n = p_1^{e_1}p_2^{e_2}\cdots p_r^{e_r}$, where the $p_i$ are distinct primes and the $e_i$ are positive integers, are of the form

$$p_1^{c_1}p_2^{c_2}\cdots p_r^{c_r},$$

where $0 \leqslant c_i \leqslant e_i$, for $i = 1, 2, \cdots, r$.

**11.** In how many different ways can the number $n$ of Problem 10 be expressed as a product of two relatively prime integers?

**12.** Show that, if $a$ is a factor of $b$, then $(b, c) = 1$ implies $(a, c) = 1$.

**13.** Are there integers $x$ and $y$ such that $x + y = 50$ and $(x, y) = 6$? Explain.

**14.** Find a set of three positive integers which is a relatively prime set such that no proper subset is a relatively prime set.

**15.** Find all positive integers $x$ and $y$ such that $(x, y) = 8$ and the L.C.M. of $\{x, y\}$ is 64. (*Hint:* Set $x = 8a$, $y = 8b$, where $(a, b) = 1$.)

**16.** Find the L.C.M. of {11, 111, 1111} by two methods.

**17.** Prove that if $a$ and $b$ are positive, relatively prime integers such that $ab = n^2$ for some integer $n$, then $a$ and $b$ are squares of integers.

**18.** Show that the rational number

$$(1/2) + (1/3) + (1/4) + \cdots + (1/n),$$

$n$ a positive integer, is never a rational integer.

## 3.6 Euler's Totient

The *counting functions* on the set of positive integers are functions which, for each positive integer $n$, count the set of positive integers which are no larger than $n$ and have some special property. We mentioned one of these functions earlier in discussing primes, viz., the prime-counting function defined by

$$\pi : n \to \pi(n) = \text{number of primes not exceeding } n.$$

No simple arithmetic formula is known for determining $\pi(n)$.

Now we consider another such function, the *totient* or *phi-function*, and derive a formula for it based on the factorization of $n$ into primes.

DEFINITION 3.7. The totient, or phi-function, is the function on $P$, the set of positive integers, determined by

$$\Phi : n \to \Phi(n) = \text{number of integers } a, \quad 1 \leqslant a \leqslant n,$$

such that $(a, n) = 1$.

Thus $\Phi(1) = 1$, $\Phi(2) = 1$, $\Phi(3) = 2$, $\Phi(4) = 2$, and $\Phi(12) = 4$. Furthermore $\Phi(p) = p - 1$ for each prime $p$ since the only positive factors of $p$ are 1 and $p$.

Before attempting to find a formula for $\Phi(n)$ we wish to point out a characterization or alternative definition of the function. This characterization is based on the rather elementary fact that $(a, b) = 1$ if and only if $(a, r) = 1$, where

$$b = aq + r, \qquad 0 \leqslant r < a.$$

Certainly the equation

$$b = aq + r$$

shows that any common factor of $a$ and $r$ is a factor of $b$, and the equation

$$r = b - aq$$

shows that any common factor of $a$ and $b$ is also a factor of $r$.

THEOREM 3.23. *If $n$ is a positive integer, then $\Phi(n)$ is exactly the number of equivalence classes modulo $n$ which contain only elements relatively prime to $n$.*

We identify the $n$ equivalence classes by the remainders:

$$[0], [1], \cdots, [n - 1].$$

Then, if $r$ is a positive integer less than $n$ such that $(r, n) = 1$, certainly by the above observation $(b, n) = 1$ for every $b \in [r]$. On the other hand, if every element of $[r]$ is relatively prime to $n$ then we must have $(r. n) = 1$. Thus $\Phi(n)$ is precisely the number of classes modulo $n$ which contain only elements relatively prime to $n$.

Note that the above argument shows that, if one element of $[r]$ is *not* relatively prime to $n$, then no element of $[r]$ is relatively prime to $n$.

The above example leads us to suspect that there should be an arithmetic formula for $\Phi(p^n)$ when $p$ is a prime, so we consider the powers of 3: $\Phi(3) = 2$, $\Phi(9) = 6$, $\Phi(27) = 18$, and so forth. The integers between 1 and 27 which are relatively prime to 27 are precisely those integers which are *not* multiples of 3. Since there are 9 positive multiples of 3 not greater than 27, viz., $3 = 1(3)$, $6 = 2(3)$, $9 = 3(3)$, $12 = 4(3)$, $15 = 5(3)$, $18 = 6(3)$, $21 = 7(3)$, $24 = 8(3)$, and $27 = 9(3)$, we conclude that $\Phi(27) = 27 - 9 = 18$.

THEOREM 3.24. *If $p$ is a prime, then $\Phi(p^n) = p^n(1 - 1/p)$ for each positive integer $n$.*

When $n = 1$, surely $\Phi(p) = p(1 - 1/p) = p - 1$ as we remarked above. Consider $p^n$ for $n > 1$; since the only distinct prime factor of $p^n$ is $p$, certainly any positive integer which is not a multiple of $p$ must be relatively prime to $p^n$. Since there are exactly $p^{n-1}$ multiples of $p$ which are positive but not greater than $p^n$ (for $0 < kp \leqslant p^n$ implies $0 < k \leqslant p^{n-1}$ by the cancellation law) we see that

$$\Phi(p^n) = p^n - p^{n-1} = p^n(1 - 1/p).$$

Now, how do we pass from this to a formula for $\Phi(r)$, where $r$ is a composite? Looking at some examples:

$$\begin{aligned}
\Phi(6) &= 2, \quad \text{since } (1, 6) = (5, 6) = 1,\\
\Phi(10) &= 4, \quad \text{since } (1, 10) = (3, 10) = (7, 10) = (9, 10) = 1,\\
\Phi(12) &= 4, \quad \text{since } (1, 12) = (5, 12) = (7, 12) = (11, 12) = 1,
\end{aligned}$$

we note that

$$\Phi(6) = \Phi(3)\Phi(2),\ \Phi(10) = \Phi(5)\Phi(2),\ \Phi(12) = \Phi(4)\Phi(3).$$

However, $\Phi(12) \neq \Phi(6)\Phi(2)$ since $4 \neq 2(1)$, so we might conjecture that the factorization into relatively prime factors is the clue.

THEOREM 3.25. *If $m$ and $n$ are positive integers such that $(m, n) = 1$, then $\Phi(mn) = \Phi(m)\Phi(n)$.*

To prove this we rely heavily on the characterization of the totient in Theorem 3.23. Denote $\Phi(m)$ by $s$ and $\Phi(n)$ by $t$. Then $s$ is the number of equivalence classes modulo $m$ which consist of elements relatively prime to $m$, and $t$ is the number of equivalence classes modulo $n$ which contain only elements relatively prime to $n$. Now select integers $x$ and $y$ such that $(x, m) = 1 = (y, n)$ and form

$$u = nx + my.$$

We claim that $(u, mn) = 1$. For suppose $p$ is a prime factor of $mn$. Since

$(m, n) = 1$ we know that $p$ is a factor of only one of the two, say $m$. Then if $p$ were a factor of $u$ we could write

$$nx = u - my,$$

which would show that $p$ is a factor of $nx$. But equations $(n, m) = (x, m) = 1$ imply that this is impossible. So we see that $(u, mn) = 1$.

If we count the number of such integers $u$ which can be formed we see that there are $st$ such integers since there are $s$ choices for $x$ and $t$ choices for $y$. If we can show that these $st$ integers lie in different equivalence classes modulo $mn$, then we will have shown that

$$\Phi(mn) \geqslant \Phi(m)\Phi(n) = st.$$

So assume that two numbers of this form are in the same class:

$$nx_1 + my_1 \equiv nx_2 + my_2 \bmod mn,$$

where $1 \leqslant x_i < m$, $(x_i, m) = 1$, $1 \leqslant y_i < n$, $(y_i, n) = 1$, for $i = 1$ and 2. Therefore

$$(nx_1 + my_1) - (nx_2 + my_2) = kmn$$

for some integer $k$, and we have

$$n(x_1 - x_2) + m(y_1 - y_2) = kmn,$$

an equation which implies, since $(m, n) = 1$, that $m$ is a factor of $x_1 - x_2$ and $n$ is a factor of $y_1 - y_2$. But $x_1$ and $x_2$ are positive integers less than $m$, and $y_1$ and $y_2$ are positive integers less than $n$ so that

$$-m < x_1 - x_2 < m \quad \text{and} \quad -n < y_1 - y_2 < n.$$

Since 0 is the only multiple of $m$ between $-m$ and $m$ we see that

$$x_1 - x_2 = 0 \quad \text{or} \quad x_1 = x_2.$$

Similarly $y_1 = y_2$. Thus the $st$ numbers of the form $nx + my$ lie in distinct classes modulo $mn$, and

$$\Phi(mn) \geqslant st.$$

Now suppose $w$ is an integer relatively prime to $mn$, $(w, mn) = 1$. Then certainly $w$ is relatively prime to each of the integers $m$ and $n$, so that $(w, m) = (w, n) = 1$. We wish to show that there are $x$ and $y$ such that $1 \leqslant x < m$, $1 \leqslant y < n$, $(x, m) = (y, n) = 1$, and

$$w \equiv xn + ym \bmod mn.$$

Since this means that

$$w = (xn + ym) + kmn$$

for some integer $k$, we see that $x$ and $y$ must satisfy congruences

$$w \equiv xn \bmod m$$

and

$$w \equiv ym \bmod n.$$

Do such integers exist? Well, we know that $(m, n) = 1$, and from this condition we get an equation

$$am + bn = 1$$

for some integers $a$ and $b$. Multiplying this by $w$ yields

$$w = wam + wbn.$$

By the Divisor Theorem,

$$\begin{aligned} wa &= q_1 n + y, \qquad 0 \leqslant y < n, \\ wb &= q_2 m + x, \qquad 0 \leqslant x < m. \end{aligned}$$

Substituting these we get

$$w = ym + (wb + q_1 m)n$$

and

$$w = xn + (wa + q_2 n)m,$$

or

$$w \equiv ym \bmod n$$

and

$$w \equiv xn \bmod m.$$

Furthermore, from these equations we see that $(y, n) = 1$, since a common factor of $y$ and $n$ would be a common factor of $w$ and $n$ as

$$w = ym + kn,$$

and similarly

$$(x, m) = 1.$$

Further substitution yields

$$\begin{aligned} w &= (q_1 n + y)m + (q_2 m + x)n, \\ &= xn + ym + (q_1 + q_2)mn, \end{aligned}$$

and so

$$w \equiv xn + ym \bmod mn.$$

This means that the number of classes consisting of elements relatively prime to $mn$ is no greater than the number of elements of the form

$$xn + ym,$$

where $(x, m) = (y, n) = 1$, $1 \leqslant x < m$, and $1 \leqslant y < n$.

Therefore $\Phi(mn) \leqslant \Phi(m)\Phi(n)$, and we conclude from this and the other inequality that

$$\Phi(mn) = \Phi(m)\Phi(n).$$

To illustrate how this proof works we will go through it again using integers.

*Example* 1. Let $m = 4$ and $n = 5$. The numbers of the two classes mod 4, $[1]_4$ and $[3]_4$, are all relatively prime to 4, and the numbers of the four classes mod 5, $[1]_5$, $[2]_5$, $[3]_5$, $[4]_5$, are all relatively prime to 5. Now by checking the numbers $1, 2, \cdots, 19$ we see that the classes mod 20 which consist of numbers relatively prime to 20 are exactly $[1]_{20}$, $[3]_{20}$, $[7]_{20}$, $[9]_{20}$, $[11]_{20}$, $[13]_{20}$, $[17]_{20}$, $[19]_{20}$.

Consider the numbers of the form

$$5x + 4y$$

where $(4, x) = (5, y) = 1$, $1 \leqslant x < 4$, $1 \leqslant y < 5$. They are $5 \cdot 1 + 4 \cdot 1 = 9$, $5 \cdot 3 + 4 \cdot 1 = 19$, $5 \cdot 1 + 4 \cdot 2 = 13$, $5 \cdot 3 + 4 \cdot 2 = 23$, $5 \cdot 3 + 4 \cdot 3 = 27$, $5 \cdot 1 + 4 \cdot 3 = 17$, $5 \cdot 1 + 4 \cdot 4 = 21$, and $5 \cdot 3 + 4 \cdot 4 = 31$. Since $9 \equiv 9 \bmod 20$, $19 \equiv 19 \bmod 20$, $13 \equiv 13 \bmod 20$, $23 \equiv 3 \bmod 20$, $27 \equiv 7 \bmod 20$, $17 \equiv 17 \bmod 20$, $21 \equiv 1 \bmod 20$, and $31 \equiv 11 \bmod 20$, we see that these eight numbers are distributed one to each of the eight classes of numbers mod 20 relatively prime to 20.

Now select a number relatively prime to 20, say 47. We shall show that there is a number $x$, $(x, 4) = 1$, $1 \leqslant x < 4$, and a number $y$, $(y, 5) = 1$, $1 \leqslant y < 5$, such that

$$47 \equiv 5x + 4y \bmod 20,$$

and we use the method of the theorem. From $(4, 5) = 1$ we obtain

$$1 = 4(4) + (-3)5$$

so that

$$47 = 47(4)(4) + 47(-3)(5).$$

Now

$$47(4) = 188 = 37(5) + 3$$

and

$$47(-3) = -141 = (-36)4 + 3;$$

thus

$$47 = (37(5) + 3)(4) + ((-36)4 + 3)(5)$$

so that

$$47 = 5(3) + 4(3) + 20(37 - 36).$$

Certainly

$$47 \equiv 5(3) + 4(3) \bmod 20.$$

From this theorem we see readily that the factorization into powers of distinct primes effectively provides us with a formula for the totient.

THEOREM 3.26. *If $n$ is a positive integer,*

$$n = p_1^{e_1} \cdots p_r^{e_r},$$

*where the $p_i$ are distinct primes and the $e_i$ are positive integers, then*

$$\Phi(n) = n(1 - 1/p_1)(1 - 1/p_2) \cdots (1 - 1/p_r).$$

The formal proof of this is a straightforward induction exercise which we will not bother writing.

To illustrate this we observe that

$$\Phi(180) = 180(1 - 1/2)(1 - 1/3)(1 - 1/5) = 48$$

since

$$180 = 2^2 \cdot 5 \cdot 3^2.$$

From

$$\Phi(4) = 2, \qquad \Phi(5) = 4, \qquad \text{and} \qquad \Phi(9) = 6,$$

we also have

$$2 \cdot 4 \cdot 6 = 48.$$

Use is made of this counting function in the following result.

THEOREM 3.27 (EULER). *If a and m are integers such that* $(a, m) = 1$ *and* $m > 1$, *then*

$$a^{\Phi(m)} \equiv 1 \bmod m.$$

This says, for example, that

$$2^4 - 1 = 5k$$

for some integer $k$ since $\Phi(5) = 4$, and we can verify that

$$2^4 - 1 = 15.$$

Similarly

$$2^6 \equiv 1 \bmod 9$$

since $\Phi(9) = 6$, and we can verify this also as

$$2^6 - 1 = 63.$$

To prove the theorem we employ the method of the following example. The minimal positive numbers relatively prime to 9 are

$$1, 2, 4, 5, 7, 8.$$

If we multiply these by an integer $a$, where $(a, 9) = 1$, we have

$$a, 2a, 4a, 5a, 7a, 8a.$$

In particular, if $a = 5$ we have

$$5, 10, 20, 25, 35, 40.$$

Reduce these modulo 9:

$$\begin{aligned} 5 &\equiv 5 \bmod 9, \\ 10 &\equiv 1 \bmod 9, \\ 20 &\equiv 2 \bmod 9, \\ 25 &\equiv 7 \bmod 9, \\ 35 &\equiv 8 \bmod 9, \\ 40 &\equiv 4 \bmod 9. \end{aligned}$$

Thus each of the multiples lies in a different class modulo 9. Multiplying the congruences we have

$$(5)(10)(20)(25)(35)(40) \equiv (5)(1)(2)(7)(8)(4) \bmod 9,$$

or

$$(5)(1)(5)(2)(5)(4)(5)(5)(5)(7)(5)(8) \equiv (1)(2)(4)(5)(7)(8) \bmod 9,$$

which states that the difference,

$$(5^6 - 1)(1)(2)(4)(5)(7)(8),$$

is divisible by 9. Since the six numbers 1, 2, 4, 5, 7, 8 are relatively prime to 9, we see that 9 is a factor of $5^6 - 1$. Thus

$$5^6 \equiv 1 \bmod 9.$$

In this example we use the fact that

$$a \equiv b \bmod m \qquad \text{and} \qquad c \equiv d \bmod m$$

imply

$$ac \equiv bd \bmod m.$$

This is verified easily by writing

$$a = b + km, \qquad c = d + hm;$$

then multiplying we get

$$ac = bd + (bh + dk + hkm)m.$$

So

$$ac \equiv bd \bmod m.$$

Obviously this can be extended to more than two congruences by a simple induction argument.

Now for the proof of the theorem. Denote $\Phi(m)$ by $n$ and the $\Phi(m)$ numbers between 0 and $m$ which are relatively prime to $m$ by $r_1, r_2, \cdots, r_n$. Multiplying each of these by $a$ we get the $n$ numbers $ar_1, ar_2, \cdots, ar_n$. As in the example we wish to show that each of these is relatively prime to $m$ and that no two are congruent modulo $m$. Certainly $(a, m) = (r_i, m) = 1$ implies $(ar_i, m) = 1$, for a common prime factor of $ar_i$ and $m$ must certainly divide either $a$ or $r_i$ by the uniqueness of prime factorization.

To show that no two of the $n$ products are congruent mod $m$, suppose

$$ar_i \equiv ar_j \bmod m.$$

Then

$$ar_i - ar_j = km$$

for some integer $k$, so that $m$ is a factor of the product $a(r_i - r_j)$. Since $(a, m) = 1$ this means that $m$ is a factor of $r_i - r_j$. But $r_i$ and $r_j$ are positive integers less than $m$, so that

$$-m < r_i - r_j < m,$$

and since zero is the only multiple of $m$ in this range, we have $r_i = r_j$. Thus the $n$ numbers $ar_1, ar_2, \cdots, ar_n$, lie in different equivalence classes mod $m$.

This means, since the $n$ classes of elements relatively prime to $m$ are represented by the least residues or remainders $r_1, r_2, \cdots, r_n$, that

$$ar_i \equiv r'_i \bmod m, \qquad i = 1, 2, \cdots, n,$$

where $r'_i$ is one of the numbers $r_1, r_2, \cdots, r_n$.

Multiplying these $n$ congruences we get

$$a^n r_1 r_2 \cdots r_n \equiv r'_1 r'_2 \cdots r'_n \bmod m,$$

and since

$$r'_1 r'_2 \cdots r'_n = r_1 r_2 \cdots r_n$$

by the Associative and Commutative Laws, this means that

$$(a^n - 1) r_1 r_2 \cdots r_n = km.$$

Since $(r_1 r_2 \cdots r_n, m) = 1$ this implies that $m$ is a factor of $a^n - 1$. Thus

$$a^{\Phi(m)} \equiv 1 \bmod m.$$

*Corollary* 3.27.1 (*Fermat's Little Theorem*). If $p$ is a prime and $a$ is an integer, then

$$a^p \equiv a \bmod p.$$

Consider $a^p - a = (a^{p-1} - 1)a$. Either $p$ is a factor of $a$ or $(a, p) = 1$. If $(a, p) = 1$ then, since $\Phi(p) = p - 1$, Theorem 3.27 implies that $p$ is a factor of $a^{p-1} - 1$. In either case $a^p - a$ is a multiple of $p$, and

$$a^p \equiv a \bmod p.$$

The methods and results of this section indicate that an arithmetic for the equivalence classes modulo $m$ is feasible and desirable. The existence of a sufficiently nice arithmetic of residue classes would enable us to shorten the above proofs and to apply the above results in a much easier manner. We shall see that the concept of congruence, which was introduced as a convenient notation, leads to the development of new mathematical systems containing only finitely many elements. These systems are useful in the study of the system of integers but are even more important as examples of a method of analyzing abstract algebraic systems. This is discussed in Chapter 5 and later chapters.

## Exercise 3.6

**1.** Evaluate $\Phi(49)$, $\Phi(50)$, $\Phi(100)$, $\Phi(1000)$.

**2.** Find all positive integers $m$ such that $\Phi(m) = 10$.

**3.** Show that, if $p$ is a prime not 2 or 5, then it is a factor of infinitely many of the numbers 9, 99, 999, $\cdots$

**4.** Show that, if $m$ is an odd, positive integer, then the numbers $2, 4, 6, \cdots, 2m$ represent the $m$ equivalence classes mod $m$.

**5.** By considering the prime power factors of $m$ show that, if $m$ is a composite greater than 4, then

$$(m - 1)! \equiv 0 \bmod m.$$

**6.** Show that $(7 - 1)! \equiv 6 \bmod 7$ by showing that the products 2(4) and 3(5) are congruent with 1 mod 7. Can you show that $(11 - 1)! \equiv 10 \bmod 11$ in the same way? How would you generalize this?

**7.** Use Euler's Theorem to show that, if $ab \equiv c \bmod m$ and $(a, m) = 1$, then $b \equiv ca^{\Phi(m)-1} \bmod m$.

**8.** From the integers of the sets $\{1, 2\}$ and $\{1, 3\}$ construct four integers relatively prime to 12 by the method used in proving Theorem 3.25.

**9.** Show that the product of the integers 3, 6, 9, and 12 is congruent mod 5 with the product of 1, 2, 3, and 4.

**10.** For what integers $m$ is $\Phi(m)$ odd?

**11.** Verify that $\Phi(1) + \Phi(2) + \Phi(4) + \Phi(6) + \Phi(12) = 12$. What conjecture does this suggest?

**12.** Prove that, if $\Phi(mn) = \Phi(m)$ and $n > 1$, then $n = 2$ and $m$ is odd.

**13.** Show that there are infinitely many integers $m$ such that $\Phi(m)$ is a multiple of $p$, where $p$ is a prime.

**14.** Show that there is no integer $m$ such that $\Phi(m) = 14$.

**15.** Find the last digit in the decimal representation of $3^{100}$ by considering $3^{100}$ modulo 10 and using Euler's Theorem.

**16.** Use mathematical induction to prove: (i) If

$$a_i \equiv b_i \bmod m \text{ for } i = 1, 2, \cdots, n,$$

then

$$a_1a_2\cdots a_n \equiv b_1b_2\cdots b_n \bmod m.$$

(ii) If

$$(a_1, m) = (a_2, m) = \cdots = (a_n, m) = 1,$$

then

$$(a_1a_2\cdots a_n, m) = 1.$$

## 3.7 Suggested Reading

*Articles*

Harris, V. C., "A modification of the sieve of Eratosthenes," *Amer. Math. Monthly*, **60** (1953), 325–326.

Herwitz, P. S., "The theory of numbers," *Sci. American*, **185**, July 1951, 52–55.

Polya, G., "Heuristic reasoning in the theory of numbers," *Amer. Math. Monthly*, **66** (1959), 375–384.

Thompson, J., "A method for finding primes," *Amer. Math. Monthly*, **60** (1953), 175.

*Books*

Bell, E. T., *The Magic of Numbers*, McGraw-Hill Book Co., New York, 1946.

Henkin, L., W. N. Smith, V. J. Varineau, and M. J. Walsh, *Retracing Elementary Mathematics*, The Macmillan Company, New York, 1962.

LeVeque, W. J., *Elementary Theory of Numbers*, Addison-Wesley Publishing Co., Reading, Mass., 1962.

Ore, O, *Number Theory and Its History*, McGraw-Hill Book Co., New York, 1948.

Stewart, B. M., *Theory of Numbers*, 2nd ed., The Macmillan Co., New York, 1964.

# 4

# Diophantine Problems

SOMETIMES WE ARE confronted with problems which require, or reduce to, the finding of integers with certain properties. Frequently these problems are such that the conditions can be stated as equations or inequalities which the integers must satisfy. Such problems, and the equations and inequalities, are often called *Diophantine* after the Greek mathematician Diophantos who wrote extensively on the subject. In this chapter we consider certain simple Diophantine problems which can be treated by using the methods and concepts of the previous chapter.

To a degree this material represents a digression from the central theme of our study, the analysis of algebraic systems. However, we feel that it does contribute to a better understanding of $J$, the system of integers, as well as being of considerable interest in its own right. Certainly everyone should know something about the topics covered here.

## 4.1 Linear Diophantine Equations

The following is a problem or puzzle of a type which often appears in a newspaper or magazine labeled as a "brain teaser."

*Problem.* Mr. Creasy purchased 100 animals for his farm at a total cost of \$2000. If the animals are calves, lambs, and piglets which cost \$50, \$20, and \$5 apiece, respectively, how many of each did he buy?

Clearly this problem can be solved in a finite number of steps by simply trying different combinations. However, we shall express the problem as a set of equations and inequalities and devise a reasonably "efficient" routine for solving the problem. If the problem has a solution (and some do not), then there must be integers $x$, $y$, and $z$ such that

$$x + y + z = 100$$

and

$$50x + 20y + 5z = 2000.$$

Furthermore, $x$, $y$, and $z$ cannot be negative, so that

$$x \geqslant 0, \ y \geqslant 0, \ z \geqslant 0,$$

and the statement of the problem seems to imply that $x$, $y$, and $z$ are in fact positive integers.

How do we treat these equations? First we list a simple theorem about the integers.

THEOREM 4.1. (1) *If $a$, $b$, and $k$ are integers, $k \neq 0$, then $a = b$ if and only if $ka = kb$.*

(2) *If $a$, $b$, $c$, $d$, $k$, and $h$ are integers, $k \neq 0$, then $a = b$ and $c = d$ if and only if $a = b$ and $ha + kc = hb + kd$.*

The first portion of the theorem has already been discussed as the Cancellation Law. The second part follows from the first and the fact that subtraction is defined on $J$. If

$$a = b \quad \text{and} \quad c = d,$$

then certainly

$$a = b \quad \text{and} \quad ha + kc = hb + kd$$

since the binary operations of multiplication and addition are well-defined.

Conversely, if

$$a = b \quad \text{and} \quad ha + kc = hb + kd$$

then

$$\begin{aligned} ha &= hb, \\ (ha + kc) - ha &= (hb + kd) - hb, \\ kc &= kd, \end{aligned}$$

and

$$c = d.$$

There is nothing surprising about this theorem nor about its applications. But by the theorem we can replace the equation

$$50x + 20y + 5z = 2000$$

by the equation

$$10x + 4y + z = 400$$

without any effect on the possible values of $x$, $y$, and $z$. For the same reasons the two equations

$$x + y + z = 100 \quad \text{and} \quad 10x + 4y + z = 400$$

can be replaced by the two equations

$$x + y + z = 100 \quad \text{and} \quad 9x + 3y = 300$$

without any effect on the values of $x$, $y$, and $z$, since

$$9x + 3y = (10x + 4y + z) + (-1)(x + y + z) = 400 - 100.$$

That is to say, any integers satisfying one pair of equations also satisfies the other pair.

Now the equation

$$9x + 3y = 300,$$

or

$$3x + y = 100,$$

is seen to be simpler than the equation it replaces since it does not explicitly involve the integer $z$. So we say the unknown $z$ has been "eliminated." But what can we do with an equation such as

$$3x + y = 100?$$

We recall in our discussion of G.C.F. and the Euclidean algorithm that the G.C.F. of two nonzero integers $a$ and $b$ can be expressed in the form

$$(a, b) = am + bn$$

for some integers $m$ and $n$. Since $(3, 1) = 1$ this means that there are integers $m$ and $n$ such that

$$1 = 3m + n,$$

and the Euclidean algorithm can be used to find one pair of integers $m$ and $n$. Therefore, multiplying by 100 we have

$$3(100m) + (100n) = 100,$$

so that integers $x$ and $y$ such that

$$3x + y = 100$$

can be obtained from $m$ and $n$.

However, all numbers obtained in this manner are going to be multiples of 100, and clearly these are too large to be of any use. Moreover, since $m$ and $n$ cannot both be positive, it seems impossible to use the numbers $m$ and $n$ to find $x$ and $y$. But all is not lost.

Definition 4.1. An equation of the form

$$ax + by = c,$$

where $a$, $b$, $c$, $x$, and $y$ are integers, is known as a *linear Diophantine equation* in $x$ and $y$. (It can also be considered a linear Diophantine equation in $a$ and $b$.)

From our work with the G.C.F. and the Euclidean algorithm we see readily that, for given integers $a$, $b$, and $c$, integers $x$ and $y$ satisfying the equation can exist only if $(a, b)$ is a factor of $c$. Certainly if $d$ is a factor of $a$ and $b$,

$$a = da_1 \quad \text{and} \quad b = db_1,$$

then

$$c = d(a_1x + b_1y),$$

so, if the integers $x$ and $y$ exist, then $d$ is a factor of $c$.

As we indicated above the converse is also true. For suppose

$$d = (a, b)$$

is a factor of $c$,

$$c = dc_1.$$

By the theory of the G.C.F. there exist integers $m$ and $n$ such that

$$d = am + bn,$$

and so

$$c = dc_1 = a(mc_1) + b(nc_1).$$

This proves the following result.

THEOREM 4.2. *There exist integers $x$ and $y$ such that*

$$ax + by = c,$$

*$a$, $b$, and $c$ nonzero integers, if and only if $d = (a, b)$ is a factor of $c$.*

We emphasize that the solutions $x$ and $y$ are integers, not necessarily positive or nonzero.

However, there can be many solutions of a linear Diophantine equation, for we see that

$$4(3) + 2(-5) = 2,$$
$$4(6) + 2(-11) = 2,$$
$$4(-2) + 2(5) = 2.$$

How then are the different pairs of solutions related?

THEOREM 4.3. *Suppose $x_1$ and $y_1$ are integers such that*

$$ax_1 + by_1 = c,$$

*where $a$, $b$, $c$ are nonzero integers, and*

$$(a, b) = 1.$$

*Then*

$$x = x_1 + qb \quad \text{and} \quad y = y_1 - qa$$

*satisfy the equation*

$$ax + by = c$$

*for every integer $q$. Conversely, if $x_2$ and $y_2$ are integers such that*

$$ax_2 + by_2 = c,$$

*then there exists an integer $q$ such that*

$$x_2 = x_1 + bq \qquad \text{and} \qquad y_2 = y_1 - aq.$$

Direct substitution verifies the first statement since

$$\begin{aligned} ax + by &= a(x_1 + bq) + b(y_1 - aq) \\ &= ax_1 + by_1 + abq - abq \\ &= ax_1 + by_1 = c. \end{aligned}$$

To prove the converse consider the two equations,

$$\begin{aligned} ax_1 + by_1 &= c, \\ ax_2 + by_2 &= c. \end{aligned}$$

By the transitivity of equality we have

$$ax_1 + by_1 = ax_2 + by_2,$$

so that

$$b(y_1 - y_2) = a(x_2 - x_1).$$

Since $(a, b) = 1$ we see that $b$, as a factor of the product $a(x_2 - x_1)$, must be a factor of $x_2 - x_1$ so that

$$x_2 - x_1 = bq$$

for some integer $q$. Thus

$$x_2 = x_1 + bq.$$

Substitution yields

$$b(y_1 - y_2) = a(bq)$$

so that, since $b \neq 0$,

$$y_1 - y_2 = aq$$

and

$$y_2 = y_1 - aq.$$

Now we go back to the example we started with; we saw that a solution in integers for

$$3x + y = 100$$

was provided by

$$3(100m) + (100n) = 100,$$

and taking $m = 0$ and $n = 1$ we have an integral solution,

$$x_1 = 0 \qquad \text{and} \qquad y_1 = 100.$$

Applying Theorem 4.3 we conclude that all integral solutions of the equation are given by

$$x = 0 + 1(q), \qquad y = 100 - 3q,$$

where $q$ is an arbitrary integer. Then substitution in the equation

$$x + y + z = 100$$

yields

$$q + (100 - 3q) + z = 100,$$

or

$$z = 2q.$$

Thus far we have concentrated our attention on the equations; now we use the inequalities

$$x > 0, \qquad y > 0, \qquad z > 0.$$

These yield the following conditions on $q$:

$$q > 0, \qquad 100 - 3q > 0, \qquad 2q > 0.$$

From these we see that $q$ is an integer between 0 and 34, and so there are exactly 33 different solutions to the problem of Mr. Creasy and the animals.

*Example* 1. Express 100, if possible, as the sum of two positive integers, one a multiple of 7 and the other a multiple of 11. That is, find positive integers $x$ and $y$ such that

$$7x + 11y = 100.$$

Since $(7, 11) = 1$ we know that the equation has integral (although not necessarily positive) solutions. If $m$ and $n$ are integers such that

$$7m + 11n = 1$$

then $100m$ and $100n$ serve as one solution pair. To find one pair of integers $m$ and $n$ we could use the Euclidean algorithm, but with integers the size of 7 and 11 trial and error is quicker. We see that

$$7(-3) + 11(2) = 1.$$

Therefore

$$x = -300 + 11q \quad \text{and} \quad y = 200 - 7q, \qquad q \text{ an integer},$$

are the integral solutions of

$$7x + 11y = 100.$$

Consider the inequalities $x > 0$ and $y > 0$. These imply

$$-300 + 11q > 0 \qquad \text{and} \qquad 200 - 7q > 0$$

or

$$11q > 300 \qquad \text{and} \qquad 200 > 7q,$$

so that $q$ must be an integer greater than 27 and less than 29. Thus $q = 28$, and we have

$$x = -300 + 308 = 8, \qquad y = 200 - 196 = 4,$$

so that

$$100 = 56 + 44$$

is the one and only solution to the problem.

*Example* 2. Find positive integers $x$ and $y$ such that

$$208x + 136y = 120.$$

By Theorem 4.1 we may consider the equation

$$26x + 17y = 15$$

since 8 is the G.C.F. of $\{208, 136, 120\}$. From the Euclidean algorithm (modified) we get

$$26 = 1(17) + 9,$$
$$17 = 2(9) - 1,$$

so that

$$1 = 2(9) - 17 = 2(26 - 17) - 17,$$
$$1 = 2(26) + (-3)(17).$$

Therefore

$$1 = (26, 17),$$

the equation $26x + 17y = 15$ has a solution in integers, and

$$x_1 = 15(2) = 30 \quad \text{and} \quad y_1 = 15(-3) = -45$$

provide one solution pair. Then the general solution is given by

$$x = 30 + 17q \quad \text{and} \quad y = -45 - 26q,$$

$q$ an integer.

The requirement that $x$ and $y$ be positive produces the inequalities

$$30 + 17q > 0 \quad \text{and} \quad -45 - 26q > 0.$$

Thus $q$ is an integer greater than $-2$ and less than $-1$. Since there is no such integer we conclude that the equation has no solution in *positive* integers.

These theorems and examples cover the simpler aspects of linear Diophantine equations in two unknown quantities and, more generally, sets of $n - 1$ linear Diophantine equations in $n$ unknown quantities with $n > 2$. There are, however, methods for finding solutions of linear Diophantine equations in $x$ and $y$ which do not explicitly involve the Euclidean algorithm. Several such methods are discussed in the books by O. Ore, J. V. Uspensky and M. H. Heaslet, and G. H. Hardy and E. M. Wright, as well as in other books on the theory of numbers.

## Exercise 4.1

**1.** A man spent \$1770 for horses and cows. If each horse cost \$31 and each cow \$21, how many of each did he buy?

**2.** Find integers $x$ and $y$ such that

$$7x + 19y = 1921$$

and $x + y$ is minimal.

**3.** Find all positive integers $x$ and $y$ (if any) such that

$$91x + 221y = 1053.$$

**4.** When Adam handed his weekly pay check to the bank cashier she misread the number of dollars for the number of cents and vice versa. Adam accepted the money without counting it, but after spending $3.20 he discovered to his dismay that he was left with just one-half the amount of his check. Assuming that Adam had no money to begin with, determine the smallest salary that he could be getting.

**5.** Find two rational integers $x/5$ and $y/7$ whose sum is $26/35$, where $x$ and $y$ are integers.

**6.** Prove that the equation

$$ax + by = c,$$

where $a$, $b$, and $c$ are nonzero integers, has a solution in integers if and only if $(a, b, c) = (a, b)$.

**7.** For what fractions of positive two-digit integers does the following incorrect rule of reduction give the correct result?

$$(10a + b)/(10b + c) = a/c, \qquad a, b, c \text{ digits}.$$

For example, $16/64 = 1/4$ by canceling the common digit 6.

**8.** Suppose $x$ and $y$ are integers such that $2x + 3y$ is a multiple of 17. Show that $9x + 5y$ is also a multiple of 17.

**9.** Find an integer $x$ such that

$$5x \equiv 16 \bmod 39$$

and

$$7x \equiv 27 \bmod 56.$$

(*Hint:* Consider the equations $5x + 39y = 16$ and $7x + 56z = 27$.)

**10.** Find all integers $x$ such that

$$x \equiv 16 \bmod 39$$

and

$$x \equiv 27 \bmod 56.$$

**11.** Find the positive integral solutions of

$$158x + 57y = 20{,}000.$$

**12.** If 30 people give a total of $50 to the Red Cross, and if each man, woman, and child gives $3, $2, and $1, respectively, how many men are in the group?

## 4.2 More Linear Diophantine Equations

A linear Diophantine equation in $n$ unknowns, $x_1, x_2, \cdots, x_n$, is obviously an equation of the form

$$a_1x_1 + a_2x_2 + \cdots + a_nx_n = c,$$

where $c$ and the $a_i$ are nonzero integers. Since our discussion of G.C.F. included the case of sets of more than two integers, we can easily obtain criteria for the existence of a set of integers $x_1, \cdots, x_n$ satisfying this equation.

THEOREM 4.4. *There exist integers $x_1, x_2, \cdots, x_n$ such that*

$$a_1x_1 + a_2x_2 + \cdots + a_nx_n = c, \qquad n > 1,$$

*where c and the $a_i$ are integers $\neq 0$, if and only if the G.C.F. $(a_1, a_2, \cdots, a_n)$ is a factor of c.*

It is clear that $(a_1, a_2, \cdots, a_n)$ must be a factor of $c$ if the integers $x_i$ exist. On the other hand, suppose

$$c = dc_1,$$

where

$$d = (a_1, a_2, \cdots, a_n).$$

From the theory of the G.C.F. there are integers $b_1, b_2, \cdots, b_n$ such that

$$d = a_1b_1 + a_2b_2 + \cdots + a_nb_n.$$

Therefore

$$c = c_1d = a_1(c_1b_1) + a_2(c_1b_2) + \cdots + a_n(c_1b_n),$$

and the equation has a solution in integers.

Moreover, we have available a routine based on the Euclidean algorithm for finding a set of integers $b_1, b_2, \cdots, b_n$.

*Example* 1. Find integers $x$, $y$, and $z$ such that

$$50x + 45y + 36z = 10.$$

First we see that

$$(50, 45) = 5,$$

and clearly

$$50(1) + 45(-1) = 5.$$

Then we compare 5 and 36:

$$(5, 36) = 1,$$

and so

$$(50, 45, 36) = (5, 36) = 1.$$

Thus the equation has a solution in integers.

Now

$$1 = 36(1) + 5(-7),$$

so substituting for 5 yields

$$1 = 36(1) + (-7)50 + 7(45).$$

Hence we get, multiplying by 10,

$$50(-70) + 45(70) + 36(10) = 10,$$

and the integers $x_1 = -70$, $y_1 = 70$, and $z_1 = 10$ furnish one solution of the equation.

Since it is evident that many different solutions can be found we should consider the problem of describing the set of *all* solutions. We do this now for the case of an equation in three unknowns, but first we need the following result.

*Lemma* 4.1. If $b$ and $c$ are nonzero integers, then four integers $h$, $k$, $r$, and $s$ can be found such that

$$hs - kr = 1 \qquad \text{and} \qquad bk + cs = 0.$$

Assume $b$ and $c$ are positive; then from the work on L.C.M. we know that

$$(b, c)m = bc,$$

where $(b, c)$ and $m$ are the G.C.F. and L.C.M., respectively, of $\{b, c\}$. Then since $m$ is a multiple of $b$,

$$m = bk,$$

we have for

$$s = -b/(b, c),$$
$$bk + cs = 0.$$

Furthermore, since this implies that

$$k = bc/b(b, c) = c/(b, c),$$

we see that $(k, s) = 1$. So by the theory of the G.C.F. there exist integers $h$ and $r$ such that

$$hs + (-k)r = 1.$$

Therefore the required integers exist, and we have a way of finding them since the Euclidean algorithm can be used to find $h$ and $r$.

*Example* 2. If $b = 12$ and $c = 20$, then we see that $k = 20/4 = 5$ and $s = -12/4 = -3$. Checking these numbers we get

$$12(5) + 20(-3) = 0.$$

Now $(5, -3) = (5, 3) = 1$, and by observation we get

$$1 = (-1)(5) + (-2)(-3).$$

So by selecting $h = -2$ and $r = 1$ we have

$$hs - kr = 1.$$

We use this result to establish a reduction theorem for an equation in three unknowns.

THEOREM 4.5. *Let $a$, $b$, $c$, and $d$ be nonzero integers and $h$, $k$, $r$, and $s$ be integers such that $hs - kr = 1$ and $bk + cs = 0$. Then, if $x$, $y$, and $z$ are integers such that*

$$ax + by + cz = d,$$

*the integers $x$, $t = sy - kz$, and $u = hz - ry$ satisfy the equation*

$$ax + (bh + cr)t + (bk + cs)u = d.$$

*Conversely, if x, t, and u are integers satisfying this last equation, then x, $y = ht + ku$, and $z = rt + su$ satisfy the equation*

$$ax + by + cz = d.$$

It is obvious that, since $bk + cs = 0$, this theorem reduces the problem of solving

$$ax + by + cz = d$$

to that of solving

$$ax + (bh + cr)t = d,$$

an equation in two unknowns.

The proof is a straightforward, manipulative verification:

$$\begin{aligned} ax + (bh + cr)(sy - kz) + (bk + cs)(hz - ry) \\ &= ax + by(hs - kr) + cz(hs - kr) + cy(rs - rs) + bz(hk - hk) \\ &= ax + by + cz = d. \end{aligned}$$

And for the converse,

$$ax + b(ht + ku) + c(rt + su) = ax + (bh + cr)t + (bk + cs)u = d.$$

Therefore if we find all the solutions of the equation in $x$ and $t$,

$$ax + (bh + cr)t = d,$$

which we know how to do already, then, by allowing $u$ to be an arbitrary integer, we have all the solutions of

$$ax + by + cz = d$$

given by

$$x = x, \qquad y = ht + ku, \qquad z = rt + su.$$

Since the solutions $x$ and $t$ will be given in terms of an arbitrary integer $q$, the solutions $x$, $y$, and $z$ will be stated in terms of two arbitrary integers (sometimes called *parameters*) $q$ and $u$.

*Example* 1 (*continued*). To solve

$$50x + 45y + 36z = 10$$

completely we must first find the integers $h$, $k$, $r$, and $s$ of Lemma 4.1. Since

$$(45, 36) = 9,$$

we get $k = 4$ and $s = -5$, so that we can choose $h = -1$ and $r = 1$. Clearly

$$hs - kr = (-5)(-5) - 4(1) = 1$$

and

$$bk + cs = (45)4 + 36(-5) = 180 - 180 = 0.$$

Then the equation in $x$ and $t$ is

$$50x - 9t = 10,$$

and the general solution of this equation is given by

$$x = 2 + 9q \qquad \text{and} \qquad t = 10 + 50q,$$

where $q$ is an arbitrary integer. Then the general solution of the original equation is given by

$$x = 2 + 9q, \quad y = -10 - 50q + 4u, \quad z = 10 + 50q - 5u,$$

where $q$ and $u$ are the parameters. The particular solution obtained previously results from the values $q = -8$ and $u = -80$.

Since this reduction is based on Lemma 4.1 we see that a linear Diophantine equation in four unknowns,

$$ax + by + cz + dw = e,$$

can be reduced to one involving three unknowns by applying Lemma 4.1 and Theorem 4.5 to the numbers $c$ and $d$. In other words the theorem sets forth a method for reducing the number of unknowns by one while introducing a parameter. Then an equation in four unknowns would require two reductions, and the general solution would be stated in terms of three parameters or arbitrary integers. Instead of stating the most general theorem we discuss an additional example.

*Example* 3. Solve the linear Diophantine equation

$$2x + 3y + 12z + 20w = 9.$$

Using the results of Example 2 we see that $-2$, 5, 1, and $-3$ are integers such that

$$12(5) + 20(-3) = 0$$

and

$$-2(-3) - 1(5) = 1.$$

In other words these integers serve as $h$, $k$, $r$, and $s$ for eliminating $(12z + 20w)$ from the equation. Then the new equation is

$$2x + 3y + \big(12(-2) + 20(1)\big)t = 9,$$

and the eliminated unknowns are given by

$$z = -2t + 5u \qquad \text{and} \qquad w = t - 3u,$$

where $u$ is an arbitrary integer.

We repeat the process on the equation

$$2x + 3y - 4t = 9,$$

this time eliminating $y$ and $t$ (although we could eliminate $x$ and $y$ or $x$ and $t$).

For $b = 3$ and $c = -4$ we choose $k = 3$ and $s = 4$; then $h$ and $r$ can be selected as both equal to 1. For these numbers our new equation in two unknowns is

$$2x + (3 - 4)v = 9,$$

and the eliminated unknowns are given by

$$y = v + 3f \quad \text{and} \quad t = v + 4f,$$

where $f$ is an arbitrary integer.

Solving the equation

$$2x - v = 9$$

we obtain the general solution

$$x = 4 + q \quad \text{and} \quad v = -1 + 1 + 2q,$$

where $q$ is an arbitrary integer. Working back through our relationship we get

$$y = (-1 + 2q) + 3f, \quad t = (-1 + 2q) + 4f,$$

and

$$z = -2(-1 + 2q + 4f) + 5u, \quad w = (-1 + 2q + 4f) - 3u.$$

Then for arbitrary integers $u$, $q$, and $f$ the general solution of the original equation is given by

$$\begin{aligned} x &= 4 + q, \\ y &= -1 + 2q + 3f, \\ z &= 2 - 4q - 8f + 5u, \\ w &= -1 + 2q + 4f - 3u. \end{aligned}$$

In particular, when $u = q = f = 0$ we get the special solution $x = 4$, $y = -1$, $z = 2$, $w = -1$.

Of course if we desired the positive integral solutions of the equation we would consider the four inequalities

$$4 + q > 0, \quad -1 + 2q + 3f > 0, \quad 2 - 4q - 8f + 5u > 0, \quad \text{and}$$
$$-1 + 2q + 4f - 3u > 0.$$

## Exercise 4.2

**1.** Show that, for arbitrary integers $q$ and $u$, the integers

$$x = 2 - 9u, \quad y = 14u - 4q - 3, \quad \text{and} \quad z = 5q - 5u + 1$$

satisfy the equation

$$50x + 45y + 36z = 1.$$

**2.** Solve the linear Diophantine equation

$$22x + 38y + 15z = 33.$$

**3.** Find a solution in integers of the equation

$$189x + 180y + 175z = 200.$$

**4.** Lemma 4.1 was proved only for the case $b$ and $c$ positive. Complete the proof for nonzero integers.

**5.** Find a solution of

$$19x + 9y + 3z = 100$$

in positive integers, if it has one.

**6.** State the general theorem for reducing a linear Diophantine equation in $n > 2$ unknowns to one in $n - 1$ unknowns.

**7.** (From the London *Times*) Every schoolboy knows that to find five unknown quantities he needs five equations, so he would no doubt think at first sight that it was impossible to solve this problem: I bought a number of articles at five different prices, namely at 17 shillings sixpence, 27 shillings sixpence, 96 shillings threepence, 115 shillings sixpence, and 128 shillings four pence each. The total cost was 57 pounds 14 shillings elevenpence. How many articles did I buy of each?

(*Note:* 1 pound = 20 shillings, and 1 shilling = twelve pence. The answer: 10 of the first, 6 of the second, 1 of the third, 4 of the fourth, and 2 of the fifth.)

**8.** Johnny bought 100 marbles, each colored green, red, silver, or blue, for 100 cents. If five green marbles cost 3 cents, seven red ones 5 cents, nine silver ones 7 cents, and each blue one 3 cents, how many of each did he get?

## 4.3 Linear Congruences

In Example 2 of Section 4.1 we found all of the integers $x$ and $y$ such that

$$208x + 136y = 120,$$

namely, $x = 30 + 17q$ and $y = -45 - 26q$, where $q$ is an arbitrary integer. In the notation of congruences this means that any integer $x$ of the form $x = 30 + 17q$ has the property that

$$208x \equiv 120 \bmod 136.$$

Conversely, if $x$ is an integer such that

$$208x \equiv 120 \bmod 136,$$

then we see that $x$ must be of the form $x = 30 + 17q$ for some integer $q$, for certainly the congruence is equivalent to the statement

$$208x - 120 = 136k$$

for some integer $k$. This means that $x$ and $-k$ form a solution of

$$208x + 136y = 120.$$

Thus our work in Section 4.1 enables us to deal with certain congruences involving unknowns.

DEFINITION 4.2. A congruence of the form

$$ax \equiv c \bmod b,$$

where $a$, $b$, and $c$ are positive integers, is called a *linear congruence* in the unknown integer $x$. An integer $x'$ such that $ax' \equiv c \bmod b$ is a solution of the congruence.

We see, then, that the problem of finding all the integers $x$ such that

$$208x \equiv 120 \bmod 136$$

is exactly the same as that of finding all the pairs of integers $x$ and $y$ such that

$$208x + 136y = 120,$$

although the role of the integer $y$ is somewhat obscured.

THEOREM 4.6. *The integer $x$ satisfies the linear congruence*

$$ax \equiv c \bmod b$$

*if and only if there is an integer $y$ such that*

$$ax + by = c.$$

For, if $ax \equiv c \bmod b$, then by definition of congruence mod $b$ the integer $ax - c$ is a multiple of $b$. Hence there is an integer $k$ such that

$$ax - c = kb.$$

Then for $y = -k$ we have

$$ax + by = c.$$

The proof of the converse is obtained by reversing these steps.

This correspondence between linear congruences and linear Diophantine equations in two unknowns enables us to use our knowledge of the latter to say exactly when a linear congruence has a solution.

THEOREM 4.7. *The linear congruence*

$$ax \equiv c \bmod b$$

*has a solution if and only if $d = (a, b)$ is a factor of $c$. If the congruence has a solution, then there are exactly $d$ different classes mod $b$ of solutions.*

The congruence has a solution if and only if the linear Diophantine equation

$$ax + by = c$$

has a solution, by Theorem 4.6. Since the equation has a solution if and only if $d = (a, b)$ is a factor of $c$, the first statement of the theorem follows.

Now consider the general solution of the equation

$$ax + by = c,$$

namely,

$$x = x_0 + (b/d)q, \qquad y = y_0 - (a/d)q,$$

where $x_0$ and $y_0$ comprise a particular solution and $q$ is an arbitrary integer.

Certainly the $d$ integers

$$x_0, x_0 + b/d, x_0 + 2b/d, \cdots, x_0 + (d - 1)b/d$$

lie in different equivalence classes mod $b$ since the difference of any two distinct elements in the list is a nonzero integer between $-b$ and $b$:

$$(x_0 + mb/d) - (x_0 + nb/d) = (m - n)b/d$$

with $m - n \neq 0$ and $-d < m - n < d$. Furthermore, if $t$ is an integer congruent with one of these $d$ integers, $x_0 + mb/d$, $0 < m < d$, then $t$ is a solution of the congruence since

$$at = a(x_0 + mb/d - kb) = a(x_0 + mb/d) - kab$$

implies that

$$at \equiv a(x_0 + mb/d) \bmod b.$$

So by the transitivity of congruence mod $b$ we have

$$at \equiv c \bmod b.$$

Thus each integer in each of the $d$ classes mod $b$

$$x_0, x_0 + b/d, \cdots, x_0 + (d - 1)b/d$$

is a solution of the congruence $ax \equiv c \bmod b$.

On the other hand, since the equations

$$x = x_0 + (b/d)q \qquad \text{and} \qquad y = y_0 - (b/d)q,$$

$q$ an arbitrary integer, describe all the solutions of the equation $ax + by = c$, we see that every solution of $ax \equiv c \bmod b$ is of the form

$$x = x_0 + (b/d)q.$$

It is clear that the integer $x_0 + (b/d)q$ must lie in one of the $d$ equivalence classes listed above.

*Example* 1. Solve, if possible, the linear congruence $9x \equiv 12 \bmod 21$.

Since $3 = (9, 21)$ is a factor of 12 we see that the congruence has a solution. Consider the difference $9x - 12$; for what integers $x$ is this integer a multiple of 21? The equations

$$9(-1) - 12 = -21, \quad 9(6) - 12 = 42, \quad 9(13) - 12 = 105$$

provide three solutions. The discussion above indicates that any integer of the form

$$x = (-1) + ((21)/3)q$$

is a solution, so let us consider these integers:

| | | | | | | | | | |
|---|---|---|---|---|---|---|---|---|---|
| $q$: | 0 | 1 | 2 | 3 | $-1$ | $-2$ | $-3$ | 6 | $\cdots$ |
| $x$: | $-1$ | 6 | 13 | 20 | $-8$ | $-15$ | $-22$ | 41 | $\cdots$ |

Modulo 21, these numbers fall into three classes

$$[-1] = -1, 20, -22, 41, \cdots,$$
$$[\ 6] = 6, -15, \cdots,$$
$$[\ 13] = 13, -8, \cdots.$$

Naturally if the integers $a$, $b$, and $c$ are large we employ the Euclidean algorithm to find $d$ and a particular solution $x_0$.

*Example* 2. Solve, if possible, the linear congruence

$$657x \equiv 18 \bmod 963.$$

$$\begin{aligned} 963 &= 657(1) + 306, \\ 657 &= 306(2) + 45, \\ 306 &= 45(6) + 36, \\ 45 &= 36(1) + 9, \\ 36 &= 9(4). \end{aligned}$$

Since $9 = (963, 657)$ is a factor of 18 we know that the congruence can be solved and that the solutions comprise 9 equivalence classes mod 963. Collapsing the above set of equations by eliminating 36, 45, and 306, in turn, we obtain

$$9 = (22)657 + (-15)963.$$

Therefore

$$657(44) \equiv 18 \bmod 963,$$

and 44 is one solution. The other solutions are the elements of the 9 classes

$$[44],\ [44 + 107],\ [44 + 214],\ \cdots,\ [44 + 856]$$

since $b/d = 963/9 = 107$.

The results on linear Diophantine equations can also be used to solve a pair of linear congruences. Suppose we wish to find, if possible, an integer $x$ such that both of the following congruences hold:

$$\begin{aligned} ax &\equiv b \bmod m, \\ cx &\equiv d \bmod n. \end{aligned}$$

By Theorem 4.6 this is equivalent to the problem of finding integers $x$, $y$, and $z$ such that

$$ax + my = b$$

and

$$cx + nz = d.$$

In other words we must solve a pair of linear Diophantine equations simultaneously. We will first treat a special case of this problem.

THEOREM 4.8. *There exists an integer $x$ such that*

$$x \equiv a \bmod m \quad \textit{and} \quad x \equiv b \bmod n,$$

*where $a$, $b$, $m$, and $n$ are positive integers, if and only if*

$$a \equiv b \bmod (m, n).$$

*If $x$ and $y$ both satisfy the congruences, then*

$$x \equiv y \bmod \langle m, n \rangle.$$

(Here $(m, n)$ and $\langle m, n\rangle$ denote the G.C.F. and L.C.M., respectively of $\{m, n\}$. The restriction that $a$ and $b$ be positive is of no significance.)

Clearly an integer $x$ exists such that

$$x \equiv a \bmod m \qquad \text{and} \qquad x \equiv b \bmod n$$

if and only if there exist integers $r$ and $s$ such that

$$x = a + rm \qquad \text{and} \qquad x = b + sn.$$

Consider the equation

$$a + rm = b + sn \qquad \text{or} \qquad rm - sn = b - a;$$

from Theorem 4.2 we know that integers $r$ and $s$ satisfying this equation exist if and only if $(m, n)$ is a factor of $(b - a)$, or

$$b \equiv a \bmod (m, n).$$

Since it is clear that the $r$ and $s$ determine $x$ we conclude that the first statement of the theorem is true.

Now if $x \equiv a \bmod m$ and $y \equiv a \bmod m$, then $x = a + km$ and $y = a + hm$ for some integers $h$ and $k$. Therefore,

$$x - y = a + km - (a + hm) = (k - h)m,$$

or

$$x \equiv y \bmod m.$$

Similarly

$$x \equiv y \bmod n$$

if $x \equiv b \bmod n$ and $y \equiv b \bmod n$. Certainly $x - y$ is a multiple of $\langle m, n\rangle$ if it is a multiple of both $m$ and $n$, since the L.C.M. of $\{m, n\}$ is a factor of every common multiple of $m$ and $n$. Therefore we conclude that

$$x \equiv y \bmod \langle m, n\rangle$$

if $x \equiv a \bmod m$, $x \equiv b \bmod n$, $y \equiv a \bmod n$, and $y \equiv b \bmod n$.

From the first part of the above proof we see that values of $x$ (if they exist) can be found from values of $r$ and $s$. So we have again the problem of solving a linear Diophantine equation.

*Example* 3. Find an integer $x$ such that

$$x \equiv 5 \bmod 12 \qquad \text{and} \qquad x \equiv 4 \bmod 17.$$

We see that such an $x$ exists since

$$5 \equiv 4 \bmod (12, 17).$$

So we must find integers $r$ and $s$ such that satisfy the conditions

$$x = 5 + 12r = 4 + 17s,$$

or solve the equation

$$12r - 17s = -1$$

in integers. The Euclid algorithm can be used, but trial and error yields

$$12(7) - 17(5) = -1,$$

or $r = 7$ and $s = 5$. Therefore

$$x = 5 + 84 = 4 + 85 = 89$$

is one solution of the pair of congruences. Clearly the congruence class [89] mod $\langle 12, 17 \rangle$ consists of all the solutions of the pair of congruences.

Although we remarked that Theorem 4.8 treated only a special case of the problem of solving a pair of linear congruences, we will show now that Theorem 4.8, or rather its proof, provides a method for solving a pair. This method is illustrated by the following.

*Example* 4. Solve the pair of congruences

$$5x \equiv 1 \bmod 12, \qquad 6x \equiv 7 \bmod 17.$$

First we find all of the solutions of

$$5x \equiv 1 \bmod 12.$$

Since the numbers are small we proceed by trial and error and obtain 5 as a particular solution. Then since $(5, 12) = 1$ we know that the elements of the congruence class [5] modulo 12 are the solutions of the congruence.

In the same manner we consider

$$6x \equiv 7 \bmod 17$$

and find that 4 is a solution. Since $(6, 17) = 1$ we conclude that the elements of the congruence class [4] modulo 17 are the solutions of this congruence.

Now suppose $x'$ is a common solution of these two congruences; then $x'$ must lie in the class [5] modulo 12 and also in the class [4] modulo 17. In other words $x'$ is a solution of the following pair of congruences:

$$x' \equiv 5 \bmod 12, \qquad x' \equiv 4 \bmod 17.$$

From Example 3 we know that the solutions of this pair are exactly the elements of the congruence class [89] modulo 204. Therefore $x'$ lies in the class [89] modulo 204.

Conversely, suppose $y$ is in [89] modulo 204. Then

$$y = 89 + 204k$$

for some integer $k$, so that

$$y = 4 + 85 + 204k = 4 + (5 + 12k)17$$

and

$$6y = 24 + 6(5 + 12k)17 = 7 + (31 + 72k)17;$$

moreover,

$$y = 5 + 84 + 204k = 5 + (7 + 17k)12$$

and

$$5y = 25 + 5(7 + 17k)12 = 1 + (37 + 85k)12.$$

Therefore we see that

$$5y \equiv 1 \bmod 12 \qquad \text{and} \qquad 6y \equiv 7 \bmod 17$$

and conclude that the solutions of the original pair of congruences are precisely the elements of [89] modulo 204.

The procedure followed in this example can be stated as a simple theorem, and this is left as an exercise for the student.

A special case of Theorem 4.8 which arises when the moduli are relatively prime integers can be extended by mathematical induction to a very old theorem that is the basis for many, many puzzles and brain teasers. It is also a useful result in the study of abstract systems.

THEOREM 4.9 (CHINESE REMAINDER THEOREM). *If the $n$ positive integers $m_1, m_2, \cdots, m_n$ are relatively prime by pairs (i.e., $(m_i, m_j) = 1$ if $i \neq j$), then the set of $n$ congruences*

$$x \equiv a_1 \bmod m_1, \cdots, x \equiv a_n \bmod m_n,$$

*has a solution $x'$. Moreover the solutions of the set are exactly the elements of congruence class $[x']$ modulo $m_1 m_2 \cdots m_n$.*

When $n = 1$ the proposition is trivially true since the congruence

$$x \equiv a_1 \bmod m_1$$

has as solutions the elements of $[a_1]$ mod $m_1$. When $n = 2$ the proposition is true by Theorem 4.8. So suppose the proposition is true for the positive integer $k$ (the induction hypothesis) and consider the set of $k + 1$ congruences

$$x \equiv a_1 \bmod m_1, \cdots, \quad x \equiv a_k \bmod m_k, \quad x \equiv a_{k+1} \bmod m_{k+1},$$

where $(m_i, m_j) = 1$ for $i \neq j$. By the induction hypothesis the set of $k$ congruences

$$x \equiv a_2 \bmod m_2, \cdots, \qquad x \equiv a_{k+1} \bmod m_{k+1},$$

has a solution $r$, and the elements of $[r]$ modulo $m$, where $m = m_2 m_3 \cdots m_{k+1}$, are precisely the solutions of the set.

Now we consider the pair of congruences,

$$x \equiv r \bmod m \qquad \text{and} \qquad x \equiv a_1 \bmod m_1.$$

First we see that the integers $m$ and $m_1$ are relatively prime since a prime divisor of $m$ is necessarily a divisor of exactly one of the $k$ integers $m_2, \cdots, m_{k+1}$. Since these numbers are relatively prime to $m_1$, we conclude that

$$(m, m_1) = 1.$$

Therefore by Theorem 4.8 this pair of congruences has a solution $x'$, and moreover the solutions of the pair are exactly the elements of the congruence class $[x']$ modulo $mm_1$. Then $x'$ is certainly a solution of the $k + 1$ congruences

$$x \equiv a_1 \bmod m_1, \cdots, \qquad x \equiv a_{k+1} \bmod m_{k+1},$$

and it is easy to see that the set of solutions of these $k + 1$ congruences is exactly the class $[x']$ modulo $m_1 m_2 \cdots m_{k+1}$. After all, a solution of these $k + 1$ congruences is certainly a solution of the $k$ congruences

$$x \equiv a_2 \bmod m_2, \cdots, \qquad x \equiv a_{k+1} \bmod m_{k+1}$$

as well as a solution of

$$x \equiv a_1 \bmod m_1.$$

This completes the induction and proves the theorem.

To illustrate the type of puzzle which can be treated systematically as a result of this theorem we shall now solve a well-known "pirate puzzle."

*Example* 5. A band of 13 pirates confiscated a box of $x$ gold coins. Uniform distribution of the coins resulted in a remainder of 8 coins. After two pirates were killed, a redistribution left a remainder of 3 coins. And a redistribution after the death of three more pirates resulted in a remainder of 5 coins. What is the minimal value of $x$?

We can immediately reduce this to the problem of solving the following set of congruences:

$$x \equiv 8 \bmod 13, \quad x \equiv 3 \bmod 11, \quad x \equiv 5 \bmod 8.$$

Since $(13, 11) = (13, 8) = (11, 8) = 1$ we know by the Chinese Remainder Theorem that this set has exactly one solution between 0 and 8(11)(13). To find this integer we first solve the pair

$$x \equiv 8 \bmod 13, \qquad x \equiv 3 \bmod 11,$$

that is, we seek integers $r$ and $s$ such that

$$x = 8 + 13r = 3 + 11s,$$

or

$$11s - 13r = 5.$$

Since

$$11(6) - 13(5) = 1$$

we can take

$$s = 30 \qquad \text{and} \qquad r = 25.$$

Then

$$8 + 13(25) = 3 + 11(30) = 333$$

is one solution of the pair, and the elements of the congruence modulo 143 (= 11(13)) classes

$$[333] = [47]$$

are the solutions of the pair.

Now we consider the pair

$$x \equiv 47 \bmod 143 \qquad \text{and} \qquad x \equiv 5 \bmod 8.$$

To solve this pair we must find integers $u$ and $v$ such that

$$x = 47 + 143u = 5 + 8v$$

or

$$143u - 8v = -42.$$

Since

$$143(7) - 8(125) = 1$$

we see that we can use

$$u = 7(-42) \qquad \text{and} \qquad v = 125(-42).$$

Then

$$47 + 143(7)(-42) = 5 + 8(125)(-42) = -41995$$

is a solution of this pair. Since all the solutions of this pair, and hence of the original three congruences, are the elements of the congruence class $[-41995]$ modulo 1144 $(=8(143))$, and since 333 is the smallest positive integer in that class,

$$-41995 = -37(1144) + 333,$$

we conclude that 333 is the answer to the puzzle.

We note that the Chinese Remainder Theorem can also be used to solve a single congruence,

$$ax \equiv b \bmod m_1m_2, \qquad (m_1, m_2) = 1.$$

For, if $r_1$ and $r_2$ are integers such that

$$ar_1 \equiv b \bmod m_1 \qquad \text{and} \qquad ar_2 \equiv b \bmod m_2,$$

and if $r$ is a number such that

$$r \equiv r_1 \bmod m_1 \qquad \text{and} \qquad r \equiv r_2 \bmod m_2,$$

then we see that

$$ar \equiv b \bmod m_1m_2.$$

For

$$ar - b = ar_1 + k_1m_1 - b = h_1m_1 + k_1m_1$$

since

$$ar_1 - b = h_1m_1.$$

Similarly $ar - b$ is a multiple of $m_2$, so since $(m_1, m_2) = 1$,

$$ar \equiv b \bmod m.$$

## Exercise 4.3

**1.** Show that an integer $x$ such that

$$-11x \equiv -92 \bmod 30$$

is a solution of

$$19x \equiv 28 \bmod 30$$

and conversely, since $-11 \equiv 19 \bmod 30$ and $-92 \equiv 28 \bmod 30$. What does this show about the assumption, $a$ and $b$ positive, in the problem $ax \equiv b \bmod m$?

**2.** Solve:

(*a*) $513x \equiv -17 \bmod 1163$.
(*b*) $213x \equiv 10002 \bmod 441$.
(*c*) $24x \equiv -2 \bmod 17$.
(*d*) $33x \equiv 22 \bmod 105$.
(*e*) $6x + 2 \equiv 0 \bmod 10$.
(*f*) $-x \equiv 6 \bmod 5$.

**3.** Solve the sets:

(*a*) $x \equiv 4 \bmod 9$ and $x \equiv 7 \bmod 12$.
(*b*) $x \equiv 2 \bmod 3$, $x \equiv 5 \bmod 7$, $x \equiv 5 \bmod 8$.
(*c*) $x \equiv 3 \bmod 17$, $x \equiv 4 \bmod 11$, $x \equiv 5 \bmod 6$.

**4.** Solve Problem 2(*d*) by the method suggested in the final remark of the section.

**5.** Solve the pair $5x \equiv -1 \bmod 12$, $35x \equiv 5 \bmod 45$.

**6.** Find three consecutive integers which are in turn divisible by $2^2$, $3^2$, and $5^2$. Generalize.

**7.** Find a pair of integers satisfying the following congruence in two unknowns:

$$38x + 15y \equiv 33 \bmod 22.$$

(Write as a linear Diophantine equation in three unknowns.)

**8.** Use Euler's Theorem ($a^{\Phi(m)} \equiv 1 \bmod m$ if $(a, m) = 1$) to find a solution of

$$5x \equiv 2 \bmod 8.$$

Is this a very practical method of solution?

**9.** Show that the integer $a$ cannot be a solution of the congruence $ax \equiv 35 \bmod 100$.

**10.** Denote by $[r_1], [r_2], \cdots, [r_m]$ the distinct congruence classes mod $m$. If the *number* of solutions of the congruence $ax \equiv b \bmod m$ is defined to be the number of $[r_i]$ such that $ar_i \equiv b \bmod m$, restate the theorems of this section using this concept. Show that the concept is independent of the particular element $r_i$ picked to represent the set $[r_i]$.

**11.** If $a$ is selected at random from the set $\{1, 2, \cdots, 9\}$ and $b$ is selected at random from the set $\{0, 1, 2, \cdots, 9\}$, what is the probability that the congruence $ax \equiv b \bmod 10$ has no solution?

**12.** Let $h$, $k$, and $p$ be positive integers with $(h, k) = 1$. Show that an integer $x$ exists such that $(hx + k, p) = 1$ when $p$ is a prime. Can you extend this result to the case where $p$ need not be prime? (Consider the Chinese Remainder Theorem.)

**13.** Review the proof of Theorem 3.25 and rewrite, using the material of this section.

**14.** If $x$, $m$, and $n$ are positive integers, when does $x^m \equiv x \bmod (10)^n$ imply $x^2 \equiv x \bmod (10)^n$?

## 4.4 Pythagorean Triples

The Theorem of Pythagoras, as every schoolboy knows, states that for a right triangle the square constructed from the hypotenuse has area equal to the sum of the areas of the squares constructed from each of the other sides.

If $c$ is the length of the hypotenuse and $a$ and $b$ are the lengths of the other two sides, then the theorem states that

$$a^2 + b^2 = c^2.$$

Since the Pythagoreans were also quite interested in the integers this result led them to pose the following problem: Find all sets of three integers $\{x, y, z\}$ such that

$$x^2 + y^2 = z^2.$$

Sets such as $\{3, 4, 5\}$, $\{5, 12, 13\}$, and $\{8, 15, 17\}$ were known to many ancient peoples. Clearly this is a Diophantine problem of somewhat greater complexity than the linear equation problem.

DEFINITION 4.3. A set $\{a, b, c\}$ of nonzero rational numbers is a *Pythagorean triple* if and only if $a^2 + b^2 = c^2$. It is a *primitive triple* if, in addition, $a$, $b$, and $c$ are positive integers and the G.C.F. of $\{a, b, c\}$ is 1.

Every Pythagorean triple can be obtained from a primitive triple through multiplication by a nonzero rational and adjusting signs; if $\{x, y, z\}$ is a primitive triple, then $\{rx, ry, rz\}$, $\{-rx, ry, rz\}$, etc., where $r$ is a nonzero rational, are Pythagorean triples.

The trivial sets such as $\{1, 0, 1\}$ and $\{0, 0, 0\}$ are excluded from consideration as holding no interest.

*Lemma* 4.2. If $\{x, y, z\}$ is a primitive triple with $x^2 + y^2 = z^2$, then:
(i) $x$ and $y$ are not both even.
(ii) $x$ and $y$ are not both odd.
(iii) $z$ is an odd integer.

To prove (i) we note that, if 2 is a factor of both $x$ and $y$, then, since

$$z^2 = x^2 + y^2,$$

2 is a factor of $z^2$, and hence of $z$. But $(x, y, z) = 1$, so we see that $x$ and $y$ are not both even.

Suppose $x$ and $y$ are both odd; then there are integers $a$ and $b$ such that

$$x = 2a + 1 \qquad \text{and} \qquad y = 2b + 1.$$

Substitution in $x^2 + y^2 = z^2$ yields

$$4(a^2 + a + b^2 + b) + 2 = z^2.$$

Consequently,

$$z^2 \equiv 2 \bmod 4.$$

Now the integer $z$ is either even or odd; $z$ even obviously implies

$$z^2 \equiv 0 \bmod 4,$$

whereas $z$ odd means that

$$z = 2c + 1$$

for some integer $c$, so that

$$z^2 = 4c^2 + 4c + 1 \equiv 1 \bmod 4.$$

Clearly, then, the congruence

$$z^2 \equiv 2 \bmod 4$$

is impossible, and so $x$ and $y$ are not both odd.

Property (iii) is a consequence of properties (i) and (ii) since the sum of an odd and an even integer is odd. Thus $z^2$, and hence $z$, is odd.

*Lemma* 4.3. If $\{x, y, z\}$ is a primitive triple with $x^2 + y^2 = z^2$ and $x$ even, then:

(i) $(z + y)/2$ and $(z - y)/2$ are positive, relatively prime integers.

(ii) Positive integers $u$ and $v$ exist such that $u^2 = (z + y)/2$ and $v^2 = (z - y)/2$.

(iii) $u > v$, $(u, v) = 1$, and exactly one of the integers $u$ and $v$ is even.

Since $x$ is even we conclude from Lemma 4.2 that $y$ and $z$ are odd integers. Therefore $z + y$ and $z - y$ are even integers. From the equation

$$x^2 + y^2 = z^2$$

we get

$$x^2 = z^2 - y^2 = (z + y)(z - y).$$

Therefore $x/2$, $(z + y)/2$, and $(z - y)/2$ are positive integers such that

$$(x/2)^2 = ((z + y)/2)((z - y)/2).$$

Now let $d$ be the G.C.F. of $(z + y)/2$ and $(z - y)/2$. From the last equation we see that $d^2$ is a factor of $(x/2)^2$ so that $d$ is a factor of $x/2$ and hence of $x$. Also, since

$$z = ((z + y)/2) + ((z - y)/2)$$

and

$$y = ((z - y)/2) - ((z - y)/2)$$

we know that $d$ is a common factor of $y$ and $z$. Therefore, since $(x, y, z) = 1$ we conclude that $(z + y)/2$ and $(z - y)/2$ are relatively prime.

Now we observe from

$$(x/2)^2 = ((z + y)/2)((z - y)/2)$$

that, if $p$ is a prime factor of $(z + y)/2$, then $p$ is a factor of $(x/2)^2$ and hence of $x/2$ by the Fundamental Theorem of Arithmetic. Therefore $p^2$ is a factor of $(x/2)^2$. Since $(z + y)/2$ and $(z - y)/2$ are relatively prime this means that $p^2$ is a factor of $(z + y)/2$. From this we conclude that each prime factor of $(z + y)/2$ occurs an even number of times as a factor of $(z + y)/2$, so that

$$(z + y)/2 = u^2$$

for some positive integer $u$. Similarly we have

$$(z - y)/2 = v^2$$

for some positive integer $v$.

To prove property (iii) we note that $u > v$ since $(z + y) > (z - y)$ and $u$ and $v$ are positive. Also $(u, v) = 1$ since a common factor of $u$ and $v$ is a common factor of $u^2$ and $v^2$. Finally we note that

$$y = y^2 - v^2 \qquad \text{and} \qquad z = u^2 + v^2;$$

if $u$ and $v$ are either both even or both odd, then these equations imply that $y$ and $z$ are even, contradicting property (iii) of Lemma 4.2. Thus exactly one of the integers $u$ and $v$ is even.

THEOREM 4.10. *The set of integers $\{x, y, z\}$ is a primitive triple with $x^2 + y^2 = z^2$ and $x$ even if and only if there are positive integers $u$ and $v$ with $(u, v) = 1$, $u > v$, and $u$ and $v$ not both odd, such that*

$$x = 2uv, \qquad y = u^2 - v^2, \qquad z = u^2 + v^2.$$

We have shown in the lemmas that the integers $u$ and $v$ of the theorem exist whenever the primitive triple $\{x, y, z\}$ does. So consider the converse. If $u$ and $v$ are any nonequal, nonzero integers we see that

$$x = 2uv, \qquad y = u^2 - v^2, \qquad z = u^2 + v^2$$

is a Pythagorean triple since

$$4u^2v^2 + (u^2 - v^2)^2 = (u^2 + v^2)^2.$$

Since $u > v > 0$ we see that the integers $x$, $y$, and $z$ are positive. Now let $p$ be a common factor of $\{x, y, z\}$. Since

$$y + z = 2u^2 \qquad \text{and} \qquad y - z = 2v^2,$$

$p$ is a common factor of $2u^2$ and $2v^2$, and since $(u, v) = 1$ this means that $p = 1$ or 2. But $y$ and $z$ are both odd integers since

$$y = u^2 - v^2 \qquad \text{and} \qquad z = u^2 + v^2,$$

owing to the fact that $u$ and $v$ are of opposite parity (i.e., one is even and one is odd). Thus

$$p = 1 = (x, y, z),$$

and so $\{x, y, z\}$ is a primitive triple with $x^2 + y^2 = z^2$ and $x$ even.

This theorem is considered to provide an effective solution of the primitive triple Diophantine problem since it describes every primitive triple in terms of pairs of positive integers with easily checked properties. In other words the problem is "solved" by reducing it to an easier or more manageable situation. We see that the theorem enables us to construct quite easily a table of several primitive triples. We observe from this small table of eight primitive

| $u$ | $v$ | $x$ | $y$ | $z$ |
|---|---|---|---|---|
| 2 | 1 | 4 | 3 | 5 |
| 3 | 2 | 12 | 5 | 13 |
| 4 | 1 | 8 | 15 | 17 |
| 4 | 3 | 24 | 7 | 25 |
| 5 | 2 | 20 | 21 | 29 |
| 5 | 4 | 40 | 9 | 41 |
| 6 | 1 | 12 | 35 | 37 |
| 6 | 5 | 60 | 11 | 61 |

triples that in each of the triples either $x$ or $y$ is a multiple of 3. Is this a general property?

THEOREM 4.11. *If $\{x, y, z\}$ is a primitive triple with $x^2 + y^2 = z^2$, then exactly one of the two numbers $x$ and $y$ is a multiple of* 3.

Consider the integers $x$, $y$, and $z$ modulo 3. Since the remainders for division by 3 are 0, 1, and $-1$ ($\equiv 2 \bmod 3$), and since $(x, y, z) = 1$ we see that, if the theorem is not true, then

$$x, y, z \equiv \pm 1 \bmod 3.$$

But this means that

$$x^2 + y^2 = 2 + 3k,$$

whereas

$$z^2 = 1 + 3h,$$

$h$ and $k$ integers, so that

$$1 = 2 - 1 = 3(h - k),$$

which is impossible. This contradiction proves the theorem.

Now we consider two examples which use the results and the method of proof of Theorem 4.10.

*Example* 1. Find all primitive triples $\{x, y, z\}$ with $x^2 + y^2 = z^2$ and $0 < z < 30$.

Since it is immaterial whether we take $x$ or $y$ to be even, we shall choose $x$ as in Theorem 4.10. Then $z = u^2 + v^2$, where $u > v > 0$, $(u, v) = 1$, and $u$ and $v$ are of opposite parity. Since

$$u^2 + v^2 < 30$$

implies that $u \leqslant 5$, we see that all the required triples are contained in our table. They are $\{4, 3, 5\}$, $\{12, 5, 13\}$, $\{8, 15, 17\}$, $\{24, 7, 25\}$, and $\{20, 21, 29\}$.

*Example* 2. Find if possible a square integer $t$ with the property that $t + 5$ and $t - 5$ are also squares of integers.

This Diophantine problem involves finding positive integers $x$, $y$, and $z$ such that

$$x^2 + 5 = y^2 \quad \text{and} \quad x^2 - 5 = z^2.$$

Subtracting the second from the first yields

$$10 = y^2 - z^2 = (y + z)(y - z).$$

This means that either $y + z$ or $y - z$ is even; suppose $y + z$ is even. Since the sum of an even and an odd integer is odd, this means that $y$ and $z$ are either both even or both odd. In either case $y - z$ is also even, implying that 4 is a factor of 10, which is not true. Therefore $y + z$ is not even. Suppose $y - z$ is even; then again $y$ and $z$ must be both even or both odd, so we have another impossibility. Thus the integers $x$, $y$, and $z$ do not exist, so that there is no integer $t$ with the required properties.

There are, however, rational solutions to the problem since

$$(41/12)^2 + 5 = (49/12)^2 \quad \text{and} \quad (41/12)^2 - 5 = (31/12)^2.$$

## Exercise 4.4

**1.** Find all primitive triples in which the largest integer is less than 60.

**2.** Find all primitive triples which form an arithmetic progression.

**3.** Find all Pythagorean triples which form a geometric progression.

**4.** Find all integral right triangles (i.e., right triangles whose sides have integral measures) in which the length of one side differs from the hypotenuse by one unit, by two or three units.

**5.** Find three integers $x > y > z > 0$ such that the differences $x - y$, $y - z$, and $x - z$ are all squares of integers. (*Hint:* Eliminate $x$, $y$, and $z$ from the equations.)

**6.** Prove that exactly one element of every primitive triple is a multiple of 5. (See Example 1.)

**7.** Show that the lengths of the sides of an isosceles right triangle can never form a Pythagorean triple.

**8.** Prove that, if $n$ is an integral multiple of 4, then there is a Pythagorean triple of integers containing $n$. Is this true if $n$ is any positive integer greater than 2? (Try 7, 11, and 19.)

**9.** Find "primitive" triples $\{x, y, z\}$ such that

(i) $$x^2 - y^2 = z;$$

(ii) $$x^2 + 2y^2 = z^2,$$

where $x = |r^2 - 2s^2|$, $y = 2rs$, and $z = r^2 + 2s^2$, $r$ and $s$ being positive integers with $(r, 2s) = 1$.

**10.** Show that there is no integer $t$ which is a square of an integer and is such that $t + 10$ and $t - 10$ are also squares of integers.

**11.** Show that there are just two primitive right triangles which contain the circle of radius $p$, $p$ an odd prime, as their inscribed circle. Show also that the sums of the lengths of the sides of each is six times a squared integer.

**12.** Find the shortest perimeter common to two different primitive right triangles. (*Note:* A right triangle is *primitive* if and only if the lengths of its sides form a primitive triple.)

## 4.5 Method of Descent

Although a variety of Diophantine equations in which the unknowns appear to powers greater than 1 have been solved, no general method for treating these equations is known yet. However, there are methods which can be used to analyze several types of Diophantine equations, and one of these is Fermat's *method of descent* for showing that an equation has no solutions in integers except the trivial ones. We illustrate this method now.

THEOREM 4.12. *There is no set $\{x, y, z\}$ of nonzero integers such that*

$$x^4 + y^4 = z^2.$$

Suppose such a set of nonzero integers $\{x, y, z\}$ does exist. Then certainly $\{|x|, |y|, |z|\}$ is a set of positive integers with the same property,

$$(|x|)^4 + (|y|)^4 = (|z|)^2,$$

so we can restrict our attention to sets of positive integers. Now consider the set $S$ of all positive integers which can serve as $z$ in a solution triple $\{x, y, z\}$ of positive integers. From our assumption that the equation has a solution in nonzero integers we conclude that $S$ is nonempty. Therefore, by the Well-Ordering Theorem, $S$ has a least element $z'$, and there are positive integers $x'$ and $y'$ such that

$$(x')^4 + (y')^4 = (z')^2.$$

From the minimality of $z'$ we conclude that $(x', y') = 1 = (x', y', z')$, for, if $p$ is a prime factor of $x'$ and $y'$, then since

$$(x')^4 + (y')^4 = (z')^2$$

we see that $p^4$ is a factor of $(z')^2$. This implies that $p^2$ is a factor of $z'$, so that

$$(x'/p)^4 + (y'/p)^4 = (z'/p^2)^4,$$

violating the minimality of $z'$. Therefore

$$(x', y', z') = 1.$$

This means that $\{(x')^2, (y')^2, z'\}$ is a primitive Pythagorean triple, so that Theorem 4.10 can be brought into play. Then there exist integers $u$ and $v$ with $u > v > 0$, $(u, v) = 1$, and one of the two integers even, such that

$$(x')^2 = 2uv, \qquad (y')^2 = u^2 - v^2, \qquad z' = u^2 + v^2.$$

Suppose $u$ is even; then $u = 2r$ and $v = 2s + 1$ for some integers $r$ and $s$.

So we would have

$$(y')^2 = 4r^2 - 4s^2 - 4s - 1 \equiv -1 \bmod 4,$$

which is impossible since the square of any integer is congruent with either 0 or 1 mod 4. Therefore we see that $u$ must be odd and $v$ even. From the equation for $(x')^2$ we get

$$(x'/2)^2 = u(v/2),$$

and since $(u, v) = 1$ this implies that $u$ and $v/2$ are squares of integers,

$$u = m^2, \qquad v = 2n^2, \qquad x' = 2mn.$$

Substituting these representations of $u$ and $v$ into the equations for $(y')^2$ yields

$$(y')^2 = m^4 - 4n^4$$

or

$$(y')^2 + 4n^4 = m^4.$$

This means that, since $u = m^2$ and $v = 2n^2$ are relatively prime, the set $\{y', 2n^2, m^2\}$ is a primitive Pythagorean triple,

$$(y')^2 + (2n^2)^2 = (m^2)^2.$$

Now we can use Theorem 4.10 again, concluding that there are relatively prime integers $a$ and $b$, not both odd, with $a > b > 0$, such that

$$2n^2 = 2ab, \qquad y' = a^2 - b^2, \qquad m^2 = a^2 + b^2.$$

Since $(a, b) = 1$ the equation

$$n^2 = ab$$

implies that $a$ and $b$ are squares of positive integers $c$ and $d$,

$$a = c^2 \quad \text{and} \quad b = d^2.$$

Substituting these in the equation for $m^2$ yields

$$c^4 + d^4 = m^2,$$

and we see that the positive integers $c$, $d$, and $m$ form a solution of the equation

$$x^4 + y^4 = z^2.$$

So $m$ is in $S$.

Compare $m$ and $z'$. From our representation of $z'$ in terms of $u$ and $v$,

$$z' = u^2 + v^2,$$

we get

$$z' = m^4 + 4n^4 > m^4 \geqslant m.$$

Thus $m$ is a positive integer smaller than $z'$. But $z'$ is the smallest element of $S$, and we have a contradiction. This contradiction proves the theorem.

In Book II of the *Arithmetic* of Diophantos Problem 8 involves the decomposing of a given squared rational into the sum of two squared rationals; i.e., for a given rational $r$ find rationals $s$ and $t$ such that

$$r^2 = s^2 + t^2.$$

The seventeenth-century mathematician Pierre Fermat noted in the margin of his copy of the *Arithmetic*: "However, a cube cannot be split into two cubes or a biquadrate into two biquadrates, and in general no power beyond the second can be split into two of the same powers. For this I have a truly remarkable proof, but the margin is too small to contain it." The statement that there exists no set $\{x, y, z\}$ of nonzero integers such that

$$x^n + y^n = z^n,$$

when $n$ is an integer greater than two, is known as *Fermat's Theorem*. However, no proof of this theorem is known.

Although Fermat's Theorem is still unproved much work has been done on the problem for particular values of $n$, and it is known that no nonzero solutions exist for $2 < n < 617$. (See the article by H. S. Vandiver in Suggested Reading.) Efforts to prove the theorem, although unsuccessful, have sometimes led to the invention of new and important concepts in mathematics. Such a contribution was made by the ninteenth-century mathematician E. Kummer, who extended the theory of numbers to number systems which fail to have the property of unique factorization into primes. For coping with this difficulty Kummer developed the concept of *ideal numbers*, an idea which is important to the development of modern abstract algebra. (We will encounter concepts which evolved from this idea in the following chapters.)

## Exercise 4.5

**1.** Show that the equation

$$x^{4m} + y^{4m} = z^{4m}$$

has no solution in nonzero integers when $m$ is a positive integer. (Assume a solution exists and consider Theorem 4.12.)

**2.** Show that Fermat's Theorem is true if and only if there exists no odd prime $p$ such that

$$x^p + y^p = z^p$$

has a solution in nonzero integers. (Write $n = kp$.)

**3.** In the equation

$$r^2 = s^2 + t^2$$

make the substitution

$$t = ms - r,$$

where $m$ is an unknown rational, and solve for $x$. Find two different pairs of values for $s$ and $t$ when $r = 3$.

**4.** Use the method of descent to prove that the equation $x^4 + 4y^4 = z^2$ has no solution in nonzero integers.

**5.** Show that $x^4 - y^4 = z^2$ has no solution in nonzero integers. (Rewrite as $x^4 = y^4 + z^2$.)

**6.** Find two different positive integers $d$ such that $x^4 + dy^4 = z^2$ has solutions in nonzero integers.

**7.** Find nonnegative integers $a$, $b$, $c$, and $d$ for each integer $n$, $1 \leqslant n \leqslant 20$, such that

$$n = a^2 + b^2 + c^2 + d^2.$$

($1 = 1^2 + 0^2 + 0^2 + 0^2$, $2 = 1^2 + 1^2 + 0^2 + 0^2$, etc.)

**8.** Can integers $a$ and $b$ be found for each integer $n > 0$ such that $n = a^2 + b^2$? (See the results of Problem 7.)

**9.** Show that the only solution in positive integers of $x^4 + y^4 = 2z^2$ is given by $x = y = z = 1$.

**10.** Show that the only integers satisfying

$$x(x + 1) = 2y^4$$

are $x = 1$ or $-2$ and $|y| = 1$.

## 4.6 Sum of Two Squares

During or after the study of factorization of integers, the decomposition of integers relative to the operation of multiplication, the student undoubtedly asked himself if a somewhat analogous investigation could be made for the decomposition of integers relative to the operation of addition. Certainly every positive integer is uniquely representable as a sum of ones, and, although every positive integer larger than 1 is either a prime or a sum of primes, such a representation is not unique since

$$6 = 2 + 2 + 2 = 3 + 3.$$

Thus we see that there are various choices for the indecomposable elements, the "primes," and these naturally lead to different results. This and similar problems make up what is known as *additive number theory*. One of the famous theorems of additive number theory states that each positive integer is expressible in at least one way as the sum of the squares of not more than four positive integers. This result was conjectured by Diophantos and the first published proof was by J. L. Lagrange in 1770. It was generalized in 1909 by D. Hilbert, who proved that each positive integer is expressible as the sum of the $k$th powers of not more than $F(k)$ positive integers, where $k$ is a positive integer and $F(k)$ is a positive integer determined by $k$.

In this section we consider the problem of determining which positive integers can be expressed as the sum of the squares of not more than two positive integers. Since

$$5 = 2^2 + 1^2 \qquad \text{and} \qquad 10 = 3^2 + 1^2$$

it is clear that some integers can be so expressed, and since the integers

$$6, 6 - 1, \text{ and } 6 - 4$$

are certainly not squares of integers we conclude that not all positive integers can be expressed as the sum of not more than two squares.

First we can show rather easily that no prime of the form $4k + 3$, $k$ an integer, can be expressed as the sum of two squares.

THEOREM 4.13. *If $p$ is a prime such that*

$$p \equiv 3 \bmod 4,$$

*then $p$ cannot be written as the sum of the two squared integers.*

Suppose $x$ and $y$ are positive integers such that

$$p = x^2 + y^2.$$

Now modulo 4, $x$ and $y$ are each congruent with one of the four remainders 0, 1, 2, or $-1$ ($\equiv 3 \bmod 4$). Thus $x^2$ and $y^2$ are congruent with either 0 or 1 mod 4, so that

$$x^2 + y^2 \equiv 0, 1, \text{ or } 2 \bmod 4.$$

Since $p \equiv 3 \bmod 4$ we see that it is impossible for $p$ to equal $x^2 + y^2$, and the theorem is proved.

What about the other primes? Since

$$2 = 1^2 + 1^2, \qquad 5 = 2^2 + 1^2, \qquad 13 = 3^2 + 2^2,$$
$$17 = 4^2 + 1^2, \qquad 29 = 5^2 + 4^2, \qquad 37 = 6^2 + 1^2,$$
$$41 = 5^2 + 4^2,$$

it seems reasonable to conjecture that the primes not congruent with 3 modulo 4 are indeed expressible as the sum of two squared integers. The proof of this conjecture is not so easy as the above.

First we develop an interesting property of all primes.

THEOREM 4.14 (WILSON'S THEOREM). *If $p$ is a prime, then $(p - 1)! \equiv -1 \bmod p$.*

We observe that

$$1! + 1 = 1, \quad 2! + 1 = 3, \quad 4! + 1 = 25, \quad 6! + 1 = 721.$$

Now to prove the theorem we consider the linear congruence

$$ax \equiv 1 \bmod p,$$

where $0 < a < p$. From our study of linear congruences we know that there is exactly one integer $b$, $0 < b < p$, such that

$$ab \equiv 1 \bmod p.$$

Can $b$ be equal to $a$, and if so, when? The congruence

$$a^2 \equiv 1 \bmod p$$

means that $a^2 - 1$ has $p$ as a factor. Therefore, since

$$a^2 - 1 = (a + 1)(a - 1),$$

either $p$ is a factor of $a + 1$, or $p$ is a factor of $a - 1$. Since $0 < a < p$, we see that either

$$a + 1 = p \qquad \text{or} \qquad a - 1 = 0.$$

We can readily verify that, if $a$ is either $p - 1$ or 1, then

$$a^2 \equiv 1 \bmod p.$$

For any other value of $a$ between 0 and $p$ there is one integer $b$, $1 < b < p - 1$, different from $a$ such that

$$ab \equiv 1 \bmod p.$$

The effect of all this is to pair off the integers between 1 and $p - 1$ into pairs whose product equals 1 plus a multiple of $p$. For example, if $p = 7$, then

$$\begin{aligned} 2(4) &= 1 + 1(7), \\ 3(5) &= 1 + 2(7); \end{aligned}$$

if $p = 13$, then

$$\begin{aligned} 2(7) &= 1 + 13, \\ 3(9) &= 1 + 2(13), \\ 4(10) &= 1 + 3(13), \\ 5(8) &= 1 + 3(13), \\ 6(11) &= 1 + 5(13). \end{aligned}$$

Therefore,

$$\begin{aligned} (7 - 1)! = 6(5)4(3)2 &= 6\big(3(5)\big)\big(2(4)\big), \\ &= 6(1 + 7)\big(1 + 2(7)\big) = 6\big(1 + 17(7)\big), \\ &= 6 \equiv -1 \bmod 7. \end{aligned}$$

The proof of the general case is exactly the same.

Now we are able to show that some multiple of a prime of the form $4k + 1$ is expressible as the sum of two squared integers.

THEOREM 4.15. *If $p$ is a prime of the form $4k + 1$, then $b = q!$, where*

$$q = (p - 1)/2,$$

*is a positive integer such that $b^2 + 1$ is a multiple of $p$.*

The first $p - 1$ positive integers can be written as

$$1, 2, 3, \cdots, q, p - q, p - (q - 1), \cdots, p - 1.$$

Then we have the $p - 1$ congruences

$$\begin{aligned} 1 &\equiv 1 \bmod p, \\ 2 &\equiv 2 \bmod p, \\ &\vdots \\ q &\equiv q \bmod p, \\ p - q &\equiv -q \bmod p, \\ p - (q - 1) &\equiv -(q - 1) \bmod p, \\ &\vdots \\ p - 2 &\equiv -2 \bmod p, \\ p - 1 &\equiv -1 \bmod p. \end{aligned}$$

Multiplying these congruences we get

$$(p - 1)! \equiv (q!)^2(-1)^q \bmod p,$$

so that, by Wilson's Theorem,

$$(q!)^2(-1)^q \equiv -1 \bmod p,$$

or

$$b^2 \equiv (-1)^{q+1} \bmod p.$$

Since $p = 4k + 1$ for some integer $k$ we have

$$q = (p - 1)/2 = 2k$$

and

$$q + 1 = 2k + 1.$$

Therefore

$$b^2 \equiv -1 \bmod p,$$

and the theorem is proved.

*Example* 1. Let $p = 13$. Then $q = 6$ and $6! = 720$. We see that

$$(720)^2 + 1 = 518401 = (13)39877.$$

Following the steps in the proof we write

$$\begin{aligned} 1 &\equiv 1, & 7 &\equiv -6, \\ 2 &\equiv 2, & 8 &\equiv -5, \\ 3 &\equiv 3, & 9 &\equiv -4, \\ 4 &\equiv 4, & 10 &\equiv -3, \\ 5 &\equiv 5, & 11 &\equiv -2, \\ 6 &\equiv 6, & 12 &\equiv -1, \end{aligned}$$

all mod 13. Then

$$(12)! \equiv (6!)^2(-1)^6 \bmod 13.$$

Now we present an intermediate result discovered by the mathematician A. Thue which combines with the above to show that the primes not of the form $4k + 3$ are expressible as the sum of two squares.

THEOREM 4.16. *If $p$ is a prime, if $r$ is the least positive integer such that $r^2 > p$, and if $n$ is an integer with $(n, p) = 1$, then there exist positive integers $a$ and $c$ less than $r$ such that*

$$n^2a^2 \equiv c^2 \bmod p.$$

Consider the set

$$S = \{nx - y\colon x \text{ and } y \text{ nonnegative integers} < r\}.$$

Clearly $S$ contains $r^2$ integers, so that two of them, say $nx' - y'$ and $nx'' - y''$, lie in the same congruence class modulo $p$ since $r^2 > p$. Thus

$$nx' - y' - (nx'' - y'') = sp$$

for some integer $s$. Therefore,

$$n(x' - x'') - (y' - y'') = sp$$

and

$$n(x' - x'') \equiv y' - y'' \bmod p.$$

Multiplying this congruence by itself gives

$$n^2(x' - x'')^2 \equiv (y - y'')^2 \bmod p,$$

so for

$$a = |x' - x''| \qquad \text{and} \qquad c = |y' - y''|$$

we have

$$n^2a^2 \equiv c^2 \bmod p.$$

If we can show that these integers $a$ and $c$ are between 0 and $r$ the theorem is proved.

Since $x'$, $x''$, $y'$, and $y''$ are elements of the set $0, 1, 2, \cdots, r - 1$, we see that

$$0 \leqslant |x' - x''| < r \qquad \text{and} \qquad 0 \leqslant |y' - y''| < r.$$

Thus we need only show that neither of these numbers is zero. Since $r < p$ it is clear that $x' = x''$ implies $y' = y''$ since

$$0 - (y' - y'') = sp$$

shows that $y' - y''$ is a multiple of $p$, and the nonnegative multiple of $p$ less than $p$ is zero. Similarly if $y' = y''$ we see that $x' = x''$, since

$$n(x' - x'') = sp$$

and

$$(n, p) = 1$$

implies that $p$ is a factor of $|x' - x''| < p$. Thus if either $a$ or $c$ is zero, then both are. But this is contrary to the way the two numbers $nx' - y'$ and

$nx'' - y''$ were chosen. Therefore $a$ and $c$ are both positive, and the theorem is proved.

THEOREM 4.17. *If $p$ is a prime of the form $4k + 1$, then $p$ is expressible as the sum of the squares of two integers.*

By Theorem 4.15 $b = q!$, where $q = (p - 1)/2$, is an integer such that

$$b^2 \equiv -1 \bmod p.$$

Taking $b$ as the integer $n$ of the previous theorem, we see, since $(b, p) = 1$, that there are integers $a$ and $c$ such that

$$0 < a^2 \leqslant (r - 1)^2 < p, \qquad 0 < c^2 \leqslant (r - 1)^2 < p,$$

and

$$b^2a^2 \equiv c^2 \bmod p.$$

From

$$b^2 \equiv -1 \bmod p$$

we get

$$b^2a^2 \equiv -a^2 \bmod p$$

so that

$$c^2 \equiv -a^2 \bmod p$$

since congruence is an equivalence relation. Thus we have

$$a^2 + c^2 = mp$$

for some integer $m$. From the inequalities

$$0 < a^2 < p \qquad \text{and} \qquad 0 < c^2 < p$$

we conclude

$$0 < a^2 + c^2 < 2p,$$

so that

$$a^2 + c^2 = p,$$

proving the theorem.

Now we will go through the basic steps again with some specific integers.

*Example* 2. Let $p = 13$. Then the least positive integer $r$ such that $r^2 > p$ is 4. The integer $n$ in this case is $6!$, and we form the $4^2 = 16$ integers of the form $nx - y$ with $x$ and $y$ selected from 0, 1, 2, 3. We get

| | | | |
|---|---|---|---|
| 0 | 720 | 1440 | 2160 |
| −1 | 719 | 1439 | 2159 |
| −2 | 718 | 1438 | 2158 |
| −3 | 717 | 1437 | 2157 |

Of the various possibilities we select 1440 and $-3$ as our pair $nx' - y'$ and $nx'' - y''$, and

$$nx' - y' - (nx'' - y'') = 1440 - (-3) = 111(13).$$

Here $x' = 2$, $x'' = 0$, $y' = 0$, and $y'' = 3$. Then

$$a = |x' - x''| = 2 \qquad \text{and} \qquad c = |y' - y''| = 3,$$

and certainly

$$13 = 2^2 + 3^2.$$

*Corollary* 4.17.1. A prime $p$ not of the form $4k + 3$ is expressible as a sum of two squared integers.

If $p$ is not of the form $4k + 3$, then it is either of the form $4k + 1$ or equal to 2. Since

$$2 = 1^2 + 1^2,$$

the result follows from Theorem 4.17.

Now we use this knowledge about the primes, together with the following simple result, to classify all of the positive integers.

*Lemma* 4.4. If $a$, $b$, $c$, and $d$ are integers, then the product $(a^2 + b^2)(c^2 + d^2)$ is expressible as a sum of squared integers.

To prove this we utilize one of the simplest of all factoring tricks.

$$\begin{aligned}(a^2 + b^2)(c^2 + d^2) &= a^2c^2 + b^2d^2 + a^2d^2 + b^2c^2 \\ &= (a^2c^2 + b^2d^2 + 2abcd) + (a^2d^2 + b^2c^2 - 2abcd) \\ &= (ac + bd)^2 + (ad - bc)^2.\end{aligned}$$

Now for the general result.

THEOREM 4.18. *The positive integer $m$ is expressible as the sum of the squares of not more than two positive integers if and only if the square-free factor $m'$ of $m$ has no prime factor of the form* $4k + 3$.

If $m'$ is the product of primes none of which has the form $4k + 3$, then it is clear from Corollary 4.17.1 and Lemma 4.3 that $m'$, and hence $m$, is expressible as the sum of not more than two squares. For example, if $m$ is the integer $234 = 2 \cdot 9 \cdot 13$, then

$$m' = 26 = (1^2 + 1^2)(2^2 + 3^2) = 5^2 + 1^2,$$

and

$$m = 234 = 9(5^2 + 1^2) = (15)^2 + 3^2.$$

To prove the converse we assume that $m'$ has a prime factor $p = 4k + 3$ and also that

$$m = x^2 + y^2 = r^2m'$$

for some integers $x$ and $y$ greater than zero. We shall obtain a contradiction from this and thereby prove the theorem. Let $d = (x, y)$; then

$$x = ds \quad \text{and} \quad y = dt, \qquad (s, t) = 1,$$

and we get the equation

$$(r/d)^2m' = s^2 + t^2$$

when we divide by $d^2$. Since $r/d$ is an integer ($m'$ is square-free) and $p$ is a factor of $m'$ we have the equation

$$s^2 + t^2 = hp$$

for some integer $h$.

Now $(s, t) = 1$ implies that at least one of these integers, say $s$, is relatively prime to $p$. This means that there is an integer $s'$ such that

$$ss' \equiv 1 \bmod p$$

by our linear congruence theory. Then, since

$$(s')^2 \equiv (s')^2 \bmod p$$

and

$$s^2 + t^2 \equiv 0 \bmod p,$$

we see that

$$(s')^2(s^2 + t^2) \equiv 0(s')^2 \bmod p.$$

Therefore

$$(s's)^2 + (s't)^2 \equiv 0 \bmod p,$$

and since

$$(s's)^2 \equiv 1 \bmod p$$

we see that $s't$ is an integer such that

$$1 + (s't)^2 \equiv 0 \bmod p$$

or

$$(s't)^2 \equiv -1 \bmod p.$$

However, if we look back to Theorems 4.16 and 4.17 we see that by choosing $n = s't$ we obtain the conclusion that

$$p = a^2 + c^2$$

just as in Theorem 4.17. Since this contradicts Theorem 4.13 we have the contradiction that proves the theorem.

Thus a criterion which is both necessary and sufficient for a positive integer to be expressible as the sum of two squared integers is established. And the method of proof of the sufficiency also provides a means of finding the squared integers; i.e., if $m'$ is the product of primes, none of the form $4k + 3$, then Theorem 4.16 applied to each prime $p$ yields integers $a$ and $c$ such that

$$p = a^2 + c^2,$$

and these can be combined by Lemma 4.3 to yield a representation of $m'$.

However, even when an integer can be expressed as the sum of two squared integers, this expression need not be unique:

$$125 = (10)^2 + 5^2 = (11)^2 + 2^2,$$
$$65 = 8^2 + 1^2 = 7^2 + 4^2,$$
$$325 = (18)^2 + 1^2 = (17)^2 + 6^2.$$

Such examples can be manufactured quite easily by use of the equation

$$ab = ((a + b)/2)^2 - ((a - b)/2)^2,$$

where $a$ and $b$ are positive integers which are both even or both odd. Then we have

$$35 = 1(35) = ((1 + 35)/2)^2 - ((35 - 1)/2)^2 = (18)^2 - (17)^2$$

and

$$35 = 7(5) = ((7 + 5)/2)^2 - ((7 - 5)/2)^2 = 6^2 - 1^2,$$

so that

$$(18)^2 - (17)^2 = 6^2 - 1^2.$$

Thus

$$(18)^2 + 1^2 = (17)^2 + 6^2 = 325.$$

## Exercise 4.6

**1.** Express 17 as the sum of two squares by the method of Theorem 4.16.

**2.** Prove that, if $p$ is a prime of the form $4k + 3$, then $(q!)^2 \equiv 1 \bmod p$, where $q = (p - 1)/2$.

**3.** Determine whether the numbers 365, 1105, and 1961 can be expressed as the sums of two squares, and find such expressions if they exist.

**4.** Prove that a positive integer $m$ is expressible as the difference of two squares,

$$m = x^2 - y^2,$$

if and only if $m$ can be written as the product of two factors which are both even or both odd.

**5.** Using Problem 4 show that there are infinitely many positive integers which can be expressed in $n$ different ways as the difference of two squares, where $n$ is an arbitrary positive integer. (Note that $105 = 3(5)7 = ((15 + 7)/2)^2 - ((15 - 7)/2)^2 = ((21 + 5)/2)^2 - ((21 - 5)/2)^2 = ((35 + 3)/2)^2 - ((35 - 3)/2)^2$.)

**6.** Let $m$ and $n$ be positive integers such that $(2m, n) = 1$ and let $a$ be an integer larger than 1. Show that $(a^m + 1, a^n - 1) = 1$ or 2 by considering the integers $x$ such that

$$x^{mn} \equiv 1 \bmod p,$$

when $p$ is an odd prime.

**7.** Find integers $x$ and $y$ such that

$$49x^2 \equiv y^2 \bmod 23.$$

**8.** Find the number $a_m$ of different positive integers $b$ such that for the integer $m$, $b^2 + m$ is a squared integer. ($a_1 = 0$, $a_2 = 0$, $a_3 = 1$, $a_{15} = 2$, etc.)

## 4.7 Suggested Reading

*Articles*

Swift, J., "Diophantus of Alexandria," *Amer. Math. Monthly*, **63** (1956), 163–170.

Vandiver, H. S., "Fermat's last theorem, its history and the nature of the known results concerning it," *Amer. Math. Monthly*, **53** (1946), 555–578.

*Books*

Dickson, L. E., *History of the Theory of Numbers*, Carnegie Institute of Washington, Washington, D.C., 1919; reprinted by Chelsea Publishing Co., New York, 1950.

Hardy, Godfrey, and E. M. Wright, *An Introduction to the Theory of Numbers*, Clarendon Press, Oxford, 1954.

Ore, O., *Number Theory and Its History*, McGraw-Hill Book Co., New York, 1949.

Stewart, B. M., *Theory of Numbers*, 2nd ed., The Macmillan Co., New York, 1964.

Uspensky, J. V., and M. H. Heaslett, *Elementary Number Theory*, McGraw-Hill Book Co., New York, 1939.

# 5

# Another Look at Congruences

IN OUR WORK with the system of integers we frequently used the idea and notation of congruence and saw that it provided a convenience for stating and suggesting results. Actually the concept of congruence is much more than a convenience. It is the key idea leading to the development of the structural approach in the study of algebraic systems. From the concept of congruence and the system of congruence classes we develop the idea of "dividing" a subsystem into a system to yield a new system. This in turn leads to the study of these subsystems and of systems which contain none of these subsystems. These minimal systems are rather analogous with prime integers, and so this method which is developed to study algebraic systems is an analog of the factorization of integers into primes. Thus we shall encounter terms such as *quotient system* and *direct product* of systems, and these are used to point up the analogy.

## 5.1 The System of Congruence Classes Modulo $m$

What do we know about the concept of congruence at the moment? For each positive integer $m$, congruence modulo $m$ is an equivalence relation which partitions the set $J$ into $m$ nonoverlapping sets, the *residue* or remainder classes, which can be represented as $[0], [1], \cdots, [m-1]$. The smallest nonnegative element of each class is referred to as a *least residue*, and these elements are frequently used to represent the residue classes. Clearly each residue class mod $m$ is a countably infinite set since the following establishes a one-to-one correspondence between the class $[k]$ and $J$:

$$\begin{array}{cccccccc} \cdots & -2 & -1 & 0 & 1 & 2 & 3 & \cdots \\ & \updownarrow & \updownarrow & \updownarrow & \updownarrow & \updownarrow & \updownarrow & \\ \cdots & -2m+k & -m+k & k & m+k & 2m+k & 3m+k & \cdots \end{array}$$

If $k$ is selected as a least residue then this correspondence, $n \leftrightarrow nm + k$, is based on the Divisor Theorem.

Now denote the collection of residue classes modulo $m$ by the symbol, $J/(m)$. (The reason for the selection of this notation is discussed later.) Then $J/(m)$ is a set of $m$ elements, and it possesses the basic equivalence relation of set equality.

THEOREM 5.1. *If* $[a]$ *and* $[b]$ *are elements of* $J/(m)$, *then* $[a] = [b]$ *if and only if* $a - b$ *is a multiple of* $m$.

Basically this is just a restatement of the definition of congruence modulo $m$. If $[a] = [b]$, then certainly $b$ is in the set $[a]$, which is the set of all integers congruent with $a$ mod $m$. Thus $a \equiv b \bmod m$ so that $a - b$ is a multiple of $m$. Conversely, if $a - b = km$, then $a \equiv b \bmod m$ and $b \equiv a \bmod m$. These imply that $[a] \supseteq [b]$ and $[b] \supseteq [a]$, respectively, and we conclude that $[a] = [b]$.

To make $J/(m)$ into a "number" system we must define binary operations on the set, which are much like the binary operations of $J$. The obvious approach to try is the following.

DEFINITION 5.1. The relations **A** and **M** on the set $(J/(m)) \times (J/(m)) \times (J/(m))$ are defined by:

$$(([a], [b]), [c]) \in \mathbf{A} \text{ if and only if } a + b = c;$$
$$(([a], [b]), [c]) \in \mathbf{M} \text{ if and only if } ab = c.$$

Evidently **A** is intended to be addition and **M** multiplication, but we must first prove that **A** and **M** are functions from $(J/(m)) \times (J/(m))$ to $J/(m)$. In other words we must show that, if addition, $\oplus$, and multiplication, $\bigcirc$, are defined by the equations

$$[a] \oplus [b] = [a + b]$$

and

$$[a] \bigcirc [b] = [ab],$$

then the definitions are independent of the integers which represent the residue classes.

THEOREM 5.2. *Addition,* $\oplus$, *and multiplication,* $\bigcirc$, *are well-defined binary operations on* $J/(m)$.

Let $a$ and $a'$ be two elements of $[a]$ and $b$ and $b'$ be two elements of $[b]$. Then

$$a = a' + hm \qquad \text{and} \qquad b = b' + km$$

for some integers $h$ and $k$, so that

$$(a + b) - (a' + b') = (h + k)m$$

and

$$(ab) - (a'b') = (hb' + ka' + hkm)m.$$

Therefore by Theorem 5.1,

$$[a + b] = [a' + b']$$

and

$$[ab] = [a'b'],$$

so that

$$[a] \oplus [b] = [a'] \oplus [b']$$

and

$$[a] \bigcirc [b] = [a'] \bigcirc [b'].$$

This proves the theorem.

Since the binary operations on $J/(m)$ are defined in terms of the binary operations on $J$, we should expect that most of the properties of these latter operations would be possessed also by the operations of $\{J/(m), \oplus, \bigcirc\}$.

THEOREM 5.3. *The operations denoted by* $\oplus$ *and* $\bigcirc$ *are commutative, associative, and possess identity elements. Moreover multiplication is distributive over addition.*

The proofs of these statements are rather simple. For example,

$$\begin{aligned}([a] \oplus [b]) \oplus [c] &= [a + b] \oplus [c] = [(a + b) + c] \\ &= [a + (b + c)] = [a] \oplus [b + c] \\ &= [a] \oplus ([b] \oplus [c]).\end{aligned}$$

Similarly,

$$\begin{aligned}[a] \bigcirc ([b] \oplus [c]) &= [a] \bigcirc [b + c] = [a(b + c)] \\ &= [ab + ac] = [ab] \oplus [ac] \\ &= [a] \bigcirc [b] \oplus [a] \bigcirc [c].\end{aligned}$$

We see that these properties of the operations on $J/(m)$ seem to be reflections or images of the properties of the operations on $J$.

The identity elements of $J/(m)$ are clearly [0] for $\oplus$ and [1] for $\bigcirc$.

*Example* 1. Construct the addition and multiplication tables for $J/(5)$.

We omit the brackets for the sake of simplicity, so that in the tables [0] is denoted by 0, [1] by 1, and so forth. To determine $[a] \oplus [b]$ in $J/(5)$ from the

$J/(5)$

| $\oplus$ | 0 | 1 | 2 | 3 | 4 |
|---|---|---|---|---|---|
| 0 | 0 | 1 | 2 | 3 | 4 |
| 1 | 1 | 2 | 3 | 4 | 0 |
| 2 | 2 | 3 | 4 | 0 | 1 |
| 3 | 3 | 4 | 0 | 1 | 2 |
| 4 | 4 | 0 | 1 | 2 | 3 |

| $\bigcirc$ | 0 | 1 | 2 | 3 | 4 |
|---|---|---|---|---|---|
| 0 | 0 | 0 | 0 | 0 | 0 |
| 1 | 0 | 1 | 2 | 3 | 4 |
| 2 | 0 | 2 | 4 | 1 | 3 |
| 3 | 0 | 3 | 1 | 4 | 2 |
| 4 | 0 | 4 | 3 | 2 | 1 |

addition table we select $a$ and $b$ as the least residues in $[a]$ and $[b]$, respectively, and locate $a$ in the leftmost column and $b$ in the top row. Then $[a] \oplus [b]$ is the class $[c]$, where $c$ is the element in the intersection of the row to the right of $a$ and the column beneath $b$. Thus $[7] \oplus [11] = [2] \oplus [1] = [3]$. Similarly $[7] \odot [11] = [2] \odot [1] = [2]$.

The symmetry of the tables about the diagonal from upper left to lower right is merely a reflection of the commutativity of the two operations. And it is evident from the tables that [0] and [1] are the identity elements for addition and multiplication, respectively. Moreover we notice that each element of $J/(5)$ appears *exactly once* in each row and in each column of the two tables, except for the row and column of zeros in the multiplication table. This very remarkable property means that each element of $J/(5)$ has an additive inverse element and that each element $\neq [0]$ has a multiplicative inverse element. That is, for each $[a]$ in $J/(5)$ there is a $[b]$ in $J/(5)$ such that

$$[a] \oplus [b] = [0],$$

and for each $[a] \neq [0]$ there is an element $[b]$ in $J/(5)$ such that

$$[a] \odot [b] = [1].$$

This means that the binary operations of subtraction and division can both be defined for the system $\{J/(5), \oplus, \odot\}$, and so this system possesses a property which $J$ does not have.

*Example* 2. Construct the addition and multiplication tables for $J/(6)$.

Again we omit the brackets. These tables are also symmetric about the main diagonal, and we see that [0] and [1] are the identity elements for addition and multiplication, respectively. Moreover the addition table for $J/(6)$ is quite regular

$J/(6)$

| $\oplus$ | 0 | 1 | 2 | 3 | 4 | 5 |
|---|---|---|---|---|---|---|
| 0 | 0 | 1 | 2 | 3 | 4 | 5 |
| 1 | 1 | 2 | 3 | 4 | 5 | 0 |
| 2 | 2 | 3 | 4 | 5 | 0 | 1 |
| 3 | 3 | 4 | 5 | 0 | 1 | 2 |
| 4 | 4 | 5 | 0 | 1 | 2 | 3 |
| 5 | 5 | 0 | 1 | 2 | 3 | 4 |

| $\odot$ | 0 | 1 | 2 | 3 | 4 | 5 |
|---|---|---|---|---|---|---|
| 0 | 0 | 0 | 0 | 0 | 0 | 0 |
| 1 | 0 | 1 | 2 | 3 | 4 | 5 |
| 2 | 0 | 2 | 4 | 0 | 2 | 4 |
| 3 | 0 | 3 | 0 | 3 | 0 | 3 |
| 4 | 0 | 4 | 2 | 0 | 4 | 2 |
| 5 | 0 | 5 | 4 | 3 | 2 | 1 |

since each element appears once and only once in each row and in each column. But the multiplication table of $J/(6)$ is very different from that of $J/(5)$. Since 1 appears only in the second and sixth rows we see that only the two elements [1] and [5] of $J/(6)$ possess multiplicative inverses,

$$[1] \odot [1] = [1] \quad \text{and} \quad [5] \odot [5] = [25] = [1].$$

Even more unusual is the fact that 0 appears so frequently in the table:

$$[2] \odot [3] = [3] \odot [4] = [0].$$

In the system of integers we know that the product of two integers is zero if and only if at least one of the integers is zero. But in $J/(6)$ we see that the product of two elements both different from [0] can be the zero element, [0]. Such elements are often referred to as *divisors of zero*. The divisors of zero in $J/(6)$ are [2], [3], and [4], and inspection of the sets

$$\begin{aligned}[2] &= \{2, 8, -4, -10, 14, 20, 26, -16, -22, \cdots\},\\ [3] &= \{3, 9, -3, -9, 15, -15, 21, -21, \cdots\},\\ [4] &= \{4, -2, 10, -8, -14, 16, 22, -20, \cdots\},\end{aligned}$$

shows that each of these sets has a common factor larger than 1 which is a factor of 6.

THEOREM 5.4. *An element* $[a]$ *of* $J/(m)$ *has a multiplicative inverse* $[b]$ *in* $J/(m)$,

$$[a] \bigcirc [b] = [1]$$

*if and only if* $(a, m) = 1$.

If $(a, m) = 1$, then there are integers $b$ and $c$ such that

$$ab + mc = 1.$$

Hence,

$$ab \equiv 1 \bmod m$$

so that

$$[a] \bigcirc [b] = [1]$$

in $J/(m)$.

Conversely, suppose $[b]$ is a multiplicative inverse of $[a]$ in $J/(m)$; then

$$\begin{aligned}[a] \bigcirc [b] &= [1],\\ [ab] &= [1],\end{aligned}$$

and

$$ab \equiv 1 \bmod m.$$

Therefore there exists an integer $k$ such that

$$ab - 1 = km,$$

and

$$ab + (-k)m = 1,$$

so that $(a, m) = 1$.

Complementary to this we note that, if the composite integer $m$ factors as

$$m = rs, \qquad 1 < r \leqslant s < m,$$

then in $J/(m)$ the elements $[r]$ and $[s]$ are nonzero divisors of zero since

$$[r] \bigcirc [s] = [rs] = [0].$$

## Exercise 5.1

**1.** Construct the operations tables for $J/(10)$ and $J/(11)$.

**2.** Complete the proof of Theorem 5.3.

**3.** Prove the cancellation law for addition in $J/(m)$.

**4.** Show that the cancellation law for multiplication is valid in $J/(m)$ if and only if $m$ is a prime.

**5.** Show that the nonzero rows of the addition and multiplication tables of $J/(p)$, $p$ a prime, are permutations of the $p$ symbols $0, 1, 2, \cdots, p - 1$.

**6.** From the tables for $J/(5)$, $J/(6)$, $J/(10)$, and $J/(11)$ compute $[4]^2, [4]^3, \cdots, [4]^{\Phi(m)}$.

**7.** For the rational number system $R$ define congruence modulo $m$, $m$ a rational integer, by $x \equiv y \bmod m$ if and only if $x - y = mn$ for some rational *integer* $n$. Show that

(*a*) The relation so defined is an equivalence relation.

(*b*) There are infinitely many congruence classes.

(*c*) $[a] \oplus [b] = [a + b]$ defines a binary relation on the collection of congruence classes mod $m$.

(*d*) $[a] \otimes [b] = [ab]$ does *not* define a binary relation on the collection of congruence classes mod $m$.

**8.** Construct the addition table for $J/(4)$, and show that the two semigroups $\{J/(4), \oplus\}$ and $\{M, \bigcirc\}$, where $M$ is the set of nonzero elements of $J/(5)$, are isomorphic systems. (*Hint:* Consider the correspondence $[1]_4 \leftrightarrow [2]_5$.)

**9.** Define $[a] < [b]$ in $J/(m)$ to mean that the least residue of $[a]$ is less than the least residue of $[b]$.

(*a*) Show that this is a linear order on $J/(m)$.

(*b*) Show by example that $[0] < [a]$ and $[0] < [b]$ do not imply that $[0] < [a] \bigcirc [b]$ or that $[0] < [a] \oplus [b]$.

**10.** Can you designate five of the nonzero classes of $J/(10)$ as "positive" elements and the other five as "negative" in such a way that the usual laws of signs hold? Explain.

**11.** Define the operation of subtraction on the system $J/(m)$, and discuss its properties.

**12.** Restate Euler's Theorem concerning the totient for the system $J/(m)$.

## 5.2 Homomorphisms

From the definitions of addition and multiplication in $J/(m)$ we saw that the commutative and associative laws for the operations of $J$ mapped onto $J/(m)$ in such a way as to yield the commutative and associative laws for $J/(m)$. That is to say, from the equation in $J$,

$$a + b = b + a,$$

we get by obvious alterations of notation the equation in $J/(m)$,

$$[a] \oplus [b] = [b] \oplus [a],$$

and from

$$a(bc) = (ab)c$$

we get

$$[a] \bigcirc ([b] \bigcirc [c]) = ([a] \bigcirc [b]) \bigcirc [c].$$

This implicit "mapping" from $\{J, +, \cdot\}$ onto $\{J/(m), \oplus, \bigcirc\}$ resembles the mapping used in the discussion of isomorphism. However, these two systems clearly cannot be isomorphic since the first is infinite while the second is finite. So we are led to the concept of homomorphism.

DEFINITION 5.2.   A mapping $F$ from $S$ onto $T$ is a *homomorphism* from the system $\{S, O\}$ onto the system $\{T, O'\}$ if and only if there exists a one-to-one correspondence between $O$ and $O'$ which is preserved by the mapping $F$. $\{T, O'\}$ is called a *homomorphic* image of $\{S, O\}$.

The mapping $F$ preserves (or is compatible with) the correspondence

$$+ \leftrightarrow \oplus$$

if and only if

$$F(a + b) = \big(F(a)\big) \oplus \big(F(b)\big).$$

It is fairly evident now that $\{J/(m), \oplus, \bigcirc\}$ is a homomorphic image of $\{J, +, \cdot\}$ since the binary operations of $J/(m)$ were defined in a way which makes the homomorphism easy to spot.

THEOREM 5.5.   *The mapping $F$ of $J$ onto $J/(m)$ defined by*

$$F: a \rightarrow [a] = F(a)$$

*preserves the nominal correspondences between the additions and the multiplications.*

By the definitions of addition and multiplication in $J/(m)$ we know that

$$F(a + b) = [a + b] = [a] \oplus [b] = F(a) \oplus F(b)$$

and

$$F(ab) = [ab] = [a] \bigcirc [b] = F(a) \bigcirc F(b).$$

*Corollary* 5.5.1.   The system $\{J/(m), \oplus, \bigcirc\}$ is a homomorphic image of the system of integers.

We noted that isomorphic systems are essentially the same, being "abstractly equal." This is certainly not true for homomorphic systems in general; a homomorphic image can be likened to a silhouette of a system projected or mapped onto a screen. Certain features (e.g., the profile) are preserved, certain features (e.g., coloration) are lost, and some features (e.g., monotonicity) are gained. In the case of the homomorphism of $J$ onto $J/(m)$ the associative laws, the commutative laws, and the distributive law are preserved. Moreover, the presence of an additive and a multiplicative identity persists under the homomorphisms. The infiniteness of $J$ is lost, however, and so are the features of the linear order on $J$. On the other hand $J/(m)$ has some properties which are not possessed by $J$; viz, if $m$ is composite, then $J/(m)$ has nonzero divisors of zero, and if $m$ is prime, then every nonzero element of $J/(m)$ has a multiplicative inverse.

The preservation of identity elements is a general feature of homomorphisms.

THEOREM 5.6. *Let $\{S, \times\}$ and $\{T, \otimes\}$ be two mathematical systems. If $\boldsymbol{F}$ is a homomorphism of $\{S, \times\}$ onto $\{T, \otimes\}$ and if $e$ is the identity element of $S$, then $\boldsymbol{F}(e)$ is the identity element of $T$.*

The condition that $e$ is the identity element of $S$ means that

$$e \times s = s \times e = s$$

for every element $s$ of $S$. Since $\boldsymbol{F}$ is a homomorphism this equation has the image

$$\boldsymbol{F}(e \times s) = \boldsymbol{F}(s) \otimes \boldsymbol{F}(e) = \boldsymbol{F}(s) = \boldsymbol{F}(e) \otimes \boldsymbol{F}(s).$$

Since $\boldsymbol{F}$ is a mapping of $S$ onto $T$, this means that

$$\boldsymbol{F}(e) \otimes t = t \otimes \boldsymbol{F}(e) = t$$

for every $t$ in $T$, for each $t$ is the image of some $s$ in $S$.

Thus, if we are trying to show that one system is a homomorphic image of another, then by checking the identity elements of the two systems we can sometimes tell what the mapping must be, if it exists. By looking at the identity elements of $J$ and $J/(m)$ we can show that the mapping described in Theorem 5.5 is in fact the only homomorphism of $J$ onto $J/(m)$.

*Corollary* 5.6.1. The only homomorphism from $\{J, +, \cdot\}$ onto $\{J/(m), \oplus, \bigcirc\}$ is given by

$$\boldsymbol{F}: a \rightarrow [a].$$

Let $\boldsymbol{F}'$ be a homomorphism of $\{J, +, \cdot\}$ onto $\{J/(m), \oplus, \bigcirc\}$. Clearly $\boldsymbol{F}'$ is also a homomorphism of the semigroup $\{J, \cdot\}$ onto the semigroup $\{J/(m), \bigcirc\}$, and since these semigroups possess identity elements relative to their binary operations, we must have

$$\boldsymbol{F}'(1) = [1].$$

Now $\boldsymbol{F}'$ must also preserve addition, so this means that

$$\boldsymbol{F}'(2) = \boldsymbol{F}'(1 + 1) = \boldsymbol{F}'(1) \oplus \boldsymbol{F}'(1) = [1] \oplus [1] = [2].$$

In this way we see that

$$\boldsymbol{F}'(a) = [a]$$

so that

$$\boldsymbol{F}' = \boldsymbol{F}$$

since

$$\boldsymbol{F}'(a) = \boldsymbol{F}(a) = [a]$$

for every integer $a$.

Not only is $J/(5)$ a homomorphic image of $J$, but it is also a homomorphic image of infinitely many of the finite systems $J/(m)$. In particular we see that, if $m$ is a multiple of 5, then

$$[k]_m \to [k]_5$$

defines a homomorphism of $J/(m)$ onto $J/(5)$. This means that, if $m = 5n$, then we have the following mapping:

$$\begin{gathered}
\{[0]_m, [5]_m, \cdots, [5(n-1)_m\} \to [0]_5 \\
\{[1]_m, [6]_m, \cdots, [5n-4]_m\} \to [1]_5 \\
\cdot \\
\cdot \\
\cdot \\
\{[4]m, [9]_m, \cdots, [5n-1]_m\} \to [4]^5.
\end{gathered}$$

Then we can show quite easily that this is a homomorphism since

$$[5r - a] \oplus [5s - b] = [5(r + s) - (a + b)]$$

in $J/(5n)$ maps onto

$$[-a] \oplus [-b] = [-(a + b)]$$

in $J/(5)$, and similarly

$$[5r - a] \bigcirc [5s - b] = [5(5rs - as - br) + ab]$$

in $J/(5n)$ maps onto

$$[-a] \bigcirc [-b] = [ab]$$

in $J/(5)$. (Strictly speaking the equation

$$[a] \oplus [b] = [a + b]$$

in $J/(m)$ should be written

$$[a]_m \oplus_m [b]_m = [a + b]_m,$$

but we omit the subscripts for the sake of simplicity. We remark, however, that $\oplus$ in $J/(m)$ and $\oplus$ in $J/(n)$ are in general two different binary operations.)

THEOREM 5.7. *There is a homomorphism of* $\{J/(m), \oplus, \bigcirc\}$ *onto* $\{J/(n), \oplus, \bigcirc\}$ *if and only if m is a multiple of n.*

If $m$ is a multiple of $n$, say

$$m = nt,$$

then the mapping defined by

$$\boldsymbol{F}: [a]_m \to [qn + r]_n = [r]_n,$$

where

$$a = qn + r, \qquad 0 \leqslant r < n,$$

in $J$, is a well-defined mapping since $a'$ in $[a]_m$ implies that

$$a' = a + km = a + ktn.$$

Hence

$$a' = (q + kt)n + r, \qquad 0 \leqslant r < n$$

and

$$\boldsymbol{F}\colon [a']_m \to [r]_n.$$

Moreover, $\boldsymbol{F}$ preserves the binary operations. This is proved as follows:

$$\boldsymbol{F}([a_1] \oplus [a_2]) = \boldsymbol{F}([a_1 + a_2]) = [r_3]_n$$

where

$$\begin{aligned} a_1 &= q_1 n + r_1, & 0 \leqslant r_1 < n, \\ a_2 &= q_2 n + r_2, & 0 \leqslant r_2 < n, \\ r_1 + r_2 &= q_3 n + r_3, & 0 \leqslant r_3 < n, \end{aligned}$$

and

$$a_1 + a_2 = (q_1 + q_2 + q_3)n + r_3.$$

Therefore

$$[r_3]_n = [r_1]_n \oplus [r_2]_n = \boldsymbol{F}([a_1]) \oplus \boldsymbol{F}([a_2]),$$

so that

$$\boldsymbol{F}([a_1] \oplus [a_2]) = \boldsymbol{F}([a_1]) \oplus \boldsymbol{F}([a_2]).$$

Thus $\boldsymbol{F}$ preserves addition. The argument for multiplication is similar.

To prove the converse we use Theorem 5.6. If $\boldsymbol{F}'$ is a homomorphism of $J/(m)$ onto $J/(n)$, then the additive identity $[0]_m$ of $J/(m)$ must be mapped onto the additive identity $[0]_n$ of $J/(n)$, and similarly,

$$\boldsymbol{F}'([1]_m) = [1]_n.$$

Now in $J$ write

$$m = qn + r, \qquad 0 \leqslant r < n.$$

Then

$$\boldsymbol{F}'([0]_m) = \boldsymbol{F}'(\underbrace{[1]_m \oplus \cdots \oplus [1]_m}_{m \text{ times}}) = \underbrace{[1]_n \oplus \cdots \oplus [1]_n}_{m \text{ times}},$$

so that, since the sum of $qn$ $[1]$'s in $J/(n)$ is $[0]_n$, we conclude that

$$[r]_n = \underbrace{[1]_n \oplus \cdots \oplus [1]_n}_{r \text{ times}} = \boldsymbol{F}'([0]_m) = [0]_n.$$

Therefore,

$$r \equiv 0 \bmod n$$

which, since $0 \leqslant r < n$, means that

$$r = 0 \qquad \text{and} \qquad m = qn.$$

*Example* 1. Show that $J/(2)$ is a homomorphic image of $J/(4)$ by considering the operation tables shown.

$J/(4)$

| $\oplus$ | 0 | 1 | 2 | 3 |
|---|---|---|---|---|
| 0 | 0 | 1 | 2 | 3 |
| 1 | 1 | 2 | 3 | 0 |
| 2 | 2 | 3 | 0 | 1 |
| 3 | 3 | 0 | 1 | 2 |

| $\bigcirc$ | 0 | 1 | 2 | 3 |
|---|---|---|---|---|
| 0 | 0 | 0 | 0 | 0 |
| 1 | 0 | 1 | 2 | 3 |
| 2 | 0 | 2 | 0 | 2 |
| 3 | 0 | 3 | 2 | 1 |

$J/(2)$

| $\oplus$ | 0 | 1 |
|---|---|---|
| 0 | 0 | 1 |
| 1 | 1 | 0 |

| $\bigcirc$ | 0 | 1 |
|---|---|---|
| 0 | 0 | 0 |
| 1 | 0 | 1 |

The homomorphism is given by

$$M_0 = \{[0]_4, [2]_4\} \rightarrow [0]_2$$
$$M_1 = \{[1]_4, [3]_4\} \rightarrow [1]_2,$$

and we observe that the sum and product of any two elements of the set $M_0$ are again in $M_0$, corresponding to the fact that

$$[0]_2 \oplus [0]_2 = [0]_2 \bigcirc [0]_2 = [0]_2.$$

Furthermore the product of any two elements of the set $M_1$ is again in $M_1$, and the sum of any two elements from $M_1$ is in $M_0$. This corresponds to the fact that

$$[1]_2 \bigcirc [1]_2 = [1]_2 \quad \text{and} \quad [1]_2 \oplus [1]_2 = [0]_2.$$

*Example* 2. The system $J/(3)$ is a homomorphic image of $J/(6)$.
This time the homomorphism is given by

$$M_0 = \{[0]_6, [3]_6\} \rightarrow [0]_3$$
$$M_1 = \{[1]_6, [4]_6\} \rightarrow [1]_3$$
$$M_2 = \{[2]_6, [5]_6\} \rightarrow [2]_3.$$

Again we notice that the sum and product of any two elements of $M_0$ are again in $M_0$ since they map onto $[0]_3$ and

$$[0]_3 \oplus [0]_3 = [0]_3 \bigcirc [0]_3 = [0]_3.$$

Also the product of any two elements of $M_1$ is in $M_1$, corresponding to the fact that

$$[1]_3 \bigcirc [1]_3 = [1]_3,$$

and the sum of an element from $M_1$ and an element from $M_2$ is in $M_0$, corresponding to the fact that

$$[1]_3 \oplus [2]_3 = [0]_3.$$

And we see that, if an arbitrary element from $M_1$ is added to each element of $M_0$, then the set $M_1$ is obtained again:

$$M_1 = M_0 \oplus [4]_6 = \{[0]_6 \oplus [4]_6, [3]_6 \oplus [4]_6\}.$$

Similarly,

$$M_2 = M_0 \oplus [2]_6 = \{[0]_6 \oplus [2]_6, [3]_6 \oplus [2]_6\}.$$

Note that the set $M_0$ is a subsystem of $J/(6)$ relative to the binary operations of $J/(6)$.

*Example* 3. Consider the homomorphism of $J$ onto $J/(5)$. We have

$$\begin{aligned} M_0 &= \{0, 5, -5, 10, -10, 15, -15, \cdots\} \rightarrow [0]_5 \\ M_1 &= \{1, 6, -4, 11, -9, 16, -14, \cdots\} \rightarrow [1]_5 \\ M_2 &= \{2, 7, -3, 12, -8, 11, -13, \cdots\} \rightarrow [2]_5 \\ M_3 &= \{3, 8, -2, 13, -7, 18, -12, \cdots\} \rightarrow [3]_5 \\ M_5 &= \{4, 9, -1, 14, -6, 19, -11, \cdots\} \rightarrow [4]_5. \end{aligned}$$

Again we see that the sum and the product of any two elements of $M_0$ are in $M_0$, and so $\{M_0, +, \cdot\}$ is a subsystem of the system of integers. Moreover, if $a$ is an arbitrary element of $M_i$, then every element of $M_i$ is equal to $a$ plus an element from $M_0$, and also $a$ plus any element from $M_0$ is always in $M_i$; we write

$$M_i = M_0 + a.$$

We note that the set $M_0$ actually equals the set $[0]_5$ in the above example. The symbolism

$$\{0, 5, -5, 10, \cdots\} \rightarrow [0]_5$$

is meant to indicate that the homomorphism maps each of the elements 0, 5, $-5$, 10, etc., onto the element [0] of $J/(5)$.

## Exercise 5.2

**1.** Show that the semigroup $\{J^*/(3), \bigcirc\}$, where $J^*/(3)$ consists of the two elements $[1]_3$ and $[2]_3$, is a homomorphic image of the semigroup $\{J/(4), \oplus\}$. (*Hint:* Define $F$ by $F([0]_4) = [1]_3$, $F([1]_4) = [2]_3$, $F([2]_4) = [1]_3$, $F([3]_4) = [2]_3$.)

**2.** Relative to Example 3, show that

$$M_0 + 199 = M_4.$$

**3.** Relative to Example 3, show that any element in $M_2$ added to any element of $M_4$ yields an element of $M_1$. How is this related to the fact that $[2]_5 \oplus [4]_5 = [1]_5$?

**4.** Determine all of the subsystems of $J/(6)$ relative to the operations of $\oplus$ and $\bigcirc$. How does the number of such subsystems correspond to the number of homomorphic images of $\{J/(6), \oplus, \bigcirc\}$ among the systems $\{J/(m), \oplus, \bigcirc\}$?

**5.** Complete the proof of the first part of Theorem 5.7.

**6.** In the homomorphism of $J/(20)$ onto $J/(5)$, what happens to the nonzero divisors of zero in $J/(20)$ under the homomorphism?

**7.** Show that $\{J/(p), \oplus, \bigcirc\}$ contains no subsystems having more than 1 and fewer than $p$ elements, when $p$ is a prime.

**8.** In Example 1 show that the system $\{J/(2), \oplus\}$ is isomorphic with a subsystem of $\{J/(4), \oplus\}$. Show that the system $\{J/(2), \bigcirc\}$ is isomorphic with two different subsystems of $\{J/(4), \bigcirc\}$.

**9.** Show that the mapping

$$F: n \to |n|$$

is a homomorphism of the semigroup $\{J^*, \cdot\}$ onto a subsemigroup of this system. $J^*$ denotes the set of nonzero integers.

**10.** Let $R^*$ denote the set of nonzero rationals. Is the mapping

$$F: r \to 1/r$$

a homomorphism of the system $\{R^*, +, \cdot\}$ onto itself? Explain.

**11.** Show that, if $[a] \neq [0]$ and $[c]$ are elements of $J/(p)$, where $p$ is a prime, then $J/(p)$ contains exactly one element $[b]$ such that

$$[a] \bigcirc [b] = [c].$$

**12.** Show that, if $[a]$ and $[c]$ are elements of $J/(m)$, then $J/(m)$ contains an element $[b]$ such that

$$[a] \bigcirc [b] = [c]$$

if and only if $[a]$ is not a divisor of zero. Is $[b]$ always unique?

## 5.3 Subsystems and Quotient Systems

In Section 5.2 the examples indicated that, if $F$ is a homomorphism of $\{J, +, \cdot\}$ onto $\{J/(m), \oplus, \bigcirc\}$, then the elements of $J$ which are mapped onto $[0]_m$ form a subsystem of $J$. Similarly, if $\{J/(n), \oplus, \bigcirc\}$ is a homomorphic image of $\{J/(m), \oplus, \bigcirc\}$, then the elements of $J/(m)$ which are mapped onto $[0]_n$ seem to form a subsystem of $J/(m)$.

DEFINITION 5.3. A nonempty set $T$ of elements of the system $\{S, O\}$ is a *subsystem* $\{T, O\}$ of $\{S, O\}$ if and only if the operations of $O$ induce operations on $T$. That is to say, $T$ is a subsystem of $S$ if and only if $T$ is closed under the operations of $S$.

This is rather obviously what is meant by the statement that the multiples of 5 form a subsystem of $J$. For the sum and the product of multiples of 5 are again multiples of 5. In fact we have already discussed many different subsystems.

Now the subsystem $M_0$ of Example 3 in Section 5.2 had a property not shared by all of the subsystems of $J$. Not only is $M_0$ closed under multiplication, but any element of $M_0$ multiplied by any element of $J$ is also in $M_0$. This of course is a reflection of the fact that

$$[0]_5 \bigcirc [a]_5 = [0]_5.$$

Not all subsystems of $J$ possess this property since the set of positive integers is certainly a subsystem of $J$ without the property. So we single out these special subsystems.

DEFINITION 5.4. An *ideal* $M$ of $J$ is a subsystem of $\{J, +, \cdot\}$ with the property that $am$ is in $M$ for each $m$ in $M$ and $a$ in $J$.

We see, then, that the set of all multiples of 2 is certainly an ideal of $J$. In fact, the set of all multiples of $m$, where $m$ is an arbitrary integer, is an ideal of $J$.

From the idea of an ideal $M$ of $J$ we develop the concept of the quotient system of $J$ relative to $M$. For the ideal $M$ of $J$ we define an *additive coset* of $M$ to be the set

$$x + M = \{x + m\colon x \text{ a fixed integer, and } m \text{ in } M\}$$

for each $x$ in $J$. Clearly these cosets of $M$ form a partition of $J$, for if $a$ is in the intersection of $x + M$ and $y + M$, then integers $m_1$ and $m_2$ exist in $M$ such that

$$a = x + m_1 = y + m_2.$$

Therefore

$$x = y + (m_2 - m_1),$$

which implies that $x$, and hence $x + m$ for any $m$ in $M$, are in $y + M$ since $m_2 - m_1$ and $m_2 - m_1 + m$ are elements of $M$. For $M$ is an ideal of $J$, and $m_1$ in $M$ implies that $-m_1 = (-1)m_1$ is also in $M$, and, since $M$ is closed under addition,

$$m_2 - m_1 \quad \text{and} \quad m_2 - m_1 + m$$

are elements of $M$. Thus

$$x + M \subseteq y + M.$$

Since

$$y = x + (m_1 - m_2)$$

the corresponding argument shows that

$$y + M \subseteq x + M.$$

Therefore

$$x + m = y + M.$$

Since 0 lies in $M$ we see that $x$ is an element of the coset $x + M$. Hence every element of $J$ lies in a coset of $M$, and distinct cosets have no common elements. So the cosets of $M$ form a partition of $J$.

Denote the collection of cosets of $M$ by $J/M$. We define addition and multiplication of cosets by the equations

$$(x + M) \boxplus (y + M) = (x + y) + M$$

and

$$(x + M) \square (y + M) = (xy) + M.$$

To show that $\boxplus$ and $\square$ are well-defined we assume

$$x' + M = x + M \qquad \text{and} \qquad y' + M = y + M$$

and consider

$$(x' + M) \boxplus (y' + M) \qquad \text{and} \qquad (x' + M) \square (y' + M).$$

Since $x'$ and $y'$ belong to the cosets $x' + M$ and $y' + M$, respectively, there exist $m_1$ and $m_2$ in $M$ such that

$$x' = x + m_1 \qquad \text{and} \qquad y' = y + m_2.$$

Then

$$x' + y' = x + y + (m_1 + m_2) = x + y + m_3$$

and

$$x'y' = xy + (xm_2 + ym_1 + m_1m_2) = xy + m_4,$$

and so $x' + y'$ is an element of both

$$(x' + y') + M \qquad \text{and} \qquad (x + y) + M$$

and $x'y'$ is an element of both

$$(x'y') + M \qquad \text{and} \qquad (xy) + M.$$

Since the cosets form a partition we conclude that

$$(x' + y') + M = (x + y) + M$$

and

$$(x'y') + M = (xy) + M.$$

Therefore,

$$(x' + M) \boxplus (y' + M) = (x + M) \boxplus (y + M)$$

and

$$(x' + M) \square (y' + M) = (x + M) \square (y + M)$$

and the operations are well-defined.

DEFINITION 5.5. The system $\{J/M, \boxplus, \square\}$ is the *quotient system* of $J$ over the ideal $M$.

Without delving into the properties of the quotient system we can show in a very straightforward fashion that $\{J/M, \boxplus, \square\}$ is a homomorphic image of $\{J, +, \cdot\}$.

THEOREM 5.8. *The mapping* $F$ *defined by*

$$F\colon x \rightarrow x + M$$

*is a homomorphism of* $\{J, +, \cdot\}$ *onto* $\{J/M, \boxplus, \square\}$, *and the set of elements of* $J$ *mapped onto the coset* $0 + M$ *is precisely the ideal* $M$.

That $F$ is a homomorphism is almost a triviality from the definitions of $\boxplus$ and $\square$. For

$$F(x + y) = (x + y) + M = (x + M) \boxplus (y + M) = F(x) \boxplus F(y)$$

and

$$F(xy) = (xy) + M = (x + M) \square (y + M) = F(x) \square F(y).$$

And surely, if $x$ is an element of $J$ such that

$$F(x) = x + M = 0 + M,$$

then $x$ is an element of $M = 0 + M$. Conversely, if $m$ is an element of $M$, then

$$F(m) = m + M = M = 0 + M.$$

Thus the elements of $M$ are exactly the elements of $J$ which are mapped onto the zero coset, $0 + M$. Note that

$$(0 + M) \boxplus (x + M) = x + M$$

and

$$(0 + M) \square (x + M) = 0 + M.$$

But how do these homomorphic images of $\{J, +, \cdot\}$ compare with the finite systems, the homomorphic images of $\{J, +, \cdot\}$ discussed previously? Have we some new systems?

THEOREM 5.9. *The set $(m)$ of all multiples of the nonnegative integer $m$ is an ideal of $J$. Furthermore, every ideal of $J$ is such an ideal.*

Obviously the set $(m)$ is an ideal since

$$(am + bm) = (a + b)m,$$
$$(am)(bm) = (abm)m,$$

and

$$n(am) = (na)m.$$

Now let $M$ be an ideal of $J$. If $M$ contains no positive integers, then it cannot contain a negative integer $n$ since $(-1)n = -n$ would then be a positive element of $M$. So, if $M$ contains no positive integer, then $M = (0)$.

If $M$ contains positive integers, then from the Well-Ordering Theorem we know that $M$ contains a minimal positive integer $m$. We shall show that every element $x$ of $M$ is a multiple of $m$. By the Divisor Theorem there exist integers $q$ and $r$ such that

$$x = qm + r, \qquad 0 \leqslant r < m.$$

Since $m$ and $x$ are in $M$, then

$$-qm = (-q)m \qquad \text{and} \qquad x + (-qm) = x - qm$$

are elements of $M$. Therefore

$$r = x - qm$$

is an element of $M$, so that, since $0 < r < m$ violates the fact that $m$ is the least positive element of $M$, we conclude that

$$r = 0 \qquad \text{and} \qquad x = qm.$$

So the set $M$ is contained in the set $(m)$. But $m$ in $M$ clearly implies that

$$(m) \subseteq M,$$

and we see that

$$M = (m).$$

Now the quotient system $J/(0)$ is basically just the system $J$ since the cosets

$$x + (0)$$

are the sets $\{x\}$ of individual elements of $J$. Actually $J$ and $J/(0)$ are isomorphic, with the correspondence being

$$x \leftrightarrow x + (0) = \{x\}.$$

If $M$ is the ideal $(m)$ with $m > 0$, then the quotient system $J/M$ is just exactly the system of congruence classes modulo $m$. This is the reason we adopted the symbolism $J/(m)$ for the system of congruence classes modulo $m$. The coset $x + M$ is just the set of all integers congruent with $x$ modulo $m$, for, if $y$ is in $x + M$, then

$$y = x + m_1$$

for some $m_1$ in $M$. But $M = (m)$, so that $m_1 = km$ for some integer $k$. Hence

$$y = x + km$$

so that

$$x \equiv y \bmod m$$

and $y$ is an element of $[x]_m$. Conversely, if $t$ is in $[x]_m$, then

$$t = x + hm$$

so that $t$ is an element of the coset $x + M$.
Therefore

$$[x]_m = x + M.$$

This means that we do *not* have any new homomorphic images of $\{J, +, \cdot\}$, but this is unimportant. What we do have is a method for obtaining these homomorphic images which depends not on the individual elements and their factorizations but is built instead on the concept of ideal, a special type of subsystem of $J$. This enables us to break away from the consideration of the elements of a system and study instead, or in addition, certain subsystems and their "quotient" systems. The power of this structural method in analyzing mathematical systems is considerable, as we shall see.

Now let us define ideals and quotient systems of $J/(m)$.

DEFINITION 5.6. A subsystem $S$ of $J/(m)$ is an *ideal* of $\{J/(m), \oplus, \bigcirc\}$ if and only if $[a] \bigcirc [s]$ is in $S$ for every $[a]$ in $J/(m)$ and $[s]$ in $S$. The sets $[x] \oplus S =$

$$\{[x] \oplus [s]: \text{all } [s] \text{ in } S\}$$

for each $[x]$ in $J/(m)$ are the *additive cosets* of $S$ in $J/(m)$.

The arithmetic of $J/(m)$ is known to us so that we can show that these cosets form a partition of $J/(m)$. For if $[a]$ lies in both $[x] \oplus S$ and $[y] \oplus S$, then

$$[a] = [x] \oplus [s_1] = [y] \oplus [s_2].$$

So

$$[x] = ([y] \oplus [s_2]) \oplus ([-1] \bigcirc [s_1]),$$

implying that $[x] \oplus S \subseteq [y] \oplus S$. Similarly,

$$[y] = [x] \oplus ([s_1] \oplus ([-1] \bigcirc [s_2]))$$

so that

$$[y] \oplus [s] = [x] \oplus ([s_1] \oplus ([-1] \bigcirc [s_2]) \oplus [s])$$

and

$$[y] \oplus S \subseteq [x] \oplus S.$$

Thus $[y] \oplus S = [x] \oplus S$, so that, since every element of $J/(m)$ belongs to some coset of $S$, for $[a]$ is in $[a] \oplus S$, we see that the distinct cosets form a partition of $J/(m)$.

The set $(J/(m))/S$ of cosets of $S$ is made into a homomorphic image of $\{J/(m), \oplus, \bigcirc\}$ in the most obvious way. Define addition and multiplication of cosets by the equations

$$([x] \oplus S) \boxplus ([y] \oplus S) = ([x] \oplus [y]) \oplus S$$

and

$$([x] \oplus S) \square ([y] \oplus S) = ([x] \bigcirc [y]) \oplus S.$$

As usual we have the problem of showing that these operations are well-defined. If

$$[x'] \oplus S = [x] \oplus S \qquad \text{and} \qquad [y'] \oplus S = [y] \oplus S,$$

then

$$[x'] = [x] \oplus [s_1]$$

and

$$[y'] = [y] \oplus [s_2].$$

Since

$$[x'] \oplus [y'] = ([x] \oplus [y]) \oplus ([s_1] \oplus [s_2])$$

and

$$[x'] \bigcirc [y'] = ([x] \bigcirc [y]) \oplus \big(([x] \bigcirc [s_2]) \oplus ([y] \bigcirc [s_1]) \oplus ([s_1] \bigcirc [s_2])\big)$$

we see that

$$([x] \oplus S) \boxplus ([y] \oplus S) = ([x'] \oplus S) \boxplus ([y'] \oplus S)$$

and

$$([x] \oplus S) \square ([y] \oplus S) = ([x'] \oplus S) \square ([y'] \oplus S).$$

The system $\{(J/(m))/S, \boxplus, \square\}$ is called the quotient system of $J/(m)$ over $S$. We illustrate with examples.

*Example* 1. Find an ideal of $J/(6)$, and form the quotient system.

We write the elements of $J/(6)$ as 0, 1, 2, 3, 4, 5 and use the simplest notation for addition and multiplication in $J/6$. Thus we write

$$1 + 5 = 0 \quad \text{for } [1] \oplus [5] = [0]$$

and

$$2(4) = 2 \quad \text{for } [2] \bigcirc [4] = [2].$$

The set $\{0\}$ is clearly an ideal but it is too trivial to bother with. Now if 1 is in an ideal $S$, then $0 = 0(1)$, $1 = 1(1)$, $2 = 2(1)$, $3 = 3(1)$, $4 = 4(1)$, and $5 = 5(1)$ are also in $S$, and this set, $S = J/(6)$, is also an ideal of $J/(6)$ which is not very interesting.

Now the sets $S_2 = \{0, 2, 4\}$ and $S_3 = \{0, 3\}$ are easily seen to be ideals of $J/(6)$ by checking the operation tables of $J/(6)$. Furthermore these are the only other ideals of $J/(6)$, for, if either 2 or 4 is in an ideal $S$, then so are both 2 and 4. And certainly 3 is either in an ideal $S$ or not in $S$.

The cosets of $S_2$ are the two sets

$$S_2 = 0 + S_2 = \{0, 2, 4\} \qquad \text{and} \qquad 1 + S_2 = \{1, 3, 5\}.$$

Clearly these two sets comprise a partition of $J/(6)$. Denote the sets $0 + S_2$ and $1 + S_2$ by 0* and 1*, respectively. Then we compute the operation tables shown for these cosets. From these we see quite easily that the system $\{(J/(6))/S_2, \boxplus, \square\}$ is isomorphic with the system $\{J/(2), \oplus, \bigcirc\}$.

$(J/(6))/S_2$

| ⊞ | 0* | 1* |
|---|---|---|
| 0* | 0* | 1* |
| 1* | 1* | 0* |

| □ | 0* | 1* |
|---|---|---|
| 0* | 0* | 0* |
| 1* | 0* | 1* |

The cosets of $S_3$ are the three sets

$0^* = 0 + S_3 = \{0, 3\}$, $1^* = 1 + S_3 = \{1, 4\}$, $2^* = 2 + S_3 = \{2, 5\}$,
and we see that these sets form a partition of $J/(6)$.

The operation tables for the quotient system are as shown. For example,

$(J/(6))/S_3$

| $\boxplus$ | 0* | 1* | 2* |
|---|---|---|---|
| 0* | 0* | 1* | 2* |
| 1* | 1* | 2* | 0* |
| 2* | 2* | 0* | 1* |

| $\square$ | 0* | 1* | 2* |
|---|---|---|---|
| 0* | 0* | 0* | 0* |
| 1* | 0* | 1* | 2* |
| 2* | 0* | 2* | 1* |

$$2^* \boxplus 1^* = (2 + S_3) \boxplus (1 + S_3) = (2 + 1) + S_3 = 0 + S_3 = 0^*$$

and

$$2^* \square 2^* = (2 + S_3) \square (2 + S_3) = ((2)(2)) + S_3 = 4 + S_3 = 1^*.$$

From these tables we see that this quotient system is isomorphic with $\{J/(3), \oplus, \bigcirc\}$.

*Example* 2. Show that $\{J/(p), \oplus, \bigcirc\}$ has no ideals when $p$ is a prime except the sets $\{[0]\}$ and $J/(p)$.

Suppose $S$ is an ideal of $J/(p)$. If $S \neq \{[0]\}$, then $S$ contains an element $[a] \neq [0]$. By the results of Section 5.1 we know that $J/(p)$ contains an element $[b]$ such that

$$[a] \bigcirc [b] = [1].$$

Therefore since $S$ is an ideal, the product of $[a]$ and $[b]$, namely, the element [1], must be in $S$. Then for the same reason, every element $[x] = [x] \bigcirc [1]$ of $J/(p)$ must be in $S$, and so

$$S = J/(p).$$

Thus the ideals of $\{J/(p), \oplus, \bigcirc\}$ are rather uninteresting.

As a complement of this result we can characterize the ideals of $\{J/(m), \oplus, \bigcirc\}$ when $m$ is composite. An ideal in this system is just the set of multiples (in $J/(m)$ of course) of $[n]$, where $n$ is some factor of $m$. This is proved by going back to the integers and proceeding as in the proof of Theorem 5.9. If $S$ is an ideal of $J/(m)$, then among the positive integers which lie in the residue classes making up $S$ there is a smallest one, $n$. Then if $s$ is an integer in some element of $S$ we have

$$s = qn + r, \qquad 0 \leqslant r < n$$

or

$$[s] = ([q] \bigcirc [n]) \oplus [r]$$

in $J/(m)$. Then we can write

$$[r] = [s] \oplus ([-q] \bigcirc [n]),$$

which means that $[r]$ lies in $S$. The minimality of $n$ among all the positive integers lying in the elements of $S$ implies, then, that

$$r = 0 \qquad \text{and} \qquad s = qn$$

or

$$[s] = [q] \bigcirc [n].$$

Now, however, we know that $[0] = [m]$ is an element of $S$, so that $n$ is a factor of $m$.

Since the elements of $J/(m)$ of the form $[a] \bigcirc [n]$, where $n$ is a factor of $m$, can easily be shown to form an ideal of $\{J/(m), \oplus, \bigcirc\}$, we have the following result.

THEOREM 5.10. *The subsystem $S$ of $\{J/(m), \oplus, \bigcirc\}$ is an ideal if and only if $S$ contains an element $[n]$, where $n$ is a factor of $m$, such that every element of $S$ is of the form $[a] \bigcirc [n]$ for some $[a]$ in $J/(m)$.*

## Exercise 5.3

**1.** Define an ideal of the rational number system $R$, and show that the only ideals of $R$ are $R$ and $\{0\}$. (*Hint:* Show that an ideal $\neq \{0\}$ must contain 1.)

**2.** Show that the collection of all multiples of 6 is an ideal of $J$. Describe the additive cosets of (6).

**3.** Find a nontrivial ideal $S$ of $J/(10)$, and describe its additive cosets. Construct the operation tables for the system of cosets.

**4.** Find three different subsystems of $\{J, +, \cdot\}$ which are not ideals. Does $\{J/(10), \oplus, \bigcirc\}$ have any subsystems which are not ideals? How about $\{J/(m), \oplus, \bigcirc\}$?

**5.** Let $S_1 = (2)$ and $S_2 = (10)$ be ideals of $J$, and define

$$S_1{}^* = \{x + S_2 : x \text{ in } S_1\}.$$

That is, $S_1{}^*$ is the collection of all cosets $x + S_2$ of $S_2$ with $x$ in $S_1$. Show that $S_1{}^*$ is an ideal of $J/(10)$. Do the cosets $y + S_2$, with $y$ in the ideal (3) form an ideal of $J/(10)$? How would you generalize these examples?

**6.** Let $T$ be the ideal $\{[0], [5]\}$ of $J/(10)$. Show that the union of the congruence classes mod 10 which make up the coset $x + T$ is the coset $x + (5)$ of the ideal (5) in $J$.

**7.** Devise an argument based on Problems 5 and 6 to show that Theorem 5.10 is a consequence of Theorem 5.9.

**8.** Show that the intersection of the two ideals (10) and (12) of $J$ is the ideal (60) of $J$. Is such a result generally true?

**9.** Is the union of the two ideals (10) and (12) of $J$ an ideal of $J$? (Consider the element $10 + 12 = 22$.)

**10.** Define (10, 12) to be the set

$$\{10n + 12m : n \text{ and } m \text{ arbitrary elements of } J\}.$$

Show that (10, 12) is the ideal (2) of $J$. How does this use of the notation (10, 12) compare with the G.C.F. notation (10, 12)?

## 5.4 System of Ideals

In Section 5.3 we learned that the additive cosets of an ideal $S$ of $J$ can be used to form a system $J/S$ which is a homomorphic image of $J$ by making appropriate definitions of sum and product of cosets. The resulting system is in fact the finite system $\{J/(m), \oplus, \bigcirc\}$ since $S$ must be the ideal $(m)$ for some positive integer $m$ (we are ignoring the rather trivial ideal (0)). Now we consider the set $I$ of all nonzero ideals of $J$.

For defining binary operations on $I$ we have at our disposal the use of four binary operations: (1) Set intersection, (2) set union, (3) addition of integers, (4) multiplication of integers.

We shall see that three of these lead to binary operations on $I$.

THEOREM 5.11. *The intersection of two ideals of J is again an ideal of J. The union of two ideals of J is in general not an ideal of J.*

Since the zero ideal (0) lies in every ideal we need only consider $(m) \cap (n)$ when $m$ and $n$ are positive integers. We shall show that

$$(m) \cap (n) = (k),$$

where $k$ is the L.C.M. of $\{m, n\}$.

Let $s$ be an element of $(m) \cap (n)$; then

$$s = um = vn$$

for some integers $u$ and $v$. Therefore $s$, as a common multiple of $m$ and $n$, is a multiple of $k$ and so lies in $(k)$. Thus

$$(k) \supseteq (m) \cap (n).$$

Conversely, suppose that $r$ is an element of $(k)$; then $r = tk$ for some integer $t$. Since $k$ is a multiple of $m$ and also of $n$,

$$k = am = bn$$

for some integers $a$ and $b$, so that

$$r = (ta)m = (tb)n,$$

proving that

$$(k) \subseteq (m) \cap (n).$$

We conclude that

$$(m) \cap (n) = (k).$$

To show that the union of two ideals is not in general an ideal we need only remark that $m + n$ is not usually in $(m) \cup (n)$.

From our knowledge of set theory we know that the system $\{I, \cap\}$ is a semigroup. That is, the operation is associative. We see, moreover, that the ideal (1) is the identity element of $\{I, \cap\}$. However, this is not quite the system we want to help us analyze $J$. We see, for example, that the correspondence

$$m \leftrightarrow (m)$$

is not an isomorphism between the systems $\{J^+, \cdot\}$ and $\{I, \cap\}$ since it does ***not*** preserve the correspondence between the two operations:

$$10 \leftrightarrow (10),$$
$$12 \leftrightarrow (12),$$
$$10 \cdot 12 = 120 \not\leftrightarrow (10) \cap (12) = (60).$$

($J^+$ denotes the set of positive integers.)

To define a binary operation $*$ so that $\{J^+, \cdot\}$ and $\{I, *\}$ are isomorphic systems is quite easy, though, and quite obvious.

DEFINITION 5.7. The *product* of two elements $(m)$ and $(n)$ of $I$ is denoted by $(m) * (n)$ and defined to be $(mn)$.

Since $(mn)$ is an element of $I$ uniquely determined by $(m)$ and $(n)$ we see that $*$ is a binary operation on $I$, and it makes $I$ into a system isomorphic with $\{J^+, \cdot\}$.

THEOREM 5.12. *The correspondence*

$$F: m \leftrightarrow (m)$$

*is an isomorphism of* $\{J^+, \cdot\}$ *with* $\{I, *\}$.

For we have

$$m \leftrightarrow (m),$$
$$n \leftrightarrow (n),$$

and

$$mn \leftrightarrow (m) * (n) = (mn).$$

Now many of the key results on the positive integers can be restated as results about the elements of $I$ in the following way.

THEOREM 5.13. (i) *The positive integer $n$ is a factor of the positive integer $m$ if and only if* $(n) \supseteq (m)$.

(ii) *The positive integer $m$ is a prime if and only if $(m)$ is a maximal ideal.*

(iii) *A proper ideal is expressible as the product of a unique set of maximal ideals.*

By a *proper ideal* we mean an element of $I$ which is different from (1). And a *maximal ideal* is a proper ideal which is a subset only of (1) and itself.

To prove (i) we note that, if $(n) \supseteq (m)$, then every element of $(m)$, and hence $m$, is a multiple of $n$. Conversely, if

$$m = qn,$$

then

$$am = (aq)n$$

so that

$$(n) \supseteq (m).$$

For example,

$$(5) = \{0, 5, -5, 10, -10, 15, -15, 20, -20, 25, -25, \cdots\}$$

and

$$(10) = \{0, 10, -10, 20, -20, 30, -30, \cdots\},$$

and clearly

$$(5) \supseteq (10).$$

To prove (ii) we suppose that $(m)$ is a maximal ideal of $J$. If $m$ is not a prime, then $m = 1$, which is ruled out by the fact that a maximal ideal is proper, or $m = qn$, where

$$1 < q \leqslant n < m.$$

This means, however, that the ideals $(q)$ and $(n)$ are such that

$$(1) \supset (q) \supseteq (n) \supset (m),$$

contradicting the maximality of $(m)$. Thus $m$ is a prime.

Conversely, suppose $m$ is a prime. Then, if $(m)$ is not maximal, either $(m) = (1)$, which is impossible since 1 is not a multiple of a prime, or there is a proper ideal $(n)$ such that

$$(1) \supset (n) \supset (m).$$

Clearly this implies that

$$m = qn \qquad \text{with } q > 1,$$

which contradicts the primeness of $m$. Hence $(m)$ is maximal.

Finally we note that (iii) is just a restatement of the Fundamental Theorem of Arithmetic. An example of such an ideal factorization is provided by

$$(20) = (5) * (2) * (2)$$

and

$$(36) = (3) * (3) * (2) * (2).$$

Thus we see that the ideal system $\{I, *\}$ enables us to state facts about the factorization of composite integers into primes as facts about the maximal and nonmaximal ideals of $J$. This brings us to the main purpose of this section, which is to check the behavior of ideals in a number system where the factorization into primes is not unique.

Denote by $T$ the system $\{T, +, \cdot\}$ of multiples of three in $J$. Then $T$ is a subsystem of $\{J, +, \cdot\}$ and is in fact the ideal (3). The feature of $T$ which interests us is the following: some elements of $T$ are expressible as products in $T$ of elements which cannot be factored into smaller elements, in more than one way. For example,

$$36 = 3 \cdot 12 = 6 \cdot 6,$$
$$225 = 3 \cdot 75 = 15 \cdot 15,$$

and

$$180 = 3 \cdot 60 = 15 \cdot 12 = 30 \cdot 6.$$

The elements 3, 6, 12, 15, 30, 60, and 75 are all primes of $T$ since their only factors in $T$ are the trivial ones.

DEFINITION 5.8. A nonempty subset $S$ of $T$ is an *ideal* of $T$ if and only if $S$ is a subsystem of $\{T, +, \cdot\}$ with the property that $st$ and $-s$ are in $S$ for each $s$ in $S$ and $t$ in $T$. If $s$ is the least positive integer in $S$, then $S$ is denoted by $(s)$.

The following are easily seen to be ideals of $T$:

$$(3) = \{0, 3, -3, 6, -6, \cdots\} = T,$$
$$(6) = \{0, 6, -6, 12, -12, \cdots\},$$
$$(9) = \{0, 9, -9, 18, -18, 27, \cdots\}.$$

We note that there is no ambiguity in denoting $S$ by $(s)$, where $s$ is the minimal positive integer in $S$, since we know that all the integers

$$\cdots, -2s, -s, 0, s, 2s, \cdots$$

are in $S$. Then, if $S$ contains an element $r$ other than one of these, $r$ or $-r$ added to the appropriate multiple of $s$ provides a positive integer in $S$ smaller than $s$. This impossibility shows that

$$S = (s) = \{0, s, -s, 2s, -2s, \cdots\}.$$

DEFINITION 5.9. The operation of *multiplication* is defined for the set $I_T$ of nonzero ideals of $T$ by the equation

$$(r) * (s) = (rs).$$

Note that this is a binary operation on $I_T$ since $rs$ is in $T$, and $(rs)$ is in $I_T$ if $r$ and $s$ are in $T$. This product clearly leads to the following isomorphism.

THEOREM 5.14. *The correspondence*

$$s \leftrightarrow (s)$$

*is an isomorphism of* $\{T^+, \cdot\}$ *with* $\{I_T, *\}$.

For

$$s \leftrightarrow (s),$$
$$r \leftrightarrow (r),$$

and

$$rs \leftrightarrow (rs) = (r) * (s).$$

Following the procedure suggested by the restatement of the factorization theorems for integers (*see* Theorem 5.13) we define ideal factors and prime ideals.

DEFINITION 5.10. The element $(r)$ of $I_T$ is a *factor* of the ideal $(s)$ if and only if

$$(r) \supseteq (s).$$

It is a *proper factor* if $T \supset (r) \supset (s)$. The idea $(s)$ is a *prime ideal* if and only if $(s)$ has no proper factors.

Consider the ideals (3), (6), (9), (12), (15), (18), and (21). The ideal $(3) = T$ is a factor of every element of $I_T$ and hence is of little interest. The ideals (6), (9), (15), and (21) are prime ideals since none is contained in the others: 9 is not in (6), neither (6) nor (9) contains 15, and 21 is not in (6), (9), or (15). On the other hand,

$$(6) = \{0, 6, -6, 12, -12, \cdots\} \supset (12) = \{0, 12, -12, \cdots\}$$

and both (6) and (9) contain (18). Thus neither (12) nor (18) is a prime ideal. Similarly (30) and (60) fail to be prime ideals.

Now we consider the factorizations

$$36 = 3 \cdot 12 = 6 \cdot 6,$$
$$225 = 3 \cdot 75 = 15 \cdot 15,$$

and

$$180 = 3 \cdot 60 = 15 \cdot 12 = 30 \cdot 6.$$

From our isomorphism we conclude

$$(36) = (3) * (12) = (6) * (6),$$
$$(225) = (3) * (75) = (15) * (15),$$
$$(180) = (3) * (60) = (15) * (12) = (30) * (6).$$

Which of these are factorizations into products of prime ideals? Clearly

$$(36) = (6) * (6)$$

and

$$(225) = (15) * (15)$$

are the prime factorizations since (12), (75), (60), and (30) are not prime ideals. Apparently, then, in $\{I_T, *\}$ we have the following situation: *Factorization into a product of primes is unique when it occurs.* This means that by the use of ideals we have ***restored*** unique factorization to the multiplicative semigroup $\{T, \cdot\}$.

The justification for these claims is furnished by a result which is based on the properties of the integers, naturally.

THEOREM 5.15. *The ideal $(s)$ of $T$ is a prime ideal if and only if $s/3$ is a prime integer of $J$.*

If $s/3 = p$, a prime integer, then

$$(s) = \{0, 3p, -3p, 6p, -6p, \cdots\},$$

so suppose the ideal $(t)$ contains $(s)$. Then every element of $(t)$ is a multiple of $t$, so that there is an integer $n$ such that

$$3p = tn.$$

Since $t$ is an element of $T$, we know that $t$ is a multiple of 3,

$$t = 3q,$$

so that

$$p = qn$$

and either

$$t = 3p \qquad \text{or} \qquad t = 3.$$

Thus the only ideals of $T$ containing $(3p)$ are $(3)$ and $(3p)$ so that $(s) = (3p)$ is a prime ideal.

Conversely, suppose $s = 3mn$, where $m$ and $n$ are integers larger than 1. Then

$$(3) \supset (3m) \supset (s)$$

and $(s)$ is not a prime ideal. Hence, if $(s)$ is a prime ideal, then $s/3$ is a prime integer.

From this we conclude quite readily that an ideal $(s)$ of $T$ is expressible as a product of prime ideals if and only if

$$s = 3^n p_1 p_2 \cdots p_n$$

where the $p_i$ are primes. For surely

$$(s) = (3p_1) * (3p_2) * \cdots * (3p_n)$$

is a factorization of $(s)$ into a product of prime ideals. And, by Theorem 5.15, if

$$(s) = (s_1) * (s_2) * \cdots * (s_n)$$

is a factorization of $(s)$ into a product of prime ideals, then surely

$$(s) = (3p_1) * (3p_2) * \cdots * (3p_n)$$

and

$$s = 3^n p_1 p_2 \cdots p_n.$$

From the uniqueness of the factorization of

$$s = 3^n p_1 p_2 \cdots p_n$$

in $J$ we conclude that the factorization

$$(s) = (3p_1) * (3p_2) * \cdots * (3p_n)$$

is unique.

*Example* 1. $(37584) = (9) * (6) * (21) * (51)$.

*Example* 2. $(12528)$ is not expressible as a product of prime ideals since $12528 = 3^4 \cdot 2 \cdot 7 \cdot 17$. There are, however, many factorizations of $(12528)$ into a product of ideals:

$$(12528) = (6) * (3) * (21) * (51) = (18) * (21) * (51).$$

This discussion of the systems of ideals of $J$ and of $T$ is an attempt to illustrate at a fairly low level of mathematical sophistication the idea developed in the latter part of the nineteenth century for the purpose of restoring the property of unique factorization to a certain type of number system. The illustration is rather artificial and strained, but it does provide a rough idea of the general method.

## Exercise 5.4

**1.** Define $(a) + (b)$ to be the set of all integers $an + bm$, where $(a)$ and $(b)$ are ideals of $J$ and $n$ and $m$ are arbitrary integers. Show that $(10) + (12) = (2)$ and $(3) + (11) = (1)$.

**2.** Show that $(a) + (b) = (c)$, where $c$ is the G.C.F. of $a$ and $b$.

**3.** Show that the union of two ideals of $J$ is an ideal of $J$ if and only if one is contained in the other.

**4.** Show that, for ideals of $J$,

$$(10) \cap (12) \neq (10) * (12) \quad \text{but} \quad (11) \cap (12) = (11) * (12).$$

What is the general theorem covering these cases?

**5.** What are the idempotents of the systems $\{I, \cap\}$, $\{I, *\}$, and $\{I_T, *\}$?

**6.** Prove that $J$ contains an infinite number of distinct maximal primes. Give some examples.

**7.** Express the elements $(99)$, $(999)$, and $(9999)$ of $\{I, *\}$ as products of maximal ideals.

**8.** List four ideals (other than those in the text) of $T$ which cannot be expressed as the products of prime ideals.

**9.** Compare the ideals of $\{T, +, \cdot\}$ with the ideals of $\{J, +, \cdot\}$.

**10.** How many ideals of $T$ contain a given element $t > 0$ of $T$? Explain for $t = 300$.

**11.** Show that, if $J'$ denotes the set of nonzero integers, then the semigroup $\{I, *\}$ is a homomorphic image of the semigroup $\{J', \cdot\}$ under the mapping $a \to (|a|)$. Show that the set of elements of $J'$ mapped onto $(1)$ is a subsystem of $\{J', \cdot\}$.

**12.** Let $t$ be a positive integer in $T$ and show that the set of all multiples $kt$, where $k$ is any element of $T$, is an ideal of $\{T, +, \cdot\}$. Show also that this ideal is *not* equal to $(t)$.

## 5.5 Remarks

In this chapter we characterized certain properties of individual integers in terms of subsystems, homomorphisms, ideals, quotient systems, etc.; for example, the positive integer $m$ is a prime if and only if the ideal $(m)$ is a maximal ideal of $J$; if and only if the quotient system $J/(m)$ contains only the trivial ideals; if and only if no nonzero element of $J/(m)$ is a divisor of zero. These characterizations are not intended to provide additional information about the integers (although they certainly do increase our understanding of the system of integers). Rather they are set forth as possible guides for the generalizing of concepts used in the study of the system of integers, and these generalizations enable us to analyze by analogy other and abstract systems. Some of these analogies are apt to be a trifle twisted and perhaps obscured by details, but the student will find that the discernment of such analogies will contribute greatly to his understanding of the analysis of the systems.

On the other hand, although an analogy can sometimes lead to a conjectured theorem from a known theorem, it often fails to provide a proof for the conjecture. And even if the conjectured theorem can be proved, the resulting proof is very likely to be totally different from the proof of the original theorem. So a clever analogy may lead to the conjecturing of a strange new theorem, but often an entirely different bit of ingenuity is required for the proof of the theorem.

## 5.6 Suggested Reading

*Articles*

Blumberg, H., "On the technique of generalization," *Amer. Math. Monthly* **47** (1940), 451–462

Lefschetz, S., "The structure of mathematics," *Amer. Scientist* **38** (1950), 105–111.

MacLane, S., "Some recent advances in algebra," *Amer. Math. Monthly* **46** (1939), 1–19.

Polya, G., "Generalization, specialization, and analogy," *Amer. Math. Monthly* **55** (1948), 241–243.

Weil, A., "The future of mathematics," *Amer. Math. Monthly* **57** (1950), 295–306.

*Books*

Albert, A., *Fundamental Concepts of Higher Algebra*, University of Chicago Press, Chicago, Ill., 1956.

Polya, G., *Induction and Analogy in Mathematics*, Princeton University Press, Princeton, N.J., 1954.

# 6

# Groups

Now we proceed from the consideration of the familiar systems and some of their associated systems to the study of a type of abstract system. These abstract systems, called groups, have a single binary operation which has most of the nice properties of the binary operations which we have already studied, so we should expect these systems to have properties not unlike the features of the systems we have been studying. And we shall see that a group can be at least partially analyzed by means of the concepts set forth in the previous chapter.

To a large extent our purpose in introducing the study of groups at this point is to illustrate some of the methods of analyzing abstract algebraic systems which have been devised by mathematicians. However, the theory of groups has important applications and uses in many areas of science, especially in physics and chemistry, as well as in other parts of mathematics. We will not consider such matters in this chapter since we are attempting only to develop some of the simpler aspects of the theory of groups, but the student is urged to use the reading list at the end of the chapter to investigate some of the simpler applications.

## 6.1 Definitions and Examples

We shall begin with an example of a type considered earlier.

*Example* 1. Consider the set $\{a, b, c\}$ of three distinct elements. Now this set has six permutations or one-to-one mappings onto itself:

$$\begin{aligned}
F_1 &= \{(a, a), (b, b), (c, c)\},\\
F_2 &= \{(a, b), (b, c), (c, a)\},\\
F_3 &= \{(a, c), (b, a), (c, b)\},\\
F_4 &= \{(a, b), (b, a), (c, c)\},\\
F_5 &= \{(a, c), (b, b), (c, a)\},\\
F_6 &= \{(a, a), (b, c), (c, b)\},
\end{aligned}$$

and if we use the composition of functions as our binary operation, denoted by $\cdot$, we obtain the table shown for the set $G$ of mappings.

| $\cdot$ | $F_1$ | $F_2$ | $F_3$ | $F_4$ | $F_5$ | $F_6$ |
|---|---|---|---|---|---|---|
| $F_1$ | $F_1$ | $F_2$ | $F_3$ | $F_4$ | $F_5$ | $F_6$ |
| $F_2$ | $F_2$ | $F_3$ | $F_1$ | $F_6$ | $F_4$ | $F_5$ |
| $F_3$ | $F_3$ | $F_1$ | $F_2$ | $F_5$ | $F_6$ | $F_4$ |
| $F_4$ | $F_4$ | $F_5$ | $F_6$ | $F_1$ | $F_2$ | $F_3$ |
| $F_5$ | $F_5$ | $F_6$ | $F_4$ | $F_3$ | $F_1$ | $F_2$ |
| $F_6$ | $F_6$ | $F_4$ | $F_5$ | $F_2$ | $F_3$ | $F_1$ |

This is true since, for example,

$$a(F_2 \cdot F_4) = (aF_2)F_4 = bF_4 = a,$$
$$b(F_2 \cdot F_4) = (bF_2)F_4 = cF_4 = c,$$

and

$$c(F_2 \cdot F_4) = (cF_2)F_4 = aF_4 = b,$$

so that

$$F_2 \cdot F_4 = \{(a, a), (b, c), (c, b)\} = F_6.$$

What do we know about the system $\{G, \cdot\}$? Since the binary operation is the composition of functions, we know from our previous work that it is an associative operation. From the table we see that $F_1$ is the identity element relative to the binary operation, and we see also that each element of $G$ possesses an inverse element relative to the binary operation since $F_1$ appears once and only once in each row and column of the table and these appearances are symmetric about the main diagonal of the table. On the other hand the entire table is not symmetric about the main diagonal (upper left to lower right) so that the binary operation is not commutative. Thus we conclude that $\{G, \cdot\}$ is a mathematical system with the following properties:

(1) The operation is associative.
(2) $G$ contains an identity element.
(3) Each element of $G$ has an inverse.
(4) The operation is not commutative.

This is an example of a finite, noncommutative group.

DEFINITION 6.1. A *group* is a mathematical system consisting of a nonempty set $G$, a binary operation denoted by $\cdot$ (and considered as *abstract multiplication*) and the axioms:

(1) $(a \cdot b) \cdot c = a \cdot (b \cdot c)$ for any elements of $G$.
(2) $G$ contains an element $e$ such that $a \cdot e = e \cdot a = a$ for each $a$ in $G$.
(3) For each $a$ in $G$ there is an element $a'$ in $G$ such that

$$a \cdot a' = a' \cdot a = e.$$

If the following additional axiom is assumed the system is a commutative or *Abelian group*:

(4) $a \cdot b = b \cdot a$ for any $a$ and $b$ in $G$.

The system is generally denoted by $G$ and sometimes by $\{G, \cdot\}$. A group is called *finite* if and only if the set $G$ is a finite set. The element $e$ of axiom (2) is called an *identity element* of the group $G$, and we shall show that a group has only one identity element. The element $a'$ of axiom (3) is called an *inverse* of $a$, and we shall show that each element of $G$ has only one inverse. The number of elements in $G$ is the *order* of $G$.

It is quite obvious that we can obtain many examples of Abelian groups, both finite and infinite ones, from the systems which we studied in the preceding chapters. Certainly $\{R, +\}$ is an infinite Abelian group, and for each positive integer $m$, $\{J/(m), \oplus\}$ is a finite Abelian group. However, it is the existence of examples other than these which makes the study of abstract groups worth while.

*Example* 2. Let $S$ be the Cartesian product of the set $Re$ of real numbers with itself, $S = Re \times Re$. Define the mappings $\boldsymbol{E}$ and $\boldsymbol{F}$ on $S$ by specifying images:

$$(x, y)\boldsymbol{E} = (x, y) \qquad \text{and} \qquad (x, y)\boldsymbol{F} = (-x, y)$$

for each element $(x, y)$ of $S$. Then this set of two functions, $G = \{\boldsymbol{E}, \boldsymbol{F}\}$, and the binary operation of function composition, denoted by $\cdot$, form an Abelian group.

| $\cdot$ | $\boldsymbol{E}$ | $\boldsymbol{F}$ |
|---|---|---|
| $\boldsymbol{E}$ | $\boldsymbol{E}$ | $\boldsymbol{F}$ |
| $\boldsymbol{F}$ | $\boldsymbol{F}$ | $\boldsymbol{E}$ |

The operation table for this group is as shown since

$$\begin{aligned}
(x, y)\boldsymbol{E} \cdot \boldsymbol{E} &= ((x, y)\boldsymbol{E})\boldsymbol{E} = (x, y)\boldsymbol{E} = (x, y),\\
(x, y)\boldsymbol{E} \cdot \boldsymbol{F} &= ((x, y)\boldsymbol{E})\boldsymbol{F} = (x, y)\boldsymbol{F} = (-x, y),\\
(x, y)\boldsymbol{F} \cdot \boldsymbol{E} &= ((x, y)\boldsymbol{F})\boldsymbol{E} = (-x, y)\boldsymbol{E} = (-x, y),
\end{aligned}$$

and

$$(x, y)\boldsymbol{F} \cdot \boldsymbol{F} = ((x, y)\boldsymbol{F})\boldsymbol{F} = (-x, y)\boldsymbol{F} = (x, y).$$

The operation we know to be associative, and $\boldsymbol{E}$ is the identity element whereas each element is its own inverse. And clearly the group is Abelian.

Although the student may not recognize this group, it is one that he was taught to use in his analytic geometry course for testing to see if the graph of an equation in $x$ and $y$ is symmetric with respect to the $y$-axis. We say that the graph of the equation

$$y = x^2 + 2$$

is symmetric with respect to the $y$-axis since the subset $S_1$ of $S$ consisting of all pairs $(x, y)$ of real numbers such that $y = x^2 + 2$, is mapped onto itself by the elements of this group $G$. This of course is boiled down to this simple test: $(x, y)$ is in $S_1$ if and only if $(-x, y) = (x, y)\boldsymbol{F}$ is in $S_1$ since $(-x)^2 = x^2$. Nevertheless when we discuss subsets of $S$, or their corresponding geometric configurations, which are symmetric with respect to the $y$-axis, we are talking about those subsets which are left invariant or unchanged (i. e., mapped onto themselves) by the elements $\boldsymbol{E}$ and $\boldsymbol{F}$.

This simple example relating the symmetry about the $y$-axis with the group $\{\{E, F\}, \cdot\}$ of two one-to-one mappings of the set $S$ illustrates a fundamental relationship between groups and geometries. This relationship is the basis of a definition of geometries given by the mathematician Felix Klein: A geometry is the study of those properties of a set $T$ which remain invariant when the elements of $T$ are subjected to the elements of a group of one-to-one mappings on $T$.

The preceding idea of testing for symmetry gives rise to another elementary example of a group.

*Example* 3. Let $S$ be the Cartesian product of $Re$ with $Re$. We define four mappings on $S$ by defining the images of $(x, y)$:

$$(x, y)F_1 = (x, y), \qquad (x, y)F_2 = (-x, y), \qquad (x, y)F_3 = (x, -y),$$

and

$$(x, y)F_4 = (-x, -y).$$

It is quite easy to show that the composite of any two of these is again in the set $G = \{F_1, F_2, F_3, F_4\}$ so that the system $\{G, \cdot\}$ is certainly a semigroup. We see from the operation table shown that $F_1$ is the identity element of $G$, that each element is its own inverse, and that $G$ is a finite, Abelian group.

| $\cdot$ | $F_1$ | $F_2$ | $F_3$ | $F_4$ |
|---|---|---|---|---|
| $F_1$ | $F_1$ | $F_2$ | $F_3$ | $F_4$ |
| $F_2$ | $F_2$ | $F_1$ | $F_4$ | $F_3$ |
| $F_3$ | $F_3$ | $F_4$ | $F_1$ | $F_2$ |
| $F_4$ | $F_4$ | $F_3$ | $F_2$ | $F_1$ |

*Example* 4. The set $G$ of all the one-to-one mappings of the nonempty set $T$ onto itself is a group relative to the composition of functions. Let $F_1$ and $F_2$ be elements of $G$. Then by definition of one-to-one function we know that each element of $T$ appears exactly once as a first and as a second element of pairs in $F_1$ and $F_2$. Since

$$F_1 \cdot F_2 = \{(a, b): (a, x) \text{ is in } F_1 \text{ and } (x, b) \text{ is in } F_2\}$$

it is clear that $F_1 \cdot F_2$ is one-to-one from $T$ onto $T$. In other words $F_1 \cdot F_2$ is one-to-one since every $t$ in $T$ is the image under $F_1 \cdot F_2$ of some element of $T$. So $\cdot$ is a binary operation.

The binary operation is associative, as we saw in Chapter 1, since, for $t$ in $T$ and $F_1$, $F_2$, and $F_3$ in $G$, the equations

$$tF_1 \cdot (F_2 \cdot F_3) = (tF_1)F_2 = ((tF_1)F_2)F_3$$

and

$$t(F_1 \cdot F_2) \cdot F_3 = (tF_1 \cdot F_2)F_3 = ((tF_1)F_2)F_3$$

imply that the functions

$$F_1 \cdot (F_2 \cdot F_3) \quad \text{and} \quad (F_1 \cdot F_2) \cdot F_3$$

both map $t$ onto the same image. Hence

$$F_1 \cdot (F_2 \cdot F_3) = (F_1 \cdot F_2) \cdot F_3.$$

The semigroup $\{G, \cdot\}$ has an identity element, namely, the function $E$ defined by

$$tE = t \text{ for each } t \text{ in } T.$$

Obviously $E$ is one-to-one, and the equations

$$t(F \cdot E) = (tF)E = tF$$

and

$$t(E \cdot F) = (tE)F = tF$$

show that

$$E \cdot F = F \cdot E = F.$$

Finally, if $F$ is an element of $G$, then the function $F'$ defined as

$$F' = \{(a, b): (b, a) \text{ is in } F\}$$

is an inverse element for $F$ in $G$. We see that $F'$ is in $G$ if and only if $F$ is in $G$ by looking at the set of first elements and at the set of second elements in the pairs which constitute $F$. In the same way we see that

$$F \cdot F' = F' \cdot F = E,$$

for, if $(a, b)$ is in $F$, then $(b, a)$ is in $F'$ so that $(a, a)$ is in $F \cdot F'$ and $(b, b)$ is in $F' \cdot F$.

Thus the system $\{G, \cdot\}$ is a group. It is in general neither finite nor Abelian. If $T$ is a finite set of $n$ elements, then $G$ is certainly finite since a finite set has only a finite collection of mappings onto itself. In that case the elements of $G$ are the permutations of $n$ elements, and everyone knows that there are $n!$ different permutations of $n$ elements. This accounts for the fact that the group in the initial example of this section contained $6 = 3!$ elements. We note that the group $\{G, \cdot\}$ is referred to as the *symmetric group* on $n$ elements when $T$ contains $n$ elements.

These examples all involve the concepts of mappings and the composition of mappings. Now we give a more numerical example.

*Example* 5. Let $m$ be an arbitrary integer greater than 1, and let $G$ be the set of $\Phi(m)$ residue classes modulo $m$ of integers which are relatively prime to $m$. Then the operation defined by $[a] \cdot [b] = [ab]$ is a binary operation on $G$ since

$$(ab, m) = 1$$

if and only if

$$(a, m) = (b, m) = 1.$$

Obviously this operation is associative since

$$[a] \cdot ([b] \cdot [c]) = [abc]$$

and

$$([a] \cdot [b]) \cdot [c] = [abc].$$

The element [1] is the identity element, and the inverse of $[a]$ is the element $[a^{\Phi(m)-1}]$ by Euler's Theorem. Thus $\{G, \cdot\}$ is a group. If we select $m = 7$, then $G$ contains six elements which we will denote by 1, 2, 3, 4, 5, 6 for the sake of simplicity, and the operation table is as shown. From this table we see that this group is Abelian since the table is symmetric about the main diagonal. Because

| $\cdot$ | 1 | 2 | 3 | 4 | 5 | 6 |
|---|---|---|---|---|---|---|
| 1 | 1 | 2 | 3 | 4 | 5 | 6 |
| 2 | 2 | 4 | 6 | 1 | 3 | 5 |
| 3 | 3 | 6 | 2 | 5 | 1 | 4 |
| 4 | 4 | 1 | 5 | 2 | 6 | 3 |
| 5 | 5 | 3 | 1 | 6 | 4 | 2 |
| 6 | 6 | 5 | 4 | 3 | 2 | 1 |

of the first example we conclude that there exist both Abelian and non-Abelian groups of order six. (6 is in fact the smallest integer for which this is true.)

The table in Example 5, the table in Example 1, and indeed the operation table of any group all have one common feature: each element of the group appears once and only once in each row and in each column of the body of the table. We shall discover the reason for this in the next section, but now let us consider the following question. If $\{G, \cdot\}$ is a mathematical system in which $G$ is a finite set and $\cdot$ is a binary operation on $G$ defined by a table in which each element of $G$ appears exactly once in each row and in each column, is the system a group? The answer to this is negative as the next example proves. (Such a system is called a *loop*.)

*Example* 6. Show that the table shown is not the operation table of a group. Note that each element appears exactly once in each row and each column of the body of the table and that the table is symmetric about the main diagonal.

| $\cdot$ | $e$ | $a$ | $b$ | $c$ | $d$ | $f$ |
|---|---|---|---|---|---|---|
| $e$ | $e$ | $a$ | $b$ | $c$ | $d$ | $f$ |
| $a$ | $a$ | $b$ | $c$ | $d$ | $f$ | $e$ |
| $b$ | $b$ | $c$ | $e$ | $f$ | $a$ | $d$ |
| $c$ | $c$ | $d$ | $f$ | $e$ | $b$ | $a$ |
| $d$ | $d$ | $f$ | $a$ | $b$ | $e$ | $c$ |
| $f$ | $f$ | $e$ | $d$ | $a$ | $c$ | $b$ |

From the table we see that

$$d \cdot f = c, \qquad c = f = a, \qquad f \cdot f = b, \qquad \text{and} \qquad d \cdot b = f.$$

Therefore

$$(d \cdot f) \cdot f = a$$

whereas

$$d \cdot (f \cdot f) = f,$$

and so the associative law is not valid in this system. This means that the system is *not* a group.

The fact that each element appears in each column exactly once means that the columns are essentially permutations of the six elements of the set.

From the columns we write down the following one-to-one mappings:

$$\begin{aligned}
\boldsymbol{E} &= \{(e, e), (a, a), (b, b), (c, c), (d, d), (f, f)\},\\
\boldsymbol{A} &= \{(e, a), (a, b), (b, c), (c, d), (d, f), (f, e)\},\\
\boldsymbol{B} &= \{(e, b), (a, c), (b, e), (c, f), (d, a), (f, d)\},\\
\boldsymbol{C} &= \{(e, c), (a, d), (b, f), (c, e), (d, b), (f, a)\},\\
\boldsymbol{D} &= \{(e, d), (a, f), (b, a), (c, b), (d, e), (f, c)\},\\
\boldsymbol{F} &= \{(e, f), (a, e), (b, d), (c, a), (d, c), (f, b)\}.
\end{aligned}$$

Using the usual composition operation for functions, we find that

$$\boldsymbol{A} \cdot \boldsymbol{B} = \{(e, c), (a, e), (b, f), (c, a), (d, d), (f, b)\}$$

is a permutation not included among the six obtained from the table. Thus the set of permutations obtained from this table do not form a group relative to the composition of functions. However, the permutations obtained from the columns of the table of Example 5 do form a group relative to function

| · | I | II | III | IV | V | VI |
|---|---|---|---|---|---|---|
| I | I | II | III | IV | V | VI |
| II | II | IV | VI | I | III | V |
| III | III | VI | II | V | I | IV |
| IV | IV | I | V | II | VI | III |
| V | V | III | I | VI | IV | II |
| VI | VI | V | IV | III | II | I |

composition. In the table of this group Roman numerals are used to represent these permutations, so that, for example,

$$\text{III} = \{(1, 3), (2, 6), (3, 2), (4, 5), (5, 1), (6, 4)\}$$

and

$$\text{V} = \{(1, 5), (2, 3), (3, 1), (4, 6), (5, 4), (6, 2)\}.$$

Then we see that

$$\begin{aligned}
\text{III} \cdot \text{V} &= \{(1, 1), (2, 2), (3, 3), (4, 4), (5, 5), (6, 6)\},\\
&= \text{I}.
\end{aligned}$$

This *representation* of a group $\{G, \cdot\}$ by a group of permutations on the set $G$ is a feature possessed by all groups, and we shall prove this in the next section. Thus we again return to groups composed of one-to-one mappings.

## Exercise 6.1

**1.** List all permutations of the set $\{a, b\}$ and using function composition write out the table of this group of permutations.

**2.** Consider the set $R$ of all one-to-one mappings of a plane onto itself which preserve distances between points of the plane (such as rotations about a line or point and translations). Does $R$ form a group relative to the usual composition of functions? Considering what you know (or should know) about plane geometry, comment on F. Klein's definition of geometries.

**3.** Devise a group which "tests" for symmetry about the line whose equation is $y = x$; about the origin; about the line whose equation is $y = 3$.

**4.** Write out the operation table of the group of Example 5 when $m = 5$. How does this group compare with Example 3?

**5.** The distance-preserving one-to-one mappings $\boldsymbol{F}$ of a plane which leave a nonempty set $S$ of points of the plane invariant (i.e., $s\boldsymbol{F}$ is in $S$ for each $s$ in $S$) are called the *symmetries* of $S$, and the set of symmetries of $S$ form a group $G_S$, the *symmetry group* of $S$, under function composition. Show that the symmetry group of a nonsquare rectangle $ABCD$ consists of four mappings: the rotation

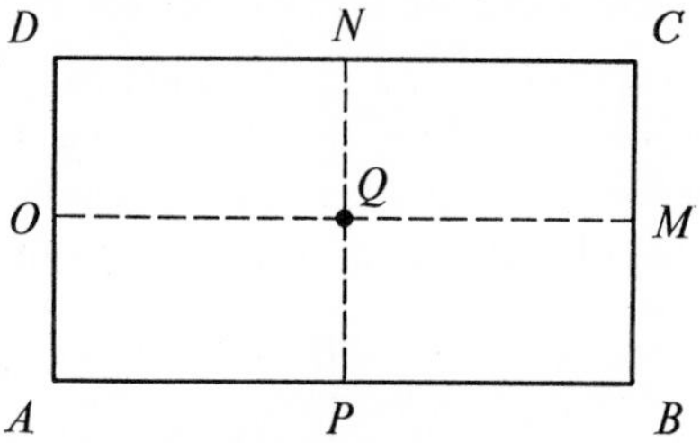


**Figure 6.1**

about the line through the midpoints $N$ and $P$, the rotation about the line through the midpoints $O$ and $M$, the rotation about the point $Q$, and the identity function. Compute the operation table of this group.

**6.** Determine the symmetry group of an equilateral triangle. Compare with the first example of this section.

**7.** Compare the symmetry group of a set of two distinct points with the symmetry group of the line segment joining the two points.

**8.** Show that a loop of three elements is necessarily a group by showing that there is only one table, except for rearrangements, for the set $\{a, b, c\}$ in which each element appears exactly once in each row and column.

**9.** Find a loop of five elements which is not a group.

**10.** How many symmetries has a five-pointed star? A noncircular ellipse? A hyperbola? A regular tetrahedron? Illustrate.

**11.** Consider the set of all one-to-one mappings of the set $J$ of integers onto $J$ which leave invariant a subset $S$ of $J$. Do these mappings form a group under function composition? Why? (Consider the case when $S$ is the set of positive integers and find the inverse of $\boldsymbol{F}$ where $\boldsymbol{F}(n) = n + 1$.)

**12.** Is the set of all rotations of a sphere a group under the usual operation of function composition? Explain.

**13.** Suppose a plane is covered with a pattern of regular hexagons. Describe some distance-preserving one-to-one mappings of the plane onto itself which leave the pattern undisturbed.

**14.** Are distance-preserving one-to-one mappings of a plane onto itself continuous functions? Are continuous one-to-one mappings with continuous inverses necessarily distance preserving? (Consider a "shrinking" of a circle onto a concentric circle.) What "geometry" might these mappings define?

**15.** Show that for each positive integer $n$ there is at least one group of order $n$.
**16.** Which symmetric groups are Abelian?

## 6.2 Elementary Properties

From our knowledge of identity elements and reciprocals or multiplicative inverses of rational numbers we naturally expect the identity element $e$ and the inverse of an element of a group to be unique.

THEOREM 6.1. *The identity element of a group is unique, and each element of a group has exactly one inverse element in the group.*

The statement that the identity element of $\{G, \cdot\}$ is unique means that, if $b$ is an element of $G$ such that for every $a$ in $G$,

$$b \cdot a = a \cdot b = a,$$

then

$$b = e.$$

To prove this we merely multiply the equation

$$a \cdot b = a$$

by $a'$, obtaining

$$a' \cdot (a \cdot b) = a' \cdot a = e.$$

Since the operation is associative this reduces to

$$a' \cdot (a \cdot b) = (a' \cdot a) \cdot b = e \cdot b = b = e.$$

To show that an element $a$ has exactly one inverse in $G$, we suppose that $c$ is an element of $G$ such that

$$c \cdot a = a \cdot c = e.$$

Multiplying the equation $a \cdot c = e$ by $a'$ yields

$$a' \cdot (a \cdot c) = a' \cdot e = a'.$$

Then by the associativity,

$$a' \cdot (a \cdot c) = (a' \cdot a) \cdot c = e \cdot c = c = a',$$

and so $a$ has only one inverse.

THEOREM 6.2. *A group possesses exactly one idempotent element, the identity.*

Certainly the equation $a \cdot e = a$ becomes

$$e \cdot e = e$$

when $a = e$. Hence $e$ is an idempotent. Now suppose $f$ is an idempotent element of $G$, so that

$$f \cdot f = f.$$

Multiplying this equation by the inverse of $f$ we obtain

$$f' \cdot (f \cdot f) = (f' \cdot f) \cdot f = e \cdot f = f = f' \cdot f = e.$$

Thus $e$ is the only idempotent element of $G$.

THEOREM 6.3. *If $a'$ is the inverse of $a$ in $G$, then $a$ is the inverse of $a'$:*

$$(a')' = a.$$

By definition of inverse, $(a')'$ is an element of $G$ such that

$$(a')' \cdot a' = a' \cdot (a')' = e.$$

Since $a'$ has the property that

$$a \cdot a' = a' \cdot a = e,$$

we conclude from the uniqueness of the inverse of $a'$ that

$$(a')' = a.$$

The uniqueness of the inverse of an element of a group enables us to prove the next result.

THEOREM 6.4. *If $a$ and $b$ are elements of a group $G$, then*

$$(a \cdot b)' = b' \cdot a'.$$

Use of the associative law yields

$$\begin{aligned}(a \cdot b) \cdot (b' \cdot a') &= a \cdot \big(b \cdot (b' \cdot a')\big),\\ &= a \cdot \big((b \cdot b') \cdot a'\big),\\ &= a \cdot (e \cdot a') = a \cdot a' = e,\end{aligned}$$

and similarly

$$(b' \cdot a') \cdot (a \cdot b) = e.$$

By the uniqueness of $(a \cdot b)'$ we conclude that

$$(a \cdot b)' = b' \cdot a'.$$

For example, in the first part of Section 6.1 we see from the operation table that

$$(\boldsymbol{F}_2 \cdot \boldsymbol{F}_4)' = \boldsymbol{F}_6' = \boldsymbol{F}_6$$

and

$$\boldsymbol{F}_4' \cdot \boldsymbol{F}_2' = \boldsymbol{F}_4 \cdot \boldsymbol{F}_3 = \boldsymbol{F}_6.$$

Thus

$$(\boldsymbol{F}_2 \cdot \boldsymbol{F}_4)' = \boldsymbol{F}_4' \cdot \boldsymbol{F}'_2,$$

and we note that

$$\boldsymbol{F}_2' \cdot \boldsymbol{F}_4' = \boldsymbol{F}_3 \cdot \boldsymbol{F}_4 = \boldsymbol{F}_5.$$

so that in this non-Abelian group

$$(\boldsymbol{F}_2 \cdot \boldsymbol{F}_4)' \neq \boldsymbol{F}_2' \cdot \boldsymbol{F}_4'.$$

In the above proofs we used the Associative Law and included the various groupings or associations. However, we recall that in any semigroup (i.e., whenever a binary operation is associative) the generalized Associative Law is valid, as we proved by induction in Chapter 2. Thus it is unnecessary for us to indicate the associations, except as a convenience to understanding.

We recall that another basic property of addition and of multiplication in the natural number system, the rational number system, etc., was embodied in the Cancellation Law. Since the operation of a group is invertible (i.e., each element possesses an inverse) we can show that the Cancellation Law is valid in a group.

THEOREM 6.5 (CANCELLATION LAW). *If a, b, and c are elements of the group* $\{G, \cdot\}$ *then either of the equations*

$$a \cdot b = a \cdot c \quad \text{or} \quad b \cdot a = c \cdot a$$

*implies that* $b = c$.

Multiplying by $a'$ on the appropriate side yields

$$a' \cdot a \cdot b = a' \cdot a \cdot c \qquad \text{or} \qquad b \cdot a \cdot a' = c \cdot a \cdot a'$$

and

$$e \cdot b = b = e \cdot c = c \qquad \text{or} \qquad b \cdot e = b = c \cdot e = c.$$

If we denote by $a \cdot G$ and $G \cdot a$, where $a$ is an arbitrary but fixed element of $G$, the sets

$$a \cdot G = \{a \cdot b: b \text{ in } G\}$$

and

$$G \cdot a = \{b \cdot a: b \text{ in } G\},$$

then this result has the following consequence.

*Corollary* 6.5.1. Each element of $G$ appears once and only once in the set $a \cdot G$ and in the set $G \cdot a$.

Let $x$ be an element of $G$. Since

$$x = x \cdot e = x \cdot a' \cdot a$$

and

$$x = e \cdot x = a \cdot a' \cdot x$$

we see that $x$ appears in each of the sets $G \cdot a$ and $a \cdot G$. That is,

$$x = b \cdot a = a \cdot c$$

where

$$b = x \cdot a' \qquad \text{and} \qquad c = a' \cdot x.$$

Now suppose

$$x = d \cdot a$$

for some element $d$ in $G$. Then

$$x = b \cdot a = d \cdot a,$$

and Theorem 6.5 implies that

$$b = d.$$

Hence $x$ appears only once in the set $G \cdot a$. Similarly $x$ appears only once in the set $a \cdot G$.

This property of groups was pointed out in Section 6.1 when we remarked that each element of the group appeared exactly once in each row and in each column of the operation table of the group. The elements of $G \cdot a$ are precisely the elements of the column headed by $a$, and the elements of $a \cdot G$ are exactly the elements of the row to the right of the element $a$.

*Corollary* 6.5.2. Each element of the group $G$ appears exactly once in each row and each column of the operation table of $G$.

As a result of this property of the group $\{G, \cdot\}$ we have a simple method for obtaining permutations or one-to-one mappings of the set $G$ onto itself. Select an element $a$ of $G$, and multiply each element of $G$ on the right by $a$. Then the mapping $\boldsymbol{F}_a$ defined by

$$\boldsymbol{F}_a\colon x \to x \cdot a$$

is a permutation of the set $G$ since the set of images is the set $G \cdot a$ and since we have shown that $G \cdot a$ contains each element of $G$ exactly once.

Now suppose we combine two of these permutations, say $\boldsymbol{F}_a$ and $\boldsymbol{F}_b$, by means of the composition of functions. Then since

$$x\boldsymbol{F}_a = x \cdot a \qquad \text{and} \qquad x\boldsymbol{F}_b = x \cdot b$$

for each $x$ in $G$, we see that

$$x(\boldsymbol{F}_a \cdot \boldsymbol{F}_b) = (x\boldsymbol{F}_a)\boldsymbol{F}_b = (x \cdot a)\boldsymbol{F}_b = x \cdot (a \cdot b),$$

where $\boldsymbol{F}_a \cdot \boldsymbol{F}_b$ is the composite function. This last equation means that the image of each element $x$ of $G$ under the combined function $\boldsymbol{F}_a \cdot \boldsymbol{F}_b$ is equal to the image of $x$ under the permutation $\boldsymbol{F}_{a \cdot b}$ obtained by multiplying on the right by $a \cdot b$ of $G$:

$$x(\boldsymbol{F}_a \cdot \boldsymbol{F}_b) = x \cdot (a \cdot b) = x\boldsymbol{F}_{a \cdot b}.$$

Therefore the set of all such mappings as $\boldsymbol{F}_a$ is closed under the operation of function composition (which we have denoted by $\cdot$ also). Moreover the product of two permutations $\boldsymbol{F}_a$ and $\boldsymbol{F}_b$ is the permutation obtained from the product of the two group elements, $a \cdot b$.

DEFINITION 6.2. Two groups $\{G, \cdot\}$ and $\{H, \bigcirc\}$ are *isomorphic* with each other if and only if there is a one-to-one correspondence between the elements of $G$ and the elements of $H$ which preserves the operations. That is, if $a$ corresponds to $h$, and $b$ corresponds to $k$, where $a$ and $b$ are in $G$ and $h$ and $k$ are in $H$, then $a * b$ corresponds to $h \bigcirc k$. We write $G \cong H$.

Although we have not shown that the set of all permutations $\boldsymbol{F}_a$ obtained in the manner described above is a group relative to function composition, it is quite evident that the correspondence

$$\boldsymbol{F}_a \leftrightarrow a$$

preserves the operations since

$$\boldsymbol{F}_a \cdot \boldsymbol{F}_b = \boldsymbol{F}_{a \cdot b}.$$

THEOREM 6.6 (CAYLEY). *The system $\{P(G), \cdot\}$ where $P(G)$ is the set of all permutations $\boldsymbol{F}_a$, is a group isomorphic with $\{G, \cdot\}$.*

The group $\{P(G), \cdot\}$ is called the *regular permutation representation* of $\{G, \cdot\}$.

It is quite easy to prove that $P(G)$ is a group by using the property established above. Certainly $\boldsymbol{F}_e$ is the identity element of $P(G)$ since

$$\boldsymbol{F}_a \cdot \boldsymbol{F}_e = \boldsymbol{F}_{a \cdot e} = \boldsymbol{F}_a \qquad \text{and} \qquad \boldsymbol{F}_e \cdot \boldsymbol{F}_a = \boldsymbol{F}_{e \cdot a} = \boldsymbol{F}_a.$$

Also the inverse of $\boldsymbol{F}_a$ is $\boldsymbol{F}_{a'}$ since

$$\boldsymbol{F}_a \cdot \boldsymbol{F}_{a'} = \boldsymbol{F}_{a \cdot a'} = \boldsymbol{F}_e \qquad \text{and} \qquad \boldsymbol{F}_{a'} \cdot \boldsymbol{F}_a = \boldsymbol{F}_{a' \cdot a} = \boldsymbol{F}_e.$$

And we know that the composition of functions is an associative operation, so we see that $\{P(G), \cdot\}$ is indeed a group.

Now consider the mapping $\boldsymbol{K}$ defined by

$$\boldsymbol{K}\colon a \to \boldsymbol{F}_a \qquad \text{for each } a \text{ in } G.$$

This is a mapping of the set $G$ onto the set $P(G)$, and we must show that it is a one-to-one mapping between the two sets. In other words we must show that the equality

$$\boldsymbol{F}_a = \boldsymbol{F}_b$$

implies that

$$a = b.$$

But $\boldsymbol{F}_a = \boldsymbol{F}_b$ means that, for each $x$ in $G$,

$$x\boldsymbol{F}_a = x\boldsymbol{F}_b$$

so that by the definition of $\boldsymbol{F}_a$ and $\boldsymbol{F}_b$,

$$x \cdot a = x \cdot b.$$

Clearly the Cancellation Law for $\{G, \cdot\}$ yields

$$a = b,$$

so $\boldsymbol{K}$ is a one-to-one correspondence between $G$ and $P(G)$.

Finally, this correspondence preserves the operations of the two groups since

$$\begin{aligned} a &\leftrightarrow \boldsymbol{F}_a, \\ b &\leftrightarrow \boldsymbol{F}_b, \\ a \cdot b &\leftrightarrow \boldsymbol{F}_{a \cdot b} = \boldsymbol{F}_a \cdot \boldsymbol{F}_b. \end{aligned}$$

Therefore the two groups are isomorphic.

*Example* 1. Find the regular permutation representation of the group $\{J/(3), \oplus\}$.

| + | 0 | 1 | 2 |
|---|---|---|---|
| 0 | 0 | 1 | 2 |
| 1 | 1 | 2 | 0 |
| 2 | 2 | 0 | 1 |

The operation table of this group is as shown. (We are using the simplified notation for the residue classes *and* the operation.) Then

$$\begin{aligned} \boldsymbol{F}_0 &= \{(0, 0 + 0), (1, 1 + 0), (2, 2 + 0)\}, \\ \boldsymbol{F}_1 &= \{(0, 0 + 1), (1, 1 + 1), (2, 2 + 1)\}, \end{aligned}$$

and

$$\boldsymbol{F}_2 = \{(0, 0 + 2), (1, 1 + 2), (2, 2 + 2)\}.$$

That is, the image of $a$ under the permutation $\boldsymbol{F}_2$ is $a + 2$, for each element $a$ of $J/(3)$. We see that the effect of $\boldsymbol{F}_1 \cdot \boldsymbol{F}_1$, the composite function, on each of the three elements of $J/(3)$ is as follows:

$$\begin{aligned} 0(\boldsymbol{F}_1 \cdot \boldsymbol{F}_1) &= (0\boldsymbol{F}_1)\boldsymbol{F}_1 = (0 + 1) + 1 = 0 + (1 + 1) = 2, \\ 1(\boldsymbol{F}_1 \cdot \boldsymbol{F}_1) &= (1\boldsymbol{F}_1)\boldsymbol{F}_1 = (1 + 1) + 1 = 1 + (1 + 1) = 0, \\ 2(\boldsymbol{F}_1 \cdot \boldsymbol{F}_1) &= (2\boldsymbol{F}_1)\boldsymbol{F}_1 = (2 + 1) + 1 = 2 + (1 + 1) = 1. \end{aligned}$$

Hence $\boldsymbol{F}_1 \cdot \boldsymbol{F}_1 = \boldsymbol{F}_{1+1} = \boldsymbol{F}_2$.

| $\cdot$ | $\boldsymbol{F}_0$ | $\boldsymbol{F}_1$ | $\boldsymbol{F}_2$ |
|---|---|---|---|
| $\boldsymbol{F}_0$ | $\boldsymbol{F}_0$ | $\boldsymbol{F}_1$ | $\boldsymbol{F}_2$ |
| $\boldsymbol{F}_1$ | $\boldsymbol{F}_1$ | $\boldsymbol{F}_2$ | $\boldsymbol{F}_0$ |
| $\boldsymbol{F}_2$ | $\boldsymbol{F}_2$ | $\boldsymbol{F}_0$ | $\boldsymbol{F}_1$ |

Continuing, we obtain the operation table of the three permutations. Examination reveals that this table is essentially the same as the preceding table.

The key to the success of this scheme is the Associative Law. In order to show that $\boldsymbol{F}_a \cdot \boldsymbol{F}_b = \boldsymbol{F}_{a \cdot b}$ we used the fact that, for each $x$ in the group $G$,

$$(x \cdot a) \cdot b = x \cdot (a \cdot b).$$

This explains why the permutations obtained from the system in Example 6 of Section 6.1 did *not* form a system.

*Example* 2. Show that the two groups $\{J/(4), \oplus\}$ and $\{J''/(5), \bigcirc\}$ are isomorphic, where $J''/(5)$ denotes the residue classes of integers relatively prime to 5.

$J/(4)$

| $\oplus$ | 0 | 1 | 2 | 3 |
|---|---|---|---|---|
| 0 | 0 | 1 | 2 | 3 |
| 1 | 1 | 2 | 3 | 0 |
| 2 | 2 | 3 | 0 | 1 |
| 3 | 3 | 0 | 1 | 2 |

$J''/(5)$

| $\bigcirc$ | 1″ | 2″ | 3″ | 4″ |
|---|---|---|---|---|
| 1″ | 1″ | 2″ | 3″ | 4″ |
| 2″ | 2″ | 4″ | 1″ | 3″ |
| 3″ | 3″ | 1″ | 4″ | 2″ |
| 4″ | 4″ | 3″ | 2″ | 1″ |

The operation tables of these two groups are shown. We are using 1 to denote $[1]_4$ and 1″ to denote $[1]_5$, etc., to simplify the notation. Inspection shows that the following correspondence is an isomorphism.

$$C_1: \begin{cases} 0 \leftrightarrow 1'' \\ 1 \leftrightarrow 2'' \\ 2 \leftrightarrow 4'' \\ 3 \leftrightarrow 3'' \end{cases}$$

We see, for example, that

$$1 \oplus 2 = 3 \quad \text{and} \quad 2'' \bigcirc 4'' = 3$$

and that

$$3 \oplus 1 = 0 \quad \text{and} \quad 3'' \bigcirc 2'' = 1''.$$

This is not, however, the only one-to-one correspondence between the two groups which preserves the operations. Consider the following:

$$C_2: \begin{cases} 0 \leftrightarrow 1'' \\ 1 \leftrightarrow 3'' \\ 2 \leftrightarrow 4'' \\ 3 \leftrightarrow 2'' \end{cases}$$

If we replace the elements in the $J/(4)$ table by the corresponding elements we get the table shown which is just a rearrangement of the table for $J''/(5)$.

| $\bigcirc$ | 1″ | 3″ | 4″ | 2″ |
|---|---|---|---|---|
| 1″ | 1″ | 3″ | 4″ | 2″ |
| 3″ | 3″ | 4″ | 2″ | 1″ |
| 4″ | 4″ | 2″ | 1″ | 3″ |
| 2″ | 2″ | 1″ | 3″ | 4″ |

So we see that there can be several isomorphisms between two isomorphic groups.

## Exercise 6.2

**1.** Let $S$ be the set of integers $\{1, 2, 3, 4, 5\}$, and define the operation $\ominus$ by the statement: $a \ominus b =$ minimum of $a$ and $b$. Show that $\{S, \ominus\}$ is an Abelian semigroup with identity element. Construct the operation table for this system. Discuss the theorems of this section relative to $\{S, \ominus\}$.

**2.** Show that isomorphism of groups is an equivalence relation on a non-empty set of groups.

**3.** Prove that, if $C$ is an isomorphism from the group $\{G, \cdot\}$ to the group $\{H, \bigcirc\}$, then $C$ maps the identity element of $G$ onto the identity element of $H$.

**4.** Consider the isomorphism $C_1$ in Example 2. Show that the image in $J''/(5)$ of the inverse of an element $a$ of $J/(4)$ is the inverse of the image in $J''/(5)$ of $a$. (For example, the image of the inverse of 3 is $3''$, and the inverse of the image of 3 is $3'' = (2'')'$.) What general principal do you deduce from this?

**5.** The element 1 of the group $\{J/(4), \oplus\}$ is said to *generate* the group since $1 \oplus 1 = 2$, $1 \oplus 1 \oplus 1 = 3$, and $1 \oplus 1 \oplus 1 \oplus 1 = 0$. Consider the tables of Example 2, and find some elements which generate each of the groups in that example.

**6.** Let $x$ be a generating element (see the previous problem) of the group $\{J/(4), \oplus\}$ and $y''$ be a generating element of $\{J''(5), \bigcirc\}$ in Example 2. Show that the following correspondence is an isomorphism of the two groups:

$$x \leftrightarrow y''$$
$$x \oplus x \leftrightarrow y'' \bigcirc y''$$
$$x \oplus x \oplus x \leftrightarrow y'' \bigcirc y'' \bigcirc y''$$
$$x \oplus x \oplus x \oplus x \leftrightarrow y'' \bigcirc y'' \bigcirc y'' \bigcirc y''.$$

How many isomorphisms of the two groups can you find this way?

**7.** Suppose a semigroup $\{S, \cdot\}$ has a left identity element $e$ (so that $e \cdot a = a$ for each $a$ in $S$) and a right identity element $f$. Prove that $e = f$.

**8.** Let $\{S, \cdot\}$ be a semigroup with the property that $S \cdot a$, the set of all $s \cdot a$ for $s$ in $S$, equals $S$ equals $a \cdot S$ for each $a$ in $S$. Show that $\{S, \cdot\}$ is a group. (*Hint:* $S = S \cdot a$ implies the existence of $e$ such that $a = e \cdot a$, and $e \cdot S = e \cdot (a \cdot S) = a \cdot S = S$ imply that $e$ is a left identity element for $S$.)

**9.** Show that a finite semigroup in which the cancellation laws (left and right) are valid is a group. (See Problem 8.)

**10.** Consider the semigroup of positive integral multiples of two under the operation of ordinary multiplication. Show that this semigroup possesses the cancellation law but is *not* a group.

**11.** Compare the group of permutations obtained in Example 1 of this section with those of Example 1 in Section 6.1.

**12.** Find the regular permutation representations for the groups of Example 2.

**13.** Comment on the statement, "If everything were known about permutation groups, then all group theory would be known."

**14.** Show that a group with no more than four elements is Abelian. (*Hint*: Compare the two sets $\{e, a, b, a \cdot b\}$ and $\{e, a, b, b \cdot a\}$.)

**15.** Prove that, if $x \cdot x = e$ for every element $x$ of the group $\{G, \cdot\}$, then it is an Abelian group. (*Hint:* Consider the inverse of $a \cdot b$.)

**16.** Show that a group of order three has a generating element. How about a group of order four? (Consider the examples of Section 6.1.)

**17.** Compare the symmetry group of a nonsquare rectangle with the symmetry group of a noncircular ellipse.

**18.** Compare the multiplicative group of positive real numbers with the additive group of real numbers. (Remember logarithms?)

**19.** The identity mapping, $\boldsymbol{I}$,

$$\boldsymbol{I}: x \rightarrow x, \text{ each } x \text{ in } G,$$

is certainly an isomorphism of the group $G$ with itself. Does the group $\{J/(4), \oplus\}$ have any other isomorphisms with itself? (See Example 2.) Can these isomorphisms be combined in any reasonably obvious way to yield another isomorphism?

**20.** Can an Abelian group be isomorphic with a non-Abelian group? Why?

**21.** Show that a loop is a group if the regular permutations obtained from the loop form a group under function composition. (See Example 6 of Section 6.1. A loop is a system $\{L, \cdot\}$, where $\cdot$ is a binary operation, $L$ contains an identity element, and each element of $L$ has an inverse.)

**22.** Let $S$ and $T$ be equivalent nonempty sets (where $\boldsymbol{F}$ is a one-to-one mapping from $S$ onto $T$). Show that the two groups $\{P(S), \cdot\}$ and $\{P(T), \cdot\}$ of all permutations on the two sets are isomorphic. (*Hint*: Use $\boldsymbol{F}$ to establish an isomorphism.)

## 6.3 Subgroups and Cyclic Groups

Thus far we have looked at some examples of groups, discussed a few properties of some distinguished elements possessed by groups, and investigated a relationship between abstract groups and permutation groups (groups of permutations). Now we begin our study of the structure of groups.

DEFINITION 6.3. A nonempty subset $H$ of $G$ is a *subgroup* of the group $\{G, \cdot\}$ if and only if

(i) $h \cdot k$ is in $H$ when $h$ and $k$ are in $H$.
(ii) $h'$ is in $H$ when $h$ is in $H$.
If $H \neq G$, then $H$ is a *proper subgroup*.

For example, the set $E$ of even integers is a subgroup of the additive group of integers since the sum of two even integers is even and the negative (i.e., the inverse) of an even integer is also an even integer. In fact the group $\{E, +\}$ is isomorphic with the group $\{J, +\}$.

Strictly speaking, by the definition above a subgroup is just a set and not a mathematical system. But the properties (i) and (ii) ensure that the binary operation of $\{G, \cdot\}$ induces a binary operation on $H$ such that $\{H, \cdot\}$ is a group.

THEOREM 6.7. *A subset $H$ of $G$ is a subgroup of the group $\{G, \cdot\}$ if and only if $\{H, \cdot\}$ is a group.*

Suppose $H$ is a subgroup of $\{G, \cdot\}$. Then $H$ is nonempty and so contains an element $h$. By property (ii) $H$ contains $h'$ also, so that using property (i) we conclude

$$e = h \cdot h'$$

is an element of $H$. Thus the system $\{H, \cdot\}$ has an identity element and an inverse for each element. So we need only show that the operation of $\{H, \cdot\}$ is associative, and this follows from the fact that the operation of $\{G, \cdot\}$ is associative.

Technically the operation symbolized by $\cdot$ in $\{G, \cdot\}$ is a certain subset $\boldsymbol{M}$ of the set $\big((G \times G) \times G\big)$, where

$$a \cdot b = c$$

if and only if $\big((a, b), c\big)$ is in $\boldsymbol{M}$. Then the operation induced on $H$ is the intersection of $\boldsymbol{M}$ with $\big((H \times H) \times H\big)$, and property (i) ensures that this is indeed a binary operation on $H$. Therefore, if $a$, $b$, and $c$ are elements of $H$, then

$$(a \cdot b) \cdot c = a \cdot (b \cdot c) = d$$

is an element of $H$, and we see that, in $\boldsymbol{M} \cap \big((H \times H) \times H\big)$,

$$\big((a \cdot b, c), d\big) = \big((a, b \cdot c), d\big).$$

Hence the operation induced on $H$ is associative and the system $\{H, \cdot\}$ is a group.

Conversely, suppose $\{H, \cdot\}$ is a group. Then certainly $H$ is a nonempty subset of $G$. Since the induced operation is indeed a binary operation on $H$ we must have $h \cdot k$ in $H$ whenever $h$ and $k$ are in $H$, for otherwise the intersection $\boldsymbol{M} \cap \big((H \times H) \times H\big)$ would not be an operation on $H$. Thus $H$ has property (i).

Now the group $\{H, \cdot\}$ has an identity element, say $f$, but is it the same identity element as that of $\{G, \cdot\}$, namely, $e$? Well, we note that

$$f \cdot f = f$$

in $H$, so that $\big((f, f), f\big)$ lies in $\boldsymbol{M}$ intersected with $\big((H \times H) \times H\big)$, and hence $f$ is an idempotent of $G$. Therefore,

$$f = e$$

and a group and its subgroup contain the same identity element. Now an element $h$ of $H$ has an inverse $h''$ in the group $\{H, \cdot\}$ so that

$$h \cdot h'' = (h'') \cdot h = f = e.$$

Hence $h''$ is the inverse of $h$ in the group $\{G, \cdot\}$, and so the set $H$ possesses property (ii). Thus $H$ is a subgroup of $\{G, \cdot\}$.

It is easy to see that each group $\{G, \cdot\}$ possesses several subgroups since the sets $\{e\}$ and $G$ are both subgroups of $\{G, \cdot\}$. These two subgroups are called the *trivial subgroups* of $\{G, \cdot\}$ since they are of little importance.

The problem of finding all the subgroups of a given group is in general a difficult one which varies sharply from one group to another.

*Example* 1. Find all the subgroups of group given in Example 1 of Section 6.1.

In this case the task is quite easy since we have an operation table for the group. The subgroups of this group are:

$$\{F_1\}, \{F_1, F_2, F_3\}, \{F_1, F_4\}, \{F_1, F_5\}, \{F_1, F_6\},$$

and the entire group. But how are these found? By looking at powers of the individual elements:

$$(F_2)^2 = F_3, \qquad (F_3)^2 = F_2, \qquad (F_4)^2 = F_1, \qquad (F_5)^2 = F_1, \qquad (F_6)^2 = F_1.$$

Since $F_2 \cdot F_3 = F_3 \cdot F_2 = F_1$, it is evident from these powers that the sets

$$\{F_1, F_2, F_3\}, \{F_1, F_4\}, \{F_1, F_5\}, \text{and } \{F_1, F_6\}$$

are subgroups. By checking the table we can see that the only subgroup containing $F_i$ and $F_j$, where $i = 2$ or 3 and $j = 4, 5$, or 6, is the whole group. For example,

$$F_2 \cdot F_4 = F_6, \quad F_4 \cdot F_2 = F_5, \quad (F_2)^2 = F_3, \quad \text{and} \quad (F_4)^2 = F_1,$$

so that a subgroup containing $F_2$ and $F_4$ must also contain $F_6$, $F_5$, $F_3$, and $F_1$, and hence is the entire group.

*Example* 2. Determine all of the subgroups of the group $\{J, +\}$.

Here of course we can use the powerful results on integers which were developed earlier. Let $H$ be a subgroup of this group. If $H = \{0\}$, then it certainly requires no discussion, so suppose $H \neq \{0\}$. Then it contains an integer $h \neq 0$, and if $h < 0$ we know that $-h > 0$ and $-h$ is in $H$. Therefore the set $H_1$ of all positive integers in $H$ is not empty. Now by the Well-Ordering Theorem the set $H_1$ contains a minimal element $m$, and we claim that $H$ is precisely the set of all integral multiples of $m$.

To show this we prove first that, if $k$ is an integer, then $km$ is in $H$. If $k$ is positive we know that $km$ is just $m$ added to itself $k$ times and surely is in H by repeated application of property (i). If $k$ is zero, then $km$ is in $H$ since zero is in $H$, and, if $k$ is negative, then $-km$ is in $H$ by the above argument, so that $km = -(-km)$ is in $H$ by property (ii). Thus all of the integral multiples of $m$ are in $H$.

Now select $h$ in $H$. By the Divisor Theorem,

$$h = qm + r, \qquad 0 \leqslant r < m,$$

and since $qm$ is in $H$ by the preceding work we know that

$$r = h + (-qm)$$

is an element of $H$. Since $m$ is the smallest positive element of $H$ we see from this that $r$ is zero and $m$ is a factor of $H$. So $H$ consists of the multiples of $m$, and the subgroups of $\{J, +\}$ are

$$(0), (1) = J, (2), (3), (4), \cdots,$$

where $(m)$ denotes the set

$$(m) = \{km\colon k \text{ any integer}\}.$$

These two examples illustrate the fact that we can often find many, if not all, of the subgroups of a group by looking at the sets generated by single elements of the group.

DEFINITION 6.4. If $x$ is an element of the group $\{G, \cdot\}$ then the *exponentiation* of $x$ for integral exponents is defined by:

(1) $$x^n = \underbrace{x \cdot x \cdot \quad \cdots \quad \cdot x}_{n \text{ times}}, \qquad \text{when } n \text{ is positive,}$$

(2) $$x^0 = e,$$

(3) $$x^{-n} = (x')^n.$$

The set of all $x^m$, $m$ in $J$, is denoted by $(x)$.

This is a simple definition for the very useful mapping of the set $G \times J$ onto the set $G$ which is suggested by the generalized Associative Law for semigroups. (A more sophisticated definition based on the Principle of Induction can be given.) We use the exponential form in this definition since we are referring to the operation of the group $\{G, \cdot\}$ as abstract multiplication. However, the exponential form is not used when the group is, or can be more conveniently thought of as, addition. Thus in Example 2 above we write

$$\underbrace{m + m + \cdots + m}_{k \text{ times}} = km$$

rather than use the exponential form, which has other meanings in this particular instance.

THEOREM 6.8. *The set $(x)$ is a subgroup of the group $\{G, \cdot\}$.*

This is a consequence of one of the laws of exponents which is easily proved for groups:

$$x^n \cdot x^m = x^{n+m} = x^m \cdot x^n.$$

If $n$ and $m$ are both nonnegative or nonpositive, then a simple counting suffices. If $n$ and $m$ are of opposite signs, then a pairing off of a sufficient quantity of $x$'s with their inverses proves the law in this case; e.g.,

$$\begin{aligned} x^3 \cdot x^{-5} &= (x \cdot x \cdot x) \cdot (x' \cdot x' \cdot x' \cdot x' \cdot x'), \\ &= (x \cdot x') \cdot (x \cdot x') \cdot (x \cdot x') \cdot (x \cdot x'), \\ &= e \cdot e \cdot e \cdot x' \cdot x' = x^{-2}. \end{aligned}$$

Here we have used two important facts: (1) an element commutes with its inverse, and (2) $e^n = e$ for any positive integer $n$. Alternatively, the latter part of the argument requires the following result, which is proved by induction.

*Lemma* 6.1. If $n$ is a positive integer, then

$$x^n \cdot x^{-n} = e, \qquad \text{for each } x \text{ in } \{G, \cdot\}.$$

When $n = 1$, then obviously

$$x^1 \cdot x^{-1} = x \cdot x' = e,$$

so suppose, for some positive integer $k$,

$$x^k \cdot x^{-k} = e.$$

Now consider

$$\begin{aligned} x^{k+1} \cdot x^{-(k+1)} &= (x^k \cdot x) \cdot (x' \cdot x^{-k}), \\ &= \big(x^k \cdot (x \cdot x')\big) \cdot x^{-k}, \\ &= (x^k \cdot e) \cdot x^{-k} = x^k \cdot x^{-k} = e. \end{aligned}$$

So the induction is complete, and the result is proved.

Then to show that $(x)$ is a subgroup we need only point out that $x^n$ is in $(x)$ for every integer $n$, and that only such elements of $G$ are in $(x)$.

The subgroup $(x)$ is the *cyclic subgroup* generated by $x$, and $x$ is said to be a *generator* of $(x)$. The *order* of $x$ is the order of $(x)$.

*Corollary* 6.8.1. The subgroup generated by $x$ is an Abelian group.

This is a consequence of the equation

$$x^n \cdot x^m = x^{n+m} = x^{m+n} = x^m \cdot x^n.$$

It may happen that one of the cyclic subgroups of $\{G, \cdot\}$ is in fact the whole group $G$. In this case the group is of a particularly elementary type.

DEFINITION 6.5. A group $\{G, \cdot\}$ is a *cyclic group* if and only if $G$ contains an element $x$ such that $G = (x)$. The element $x$ is a *generator* of $G$.

We see from the preceding result that a cyclic group is Abelian. However, the concept of exponentiation, by tying the idea of a cyclic group in so closely with the integers, enables us to completely classify the cyclic groups up to an isomorphism.

THEOREM 6.9. *If the group $\{G, \cdot\}$ is cyclic and contains $m$ elements, then it is isomorphic with $\{J/(m), \oplus\}$. If the group $\{G, \cdot\}$ is cyclic and infinite, then it is isomorphic with $\{J, +\}$.*

Suppose $G = (x)$ contains $m$ elements, and consider the following $m + 1$ elements of $G$:

$$e = x^0, x, x^2, \cdots, x^m.$$

Evidently two of these elements are equal (since otherwise $G$ would contain more than $m$ elements), say

$$x^h = x^k,$$

with $h > k$. This means that

$$x^{h-k} = e,$$

and so we see that a critical feature of a finite cyclic group is that it determines a least positive integer $n$ such that

$$x^n = e.$$

And since $G$ contains $m$ elements it is clear from the Divisor Theorem and the above argument that $m = n$. For, if $k$ is an arbitrary integer and $n$ is a positive integer such that

$$x^n = e,$$

then

$$k = qn + r, \qquad 0 \leqslant r < n,$$

implies that

$$x^k = (x^n)^q \cdot x^r = e^q \cdot x^r = x^r.$$

Thus

$$e = x^0, x, x^2, \cdots, x^{n-1}$$

are the distinct powers of $x$.

Now the mapping

$$[i] \to x^i, \qquad i = 0, 1, \cdots, m - 1,$$

is certainly a one-to-one mapping from $J/(m)$ onto the $m$ distinct powers of $x$. Furthermore this correspondence preserves the operations of the groups because of the law of exponents:

$$[i] \to x^i,$$
$$[j] \to x^j,$$
$$[i + j] = [i] \oplus [j] \to x^i \cdot x^j = x^{i+j}.$$

By the same argument, essentially, if $(x) = G$ is infinite then

$$x^i = x^j$$

if and only if $i = j$. For otherwise one of the two integers $i$ and $j$ is larger, say $i$, so that

$$x^{i-j} = e,$$

and hence there is a least positive integer $n$ such that

$$x^n = e.$$

Then $(x)$ contains only $n$ distinct elements, contradicting the infiniteness of the group. This means that the mapping

$$i \to x^i, \qquad \text{each } i \text{ in } J,$$

is a one-to-one mapping from $J$ onto $(x) = G$. Clearly it preserves the operations, so that in this case $\{G, \cdot\}$ is isomorphic with $\{J, +\}$.

An important consequence of this method is that we know all of the subgroups of a cyclic group, and they are cyclic also.

THEOREM 6.10. *Every subgroup of a cyclic group is cyclic.*

Suppose $G = (x)$, and consider a subgroup $H$ of $G$. If $H \neq \{e\}$, then $H$ contains positive powers of $x$, and hence a minimal positive power of $x$, say $x^k$. Then as in the above proof and in Example 2 we see that $H = (x^k)$.

THEOREM 6.11. *If $\{G, \cdot\}$ is a cyclic group $(x)$ of order $m$ and $k$ is an integer such that $1 < k \leqslant m$, then $(x^k)$ is a proper subgroup of $G$ if $k$ is a factor of $m$.*

If $k$ divides $m$, then there is a positive integer $h$ such that $m = kh$. Since

$$x^m = (x^k)^h = e^h = e$$

we see that the $h$ elements

$$x^k, x^{2k}, \cdots, x^{hk} = e$$

form a cyclic subgroup of $G$ which is proper since $h < m$.

Conversely, suppose $H$ is a proper subgroup of $G$. If $H = \{e\}$, then $H = (x^m) = (x^k)$ with $k = m$. If $H \neq \{e\}$, then as in the previous theorem there is a minimal positive integer $k$ such that $x^k$ is in $H$. Now let $x^n$ be in $H$; then, since

$$n = kq + r, \qquad 0 \leqslant r < k,$$

we have

$$x^n = x^{kq+r} = (x^k)^q \cdot x^r.$$

This means that

$$x^r = x^n \cdot x^{-kq}$$

is an element of $H$ since $x^n$ and $x^{-kq} = (x^{kq})'$ are elements of $H$. But $k$ is the least *positive* integer such that $x^k$ is in $H$, so we see that $r$ has to be zero. Hence $k$ is a factor of $n$ and so only powers of $x^k$ lie in $H$. In particular $e = x^m$ is in $H$ so that $k$ divides $m$, and

$$m = hk,$$

so that the distinct elements of $H$ are the $h$ powers

$$x^k, x^{2k}, \cdots, x^{hk} = e.$$

Since $H \neq G$ we see that $h < m$, and so $1 < k \leqslant m$. This proves the following proposition.

THEOREM 6.12. *If $H$ is a proper subgroup of the cyclic group $\{G, \cdot\}$ of order $m$, $G = (x)$, then there is a factor $k$ of $m$, $1 < k \leqslant m$, such that $H = (x^k)$.*

*Example* 3. Find all of the subgroups of the group $\{J/(100), \oplus\}$.

This group has the generator [1] and is of order 100. Since the factors of 100 are 1, 2, 4, 5, 10, 20, 25, 50, and 100, we see that the subgroups of this group are the cyclic subgroups

$$J/(100) = ([1]), ([2]), ([4]), ([5]), ([10]), ([20]), ([25]), ([50]), \text{ and } ([100]) = ([0]).$$

Here we write

$$k[1] = [k]$$

instead of $x^k$ since the operation of this system is addition.

We note that any of the classes of integers relatively prime to 100 can serve as a generator of $\{J/(100), \oplus\}$, for, if $(t, 100) = 1$, then

$$k[t] = \underbrace{[t] \oplus \cdots \oplus [t]}_{k \text{ times}} = [0]$$

if and only if $k$ is a multiple of 100. Hence the 100 classes

$$[t], [2t], \cdots, [99t], [100t]$$

are precisely the 100 elements of $J/(100)$, and $J/(100) = ([t])$.

## Exercise 6.3

**1.** Find all the subgroups of the group of Example 3 in Section 6.1.

**2.** Find all subgroups of the group of order six in Example 5 of Section 6.1.

**3.** Is the multiplicative group of all positive rationals a cyclic group? Find two cyclic subgroups of this group.

**4.** Can an infinite Abelian group contain a nontrivial finite cyclic subgroup? (Consider the Cartesian product $J \times (J/(3))$ with $(a, b) \cdot (c, d) = (a + c, b \oplus d)$.)

**5.** Show that the intersection of two subgroups of the group $\{G, \cdot\}$ is a subgroup of $\{G, \cdot\}$.

**6.** Show that, if $H$ is a subgroup of $\{G, \cdot\}$ and $K$ is a subgroup of $\{H, \cdot\}$, then $K$ is a subgroup of $\{G, \cdot\}$.

**7.** For the subgroup $H$ of order three in Problem 2 write out the operation induced on $H$ (i.e., the intersection of $M$ with $((H \times H) \times H)$).

**8.** Prove that, if $e$ is the identity element of $\{G, \cdot\}$, then $e^m = e$ for every integer $m$.

**9.** Show that, if $x$ and $y$ are elements of the group $\{G, \cdot\}$ such that $x \cdot y = y \cdot x$, then $(x \cdot y)^m = x^m \cdot y^m$ for every integer $m$.

**10.** If $\{G, \cdot\}$ is a cyclic group of order 75, then how many subgroups of order five does $G$ have? Why? How many generators has the group $G$?

**11.** Describe the subgroups of the multiplicative group of all integral powers of 1,000,000.

**12.** Use Example 1 of Section 6.1 to show that, if $a \cdot b \neq b \cdot a$, then $(a \cdot b)^m$ need not equal $a^m \cdot b^m$.

**13.** Prove that, if $\{G, \cdot\}$ is a group such that $(a \cdot b)^2 = a^2 \cdot b^2$ for each $a$ and each $b$ in $G$, then it is an Abelian group.

**14.** If $H$ is a nonempty subset of the finite group $\{G, \cdot\}$ with the property that $x \cdot y$ is in $H$ when $x$ and $y$ are in $H$, is $H$ a subgroup of $G$? How is the finiteness used?

**15.** If $\{G, \cdot\}$ is a cyclic group of order $m$, $G = (x)$, what form does the inverse of $x$ take?

**16.** Let $Z$ be the set of all elements $z$ of the group $\{G, \cdot\}$ with the property that

$$x \cdot z = z \cdot x$$

for every $x$ in $G$. Show that $Z$ is a subgroup of $G$. This is the *center* of $G$.

**17.** Find the center of Example 1 of Section 6.1.

**18.** Let $\{P(S), \cdot\}$ be the group of all permutations of the set $S$. Show that the functions which map an element $s$ of $S$ onto itself form a subgroup of the group. If $S = \{1, 2, 3\}$ find the permutations of $S$ which map 2 onto 2 and construct their multiplication table.

**19.** Does the group $\{G, \cdot\}$ have to be cyclic if all of its proper subgroups are cyclic? Explain.

**20.** Show that a group of order three is cyclic. What about four?

**21.** Describe in your own words the classification of cyclic groups and their subgroups.

## 6.4 Cosets

In discussing the ideals of the system of integers we discovered that from an ideal we could form a collection of sets which made up a partition of $J$. Now we could do the same thing for groups and subgroups.

DEFINITION 6.6. If $H$ is a subgroup of $\{G, \cdot\}$, then the set $aH = \{a \cdot h: h \text{ in } H\}$ for an element $a$ of $G$ is a *left coset* of $H$. The element $a$ is a *representative* of $aH$.

Right cosets are defined similarly.

*Example* 1. Find a nontrivial subgroup of the group $G$ having the operation table shown and find its cosets.

| $\cdot$ | $e$ | $a$ | $b$ | $c$ | $d$ | $f$ |
|---|---|---|---|---|---|---|
| $e$ | $e$ | $a$ | $b$ | $c$ | $d$ | $f$ |
| $a$ | $a$ | $b$ | $e$ | $f$ | $c$ | $d$ |
| $b$ | $b$ | $e$ | $a$ | $d$ | $f$ | $c$ |
| $c$ | $c$ | $d$ | $f$ | $e$ | $a$ | $b$ |
| $d$ | $d$ | $f$ | $c$ | $b$ | $e$ | $a$ |
| $f$ | $f$ | $c$ | $d$ | $a$ | $b$ | $e$ |

It is quite easy to see that this group is isomorphic with the symmetric group on three elements, Example 1 of Section 6.1. One subgroup of this group is the cyclic subgroup of order three,

$$H = \{e, a, b\}.$$

The left cosets of $H$ are

$$eH = aH = bH = H = \{e, a, b\}$$

and

$$cH = dH = fH = \{c, d, f\}.$$

Note that each coset contains three elements and that the two different cosets are disjoint.

The set $K = \{e, c\}$ is also a cyclic subgroup of $G$, and its left cosets are

$$eK = cK = K = \{e, c\},$$
$$aK = fK = \{a, f\},$$

and

$$bK = dK = \{b, d\}.$$

Here again the cosets each contain two elements and are disjoint if different. We see also that the right cosets of $K$ are

$$Ke = Kc = K = \{e, c\},$$
$$Ka = Kd = \{a, d\},$$

and

$$Kb = Kf = \{b, f\}.$$

showing that in general left and right cosets are unequal even though they overlap.

Abstracting from these simple examples we show that the cosets of a subgroup $H$ provide much information about $H$.

THEOREM 6.13. *If $H$ is a subgroup of $\{G, \cdot\}$ and $aH$ and $bH$ are cosets of $H$, then:*

(1) *$aH = bH$, or $aH$ and $bH$ are disjoint.*
(2) *$aH$ and $bH$ are equivalent sets.*

Suppose that $aH$ and $bH$ contain a common element $x$; then we must show that $aH = bH$ in this case. Since $x$ is in $aH$ there exists an $h_1$ in $H$ such that

$$x = a \cdot h_1$$

because of the definition of $aH$. Similarly,

$$x = b \cdot h_2$$

for some $h_2$ in $H$. Consequently

$$a \cdot h_1 = b \cdot h_2,$$

so that

$$a = b \cdot h_2 \cdot h_1{}^{-1}$$

and

$$b = a \cdot h_1 \cdot h_2{}^{-1}.$$

Therefore, for each $h$ in $H$,

$$a \cdot h = b \cdot (h_2 \cdot h_1{}^{-1} \cdot h),$$

and since the product $h_2 \cdot h_1{}^{-1} \cdot h$ is in the subgroup $H$, we conclude from this that

$$aH \subseteq bH.$$

Similarly,

$$b \cdot H = a \cdot (h_1 \cdot h_2{}^{-1} \cdot h)$$

implies that

$$bH \subseteq aH.$$

Hence we see that

$$bH = aH,$$

proving (1) of the theorem.

To prove (2) we show that the mapping $F$ from $aH$ to $bH$ defined as

$$F: a \cdot h \to b \cdot h \qquad \text{for each } h \text{ in } H,$$

is a one-to-one mapping from $aH$ onto $bH$. For clearly

$$b \cdot h_1 = b \cdot h_2$$

implies

$$h_1 = b^{-1} \cdot b \cdot h_1 = b^{-1} \cdot b \cdot h_2 = h_2,$$

so that the mapping is one-to-one, and it is onto $bH$ because of the definition

$$bH = \{b \cdot h\text{: each } h \text{ in } H\}.$$

When we restrict our attention to finite groups we have as a consequence of this theorem a relationship between groups and positive integers which has led to much of the development of the theory of finite groups. It suggests an analogy and some problems whose study is one of the keys to the understanding of group theory.

THEOREM 6.14 (LAGRANGE'S THEOREM). *If $H$ is a subgroup of the finite group $\{G, \cdot\}$, then the order of $H$ is a factor of the order of $G$.*

This result is a corollary of the preceding theorem since finite sets are equivalent if and only if they contain the same number of elements. Then by (1) and (2) of Theorem 6.13 we see that every coset of $H$ contains the same number of elements as $H$, which we denote by $|H|$, and selecting distinct cosets of $H$ we have the *left coset decomposition* of $G$ relative to $H$:

$$G = a_1H \cup a_2H \cup \cdots \cup a_nH.$$

Since each element of $G$ appears exactly once in each of these cosets we have

$$|G| = n|H| \qquad \text{or} \qquad |G|/|H| = n.$$

That is, the order of $G$ divided by the order of $H$ equals the positive integer $n$, which is the number of distinct left cosets of $H$ in $G$.

*Example* 2. Find a subgroup of the group $G$ of Example 1 above, and write out the left coset decomposition of $G$.

Select $H = \{e, d\}$. Then $H$ has three distinct left cosets, viz.,

$$eH = dH = \{e, d\},$$
$$aH = cH = \{a, c\},$$

and

$$bH = fH = \{b, f\}.$$

The decomposition of $G$ is

$$G = \{e, d\} \cup \{a, c\} \cup \{b, f\}.$$

Relative to the subgroup $K$ of Example 1, $G$ has the left coset decomposition

$$G = \{e, c\} \cup \{a, f\} \cup \{b, d\}$$

and the right coset decomposition

$$G = \{e, c\} \cup \{a, d\} \cup \{b, f\}.$$

These all correspond to the fact that 6 factors as 2 times 3.

DEFINITION 6.7. The number of distinct cosets of the subgroup $H$ in $\{G, \cdot\}$ is the *index* of $H$ in $G$ and is denoted by $[G:H]$.

*Example* 3. Find a nontrivial subgroup of the infinite group $\{J, +\}$, describe its cosets, and decompose $J$ as a union of distinct cosets.

We saw earlier that the subgroups of $J$ are all cyclic and that there is one for each nonnegative integer:

$$(0), (1), (2), (3), \cdots.$$

Take $H$ to be the subgroup (5). Then the cosets of $H$ are easily seen to be the five residue classes modulo 5:

$$\begin{aligned} 0 + H &= [0], \\ 1 + H &= [1], \\ 2 + H &= [2], \\ 3 + H &= [3], \\ 4 + H &= [4]. \end{aligned}$$

Thus the index of $H$ in $J$, $[J:H]$, equals 5, and the coset decomposition of $J$ relative to $H$ is

$$J = [0] \cup [1] \cup [2] \cup [3] \cup [4].$$

(We note that by using infinite cardinal numbers Lagrange's Theorem can be extended to infinite groups. This will not be discussed here.)

Consideration of Lagrange's Theorem leads to the formulation of two basic questions which we shall study.

*Question* 1. If $d$ is a positive integral factor of the order of the group $\{G, \cdot\}$, does $G$ contain a subgroup of order $d$?

*Question* 2. If $H$ is a subgroup of the group $\{G, \cdot\}$, is it possible to "divide" $H$ into $G$ to obtain a group $K$ as we divide $|H|$ into $|G|$ and obtain an integer?

In the next two sections we shall show that for finite Abelian groups both questions have affirmative answers. For an indication of what the situation is in that case consider the following Abelian group.

*Example* 4. Let $G$ be the set of all ordered pairs $(x, y)$ where $x$ and $y$ are elements of the two groups $\{J/(2), +\}$ and $\{J/(3), +\}$, respectively. Using simplified notation the elements of $G$ are precisely (0, 0), (0, 1), (0, 2), (1, 0), (1, 1), and (1, 2); we understand of course that (0, 0) is the element $([0]_2, [0]_3)$.

The equation

$$(a, b) \cdot (c, d) = (a + c, b + d)$$

is easily seen to define a binary operation on $G$ such that $\{G, \cdot\}$ is a group. The identity element of $G$ is the pair $(0, 0)$, and the inverse of $(a, b)$ is the element $(a', b')$, so that the inverse of $(1, 1)$ is $(1, 2)$:

$$(1, 1) \cdot (1, 2) = (1 + 1, 1 + 2) = (0, 0).$$

If we compute the powers of the element $(1, 1)$ we get

$$\begin{aligned}
(1, 1)^2 &= (1, 1) \cdot (1, 1) = (1 + 1, 1 + 1) = (0, 2),\\
(1, 1)^3 &= (0, 2) \cdot (1, 1) = (0 + 1, 2 + 1) = (1, 0),\\
(1, 1)^4 &= (1, 0) \cdot (1, 1) = (1 + 1, 0 + 1) = (0, 1),\\
(1, 1)^5 &= (0, 1) \cdot (1, 1) = (0 + 1, 1 + 1) = (1, 2),\\
(1, 1)^6 &= (1, 2) \cdot (1, 1) = (1 + 1, 2 + 1) = (0, 0).
\end{aligned}$$

These mean that $\{G, \cdot\}$ is a cyclic group with generating element $(1, 1)$. The correspondence

$$F\colon (1, 1)^i \to [i], \qquad i = 0, 1, 2, 3, 4, 5,$$

is an isomorphism between $\{G, \cdot\}$ and $\{J/(6), +\}$ as we saw in the last section.

Now the group $\{G, \cdot\}$ is called the *outer direct product* of the two groups $\{J/(2), +\}$ and $\{J/(3), +\}$, and since $\{J/(6), +\}$ is isomorphic with this product we ask whether $\{J/6, +\}$ can be written as a "product" of two of its subgroups in a similar fashion. The subgroup $H = \{0, 3\}$ is isomorphic with $\{J/(2), +\}$, and the subgroup $K = \{0, 2, 4\}$ is isomorphic with $\{J/(3), +\}$. We see that each element of $J/(6)$ is expressible in exactly one way as $h + k$ with $h$ in $H$ and $k$ in $K$:

$$0 = 0 + 0,\quad 1 = 3 + 4,\quad 2 = 0 + 2,\quad 3 = 3 + 0,\quad 4 = 0 + 4,\quad \text{and}\quad 5 = 3 + 2.$$

Thus surely $h + k$ corresponds uniquely to the pair $(h, k)$.

We write $J/(6) = H \otimes K$ and say that the group $\{J/(6), +\}$ is expressed as the *direct product* of the two subgroups $H$ and $K$. Since $H$ and $K$ are of order two and three respectively, we see that such a subgroup decomposition compares favorably with the decomposition of the integer 6.

Note that, under the isomorphism $F$ above, the subgroup $H$ of J/(6) corresponds to the subgroup $H' = \{(0, 0), (1, 0)\}$ of $G$,

$$\begin{aligned}
0 &\leftrightarrow (0, 0),\\
3 &\leftrightarrow (1, 0),
\end{aligned}$$

which is also isomorphic with the group $\{J/(2), +\}$. Similarly subgroup $K$ is isomorphic with subgroup $K' = \{(0, 0), (0, 1), (0, 2)\}$ of $G$, which is also isomorphic with $\{J/(3), +\}$,

$$\begin{aligned}
(0, 0) &\leftrightarrow 0,\\
(0, 1) &\leftrightarrow 1,\\
(0, 2) &\leftrightarrow 2.
\end{aligned}$$

*Example* 5. Show that a group $\{G, \cdot\}$ of order four which is not cyclic is isomorphic with the group of Example 3, Section 6.1.

Let $G = \{e, a, b, c\}$. Since $G$ is not cyclic we know that the subgroups $(a)$, $(b)$, and $(c)$ are of order two, $a^2 = b^2 = c^2 = e$. Since $a \cdot b$ cannot equal

$a = a \cdot e$, $b = e \cdot b$, or $e = a \cdot a$ because of the cancellation law, we have

| $\cdot$ | $e$ | $a$ | $b$ | $c$ |
|---|---|---|---|---|
| $e$ | $e$ | $a$ | $b$ | $c$ |
| $a$ | $a$ | $e$ | $c$ | $b$ |
| $b$ | $b$ | $c$ | $e$ | $a$ |
| $c$ | $c$ | $b$ | $a$ | $e$ |

$a \cdot b = c$. In this manner we construct the multiplication table shown for this group. Then by inspecting Example 3 of Section 6.1 we establish the isomorphism

$$e \leftrightarrow F_1,$$
$$a \leftrightarrow F_2,$$
$$b \leftrightarrow F_3,$$
$$c \leftrightarrow F_4.$$

## Exercise 6.4

**1.** Find a nontrivial subgroup of the group of Example 3, Section 6.1, find the cosets of the subgroup, and write out the coset decomposition of the group.

**2.** Compare the outer direct product of $\{J/(2), +\}$ and $\{J/(2), +\}$ with the group $G$ of Problem 1. Can you obtain a corresponding decomposition for the group $G$ as a direct product of subgroups?

**3.** Find a lower bound for the number of subgroups contained in a group $G$ of order 6; 12; 25; $n$? Can $G$ have more than this number of subgroups? Explain. (See hint to Problem 5.)

**4.** Discuss the equivalence of the cosets of the subgroup (6) of $\{J, +\}$. Show that these cosets are equivalent with the set $J$.

**5.** Let the order of the group $\{G, \cdot\}$ be $p^n$, where $p$ is a prime. Show that the order of each element in $G$ is a power of $p$. (Consider the cyclic subgroups.)

**6.** Prove that a group of prime order is cyclic.

**7.** Show that the number of distinct left cosets of a subgroup of a finite group equals the number of distinct right cosets of $H$.

**8.** Show that right cosets and left cosets of a subgroup are equivalent sets.

**9.** Use Lagrange's Theorem and the groups of Example 5, Section 6.1, to give another proof of Euler's Theorem (i.e., that $a^{\Phi(m)} \equiv 1 \bmod m$ if $m$ is a positive integer and $(a, m) = 1$).

**10.** Show that a group of order $p^n$, $p$ a prime, has at least one subgroup of order $p$.

**11.** Prove that, if $H$ and $K$ are subgroups of orders $p^n$ and $q^m$, respectively, where $p$ and $q$ are unequal primes, then $H \cap K = \{e\}$.

**12.** Let $H$ be the set of those permutations of the set $\{1, 2, 3\}$ which fix the element 1. Show that $H$ is a subgroup of the group of all permutations of the set, and find the cosets of $H$.

**13.** Prove that a group of order six is isomorphic with either $\{J/(6), +\}$ or the symmetric group on three elements.

**14.** Let $H$ be a subgroup of $\{G, \cdot\}$ and define

$$x \equiv y \bmod H$$

if and only if $y^{-1} \cdot x$ is in $H$. Show that this defines an equivalence relation on $G$, and discuss the corresponding partition of $G$.

**15.** Let $H$ and $K$ be subgroups of the Abelian group $G$ such that the indices $[G:H]$ and $[G:K]$ are finite. Show that the index $[G:H \cap K]$ is also finite.

## 6.5 Abelian Groups

In this section we consider only Abelian groups, and to emphasize this we adopt additive notation for these groups. Thus we denote the operation of the Abelian group $A$ by $+$, so that an equation such as

$$a + b = c$$

is not to be interpreted as a statement about addition of integers (unless, of course, we specify that $a$, $b$, and $c$ are integers). Here the identity element of $A$ will be denoted by $z$.

The problems we consider here center about the "factorization" of an Abelian group. We begin with "quotient" groups.

Denote by $A/H$ the set of distinct cosets of the subgroup $H$ of the group $A$. Since $A$ is Abelian we do not need to distinguish between right and left cosets. Then $A/H$ consists of the distinct sets of elements of $A$ of the form

$$x + H = \{x + h : h \text{ in } H\}.$$

Our problem is this: Can we use the binary operation of $A$ to define a binary operation on $A/H$ such that the resulting system is a group closely related to $A$?

Using the methods which worked for congruence classes of integers we define the *sum* of two cosets:

$$(x + H) \oplus (y + H) = (x + y) + H.$$

THEOREM 6.15. *The relation $\oplus$ is an associative binary operation on $A/H$.*

First we must show that the above definition is independent of the representatives $x$ and $y$. Suppose $a + H = x + H$ and $b + H = y + H$. Then $a = a + z$, where $z$ denotes the identity element of $A$, is in the coset $x + H$ and $b = b + z$ is in $y + H$. Therefore, for some $h_1$, $h_2$, in $H$, $a + b = (x + h_1) + (y + h_2) = (x + y) + (h_1 + h_2)$ so that the cosets $(a + b) + H$ and $(x + y) + H$ both contain $a + b$. Thus by the basic property (1) of Theorem 6.13,

$$(a + b) + H = (x + y) + H$$

so that

$$(x + H) \oplus (y + H) = (a + H) \oplus (b + H).$$

The associativity of $\oplus$ follows easily from the associativity of + in $A$:

$$\begin{aligned}\big((x + H) \oplus (y + H)\big) \oplus (u + H) &= \big((x + y) + H\big) \oplus (u + H)\\ &= \big((x + y) + u\big) + H\\ &= \big(x + (y + u)\big) + H\\ &= (x + H) \oplus \big((y + H) \oplus (u + H)\big).\end{aligned}$$

It is easy to see from the definition of "addition" that the coset $H = z + H$ is the identity of the system $\{A/H, \oplus\}$ since

$$(x + H) \oplus (z + H) = x + H = (z + H) \oplus (x + H).$$

Furthermore, if $-x$ denotes the inverse of $x$ in $A$, then the equations

$$(x + H) \oplus (-x + H) = z + H = (-x + H) \oplus (x + H)$$

show that the element $-x + H$ of $A/H$ is the inverse of $x + H$.

Thus we see that $\{A/H, \oplus\}$ is a group, called the *quotient group* of $A$ over $H$.

THEOREM 6.16. *The system $\{A/H, \oplus\}$ is a group. Furthermore, if $A$ is a finite group, then the order of the quotient group is $|A|/|H|$.*

The order of the quotient group is the index of $H$ in $A$ since that is the number of distinct cosets of $H$ in $A$.

*Example* 1. Let $H$ be a subgroup of order two in the group $A = J/(8)$, and form the group $\{A/H, \oplus\}$ and its operation table.

The group $A = J/(8)$ is a cyclic group since it is generated by 1 (which stands for the class [1] in this case). Then the only subgroup of $\{J/(8), +\}$ of order two is

$$H = \{0, 4\}.$$

The cosets of $H$, the elements of $A/H$, are

$$H_0 = 0 + H = \{0, 4\},\ H_1 = 1 + H = \{1, 5\},$$
$$H_2 = 2 + H = \{2, 6\},\ H_3 = 3 + H = \{3, 7\}.$$

| $\oplus$ | $H_0$ | $H_1$ | $H_2$ | $H_3$ |
|---|---|---|---|---|
| $H_0$ | $H_0$ | $H_1$ | $H_2$ | $H_3$ |
| $H_1$ | $H_1$ | $H_2$ | $H_3$ | $H_0$ |
| $H_2$ | $H_2$ | $H_3$ | $H_0$ | $H_1$ |
| $H_3$ | $H_3$ | $H_0$ | $H_1$ | $H_2$ |

The operation table of $\{A/H, \oplus\}$ is as shown. We compute, for example,

$$H_3 \oplus H_2 = (3 + H) \oplus (2 + H) = 5 + H = \{5, 1\} = H_1$$

and

$$H_1 \oplus H_3 = (1 + H) \oplus (3 + H) = 4 + H = \{4, 0\} = H_0.$$

*Example* 2. Describe the quotient group of $\{J, +\}$ over the subgroup (4).

The notation for this quotient group is $\{J/(4), \oplus\}$, which is the same as the notation for the additive group of residue classes mod 4, and this is no accident or lapse. The cosets of the subgroup (4) are precisely the congruence classes modulo 4:

$$\begin{aligned}0 + (4) &= \{0, 4, -4, 8, -8, \cdots\} = [0],\\ 1 + (4) &= \{1, 5, -3, 9, -7, \cdots\} = [1],\\ 2 + (4) &= \{2, 6, -2, 10, -6, \cdots\} = [2],\\ 3 + (4) &= \{3, 7, -1, 11, -5, \cdots\} = [3].\end{aligned}$$

We see that $[2] \oplus [3] = [2 + 3] = [1]$, etc.

*Example* 3. Describe the quotient group of $\{R, +\}$ over the subgroup $J$, where $R$ denotes the set of rationals.

The cosets of $J$ in $\{R, +\}$ which are different from $J$ are certainly in one-to-one correspondence with the positive rationals of the form $a/b$, where $(a, b) = 1$ and $0 < a < b$. For the equation

$$a/b + J = c/d + J$$

is equivalent to the statement that $a/b - c/d$ is an integer. Hence the positive rationals of the form $a/b$ with $(a, b) = 1$ and $0 < a < b$ must lie in distinct cosets. Furthermore every coset of $J$ except $J$ contains such a number. Thus the cosets of $J$ are of the following type:

$$\begin{aligned}0 + J &= \{0, -1, 1, -2, -3, 3, \cdots\},\\ 1/2 + J &= \{1/2, -1/2, 3/2, -3/2, \cdots\},\\ 2/3 + J &= \{2/3, -1/3, 5/3, -4/3, \cdots\},\\ 7/8 + J &= \{7/8, -1/8, 15/8, -9/8, \cdots\},\end{aligned}$$

etc.

The group $\{R/J, \oplus\}$ has several very curious features. For each integer $n > 1$, this group contains a cyclic subgroup of order $n$; namely, the subgroup generated by the coset $1/n + J$. Furthermore, every finite subgroup of the group $A/J$ is cyclic.

Very similar to the idea of "division" is the concept of "factorization," so we consider the possibility of expressing an Abelian group as a "product" of subgroups.

Definition 6.8. The Abelian group $\{A, +\}$ is the *direct product* of the $n$ nontrivial subgroups $H_1, \cdots, H_n$ if and only if for each $x$ in $A$ there is exactly one element $x_i$ in $H_i$, $i = 1, 2, \cdots, n$, such that

$$x = x_1 + x_2 + \cdots + x_n.$$

In this case we write $A = H_1 \otimes H_2 \otimes \cdots \otimes H_n$.

The term *direct product* is used here because of the analogy with the factorization of integers as products afforded by the next result.

Theorem 6.17. *If the Abelian group $A$ is finite, then*

$$A = H_1 \otimes H_2 \otimes \cdots \otimes H_n$$

*implies that*

$$|A| = |H_1| \cdot |H_2| \cdot \quad \cdots \quad \cdot |H_n|.$$

To show that the order of $A$ is the product of the orders of the subgroups $H_i$ we need only look at the form of the arbitrary element $x$ of $A$,

$$x = x_1 + x_2 + \cdots + x_n,$$

where $x_i$ is an element of $H_i$ uniquely determined by $x$. Since there are $|H_i|$ distinct choices for $x_i$ we see that there are exactly

$$|H_1| \cdot |H_2| \cdot \quad \cdots \quad \cdot |H_n|$$

values of $x$, proving the theorem.

*Example* 4. Write the group $A = J/(10)$ as a direct product of subgroups. This particular group contains exactly two nontrivial subgroups, namely,

$$H = \{0, 5\} \qquad \text{and} \qquad K = \{0, 2, 4, 6, 8\}.$$

Since

$$\begin{array}{lll} 0 = 0 + 0, & 1 = 5 + 6, & 2 = 0 + 2, \\ 3 = 5 + 8, & 4 = 0 + 4, & 5 = 5 + 0, \\ 6 = 0 + 6, & 7 = 5 + 2, & 8 = 0 + 8, \end{array}$$

and

$$9 = 5 + 4,$$

and since these are the only combinations $h + k$, for $h$ in $H$ and $k$ in $K$, we see that

$$A = H \otimes K.$$

A crucial point in the last example was the fact that $H \cap K = (0)$, for this is the feature which made the ten sums $h + k$ run through the elements of $A$ exactly once. We extract from this the following criteria.

THEOREM 6.18. *The finite Abelian group $A$ is the direct product of subgroups $H$ and $K$ if and only if* (i) $H \cap K = \{z\}$ *and* (ii) $|A| = |H| \cdot |K|$.

If $|A| = |H| \cdot |K|$, then there are exactly $|A|$ of the sums $h + k$ with $h$ in $H$ and $k$ in $K$. Since $H \cap K = \{z\}$ no two of these sums are equal unless the summands are equal. For

$$h_1 + k_1 = h_2 + k_2$$

implies that

$$x = h_1 - h_2 = k_2 - k_1$$

is an element of both $H$ and $K$. Since $H \cap K = \{z\}$ this means that

$$x = z = h_1 - h_2 = k_2 - k_1$$

so that

$$h_1 = h_2 \qquad \text{and} \qquad k_1 = k_2.$$

Thus we see that $A = H \otimes K$.

Conversely, suppose $A = H \otimes K$ and consider an element $x$ which is in both $H$ and $K$.

Since $x$ is in $H$ and $z$ is in $K$,

$$x = x + z$$

is a presentation of $x$ as a sum of an element from $H$ and an element from $K$.

However, $x$ is in $K$ and $z$ is in $H$, so that

$$x = z + x$$

is another such expression for $x$. But such expressions are unique by the definition of $H \otimes K$, and this can only be true if $x = z$. Thus $A = H \otimes K$ implies that $H \cap K = \{z\}$ whether $A$ is finite or not.

Another and similar criterion which we shall use in the next section is the following.

THEOREM 6.19. *If $H$ and $K$ are subgroups of the finite Abelian group $\{A, +\}$ such that*

$$|A| = |H| \cdot |K| \qquad \textit{and} \qquad (|H|, |K|) = 1$$

*then $A = H \otimes K$.*

To prove this we can use the condition that $|H|$ and $|K|$ are relatively prime integers to show that $H \cap K = \{z\}$. So suppose $x$ is in both $H$ and $K$. Then $x$ as an element of $H$ has order a divisor of $|H|$, and $x$ as an element of $K$ has order a divisor of $|K|$. Thus the order of $x$ is 1 so that $x = z$ and $H \cap K = \{z\}$. Therefore

$$A = H \otimes K.$$

We note that both of these results are illustrated by Example 4.

Now we consider the possibility of relating quotient groups and direct products and re-examine Example 4 in this light.

*Example* 4 (*Continued*). The quotient group of this Abelian group over $H$ consists of the five cosets

$$0 + H, 1 + H, 2 + H, 3 + H, \quad \text{and} \quad 4 + H.$$

Using the definition of the operation $\oplus$ we see that the coset $1 + H$ generates the group $\{A/H, \oplus\}$ since

$$(1 + H) \oplus (1 + H) = 2 + H,$$
$$(1 + H) \oplus (2 + H) = 3 + H,$$
$$(1 + H) \oplus (3 + H) = 4 + H,$$

and

$$(1 + H) \oplus (4 + H) = 0 + H.$$

Thus $\{A/H, \oplus\}$ is a cyclic group of order five and is isomorphic with the subgroup $K = \{0, 2, 4, 6, 8\} = (2)$ which is also cyclic of order five. Thus we have

$$A = H \otimes K \qquad \text{and} \qquad A/H \cong K.$$

Similarly, $A/K \cong H$ since $A/K$ and $H$ are both cyclic groups of order two and hence isomorphic.

THEOREM 6.20. *If the Abelian group $\{A, +\}$ is a direct product of subgroups $H$ and $K$, then the quotient groups $A/H$ and $A/K$ are isomorphic with the subgroups $K$ and $H$, respectively.*

Since $A = H \otimes K$ we know that $H \cap K = \{z\}$. We will extend this and show that exactly one element of $K$ lies in each coset of $H$. Consider the coset $x + H$ where $x$ is not in $H$. Then there are unique elements $h$ and $k$ of $H$ and $K$, respectively, such that

$$x = h + k.$$

Hence the element

$$k = x + (-h)$$

is in the coset $x + H$, so we know that each coset of $H$ contains at least one element of $K$.

Now suppose both $k_1$ and $k_2$ are elements of $K$ in $x + H$; then $H$ contains elements $h_1$ and $h_2$ such that

$$k_1 = x + h_1 \qquad \text{and} \qquad k_2 = x + h_2.$$

Therefore we have

$$x = k_1 + (-h_1) = k_2 + (-h_2)$$

which means that

$$k_1 = k_2 \qquad \text{and} \qquad -h_1 = -h_2$$

because of the uniqueness of such expressions in direct products.

Finally we claim that the correspondence between $K$ and $A/H$ given by

$$k \leftrightarrow k + H$$

for each $k$ in $K$ is an isomorphism. For surely we have

$$(k_1 + H) \oplus (k_2 + H) = (k_1 + k_2) + H,$$

and this shows that the correspondence preserves the operations. Hence the two groups $\{K, +\}$ and $\{A/H, \oplus\}$ are isomorphic, and, similarly, $H \cong A/K$.

*Example* 5. The group $A = J/(12)$ contains the subgroup $H = \{0, 4, 8\}$ and the subgroup $K = \{0, 3, 6, 9\}$. The cosets of $H$ are as follows:

$$H_0 = 0 + H = \{0, 4, 8\},$$
$$H_9 = 1 + H = \{1, 5, 9\},$$
$$H_6 = 2 + H = \{2, 6, 10\},$$

and

$$H_3 = 3 + H = \{3, 7, 11\}.$$

We observe that the elements of $K$ are dispersed uniformly among these four cosets, and the operation tables of $K$ and $A/H$ are as shown.

| $\oplus$ | 0 | 3 | 6 | 9 |
|---|---|---|---|---|
| 0 | 0 | 3 | 6 | 9 |
| 3 | 3 | 6 | 9 | 0 |
| 6 | 6 | 9 | 0 | 3 |
| 9 | 9 | 0 | 3 | 6 |

| $\oplus$ | $H_0$ | $H_3$ | $H_6$ | $H_9$ |
|---|---|---|---|---|
| $H_0$ | $H_0$ | $H_3$ | $H_6$ | $H_9$ |
| $H_3$ | $H_3$ | $H_6$ | $H_9$ | $H_0$ |
| $H_6$ | $H_6$ | $H_9$ | $H_0$ | $H_3$ |
| $H_9$ | $H_9$ | $H_0$ | $H_3$ | $H_6$ |

## Exercise 6.5

**1.** Describe the quotient group $A/H$ when $A$ is the group $\{J/(15), +\}$ and $H$ is a subgroup of order three. Construct the operation table for $A/H$.

**2.** Describe the quotient group $A/H$ when $A$ is the group $\{J/(3), +\}$ and $H$ is a subgroup of order three.

**3.** Describe the quotient group $A/H$ when $A$ is the group of all integral powers of 5 relative to multiplication and $H = (625)$.

**4.** Express the group $\{J/(15), +\}$ as the direct product of a subgroup $H$ of order three and a subgroup $K$ of order five. Establish an isomorphism between $A/H$ and $K$.

**5.** Show that the group $\{J/(4), +\}$ cannot be written as the direct product of two subgroups of order two.

**6.** Show that the group $\{J/(8), +\}$ cannot be written as the direct product of two nontrivial subgroups. What conjecture do you make from this?

**7.** Show that, if the finite group $A$ is the direct product of two cyclic subgroups $H$ and $K$, then $A$ is cyclic if and only if $(|H|, |K|) = 1$. (If $H = (x)$ and $K = (y)$, then when does $A = (x + y)$?)

**8.** Let $H$ be a finite subgroup of the group $R/J$ (see Example 3), and let $\{a/b\}$ be the set of elements in the cosets of $J$ comprising $H$ such that $(a, b) = 1$ and $0 < a < b$. From the set $\{a/b\}$ select the fraction $c/d$ such that $c$ is minimal among the numerators and $d$ is maximal among the denominators in $\{a/b\}$. Show that $H$ is generated by the coset $c/d + J$.

**9.** The Abelian group $A$ is the direct product of a cyclic subgroup of order $p^2$ and a cyclic subgroup of order $p^3$, where $p$ is a prime. How many subgroups of order $p$ has $A$?

**10.** Use the outer direct product to construct four nonisomorphic Abelian groups of order 36. What feature prevents them from being isomorphic?

**11.** If $\{A, +\}$ and $\{G, \cdot\}$ are isomorphic groups and $\{A, +\}$ is Abelian, what can you say about $G$? Justify.

**12.** A subgroup $H$ of a group $G$ is *maximal* in $G$ if and only if $H$ is proper but is contained in no other proper subgroup of $G$. Find two different maximal subgroups of $\{J/(12), +\}$.

**13.** Show that a subgroup of an Abelian group $\{A, +\}$ is maximal if and only if its index in $A$ is a prime.

## 6.6 Finite Abelian Groups

Now we shall show that, if the positive integer $m$ is a factor of the order $n$ of the Abelian group $A$, then $A$ contains a subgroup of $m$. This is done by considering elements of order a power of a prime.

THEOREM 6.21. *If every element of the finite Abelian group $A$ has order a power of the prime $p$, then $|A| = p^k$.*

This result is proved by mathematical induction on $n$, the order of $A$. Certainly if $n = 1$, then the only element of $A$ is $z$, which is of order $p^0 = 1$.

So our induction hypothesis states that if an Abelian group of order $r < n$ contains only elements whose orders are powers of $p$, then $r$ is a power of $p$.

Now select an element $x$ of order $p$ from $A$; we know such an element exists from our discussion of subgroups of a cyclic group. Form the quotient group $A/(x)$. Since the order of $A/(x)$ is $n/p$ we can apply the induction hypothesis to $A/(x)$ if we show that every element of $A/(x)$ is of order a power of $p$. (Obviously $A/(x)$ is Abelian.) So let $y + (x)$ be an element different from $z + (x)$ in $A/(x)$. If the positive integer $s$ is the order of $y + (x)$, so that, using additive notation,

$$\begin{aligned} s(y + (x)) &= (y + (x)) \oplus \cdots \oplus (y + (x)), \qquad s \text{ times}, \\ &= z + (x), \end{aligned}$$

then we see that $sy$ is an element of the subgroup $(x)$. If

$$sy = z,$$

then surely $s$ is the order of $y$ in $A$. If $sy \neq z$, then since $(x)$ is of order $p$ we see that

$$p(sy) = (ps)y = z.$$

In either case we conclude, from the fact that $y$ is of order a power of $p$, that $s$ is certainly a power of $p$. This means that every element of $A/(x)$ has order a power of $p$, so that, by the induction hypothesis, the order of $A/(x)$, namely $n/p$, is a power of $p$. Hence $n$ is a power of $p$, and the induction is completed, proving the theorem.

For such groups we are able to answer Question 1, Section 6.4, affirmatively.

THEOREM 6.22. *If $A$ is an Abelian group of order $p^r$, then $A$ contains a subgroup of order $p^s$, $0 \leqslant s \leqslant r$.*

Again we proceed by induction on the order of $A$. If $A$ is of order $1 = p^0$, then there is nothing to prove, so select $x$ of order $p$ in $A$ and form $A/(x)$. Since $A/(x)$ is Abelian of order $p^{r-1}$, by the induction hypothesis (unstated) $A/(x)$ contains a subgroup of order $p^{s-1}$, $1 < s < r$, which we shall label $H'$. Now the $p^{s-1}$ elements of $H'$ are cosets of $(x)$, each containing $p$ elements. Therefore the set $H$ of elements of $A$ lying in these cosets contains $p^s$ distinct elements of $A$ since cosets do not overlap. This set $H$ is a subgroup of $A$, for suppose $u$ and $v$ are in $H$. Then $u + (x)$ and $v + (x)$ are elements of $H'$ so that

$$(u + (x)) \oplus (v + (x)) = (u + v) + (x)$$

is in $H'$. Therefore $u + v$ is in $H$. Furthermore, if $y$ is in $H$, then $y + (x)$ is in $H'$, which implies that $-y + (x)$ is in $H'$ and $-y$ is in $H$. Thus $H$ is a subgroup of $A$ of order $p^s$, $1 < s < r$. Since $\{z\}$ is a subgroup of order $p^0$, $(x)$ is a subgroup of order $p^1$, and $A$ is a subgroup of order $p^r$, the theorem is proved.

The basic ideas behind these proofs are illustrated by the following example.

*Example* 1. Let $A$ be the additive group $J/(8)$ and $K$ be the subgroup of order two. Then $A/K$ is of order four and consists of the cosets

$$\begin{aligned} 0 + K &= \{0, 4\} = K, \\ 1 + K &= \{1, 5\}, \\ 2 + K &= \{2, 6\}, \\ 3 + K &= \{3, 7\}. \end{aligned}$$

We note first that the element $2 + K$ of $A/K$ is of order two since

$$(2 + K) \oplus (2 + K) = 4 + K = 0 + K.$$

The element $2 + 2 = 4$ is in $K$ so that $y = 2$ is of order four in $A$.

Now the two elements $2 + K$ and $0 + K$ form a subgroup $H'$ of $A/K$ since $2 + K$ is of order two. Then the set $H$ of elements of $A$ comprising these cosets is

$$H = \{0, 4, 2, 6\},$$

and this set is easily seen to be the cyclic subgroup (2) of $A$.

The general finite Abelian group is handled by expressing it as the direct product of subgroups of prime power order. This result is an analog of the Fundamental Theorem of Arithmetic.

THEOREM 6.23. *Let $A$ be an Abelian group of order $n$ and $n = p_1^{e_1} \cdots p_r^{e_r}$ be the factorization of $n$ into distinct prime powers. Then $A$ contains exactly one subgroup $A_i$ of order $p_i^{e_i}$ for each $i = 1, 2, \cdots, r$, and*

$$A = A_1 \otimes \cdots \otimes A_r.$$

We define $A_i$ to be the set of all elements of $A$ of order a power of $p_i$. To show that $A_i$ is a subgroup of $A$ we take $x$ and $y$ to have orders $p^a$ and $p^b$, respectively, where $p = p_i$. Taking $c$ to denote the larger of $a$ and $b$ we see that

$$p^c(x + y) = p^c x + p^c y = z,$$

so that the order of $x + y$ is a divisor of $p^c$. Hence $x + y$ is in $A_i$. And if $x$ is in $A_i$, then certainly $-x$ is in $A_i$ since

$$-x = (p^a - 1)x = x + \cdots + x, \qquad p^a - 1 \text{ times}.$$

Therefore $A_i$ is a subgroup of $A$, and by Theorem 6.21 we know that the order of $A_i$ is a power of $p_i$.

Now select an arbitrary element $w$ of $A$. The order of $w$, say $m$, is a factor of $n$, so that $m$ factors as

$$m = m_1 m_2 \cdots m_r$$

where $m_i$ is a factor of $p_i^{e_i}$. Denote by $q_i$ the positive integer

$$q_i = m/m_i, \qquad i = 1, 2, \cdots, r.$$

Then the set of $r$ integers $\{q_1, \cdots, q_r\}$ is a relatively prime set, and we know from our study of the G.C.F. that integers $t_i$ exist such that

$$1 = q_1t_1 + \cdots + q_rt_r.$$

Therefore in $A$ we have

$$\begin{aligned} w = 1w &= (q_1t_1 + \cdots + q_rt_r)w \\ &= (q_1t_1)w + \cdots + (q_rt_r)w, \end{aligned}$$

a decomposition of $w$ as a sum of certain elements $w_i = q_it_iw$ of $A$. We know that

$$q_im_i = m,$$

so that

$$m_iw_i = t_i(m)w = t_iz = z.$$

Therefore the order of the element $w_i$ is a factor of $m_i$ which is a factor of $p_i^{e_i}$. This means that $w_i$ is in $A_i$ so that we have expressed $w$ as a sum of elements, one from each subgroup $A_i$.

Since the orders of the subgroups $A_i$ are powers of different primes we see from our work in the previous section that

$$A_1 \otimes A_2, (A_1 \otimes A_2) \otimes A_3, \cdots, A_1 \otimes A_2 \otimes A_3 \otimes \cdots \otimes A_r$$

are subgroups of A which are expressible as direct products. But the above decomposition of $w$, an arbitrary element of $A$, shows that the subgroup $A_1 \otimes \cdots \otimes A_r$ contains every element of $A$. Hence

$$A = A_1 \otimes A_2 \otimes \cdots \otimes A_r.$$

This means that the order of $A$ is the product of the orders of the $A_i$, so that

$$|A_i| = p_i^{e_i}, \qquad i = 1, 2, \cdots, r,$$

and the theorem is proved.

*Example* 2. Illustrate the above proof by decomposing the group $\{J/(30), \oplus\}$.

Using the sharper notation for $J/(30)$ to indicate distinctions between integers and elements of $J/(30)$, we see by examining the group elements that corresponding to the factorization, $30 = 2 \cdot 3 \cdot 5$, we have

$$\begin{aligned} A_1 &= \{[0], [15]\}, \qquad \text{for } p_1 = 2, \\ A_2 &= \{[0], [10], [20]\}, \qquad \text{for } p_2 = 3, \end{aligned}$$

and

$$A_3 = \{[0], [6], [12], [18], [24]\}, \qquad \text{for } p_3 = 5.$$

Certainly these are subgroups of $J/(30)$.

Now select as $w$ the element [8]. Then the order of this element is 15 since 120 is the least positive multiple of 8 which is divisible by 30. Thus $m = 15$ with

$m_1 = 1$, $m_2 = 3$, and $m_3 = 5$, and so $q_1 = 15$, $q_2 = 5$, and $q_3 = 3$. Certainly the G.C.F. (15, 5, 3) is 1, and we can find integers $t_i$ such that

$$1 = t_1q_1 + t_2q_2 + t_3q_3 = 0 \cdot 15 + (-1)5 + 2 \cdot 3.$$

The corresponding decomposition of $w = [8]$ is

$$\begin{aligned}[8] &= (0 + (-5) + 6)[8] = 0[8] \oplus (-5)[8] \oplus 6[8] \\ &= [0] \oplus [20] \oplus [18]\end{aligned}$$

since

$$[-40] = [20] \quad \text{and} \quad [48] = [18].$$

Thus $w_1 = [0]$ is in $A_1$, $w_2 = [20]$ is in $A_2$, and $w_3 = [18]$ is in $A_3$, and

$$J/(30) = A_1 \otimes A_2 \otimes A_3.$$

A key point in the proof is the fact that, if $H$ and $K$ are subgroups of a finite Abelian group $A$ and if $(|H|, |K|) = 1$, then the set $\{h + k: h \text{ in } H$ and $K$ in $K\}$ is a subgroup of $A$ which is the direct product of $H$ and $K$, $H \otimes K$. That the set $\{h + k: h \text{ in } H \text{ and } k \text{ in } K\}$ is a subgroup of $A$ is quite obvious, and it is the direct product of $H$ and $K$ by Theorem 6.19, essentially.

THEOREM 6.24. *If $d$ is a factor of the order of the finite Abelian group $A$, then $A$ contains a subgroup of order $d$.*

Since $d$ is a factor of $|A| = n = p_1^{e_1} \cdots p_r^{e_r}$ we know that $d$ is a product of powers of the primes $p_i$,

$$d = p_1^{f_1} \cdots p_r^{f_r}, \qquad 0 \leqslant f_i \leqslant e_i.$$

From $A_i$ we select a subgroup of order $p_i^{f_i}$, which exists by Theorem 6.22, and form the subgroup

$$B = B_1 \otimes B_2 \otimes \cdots \otimes B_r.$$

From the above observation we see that the order of $B$ is $d$.

*Example* 3. Select from the group $J/(30)$ a subgroup of order six and a subgroup of order 15 by the above method.

Since the group $J/(30)$ is factored in Example 2 we note that

$$A_1 \otimes A_2 = \{[0] \oplus [0], [0] \oplus [10], [0] \oplus [20], [15] \oplus [0], [15] \oplus [10], [15] \oplus [20]\}$$

is the cyclic group ([5]) of order six in $J/(30)$. Similarly, $A^2 \otimes A_3$ is the cyclic group ([2]) of order 15.

These results do not exhaust the known theory of Abelian, even finite Abelian, groups in any sense. They do, however, serve to illustrate some of the ideas used in developing these subjects.

## Exercise 6.6

**1.** Let $A$ be the outer direct product of the two groups $\{J/(4), \oplus\}$ and $\{J/(6), \oplus\}$.

(i) Find the prime power subgroups $A_i$ of $A$.

(ii) Find all of the subgroups of $A$.

**2.** Decompose the group $\{J/(24), \oplus\}$ by the method of Theorem 6.23. Compare with the results of Problem 1.

**3.** How many subgroups of order eight does an Abelian group of order 120 possess? Why? Can you answer this question for 4 instead of 8 without more information about the group?

**4.** Why are the subgroups $A_i$ of Theorem 6.23 the only subgroups of order $p_i^{e_i}$?

**5.** Show that an Abelian group of order 10 is isomorphic with some subgroup of an Abelian group of order 9000.

**6.** Is a group of order four necessarily isomorphic with some subgroup of an Abelian group of order 100? Explain.

**7.** If the Abelian group $A$ is the direct product of a cyclic subgroup $H$ of order 12 and a cyclic subgroup $K$ of order 15, how many different cyclic subgroups of order 12 does $A$ contain?

**8.** Let $\{A, +\}$ be an Abelian group of order $n$ containing elements $a_1, a_2, \cdots, a_n$. If the sum of the $n$ elements, $a_1 + a_2 + \cdots + a_n$, is not the identity element, then what can you say about $A$ and $n$?

**9.** Show that the set $H$ of all elements of finite order in the Abelian group $\{A, +\}$ is a subgroup of $A$ with the property that $A/H$ contains only one element of finite order (viz., the identity element).

**10.** Prove that, if the Abelian group $\{A, +\}$ of order $p^r$ contains exactly one subgroup of order $p, p^2, \cdots,$ and $p^{r-1}$, then $A$ is a cyclic group.

## 6.7 Normal Subgroups

For groups which are not Abelian the problems are more difficult and the answers less satisfactory. It is, perhaps, astonishing that the results of the last two sections can even be partially extended to non-Abelian groups.

To emphasize the fact that we are no longer dealing exclusively with Abelian groups we again adopt the multiplicative-exponential notation.

The first thing we observe is that the definition of a binary operation on the cosets of a subgroup of an Abelian group does not always yield a binary operation on the set of left cosets of a subgroup of a non-Abelian group. Suppose $H$ is a subgroup of the group $\{G, \cdot\}$, and consider the two left cosets $aH$ and $bH$. Our success in defining $A/H$ for an Abelian group leads us to define, for **arbitrary** $a$ and $b$ in $G$,

$$aH \cdot bH = (a \cdot b)H.$$

To prove that this defines a binary operation on the set of left cosets of $H$ we have to show that

$$aH = a_1H \qquad \text{and} \qquad bH = b_1H$$

imply that $(a \cdot b)H = (a_1 \cdot b_1)H$. Now $aH = a_1H$ implies that $a = a_1 \cdot h_1$ for some $h_1$ in $H$, and $bH = b_1H$ implies that $b = b_1 \cdot h_2$ for some $h_2$ in $H$. Therefore,

$$a \cdot b \cdot h = a_1 \cdot h_1 \cdot b_1 \cdot h_2 \cdot h$$

so that

$$(a \cdot b)H = (a_1 \cdot h_1 \cdot b_1)H,$$

and, because of the lack of commutativity in $G$, there is in general no way to get rid of the unwanted $h_1$. Thus a binary operation is *not* defined, in general.

*Example* 1. Let $H$ be a subgroup of order two in the symmetric group $S_3$ on three elements, and attempt to "multiply" the left cosets of $H$.

Using the notation and operation table of Example 1 of Section 6.4, we take as $H$ the subgroup $\{e, c\}$. Then the left cosets of $H$ are

$$eH = \{e, c\} = cH$$
$$aH = \{a, f\} = fH$$
$$bH = \{b, d\} = dH.$$

Now the "product" of $aH$ and $bH$ is

$$aH \cdot bH = (a \cdot b)H = eH,$$

whereas the "product" of $fH$ and $dH$ is

$$fH \cdot dH = (f \cdot d)H = bH.$$

Since $aH = fH$ and $bH = dH$ but $eH \neq bH$ we see that a unique "product" is not obtained, and so we do not have a binary operation on the left cosets of $H$.

Now let $K$ be the subgroup $\{e, a, b\}$ of $S_3$. The left cosets of $K$ are

$$eK = aK = bK = \{e, a, b\}$$

and

$$cK = dK = fK = \{c, d, f\}.$$

A little calculating shows us that

$$eK \cdot eK = eK \cdot aK = aK \cdot bK = bK \cdot aK = bK \cdot bK = eK$$

and

$$aK \cdot cK = bK \cdot dK = eK \cdot fK = cK,$$

and these equations indicate that the "product" is well defined for the left cosets of *some* subgroups of a non-Abelian group. Consequently we are led to the following weak commutativity condition.

DEFINITION 6.9. The subgroup $H$ of the group $G$ is *normal* in $G$ if and only if for every $x$ in $G$ the left coset $xH$ equals the right coset $Hx$.

We see that every subgroup of an Abelian group is normal. Also the subgroup $K$ of the example above is normal in $S_3$ since the right cosets of $K$ are

$$Ke = \{e, a, b\} = Ka = Kb$$

and

$$Kc = \{c, d, f\} = Kd = Kf.$$

THEOREM 6.25. *If $H$ is a normal subgroup of $\{G, \cdot\}$ then the relation $aH \cdot bH = (a \cdot b)H$ for each $a$ and $b$ in $G$ defines an associative binary operation on $G/H$, the set of cosets of $H$ in $G$.*

Let $a_1$ and $b_1$ be elements of $aH$ and $bH$, respectively. Then $a = a_1 \cdot h_1$ for some $h_1$ in $H$ and $b = b_1 \cdot h_2$ for some $h_2$. Furthermore, since $Hb_1 = b_1H$, there is an element $h_3$ in $H$ such that $h_1 \cdot b_1 = b_1 \cdot h_3$. Therefore

$$\begin{aligned} a \cdot b &= a_1 \cdot h_1 \cdot b_1 \cdot h_2 \\ &= a_1 \cdot b_1 \cdot (h_3 \cdot h_2), \end{aligned}$$

so that $a \cdot b$ lies in both of the cosets $(a \cdot b)H$ and $(a_1 \cdot b_1)H$. Hence

$$aH \cdot bH = a_1H \cdot b_1H,$$

and we have a binary operation on $G/H$.

The associativity is immediate from that property in $\{G, \cdot\}$.

*Corollary* 6.25.1. The system $\{G/H, \cdot\}$ is a group when $H$ is a normal subgroup of $G$.

Obviously the coset $eH = He$ is the identity element of $G/H$, and the inverse of the coset $aH$ is the coset $a^{-1}H = Ha^{-1}$.

DEFINITION 6.10. The system $\{G/H, \cdot\}$ is the *quotient group* of the group $G$ over the normal subgroup $H$.

The concept of normal subgroup can also be approached through the concept of homomorphism. This of course should be expected from our discussion in the previous chapter in which we related certain subsystems with homomorphisms.

DEFINITION 6.11. A mapping $F$ from a group $\{G, \cdot\}$ onto a group $\{C, \bigcirc\}$ is a *homomorphism* of $G$ onto $C$ if and only if $F(a \cdot b) = F(a) \bigcirc F(b)$.

Clearly an isomorphism is a special case of a homomorphism, but let us look at a homomorphism which is not an isomorphism.

*Example* 2. Find a homomorphism, if one exists, from the symmetric group $S_3$ onto the group $\{J/(2), +\}$.

Define the mapping $F$ by its images:

$$F(e) = F(a) = F(b) = 0$$

and

$$F(c) = F(d) = F(f) = 1.$$

Then

$$F(a \cdot b) = F(e) = 0 = F(a) + F(b) = 0 + 0,$$

and

$$F(a \cdot c) = F(f) = 1 = F(a) + F(c) = 0 + 1.$$

In this manner we can verify that $F$ is a homomorphism of $S_3$ onto $J/(2)$.

We observe in this example that the image of the identity of $S_3$ is the identity of $J/(2)$ and that the inverse of an image element is the image of the inverse. Thus the inverse of $F(a)$ is $F(a^{-1}) = F(b)$ and the inverse of $F(c)$ is $F(c^{-1}) = F(c)$.

THEOREM 6.26. *If $F$ is a homomorphism of the group $\{G, \cdot\}$ onto the group $\{C, \bigcirc\}$, then $F(e)$ is the identity element of $C$ and the inverse of $F(a)$ is $F(a^{-1})$.*

This requires only a verification. Certainly the equations

$$F(e) \bigcirc F(a) = F(e \cdot a) = F(a) = F(a \cdot e) = F(a) \bigcirc F(e)$$

show that $F(e)$ is the identity element of $C$ since every element of $C$ is of the form $F(a)$ for some $a$ in $G$. Then the equations

$$F(a) \bigcirc F(a^{-1}) = F(a \cdot a^{-1}) = F(e) = F(a^{-1} \cdot a) = F(a^{-1}) \bigcirc F(a)$$

show that $F(a^{-1})$ is the inverse of $F(a)$.

Example 2 above also illustrates the fact that the elements of $G$ which map onto the identity element of $C$ form a normal subgroup of $G$. This set is called the *kernel* of the homomorphism.

THEOREM 6.27. *The kernel of the homomorphism $F$ from the group $\{G, \cdot\}$ onto the group $\{C, \bigcirc\}$ is a normal subgroup $K$ of $G$. Moreover $\{G/K, \cdot\}$* and *$\{C, \bigcirc\}$ are isomorphic groups.*

The kernel $K$ of $F$ is not empty since $e$ is in $K$ by Theorem 6.26. Now let $h$ and $k$ be two elements of $K$. By definition of $K$ we know that $F(h) = F(k) = F(e)$, the identity of $C$. Therefore

$$F(h \cdot k) = F(h) \bigcirc F(k) = F(e) \bigcirc F(e) = F(e)$$

so that $h \cdot k$ is in $K$. Also, since $F(e)$ is its own inverse in $C$ we see from the previous result that if $F(h) = F(e)$ then certainly $F(h^{-1}) = F(e)$, the inverse of $F(e)$. Thus we see that $K$ is a subgroup of $G$.

Consider the left coset $xK$; an element of this set is of the form $x \cdot k$ with $k$ in $K$. Then

$$\begin{aligned} F(x \cdot k \cdot x^{-1}) &= F(x) \bigcirc F(k) \bigcirc F(x^{-1}) = F(x) \bigcirc F(e) \bigcirc F(x^{-1}) \\ &= F(x \cdot e \cdot x^{-1}) = F(x \cdot x^{-1}) = F(e), \end{aligned}$$

so that $x \cdot k \cdot x^{-1}$ is an element $h$ of $K$. This means that

$$x \cdot k \cdot x^{-1} = h, \qquad x \cdot k \cdot x^{-1} \cdot x = h \cdot x$$

and

$$x \cdot k = h \cdot x.$$

Therefore the left coset $xK$ is a subset of the right coset $Kx$. A similar argument, starting with $k \cdot x$ from $Kx$ and dealing with the product $x^{-1} \cdot k \cdot x$, shows that $Kx \subseteq xK$. Hence we conclude that $xK = Kx$ for every $x$ in $G$ so that $K$ is a normal subgroup of $G$.

Finally we claim that the mapping $E$ from $C$ to $G/K$ defined by

$$E\colon F(a) \to aK$$

is an isomorphism between $\{C, \bigcirc\}$ and $\{G/K, \cdot\}$. The mapping certainly preserves the binary operations since

$$E\colon F(a) \bigcirc F(b) = F(a \cdot b) \to (a \cdot b)K = aK \cdot bK,$$

so we need only to show that $E$ is one-to-one. Suppose $F(a)$ and $F(b)$ are mapped onto the same element of $G/K$. This means that

$$aK = bK$$

which implies that, for some $k$ in $K$,

$$a = b \cdot k.$$

Therefore

$$F(a) = F(b \cdot k) = F(b) \bigcirc F(k) = F(b) \bigcirc F(e) = F(b)$$

and we conclude that distinct elements of $C$ are mapped onto distinct elements of $G/K$. Hence $C$ and $G/K$ are isomorphic groups.

This result suggests that, if $H$ is a normal subgroup of the group $\{G, \cdot\}$, then $\{G/H, \cdot\}$ is a homomorphic image of $G$, and that is indeed the case. Thus to find a normal subgroup we need only find a homomorphism, and to find a homomorphic image we need only find a normal subgroup.

THEOREM 6.28. *If $H$ is a normal subgroup of $\{G, \cdot\}$, then the mapping $F$: $a \to aH$, each $a$ in $G$, is a homomorphism of $\{G, \cdot\}$ onto $\{G/H, \cdot\}$ with kernel $H$.*

The mapping is surely a homomorphism since

$$(a \cdot b)H = aH \cdot bH$$

implies that

$$F(a \cdot b) = F(a) \cdot F(b).$$

And since the identity element of $G/H$ is the coset $H = eH$ we see that the kernel of the homomorphism is the set of elements $x$ of $G$ such that $xH = H$. Certainly this set is precisely $H$.

We note that in the last part of the proof of Theorem 6.27 a characterization of a normal subgroup which is quite commonly used was touched upon. The set of all products $x \cdot h \cdot x^{-1}$ for each $h$ in the subgroup $H$ and a fixed element $x$ of $G$ is denoted by $xHx^{-1}$.

THEOREM 6.29. *The subgroup $H$ of the group $\{G, \cdot\}$ is normal in $G$ if and only if $H = xHx^{-1}$ for every $x$ in $G$.*

Suppose $H = xHx^{-1}$; then we must show that $xH = Hx$. This was done essentially in the latter part of the proof of Theorem 6.27. Let $x \cdot h$ be in $xH$. Then $x \cdot h \cdot x^{-1} = k$ for some $k$ in $H$ from the condition $xHx^{-1} = H$.

Therefore

$$x \cdot h = x \cdot h \cdot x^{-1} \cdot x = k \cdot x,$$

implying that $xH \subseteq Hx$. Let $h \cdot x$ be in $Hx$. Since $H = xHx^{-1}$ there is an element $g$ in $H$ such that $h = x \cdot g \cdot x^{-1}$. Then

$$h \cdot x = (x \cdot g \cdot x^{-1}) \cdot x = x \cdot g$$

so that $Hx \subseteq xH$. Hence $Hx = xH$, and since $x$ is arbitrary we conclude that $H$ is normal in $G$.

Conversely suppose $Hx = xH$ for every $x$ in $G$. Let $h$ be an element of $H$. Then $h \cdot x = x \cdot k$ for some element $k$ in $H$, and we see that

$$h = h \cdot x \cdot x^{-1} = x \cdot k \cdot x^{-1}$$

so that $H \subseteq xHx^{-1}$. And let $x \cdot h \cdot x^{-1}$ be an element of $xHx^{-1}$. Since $xH = Hx$ there exists an element $g$ in $H$ such that $x \cdot h = g \cdot x$. Then

$$x \cdot h \cdot x^{-1} = (g \cdot x) \cdot x^{-1} = g$$

so that $xHx^{-1} \subseteq H$. So we conclude that

$$H = xHx^{-1}.$$

*Example* 3. Find a homomorphic image of order four of the symmetry group of a square.

Consider the square with vertices $a$, $b$, $c$, $d$ in Fig. 6.2. The two mappings

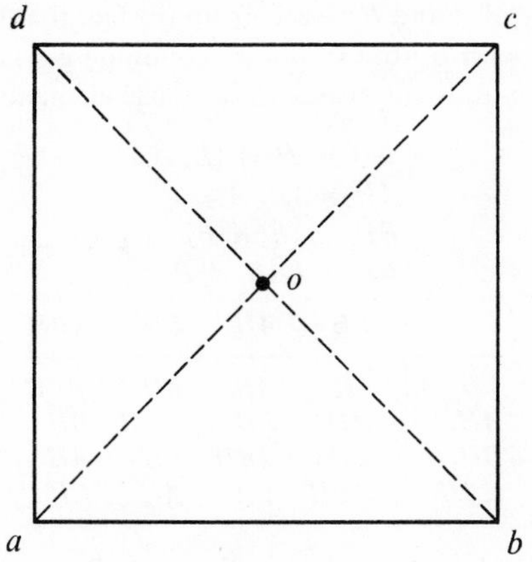


**Figure 6.2**

$$A = \{(a, b), (b, c), (c, d), (d, a)\}$$

and

$$B = \{(a, c), (b, b), (c, a), (d, d)\},$$

which are the rotation of 90° about the point $o$ and the rotation of 180° about the line through $b$ and $d$, respectively, generate the entire group. That is, the eight elements

$$E = A^4 = B^2, A, A^2, A^3, B, AB, A^2B, A^3B$$

make up the group $G$ of symmetries of the square. The verification of this is a simple computational problem. We note, for example, that the composite function $AB$ is

$$AB = \{(a, b), (b, a), (c, d), (d, c)\}.$$

This is the rotation about the line through the midpoints of the sides joining $a$ with $b$ and $c$ with $d$.

| | $E$ | $A$ | $A^2$ | $A^3$ | $B$ | $AB$ | $A^2B$ | $A^3B$ |
|---|---|---|---|---|---|---|---|---|
| $E$ | $E$ | $A$ | $A^2$ | $A^3$ | $B$ | $AB$ | $A^2B$ | $A^3B$ |
| $A$ | $A$ | $A^2$ | $A^3$ | $E$ | $AB$ | $A^2B$ | $A^3B$ | $B$ |
| $A^2$ | $A^2$ | $A^3$ | $E$ | $A$ | $A^2B$ | $A^3B$ | $B$ | $AB$ |
| $A^3$ | $A^3$ | $E$ | $A$ | $A^2$ | $A^3B$ | $B$ | $AB$ | $A^2B$ |
| $B$ | $B$ | $A^3B$ | $A^2B$ | $AB$ | $E$ | $A^3$ | $A^2$ | $A$ |
| $AB$ | $AB$ | $B$ | $A^3B$ | $A^2B$ | $A$ | $E$ | $A^3$ | $A^2$ |
| $A^2B$ | $A^2B$ | $AB$ | $B$ | $A^3B$ | $A^2$ | $A$ | $E$ | $A^3$ |
| $A^3B$ | $A^3B$ | $A^2B$ | $AB$ | $B$ | $A^3$ | $A^2$ | $A$ | $E$ |

The operation table of this group is as shown. From this table we see that the set $H = \{E, A^2\}$ is a subgroup, and checking the two products

$$AA^2 = A^2A = A^3 \qquad \text{and} \qquad BA^2 = A^2B$$

we conclude that $H$ is a normal subgroup of $G$. For since every element of $G$ is composed of products of $A$ and $B$ we see, from the fact that the elements $E$ and $A^2$ commute with $A$ and with $B$, that $C$ and $A^2$ commute with every element of $G$.

Now we form the quotient group $G/H$ whose elements are the cosets of $H$:

$$EH = H = \{E, A^2\}$$
$$AH = \{A, A^3\}$$
$$BH = \{B, A^2B\}$$
$$ABH = \{AB, A^3B\}.$$

| | $EH$ | $AH$ | $BH$ | $ABH$ |
|---|---|---|---|---|
| $EH$ | $EH$ | $AH$ | $BH$ | $ABH$ |
| $AH$ | $AH$ | $EH$ | $ABH$ | $BH$ |
| $BH$ | $BH$ | $ABH$ | $EH$ | $AH$ |
| $ABH$ | $ABH$ | $BH$ | $AH$ | $EH$ |

The operation table for $G/H$ is as shown. By using this table it is easy to see that the mapping $F$ defined by

$$F: x \to xH, \qquad \text{each } x \text{ in } G,$$

is a homomorphism. Note that $G/H$ is an Abelian group although $G$ is non-Abelian.

*Example* 4. Find a nonnormal subgroup of the symmetry group of a square.

Using the notation and table for $G$ of the preceding example, we see that the set

$K = \{E, B\}$ is a subgroup since $B^2 = E$. However, since $ABA^{-1} = ABA^3 = A^2B$ we see that

$$AKA^{-1} \neq K.$$

Therefore $K$ is not a normal subgroup of $G$ by Theorem 6.29. Or, we see that the two cosets $AK$ and $KA$ are not equal since

$$AK = \{A, AB\} \quad \text{and} \quad KA = \{A, A^3B = BA\}.$$

## Exercise 6.7

**1.** Analyze the group of symmetries of the square (see Example 3) as follows: (*a*) Find all of the subgroups of $G$. (*b*) Find all of the normal subgroups of $G$. (*c*) Find all of the nonisomorphic homomorphic images of $G$. (*d*) Find the center of $G$. (See Problem 3.)

**2.** Show that the outer direct product of $\{J/(2), +\}$ with $\{J/(2), +\}$ is a homomorphic image of the symmetry group of a square.

**3.** Prove that the center of a group $G$, namely, the set of $x$ in $G$ such that $gx = xg$ for every $g$ in $G$, is a normal subgroup of $G$.

**4.** Prove that the intersection of two normal subgroups of $G$ is a normal subgroup of $G$.

**5.** Show that the set $T = \{E, A^2, B, A^2B\}$ of $G$ in Example 3 is a normal subgroup of $G$, and that $K = \{E, B\}$ is a normal subgroup of $T$. Compare with Example 4, and show that normality does not lead to a transitive relation on the set of subgroups of a group.

**6.** Let $H$ and $K$ be normal subgroups of the group $G$. Show that, if $H \cap K = \{e\}$, then $hk = kh$ for any $h$ in $H$ and $k$ in $K$.

**7.** In the group $G/H$ of Example 3 find a subgroup $S''$ of order two. Show that the set $S$ of all elements of $G$ which are mapped onto the elements of $S''$ by the homomorphism described is a subgroup of $G$.

**8.** Let $F$ be a homomorphism of the group $\{G, \cdot\}$ onto the group $\{C, \bigcirc\}$. Show that, if $H$ is a subgroup of $G$, then the images $F(h)$ of the elements $h$ of $H$ form a subgroup of $C$. Illustrate with the groups of Example 3.

**9.** Let $\{C, \bigcirc\}$ be a homomorphic image of the group $\{G, \cdot\}$, and let $H''$ be a normal subgroup of $C$. Prove that the set $H$ of elements of $G$ which are mapped onto elements of $H''$ is a normal subgroup of $G$. (See Problem 7.)

**10.** What are the properties of the relation, homomorphism, on a set $M$ of groups?

**11.** The following define functions from the multiplicative group $R'$ of nonzero rationals to itself. Which, if any, are homomorphisms? Explain and describe the homomorphic images and the kernels.

(*a*) $r \to 1/r.$
(*b*) $r \to |r|.$
(*c*) $r \to r^n,$ $n$ some fixed integer.
(*d*) $r \to -r + a,$ $a$ some fixed integer.

**12.** If $H$ and $K$ are subgroups of $G$ such that $H$ is normal in $G$, $G = HK$, and $H \cap K = \{e\}$, show that $G/H$ is isomorphic with $K$. (Show that each coset of $H$ contains one and only one element of $K$ as in the proof of Theorem 6.20.)

**13.** Let $H$ and $K$ be subgroups of the group $G$. We say that $H$ is *conjugate* with $K$ in $G$ if and only if $G$ contains an element $x$ such that $H = xKx^{-1}$. Show that this defines an equivalence relation on the set of subgroups of $G$. Illustrate with the subgroups of the group of Example 3.

**14.** Prove that the set $xHx^{-1}$ is a subgroup of $G$ for each $x$ in $G$ if and only if $H$ is a subgroup of $G$.

**15.** Show that the mapping $F_x$ of the group $G$ onto $G$ defined for an element $x$ of $G$ by

$$F_x: g \to xgx^{-1}$$

for each $g$ in $G$, is an isomorphism of the group $G$ with itself. This mapping is called an *inner automorphism* of $G$. Find all of the inner automorphisms of the group $G$ of Example 3.

**16.** Show that the set of all inner automorphisms of a group $G$ is a group relative to the composition of functions. Calculate the operation table for the inner automorphism group of the group $G$ of Example 3.

**17.** Prove that a group is Abelian if and only if its inner automorphism group is of order 1.

**18.** Analyze the symmetry group of a regular hexagon.

**19.** Analyze the group of permutations on the set $\{1, 2, 3, 4\}$.

**20.** Find a normal subgroup of order 12 in the symmetric group on four elements, and analyze this group of order 12.

## 6.8 Sylow's Theorem

The alternative characterization of a normal subgroup in the previous section leads us to the consideration of elements of the form $xyx'$ or $xyx^{-1}$. From this we obtain an equivalence relation on the elements of the group $G$. (Note that we are now writing $x \cdot y$ as $xy$.)

DEFINITION 6.12. The element $a$ is *conjugate* with $b$ in the group $G$ if and only if $G$ contains an element $x$ such that $a = xbx^{-1}$.

If we inspect the group of Example 3 in the previous section we see that $A^3$ is conjugate with (or a conjugate of) $A$ since

$$A^3 = BAB^{-1} = BAB = A^3BB.$$

In an Abelian group, of course, each element is conjugate only with itself.

THEOREM 6.30. *The relation of conjugacy is an equivalence relation on* $G$.

Certainly each element $g$ of $G$ is conjugate with itself since $g = ege$. Also from $h = xgx^{-1}$ we get

$$g = ege = x^{-1}xgx^{-1}x = x^{-1}(xgx^{-1})(x^{-1})^{-1}$$

so that

$$g = x^{-1}h(x^{-1})^{-1}.$$

Hence the relation is symmetric. Finally, if

$$h = xgx^{-1} \qquad \text{and} \qquad k = yhy^{-1},$$

then

$$k = yxgx^{-1}y^{-1},$$

and since $(yx)^{-1} = x^{-1}y^{-1}$ we see that

$$k = (yx)g(yx)^{-1}.$$

Thus, if $k$ is conjugate with $h$ and $h$ is conjugate with $g$, then $k$ is conjugate with $g$, and the relation is transitive.

This equivalence relation naturally effects a partition of the group $G$, and the subsets of $G$ which make up this partition are the *conjugate classes* of $G$.

*Example* 1. Determine the conjugate classes of the symmetry group of the square.

Examining the operation table of Example 3 of Section 6.7 we find that the conjugate classes of $G$ are as follows:

$$\begin{aligned} &C_1 = \{\mathbf{E}\}, \qquad C_2 = \{\mathbf{A}^2\} \\ &C_3 = \{\mathbf{A}, \mathbf{A}^3\} \\ &C_4 = \{\mathbf{B}, \mathbf{A}^2\mathbf{B}\} \\ &C_5 = \{\mathbf{AB}, \mathbf{A}^3\mathbf{B}\}. \end{aligned}$$

Clearly all those elements which lie in conjugate classes of a single element together comprise a normal Abelian subgroup $Z$ of $G$, and the elements of $Z$ commute with every element of $G$. This set $Z$ is the *center* of $G$.

In the example above the number of elements in each conjugate class is a divisor of the order of $G$. Another simple example shows this property also.

*Example* 2. Determine the conjugate classes of the symmetric group $S_3$ on three elements.

Using the notation of Example 1 of Section 6.4 we see from the operation table that the conjugate classes of $S_3$ are three in number:

$$\begin{aligned} C_1 &= \{e\} \\ C_2 &= \{a, b\} \\ C_3 &= \{c, d, f\}. \end{aligned}$$

THEOREM 6.31. *The number of elements in a conjugate class of a finite group $G$ is a factor of the order of $G$. If $a$ is an element of the class $C$, then the number of elements in $C$ is the index of the subgroup of elements of $G$ which commute with $a$.*

Let $N_a = \{x\colon x \text{ is in } G \text{ and } xa = ax\}$. This is called the *centralizer* of $a$.

If $x$ and $y$ belong to $N_a$, then

$$xya = x(ya) = x(ay) = (xa)y = axy$$

so that $xy$ is in $N_a$. Furthermore, if $x$ is in $a$, then multiplying the equation

$$xa = ax$$

by $x^{-1}$ on the left and on the right yields

$$x^{-1}xax^{-1} = x^{-1}axx^{-1}$$

or

$$ax^{-1} = x^{-1}a.$$

Therefore $N_a$ is a subgroup of $G$ (whether $G$ is a finite group or not).

Let the index of $N_a = N$ in $G$ be $n$. Then $G$ contains $n$ elements $g_1, \cdots, g_n$ such that the $n$ distinct left cosets of $N$ in $G$ are $g_1N, \cdots, g_nN$. Form the $n$ products

$$g_1ag_1^{-1}, \cdots, g_nag_n^{-1};$$

if two of these were equal, say

$$g_iag_i^{-1} = g_jag_j^{-1},$$

then

$$g_j^{-1}g_ia = ag_j^{-1}g_i$$

so that $g_j^{-1}g_i$ is an element of $N$. But this means that $g_iN = g_jN$, contradicting the distinctness of the cosets unless $i = j$. Thus the class $C$ to which $a$ belongs contains at least $n$ distinct elements, namely, those listed above.

Now suppose $C$ contains $m$ elements, denoted by $a_1 = a, a_2, \cdots, a_m$. From the transitivity of conjugacy we know that $G$ contains elements $x_1 = e, x_2, \cdots, x_m$ such that $a_i = x_iax_i^{-1}$. We shall show that two of these $x$'s cannot lie in the same left coset of $N$. Suppose otherwise; if $x_i$ and $x_j$ lie in $yN$, then

$$x_i = yu \qquad \text{and} \qquad x_j = yv$$

for elements $u$ and $v$ in $N$. Then

$$a_i = x_iax_i^{-1} = yua(yu)^{-1} = yuau^{-1}y^{-1} = yay^{-1},$$

and similarly,

$$a_j = x_jax_j^{-1} = yvav^{-1}y^{-1} = yay^{-1}.$$

This means that

$$a_i = a_j,$$

so that distinct $x$'s lie in different left cosets of $N$. Hence the number of left cosets of $N$ is at least $m$.

From these two arguments we have $m \geq n$ and $n \geq m$. Therefore $m = n$, and the theorem is proved.

*Example* 3. Find the centralizer of the element $B$ of the group of Example 3 in Section 6.7.

By inspecting the operation table we find that

$$B = EBE = A^2BA^2 = BBB = A^2B(B)A^2B.$$

Hence $N_B = \{E, A^2, B, A^2B\}$. The left cosets of $N = N_B$ are $EN$ and $AN$, and the elements of the conjugate class $C_4$ to which $B$ belongs are

$$B = EBE \quad \text{and} \quad A^2B = ABA^3.$$

Using Theorem 6.31 we can prove a very useful result for groups of prime power order.

THEOREM 6.32. *A group $G$ of order $p^r$, $p$ a prime, contains an element $x \neq e$ which commutes with every element of $G$. That is, a group of prime power order has a nontrivial center.*

Consider the distinct conjugate classes $C_1, C_2, \cdots, C_s$ of $G$. If $c_i$ denotes the number of elements in $C_i$, then since every element of $G$ lies in exactly one of these classes, we have

$$p^r = c_1 + c_2 + \cdots + c_s.$$

This *class equation* for $G$ represents nothing more than a counting of the elements of $G$, class by class. Now each of the positive integers $c_i$ is a power of $p$ since by Theorem 6.31 $c_i$ is a factor of $p^r$. Reducing the class equation modulo $p$ shows either that all of the $c_i$ are powers of $p$ greater than 1, or that at least $p$ of the $c_i$ equal 1. But one of the classes, say $C_1$, consists of the identity element only. Therefore $c_1 = 1$, and we see that there must be at least $p - 1$ other classes consisting of single elements, and that any one of these elements has the desired property.

The existence of this element $x$ means that we are able to prove many theorems about groups of prime power order using mathematical induction. To illustrate we shall answer Question 1 of Section 6.4 affirmatively for such groups.

THEOREM 6.33. *If $G$ is a group of order $p^r$, $p$ a prime, then $G$ contains a subgroup of order $p^s$, where $s$ is an integer such that $0 \leqslant s \leqslant r$.*

The proof of this is almost identical with the proof of the corresponding theorem for Abelian $p$-groups. Select an element $y$ of order $p$ which permutes with every element of the group $G$; a suitable power of the element $x$ of Theorem 6.32 will suffice. Then the cyclic subgroup $(y)$ is surely normal in $G$, so we can form the quotient group $G/(y)$ which is of order $p^{r-1}$. By the induction hypothesis for groups of order $p^t$, $t < r$, we know that $G/(y)$ contains a subgroup $H''$ of order $p^{s-1}$ for an integer $s$ such that $1 \leqslant s \leqslant r$. (The case for $s = 0$ is trivial, of course.) Then we claim that the set $H$ of all elements of

$G$ which lie in the cosets of $(y)$ which make up $H''$ (i.e., the elements of $G$ which are mapped onto the elements of $H''$ by the "natural" homomorphism, $F: a \to a(y)$) is a subgroup of order $p^s$ in $G$. This is a simple verification which was worked out earlier in the Abelian case. So the induction step is completed.

For groups of composite order we can prove the existence of subgroups of *prime power order* by using the preceding ideas. First we prove the existence of a subgroup of maximal prime power order, and then invoke the above result.

THEOREM 6.34. *If the order $n$ of the finite group $G$ factors as $n = mp^r$, where $p$ is a prime and $(m, p) = 1$, then $G$ contains a subgroup of order $p^r$.*

If the theorem is not true, then the set of the orders of those groups for which the statement is false for some prime, contains a least positive integer. We shall call this least integer $n$ and take the group $G$ to be a group of this order for which the statement is false ($G$ is sometimes referred to as a "least rascal"). Then for some prime $p$, $n = mp^r$ with $(p, m) = 1$ but $G$ contains no subgroup of order $p^r$. (Note that $r$ is positive.)

Now let $M$ be a proper subgroup of $G$. If $p^r$ is a factor of $|M|$, then we know from the minimality of $n$, which is of course greater than the order of $M$, that $M$ contains a subgroup of order $p^r$. Since a subgroup of $M$ is also a subgroup of $G$ we see that this cannot happen as $G$ contains no subgroup of order $p^r$. Hence we must conclude that $G$ has no proper subgroup whose order is divisible by $p^r$. This means, since the order $n$ of $G$ is the product of the order and the index of each subgroup $H$ of $G$,

$$n = mp^r = |H|[G:H],$$

that the index of every proper subgroup of $G$ is a multiple of $p$.

Consider the number $c_i$ of elements in the conjugate class $C_i$. If $C_i$ contains more than one element, then $c_i$ is the index of a proper subgroup of $G$ and hence is a multiple of $p$. Therefore when we consider the class equation

$$n = mp^r = c_1 + c_2 + \cdots + c_s$$

modulo $p$ we see that the set $Z$ of elements of $G$ which individually form conjugate classes contains $kp$ elements since the above equation becomes

$$0 \equiv c_1 + c_2 + \cdots + c_s \bmod p.$$

Since $Z$ contains the element $e$ we know that $kp \neq 0$. This set $Z$ is a normal Abelian subgroup of $G$ whose elements commute with every element of $G$. Then from our theory of Abelian groups we know that $Z$ contains an element $x$ of order $p$, and certainly the cyclic subgroup $(x)$ is normal in $G$.

Form the quotient group $G/(x)$. Since the order of this group is $mp^{r-1} < n$ we conclude that $G/(x)$ contains a subgroup $H''$ of order $p^{r-1}$. Then the set $H$ of elements of $G$ which lie in the cosets of $(x)$ that make up $H''$ contains $p^r$ elements. Moreover $H$ is easily seen to be a subgroup of $G$. So we have arrived at the impossible conclusion that $G$ does not but does contain a subgroup of order $p^r$. This contradiction is a result of the original assumption that the theorem is false. Hence the theorem is true.

This result is called a *Sylow Theorem* after the nineteenth-century mathematician Sylow, and the subgroups of maximal prime power order, $p^r$, are called *Sylow subgroups.* When the Sylow Theorem is combined with Theorem 6.33 we obtain just about the most general theorem possible on the existence of subgroups of non-Abelian groups.

*Corollary* 6.34.1. If $p^t$ is a factor of the order of the group $G$ and $p$ is a prime, then $G$ contains a subgroup of order $p^t$.

For surely a Sylow subgroup of $G$ of order the maximal power of $p$ dividing the order of $G$ contains a subgroup of order $p^t$ by Theorem 6.33. This is, then, a subgroup of $G$ of order $p^t$.

That it is difficult to say more about the existence of subgroups of $G$ of order $d$ when $d$ is a divisor of the order of $G$ follows from an analysis of the group $A_4$, which is a normal subgroup of order 12 of the symmetric group on four elements. The group $A_4$, which is called the *alternating group* on four elements, has the operation table shown below.

| | $e$ | $x$ | $x^2$ | $y$ | $xy$ | $x^2y$ | $z$ | $xz$ | $x^2z$ | $yz$ | $xyz$ | $x^2yz$ |
|---|---|---|---|---|---|---|---|---|---|---|---|---|
| $e$ | $e$ | $x$ | $x^2$ | $y$ | $xy$ | $x^2y$ | $z$ | $xz$ | $z^2z$ | $yz$ | $xyz$ | $x^2yz$ |
| $x$ | $x$ | $x^2$ | $e$ | $xy$ | $x^2y$ | $y$ | $xz$ | $x^2z$ | $z$ | $xyz$ | $x^2yz$ | $yz$ |
| $x^2$ | $x^2$ | $e$ | $x$ | $x^2y$ | $y$ | $xy$ | $x^2z$ | $z$ | $xz$ | $x^2yz$ | $yz$ | $xyz$ |
| $y$ | $t$ | $xyz$ | $x^2z$ | $e$ | $xz$ | $x^2yz$ | $yz$ | $xy$ | $x^2$ | $z$ | $x$ | $x^2y$ |
| $xy$ | $xy$ | $x^2yz$ | $z$ | $x$ | $x^2z$ | $yz$ | $xyz$ | $x^2y$ | $e$ | $xz$ | $x^2$ | $y$ |
| $x^2y$ | $x^2y$ | $yz$ | $xz$ | $x^2$ | $z$ | $xyz$ | $x^2yz$ | $y$ | $x$ | $x^2z$ | $e$ | $xy$ |
| $z$ | $z$ | $xy$ | $x^2yz$ | $yz$ | $x$ | $x^2z$ | $e$ | $xyz$ | $x^2y$ | $y$ | $xz$ | $x^2$ |
| $xz$ | $xz$ | $x^2y$ | $yz$ | $xyz$ | $x^2$ | $z$ | $x$ | $x^2yz$ | $y$ | $xy$ | $x^2z$ | $e$ |
| $x^2z$ | $x^2z$ | $y$ | $xyz$ | $x^2yz$ | $e$ | $xz$ | $x^2$ | $yz$ | $xy$ | $x^2y$ | $z$ | $x$ |
| $yz$ | $yz$ | $xz$ | $x^2y$ | $z$ | $xyz$ | $x^2$ | $y$ | $x$ | $x^2yz$ | $e$ | $xy$ | $x^2z$ |
| $xyz$ | $xyz$ | $x^2z$ | $y$ | $xz$ | $x^2yz$ | $e$ | $xy$ | $x^2$ | $yz$ | $x$ | $x^2y$ | $z$ |
| $x^2yz$ | $x^2yz$ | $z$ | $xy$ | $x^2z$ | $yz$ | $x$ | $x^2y$ | $e$ | $xyz$ | $x^2$ | $y$ | $xz$ |

From this table we can show that this group contains no subgroup of order six. Suppose that $H$ is a subgroup of order six. Then $H$ contains a subgroup of order three and a subgroup of order two by the Sylow Theorem. Since the only subgroups of $A_4$ of order two are the three sets $\{e, y\}$, $\{e, z\}$, and $\{e, yz\}$, one of these is in $H$. But combining any one of these with any one of the four subgroups of order three by writing all possible products reveals that such an $H$ cannot exist. For example, if we combine $\{e, y\}$ with $\{e, x, x^2\}$, we get the 12 elements

$$e, y, x, x^2, xy, x^2y, yx = xyz, yx^2 = x^2z, z = xyx_2, x^2yz = xyz,$$
$$yz = x^2yx, xz = x^2yx^2.$$

Thus a subgroup of order six cannot contain $\{e, y\}$ and $\{e, x, x^2\}$. In this manner we show that $A_4$, although of order 12, contains no subgroup of order six.

## Exercise 6.8

**1.** Find all of the Sylow subgroups of $A_4$.

**2.** Find all of the Sylow subgroups for $p = 3$ of the symmetric group on four elements. (How do they compare with the Sylow subgroups of $A_4$?)

**3.** Find the conjugate classes and the class equation for $A_4$.

**4.** Find the class equation of the symmetry group of a square.

**5.** Find the class equation of the symmetry group of a regular hexagon.

**6.** Describe the class equation of an Abelian group.

**7.** Show that, if the group $G$ has exactly one Sylow subgroup $P$ for the prime $p$, then $P$ is normal in $G$. (The converse is also true by another theorem of Sylow.)

**8.** Let $H$ be a normal subgroup of prime power order in the finite group $G$. Show that $H$ is contained in every Sylow subgroup of $G$ for that particular prime.

**9.** Show that the center $Z$ of $G$ is the intersection of all of the element centralizers $N_a$.

**10.** In the group $A_4$ find the centralizer of $x$ and of $y$.

**11.** Let $H$ be a subgroup of the group $G$. Show that the set $N_H$ of all elements $x$ of $G$ such that $xHx^{-1} = H$, is a subgroup of $G$ which contains $H$ as a normal subgroup. ($N_H$ is called the *normalizer* of $H$ in $G$.)

**12.** Show that, if $H$ is a subgroup of a finite group $G$, then the index $[G:N_H]$ equals the number of distinct conjugates of $H$ in $G$.

**13.** In $A_4$ find the normalizer of $H = \{e, y\}$ and find the conjugates of $H$. Compare with the statement of Problem 12.

**14.** If $G$ is a group of order $pq$, where $p$ and $q$ are primes and $p < q$, show that $G$ contains exactly one subgroup of order $q$.

**15.** Show that the only finite groups with two conjugate classes are of order two.

**16.** Let $H$ be a proper subgroup of the finite group $G$. Show that $G$ contains at least one element which is in no conjugate of $H$. Illustrate with $G = S_3$ and $H$ a subgroup of order two. (Use the result of Problem 12.)

**17.** Let $H$ be a normal subgroup of the finite group $G$. Show that, if $p$ is not a factor of the index $[G:H]$, then every $p$-Sylow subgroup of $G$ is a subgroup of $H$.

**18.** Describe all (up to an isomorphism) abstract groups of order 10; of order 15.

## 6.9 Additional Remarks

Although there exists no exact analog in the theory of non-Abelian finite groups of the factorization of a positive integer into a product of prime powers, there is a remarkable type of "unique factorization" for such groups which is of importance to the theory of equations. This relationship will be commented upon later.

Let $G$ be a finite group, and choose $H_1$ to be a normal subgroup of $G$ which is (1) not equal to $G$, and (2) not contained in any proper normal subgroup of $G$ except $H_1$. Such a subgroup is called a *maximal normal subgroup* of $G$. There can be several choices for $H_1$. Then in $H_1$ select $H_2$ to be a maximal normal subgroup of $H_1$. Although $H_2$ is normal in $H_1$ it need not be normal in $G$. Select $H_3$ to be a maximal normal subgroup of $H_2$, etc. Since $G$ is finite this procedure must terminate with $H_r = \{e\}$. The resulting ordered collection of subgroups,

$$G \supset H_1 \supset H_2 \supset \cdots \supset H_r = \{e\},$$

is called a *composition series of length r* for the group $G$, and the $r$ factor groups

$$G/H_1, H_1/H_2, \cdots, H_{r-1}/H_r$$

are called the *composition factors* of $G$.

THEOREM 6.35 (JORDAN-HOELDER THEOREM). *The composition factors of the finite group G are unique (up to an isomorphism).*

We shall not prove this theorem (a proof can be found in any of the books listed in the reading list) but give an example instead. Let $G$ be the group of symmetries of a square (Example 3 of Section 6.7). $G$ contains two different maximal normal subgroups:

$$H_1 = \{E, A, A^2, A^3\}$$

and

$$K_1 = \{E, A^2, B, A^2B\}.$$

The subgroup $H_1$ contains exactly one maximal normal subgroup, $H_2 = \{E, A^2\}$. But the group $K_1$ contains three different maximal normal subgroups (so that $G$ has four different composition series). We select $K_2 = \{E, B\}$; note that $K_2$ is normal in $K_1$ but not in $G$. Thus we have two different composition series for $G$, each of length 3:

$$G \supset H_1 \supset H_2 \supset H_3 = \{E\}$$

and

$$G \supset K_1 \supset K_2 \supset K_3 = \{E\}.$$

The composition factors are in each case three groups of order two.

## Exercise 6.9

**1.** Write out all of the composition series of the symmetry group of a square.

**2.** Find the composition factors of the group $\{J/(8), +\}$. How do they compare with the composition factors of the symmetry group of a square?

**3.** Find two composition series for the alternating group $A_4$.

**4.** Show that, if a cyclic group of order $n$ has exactly one composition series, then $n$ is a prime power. Is the converse true?

**5.** What can you say about the composition factors of a cyclic group?

**6.** Prove that all of the composition factors of a group of order $p^n$, $p$ prime, are of order $p$. (Show that in this case a maximal normal subgroup has index $p$.)

**7.** A group is *solvable* if and only if its composition factors have prime orders. Search the references for a description of the smallest nonsolvable group. (It has order 60.)

## 6.10 Suggested Reading

*Articles*

Andree, R., and G. Peterson, "Two theorems on groups," *Amer. Math. Monthly* **61** (1954) 641

Deskins, W., and J. Hill, "On the axioms of a group," *Amer. Math. Monthly* **68** (1961), 795–796.

Johnston, F. E., "The postulational treatment of mathematics as exemplified in the theory of groups," *Amer. Scientist* **33** (1945), 39–48.

MacKay, J., "Another proof of Cauchy's group theorem," *Amer. Math. Monthly* **66** (1959) 119.

MacLane, S., "Algebra," 23d *Yearbook, National Council of Teachers of Mathematics* (1957), 100–144.

Utz, W. R., "Square roots in groups," *Amer. Math. Monthly* **60** (1953), 185–186.

Whittaker, E. T., "On group postulates," *Amer. Math. Monthly* **62** (1955), 631–635.

*Books*

Burnside, W., *Theory of Groups of Finite Order*, 2nd ed., Dover Press, New York, 1955.

Carmichael, R., *Introduction to the Theory of Groups*, Ginn & Company, New York, 1937.

Hall, M., Jr., *The Theory of Groups*, The Macmillan Co., New York, 1959.

Speiser, A., *Theorie der Gruppen von endlicher Ordnung*, Springer, Berlin, 1937.

Zassenhaus, H., *Lehrbuch der Gruppentheorie*, Teubner, Leipzig, 1937.

# 7

# Rings, Domains, and Fields

IN THIS CHAPTER we commence the study of systems which can be thought of as generalized number systems. These systems have two binary operations which will be called addition and multiplication; for the most part we will use the common symbolism for these operations. This convention is more than just a convenience since it serves to highlight the analogy between these new systems and the number systems we already know. However, analogies are not proofs, and the student is warned not to assume that a statement concerning addition and multiplication in these new systems is true simply because it is known to be true in familiar number systems. Rather, these analogies are intended to suggest statements to be proved or disproved. Furthermore the familiar systems should be used as testing places for conjectures and theorems about other systems (of appropriate type, of course).

## 7.1 Definitions and Examples

The most common variety of mathematical system with two binary operations that is widely studied is the ring. This general category is in turn divided into special but often overlapping types of abstract rings.

DEFINITION 7.1. A system consisting of a nonempty set $S$ and two binary operations, called addition and multiplication, on $S$ is a *ring* if and only if the following conditions are satisfied:

Addition: $S$ is an Abelian group relative to addition.
Multiplication: $S$ is a semigroup relative to multiplication.
Distribution: For any elements $a$, $b$, and $c$ of $S$,

$$a(b + c) = ab + ac \qquad \text{and} \qquad (b + c)a = ba + ca.$$

The identity element for addition is denoted by $z$ (for zero), and the additive inverse of $a$ is written as $-a$. The ring is usually denoted by $S$.

By specifying various conditions for the multiplicative semigroup to satisfy we obtain special types of rings which are often more amenable to study than the most general case.

DEFINITION 7.2. A ring $S$ is

(1) A *field* if the nonzero elements of $S$ form an Abelian group relative to multiplication.

(2) A *sfield* (*skew field* or *division ring*) if the nonzero elements of $S$ form a group relative to multiplication.

(3) An *integral domain* if $S$ is a commutative semigroup with an identity $e \neq z$ and without divisors of zero, relative to multiplication.

(4) A *commutative ring* if the multiplicative semigroup $S$ is commutative.

(5) A *ring with identity* if $S$ contains a multiplicative identity element $e \neq z$.

If the defining properties of a field are set down explicitly we have a sizable list. The binary operations of a field satisfy the following:

A1. Addition is associative.

A2. There is an additive identity $z$ such that $a + z = z + a = a$ for each $a$ in $S$.

A3. Each element $a$ has an additive inverse, $-a$.

A4. $a + b = b + a$ for each $a$ and $b$ in $S$.

M1. Multiplication is associative.

M2. There exists in $S$ a nonzero element $e$ such that $ea = ae = a$ for each $a \neq z$ in $S$.

M3. Each element $a \neq z$ has a multiplicative inverse, $a^{-1}$, such that $aa^{-1} = a^{-1}a = e$.

M4. $ab = ba$ for each $a$ and $b$ different from $z$ in $S$.

D. For any elements $a$, $b$, and $c$ of $S$, $a(b + c) = ab + ac$ and $(b + c)a = ba + ca$.

Similar lists can and should be written out for the other types of rings listed above. An integral domain, then, is a nonempty set $S$ with binary operations addition and multiplication satisfying conditions A1, A2, A3, A4, M1, and D from the list above, in addition to

M2′. There is a multiplicative identity $e \neq z$ such that $ea = ae = a$ for every $a$ in $S$.

M3′. $S$ has no divisors of zero (i.e., if $ab = z$, then $a$ and/or $b$ equals $z$).

M4′. $ab = ba$ for each $a$ and $b$ in $S$.

Although properties M2′ and M4′ differ slightly from M2 and M4, respectively, in their statements, the special properties which $z$ possesses eliminate these distinctions as we shall see.

It is quite evident that the same ring can fall into several of these classifications. Certainly any field is also a skew field, and an integral domain is also a ring with identity as well as a commutative ring. We can represent this overlapping of these categories of rings schematically as is shown in Fig. 7.1.

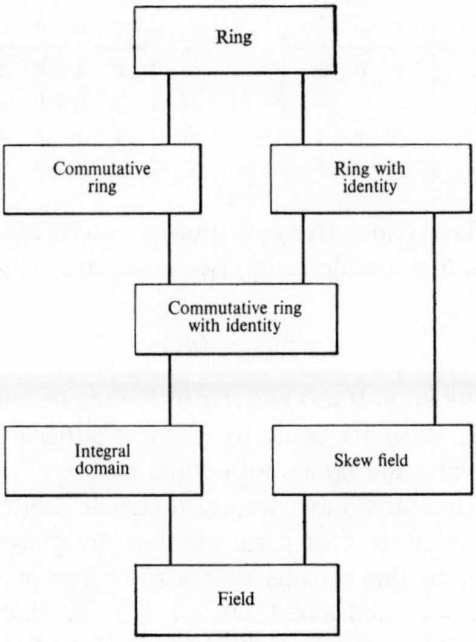


**Figure 7.1**

This figure indicates that an integral domain is a commutative ring with identity, certainly, but it also implies that not every commutative ring with identity is an integral domain. It indicates that a field is an integral domain but that not every integral domain is a field, and so forth. How do we justify these implications? Consider the following examples.

*Example* 1. The system $J$ of rational integers is an integral domain which is not a field. We know from our study of this system that it contains no divisors of zero, that multiplication is commutative, that it has an identity, and that it possesses elements which do not have multiplicative inverses.

*Example* 2. The system $J/(m)$ of the integers mod $m$ is also a ring that we know well. When $m$ is composite, say 6, then the resulting ring is a commutative ring with identity that has divisors of zero. Thus a commutative ring with identity is not necessarily an integral domain.

*Example* 3. The subsystems of $J$ were determined in Chapter 5, so we know that the set of all integral multiples of $k$, where $k$ is an integer larger than 1, is a ring relative to the operations of $J$. Then it is a commutative ring without a multiplicative identity element.

This much we can prove about the diagram in Fig. 7.1 just by using very familiar examples. (We note that the system of rational numbers and the ring $J/(p)$, where $p$ is a prime, are fields so that this classification is not empty.) To say more about the diagram we must invent some new systems.

*Example* 4. Let $S$ consist of the set $\{z, a, b, c\}$ and the binary operations defined by the tables shown. The additive system is easily seen to be isomorphic with the outer direct product of the two groups $\{J/(2), +\}$ and $\{J/(2), +\}$, and

| $+$ | $z$ | $a$ | $b$ | $c$ |
|---|---|---|---|---|
| $z$ | $z$ | $a$ | $b$ | $c$ |
| $a$ | $a$ | $z$ | $c$ | $b$ |
| $b$ | $b$ | $c$ | $z$ | $a$ |
| $c$ | $c$ | $b$ | $a$ | $z$ |

| $\cdot$ | $z$ | $a$ | $b$ | $c$ |
|---|---|---|---|---|
| $z$ | $z$ | $z$ | $z$ | $z$ |
| $a$ | $z$ | $a$ | $b$ | $c$ |
| $b$ | $z$ | $z$ | $z$ | $z$ |
| $c$ | $z$ | $a$ | $b$ | $c$ |

hence it is a group. The associativity of multiplication can be verified by simple calculation. If $u$, $v$, and $w$ are elements, not necessarily distinct, from $S$ then we prove that

$$u(vw) = (uv)w$$

by considering the element $u$. If $u$ is either $z$ or $b$, then $uv$ and $u(vw)$ are both equal to $z$ so that $(uv)w$ and $u(vw)$ are equal to $z$. If $u$ is either $a$ or $c$, then $uv = v$ and $u(vw) = vw$ so that $(uv)w$ and $u(vw)$ both equal $vw$.

To verify the Distributive Laws we again choose arbitrary elements $u$, $v$, and $w$ from $S$. Then if $u$ is either $z$ or $b$ we see that the three elements $uv$, $uw$, and $u(v + w)$ are all zero, so that in this case $u(v + w) = uv + uw$. If $u$ is either $a$ or $c$, then $uv = v$, $uw = w$, and $u(v + w) = v + w$, so that we have $u(v + w) = uv + uw$ in this case. Hence the Left Distributive Law holds.

To prove the Right Distributive Law we note that

$$(v + w)u = vu + wu$$

if any one of the elements is $z$, or if $v = w$ since

$$(v + v)u = zu = z = vu + vu.$$

This and commutativity of addition cause only nine cases to be left:

$$\begin{aligned}
(a + b)a &= ca = a = aa + ba, & (a + b)b &= cb = b = ab + bb,\\
(a + b)c &= cc = c = ac + bc, & (a + c)a &= ba = z = aa + aa,\\
(a + c)b &= bb = z = ab + cb, & (a + c)c &= bc = z = ac + cc,\\
(b + c)a &= aa = a = ba + ca, & (b + c)b &= ab = b = bb + cb,
\end{aligned}$$

$$(b + c)c = ac = c = bc + cc.$$

Thus the Right Distributive Law holds in $S$.

Then this rather trivial system is a ring in which multiplication is not commutative and which has no identity element. Hence this is a system which lies only in the top bracket of the diagram.

The problems of finding a skew field which is not a field and of finding a noncommutative ring with identity which is not a sfield are a bit more difficult to solve. For this purpose we discuss in a rather brief fashion a very famous algebraic system, the *quaternions* of W. R. Hamilton.

*Example* 5. Denote by $Q$ the set $R \times R \times R \times R$ of all ordered quadruples of rational numbers, and define addition and multiplication of elements of $Q$ as follows:

$$(a_1, a_2, a_3, a_4) + (b_1, b_2, b_3, b_4) = (a_1 + b_1, a_2 + b_2, a_3 + b_3, a_4 + b_4)$$

and

$$(a_1, a_2, a_3, a_4)(b_1, b_2, b_3, b_4) = (c_1, c_2, c_3, c_4)$$

where

$$\begin{aligned} c_1 &= a_1b_1 - a_2b_2 - a_3b_3 - a_4b_4, \\ c_2 &= a_1b_2 + a_2b_1 + a_3b_4 - a_4b_3, \\ c_3 &= a_1b_3 - a_2b_4 + a_3b_1 + a_4b_2, \end{aligned}$$

and

$$c_4 = a_1b_4 + a_2b_3 - a_3b_2 + a_4b_1.$$

The resulting system is the division ring of *rational quaternions.*

To verify that $Q$ is a ring involves a certain amount of simple, straightforward calculation, especially in the case of addition. We shall focus our attention here on multiplication, and introduce some simplifying notation that is commonly used. For an element $r$ of $R$ we define the *scalar product*

$$\begin{aligned} r(a_1, a_2, a_3, a_4) &= (ra_1, ra_2, ra_3, ra_4) \\ &= (a_1r, a_2r, a_3r, a_4r) = (a_1, a_2, a_3, a_4)r \end{aligned}$$

for elements of $R$ and $Q$. Now we introduce some simple symbols for certain elements of $Q$:

$$e = (1, 0, 0, 0), \quad i = (0, 1, 0, 0), \quad j = (0, 0, 1, 0)$$

and

$$k = (0, 0, 0, 1).$$

Then the element $q = (a_1, a_2, a_3, a_4)$ of $Q$ is expressible uniquely as

$$q = ea_1 + ia_2 + ja_3 + ka_4.$$

The elements $e$, $i$, $j$, and $k$ have very distinctive properties. $e$ is the multiplicative identity of $Q$, and

$$\begin{gathered} e^2 = e, \quad i^2 = -e, \quad j^2 = -e, \quad k^2 = -e, \\ ij = k, \quad ji = -k, \quad ik = -j, \quad ki = j, \quad jk = i, \end{gathered}$$

and

$$kj = -i.$$

These are easy arithmetic observations from the definition of multiplication. In fact, this definition can be rewritten as

$$\begin{aligned} (ea_1 + ia_2 + ja_3 + ka_4)&(eb_1 + ib_2 + jb_3 + kb_4) \\ &= e(a_1b_1 - a_2b_2 - a_3b_3 - a_4b_4) \\ &\quad + i(a_1b_2 + a_2b_1 + a_3b_4 - a_4b_3) \\ &\quad + j(a_1b_3 - a_2b_4 + a_3b_1 + a_4b_2) \\ &\quad + k(a_1b_4 + a_2b_3 - a_3b_2 + a_4b_1), \end{aligned}$$

so that by assigning appropriate values of zeros and 1's to the $a_i$ and $b_i$ we obtain all of the above equations. Furthermore we observe that we have the important distributivity equation,

$$\begin{aligned} (ea_1 + ia_2 + ja_3 + ka_4)&(eb_1 + ib_2 + jb_3 + kb_4) \\ &= (ea_1eb_1 + ia_2ib_2 + ja_3jb_3 + ka_4kb_4) \\ &\quad + (ea_1ib_2 + ia_2eb_2 + ja_3kb_4 + ka_4jb_3) \\ &\quad + (ea_1jb_3 + ia_2kb_4 + ja_3eb_1 + ka_4ib_2) \\ &\quad + (ea_1kb_4 + ia_2jb_3 + ja_3ib_2 + ka_4eb_1). \end{aligned}$$

Here we are using properties of the scalar product: for $r$ and $s$ in $R$ and $q$ and $q_1$ in $Q$,

$$r(sq) = (rs)q = r(qs) = (rq)s$$

and

$$r(q + q_1) = rq + rq_1 = qr + q_1r.$$

Then to show that multiplication in $Q$ is associative we need only verify the Associative Law for the elements $i, j$, and $k$. This program leaves 27 cases to verify; for example,

$$i(jk) = i(i) = -e = (ij)k = kk,$$
$$i(ik) = i(-j) = -k = (ii)k = (-e)k,$$

and

$$i(kj) = i(-i) = e = (ik)j = (-j)j.$$

The remainder is left to the student to verify.

Application of the definition of multiplication shows that a nonzero element of $Q$, where $z = (0, 0, 0, 0)$, denoted as

$$q = (a_1, a_2, a_3, a_4)$$

has the multiplicative inverse

$$q^{-1} = (1/t)(a_1, -a_2, -a_3, -a_4)$$

where $t = a_1^2 + a_2^2 + a_3^2 + a_4^2$. Setting $b_1 = a_1$, $b_2 = -a_2$, $b_3 = -a_3$, and $b_4 = -a_4$ in the definition of multiplication yields

$$\begin{aligned} tqq^{-1} &= (a_1^2 + a_2^2 + a_3^2 + a_4^2, -a_1a_2 + a_2a_1 - a_3a_4 + a_4a_3, \\ &\qquad -a_1a_3 + a_2a_4 + a_3a_1 - a_4a_2, -a_1a_4 - a_2a_3 + a_3a_2 + a_4a_1) \\ &= (t, 0, 0, 0) = te. \end{aligned}$$

Hence $qq^{-1} = e$, and similarly $q^{-1}q = e$.

In this manner we can show that the system of rational quaternions is a skew field which is not a field. The student should recognize that this system rather resembles the complex field whose properties undoubtedly guided Hamilton somewhat in his development of the quaternions.

*Example* 6. Let $Q'$ be the set of all elements $q$ of $Q$, $q = (a_1, a_2, a_3, a_4)$, where the numbers $a_n$ are all integers. Relative to the binary operations induced by the operations of $Q$ this system is a noncommutative ring with an identity element $e$. It is not a division ring since the multiplicative inverses of such elements as $e + i$ and $i - j$ are not in $Q'$.

Simple arithmetic problems in $Q$ and $Q'$ are rather easily worked out, and these sometimes help us realize both the similarities and differences between quaternions and ordinary numbers.

*Example* 7. Find a quaternion $q$ such that

$$(3e - j)q = i.$$

The inverse of $3e - j$ is $(1/10)(3e + j)$, so multiplying the above equation by this inverse yields

$$(1/10)(3e + j)(3e - j)q = (1/10)(3e - j)i$$

and

$$eq = q = (3/10)(3i + k).$$

Thus linear equations are handled exactly as linear equations over the rational field.

*Example* 8. Find three different quaternions whose squares all equal $-2e$. If

$$(a, b, c, d)^2 = (-2, 0, 0, 0),$$

then $a$, $b$, $c$, and $d$ are rational numbers such that

$$\begin{aligned} a^2 - b^2 - c^2 - d^2 &= -2 \\ ab + ba + cd - dc &= 0 = 2ab \\ ac - bd + ca + db &= 0 = 2ac \\ ad + bc - cb + da &= 0 = 2ad. \end{aligned}$$

Surely the quaternions $i - j$, $i - k$, and $j - k$ all satisfy this condition.

## Exercise 7.1

**1.** List the axioms for (*a*) a skew field; (*b*) a ring with identity; (*c*) a commutative ring.

**2.** Make a Venn diagram illustrating the classifications of rings.

**3.** List all implications from the classification diagram for rings.

**4.** Let $S$ be the set $\{z, a, b, c\}$, and define addition on $S$ by the table of Example 4 and multiplication by the table shown here.

| $\cdot$ | $z$ | $a$ | $b$ | $c$ |
|---|---|---|---|---|
| $z$ | $z$ | $z$ | $z$ | $z$ |
| $a$ | $z$ | $a$ | $b$ | $c$ |
| $b$ | $z$ | $b$ | $z$ | $z$ |
| $c$ | $z$ | $c$ | $b$ | $c$ |

Show that multiplication is associative but that $S$ is not a ring.

**5.** Let $S$ be any Abelian group, written additively, and define $ab = z$ for each $a$ and each $b$ in $S$. Show that the resulting system is a ring. (These are called *zero rings*. Where do they fit in Fig. 7.1?)

**6.** Let $S$ be the set of rational integers, $S = J$, and define new operations on this set by the equations

$$a \oplus b = a + b - 1 \quad \text{and} \quad a \odot b = a + b - ab.$$

Show that this new system is an integral domain. Is it a field? (Note that $z = 1$ and $e = 0$ in this system.)

**7.** Denote as usual by $\sqrt{2}$ the positive real number whose square is 2. Show that the set of all real numbers of the form $a + b\sqrt{2}$, where $a$ and $b$ are rational, is a field relative to the usual operations.

**8.** Prove that the quaternions form an Abelian group under addition.

**9.** Let $S$ and $T$ be two rings. Show that the set $S \times T$ is a ring when addition and multiplication are defined by the relations

$$(a_1, b_1) + (a_2, b_2) = (a_1 + a_2, b_1 + b_2)$$

and

$$(a_1, b_1)(a_2, b_2) = (a_1a_2, b_1b_2).$$

**10.** Compute the products in $Q$:

(*a*) $((e + 2i + 3j + 4k)(-e - i + 3j + k))(2e + i - k)$;
(*b*) $(e + 2i + 3j + 4k)((-e - i + 3j + k)(2e + i - k))$.

**11.** Compute the inverse of each of the quaternions of Problem 10.

**12.** Find a quaternion $q$ such that:

(*a*) $(e + i)q = i - j$;
(*b*) $q(e + i) = i - j$;
(*c*) $q(j + k) = i + j - 2k$.

**13.** How many elements $q$ does $Q$ contain such that $q^2 = -5e$?

**14.** Prove that quaternion multiplication is associative.

**15.** Let $C = R \times R$, and define operations as follows:

$$(a, b) + (c, d) = (a + c, b + d) \quad \text{and} \quad (a, b)(c, d) = (ac - bd, ad + bc).$$

Show that the resulting system is a field.

**16.** Show that the eight quaternions $e$, $-e$, $i$, $-i$, $j$, $-j$, $k$, and $-k$ form a group under multiplication. (This is the *quaternion group*.) Can the regular permutation representations be used to verify the Associative Law?

**17.** If the real field is used instead of the rational field in forming the quaternions, then the resulting system is the ring of real quaternions. It is also a skew field. Show that there are infinitely many real quaternions $q$ such that $q^2 = -e$.

**18.** Show that it is impossible to define multiplication in $S = R \times R \times R$ in such a way that the resulting system, with addition defined componentwise as for the quaternions, is a field.

**19.** Show that a ring with divisors of zero cannot satisfy the Cancellation Law for Multiplication.

**20.** If in the definition of quaternions the field of integers mod 2 is used instead of the rational field, what sort of system results? How many elements has it? Is it a sfield? What if $J/(p)$ is used?

## 7.2 Elementary Properties

From our knowledge of special rings and from our study of groups we expect the identity elements and the inverse elements of a ring to be quite special. Since the elements of a ring $S$ form an Abelian group under addition, we already know something about the additive identity $z$ and the inverse $-a$ of $a$.

THEOREM 7.1. *If $S$ is a ring, then*

(1) *$z$ is the only element of $S$ such that $a + z = z + a = a$ for every $a$ in $S$.*

(2) *For each $x$ in $S$ there is exactly one element $-x$ in $S$ such that*

$$-x + x = x + (-x) = z.$$

(3) *For each $x$ in $S$,*

$$xz = zx = z.$$

(4) $(-a)b = a(-b) = -(ab)$ *for each a and each b in S.*
(5) $-(-a) = a$ *for each a in S.*
(6) $(-a)(-b) = ab$ *for each a and each b in S.*

The three statements (1), (2), and (5) are familiar properties of the additive group $\{S, +\}$. Certainly if $u$ has the additive property of $z$, then

$$u + z = z + u = u = z.$$

And if $y$ has the additive property of $-x$, then

$$\begin{aligned} y = y + z = y + \big(x + (-x)\big) &= (y + x) + (-x) \\ &= z + (-x) = -x. \end{aligned}$$

Finally, $-(-a) = a$ from (2) and from the equation

$$a + (-a) = (-a) + a = z.$$

To verify (3) we use the Distributive Law:

$$xz = x(z + z) = xz + xz.$$

Adding the negative of $xz$ to this yields

$$z = xz + \big(-(xz)\big) = (xz + xz) + \big(-(xz)\big) = xz.$$

Similarly we can show that $zx = z$.

The verification of (4) depends on (2), (3), and the Distributive Law:

$$ab + (-a)b = \big(a + (-a)\big)b = zb = z.$$

Hence by the uniqueness of $-(ab)$ we see that $(-a)b = -(ab)$. Similarly,

$$a(-b) + ab = a\big((-b) + b\big) = az = z,$$

so that

$$a(-b) = -(ab).$$

Finally, we use (4) and (5) to prove (6). First,

$$(-a)(-b) = -\big(a(-b)\big)$$

so that since $a(-b) = -(ab)$ we have

$$(-a)(-b) = -\big(-(ab)\big).$$

This means, by (5) that

$$(-a)(-b) = -\big(-(ab)\big) = ab.$$

From (3) of this result we obtain a corollary.

*Corollary* 7.1.1. A field is an integral domain.

If $S$ is a field we know that the nonzero elements of $S$ form an Abelian multiplicative group. We must show that $S$ is a multiplicative semigroup which is commutative, has an identity, but has no divisors of zero. So we must show that $z$ commutes multiplicatively with every element of $S$, and that $ez = ze = z$ for the multiplicative identity $e$ of the group of nonzero elements. Both of these facts follow from (3). Also, if

$$ab = z,$$

where $a \neq z$, then

$$b = eb = a^{-1}ab = a^{-1}z = z$$

by (3), so that a field has no divisors of zero.

Although an integral domain is not always a field, we can show that it has a type of divisibility, just as the ring $J$ has.

THEOREM 7.2. *If the ring $S$ contains no divisors of zero, then the Cancellation Law for Multiplication is valid in $S$.*

Suppose $ax = ay$ in $S$, where $a \neq z$. Then we can write

$$ax + (-(ay)) = z$$

so that by (4) of Theorem 7.1,

$$z = ax + a(-y) = a(x + (-y)).$$

Since S has no divisors of zero this equation implies that

$$x + (-y) = z$$

so that

$$x = z + y = y.$$

In the same manner we conclude from

$$xa = ya, \qquad a \neq z,$$

that $x = y$.

The regular properties of the additive inverse lead us to define subtraction in a ring exactly as we defined subtraction for $J$.

DEFINITION 7.3. The operation of *subtraction* is defined for the ring $S$ by the equation

$$a - b = a + (-b).$$

This operation must be used carefully since it is neither associative nor commutative. However, multiplication is distributive over subtraction.

THEOREM 7.3. *If $a$, $b$, and $c$ are elements of the ring $S$, then*

$$a(b - c) = ab - ac \quad \text{and} \quad (b - c)a = ba - ca.$$

By definition,

$$b - c = b + (-c) \quad \text{and} \quad ab - ac = ab + (-(ac)).$$

Using the fact that multiplication distributes over addition we have

$$a(b + (-c)) = ab + a(-c),$$

and, since $a(-c) = -(ac)$ by Theorem 7.1, we conclude that

$$a(b - c) = ab - ac.$$

The right-sided distributivity is handled in the same manner.

In the previous section we saw that a ring need not have a multiplicative identity, and we know from the ring $J$ that even in an integral domain multiplicative inverses may not exist. However, these elements are unique when they do exist.

THEOREM 7.4. (1) *A ring has at most one multiplicative identity.*

(2) *A ring has a multiplicative identity if and only if it has exactly one left (or right) multiplicative identity.*

(3) *An element in a ring with identity has at most one multiplicative inverse.*

Suppose

$$ex = xe = x \quad \text{and} \quad fx = xf = x$$

for every element $x$ of the ring $S$. Then for $x = f$ we have from the first equation

$$ef = fe = f,$$

and for $x = e$ we get from the second

$$fe = ef = e.$$

Hence $e = f$, and (1) is proved.

Suppose $e$ is the only left identity of $S$,

$$ex = x$$

for every $x$ in $S$, and consider the equation, for $a$ in $S$,

$$\begin{aligned}(a - ae + e)x &= ax - aex + ex \\ &= ax - ax + x = z + x = x.\end{aligned}$$

Hence the element $(a - ae + e)$ is a left identity for every $x$ in $S$. By the uniqueness of $e$, we have

$$a - ae + e = e$$

so that

$$a = ae.$$

Since $a$ is an arbitrary element of $S$ this means that $e$ is also a right identity.

The converse is proved by the method used to prove (1).

Finally, suppose

$$aa^{-1} = a^{-1}a = e,$$

and

$$ab = ba = e.$$

Then $a^{-1}ab = eb = a^{-1}e = b = a^{-1}$.

From (2) one receives the impression that a ring without an identity can have several one-sided identities, and this is indeed the case.

*Example* 1. Let $S$ be the ring of Example 4 in Section 7.1. Certainly $a$ and $c$ are both right identity elements for multiplication, but the ring does not have a two-sided multiplicative element.

*Example* 2. Consider the ring $J/(8)$. This ring has a multiplicative identity 1, but only some of the elements have inverses. We see that 1, 3, 5, and 7 have inverses and that these inverses are unique in $J/(8)$, by inspecting the table.

| · | 1 | 2 | 3 | 4 | 5 | 6 | 7 |
|---|---|---|---|---|---|---|---|
| 1 | 1 | 2 | 3 | 4 | 5 | 6 | 7 |
| 2 | 2 | 4 | 6 | 0 | 2 | 4 | 6 |
| 3 | 3 | 6 | 1 | 4 | 7 | 2 | 5 |
| 4 | 4 | 0 | 4 | 0 | 4 | 0 | 4 |
| 5 | 5 | 2 | 7 | 4 | 1 | 6 | 3 |
| 6 | 6 | 4 | 2 | 0 | 6 | 4 | 2 |
| 7 | 7 | 6 | 5 | 4 | 3 | 2 | 1 |

## Exercise 7.2

**1.** Find a ring with more than one left identity element.

**2.** Prove that subtraction is not in general association. Describe subtraction in $J/(2)$.

**3.** Show that, if a ring has a left identity $e$ and a right identity $f$, then $e = f$.

**4.** Prove that $-(a + b) = -a + (-b) = -a - b = -b - a$ in a ring $S$.

**5.** Complete the proof of Theorem 7.3.

**6.** If $ab = z$ in the ring $S$, what conclusions can you reach about $a$ and $b$?

**7.** Show that $(-a)(-b)(-c) = -(abc)$.

**8.** For given elements $a$ and $b$ in the ring $S$, can there exist more than one $x$ in $S$ such that $ax = b$? (See Example 2.)

**9.** Show that the commutativity of addition in a ring with identity can be proved from the other axioms. (Consider $(a + b)(e + e)$.)

**10.** Determine the set of those quaternions which commute multiplicatively with every element of $Q$.

**11.** Show that, if $e$ is the multiplicative identity of ring $S$, then $-a = -e(a)$.

**12.** Give an example to show that a ring $S$ can have a nonzero element $a$ such that $ax = z$ for every $x$ in $S$. (Such an element is called a *right annihilator*.)

## 7.3 Exponentiation and Scalar Product

The subject of exponentiation was discussed earlier for semigroups and for groups. This method of relating an abstract ring to the ring of integers is, however, so basic and so important that we are discussing it again for emphasis. Besides it is possible that understanding of the concept has only been partial.

DEFINITION 7.4. For an element $a$ in the ring $S$ and the integer $n$ the *scalar product* $an = na$ is defined to be:

(1) $a + a + \cdots + a,$ $n$ times when $n > 0$,

(2) $z$ when $n = 0$,

and

(3) $-a - a - \cdots - a,$ $|n|$ times when $n < 0$.

As we noted earlier, the feasibility of this definition rests on the Generalized Associative Law which we proved for any associative binary operation. No special symbolism is employed here for the scalar product although it should be understood that in general the product $ab$, for $a$ and $b$ in $S$, and the scalar product, $an = na$, are two different concepts entirely. The concept of scalar multiplication for integral scalars is derived from a shorthand notation for certain statements about addition.

THEOREM 7.5. *If $a$ is an element of the ring $S$ and $m$ and $n$ are integers, then*

$$a(m + n) = (m + n)a = am + an.$$

The proof is divided into several cases.

(1) If $m$ and $n$ are positive, then the equation $a(m + n) = am + an$ is merely a statement about the association of the sum of $m + n$ $a$'s, and as such is true by the Generalized Associative Law.

(2) If $m$ and $n$ are negative, then the argument is the same as in case (1) except that $-a$ is added $-m - n$ times.

(3) If either $m$ or $n$ is zero, then the corresponding $am$ or $an$ is $z$, and the truth of the statement is a consequence of the property of $z$.

(4) If $m$ and $n$ have opposite signs, say $-m + r = n$ where $-m$, $r$, and $n$ are positive, then

$$a(m + n) = ar,$$
$$am = -a - a - \cdots - a \qquad -m \text{ times},$$

and

$$an = a + a + \cdots + a, \qquad -m + r \text{ times}.$$

Therefore,

$$am + an = (-a)(-m) + a(-m) + ar,$$

and we need to show that

$$(-a)(-m) + a(-m) = z$$

to complete the proof. This equality is a consequence of our next two theorems.

THEOREM 7.6. *If n is a positive integer and a and b are elements of the ring S, then*

$$(a + b)n = an + bn.$$

We proceed by induction on $n$. If $n = 1$, then certainly

$$(a + b)1 = a + b = a1 + b1,$$

so assume that

$$(a + b)k = ak + bk$$

for some integer $k \geq 1$. Consider the element $(a + b)(k + 1)$; by definition

$$(a + b)(k + 1) = (a + b) + \cdots + (a + b), \quad k + 1 \text{ times},$$

so by the generalized Associative Law,

$$(a + b)(k + 1) = \underbrace{\big((a + b) + \cdots + (a + b)\big)}_{k \text{ times}} + (a + b).$$

Applying the induction hypothesis we get

$$\begin{aligned}(a + b)(k + 1) &= ak + bk + a + b,\\ &= (ak + a) + (bk + b).\end{aligned}$$

Since $ak + a = a(k + 1)$ and $bk + b = b(k + 1)$ by case (1) of Theorem 7.5, we see that

$$(a + b)(k + 1) = a(k + 1) + b(k + 1).$$

This completes the induction and proves the theorem.

*Corollary* 7.6.1. If $n$ is an integer and $a$ and $b$ are elements of the ring $S$, then

$$(a + b)n = an + bn.$$

If $n = 0$, then

$$(a + b)0 = z = a0 = b0$$

so that

$$(a + b)0 = a0 + b0.$$

If $n < 0$, then $-n = r > 0$, and we apply the result above to $(-(a + b))r$:

$$(-(a + b))r = ((-a) + (-b))r = (-a)r + (-b)r.$$

Hence we have

$$(a + b)n = an + bn.$$

THEOREM 7.7. *If $n$ is a positive integer, then*

$$nz = zn = z.$$

This is also proved by induction on $n$. When $n = 1$ we know that

$$z1 = z,$$

so we assume as our induction hypothesis that

$$zk = z$$

for some integer $k \geq 1$. Consider $z(k + 1)$; by case (1) of Theorem 7.5 we have

$$z(k + 1) = zk + z1,$$

so surely

$$z(k + 1) = z.$$

This completes the induction.

Now the completion of the proof of Theorem 7.5 is immediate.

By very similar methods we can prove the following additional properties of scalar multiplication.

THEOREM 7.8. *If $a$ and $b$ are elements of the ring $S$ and $m$ and $n$ are integers, then*

(i) $$(ab)n = a(bn) = (an)b,$$

*and*

(ii) $$a(mn) = (am)n.$$

The proof of this theorem is left as an exercise for the student. We note that the proof involves the Generalized Distributive Law.

THEOREM 7.9. *If the elements $a, b_1, \cdots, b_n$ are from a ring $S$, then*

$$a(b_1 + \cdots + b_n) = ab_1 + \cdots + ab_n,$$

*and*

$$(b_1 + \cdots + b_n)a = b_1a + \cdots + b_na.$$

The proof is a simple induction on $n$. Surely if

$$a(b_1 + \cdots + b_k) = ab_1 + \cdots + ab_k,$$

then

$$a(b_1 + \cdots + b_k + b) = a(b_1 + \cdots + b_k) + ab$$

by the Generalized Associative Law and the Distributive Law for $S$. This is the principal observation needed to prove the theorem.

Of course the exponentiation of a ring $S$ has fewer of these nice properties since it is based upon the multiplication of $S$. Since elements of $S$ do not usually have multiplicative inverses we must restrict the exponents to the set of positive integers. Rather than repeat, in a different notation, the preceding work we adopt a slightly more sophisticated approach to exponentiation.

DEFINITION 7.5. If $a$ is an element of the ring $S$, then we define

$$a^1 = a, \tag{1}$$

and

$$a^{k+1} = a^k a, \tag{2}$$

where $k$ is a positive integer.

This is an example of a *recursive definition.*

THEOREM 7.10. *Exponentiation is a mapping from the set $S \times P$ onto $S$, where $P$ is the set of all positive integers.*

To prove this we must show that, for each $a$ in $S$ and $n$ in $p$, the image element $a^n$ is a uniquely specified element of $S$. This is a consequence of the recursive definition and the Induction Axiom. Let $M$ be the subset of $P$ consisting of those positive integers $n$ for which $a^n$ is uniquely defined for every $a$ in $S$. Certainly 1 is in $M$ since $a^1 = a$. Furthermore $k + 1$ is in $M$ whenever $k$ is since $a^{k+1} = a^k \cdot a$. Therefore $M = P$ by the Induction Axiom, and exponentiation is a function from $S \times P$ to $S$. Obviously it is onto $S$ since $a^1 = a$.

THEOREM 7.11. *If $a$ is an element of the ring $S$ and $m$ and $n$ are positive integers, then*

$$a^m a^n = a^{m+n}; \tag{1}$$
$$(a^m)^n = a^{mn}. \tag{2}$$

These too are proved by mathematical induction. To prove (1) we proceed by induction on $n$. When $n = 1$ we see that

$$a^1 = a \qquad \text{and} \qquad a^{m+1} = a^m a;$$

thus

$$a^m a^1 = a^m a = a^{m+1}.$$

Our induction hypothesis is the statement

$$a^m a^k = a^{m+k} \qquad \text{for some } k \text{ in } P,$$

and we consider the product

$$a^m a^{k+1}.$$

By Definition 7.5 and the Associative Law,

$$a^m a^{k+1} = a^m(a^k a) = (a^m a^k)a.$$

Applying the induction hypothesis we obtain

$$a^m a^{k+1} = a^{m+k}a,$$

so that, by the definition,

$$a^m a^{k+1} = a^{(m+k)+1}.$$

Since exponentiation is a mapping from $S \times P$ onto $S$ we know that

$$a^{m+(k+1)} = a^{(m+k)+1} = a^{m+k+1}$$

since

$$m + (k + 1) = (m + k) + 1 = m + k + 1$$

in $P$. Hence

$$a^m a^{k+1} = a^{m+(k+1)},$$

and the induction is completed.

If multiplication has special properties, then naturally more can be said about the exponentiation. For example, when multiplication is commutative we get the following familiar properties.

THEOREM 7.12. *If a and b are elements of the commutative ring S and n is a positive integer, then*

(1) $$(ab)^n = a^n b^n,$$

*and*

(2) $$(a + b)^n = a^n + b^n + \sum_{i=1}^{n-1} m_i a^{n-i} b^i$$

*where* $m_i = n!/(i!(n - i)!)$.

The student should recognize (2) as the *binomial expansion* which is so well known to all school children. The proof is a straightforward induction and can be found in all good high school advanced algebra books.

*Example* 1. Evaluate the element $(a + b)^7$ two ways when $a$ and $b$ are the elements [2] and [3], respectively, of the field $J/(7)$.

We know from Fermat's Little Theorem that $([2] + [3])^7 = ([5])^7 = [5]$. Now consider the binomial coefficients; certainly the integer $7!/(i!(7 - i)!)$ is always a multiple of 7 since neither $i!$ nor $(7 - i)!$ is a multiple of 7 for $i = 1, 2, \cdots, 6$. Now we note that

$$\begin{aligned} 7[a] &= [a] + \cdots + [a], \qquad 7 \text{ times}, \\ &= [a](\underbrace{[1] + \cdots + [1]}_{7 \text{ times}}) \\ &= [a]([7]) = [7a] = [0]. \end{aligned}$$

Therefore all of the middle terms in the expansion of $([a] + [b])^7$ are equal to $[0]$ in $J/(7)$. This means that

$$\begin{aligned}([2] + [3])^7 &= [2]^7 + [3]^7 \\ &= [2] + [3] = [5].\end{aligned}$$

*Example* 2. Show that the scalar 2 is an *annihilator* of every element of the ring of Example 4 in Section 7.1.

We observed earlier that the additive group of that ring has the special property that each element is its own additive inverse:

$$\begin{aligned}z + z &= z \\ a + a &= z \\ b + b &= z \\ c + c &= z.\end{aligned}$$

Rewriting these by using the scalar 2 we get $2z = z2 = z$, $2a = a2 = z$, $2b = b2 = z$, and $2c = c2 = z$.

This example suggests that the concept of scalar multiplication relates a ring, sometimes, to rings other than the ring of integers (such as the rings $J/(m)$). We shall investigate that idea in the next section. It is of course just a way of talking about the cyclic subgroups of the additive group of a ring.

*Example* 3. Attempt to evaluate the quaternion $(j + k)^2$ by the binomial expansion.

Now

$$\begin{aligned}(j + k)^2 &= (j + k)(j + k) \\ &= j(j + k) + k(j + k) \\ &= -e + i - i - e = -2e,\end{aligned}$$

and

$$j^2 + 2jk + k^2 = -e + 2i - e.$$

Since $-2e \neq -2e + 2i$ we see that the binomial expansion does not hold in general for a ring.

## Exercise 7.3

1. Define $na$, for $n$ in $P$ and $a$ in the ring $S$, recursively as in Definition 7.5, and prove that this is the image of a function from $P \times S$ onto $S$.
2. Complete the proof of Theorem 7.5.
3. Prove parts (i) and (ii) of Theorem 7.8.
4. Give a proof of part (2) of Theorem 7.11.
5. Show that Theorem 7.12 does not hold for the ring of Example 4, Section 7.1.
6. Calculate $(a + b)^{121}$ when $a$ and $b$ are the elements [3] and [4] of $J/(11)$.
7. Calculate $([3] + [4])^6$ over the system $J/(6)$.
8. Prove that $(a + b)^p = a^p + b^p$ if every additive cyclic subgroup of the commutative ring $S$ is of order $p$, except the zero subgroup.
9. Prove that $n!/(k!(n - k)!)$ is an integer for $n > k > 0$.
10. Prove the binomial expansion valid for commutative rings.

**11.** Show that a ring can contain several idempotent elements, $i^2 = i \neq z$, even though it has no multiplicative identity.

**12.** Can an additively written Abelian group have scalar multipliers from a system other than the ring of integers? Explain. (Consider the additive group of a ring.)

**13.** Can nonzero integers be divisors of "zero" as scalars for an integral domain? Explain.

**14.** Distinguish between the different binary operations in the following expressions, where $a$ and $b$ are elements of the ring $S$ and $n$ and $m$ are integers:

$$(ab)n,\ a(bn),\ (a + b)n,\ (n + m)a,\ (n - m)a,\ n(a - b).$$

When do the expressions $a + m$ and $n - b$ make sense?

**15.** Let $n$ be the least positive integer such that $na = [0]$ for the element $a$ of the ring $J/(m)$.

(1) Show that $n$ is a factor of $m$.

(2) Show that $ab \neq [0]$ when $b$ is any of the $n - 1$ elements $[1], [2], \cdots, [n - 1]$.

(3) Show that $ab$ takes on exactly $n$ distinct values in $J/(m)$.

(4) What must be true of the powers $a, a^2, \cdots, a^n$?

(5) Illustrate the above with $a = [9]$ and $m = 21$.

## 7.4 Subsystems and Characteristic

The structural approach to the study of rings requires knowledge of some of the subsystems of a ring. Here we introduce some of the simpler aspects.

DEFINITION 7.6. Let $T$ be a nonempty subset of the ring $S$. Then $T$ is defined to be a *subring* of $S$ if and only if, for each $x$ and $y$ in $T$,

(1) $xy$ is in $T$.

(2) $x + y$ is in $T$.

(3) $x - y$ is in $T$.

The justification for the term subring comes from the following result.

THEOREM 7.13. *If $T$ is a subring of the ring $S$, then $T$ is a ring (relative to the binary operations induced on $T$ by the binary operations of $S$).*

The induced operations, $A' = A \cap ((T \times T) \times T)$ and $\mathbf{M}' = \mathbf{M} \cap ((T \times T) \times T)$, where $A$ and $\mathbf{M}$ are the subsets of $(S \times S) \times S$ called addition and multiplication, respectively, naturally inherit the properties of associativity, commutativity, and distributivity, so we need only concern ourselves with showing the existence of an additive identity and an additive inverse for each element in $T$. From condition (3) we see that $x - x = z$ is in $T$, so surely $T$ has an additive identity, namely, $z$. And, if $y$ is an element of $T$, then by (3) $z - y = -y$ is in $T$, so that each element of $T$ has an additive inverse in $T$.

The conditions (1) and (2) are essential to the conclusions that $A'$ and $\mathbf{M}'$ are binary operations on $T$. For, if $xy$ were not in $T$, then $((x, y), xy)$ would not be in $\mathbf{M}'$ and so $\mathbf{M}'$ would not be a mapping from $T \times T$ to $T$. Similarly $x + y$ in $T$ is necessary for $\mathbf{M}'$ to be a binary operation on $T$.

In our earlier studies we encountered many subrings. The even integers form a subring of the ring of integers. The ring of rational integers is a subring of the ring of rational numbers. And there are many others. In fact, from two subrings of a ring we can get other subrings.

THEOREM 7.14. *If $T$ and $W$ are subrings of the ring $S$, then $T \cap W$ is a subring of $S$ also.*

Consider $T \cap W$. If $x$ and $y$ are in both $T$ and $W$, then we see immediately that the three elements $xy$, $x + y$, and $x - y$ are in both $T$ and $W$. Hence $T \cap W$ is a subring of $S$.

Note that $T \cap W \subseteq T$. This suggests that a subring of $T$ is also a subring of $S$, and that is easily proved true since the binary operations of $T$ are induced by the operations of $S$.

Although it is true that a subring $T$ inherits many properties from the ring $S$, the two rings $S$ and $T$ can have some rather different properties. We list a few simple illustrations.

*Example* 1. A subring $T$ of a ring $S$ with identity need not be a ring with identity. For the subring of $J$ consisting of all even integers has no identity element.

*Example* 2. A subring $T$ of a ring $S$ without an identity can have a multiplicative identity. The subset $\{z, a\}$ of the ring of Example 4, Section 7.1, is a ring with identity. Moreover, it is commutative.

*Example* 3. A subring $T$ of a noncommutative ring $S$ can be a commutative ring. See the preceding remark.

*Example* 4. A subring $T$ of a field $S$ need not be a field as we see by looking at the set of rational integers of the rational field.

*Example* 5. A subring $T$ of a ring $S$ can have a multiplicative identity $f$ which is different from the multiplicative identity $e$ of $S$. For let $S = \{z, e, b, f\}$ with addition and multiplication defined by the tables shown. This system is

| $+$ | $z$ | $e$ | $b$ | $f$ |
|---|---|---|---|---|
| $z$ | $z$ | $e$ | $b$ | $f$ |
| $e$ | $e$ | $z$ | $f$ | $b$ |
| $b$ | $b$ | $f$ | $z$ | $e$ |
| $f$ | $f$ | $b$ | $e$ | $z$ |

| $\cdot$ | $z$ | $e$ | $b$ | $f$ |
|---|---|---|---|---|
| $z$ | $z$ | $z$ | $z$ | $z$ |
| $e$ | $z$ | $e$ | $b$ | $f$ |
| $b$ | $z$ | $b$ | $b$ | $z$ |
| $f$ | $z$ | $f$ | $z$ | $f$ |

easily verified to be a ring with identity $e$. The subset $T = \{z, f\}$ is a subring with identity $f$. Furthermore, the subsets $V = \{z, e\}$ and $W = \{z, b\}$ are subrings with identity elements.

There are, however, some positive statements which can be made. Certainly any subring of a commutative ring is also a commutative ring. Moreover, no subring of an integral domain has divisors of zero since a ring and its subrings have the same zero element, $z$. Then

$$ab = z$$

in $T$ certainly means that $ab = z$ in $S$.

DEFINITION 7.7. A subring $T$ of a field $S$ is a *subfield* of $S$ if and only if $T$ is a field. A subring $T$ of an integral domain $S$ is a *subdomain* if and only if $T$ is an integral domain.

Surely the domain of rational integers is a subdomain of the field (and integral domain) of rational numbers. And the set of rational cuts (or rational numbers) is a subfield of the real field.

From each element $a$ of a ring $S$ we obtain a subring which is denoted by $aJ$. $aJ$ consists of all the scalar multiples $an$ of $a$ as $n$ ranges over $J$. Using the properties of scalar multiplication we see that

$$(an)(am) = amn,$$
$$an + am = a(n + m),$$

and

$$an - am = a(n - m),$$

so that $aJ$ is certainly a subring of $S$.

Now it is clear that $aJ$ is a finite system if and only if there is a positive integer $k$ such that

$$ak = z.$$

For otherwise the set $\{a, 2a, 3a, \cdots\}$ is an infinite subset of $aJ$. The least positive integer $k$ with this property is defined to be the *characteristic* of $a$ and of $aJ$. If no such positive integer exists, then $a$ and $aJ$ are said to have *characteristic zero* (or characteristic infinity).

Now in general the elements of a ring vary widely in their characteristics. In the ring $J/(4)$ the two elements [1] and [3] have characteristic 4, and the element [2] has characteristic 2.

*Example* 6. Consider the additive group $R_1$ of rational numbers modulo (1). We make this group into a ring by defining the product of each two elements to be [0]. The element [1/2] is of characteristic 2, the element [1/3] of characteristic 3, the element $[1/m]$ of characteristic $m$ when $m$ is a positive integer. In fact this ring has elements of every possible positive characteristic.

However, if the multiplication in a ring is sufficiently restricted or special, it exerts influence on the additive structure of the ring through the distributive law and enables us to make some very strong statements about the characteristics.

THEOREM 7.15. *If $S$ is a ring with identity and without divisors of zero, then all of the elements $\neq z$ have the same characteristic which is either 0 or a prime $p$.*

Let $e$ be the identity of $S$, $e \neq z$. If $e$ has positive characteristic we denote it by $k$. Now suppose $k$ has a factor $h$, $1 < h < k$. Then $k = hq$ and

$$z = ke = hqe = hqe^2 = (he)(qe),$$

and since $S$ has no divisors of zero one of the two elements $he$ and $qe$ must equal $z$. But this contradicts the definition of the characteristic $k$. Hence $k$ has no such factors and we see that $e$ has prime characteristic $k = p$.

Now let $x \neq z$ be an arbitrary element of $S$. Since

$$px = p(ex) = (pe)x = zx = z,$$

we know that $x$ has positive characteristic $m$ and $m \leqslant p$. However,

$$z = mx = m(ex) = (me)x$$

implies that $me = z$ since $S$ has no divisors of zero. Hence, since $p$ is the characteristic of $e$, $p \leqslant m$. Thus $m = p$ and every nonzero element of $S$ has characteristic $p$.

Suppose $e$ has characteristic 0; then there is no positive integer $k$ such that $ke = z$. If $x \neq z$ were an element of positive characteristic $m$ in $S$, then

$$z = mx = m(ex) = (me)x,$$

and we would have $me = z$ since $S$ has no divisors of zero. This contradiction shows that, if $e$ has characteristic 0, then all nonzero elements of $S$ have characteristic 0, proving the theorem.

DEFINITION 7.8. The *characteristic of the ring $S$* is the least positive integer $k$ such that $kx = z$ for every $x$ in $S$, or zero if $k$ does not exist.

*Corollary* 7.15.1. A ring with identity and without divisors of zero is a ring of characteristic 0 or $p$.

Now consider an integral domain $D$. It has an identity $e$ and no divisors of zero so it has characteristic 0 or $p$. In either case $eJ$ is a subdomain of $D$ since the subring $eJ$ is surely an integral domain: it has an identity $e = e1$; it is commutative since

$$(en)(em) = e(nm) = e(mn) = (em)(en);$$

and it certainly has no divisors of zero since $D$ has none. As a matter of fact, $eJ$ is the minimal subdomain of $D$ in that it is contained in every subdomain of $D$.

THEOREM 7.16. *The subdomain $eJ$ of the domain $D$ is contained in every subdomain of $D$.*

To prove this we need only to show that $e$ is contained in every subdomain of $D$. Let $D'$ be a subdomain of $D$. As such it has a multiplicative identity element $f \neq z$. Now $f$ is idempotent,

$$f^2 = f,$$

and since $f$ is in $D$ also,

$$fe = f.$$

Hence

$$f^2 - fe = f(f - e) = z,$$

and since $D$ has no divisors of zero we know that

$$f - e = z \qquad \text{and} \qquad f = e.$$

Thus $e$ is in $D'$, so that $D' \supseteq eJ$.

The commutativity of $D$ is of no special consequence in this work.

THEOREM 7.17. *The subdomain $eJ$ of the domain $D$ is a field if and only if $D$ has characteristic $p$.*

If $D$ has characteristic $p$, then $eJ$ contains $p$ elements, namely,

$$z = 0e, e = 1e, \cdots, (p - 1)e.$$

Let $qe \neq z$ be in $eJ$; since $qe \neq z$ we know that $p$ is not a factor of $q$. Hence $(q, p) = 1$ and there are integers $r$ and $s$ such that

$$1 = rp + qs.$$

Therefore,

$$e = e1 = e(rp + qs) = r(ep) + (qe)(se),$$

and since

$$ep = z$$

we have

$$e = (qe)(se)$$

so that $se$ is the multiplicative inverse of $qe$ in $eJ$. Thus $eJ$ is a field.

Conversely, suppose $eJ$ is a field, and consider $me \neq 1e$, $me \neq z$. Then $me$ has a multiplicative inverse, $ne$, and

$$e = (ne)(me).$$

Write this as

$$(nm)e - 1e = (nm - 1)e = z.$$

Since $m \neq 1$ we know that $nm \neq 1$ in $J$, and so $e$ has positive characteristic. Thus $D$ has characteristic $p$, a prime.

## Exercise 7.4

**1.** Determine the characteristic of every example of a ring given thus far in this chapter.

**2.** Show that a ring exists of every possible characteristic. (What is the characteristic of $J/(m)$?)

**3.** Prove that every subsfield of a sfield contains $eJ$, where $e$ is the sfield identity.

**4.** Find a skew field which contains a subring which is a field.

**5.** Let $T$ be a subring of the ring $S$ and $W$ be a subring of the ring $T$. Show that $W$ is a subring of $S$.

**6.** Find all of the subrings of $J/(12)$, and determine the characteristic of each.

**7.** Find $T$, a subring of characteristic 3 of $J/(21)$, and $W$, a subring of characteristic 7 of $J/(21)$. Show that each element $x$ of $J/(21)$ is expressible uniquely as

$$x = t + w, \qquad t \text{ in } T, \qquad w \text{ in } W.$$

Moreover, show that, if $x_i = t_i + w_i$, then

$$x_1x_2 = t_1t_2 + w_1w_2 \qquad \text{and} \qquad x_1x_2 = (t_1 + t_2) + (w_1 + w_2).$$

**8.** Which of the following sets are subfields of the real field?

(*a*) $\{a + b\sqrt{3}: a \text{ and } b \text{ in } R\}$.

(*b*) $\{a + b\sqrt[3]{2}: a \text{ and } b \text{ in } R\}$.

(*c*) $\{a - b\sqrt{2}: a \text{ and } b \text{ in } R\}$.

(*d*) $\{a + b\sqrt[3]{9} + c\sqrt[3]{3}: a, b, \text{ and } c \text{ in } R\}$.

**9.** Prove that, if $x$ and $y$ are elements of a commutative ring of characteristic $p$, where $p$ is a prime, then

$$(x + y)^p = x^p + y^p \qquad \text{and} \qquad (x - y)^p = x^p - y^p.$$

**10.** Let $D$ be an integral domain of characteristic $p$. What can you say about the mapping of $D$ to $D$ defined for each $x$ in $D$ by $x \to x^p$? What mapping is this when $D = J/(p)$?

**11.** What can you say about every subfield of the real field?

**12.** Show that the rational field contains no proper subfields.

**13.** Prove that the only proper subdomain of the integral domain, the rational field, is the ring of rational integers.

## 7.5 Isomorphisms and Extensions

An inspection of the subring $eJ$ of a domain of characteristic zero reveals it to be astonishingly like the system $J$. This naturally brings up the concept of isomorphism.

DEFINITION 7.9. The ring $\{S, +, \cdot\}$ is *isomorphic* with the ring $\{S^*, \oplus, \odot\}$

if and only if there is a one-to-one mapping $F$ from $S$ onto $S^*$ such that for $x$ and $y$ in $S$

$$F(x + y) = F(x) \oplus F(y)$$

and

$$F(x \cdot y) = F(x) \odot F(y).$$

The mapping $F$ is called an *isomorphism* from $S$ onto $S'$.

This agrees with our earlier discussions of isomorphic systems. Applied to the material of the preceding section it yields the following result.

THEOREM 7.18. *An integral domain of characteristic zero contains a subdomain which is isomorphic with $J$. An integral domain of characteristic $p$ contains a subdomain isomorphic with $J/(p)$.*

If the domain $D$ has characteristic 0, then the subdomain $eJ$ is certainly isomorphic with $J$. An isomorphism of $eJ$ onto $J$ is given by

$$F\colon en \to n, \qquad \text{for each } n \text{ in } J.$$

We see that

$$F(en \cdot em) = F(enm) = nm = F(en)F(em)$$

and

$$F(en + em) = F\big(e(n + m)\big) = n + m = F(en) + F(em).$$

Furthermore $F$ is a mapping of $eJ$ onto $J$ since $en = em$ if and only if $n = m$ because of the fact that $D$ has characteristic 0. Thus $eJ$ is isomorphic with $J$, and we say that an integral domain of characteristic zero "contains" the domain $J$ of rational integers.

If the domain $D$ has characteristic $p$, then we define $F$ by

$$F\colon em \to [m]$$

for each of the $p$ elements $e0, e1, \cdots, e(p - 1)$ of $eJ$, where $[m]$ denotes the congruence class of integers mod $p$. Since the $p$ integers $0, 1, \cdots, p - 1$ are distributed one to each of the congruence classes mod $p$, we know that $F$ is a one-to-one mapping of $eJ$ onto $J/(p)$. Now consider $F(en \cdot em)$. Clearly

$$en \cdot em = enm = er$$

where $0 \leqslant r < p$ and $nm = qp + r$. Moreover we know from our study of the ring $J/(p)$ that

$$[n][m] = [nm] = [r].$$

Hence

$$F(en \cdot em) = F(er) = [r] = [n][m].$$

Consider

$$en + em = e(n + m).$$

Again by the Divisor Theorem for $J$ we have

$$n + m = pq^* + r^*, \qquad 0 \leqslant r^* < p,$$

so that

$$en + em = e(pq^* + r^*) = er^*.$$

Moreover,

$$[n] + [m] = [n + m] = [r^*],$$

so that

$$\boldsymbol{F}(en + em) = \boldsymbol{F}(er^*) = [r^*] = [n] + [m].$$

Hence $\boldsymbol{F}$ is an isomorphism from $eJ$ onto $J/(p)$. We say that an integral domain of characteristic $p$ "contains" the finite field $J/(p)$, identifying $eJ$ with $J/(p)$.

*Corollary* 7.18.1. An integral domain $D$ contains (a subdomain isomorphic with) the ring of integers or one of the fields $J/(p)$.

This means that the integral domains, and the fields also, are anchored to the familiar systems which we have already studied. Thus our knowledge of the systems $J$ and $J/(p)$ provides us with an entry into any integral domain.

THEOREM 7.19. *A field $S$ of characteristic zero contains a subfield isomorphic with $R$, the rational field.*

As we have already seen, $S$ contains the system $eJ$ which is isomorphic with $J$. Now each element $en \neq z$ in $eJ$ has a multiplicative inverse $(en)^{-1}$ in $S$, and we claim that the set $T$ of all elements of $S$ of the form

$$(em)(en)^{-1}$$

for some $m$ and $n \neq 0$ in $J$ is a subfield of $S$. Furthermore the mapping $\boldsymbol{F}$ defined as

$$\boldsymbol{F}: m/n \to (em)(en)^{-1}$$

is an isomorphism of $R$ onto $T$.

That $T$ is a subfield of $S$ is easily shown. If $(em)(en)^{-1}$ and $(ep)(eq)^{-1}$ are elements of $T$, then

$$(em)(en)^{-1} \pm (ep)(eq)^{-1} = \big(e(qm \pm pn)\big)(eqn)^{-1}$$

and

$$\big((em)(en)^{-1}\big)\big((ep)(eq)^{-1}\big) = (emp)(enq)^{-1},$$

so that $T$ is a subring of $S$. Since

$$e = (e1)(e1)^{-1}$$

we see that $eJ \subset T$, and for $m \neq 0$ we have $(en)(em)^{-1}$ in $T$, and this is the multiplicative inverse of $(em)(en)^{-1}$. Thus $T$ is a subfield of $S$. (The student should notice that we are just working with the fractions $m/n$ and $p/q$ in slightly disguised form.)

To show that $\boldsymbol{F}$ is an isomorphism we first show that $\boldsymbol{F}$ is a mapping, and this means we must show that the definition of $\boldsymbol{F}$ is independent of the integers $m$ and $n$ which appear in the representation of $m/n$. So we have to show that, if

$$m/n = m_1/n_1 \qquad \text{in } R,$$

then

$$(em)(en)^{-1} = (em_1)(en_1)^{-1} \qquad \text{in } S$$

(proving that, for example, 1/2 and 2/4 have the same image in $S$ under $\boldsymbol{F}$). From $m/n = m_1/n_1$ we obtain the equation (*in* $J$)

$$mn_1 = m_1n$$

so that in $S$

$$e(mn_1) = e(m_1n).$$

Then

$$e^2(mn_1) = (em)(en_1) = e^2(m_1n) = (em_1)(en)$$

so that multiplication by $(en)^{-1}(en_1)^{-1}$ yields

$$(em)(en)^{-1} = (em_1)(en_1)^{-1},$$

and we see that $\boldsymbol{F}$ is a mapping from $R$ to $S$.

Next we point out that the mapping $F$ is one-to-one. This follows from the fact that

$$(em)(en)^{-1} = (ep)(eq)^{-1}$$

implies

$$\begin{aligned}(em)(en)^{-1}(en)(eq) &= (ep)(eq)^{-1}(eq)(en),\\ (em)(eq) &= (ep)(en),\\ emq &= epn,\end{aligned}$$

and

$$e(mq - pn) = z.$$

Since $S$ has characteristic 0 this means that

$$mq - pn = 0$$

and

$$m/n = p/q.$$

Hence the mapping $\boldsymbol{F}$ is one-to-one.

That $\boldsymbol{F}$ is an isomorphism follows from the discussion of addition and multiplication in $T$:

$$\begin{aligned}\boldsymbol{F}(m/n + p/q) &= \boldsymbol{F}\big((mq + pn)/qn\big) = \big(e(mq + pn)\big)(eqn)^{-1},\\ &= \boldsymbol{F}(m/n) + \boldsymbol{F}(p/q),\end{aligned}$$

and

$$\begin{aligned}\boldsymbol{F}\big((m/n)(p/q)\big) &= \boldsymbol{F}(mp/nq) = (emp)(enq)^{-1},\\ &= \boldsymbol{F}(m/n)\boldsymbol{F}(p/q).\end{aligned}$$

DEFINITION 7.10. The ring $T$ is said to be an *extension* of the ring $S$ if and only if $T$ contains a proper subring $S'$ which is isomorphic with $S$.

*Corollary* 7.19.1. A field $S$ is an extension of the rational field $R$ if $S$ has characteristic 0, and of the finite field $J/(p)$ if $S$ has characteristic $p$.

The fields $R$, $J/(2)$, $J/(3)$, $\cdots$, are sometimes called *prime fields* since every field is an extension of exactly one of them. This reduces the problem of studying fields and domains to the problem of studying extensions of the basic systems that we have already encountered. Thus far we have encountered a few special extensions of certain special rings, e.g., the extension of $J$ to $R$ and the extension of $R$ to $Q$, the sfield of rational quaternions. These methods can also be used to extend some other rings, but another and more general method of extension is studied in the next chapter.

Now the preceding work characterizes the integral domain $J$ as the minimal integral domain of characteristic 0. That is, an integral domain which contains no proper subdomain is isomorphic with $J$ if and only if it is of characteristic 0. There is another way of characterizing $J$ which involves the concept of induction.

Let $S$ be an integral domain. A subset $L$ of $S$ is called an *induction set* if (i) the multiplicative identity $e$ of $S$ is in $L$, and (ii) the sum $a + e$ is in $L$ whenever the element $a$ is in $L$.

*Lemma* 7.1. An integral domain $S$ contains exactly one induction set $M$ which is contained in every induction set of $S$.

Since $S$ is surely an induction set of $S$ we know that the class of induction sets of $S$ is not empty. So we form $M$, the intersection of all induction sets of $S$. We shall show that $M$ is an induction set of $S$ and thereby prove the lemma. First we note that $e$ belongs to each of the sets which intersect to form $M$, and so $e$ is in $M$. Now suppose $a$ is in $M$. Then by definition of intersection $a$ is an element of every induction set of $S$, and so $a + e$ is in every induction set of $S$. This means, then, that $a + e$ is in $M$, and we conclude that $M$ is the minimal induction set of $S$.

It is quite clear from the axiom of induction that the set $P$ of positive integers is the minimal induction set of $J$ and also of the field $R$. Inspection of the integral domain $J/(p)$ shows that $J/(p)$ is the only induction set of that system.

*Lemma* 7.2. The set $eP = \{en\colon n \text{ in } P\}$ is the minimal induction set $M$ of the domain $S$.

Consider the set $eP$. It contains $e = e1$, and, if $a$ is in $eP$, then $a = ek$ for some positive integer $k$ so that

$$a + e = ek + e1 = e(k + 1)$$

is in $eP$ also. Thus $eP$ is an induction set of $S$ and so $eP \supseteq M$.

On the other hand, if we denote by $M'$ the set of all positive integers $m$ such that $em$ is in $M$, then we see first of all that 1 is in $M'$. Now suppose $k$ is in $M'$. Then $ek$ is in $M$ so that

$$e(k + 1) = ek + e$$

is in $M$ and $k + 1$ is in $M'$. Therefore by the Induction Axiom, $M' = P$, and we see that $eP \subseteq M$. Hence $M = eP$.

Now the characterization of $J$ is rather evident.

THEOREM 7.20. *The integral domain $S$ is isomorphic with $J$ if and only if exactly one of the following holds for each element $x$ of $S$:*

(i) $x = z$; (ii) *$x$ is in $M$; or* (iii) *$-x$ is in $M$, where $M$ denotes the minimal induction set of $S$.*

Suppose the elements of $S$ are split in the above manner. Then we know that, for an arbitrary element $x$ of $S$, either

$$x = z = x0,$$
$$x = en, \qquad n \text{ a positive integer,}$$

or

$$-x = en, \qquad n \text{ a positive integer.}$$

Since $-x = en$ implies that $x = e(-n)$ we clearly have a one-to-one correspondence between the elements of $S$ and the elements of $J$, given by

$$\mathbf{F}: m \to x = em.$$

For, if $em = en$ with $m \neq n$, then

$$em - en = e(m - n) = z$$

puts $x = z = e(m - n)$ into two of the above categories simultaneously. Thus $\mathbf{F}$ is one-to-one. That $\mathbf{F}$ is an isomorphism is proved easily as in Theorem 7.18.

Conversely, suppose $S$ and $J$ are isomorphic domains with isomorphism $\mathbf{F}$ from $J$ to $S$. Since $\mathbf{F}(1) = e$ and $\mathbf{F}(0) = z$ by the next theorem we see that the elements of $S$ fall into three nonoverlapping sets,

$$\{z\},\ eP, \text{ and } -eP = \{em\colon -m \text{ in } P\},$$

which correspond to the partition of $J$ into $\{0\}$, $P$, and $-P = \{$set of all negative integers$\}$.

The result concerning the correspondences between the respective identity elements is a simple consequence of the uniqueness of these elements.

THEOREM 7.21. *If $\mathbf{F}$ is an isomorphism from the ring $S$ with identity $e$ onto the ring $S''$, then $\mathbf{F}(z) = z''$ and $\mathbf{F}(e) = e''$ are the additive and multiplicative identity elements, respectively, of $S''$.*

Let $x''$ be an arbitrary element of $S''$. Since $\boldsymbol{F}$ maps $S$ onto $S''$ there is exactly one element $x$ in $S$ such that $\boldsymbol{F}(x) = x''$. Now

$$\boldsymbol{F}(x + z) = x'' + z'' = \boldsymbol{F}(x) = x'' = \boldsymbol{F}(z + x) = z'' + x''$$

so that $z''$ is the additive identity of $S''$, and $e'' = \boldsymbol{F}(e)$ is the multiplicative identity of $S''$ since

$$\boldsymbol{F}(xe) = x''e'' = \boldsymbol{F}(x) = x'' = \boldsymbol{F}(ex) = e''x''.$$

An example of an isomorphism between two rings was studied in Chapter 2 when we saw that the ring $J$ is isomorphic with the ring of rational integers, a subring of the field $R$. Now we shall give an example of a ring which has a nontrivial isomorphism with itself (or an *automorphism*).

*Example* 1. Let $S$ be the set of all real numbers of the form $a + b\sqrt{5}$, where $a$ and $b$ are rational numbers. $S$ is certainly a subring of the field of real numbers since the elements

$$(a + b\sqrt{5}) \pm (c + d\sqrt{5}) = (a \pm c) + (b \pm d)\sqrt{5}$$

and

$$(a + b\sqrt{5})(c + d\sqrt{5}) = (ac + 5bd) + (ad + bc)\sqrt{5}$$

are in $S$ whenever $a$, $b$, $c$, and $d$ are rational numbers. Moreover $S$ is a subfield of $Re$ since $a + b\sqrt{5}$ has a multiplicative inverse if

$$a + b\sqrt{5} \neq 0.$$

For in $S$

$$a + b\sqrt{5} = 0$$

implies that $a$ and $b$ are both 0 since otherwise the equation

$$a/b = -\sqrt{5}$$

contradicts the fact that there is no rational number whose square is 5. Hence

$$a + b\sqrt{5} \neq 0$$

is equivalent to the condition

$$a^2 - 5b^2 \neq 0,$$

and since

$$(a + b\sqrt{5})(a - b\sqrt{5}) = a^2 - 5b^2$$

we see that the inverse of $a + b\sqrt{5}$ is

$$(a/(a^2 - 5b^2)) - (b/(a^2 - 5b^2))\sqrt{5}.$$

Now define the mapping $\boldsymbol{F}$ of $S$ onto $S$ by the equation

$$\boldsymbol{F}(a + b\sqrt{5}) = a - b\sqrt{5}.$$

Thus

$$\boldsymbol{F}(1) = \boldsymbol{F}(1 + 0\sqrt{5}) = 1 - 0\sqrt{5} = 1$$

and

$$\boldsymbol{F}(2 - \sqrt{5}) = 2 + \sqrt{5}.$$

Clearly the equations

$$(a - b\sqrt{5}) + (c - d\sqrt{5}) = (a + c) - (b + d)\sqrt{5}$$

and

$$(a - b\sqrt{5})(c - d\sqrt{5}) = (ac + 5bd) - (ad + bc)\sqrt{5}$$

show that $F$ is an automorphism of $S$. Note that the rational field $R$, which is a subfield of $S$, is left elementwise unchanged by $F$ since

$$F(r) = F(r + 0\sqrt{5}) = r - 0\sqrt{5} = r.$$

The automorphisms of a ring are rather like the symmetries of a geometrical figure or geometry. The example above is analogous to the rotation of a plane 180° about a line in the plane, shown in Fig. 7.2.

**Figure 7.2**

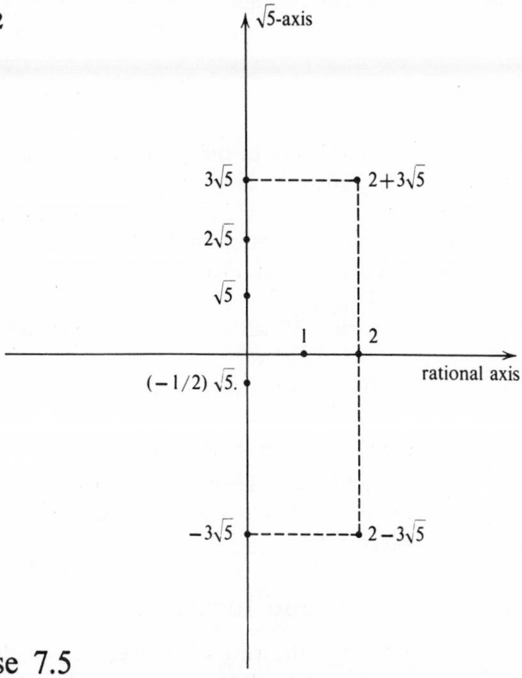


## Exercise 7.5

**1.** Show that the ring of Example 4, Section 7.1, is an extension of $J/(2)$.

**2.** Show that quaternion ring $Q$ is an extension of the rational field $R$ by considering the quaternions of the form $(r, 0, 0, 0) = re + 0i + 0j + 0k$.

**3.** Show that, if $F$ is an isomorphism from field $S$ onto field $T$, then $-F(x) = F(-x)$ and the multiplicative inverse $(F(x))^{-1}$ is $F(x^{-1})$. Illustrate with Example 1 of this section.

**4.** Find an infinite collection of different induction sets in the domain $J$.

**5.** What can you say about a ring which contains a subring isomorphic with $J$ and another subring isomorphic with $J/(3)$?

**6.** Show from Theorem 7.21 that the only automorphism of $J/(m)$ is the identity mapping $E$, $E(x) = x$. Connect this with the fact that the only induction set of $J/(m)$ is $J/(m)$.

**7.** Prove that the only automorphism of $J$ is the identity mapping $E$, $E(x) = x$.

**8.** Complete the proof of Theorem 7.20.

**9.** Show that $J/(p)$ is isomorphic with a subring of $J/(m)$ if and only if $p$ is a factor of $m$.

**10.** Find a nontrivial automorphism of the rational quaternion ring.

**11.** Show that the subsets

$$\{m + n\sqrt{2}: m \text{ and } n \text{ integral}\}$$

and

$$\{m + n\sqrt{3}: m \text{ and } n \text{ integral}\}$$

of the field of real numbers are nonisomorphic subdomains of *Re*. (*Hint:* If an isomorphism exists, then $\sqrt{2}$ corresponds to an element $m + n\sqrt{3}$ so that $2 = (\sqrt{2})^2$ corresponds to $m^2 + 9n^2 + 2mn\sqrt{3}$. But $2 = 1 + 1$ corresponds to $2 = 1 + 1$.)

**12.** Prove that an integral domain with $p$ elements, $p$ prime, is isomorphic with $J/(p)$.

**13.** Find all of the automorphisms of the example of this section, and show that they form a group under function composition.

**14.** Show that the map $F$, $F(x) = x^p$, of the integral domain $S$ of characteristic $p$ to $S$, is an isomorphism of $S$ onto a subdomain of itself.

**15.** Show that the isomorphism of Problem 14 is an automorphism if $S$ is finite.

**16.** Extend a ring $S$ to a ring $S^*$ with identity by considering $S^* = S \times J$ and defining

$$(s, h) + (t, k) = (s + t, h + k)$$

and

$$(s, h)(t, k) = (st + sk + ht, hk)$$

where $sk$ and $ht$ are scalar multiples. Then $S_1 = \{(s, 0): s \text{ in } S\}$ is isomorphic with $S$ and $(z, 1)$ is the identity of $S^*$. What could be used instead of $J$ so that $S$ and $S^*$ have the same characteristic?

## 7.6 Homomorphisms and Ideals

From our earlier work with the ring of integers in which subrings and homomorphisms of $J$ were linked, and from our knowledge of the relations between normal subgroups and homomorphisms of a group we should naturally expect the concept of homomorphism to be of considerable importance in the study of rings. In particular it should single out those subrings of a ring which can be "divided into" the ring.

DEFINITION 7.11. A mapping $F$ from a ring $S$ onto a ring $S''$ is a *homomorphism* of $S$ onto $S''$ if and only if

$$F(a + b) = F(a) + F(b)$$

and

$$F(ab) = F(a)F(b)$$

for each $a$ and $b$ in $S$. $S''$ is a *homomorphic image* of $S$.

Obviously an isomorphism is just a special type of homomorphism, viz., a one-to-one homomorphism.

It can happen that neither of the rings, $S$ nor $S''$, has a multiplicative identity. But both will always have additive identities, and we concentrate our attention on the zero element $z''$ of $S''$. As in the proof of Theorem 7.21 we can show easily that $z''$ is the image $\mathbf{F}(z)$ of the zero $z$ of $S$. We can in fact prove considerably more.

THEOREM 7.22. *If $\mathbf{F}$ is a homomorphism from ring $S$ onto ring $S''$, then the set $K$ of all elements $k$ in $S$ such that $\mathbf{F}(k) = z''$ is a subring of $S$ with the special property that $ks$ and $sk$ are in $K$ whenever $k$ is in $K$ and $s$ is in $S$.*

Let $h$ and $k$ be two elements of $K$. Then

$$\mathbf{F}(h) = \mathbf{F}(k) = z''$$

so that

$$\mathbf{F}(hk) = \mathbf{F}(h)\mathbf{F}(k) = z''z'' = z''$$

and

$$\mathbf{F}(h + k) = \mathbf{F}(h) + \mathbf{F}(k) = z'' + z'' = z''.$$

Therefore $hk$ and $h + k$ are in $K$. Moreover, $z$ is in $K$ since for each $x'' = \mathbf{F}(x)$ in $S'$ we have

$$x'' + \mathbf{F}(z) = \mathbf{F}(x) + \mathbf{F}(z) = \mathbf{F}(x + z) = \mathbf{F}(x) = \mathbf{F}(z) + x''.$$

Since $z''$ is unique in this property,

$$\mathbf{F}(z) = z''$$

and $z$ is in $K$.

Now consider $z = k + (-k)$ for $k$ in $K$;

$$z'' = \mathbf{F}(z) = \mathbf{F}(k + (-k)) = \mathbf{F}(k) + \mathbf{F}(-k) = z'' + \mathbf{F}(-k)$$

so that $\mathbf{F}(-k) = z''$. Hence $-k$ is in $K$ also, and we see that $K$ is a subring of $S$.

For any $s$ in $S$ and $k$ in $K$ we have

$$\mathbf{F}(sk) = \mathbf{F}(s)\mathbf{F}(k) = \mathbf{F}(s)z'' = z''$$

and

$$\mathbf{F}(ks) = \mathbf{F}(k)\mathbf{F}(s) = z''\mathbf{F}(s) = z''.$$

Thus the subring $K$ contains the elements $sk$ and $ks$. $K$ is called the *kernel* of the homomorphism $\mathbf{F}$.

*Example* 1. Let $S$ be the ring of Example 4, Section 7.1, and $S''$ be $J/(2)$. The operation tables of these rings are as shown.

$S$

| + | z | a | b | c |
|---|---|---|---|---|
| z | z | a | b | c |
| a | a | z | c | b |
| b | b | c | z | a |
| c | c | b | a | z |

| · | z | a | b | c |
|---|---|---|---|---|
| z | z | z | z | z |
| a | z | a | b | c |
| b | z | z | z | z |
| c | z | a | b | c |

$S''$

| + | 0 | 1 |
|---|---|---|
| 0 | 0 | 1 |
| 1 | 1 | 0 |

| · | 0 | 1 |
|---|---|---|
| 0 | 0 | 1 |
| 1 | 0 | 1 |

The mapping $F$ of $S$ onto $S''$,

$$F = \{(z, 0), (b, 0), (a, 1), (c, 1)\},$$

is a homomorphism of $S$ onto $S''$ as we can show by checking the operation tables. We note, for example, that

$$F(z + a) = F(z) + F(a) = 0 + 1 = 1 = F(a),$$
$$F(a + b) = F(a) + F(b) = 1 + 0 = 1 = F(c),$$
$$F(ab) = F(a)F(b) = 1 \cdot 0 = 0 = F(b),$$

and

$$F(ca) = F(c)F(a) = 1 \cdot 1 = 1 = F(a).$$

The kernel of this homomorphism is $K = \{z, b\}$ which is easily seen to be a subring of $S$. Moreover, we see by looking at the first and third rows and columns of the multiplication table of $S$ that $K$ in this example does possess the special left and right multiplication property.

Now we investigate the type of subring that all kernels seem to be.

DEFINITION 7.12. A subring $T$ of the ring $S$ is an *ideal* of $S$ if and only if the sets $TS = \{ts: t \text{ in } T, s \text{ in } S\}$ and $ST = \{st: s \text{ in } S, t \text{ in } T\}$ are subsets of $T$.

Clearly we proved in Theorem 7.22 that the kernel of a homomorphism of $S$ onto $S''$ is an ideal of $S$. Is the converse true? Can we define a homomorphic image of $S$ for each ideal $T$ of $S$? The answer, as we shall see, is affirmative.

Since addition is in general the nicer operation of a ring $S$, and since an ideal $T$ of $S$ is certainly a subgroup of the additive, Abelian group $S$, we consider the additive cosets

$$a + T = \{a + t: t \text{ in } T\}$$

of $T$ in $S$. These form a partition of the set $S$.

THEOREM 7.23. *The additive cosets $a + T$ of the ideal $T$ form a partition of the set $S$ of the ring $S$.*

First we know that $x$ is in $x + T$ for each $x$ in $S$ since $z$ is in $T$ and $x = x + z$. Now suppose $c$ is an element in both the cosets $a + T$ and $b + T$. Then $T$ contains elements $t$ and $v$ such that

$$c = a + t = b + v.$$

Therefore

$$a = b + (v - t)$$

so that

$$a + T \supseteq b + T,$$

and

$$b = a + (t - v),$$

so that

$$a + T \subseteq b + T.$$

Hence the cosets form a partition of $S$. (Note that the multiplicative properties of $T$ were not used.)

*Example* 1 (*Continued*). The additive cosets of the ideal $K = \{z, b\}$ in $S$ are

$$z + K = b + K = K = \{z, b\}$$

and

$$a + K = c + K = \{a, c\}.$$

Clearly the two subsets form a partition of $S = \{z, a, b, c\}$.

Denote by $S/T$ the collection $\{a + T\colon a \text{ in } S\}$ of cosets. How can we make this set into a ring which is a homomorphic image of $S$? Guided by our earlier successes in analogous situations and by the above example we define addition and multiplication as follows.

*Addition:*

$$(a + T) \oplus (b + T) = (a + b) + T$$

*Multiplication:*

$$(a + T) \odot (b + T) = ab + T.$$

Since these definitions are stated in terms of the coset representatives $a$, $b$, $a + b$, and $ab$, we must prove they are actually independent of the particular representatives. So let

$$a + T = a_1 + T \quad \text{and} \quad b + T = b_1 + T.$$

Then

$$a_1 = a + t \quad \text{and} \quad b_1 = b + v$$

for some elements $t$ and $v$ of $T$. This means that

$$a_1 + b_1 = a + b + (t + v)$$

and

$$a_1 b_1 = (a + t)(b + v) = ab + (tb + av + tv).$$

Since $T$ is an ideal the elements $tb$ and $av$ are in $T$, so that $(t + v)$ and $(tb + av + tv)$ are elements of $T$. Thus

$$(a_1 + b_1) + T = (a + b) + T$$

and

$$a_1 b_1 + T = ab + T,$$

and the two relations are binary operations on $S/T$.

*Example* 2. In the ring $S$ of Example 1 we see that the set $H = \{z, a\}$ is a subring of $S$ which is not an ideal of $S$. Clearly $HS = \{z, a, b, c\}$ is not a subset of $H$. Now we can form the additive cosets of $H$ without any difficulty, and they form a partition of $S$:

$$z + H = a + H = H = \{a, z\}$$

and

$$b + H = c + H = \{b, c\}.$$

But suppose we try multiplying these by the above method:

$$(b + H) \odot (b + H) = b^2 + H = z + H$$

and

$$(c + H) \odot (c + H) = c^2 + H = c + H.$$

Clearly we get two unequal values when we multiply the same coset

$$b + H = c + H$$

by itself. Thus we do not get a binary operation of multiplication on the cosets of a subring which is not an ideal.

THEOREM 7.24. *The system $\{S/T, \oplus, \odot\}$ is a ring, and the natural mapping*

$$a \to a + T, \qquad \textit{for each } a \textit{ in } S,$$

*is a homomorphism of $S$ onto $S/T$ with kernel $T$.*

That $S/T$ is a ring is quite evident:

$$\begin{aligned}(1)\ (a + T) \oplus (b + T) &= (a + b) + T \\ &= (b + a) + T = (b + T) + (a + T).\end{aligned}$$

$$\begin{aligned}(2)\ \big((a + T) \oplus (b + T)\big) \oplus (c + T) &= \big((a + b) + T\big) \oplus (c + T) \\ &= (a + b + c) + T \\ &= (a + T) \oplus \big((b + T) \oplus (c + T)\big).\end{aligned}$$

(3) $(a + T) \oplus (z + T) = a + T.$

(4) $(a + T) \oplus (-a + T) = z + T.$

(5) Multiplication is associative since

$$(ab)c + T = a(bc) + T = abc + T.$$

$$\begin{aligned}(6)\ (a + T) \odot \big((b + T) \oplus (c + T)\big) &= a(b + c) + T = (ab + ac) + T \\ &= \big((a + T) \odot (b + T)\big) \\ &\quad \oplus \big((a + T) \odot (c + T)\big),\end{aligned}$$

and similarly on the other side.

The natural mapping preserves the operations of the two rings since

$$a \to a + T, \qquad b \to b + T,$$
$$a + b \to (a + b) + T = (a + T) \oplus (b + T),$$

and

$$ab \to ab + T = (a + T) \odot (b + T).$$

Clearly the kernel of this mapping is $T$ since $x$ maps onto the zero of $S/T$, namely, $z + T$, if and only if

$$x + T = z + T = T,$$

and $x + T = T$ if and only if $x$ is in $T$.

(Note that the additive group $\{S/T, \oplus\}$ is just the quotient group of the additive group $\{S, +\}$ over the subgroup $T$.)

DEFINITION 7.13. The ring $\{S/T, \oplus, \odot\}$ is the *quotient ring* (sometimes *difference ring*) of the ring $S$ over the ideal $T$.

The adjective "difference" is sometimes used to emphasize the prominent role of addition. In this case the system is denoted by $S - T$, and should not be confused with the set difference.

*Example* 3. Find an ideal $T$ of the ring $S = \{z, a, b, c\}$ of Example 1, and form the quotient ring $S/T$.

We have already noted that $T = \{z, b\}$ is an ideal of $S$, so we denote the two cosets $z + T$ and $a + T$ by $T$ and $A$, respectively. Then the operation tables of the quotient ring are as shown.

| $\oplus$ | $T$ | $A$ |
|---|---|---|
| $T$ | $T$ | $A$ |
| $A$ | $A$ | $T$ |

| $\odot$ | $T$ | $A$ |
|---|---|---|
| $T$ | $T$ | $T$ |
| $A$ | $T$ | $A$ |

The mapping $F_1$ of $S$ onto $S/T$,

$$F_1 = \{(z, T), (b, T), (a, A), (c, A)\},$$

is easily checked to be a homomorphism as in Example 1. In fact, the system $S/T$ looks astonishingly like the system $S' = J/(2)$ used in Example 1, and this is of course no accident.

THEOREM 7.25. *If $S''$ is a homomorphic image of the ring $S$ with homomorphism $F$, $F(a) = a''$, and kernel $K$, then the mapping $F_2$, $F_2(a + K) = a''$, is an isomorphism of $S/K$ with $S''$.*

Consider the definition of $F_2$:

$$F_2(a + K) = a'' = F(a).$$

Since it involves the coset representative $a$ we must show that this is not vital. In other words, we must show that, if $b$ is in the coset $a + K$, then

$$b'' = a''.$$

Now $b$ in $a + K$ implies that $K$ contains $k$ such that

$$b = a + k.$$

Therefore

$$\begin{aligned} b'' &= \boldsymbol{F}(b) = \boldsymbol{F}(a + k) = \boldsymbol{F}(a) + \boldsymbol{F}(k) \\ &= a'' + z'' = a'', \end{aligned}$$

and so

$$\boldsymbol{F}_2(a + K) = \boldsymbol{F}_2(b + K) = a'' = b'',$$

and $\boldsymbol{F}_2$ is a function from $S/K$ onto $S'$.

Moreover $\boldsymbol{F}_2$ is a one-to-one mapping since

$$\boldsymbol{F}_2(a + K) = a'' = \boldsymbol{F}_2(c + K) = c''$$

implies that

$$a'' - c'' = z''.$$

Therefore $a - c$ is in $K$ and

$$a - c = k.$$

Thus

$$a = c + k \qquad \text{so that} \qquad a + K = c + K,$$

and so distinct cosets of $K$ go onto distinct elements of $S''$.

To show that $\boldsymbol{F}_2$ is an isomorphism we check the images:

$$\begin{aligned} \boldsymbol{F}_2\big((a + K) \oplus (b + K)\big) &= \boldsymbol{F}_2\big((a + b) + K\big) = (a + b)'', \\ &= \boldsymbol{F}(a + b) = \boldsymbol{F}(a) + \boldsymbol{F}(b) = a'' + b'', \\ &= \boldsymbol{F}_2(a + K) + \boldsymbol{F}_2(b + K); \\ \boldsymbol{F}_2\big((a + K) \odot (b + K)\big) &= \boldsymbol{F}_2(ab + K) = (ab)'', \\ &= \boldsymbol{F}(ab) = \boldsymbol{F}(a)\boldsymbol{F}(b) = a''b'', \\ &= \boldsymbol{F}_2(a + K)\boldsymbol{F}_2(b + K). \end{aligned}$$

This completes the description of the very basic relationships between ideals of the ring $S$ and homomorphic images of $S$. For each homomorphic image $S''$ of $S$ there exists an ideal $K$ in $S$, where $K$ is the kernel of the homomorphism from $S$ to $S''$, and $S''$ and $S/K$ are isomorphic. And, if $T$ is an ideal of $S$, then $S/T$ is a homomorphic image of $S$.

In the chapters that follow we will encounter a variety of different rings and have ample opportunity to observe many different ideals. These will be used to study the rings in question, to invent new systems, and to add to our understanding of rings in general. For the moment, however, our supply of slightly exotic rings on which to practice is a trifle low.

*Example* 4. Find all of the ideals of the field $R$.

Let $T$ be an ideal of $R$. If $T$ contains a nonzero rational $r$, then $T$ contains the identity 1 which equals $r(1/r)$, by the special multiplicative property of $T$.

Then by this same property every $x = x1$ of $R$ is in $T$ so that $T = R$. Hence $R$ has two ideals only, the zero ideal $\{0\}$ and the entire field $R$.

*Example* 5. Show that the set $C$ of all elements of the ring $S$ having positive characteristic is an ideal of $S$. Moreover, the ring $S/C$ has characteristic 0 if $C \neq S$.

If $x$ and $y$ are elements of $C$ and have characteristics $m$ and $n$, respectively, then

$$mn(x \pm y) = n(mx) \pm n(ny) = z \pm z = z,$$

using the properties of scalar multiplication, so that $x + y$ and $x - y$ have positive characteristics and are in $C$. Furthermore, if $s$ is any element of $S$ and $x$ is an element of $C$ of characteristic $m$, then

$$m(xs) = (mx)s = zs = z$$

and

$$m(sx) = s(mx) = sz = z,$$

so that $xs$ and $sx$ are both in $C$. Thus $C$ is certainly an ideal of $S$. $C$ is sometimes called the *torsion ideal* of $S$.

Suppose $S/C$ contains a nonzero element

$$x + C \neq z + C = C$$

of positive characteristic $n$. Then

$$n(x + C) = nx + C = C$$

so that $nx$ is an element of $C$. As an element of $C$, $nx$ has positive characteristic $m$ so that we have

$$m(nx) = (mn)x = z.$$

But this means that $x$ has positive characteristic and hence is in $C$, so that

$$x + C = C = z + C.$$

Consequently all of the nonzero elements of $S/C$ have characteristic 0.

## Exercise 7.6

**1.** Find an ideal $T$, $\{0\} \subset T \subset D$, of the domain $D = \{m + n\sqrt{2}: m \text{ and } n \text{ integers}\}$, and describe $D/T$.

**2.** Show that a homomorphic image $S''$ of the ring $S$ is: (*a*) commutative if $S$ is commutative; (*b*) not necessarily noncommutative if $S$ is noncommutative; (*c*) a ring with identity if $S$ is; (*d*) not necessarily lacking an identity even though $S$ has no identity.

**3.** Show that a homomorphic image of an integral domain need not be an integral domain.

**4.** Prove that a skew field $S$ has only the trivial ideals $\{z\}$ and $S$.

**5.** Let $C_n$ consist of those elements of $S$ which have positive characteristics less than or equal to $n$. Show that $C_n$ is an ideal of $S$.

**6.** Relative to Problem 5, find $C_2$ for $J/(8)$; find $C_4$ for $J/(8)$.

**7.** For the ring $S$ and the positive integer $n$ define $nS = \{nx: x \text{ in } S\}$. Show that $nS$ is an ideal of $S$. What is true about $S/nS$? Illustrate with $S = J/(8)$ and $n = 20$; $n = 3$.

**8.** Show that the intersection of two ideals $T$ and $W$ of the ring $S$ is also an ideal of $S$.

**9.** In the ring $S$ let $A_1 = \{a\colon ax = z \text{ for all } x \text{ in } S\}$ and $A_2 = \{b\colon xb = z \text{ for all } x \text{ in } S\}$. Show that $A = A_1 \cap A_2$ is an ideal of $S$.

**10.** Let $T$ be an ideal of the ring $S$, and define $x$ to be *congruent* with $y$ modulo $T$ if and only if $x - y$ is in $T$. Show that this is an equivalence relation on $S$.

**11.** Show that the set theoretic union of two ideals of a ring $S$ need not be an ideal. When is the union of two ideals an ideal?

**12.** Show that the set $\{m + n\sqrt{3}\colon m \text{ and } n \text{ integral multiples of } 24\}$ is an ideal $T$ of the integral domain $D = \{m + n\sqrt{3}\colon m \text{ and } n \text{ in } J\}$. Find a subring $W$ of $D$ which contains $T$, show that $T$ is an ideal of $W$, and relate $W/T$ with $D/T$.

**13.** Let $V$ be the set of all elements of the ring $S$ which are mapped onto the ideal $V''$ of the homomorphic image $S''$ by the homomorphism $\boldsymbol{F}$. Show that $V$ is an ideal of $S$. Illustrate with the rings $D$ and $D/T$ in Problem 12.

**14.** Find all of the homomorphic images of the examples of Section 7.1.

**15.** Let $f''$ be a nonzero idempotent of the homomorphic image $S''$ of the ring $S$. Prove that the set of all elements which map onto $f''$ is a subsemigroup of the multiplicative semigroup $(S, \cdot\}$.

**16.** Find all of the idempotents of $J/(12)$, and illustrate Problem 15.

**17.** Can two different homomorphisms of the ring $S$ have the same kernel? Can two different homomorphisms of the ring $S$ be onto the same image ring $S''$? Explain. (See Example 1 of Section 7.5.)

## 7.7 Ring of Functions

For each ring there exists an extension ring, the ring $FS$ of all functions from $S$ to $S$. Although such rings seem quite difficult to analyze in general, they do provide us with a variety of different examples in a fairly simple fashion.

The set $FS$ is already known since the concept of function from $S$ to $S$ has certainly been defined. Now we must define two binary operations on $FS$, and we do this by using the binary operations of $S$ and the fact that a function is determined uniquely by the images it maps elements onto.

Let $\boldsymbol{F}$ and $\boldsymbol{G}$ be two elements of $FS$.

DEFINITION 7.14. The function $\boldsymbol{H}$ is the *sum* of $\boldsymbol{F}$ and $\boldsymbol{G}$, $\boldsymbol{H} = \boldsymbol{F} \oplus \boldsymbol{G}$, if and only if

$$\boldsymbol{H}(x) = \boldsymbol{F}(x) + \boldsymbol{H}(x) \qquad \text{for every } x \text{ in } S.$$

The function $\boldsymbol{K}$ is the *product* of $\boldsymbol{F}$ and $\boldsymbol{G}$, $\boldsymbol{K} = \boldsymbol{F} \odot \boldsymbol{G}$, if and only if

$$\boldsymbol{K}(x) = \boldsymbol{F}(x)\boldsymbol{G}(x) \qquad \text{for every } x \text{ in } S.$$

The student is warned not to confuse this product of functions with function composition which is an entirely different binary operation. Here we are multiplying the images, whereas we obtain the image of the image in the case of composition.

THEOREM 7.26. *The system* $\{FS, \oplus, \odot\}$ *is a ring, the* function ring *of S.*

First we must show that addition and multiplication are binary operations on $FS$. This means that we have to verify that the sum and the product of any two elements $\boldsymbol{F}$ and $\boldsymbol{G}$ of $FS$ are defined, and that task is quite simple. Surely the subsets of $S \times S$,

$$\boldsymbol{F} \oplus \boldsymbol{G} = \{(a, \boldsymbol{F}(a) + \boldsymbol{G}(a)) : a \text{ in } S\}$$

and

$$\boldsymbol{F} \odot \boldsymbol{G} = \{(a, \boldsymbol{F}(a)\boldsymbol{G}(a)) : a \text{ in } S\},$$

satisfy the requirements of a function since each element of $S$ appears exactly once as a first element of a pair in both subsets.

Let $\boldsymbol{F}$, $\boldsymbol{G}$, and $\boldsymbol{H}$ be elements of $FS$. Since $\boldsymbol{F}(a)$, $\boldsymbol{G}(a)$, and $\boldsymbol{H}(a)$ are elements of $S$, then certainly

$$\begin{aligned} \boldsymbol{F}(a) + (\boldsymbol{G}(a) + \boldsymbol{H}(a)) &= (\boldsymbol{F}(a) + \boldsymbol{G}(a)) + \boldsymbol{H}(a), \\ \boldsymbol{F}(a) + \boldsymbol{G}(a) &= \boldsymbol{G}(a) + \boldsymbol{F}(a), \\ \boldsymbol{F}(a)(\boldsymbol{G}(a)\,\boldsymbol{H}(a)) &= (\boldsymbol{F}(a)\boldsymbol{G}(a))\boldsymbol{H}(a), \\ \boldsymbol{F}(a)(\boldsymbol{G}(a) + \boldsymbol{H}(a)) &= \boldsymbol{F}(a)\boldsymbol{G}(a) + \boldsymbol{F}(a)\boldsymbol{H}(a), \end{aligned}$$

and

$$(\boldsymbol{G}(a) + \boldsymbol{H}(a))\boldsymbol{F}(a) = \boldsymbol{G}(a)\boldsymbol{F}(a) + \boldsymbol{H}(a)\boldsymbol{F}(a).$$

These images determine the sums and products of the functions, so we see that corresponding to the above equations in $S$ we have in $FS$,

$$\begin{aligned} \boldsymbol{F} \oplus (\boldsymbol{G} \oplus \boldsymbol{H}) &= (\boldsymbol{F} \oplus \boldsymbol{G}) \oplus \boldsymbol{H}, \\ \boldsymbol{F} \oplus \boldsymbol{G} &= \boldsymbol{G} \oplus \boldsymbol{F} \\ \boldsymbol{F} \odot (\boldsymbol{G} \odot \boldsymbol{H}) &= (\boldsymbol{F} \odot \boldsymbol{G}) \odot \boldsymbol{H}, \\ \boldsymbol{F} \odot (\boldsymbol{G} \oplus \boldsymbol{H}) &= \boldsymbol{F} \odot \boldsymbol{G} \oplus \boldsymbol{F} \odot \boldsymbol{H}, \end{aligned}$$

and

$$(\boldsymbol{G} \oplus \boldsymbol{H}) \odot \boldsymbol{F} = \boldsymbol{G} \odot \boldsymbol{F} \oplus \boldsymbol{H} \odot \boldsymbol{F}.$$

Because of the close tie between the relations in $S$ and the relations in $FS$ we shall henceforth use the same symbols for both additions and both multiplications. Thus the associativity conditions above are written

$$\boldsymbol{F} + (\boldsymbol{G} + \boldsymbol{H}) = (\boldsymbol{F} + \boldsymbol{G}) + \boldsymbol{H}$$

and

$$\boldsymbol{F}(\boldsymbol{G}\boldsymbol{H}) = (\boldsymbol{F}\boldsymbol{G})\boldsymbol{H}.$$

The additive identity, the zero of $FS$, is the function $\boldsymbol{Z}$ defined image-wise as

$$\boldsymbol{Z}(a) = z.$$

Clearly

$$\boldsymbol{F} + \boldsymbol{Z} = \boldsymbol{Z} + \boldsymbol{F} = \boldsymbol{F}$$

since

$$\boldsymbol{F}(a) + \boldsymbol{Z}(a) = \boldsymbol{F}(a) + z = \boldsymbol{F}(a) = z + \boldsymbol{F}(a).$$

And the additive inverse of the element $F$ of $FS$ is the function $-F$ defined by

$$(-F)(a) = -(F(a)).$$

That is, the image of $a$ under the function $-F$ is the element $-(F(a))$ of $S$. Certainly

$$F + (-F) = -F + F = Z$$

since

$$z = Z(a) = F(a) - F(a) = -(F(a)) + F(a).$$

This completes the proof.

It was stated above that $FS$ is an extension of $S$, so we must be able to find a subring of $FS$ which is isomorphic with $S$. For this purpose we single out the familiar constant functions, which are defined in the same fashion as $Z$. Let $s$ be an arbitrary but fixed element of $S$; then the *constant function* $F_s$ is defined by

$$F_s(x) = s \qquad \text{for every } x \text{ in } S.$$

THEOREM 7.27. *The set $CS$ of all constant functions on $S$ is a subring of $FS$ which is isomorphic with $S$.*

Clearly the sum, the product, and the difference of two constant functions are constant functions. In fact,

$$F_s + F_t = F_{s+t},$$
$$F_sF_t = F_{st},$$

and

$$F_s - F_t = F_{s-t}$$

since

$$F_s(x) \pm F_t(x) = s \pm t$$

and

$$F_s(x)F_t(x) = st \qquad \text{for each } x \text{ in } S.$$

The obvious correspondence,

$$s \leftrightarrow F_s \qquad \text{for each } s \text{ in } S,$$

is an isomorphism between the ring $S$ and the ring $CS$ by the above relations. It is a one-to-one correspondence since

$$F_s = F_t$$

if and only if

$$s = t,$$

since equality of functions is determined by the images.

*Example* 1. Let $S$ be the ring $J/(3)$. Then the ring $FS$ contains exactly 27 elements since a typical function $F$ from $S$ to $S$ has the form

$$F = \{(0, a), (1, b), (2, c)\},$$

where $a$, $b$, and $c$ are any elements from $J/(3)$. So there are three choices for $a$, three for $b$, and three for $c$, making 27 possibilities in all. The constant functions of this ring are

$$F_0 = \{(0, 0), (1, 0), (2, 0\},$$
$$F_1 = \{(0, 1), (1, 1), (2, 1)\},$$

and

$$F_2 = \{(0, 2), (1, 2), (2, 2)\},$$

and we can easily compute the operation tables shown for $CS$.

| $+$ | $F_0$ | $F_1$ | $F_2$ |
|---|---|---|---|
| $F_0$ | $F_0$ | $F_1$ | $F_2$ |
| $F_1$ | $F_1$ | $F_2$ | $F_0$ |
| $F_2$ | $F_2$ | $F_0$ | $F_1$ |

| $\cdot$ | $F_0$ | $F_1$ | $F_2$ |
|---|---|---|---|
| $F_0$ | $F_0$ | $F_0$ | $F_0$ |
| $F_1$ | $F_0$ | $F_1$ | $F_2$ |
| $F_2$ | $F_0$ | $F_2$ | $F_1$ |

When compared with the operation tables of $J/(3)$ the isomorphism shows up very clearly.

Another subring of $FS$ which can be described rather easily is the subring of polynomial functions. These are elementary functions which are generally more amenable to study than most other types (as the student should remember from his calculus course). Polynomial functions can be considered as generalizations of the constant functions. A constant function is determined by a single element $s$ of $S$ and the rule,

$$F_s(x) = s, \qquad \text{for each } x \text{ in } S.$$

A *polynomial function* $\boldsymbol{P}$ is determined by a set of elements from $S$,

$$\{s_0, s_1, \cdots, s_n\}$$

and the rule

$$\boldsymbol{P}(x) = s_0 + s_1x + \cdots + s_nx^n \qquad \text{for each } x \text{ in } S.$$

*Example* 2. Determine two different polynomial functions for the ring of Example 1.

The function

$$\boldsymbol{P}_1 = \{(0, 1), (1, 0), (2, 1)\}$$

is a polynomial function determined by the set

$$\{s_0 = 1, s_1 = 1, s_2 = 1\}$$

and the rule

$$\boldsymbol{P}_1(x) = 1 + 1x + 1x^2 \qquad \text{for each } x \text{ in } S.$$

For $\boldsymbol{P}_1(0) = 1$, $\boldsymbol{P}_1(1) = 0$, and $\boldsymbol{P}_1(2) = 1$.

Similarly the function

$$\boldsymbol{P}_2 = \{(0, 1), (1, 1), (2, 0)\}$$

is a polynomial function determined by the rule

$$\boldsymbol{P}_2(x) = 1 + 2x + 1x^2 \qquad \text{for each } x \text{ in } S.$$

If we apply the rules for addition and multiplication of the functions on $S$ to these two functions, we obtain by working with the images:

$$(P_1 + P_2)\colon x \to P_1(x) + P_2(x) = 2 + 0x + 2x^2$$

for each $x$ in $S$, and

$$\begin{aligned}(P_1P_2)\colon x \to P_1(x)P_2(x) &= (1 + 1x + 1x^2)(1 + 2x + 1x^2),\\ &= 1 + 0x + 1x^2 + 0x^3 + 1x^4.\end{aligned}$$

Using the statement of Fermat's Little Theorem for $J/(3)$ which means that $x^3 = x$ in $J/(3)$ we have

$$P_1P_2(x) = 1 + 0x + 2x^2,$$

and we can check this by direct computation:

$$P_1P_2 = \{(0, 1), (1, 0), (2, 0)\}.$$

This use of Fermat's Little Theorem suggests that every function from $J/(3)$ to $J/(3)$ is a polynomial function. For each element $x$ of that field, $x^3 = x$, $x^4 = x^2$, $x^5 = x$, $x^6 = x^2, \cdots$, so that there are at most 27 rules for polynomial functions:

$$a + bx + cx^2 \qquad \text{for each } x \text{ in } J/(3),$$

where $a$, $b$, and $c$ are any elements of $J/(3)$. However, if two of these rules yield the same function, say

$$\begin{aligned}P(0) &= a + b0 + c0^2 = d + e0 + f0^2,\\ P(1) &= a + b1 + c1^2 = d + e1 + f1^2,\end{aligned}$$

and

$$P(2) = a + b2 + c2^2 = d + e2 + f2^2,$$

then we see that

$$\begin{aligned}a &= d,\\ a + b + c &= d + e + f,\end{aligned}$$

and

$$a + 2b + c = d + 2e + f.$$

Adding the second and third equations yields

$$a + 2c = d + 2f$$

so that

$$c = f,$$

and from these we conclude that

$$b = e.$$

Hence $FS$ contains at least 27 polynomial functions when $J/(3) = S$, so we see that all of the elements of $FS$ are polynomial functions.

*Example* 3. Show that not every function on $S = J/(9)$ is a polynomial function.

The system $FS$ in this case contains $9^9$ elements since each of nine positions can be filled by any of the nine elements of $J/(9)$. Now consider the possible rules for forming polynomial functions,

$$s_0 + s_1x + \cdots + s_nx^n \qquad \text{for each } x \text{ in } J/(3).$$

By Euler's Theorem, if $x$ is one of the classes of integers 1, 2, 4, 5, 7, or 8, then, since $\Phi(9) = 6$, we have

$$x^6 = 1, x^7 = x, x^8 = x^2, \cdots, x^n = x^m,$$

where $0 \leqslant m < 6$. On the other hand, if $x = 0$, 3, or 6, then

$$x^2 = x^3 = x^4 = \cdots = 0.$$

Therefore there are not more than $9^6$ polynomial functions since the only possibly distinct rules are

$$s_0 + s_1x + s_2x^2 + s_3x^3 + s_4x^4 + s_5x^5$$

for each $x$ in $J/(9)$, where the $s_i$ are elements of $J/(9)$. Since $9^6 < 9^9$ there must exist functions which are not polynomial functions.

THEOREM 7.28. *The set PS of polynomial functions on S is a subring of FS when S is a commutative ring.*

Let the polynomial functions $P_1$ and $P_2$ be determined by the rules,

$$P_1(x) = s_0 + s_1x + \cdots + s_nx^n \qquad \text{for every } x \text{ in S}$$

and

$$P_2(x) = t_0 + t_1x + \cdots + t_mx^m \qquad \text{for every } t \text{ in } S,$$

where $m \geq n$. Then the functions $P_1 \pm P_2$ are determined by the rules

$$v_0 + v_1x + \cdots + v_mx^m \qquad \text{for every } x \text{ in } S,$$

where

$$v_i = s_i \pm t_i, \qquad 0 \leqslant i \leqslant n,$$

and

$$v_i = \pm t_i \qquad \text{for } n < i \leqslant m$$

if $m > n$. Thus $P_1 \pm P_2$ are polynomial functions. Furthermore the product $P_1P_2$ is determined by the rule

$$P_1P_2(x) = u_0 + u_1x + \cdots + u_rx^r \qquad \text{for every } x \text{ in } S,$$

where $r = m + n$ and

$$u_i = \sum_{j+k=i} s_jt_k, \qquad \text{for } i = 0, 1, \cdots, m + n = r.$$

This last symbolism is an abbreviation for the $r + 1$ equations

$$\begin{aligned} u_0 &= s_0t_0, \\ u_1 &= s_0t_1 + s_1t_0, \\ u_2 &= s_0t_2 + s_1t_1 + s_2t_0, \\ &\vdots \\ u_r &= s_nt_m. \end{aligned}$$

To obtain these rules we merely make use of the Distributive Laws, the Associative Laws, and the Commutative Laws. Note that we have used the commutativity of multiplication in $S$ extensively to obtain the above rules.

An interesting link between the elements of $FS$ and elements of $PS$ when $S$ is a field is provided by the following interpolation formula of Lagrange.

THEOREM 7.29. *If $a_1, \cdots, a_n$ are $n$ distinct elements of the field $S$ and $\boldsymbol{F}$ is an element of $FS$, then $PS$ contains a polynomial function $\boldsymbol{P}$ such that*

$$\boldsymbol{F}(a_i) = \boldsymbol{P}(a_i), \qquad i = 1, 2, \cdots, n.$$

Geometrically this means that given $n$ points on the graph of a function $\boldsymbol{F}$ we can find a polynomial function $\boldsymbol{P}$ whose graph passes through these $n$ points. (This should remind the student of the "two-point form" from analytic geometry.)

The theorem is established by the following rule:

$$\boldsymbol{P}(x) = \sum_{i=1}^{n} \boldsymbol{F}(a_i)(x - a_1)\cdots(x - a_{i-1})(x - a_{i+1})\cdots(x - a_n)b_i$$

for every $x$ in $S$, where

$$b_i = (a_i - a_1)^{-1}\cdots(a_i - a_{i-1})^{-1}(a_i - a_{i+1})^{-1}\cdots(a_i - a_n)^{-1}$$

for each $i$ from 1 to $n$.

*Example* 4. If $S$ is the rational field $R$, if $a_1 = 2$, $a_2 = -1$, and $a_3 = 10$, and if $\boldsymbol{F}(2) = 24$, $\boldsymbol{F}(-1) = 66$, and $\boldsymbol{F}(10) = -176$, then the polynomial $\boldsymbol{P}$ described above is given by the rule

$$\begin{aligned}\boldsymbol{P}(x) = {} & \boldsymbol{F}(2)(x + 1)(x - 10)(1/3)(-1/8) \\ & + \boldsymbol{F}(-1)(x - 2)(x - 10)(-1/3)(-1/11) \\ & + \boldsymbol{F}(10)(x - 2)(x + 1)(1/8)(1/11) = 26 - 35x + 5x^2.\end{aligned}$$

As for the ideals of $FS$ we can use that element of many properties, the zero, to locate a number of ideals. Let $s$ be an arbitrary but fixed element of $S$ and denote by $(F\colon s)$ the set of all functions $\boldsymbol{F}$ on $S$ such that

$$\boldsymbol{F}(s) = z.$$

THEOREM 7.30. *The set $(F\colon s)$ of all functions $\boldsymbol{F} \in FS$ such that $\boldsymbol{F}(s) = z$ is an ideal of $FS$ with the property that $FS/(F\colon S)$ is isomorphic with $S$.*

If $\boldsymbol{F}$ and $\boldsymbol{G}$ are elements of $(F\colon s)$ then

$$\boldsymbol{F}(s) = \boldsymbol{G}(s) = z,$$

so that

$$(\boldsymbol{F} \pm \boldsymbol{G})(s) = \boldsymbol{F}(s) \pm \boldsymbol{G}(s) = z \pm z = z,$$

and thus $\boldsymbol{F} \pm \boldsymbol{G}$ are in $(F\colon S)$. If $\boldsymbol{F}$ has the property that

$$\boldsymbol{F}(s) = z$$

and $H$ is any element of $FS$, then

$$(FH)(s) = F(s)H(s) = zH(s) = z$$

and

$$(HF)(s) = H(s)F(s) = H(s)z = z,$$

so that $HF$ and $FH$ are in $(F: s)$. Thus $(F: s)$ is an ideal of $FS$.

Now let $H$ be an arbitrary element of $FS$. If $H(s) = t$, then $H$ belongs to the additive coset

$$F_t + (F: s)$$

of $(F: S)$, where $F_t$ is the constant function which maps every element of $S$ onto $t$. Conversely, every element $G$ of the coset $F_t + (F: s)$ has the property that

$$G(s) = t.$$

Then the correspondence

$$t \leftrightarrow F_t + (F: S)$$

is an isomorphism of $S$ with $FS/(F: s)$ by Theorem 7.27.

If $S$ is the real field then the above work can be pictured geometrically, as is shown in Fig. 7.3. The ideal $(F: s)$ is the set of all functions whose graphs

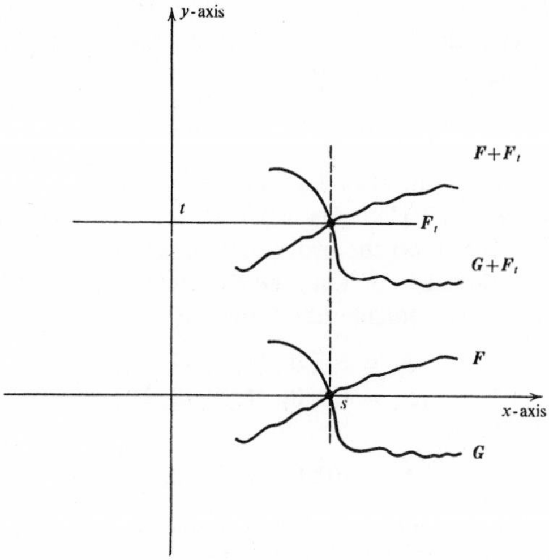


**Figure 7.3**

cross the $x$-axis at the point corresponding to $s$. The coset $F_t + (F: s)$ is the set of all functions whose graphs pass through the point having coordinates $(s, t)$. The isomorphism is the one-to-one correspondence between the point labeled $t$ on the $y$-axis and the point labeled $(s, t)$ on the dashed vertical line.

The underlying homomorphism from $FS$ onto $S$ can be described in another way. For the fixed element $s$ of $S$ the mapping of $FS$ onto $S$ defined by

$$F \to F(s) \qquad \text{for each } F \text{ in } FS,$$

is a *specialization* of $FS$ at $s$. Using the geometrical picturization of Fig. 7.3 we see that a function $F$ is specialized onto $t$ at $s$ if and only if the graph of $F$ passes through the point having coordinates $(s, t)$.

THEOREM 7.31. *The specialization of FS onto S at s is a homomorphism of FS onto S with kernel* $(F: s)$.

Clearly if

$$F \to t = F(s)$$

and

$$G \to u = G(s)$$

then

$$F + G \to t + u = F(s) + G(s)$$

and

$$FG \to tu = F(s)G(s).$$

Furthermore $(F: s)$ is the kernel of this homomorphism since it was defined as the set of all functions $F$ such that

$$F(s) = z, \qquad \text{the zero of } S.$$

*Example* 5. Find an ideal of $FS$ when $S = J/(3)$.

Since $FS$ contains 27 elements whereas $S = J/(3)$ contains three we see from Lagrange's Theorem on the order of a subgroup of a finite group that the ideals $(F: 0)$ and $(F: 1)$ each contain nine elements. Then the ideal $T = (F: 0) \cap (F: 1)$ contains just three elements, the functions

$$F_0 = \{(0, 0), (1, 0), (2, 0)\},$$
$$F_1 = \{(0, 0), (1, 0), (2, 1)\},$$

and

$$F_2 = \{(0, 0), (1, 0), (2, 2)\}.$$

The subring $T$ is not only an ideal, but it is also a field isomorphic with $J/(3)$ and has the same operation tables as the system of Example 1.

## Exercise 7.7

**1.** Write out the operation tables for $FS$ when $S = J/(2)$.

**2.** Find all of the ideals and homomorphic images of the ring $FS$ of Problem 1.

**3.** Show that all of the elements of $FS$ in Problem 1 are polynomial functions, and determine the rule for each function.

**4.** Exhibit an element of $FS$ for $S = J/(4)$ which is not a polynomial function.

**5.** Determine the quotient ring $FS/T$ for the ideal $T$ of Example 5.

**6.** How many elements of $FS$ are in $(F: 1)$ when $S = J/(4)$? Determine three of them.

**7.** Show that every element of $FS$ is a polynomial function when $S = J/(p)$, $p$ prime.

**8.** For $S = R$ find a polynomial function containing the pairs (0, 1), (1, 1), (2, 0), and (3, 4). How many different polynomial functions contain these pairs?

**9.** Show that $CS$ is a subring of $PS$ when $S$ is a commutative ring.

**10.** Show that the ring $FS$ always contains divisors of zero when $S$ is a ring with more than one element.

**11.** Prove that $FS$ is a commutative ring with identity if and only if $S$ is a commutative ring with identity.

**12.** Show that $FS$ contains elements which are not polynomial functions when $S = J/(m)$ and $m$ is composite.

**13.** Let $S''$ be a homomorphic image of the ring $S$. Can this homomorphism be extended to a homomorphism of $FS$ onto $FS''$? Explain.

**14.** Show that the ideal $(F: s)$ is a *maximal ideal* of $FS$ when $S$ is a field in that $FS$ is the only larger ideal which contains $(F: s)$.

**15.** Let $W$ be a nonempty subset of the ring $S$. Show that the set $(F: W)$ of those functions which map *all* of the elements of $W$ onto zero is an ideal of $FS$.

**16.** Let $W$ be a nonempty subset of the ring $S$. Show that the set $F_W$ of those functions which map at least one element of $W$ onto zero is an ideal of $FS$. Determine $F_W$ when $S = J/(4)$ and $W = \{0, 1, 2\}$; $W = \{0, 1\}$; $W = \{0, 1, 2, 3\}$.

**17.** How does the characteristic of $FS$ compare with the characteristic of $S$?

## 7.8 Suggested Reading

*Articles*

MacDuffee, C. C., "Algebra's debt to Hamilton," *Scripta Mathematica*, Vol. X, Nos. 1–4, 1953, 25–35.

Whittaker, E., "W. R. Hamilton," *Sci. American* 190, May 1954, 82–87.

*Books*

McCoy, N. H., *Rings and Ideals*, Carus Monograph No. 8, Mathematics Association of America, Inc., Buffalo, N.Y., 1948.

McCoy, N. H., *The Theory of Rings*, The Macmillan Company, New York, 1964.

# 8

# Polynomial Rings

EVERY STUDENT OF mathematics knows that of all functions the polynomial functions are probably the easiest to handle and consequently are of great importance. Therefore an analysis of the ring of polynomial functions of a field or domain should be possible to carry out and should be useful as well. However, there are several other facts to be considered. The ring of polynomial functions of a domain need not be a domain, so that algebraically speaking this ring may not be so nice. Moreover, the polynomial rules which are the basic ingredients of the polynomial functions arise elsewhere, such as in the handling of repeated differentiations and of differential equations. This suggests that the rules rather than the functions themselves should be studied. Following this idea we develop a polynomial ring based on the use and behavior of these rules, and the result is a system which is very much like the ring of polynomial functions. But it is also more general and the theory can be applied in other situations.

Although much of the work at the beginning involves abstract fields and integral domains we are primarily interested in certain extensions of the rational field in this chapter.

## 8.1 Polynomial Rings

An essential ingredient of the rule for a polynomial function on the ring $S$ is the set $(a_0, a_1, \cdots, a_n)$ of elements from the ring $S$. The subscripts on the elements of this set indicate that it is a mapping from the set $\{0, 1, \cdots, n\}$ to the ring $S$, and in this case $a_i$ is a symbol for the pair $(i, a)$ and indicates that $a_i$ is the image of $i$. Such mappings are the *finite ordered subsets* of $S$, or the *ordered m-tuples* of $S$ (with $m = n + 1$ in the case above).

Now let $S$ be a ring with multiplicative identity element $e$, and denote by $S[\lambda]$ the collection of all finite ordered subsets $(a_0, a_1, \cdots, a_n)$ of $S$ where

(1) $n$ is an arbitrary nonnegative integer.

(2) Either $a_n \neq z$ or $n = 0$ and $a_0 = z$.

The second restriction seems a reasonable one from our experience with polynomial functions and their rules since additional zeros contribute nothing. The reason for denoting this collection by $S[\lambda]$ will appear later.

To make $S[\lambda]$ into a ring we define addition and multiplication by copying the effect of addition and multiplication of functions on the rules for polynomial functions.

*Addition.* Let $a = (a_0, a_1, \cdots, a_n)$ and $b = (b_0, \cdots, b_m)$ be two elements of $S[\lambda]$ where $m \geqslant n$. Then addition is defined by the equation

$$a + b = (c_0, c_1, \cdots, c_r)$$

where

$$\begin{aligned} c_i &= a_i + b_i, \qquad i = 0, 1, \cdots, n, \\ c_i &= b_i \qquad \text{if } n < i \leqslant m, \end{aligned}$$

and either $r$ is the largest integer such that $c_r \neq 0$ or $r = 0$ and $c_r = z$.

For example, in $J[\lambda]$ we have

$$\begin{aligned} (0, 1, 0, -1) + (1, 1, 1, 1) &= (1, 2, 1), \\ (0, 1, 0, -1) + (1, -1) &= (1), \\ (1, 1) + (-1, -1) &= (0), \end{aligned}$$

and

$$(1, 1, 1, 1) + (2) = (3, 1, 1, 1).$$

Here of course we use the position instead of the more cumbersome subscripts which are used to describe general elements. Thus (1, 0, 1, 1) is the ordered quadrupole with $a_0 = 1$, $a_1 = 0$, $a_2 = 1$, and $a_3 = 1$.

This coordinate-wise definition of addition rather obviously extends all of the nice features of addition in $S$ to $S[\lambda]$.

THEOREM 8.1. *The system $\{S[\lambda], +\}$ is an Abelian group.*

Obviously the element $(z)$ of $S[\lambda]$ is the zero element of $S[\lambda]$, and the inverse or negative of $a = (a_0, a_1, \cdots, a_n)$ is surely the element

$$-a = (-a_0, -a_1, \cdots, -a_n)$$

which is in $S[\lambda]$ since $-a_n \neq z$ if and only if $a_n \neq z$.

To check the Associative and Commutative Laws we need only look at the formula for the $i$th component. Let

$$\begin{aligned} a &= (a_0, a_1, \cdots, a_n), \\ b &= (b_0, b_1, \cdots, b_m), \end{aligned}$$

and

$$c = (c_0, c_1, \cdots, c_r)$$

be elements of $S[\lambda]$, with $n \leqslant m \leqslant r$. For the sum $a + (b + c)$ we have as components

$$\begin{aligned} a_i + (b_i + c_i), &\qquad 0 \leqslant i \leqslant n, \\ (b_i + c_i), &\qquad n < i \leqslant m, \end{aligned}$$

and

$$c_i, \qquad m < i \leqslant r,$$

whereas in the sum $(a + b) + c$ we have the components

$$\begin{aligned} (a_i + b_i) + c_i, &\qquad 0 \leqslant i \leqslant n, \\ b_i + c_i, &\qquad n < i \leqslant m, \end{aligned}$$

and

$$c_i, \qquad m < i \leqslant r.$$

From the Associative Law in $S$ we conclude that

$$a + (b + c) = (a + b) + c,$$

for any $a$, $b$, and $c$ in $S[\lambda]$.

Similarly the $i$th component of $a + b$ is either $a_i + b_i$ or $b_i$, whereas the $i$th component of $b + a$ is either $b_i + a_i$ or $b_i$. Since

$$a_i + b_i = b_i + a_i$$

in $S$ we conclude that

$$a + b = b + a$$

in $S[\lambda]$.

Multiplication is also abstracted from the polynomial rule obtained when two polynomial functions are multiplied. The resulting operation is perhaps a bit cumbersome, but it accomplishes what needs to be done.

*Multiplication.* Let $a = (a_0, a_1, \cdots, a_n)$ and $b = (b_0, b_1, \cdots, b_m)$ be two elements of $S[\lambda]$. Then multiplication of these two elements is defined by the equation

$$ab = (c_0, c_1, \cdots, c_r)$$

where

$$c_i = \sum a_j b_k \qquad \text{with } j + k = i,$$

and either $r$ is the largest integer less than or equal to $n + m$ such that $c_r \neq z$ or $r = 0$ and $c_r = z$.

For example, the product of $a = (a_0, a_1, a_2)$ and $b = (b_0, b_1)$ is

$$ab = (a_0b_0, a_0b_1 + a_1b_0, a_1b_1 + a_2b_0, a_2b_0)$$

with the necessary adjustments for the occurrence of zeros.

The symbolism

$$c_i = \sum a_j b_k \qquad \text{with } j + k = i$$

means that we select all possible pairs $j$ and $k$ such that

$$0 \leqslant j \leqslant n, \qquad 0 \leqslant k \leqslant m,$$

and

$$j + k = i.$$

In general this means

$$c_0 = a_0 b_0,$$
$$c_1 = a_0 b_1 + a_1 b_0,$$
$$c_2 = a_0 b_2 + a_1 b_1 + a_2 b_0,$$

etc. Thus in $J[\lambda]$ we have

$$(1, -1)(1, 1) = (1, 0, -1),$$
$$(1, -1)(1, -1) = (1, -2, 1),$$

and

$$(1)(2) = (2).$$

THEOREM 8.2. *The system* $\{S[\lambda], +, \cdot\}$ *is a ring with identity element.*

It is easy to see that the element $(e)$ is the identity element of $S[\lambda]$ since setting $b$ equal to $(e)$ in the definition above yields

$$c_i = a_i b_0 = a_i e = a_i$$

so that

$$a(e) = a.$$

Similarly, setting $a$ equal to $(e)$ yields

$$(e)b = b.$$

The proofs of the Associative and Distributive Laws are straightforward exercises in handling summations. Let

$$a = (a_0, a_1, \cdots, a_n),$$
$$b = (b_0, b_1, \cdots, b_m),$$

and

$$c = (c_0, c_1, \cdots, c_r)$$

be elements of $S[\lambda]$. Then the $i$th component of $a(bc)$ is

$$\sum a_h(b_j c_k) \qquad \text{with } h + (j + k) = i,$$

whereas the $i$th component of $(ab)c$ is

$$\sum (a_h b_j) c_k \qquad \text{with } (h + j) + k = i.$$

From the Associative Law for Multiplication in $S$ we conclude that

$$a(bc) = (ab)c$$

in $S[\lambda]$.

Using the same notation we note that the $i$th component of $a(b + c)$ is

$$\sum a_j(b_k + c_k) \qquad \text{with } j + k = i,$$

whereas the $i$th component of $ab + ac$ is the sum of the two elements

$$\sum a_j b_k \qquad \text{with } j + k = i$$

and

$$\sum a_j c_k \qquad \text{with } j + k = i.$$

Thus the distributivity of multiplication over addition in $S[\lambda]$ follows from the corresponding property in $S$.

DEFINITION 8.1. The system $\{S[\lambda], +, \cdot\}$ is the *polynomial ring* of the ring $S$ with multiplicative identity.

In the theorems above we have used the fact that two functions are equal if and only if they have the same domain and map equal elements onto equal elements. That is, the ordered set $(a_0, a_1, \cdots, a_n)$ equals the ordered set $(b_0, b_1, \cdots, b_m)$ if and only if $n = m$ and corresponding components (i.e., images) are equal,

$$a_0 = b_0, \qquad a_1 = b_1, \cdots,$$

or $a_i = b_i$ for $0 \leqslant i \leqslant n$. Thus in discussing the $i$th components we are dealing with the images of $i$ under functions which make up $S[\lambda]$.

Now we shall develop a more convenient notation for the elements of $S[\lambda]$, one which is suggested by the rules for polynomial functions. But first we note that $S[\lambda]$ is an extension of $S$.

THEOREM 8.3. *The set of all one-tuples of $S[\lambda]$ is a subring of $S[\lambda]$ which is isomorphic with $S$.*

Let $(a)$ and $(b)$ be two one-tuples of $S[\lambda]$. Then we see that

$$(a) \pm (b) = (a + b)$$

and

$$(a)(b) = (ab),$$

so that the one-tuples certainly form a subring of $S[\lambda]$. Furthermore the correspondence

$$a \leftrightarrow (a)$$

for every $a$ in $S$ is certainly an isomorphism since

$$a + b \leftrightarrow (a + b) = (a) + (b)$$

and

$$ab \leftrightarrow (ab) = (a)(b).$$

Therefore we shall identify the element $a$ of $S$ and the one-tuple $(a)$ of $S[\lambda]$ and use the same symbol $a$ for both. In this case $z$ and $e$ are the additive and multiplicative identities for both $S$ and $S[\lambda]$.

To develop a new notation for $S[\lambda]$ we single out the element $(z, e)$ and label it as $\lambda$. This particular element of $S[\lambda]$ is sometimes called an *indeterminate* of $S$.

*Lemma* 8.1. For each positive integer $n$, $\lambda^n$ is the $(n + 1)$-tuple $(a_0, a_1, \cdots, a_n)$ where $a_0 = a_1 = \cdots = a_{n-1} = z$ and $a_n = e$.

This is proved by induction on $n$. The statement is certainly true for $n = 1$ by definition, so we consider the nature of $\lambda^{k+1}$, having the induction hypothesis that

$$\lambda^k = (z, \cdots, z, e), \qquad \text{with } k\ z\text{'s}.$$

By definition of multiplication in $S[\lambda]$,

$$\lambda^{k+1} = \lambda\lambda^k = (c_0, c_1, \cdots, c_{k+1})$$

where

$$c_i = zz + ez = z, \qquad 0 < i < k + 1,$$
$$c_0 = zz = z$$

and

$$c_{k+1} = ee = e.$$

Thus we see that

$$\lambda^{k+1} = (z, \cdots, z, e) \qquad \text{with } k + 1\ z\text{'s},$$

completing the induction.

THEOREM 8.4. *The element $a = (a_0, a_1, \cdots, a_n)$ of $S[\lambda]$ is expressible uniquely in the form*

$$a = a_0 + a_1\lambda + a_2\lambda^2 + \cdots + a_n\lambda^n.$$

The element $a_i\lambda^i$, which is the product of the one-tuple $(a_i)$ and the $(i + 1)$-tuple $(z, \cdots, z, e) = \lambda^i$, is either zero (when $a_i = z$) or the $(i + 1)$-tuple

$$(z, \cdots, z, a_i).$$

In either case we see that the sum

$$a_0 + a_1\lambda + a_2\lambda^2 + \cdots + a_n\lambda^n$$

equals $(a_0, a_1, \cdots, a_n)$. The uniqueness follows from the fact that two tuples are equal if and only if they are componentwise equal. Thus we can say that the polynomial ring $S[\lambda]$ of the ring $S$ with identity element is the collection of all expressions in the element $\lambda$ of the form

$$a_0 + a_1\lambda + a_2\lambda^2 + \cdots + a_n\lambda^n$$

with $a_i$ in $S$ and $a_n \neq z$.

*Warning.* The element $\lambda$ is not an unknown or "variable" element of $S$. It is not an element of $S$ in any sense, and the student should avoid thinking of it as an element of $S$. It is a definite, fixed element of $S[\lambda]$.

However, we can map the ring $S[\lambda]$ onto the ring $S$ in much the same manner as the ring of polynomial functions of a commutative ring was mapped onto that ring. This mapping can be thought of as "substitution" although the term *specialization* is probably preferable.

DEFINITION 8.2. The mapping $\boldsymbol{F}_s$ of the ring $S[\lambda]$ onto the ring $S$ defined for the arbitrary element $s$ of $S$ by

$$\boldsymbol{F}_s\colon a_0 + a_1\lambda + \cdots + a_n\lambda^n \to a_0 + a_1 s + \cdots + a_n s^n,$$

is the *specialization* of $S[\lambda]$ for $s$.

The effect of the specialization $\boldsymbol{F}_s$ on a particular element of $S[\lambda]$ is discovered by simply substituting $s$ for $\lambda$ and computing the image.

*Example* 1. What happens to the elements $1 - \lambda$ and $2 + \lambda + \lambda^2$ of $J[\lambda]$ under the specialization for $s = 1$?

Clearly $\boldsymbol{F}_1$ maps $1 - \lambda$ onto $1 - 1 = 0$ and $2 + \lambda + \lambda^2$ onto $2 + 1 + 1^2 = 4$. Moreover, we see that the elements

$$3 + \lambda^2 = (1 - \lambda) + (2 + \lambda + \lambda^2)$$

and

$$2 - \lambda - \lambda^2 = (1 - \lambda)(2 + \lambda + \lambda^2)$$

map onto $4 = 0 + 4$ and $0 = 0 \cdot 4$, respectively. This suggests that the specialization is a homomorphism.

THEOREM 8.5. *If $S$ is a commutative ring, then the specialization of $S[\lambda]$ onto $S$ for $t$ is a homomorphism of $S[\lambda]$ onto $S$.*

The definitions of addition and multiplication in $S[\lambda]$ were made by abstracting from the polynomial rules so that this theorem is a natural result. The two elements

$$a(t) = a_0 + a_1 t + \cdots + a_n t^n$$

and

$$b(t) = b_0 + b_1 t + \cdots + b_m t^m$$

of $S$ can be added and multiplied in $S$ so that the forms are preserved:

$$a(t) + b(t) = (a_0 + b_0) + (a_1 + b_1)t + \cdots$$

and

$$a(t)b(t) = a_0 b_0 + (a_0 b_1 + a_1 b_0)t + \cdots.$$

Clearly as the components in the sum and products here are the same as the corresponding components of the sum and product of

$$a(\lambda) = a_0 + a_1\lambda + \cdots + a_n\lambda^n$$

and

$$b(\lambda) = b_0 + b_1\lambda + \cdots + b_m\lambda^m$$

in $S[\lambda]$. This establishes the homomorphism.

*Example* 2. Determine some elements of the kernel of the specialization of $J[\lambda]$ onto $J$ for $t = 1$.

Clearly the elements $1 - \lambda$, $1 - \lambda^2$, $1 - \lambda^3$, and in general $1 - \lambda^n$ all lie in the kernel of this homomorphism since they are mapped onto 0.

*Example* 3. Show that a specialization is never an isomorphism.

If $F_t$ is an isomorphism, then its kernel must consist of only one element, the zero element $z$ of $S[\lambda]$. But the polynomial $t - \lambda$ is certainly mapped onto $z$ in $S$ since $t - t = z$ in $S$, and

$$t - \lambda = (t, e)$$

as a pair cannot be equal to the one-tuple $(z)$.

The notation $a(\lambda)$ is used to denote an element of $S[\lambda]$,

$$a(\lambda) = a_0 + a_1\lambda + \cdots + a_n\lambda^n,$$

although $a(\lambda)$ is *not* a function of $\lambda$. The maximal nonnegative integer $n$ such that $a_n \neq z$ is called the *degree* of $a(\lambda)$, and we note that the zero element of $S[\lambda]$ has no degree. The notation

$$\deg(a(\lambda))$$

is frequently used to denote the degree of $a(\lambda)$.

Also an element $t$ of $S$ is called a *root* or *zero* of the element $a(\lambda)$ of $S[\lambda]$ if and only if $a(\lambda)$ is mapped onto $z$ by the specialization of $S[\lambda]$ onto $S$ for $t$. That is, $t$ is a zero of $a(\lambda)$ if and only if

$$a(t) = a_0 + a_1t + \cdots + a_nt^n = z.$$

This notation and terminology is quite standard and should agree with that which the student has already learned.

## Exercise 8.1

**1.** Complete the indicated computations in $S[\lambda]$ for $S = J/(4)$:
(*a*) (1, 2, 3, 2) + (3, 2, 2, 2) = ?
(*b*) (1, 2, 3, 1) + (0, 0, 1) = ?
(*c*) (1, 2, 3) + (3, 2, 1, 1, 1) = ?
(*d*) (1, 2, 3)(2, 2, 2, 3) = ?
(*e*) (2, 3)(2, 1, 2)(1, 1, 1, 1, 1) = ?

**2.** Rewrite the above equations using the polynomial expression in $\lambda$ form.

**3.** Compare the number of polynomial functions on $S = J/(p)$ with the number of elements in $S[\lambda]$.

**4.** If $a_0 + a_1\lambda + a_2\lambda^2 = 1 + \lambda^2$ in $S[\lambda]$ what can you say about the components $a_i$?

**5.** How does $\deg(a(\lambda))(b(\lambda))$ compare with $\deg(a(\lambda))$ and $\deg(b(\lambda))$? Compute $(1 + 2\lambda)(1 + 2\lambda)$ for $S = J/(4)$, and comment on the degrees.

**6.** How does $\deg(a(\lambda) + b(\lambda))$ compare with $\deg(a(\lambda))$ and $\deg(b(\lambda))$?

**7.** How many zeros has the element

$$a(\lambda) = 2 + 3\lambda + \lambda^2$$

when $S = J/(4)$?

**8.** Describe the elements of $S[\lambda]$ for $S = J/(2)$, and describe the two specializations onto $S$. What are the kernels of these specializations?

**9.** Why is $S$ required to be commutative in Theorem 8.5? Consider the specialization for $t = i$ when $S = Q$, the sfield of rational quaternions, and $a(\lambda) = j + \lambda$ and $b(\lambda) = k + \lambda$.

**10.** Prove that $\lambda^n$ commutes multiplicatively with every element of $S[\lambda]$.

**11.** Discuss the description of $\lambda$ in $S[\lambda]$ as a "placeholder."

**12.** Define the elements of $S[\lambda]$ as the functions from $P$, the set of nonnegative integers, to the set $S$ which map all but possibly a finite subset of elements of $P$ onto $z$ of $S$. Thus $S[\lambda]$ consists of the infinite sequences $(a_0, a_1, \cdots)$ in which all but at most a finite collection of terms are $z$. Compare this with definition given in this section. How would addition and multiplication be defined? Is it necessary to have all but a finite number of the $a_i$ equal to $z$?

**13.** Compute the product

$$(1 - \lambda + \lambda^2)(7 - \lambda^3)(-2 + 7\lambda - \lambda^3)$$

in three different ways in $J[\lambda]$.

**14.** Show that, if $S$ and $T$ are isomorphic rings, then their polynomial extensions are isomorphic. Is the converse true?

**15.** Let $T$ be an ideal of $S$. Show that $T[\lambda]$ is an ideal of $S[\lambda]$.

**16.** Find a nontrivial ideal in $R[\lambda]$. What is it mapped onto by the specialization for $t = 0$? $t = 1$?

## 8.2 Polynomial Domains

When the ring $S$ has special properties these are usually reflected in the polynomial ring $S[\lambda]$. If $S$ is an integral domain, then $S[\lambda]$ is also an integral domain, and we shall see that the polynomial domain of a field can be analyzed in a manner quite analogous to that used with $J$.

THEOREM 8.6. *The ring $S[\lambda]$ is an integral domain if and only if $S$ is an integral domain.*

Let $S$ be an integral domain. We saw in the previous section that $S[\lambda]$ has an identity, so we must show that multiplication in $S[\lambda]$ is commutative and that it contains no divisors of zero. The commutativity is quite simple. For elements

$$a(\lambda) = a_0 + a_1\lambda + \cdots + a_n\lambda^n$$

and

$$b(\lambda) = b_0 + b_1\lambda + \cdots + b_m\lambda^m$$

of $S[\lambda]$ we have the product

$$a(\lambda)b(\lambda) = c_0 + c_1\lambda + \cdots + c_r\lambda^r$$

where

$$c_i = \sum a_j b_k \qquad \text{with } j + k = i.$$

Since multiplication is commutative in $S$ we know that

$$c_i = \sum b_k a_j \qquad \text{with } j + k = i.$$

This means that

$$a(\lambda)b(\lambda) = b(\lambda)a(\lambda)$$

so that multiplication in $S[\lambda]$ is commutative. Furthermore, if neither $a(\lambda)$ nor $b(\lambda)$ equals $z$, then $\deg\big(a(\lambda)\big) = n$, $a_n \neq z$, $\deg\big(b(\lambda)\big) = m$, and $b_m \neq z$. Hence the degree of $a(\lambda)b(\lambda)$ is

$$r = n + m$$

since $r$ is the largest integer such that

$$c_r = \sum a_j b_k, \qquad \text{with } j + k = r$$

and $0 \leqslant j \leqslant n$ and $0 \leqslant k \leqslant m$, is nonzero, and certainly $a_n b_m \neq z$. This means that $S[\lambda]$ has no divisors of zero since the set of nonzero elements of $S[\lambda]$, which is the set of elements with degrees, is closed under multiplication.

The converse is true since $S$ is (isomorphic with) a subring of $S[\lambda]$. This means that $S$ is commutative and has no divisors of zero. Since $S$ has an identity element we conclude that $S$ is a domain when $S[\lambda]$ is.

*Corollary* 8.6.1. If $S$ is a domain and $a(\lambda)$ and $b(\lambda)$ are nonzero elements of $S[\lambda]$, then

$$\deg\big(a(\lambda)b(\lambda)\big) = \deg\big((\lambda)\big) + \deg\big(b(\lambda)\big).$$

This was proved above when we showed that $r = m + n$.

The concept of degree provides an important link between $S[\lambda]$ and the integers which enables us to prove an analog of the Divisor Theorem for the polynomial domain of an integral domain $S$.

THEOREM 8.7 (DIVISOR THEOREM). *If $S$ is a domain and $a(\lambda)$ and $b(\lambda)$ are elements of $S[\lambda]$ with $b(\lambda)$ monic, then $S[\lambda]$ contains a unique pair of elements $q(\lambda)$ and $r(\lambda)$ such that*

$$a(\lambda) = q(\lambda)b(\lambda) + r(\lambda)$$

*with*

$$r(\lambda) < b(\lambda).$$

First we must explain the terms and notation. An element of $S[\lambda]$ is *monic* if and only if the component with maximal subscript (i.e., the leading coefficient) is $e$, the multiplicative identity of $S$. Thus the elements $1 + 2\lambda - 7\lambda^3 + \lambda^4$, $1$, $1 + \lambda$, $\lambda^2$, and $\lambda^{100}$ are monic elements of $J[\lambda]$, whereas $1 + 2\lambda$, $-\lambda^2$, $7\lambda$, and $0$ are *not* monic.

The notation

$$r(\lambda) < b(\lambda)$$

means that either $z = r(\lambda)$ or $\deg\big(r(\lambda)\big) < \deg\big(b(\lambda)\big)$. Thus in $J[\lambda]$ we have

$$0 < 1 + \lambda,$$
$$1 + \lambda < \lambda^2,$$

and

$$1 + \lambda < -\lambda^3.$$

Note that two elements with the same degree are *not* related by this inequality.

To prove the theorem we proceed by induction on the degree of $a(\lambda)$ and show that $q(\lambda)$ and $r(\lambda)$ exist. (Of course if $a(\lambda)$ has no degree, then $a(\lambda) = q(\lambda) = r(\lambda) = z$.) If $a(\lambda) < b(\lambda)$, then we can select $q(\lambda) = z$ and $r(\lambda) = a(\lambda)$, so we need only consider the case where

$$n = \deg\big(a(\lambda)\big) \geqslant m = \deg\big(b(\lambda)\big).$$

Denote the leading coefficient of $a(\lambda)$ by $a_n$ and form the polynomial

$$c(\lambda) = a(\lambda) - a_n\lambda^{n-m}b(\lambda).$$

Now

$$a(\lambda) = a_0 + a_1\lambda + \cdots + a_n\lambda^n,$$
$$b(\lambda) = b_0 + b_1\lambda + \cdots + e\lambda^m,$$

and

$$a_n\lambda^{n-m}b(\lambda) = a_nb_0\lambda^{n-m} + \cdots + a_n\lambda^n,$$

so that $c(\lambda)$, the difference of the first and third equations, would have degree less than $n$ or be zero. The student should note that this is precisely the first step in the usual long division process for polynomials.

This reduction step is the heart of the proof, for we can now apply the induction hypothesis to $c(\lambda)$ for the monic divisor $b(\lambda)$, thereby obtaining

$$c(\lambda) = q_1(\lambda)b(\lambda) + r(\lambda) \qquad \text{with } r(\lambda) < b(\lambda).$$

Therefore

$$a(\lambda) - a_n\lambda^{n-m}b(\lambda) = q_1(\lambda)b(\lambda) + r(\lambda)$$

or

$$a(\lambda) = \big(a_n\lambda^{n-m} + q_1(\lambda)\big)b(\lambda) + r(\lambda)$$

with $r(\lambda) < b(\lambda)$. Thus for

$$q(\lambda) = a_n\lambda^{n-m} + q_1(\lambda)$$

we have

$$a(\lambda) = q(\lambda)b(\lambda) + r(\lambda) \qquad \text{with } r(\lambda) < b(\lambda).$$

This completes the induction argument.

To show that $q(\lambda)$ and $r(\lambda)$, the *quotient* and *remainder*, are unique we assume that

$$a(\lambda) = q^*(\lambda)b(\lambda) + r^*(\lambda) \qquad \text{with } r^*(\lambda) < b(\lambda).$$

Then we see that

$$q(\lambda)b(\lambda) = q^*(\lambda)b(\lambda) = r^*(\lambda) - r(\lambda)$$

and

$$\big(q(\lambda) = q^*(\lambda)\big)b(\lambda) = r^*(\lambda) - r(\lambda).$$

Since $b(\lambda) \neq z$ and $S$ is an integral domain, then either both the elements $(q(\lambda) = q^*(\lambda))$ and $(r^*(\lambda) - r(\lambda))$ are zero or neither is. If neither is zero, then we consider the degrees:

$$\deg\,(q(\lambda) = q^*(\lambda)) + \deg\,(b(\lambda)) = \deg\,(r^*(\lambda) - r(\lambda)).$$

This equation means that

$$\deg\,(b(\lambda)) \leqslant \deg\,(r^*(\lambda) - r(\lambda)),$$

but this contradicts both of the conditions

$$r(\lambda) < b(\lambda) \qquad \text{and} \qquad r^*(\lambda) < b(\lambda).$$

Thus we must conclude that

$$q(\lambda) - q^*(\lambda) = z = r^*(\lambda) - r(\lambda)$$

so that

$$q(\lambda) = q^*(\lambda) \qquad \text{and} \qquad r^*(\lambda) = r(\lambda),$$

and the theorem is proved.

To find the polynomials $q(\lambda)$ and $r(\lambda)$ for a particular pair $a(\lambda)$ and $b(\lambda)$ we merely repeat the above reduction a sufficient number of times.

*Example* 1. Find the quotient and remainder for

$$a(\lambda) = 2 + 3\lambda + 4\lambda^2 + 5\lambda^3 \quad \text{and} \quad b(\lambda) = 2 + \lambda + \lambda^2 \quad \text{in } J[\lambda].$$

We write the successive reductions in the following form:

$$\begin{array}{r|l}
 & 5\lambda \; - 1 \\ \hline
\lambda^2 + \lambda + 2 & 5\lambda^3 + 4\lambda^2 + 3\lambda + 2 \\
 & 5\lambda^3 + 5\lambda^2 + 10\lambda \\ \cline{2-2}
 & \quad - \lambda^2 - 7\lambda + 2 \\
 & \quad - \lambda^2 - \lambda - 2 \\ \cline{2-2}
 & \qquad - 6\lambda + 4
\end{array}$$

There are two reductions here. First we have

$$5\lambda^3 + 4\lambda^2 + 3\lambda + 2 = 5\lambda b(\lambda) + (-\lambda^2 - 7\lambda + 2),$$

and then

$$-\lambda^2 - 7\lambda + 2 = -1b(\lambda) + (-6\lambda + 4).$$

Collecting and combining these yields

$$5\lambda^3 + 4\lambda^2 + 3\lambda + 2 = (5\lambda - 1)b(\lambda) + (-6\lambda + 4)$$

so that in this case

$$q(\lambda) = 5\lambda - 1 \qquad \text{and} \qquad r(\lambda) = -6\lambda + 4.$$

(Note that we have reversed the order of writing the components of the polynomials to agree with the radial notation for integers (as powers of 10). This is merely a convention.)

This result can be combined with Theorem 8.5 on specializations to yield the important *Remainder Theorem.*

THEOREM 8.8. *If $t$ is an element of the domain $S$, then the remainder upon dividing $a(\lambda)$ by $b(\lambda) = \lambda - t$ is the element $a(t)$ of $S$ which $a(\lambda)$ is specialized onto by $\boldsymbol{F}_t$.*

Applying the result above we have

$$a(\lambda) = q(\lambda)(\lambda - t) + r(\lambda),$$

where $r(\lambda) < (\lambda - t)$. Since the degree of $\lambda - t$ is one we see from $r(\lambda) < (\lambda - t)$ that $r(\lambda)$ is in $S$. Now the specialization $\boldsymbol{F}_t$ is a homomorphism of $S[\lambda]$ onto $S$, so that the equation above is mapped onto

$$a(t) = q(t)(t - t) + r(t).$$

Hence the constant $r(\lambda) = r(t)$ of $S$ equals $a(t)$.

*Example* 2. In $J[\lambda]$ divide $b(\lambda) = \lambda - 2$ into $a(\lambda) = 5\lambda^3 + 4\lambda^2 + 3\lambda + 2$. Proceeding as above we have

$$\begin{array}{r|l}
 & 5\lambda^2 + 14\lambda + 31 \\
\hline
\lambda - 2 & 5\lambda^3 + 4\lambda^2 + 3\lambda + 2 \\
 & 5\lambda^3 - 10\lambda^2 \\
\cline{2-2}
 & \qquad 14\lambda^2 + 3\lambda + 2 \\
 & \qquad 14\lambda^2 - 28\lambda \\
\cline{2-2}
 & \qquad\qquad 31\lambda + 2 \\
 & \qquad\qquad 31\lambda - 62 \\
\cline{2-2}
 & \qquad\qquad\qquad 64
\end{array}$$

This can be checked by computing

$$a(2) = 5(2)^3 + 4(2)^2 + 3(2) + 2 = 64.$$

DEFINITION 8.3. The element $b(\lambda) \neq z$ of the domain $S[\lambda]$ is a *factor* of $a(\lambda)$ if and only if $S[\lambda]$ contains an element $q(\lambda)$ such that

$$a(\lambda) = b(\lambda)q(\lambda).$$

*Corollary* 8.8.1. The element $r$ of the domain $S$ is a zero of $a(\lambda)$ if and only if $b(\lambda) = \lambda - r$ is a factor of $a(\lambda)$.

This is an immediate consequence of the Remainder Theorem.

*Corollary* 8.8.2. If $\deg(a(\lambda)) = n$, then $a(\lambda)$ cannot have more than $n$ zeros in the domain $S$.

This is proved by induction on $n$. If $n = 1$ and $r$ is a zero of $a(\lambda)$, then from the above and Corollary 8.6.1 we conclude that

$$a(\lambda) = a_1(\lambda - r) = a_1\lambda + a_0 = a_0 + a_1\lambda,$$

with $a_1 \neq z$. If $t \neq r$ were another zero of $a(\lambda)$ in $S$ then

$$z = a(t) = a_1(t - r).$$

Since $a_1$ and $t - r$ are nonzero elements of the domain $S$, which has no divisors of zero, this is impossible. Hence $a(\lambda)$ has at most one zero.

Now suppose the statement is true for any polynomial of degree less than $n$, and consider $a(\lambda)$ of degree $n$. If $a(\lambda)$ has no zeros in $S$ there is nothing to prove, so suppose $r$ is a zero of $a(\lambda)$. Then

$$a(\lambda) = q(\lambda)(\lambda - r),$$

and $\deg\big(q(\lambda)\big) = n - 1 < n$. Hence $q(\lambda)$ has at most $n - 1$ zeros in $S$. How are the zeros of $a(\lambda)$ and $q(\lambda)$ related? If $t \neq r$ is a zero of $a(\lambda)$, then $a(t) = z$ and

$$a(t) = z = q(t)(t - r).$$

Since $t - r \neq z$ and $S$ is a domain, this equation implies that $t$ is a zero of $q(t)$. Hence $a(t)$ cannot have more than $n$ different zeros in $S$, and the induction is completed.

*Example* 3. Determine all of the zeros of the polynomial $\lambda^2 + (p - 1)$ over the domain $S = J/(p)$

We see that $\lambda^2 + (p - 1)$ has the two factors $\lambda - 1$ and $\lambda - (p - 1)$ so that 1 and $p - 1$ are zeros of this polynomial. Since it has degree 2, these are the only zeros of the polynomial.

*Example* 4. Show that Corollary 8.8.2 need not be true if $S$ has divisors of zero.

Let $S = J/(10)$. We note that the polynomial $4 + 5\lambda + \lambda^2$ has four distinct zeros in $S$, namely, 1, 4, 6, and 9.

This last corollary is the basis for an interesting test for equality of polynomials over a domain.

*Corollary* 8.8.3. If the elements $a(\lambda)$ and $b(\lambda)$ of the domain $S[\lambda]$ have degrees less than $n$ and if $a(t_i) = b(t_i)$ for $n$ distinct elements $t_1, \cdots, t_n$ of $S$, then $a(\lambda) = b(\lambda)$.

Form the polynomial $c(\lambda) = a(\lambda) - b(\lambda)$. If $c(\lambda) \neq z$, then $c(\lambda)$ is a polynomial of degree less than $n$ which has $n$ or more distinct zeros since

$$c(t_i) = a(t_i) - b(t_i) = z.$$

This contradicts Corollary 8.8.2, and so we conclude that

$$c(\lambda) = z \qquad \text{and} \qquad a(\lambda) = b(\lambda).$$

## Exercise 8.2

**1.** Compute $q(\lambda)$ and $r(\lambda)$ when:

(*a*) $a(\lambda) = 3\lambda^4 - 2\lambda^3 + \lambda^2 - \lambda + 7$ and $b(\lambda) = \lambda^2 - \lambda - 1$ for $S = J$.

(*b*) $a(\lambda) = 3\lambda^4 + \lambda^2 - 7$ and $b(\lambda) = \lambda^2 - 1$ for $S = J$.

(*c*) $a(\lambda) = 3\lambda^4 + \lambda^2 - 7$ and $b(\lambda) = \lambda + 1$ for $S = J$.

(*d*) $a(\lambda) = 3\lambda^4 + \lambda^2 - 7$ and $b(\lambda) = \lambda - 1$ for $S = J$.

**2.** Show that $a(\lambda) = \lambda^2 + \lambda + 1$ has no factors when $S = J/(2)$ except 1 and $a(\lambda)$.

**3.** Determine all factors of $a(\lambda) = \lambda^4 + 1$ of degree one when $S = J/(5)$.

**4.** Compute the quotient and remainder for $a(\lambda) = 3\lambda^3 + 2\lambda^2 + \lambda$ and $b(\lambda) = \lambda^2 + 1$ when $S = J/(5)$.

**5.** What is the induction hypothesis in the proof of the Divisor Theorem? How is the proof carried out when $\deg(a(\lambda)) = \deg(b(\lambda)) = 0$?

**6.** Show that, if $r$ and $t$ are elements of the domain $S$, $r \neq t$, such that $a(r) = a(t) = z$, then the monic polynomial $\lambda^2 - (r + t)\lambda + rt$ is a factor of $a(\lambda)$. Is the converse also true?

**7.** Let $S = J/(5)$. Show that, for $a(\lambda) = \lambda^4 + \lambda^3 + \lambda^2$ and $b(\lambda) = \lambda^5 + \lambda^4 + \lambda^3 + \lambda^2 + \lambda$, we have $a(t) = b(t)$ for every $t$ in $S$. Compare this with Corollary 8.8.3.

**8.** The last corollary can be used to prove that for $S = J$ the ring $PS$ of polynomial functions and the domain $S[\lambda]$ are isomorphic. Define the map $F$ from $S[\lambda]$ to $PS$ to send $a(\lambda) = a_0 + a_1\lambda + \cdots + a_n\lambda^n$ onto the polynomial function determined by the rule

$$x \to a_0 + a_1x + \cdots + a_nx^n \qquad \text{for each } x \text{ in } J.$$

Show that $F$ is one-to-one. (Let $a(\lambda)$ and $b(\lambda)$ map onto the same element of $PS$, and then specialize to $J$.)

**9.** Determine the kernel of the specialization of $J[\lambda]$ onto $J$ for $t = 1$; for $t = 0$.

**10.** Describe the properties of the relation "less than" on $S[\lambda]$ defined by $a(\lambda) < b(\lambda)$ if and only if $a(\lambda) = z$ or $\deg(a(\lambda)) < \deg(b(\lambda))$. Compare the elements $\lambda^3$, $2\lambda^2$, $1 + \lambda^2$, $3$, $-1$, and $0$ of $J[\lambda]$, and construct a nodal diagram.

**11.** Note that the role of the powers of $\lambda$ in Examples 1 and 2 is a minor one. Devise a way of dividing $\lambda + r$ into $a(\lambda)$ which utilizes position and eliminates the need for writing all of the powers of $\lambda$. *Example*: Instead of

$$\begin{array}{r|rrr} & 2\lambda & +\,1 & \\ \hline \lambda + 1 & 2\lambda^2 & +\,3\lambda & -\,1 \\ & 2\lambda^2 & +\,2\lambda & \\ \cline{2-4} & & \lambda & -\,1 \\ & & \lambda & +\,1 \\ \cline{3-4} & & & -\,2 \end{array}$$

write

$$\begin{array}{r|rrr} & 2 & 1 & \\ \hline 1 & 2 & 3 & -1 \\ & 2 & 2 & \\ \cline{2-3} & & 1 & -1 \\ & & 1 & 1 \\ \cline{3-4} & & & -2 \end{array}$$

or the even briefer

$$\begin{array}{r|rrr} 1 & 2 & 3 & -1 \\ & & 2 & 1 \\ \hline & 2 & 1 & -2 \end{array}$$

This is sometimes called *synthetic division*.

**12.** Show that, if $r$ is an element of the domain $S$, then $\lambda - r$ is a factor of $\lambda^n - r^n$ for every natural number $n$. Give two proofs.

**13.** If $\lambda^2 - 1$ is divided into the polynomial $\lambda^{100} + \lambda^{37} + 2$ in $J[\lambda]$, what is the remainder? (*Ans.* $\lambda + 3$.)

**14.** Complete the following proof of the Divisor Theorem: Consider the set $B$ of all elements of $S[\lambda]$ of the form $a(\lambda) - b(\lambda)c(\lambda)$ for every $c(\lambda)$ in $S[\lambda]$. If $z$ is in $B$, then $b(\lambda)$ is a factor of $a(\lambda)$. Otherwise consider the set $D(B)$ of all the degrees of the elements of $B$. Now $D(B)$ has a minimal element $d$, and if

$$r(\lambda) = a(\lambda) - b(\lambda)q(\lambda)$$

is of degree $d$, then $r(\lambda) < b(\lambda)$. (Assume otherwise and reduce further.)

## 8.3 Reducibility in the Domain of a Field

In this section and in most of the subsequent work in this chapter we restrict our attention to the polynomial domain of a field. To emphasize this restriction we label the field $F$ and the domain $F[\lambda]$.

DEFINITION 8.4. An element $a(\lambda)$ not in $F$ is *irreducible* (or *prime*) over $F$ if and only if the only factors of $a(\lambda)$ have degree zero or the same degree as $a(\lambda)$.

We note that the polynomial $\lambda^2 - 2$ of $R[\lambda]$ has many different factors of degree 0 and of degree 2 since

$$\lambda^2 - 2 = (1/m)(m\lambda^2 - 2m)$$

for any rational number $m \neq 0$. However, it has no factor of degree 1, for, if $r\lambda - t$ is a factor of $\lambda^2 - 2$, $r \neq 0$, then so is $\lambda - (t/r)$. But by the results of the previous section $\lambda - (t/r)$ is a factor of $\lambda^2 - 2$ if and only if

$$(t/r)^2 - 2 = 0.$$

Since there is no element of $R$ whose square is 2 we know that this cannot be. Hence $\lambda^2 - 2$ is irreducible over $R$.

THEOREM 8.9. *The domain $R[\lambda]$ has an infinite collection of irreducible monic elements.*

For the monic element $\lambda^2 - p$, where $p$ is a rational prime integer, is irreducible over $R$ since $R$ contains no element whose square is $p$.

The elements of $F[\lambda]$ fall into four categories, which form a partition:

(i) The zero element, $z$.
(ii) The units or elements with multiplicative inverses.
(iii) The irreducible elements.
(iv) The other or reducible elements of $F[\lambda]$.

The units of $F[\lambda]$ are clearly the nonzero elements of $F$ because of the fact that degrees are added when polynomials are multiplied. Since the identity $e$ has degree 0, no element of positive degree can be a unit.

The class of irreducible elements is never empty since all of the polynomials of degree one are irreducible. And the class of reducible elements certainly contains the products of the irreducible elements.

This classification is much like the familiar one for that model integral domain $J$, and it suggests that we might be able to parallel the arithmetic of $J$ for $F[\lambda]$. We shall now do that.

THEOREM 8.10. *An element $a(\lambda)$ of $F[\lambda]$ not in $F$ can be expressed as the product of a unit and monic irreducible elements.*

The proof is by induction on the degree of $a(\lambda)$. If $\deg\big(a(\lambda)\big) = 1$, then

$$a(\lambda) = a_0 + a_1\lambda = a_1(\lambda + b_0)$$

where $a_1b_0 = a_0$. Since $a_1$ is in $F$ and $\lambda + b_0$ is certainly monic and irreducible, this completes the first step of the induction.

Now we take as our induction hypothesis the statement that any nonconstant polynomial of degree less than $n$ can be written as the product of a unit and monic irreducible elements. Consider the reducible element

$$a(\lambda) = a_0 + a_1\lambda + \cdots + a_n\lambda^n$$

of degree $n$. Since it is reducible we have

$$a(\lambda) = b(\lambda)c(\lambda)$$

where $\deg\big(b(\lambda)\big)$ and $\deg\big(\lambda(\lambda)\big)$ are less than $n$. Applying the induction hypothesis to both $b(\lambda)$ and $c(\lambda)$, and multiplying the two unit elements obtained, we get the desired expression for $a(\lambda)$.

Of course if $a(\lambda)$ is irreducible we need only to divide by the leading coefficient,

$$a(\lambda) = a_n\lambda^n + \cdots + a_0 = a_n(\lambda^n + \cdots + b_0)$$

where $a_nb_i = a_i$, $i = 0, 1, \cdots, n - 1$. The monic polynomial

$$\lambda^n + \cdots + b_1\lambda + b_0$$

is irreducible since a factor of it is a factor of $a(\lambda)$. This completes the induction.

Now this "factorization into primes" is the analog of the Fundamental Theorem of Arithmetic, and we shall prove that it is unique also. For this purpose we develop the theory of the greatest common factor in $F[\lambda]$.

DEFINITION 8.5. Let $a(\lambda)$ and $b(\lambda)$ be two nonzero elements of $F[\lambda]$. The element $d(\lambda)$ of $F[\lambda]$ is a *greatest common factor* of these two elements if and only if

(1) $d(\lambda)$ is a factor of both $a(\lambda)$ and $b(\lambda)$.
(2) Every common factor of $a(\lambda)$ and $b(\lambda)$ is a factor of $d(\lambda)$.
(3) $d(\lambda)$ is monic.

In making this definition we have of course singled out the critical properties of the G.C.F. in $J$. Since $F[\lambda]$ is not (apparently) well ordered, we have subordinated the maximality feature in the definition of G.C.F. given for $J$.

There are several ways of proving that the G.C.F. exists and is unique. One way involves the use of ideals.

THEOREM 8.11. *The nonzero elements $a(\lambda)$ and $b(\lambda)$ possess a unique G.C.F. $d(\lambda)$. Moreover $F[\lambda]$ contains elements $f(\lambda)$ and $g(\lambda)$ such that*

$$d(\lambda) = a(\lambda)f(\lambda) + b(\lambda)g(\lambda).$$

Form the subset $T$ of $F[\lambda]$ consisting of all elements of the form

$$a(\lambda)f(\lambda) + b(\lambda)g(\lambda)$$

where $f(\lambda)$ and $g(\lambda)$ are arbitrary elements of $F[\lambda]$. Denote by $T'$ the set of nonzero elements of $T$ and by $D(T')$ the collection of degrees of the elements of $T'$. Then $D(T')$ contains a minimal element $n \geqslant 0$, and of course $T'$ contains an element

$$d_1(\lambda) = a(\lambda)f_1(\lambda) + b(\lambda)g_1(\lambda)$$

of degree $n$. Dividing through by the leading coefficient of $d_1(\lambda)$ we obtain the monic polynomial

$$d(\lambda) = a(\lambda)f(\lambda) + b(\lambda)g(\lambda)$$

of degree $n$ in $T'$. Now we shall show that $d(\lambda)$ is a G.C.F. of $a(\lambda)$ and $b(\lambda)$.

First we prove that $d(\lambda)$ is a factor of every element of $T'$. Let $h(\lambda)$ be in $T'$, and form

$$h(\lambda) = d(\lambda)q(\lambda) + r(\lambda), \qquad r(\lambda) < d(\lambda).$$

Now $r(\lambda)$ is either zero or an element of $T'$ of degree less than $n = \deg\big(d(\lambda)\big)$. For $h(\lambda)$, as an element of $T$, is of the form

$$h(\lambda) = a(\lambda)f_2(\lambda) + b(\lambda)g_2(\lambda)$$

for some elements $f_2(\lambda)$ and $g_2(\lambda)$ in $F[\lambda]$. Thus

$$\begin{aligned} r(\lambda) &= h(\lambda) - q(\lambda)d(\lambda), \\ &= a(\lambda)\big(f_2(\lambda) - q(\lambda)f(\lambda)\big) + b(\lambda)\big(g_2(\lambda) - q(\lambda)g(\lambda)\big), \end{aligned}$$

and so is an element of $T$. If $r(\lambda) \neq z$, then $r(\lambda)$ is an element of $T'$ of degree less than $n$, which contradicts the way $n$ was selected. Therefore

$$r(\lambda) = z$$

and

$$h(\lambda) = q(\lambda)d(\lambda).$$

This means that $d(\lambda)$ is a common factor of $a(\lambda)$ and $b(\lambda)$ since both of these elements lie in $T'$:

$$a(\lambda) = ea(\lambda) + zb(\lambda)$$

and

$$b(\lambda) = za(\lambda) + eb(\lambda).$$

On the other hand, if $c(\lambda)$ is a common factor of $a(\lambda)$ and $b(\lambda)$,

$$a(\lambda) = a_1(\lambda)c(\lambda) \quad \text{and} \quad b(\lambda) = b_1(\lambda)c(\lambda),$$

then from the equation

$$d(\lambda) = a(\lambda)f(\lambda) + b(\lambda)g(\lambda)$$

we have

$$d(\lambda) = \big(a_1(\lambda)f(\lambda) + b_1(\lambda)g(\lambda)\big)c(\lambda).$$

Thus $c(\lambda)$ is a factor of $d(\lambda)$. Since $d(\lambda)$ is monic this proves that $d(\lambda)$ is a G.C.F. of $a(\lambda)$ and $b(\lambda)$.

To prove the uniqueness of $d(\lambda)$ we let $m(\lambda)$ be another G.C.F. of $a(\lambda)$ and $b(\lambda)$. Then $d(\lambda)$ is a factor of $m(\lambda)$ since every common factor of $a(\lambda)$ and $b(\lambda)$ is a factor of a G.C.F. Similarly $m(\lambda)$ is a factor of $d(\lambda)$. Hence there exist polynomials $s(\lambda)$ and $t(\lambda)$ such that

$$m(\lambda) = d(\lambda)s(\lambda)$$

and

$$d(\lambda) = m(\lambda)t(\lambda);$$

therefore

$$d(\lambda) = d(\lambda)s(\lambda)t(\lambda)$$

and

$$d(\lambda)\big(e - s(\lambda)t(\lambda)\big) = z.$$

Since $F[\lambda]$ is an integral domain this means that

$$e = s(\lambda)t(\lambda),$$

and thus the elements $s(\lambda)$ and $t(\lambda)$ are units of $F[\lambda]$ and so are in $F$. From

$$m(\lambda) = sd(\lambda)$$

and the fact that $m(\lambda)$ and $d(\lambda)$ are monic we conclude that

$$s = t = e \quad \text{and} \quad m(\lambda) = d(\lambda).$$

Therefore the G.C.F. is unique.

The problem of finding the G.C.F. of two particular elements of $F[\lambda]$ is solved by extending the Divisor Theorem to obtain the Euclidean algorithm for $F[\lambda]$.

THEOREM 8.12. *If $a(\lambda)$ and $b(\lambda)$ are nonzero elements of $F[\lambda]$, then the element $r_n(\lambda)$ of the following algorithm is the G.C.F. of $a(\lambda)$ and $b(\lambda)$:*

$$\begin{aligned}
b(\lambda) &= c_0 r_0(\lambda), \\
a(\lambda) &= q_1(\lambda)r_0(\lambda) + c_1 r_1(\lambda), \qquad z < r_1(\lambda) < r_0(\lambda), \\
r_0(\lambda) &= q_2(\lambda)r_1(\lambda) + c_2 r_2(\lambda), \qquad z < r_2(\lambda) < r_1(\lambda), \\
&\;\;\vdots \\
r_{n-2}(\lambda) &= q_n(\lambda)r_{n-1}(\lambda) + c_n r_n(\lambda), \quad z < r_n(\lambda) < r_{n-1}(\lambda), \\
r_{n-1}(\lambda) &= q_{n+1}(\lambda)r_n(\lambda),
\end{aligned}$$

*where the $c_i$ are all units and the $r_i(\lambda)$ are monic.*

This is so much like the algorithm we used in $J$ that there is hardly any need to comment upon it. Working down from the top we see that any common factor $m(\lambda)$ of $a(\lambda)$ and $b(\lambda)$ is also a factor of $r_1(\lambda)$. Then $m(\lambda)$ is a common factor of $b(\lambda)$ and $r_1(\lambda)$ and hence of $r_0(\lambda)$ and $r_1(\lambda)$, so that from the next equation $m(\lambda)$ is a factor of $r_2(\lambda)$. In this way we see that $m(\lambda)$ is a factor of every $r_i(\lambda)$. To *prove* this we assume otherwise and take $u$ to be the least integer such that $r_u(\lambda)$ is not divisible by $m(\lambda)$. But the $u$th equation,

$$r_{u-2}(\lambda) = q_u(\lambda)r_{u-1}(\lambda) + c_u r_u(\lambda)$$

or

$$r_u(\lambda) = (c_u^{-1})\big(r_{u-2}(\lambda) - q_u(\lambda)r_{u-1}(\lambda)\big),$$

shows clearly that any common factor of $r_{u-2}(\lambda)$ and $r_{u-1}(\lambda)$, such as $m(\lambda)$, is also a factor of $r_u(\lambda)$. Hence the assumption leads to a contradiction, and we know that $m(\lambda)$ divides all $r_i(\lambda)$. In particular, $m(\lambda)$ divides $r_n(\lambda)$.

Working up from the bottom we see that $r_n(\lambda)$ is a factor of $r_{n-1}(\lambda)$ by the last equation. From the next-to-last equation we see that $r_n(\lambda)$ is a factor of $r_{n-2}(\lambda)$. Continuing in this fashion (the proof is like the one above) we conclude that $r_n(\lambda)$ is a factor of every $r_i(\lambda)$. Then from the first equation,

$$a(\lambda) = q_1(\lambda)r_0(\lambda) + c_1 r_1(\lambda),$$

we see that $r_n(\lambda)$ is a common divisor of $a(\lambda)$ and $r_0(\lambda)$ and hence of $a(\lambda)$ and $b(\lambda)$. Since $r_n(\lambda)$ is monic we conclude that $r_n(\lambda)$ is the G.C.F. $d(\lambda) = \big(a(\lambda), b(\lambda)\big)$.

We remark that the number of steps in the algorithm never exceeds the degree of $b(\lambda)$, which is always selected as the element of lesser degree. Also the elements $c_i$ in the algorithm can all be ignored except for $c_n$, which serves the purpose of making $r_n(\lambda)$ monic.

*Example* 1. Find the G.C.F. of $\lambda^4 + 3\lambda^2 + 4\lambda$ and $2\lambda^2 - 2\lambda - 4$ from $R[\lambda]$, and express the G.C.F. in terms of $a(\lambda)$ and $b(\lambda)$.

The algorithm is quite simple:

$$\begin{aligned}
b(\lambda) &= 2r_0(\lambda) = 2(\lambda^2 - \lambda - 2), \\
a(\lambda) &= \lambda^4 + 3\lambda^2 + 4\lambda = (\lambda^2 + \lambda + 6)r_0(\lambda) + 12(\lambda + 1), \quad r_1(\lambda) = \lambda + 1, \\
r_0(\lambda) &= (\lambda + 2)r_1(\lambda) - 4, \quad r_2(\lambda) = 1, \\
r_1(\lambda) &= (\lambda + 1)1.
\end{aligned}$$

Clearly 1 is the G.C.F. of the two polynomials,

$$1 = (\lambda^4 + 3\lambda^2 + 4\lambda,\ 2\lambda^2 - 2\lambda - 4),$$

and collapsing the set of equations we get

$$\begin{aligned} 1(-4) &= r_0(\lambda) - (\lambda + 2)r_1(\lambda), \\ 12r_1(\lambda) &= a(\lambda) - (\lambda^2 + \lambda + 6)r_0(\lambda), \\ 1 &= (-1/4)\{(1/2)b(\lambda) - (\lambda + 2)[(1/12)(a(\lambda) - (\lambda^2 + 2\lambda + 6)r_0(\lambda))]\} \end{aligned}$$

or

$$1 = a(\lambda)[(1/48)(\lambda + 2)] + b(\lambda)[(-1/96)(\lambda^3 + 3\lambda^2 + 8\lambda + 24)].$$

This can be checked by collapsing the right side.

DEFINITION 8.6. Two nonzero elements of $F[\lambda]$ are *relatively prime* if and only if their G.C.F. is $e$, the identity of $F$.

The polynomials in the example above are relatively prime.

Now the theory of the G.C.F. is important in proving the uniqueness of the factorization in Theorem 8.10 since it enables us to prove the following key result.

*Lemma* 8.2. If $a(\lambda)$, $b(\lambda)$, and $c(\lambda)$ are polynomials over the field $F$ such that (i) $a(\lambda)$ is a factor of the product $b(\lambda)c(\lambda)$, and (ii) $a(\lambda)$ and $b(\lambda)$ are relatively prime, then $a(\lambda)$ is a factor of $c(\lambda)$.

From $e = (a(\lambda), b(\lambda))$ and from Theorem 8.11 we conclude that

$$e = a(\lambda)f(\lambda) + b(\lambda)g(\lambda)$$

for some $f(\lambda)$ and $g(\lambda)$ in $F(\lambda)$. Then multiplying by $c(\lambda)$ yields the equation

$$c(\lambda) = a(\lambda)f(\lambda)c(\lambda) + g(\lambda)b(\lambda)c(\lambda).$$

Since $a(\lambda)$ is a factor of both summands on the right we see that $a(\lambda)$ is a factor of $c(\lambda)$, and the lemma is proved.

THEOREM 8.13 (UNIQUE FACTORIZATION THEOREM). *Each nonconstant element of $F[\lambda]$ is uniquely expressible as the product of a unit and monic irreducible polynomials.*

Let $m(\lambda)$ be a nonconstant element of $F[\lambda]$. From Theorem 8.10 we know that $m(\lambda)$ can be expressed in the form

$$m(\lambda) = sp_1(\lambda)\cdots p_n(\lambda),$$

where $s$ is a unit and the $p_i(\lambda)$ are monic irreducible polynomials of $F[\lambda]$. Now suppose that polynomials of degree less then deg $(m(\lambda))$ are uniquely factorable into this form (the induction hypothesis) and consider another factorization of $m(\lambda)$,

$$m(\lambda) = tq_1(\lambda)\cdots q_r(\lambda),$$

where $t$ is a unit and the $q_i(\lambda)$ are monic irreducible polynomials of $F[\lambda]$.

Since

$$sp_1(\lambda)\cdots p_n(\lambda) = tq_1(\lambda)\cdots q_r(\lambda)$$

we see that $p_1(\lambda)$ is a factor of the product $b(\lambda)c(\lambda)$, where

$$b(\lambda) = q_1(\lambda)$$

and

$$c(\lambda) = tq_2(\lambda)\cdots q_r(\lambda).$$

Now either

$$p_1(\lambda) = q_1(\lambda) = \big(p_1(\lambda),\ \ q_1(\lambda)\big), \tag{8.1}$$

or

$$e = \big(p_1(\lambda),\ \ q_1(\lambda)\big) \tag{8.2}$$

since the only monic factors of $p_1(\lambda)$ are $p_1(\lambda)$ and $e$.

If $e = (p_1, q_1)$, then by the preceding lemma we know that $p_1(\lambda)$ is a factor of $c(\lambda) = tq_2(\lambda)\cdots q_r(\lambda)$. Applying the induction hypothesis to $c(\lambda)$, which is permissible since $\deg\big(c(\lambda)\big) = \deg\ \ \big(q_1(\lambda)\big) < \deg\big(m(\lambda)\big)$, we conclude that the $q_i(\lambda)$, $i = 2, \cdots, r$, are the only monic irreducible factors of $c(\lambda)$. Hence $p_1(\lambda)$ equals one of the $q_i(\lambda)$.

Thus in both of the cases (1) and (2) we see that $p_1(\lambda)$ equals one of the elements $q_i(\lambda)$. Then by relabeling this $q_i(\lambda)$ as $q_1(\lambda)$, if necessary, we have

$$m(\lambda) = sp_1(\lambda)\cdots p_n(\lambda) = tp_1(\lambda)q_2(\lambda)\cdots q_r(\lambda).$$

Now we use the fact that $F[\lambda]$ is a domain so that the Cancellation Law for multiplication holds here. Thus

$$m_1(\lambda) = sp_2(\lambda)\cdots p_n(\lambda) = tq_2(\lambda)\cdots q_r(\lambda),$$

and from the induction hypothesis we conclude that

$$s = t, \qquad n = r,$$

and the monic irreducible factors are equal in some order. Since $p_1(\lambda) = q_1(\lambda)$ we see that the two factorizations of $m(\lambda)$ are identical except possibly for the arrangement of factors.

*Example* 2. Factor the element

$$m(\lambda) = 2\lambda^3 + 3\lambda^2 + 2\lambda + 3$$

when $F = J/(5)$, using Theorem 8.13 and the zeros of $m(\lambda)$.

We note that

$$m(1) = m(2) = m(3) = 0$$

so that $\lambda - 1 = \lambda + 4$, $\lambda - 2 = \lambda + 3$, and $\lambda - 3 = \lambda + 2$ are irreducible factors of $m(\lambda)$. Since the degree of $m(\lambda)$ is three we conclude that

$$m(\lambda) = 2(\lambda + 4)(\lambda + 3)(\lambda + 2).$$

*Example* 3. Show that the element

$$m(\lambda) = \lambda^3 + \lambda + 1$$

is irreducible over $F = J/(5)$.

If $m(\lambda)$ is reducible it must have a linear factor $\lambda - r$, where $r$ is a zero of $m(\lambda)$. By checking the five numbers

$$m(0) = 1, \quad m(1) = 3, \quad m(2) = 1, \quad m(3) = 1, \quad m(4) = 4,$$

we see that $m(\lambda)$ has no zeros in $J/(5)$, and so we know that the polynomial is irreducible.

## Exercise 8.3

**1.** Find the G.C.F. of

(*a*) $2\lambda^3 + \lambda^2 + \lambda - 2$ and $\lambda^3 - \lambda^2 - \lambda + 2$ over $R$.
(*b*) $\lambda^3 - 2\lambda^2 - 3\lambda + 2$ and $\lambda^2 + 4$ over $R$.
(*c*) $\lambda^4 + \lambda + 1$ and $\lambda^2 + \lambda + 1$ over $J/(2)$.

**2.** Express the answers for Problem 1 in the form

$$d(\lambda) = a(\lambda)f(\lambda) + b(\lambda)g(\lambda).$$

Are the elements $f(\lambda)$ and $g(\lambda)$ unique? Explain.

**3.** Find the G.C.F. of $\lambda^2 + \lambda + 1$ and $\lambda^3 + \lambda + 1$ over $J/(3)$ in two ways.

**4.** Find all irreducible polynomials of degree five or less over $J/(2)$.

**5.** Prove that the set $T$ in the proof of Theorem 8.11 is an ideal of $F[\lambda]$.

**6.** Discuss and factor the following when possible:

(*a*) $\lambda^2 + 2\lambda - 2$ over $J/(3)$.
(*b*) $\lambda^2 + \lambda + 1$ over $J/(13)$.
(*c*) $\lambda^3 + \lambda^2 + 1$ over $J/(13)$.
(*d*) $\lambda^4 + 1$ over $J/(5)$.
(*e*) $\lambda^3 - (1/5)\lambda^2 - 4\lambda + 4/5$ over $R$.

**7.** Prove that, if $p$ is a prime rational integer, then $\lambda^n - p$ is irreducible over $R$. (Assume $r/s$ is a zero of the polynomial in $R$, and use the unique factorization for $J$.)

**8.** Of the $p - 1$ polynomials $\lambda^2 + t$ for $t = 1, 2, \cdots, p - 1$ in $J/(p)$, $p$ an odd prime, exactly $(p - 1)/2$ are irreducible. Verify this for $p = 5; 7; 11$.

**9.** Show that $\lambda^2 + 1$ is an irreducible element of $R[\lambda]$. Show that the set $T = (\lambda^2 + 1)$ of all multiples of $\lambda^2 + 1$ is an ideal of $R[\lambda]$. Compute the square of the coset $\lambda + T$ in $T[\lambda]/T$.

**10.** The domain $R[\lambda]$ is a subdomain of Re$[\lambda]$. Describe the behavior of the element $\lambda^2 - 2$ in the two domains.

**11.** Show that, if the monic polynomial $m(\lambda)$ of degree $n$ in $F[\lambda]$ has $n$ distinct roots or zeros $r_i$ in $F$, then $m(\lambda) = (\lambda - r_1)\cdots(\lambda - r_n)$.

**12.** Describe the coefficients of $m(\lambda)$ in Problem 11 in terms of the $r_i$. (If $m(\lambda) = a_0 + \cdots + a_{n-1}\lambda^{n-1} + \lambda^n$, then $a_{n-1} = -r_1 - r_2 - \cdots - r_n$, for example.)

**13.** Show that over $F = J/(p)$ the polynomial $\lambda^p - t$, $t$ in $F$, factors as $(\lambda - t)^p$.

**14.** Define and find the G.C.F. of $\lambda^4 - 1$, $\lambda^5 - 1$, and $\lambda^6 - 1$.

**15.** Define the L.C.M. of two polynomials $a(\lambda)$ and $b(\lambda)$. How is it related to the G.C.F.?

**16.** Let $F_1$ be a subfield of $F$, and let $a(\lambda)$ and $b(\lambda)$ be nonconstant elements of $F_1(\lambda)$. Show that the G.C.F. of $a(\lambda)$ and $b(\lambda)$ in $F_1[\lambda]$ is also the G.C.F. of $a(\lambda)$ and $b(\lambda)$ in $F[\lambda]$.

**17.** Factor the polynomial $\lambda^4 - 10\lambda^2 + 1$ over the field of all elements of the form $a + b\sqrt{2}$, $a$ and $b$ in $R$.

**18.** Define the G.C.F. of any finite set of elements of $F[\lambda]$, and prove that it exists and is unique.

**19.** Prove that $(a(\lambda), b(\lambda)) = (a(\lambda), c(\lambda)) = e$ in $F[\lambda]$ implies that

$$(a(\lambda), b(\lambda)c(\lambda)) = e.$$

## 8.4 Reducibility over the Rational Field

The problem of determining whether a polynomial is reducible or not is generally a very difficult one. If we restrict our attention to the rational field we are able to develop a few rather simple criteria which sometimes reveal some information on reducibility.

First we note that, if an element $a(\lambda)$ of $R[\lambda]$ factors as

$$a(\lambda) = b(\lambda)c(\lambda),$$

then by multiplying this equation by the L.C.M. of the denominators of the components of the three polynomials we obtain a factorization of an element of $J[\lambda]$ in $J[\lambda]$. There is nothing very surprising about this. But consider an unfactored element $a(\lambda)$ of $R(\lambda)$; by the same method it can be lifted into $J[\lambda]$. If

$$a(\lambda) = (1/2)\lambda^2 - (1/3)\lambda + 1/4,$$

then

$$12a(\lambda) = 6\lambda^2 - 2\lambda + 3$$

is in $J[\lambda]$ and the set of components is a relatively prime set. Now the astonishing thing is this: If $ka(\lambda)$ has no factors in $J[\lambda]$, then $a(\lambda)$ is irreducible in $R[\lambda]$.

THEOREM 8.14. *If the polynomial $a(\lambda)$ of $J[\lambda]$ factors in $R[\lambda]$, then it factors in $J[\lambda]$. That is, if $a(\lambda) = b(\lambda)c(\lambda)$ in $R[\lambda]$, then there are rationals $s$ and $t$ such that $sb(\lambda)$ and $tc(\lambda)$ are in $J[\lambda]$ and $a(\lambda) = sb(\lambda)tc(\lambda)$.*

We note for example that

$$\lambda^2 - 1 = ((1/8)\lambda - (1/8))(8\lambda + 8) = (\lambda - 1)(\lambda + 1).$$

In this case $b(\lambda) = (1/8)\lambda - (1/8)$, $s = 8$, $c(\lambda) = 8\lambda + 8$, and $t = (1/8)$.

Take the components of $a(\lambda)$ to be relatively prime since otherwise we can divide the equation by the G.C.F. of those integers. Denote by $s$ the rational number whose numerator is the L.C.M. of the denominators of

$b(\lambda)$ and whose denominator is the G.C.F. of the numerators of $b(\lambda)$. (Check the example above.) Similarly $t$ is the rational number $m/n$ such that $m$ is the L.C.M. of the denominators of the components of $c(\lambda)$ and $n$ is the G.C.F. of the numerators of those components.

So, if

$$c(\lambda) = (2/3)\lambda^2 + (4/5)\lambda - (6/7),$$

then $t = 105/2$, and certainly the polynomial

$$tc(\lambda) = 35\lambda^2 + 42\lambda - 45$$

is in $J[\lambda]$ and has relatively prime components. The G.C.F. of 35, 42, and $-45$ is 1.

To prove the theorem we must show that $st = 1$ in $R$, so write in $J[\lambda]$

$$sta(\lambda) = sb(\lambda)tc(\lambda).$$

The polynomials

$$sb(\lambda) = b_0 + b_1\lambda + \cdots + b_n\lambda^n$$

and

$$tc(\lambda) = c_0 + c_1\lambda + \cdots + c_r\lambda^r$$

are in $J[\lambda]$ because of the way $s$ and $t$ were selected. Certainly that means $sta(\lambda)$ is in $J[\lambda]$, too. This means that the product $st$ is an integer, since the components of $a(\lambda)$ were taken to be relatively prime, and for

$$sta(\lambda) = sta_0 + sta_1\lambda + \cdots + sta_{n+r}\lambda^{n+r}$$

to be in $J[\lambda]$ the least positive denominator of $st$ must be the G.C.F. of the $a_i$. Hence $st$ is an integer.

Now suppose $st > 1$. Then a prime $p$ divides $st$, and we shall show that $p$ divides either all $b_i$ in $sb(\lambda)$ or all $c_i$ in $tc(\lambda)$, contradicting the choice of $s$ or $t$, respectively. Assume $j$ and $k$ are integers, $0 \leqslant j \leqslant n$ and $0 \leqslant k \leqslant r$, such that $(b_j, p) = (c_k, p) = 1$, and $p$ is a factor of all the components

$$b_0, b_1, \cdots, b_{j-1} \qquad (\text{if } j \neq 0)$$

and

$$c_0, c_1, \cdots, c_{k-1} \qquad (\text{if } k \neq 0).$$

Then consider the $(j + k)$th component in the product $sb(\lambda)tc(\lambda)$, namely

$$sta_{j+k} = \sum b_i c_u \qquad \text{with } i + u = j + k.$$

In this equation $p$ divides every term except the term $b_j c_k$ since $p$ divides $sta_{j+k}$, certainly, and $p$ divides $b_i c_u$ if $0 \leqslant i < j$ or $0 \leqslant u < k$. If $i + u = j + k$, then either $0 \leqslant i < j$ or $0 \leqslant u < k$ always except when

$$i = j \qquad \text{and} \qquad u = k.$$

But it is impossible for every term except one in an equation to be divisible by $p$, and hence this situation cannot occur. Therefore, if $p$ divides $st$, then $p$ divides every component of $sb(\lambda)$ or $tc(\lambda)$. But these components form relatively prime sets in each case. Hence we must conclude that $st = 1$, so that

$$a(\lambda) = sb(\lambda)tc(\lambda).$$

*Example* 1. In the argument above write out the summation equation for $j = 3$ and $k = 4$ when $n = 8$ and $r = 9$.

Here we have

$$sta_7 = b_0c_7 + b_1c_6 + b_2c_5 + b_3c_4 + b_4c_3 + b_5c_2 + b_6c_1 + b_7c_0.$$

Then only the term $b_3c_4$ is not divisible by the prime $p$, and modulo $p$ would have the impossible congruence

$$0 \equiv 0 + 0 + 0 + b_3c_4 + 0 + 0 + 0 + 0.$$

This result, sometimes known as the *Lemma of Gauss* (after the great mathematician Karl Friedrich Gauss) reduces the problem of studying reducibility in $R[\lambda]$ to the consideration of elements in $J[\lambda]$. As an example of what can be done there we have the following theorem.

THEOREM 8.15 (EISENSTEIN). *If $a(\lambda) = a_0 + \cdots + a_n\lambda^n$ is an element of $J[\lambda]$ such that $a_i \equiv 0 \bmod p$ for $i = 0, 1, \cdots, n - 1$, and $(a_n, p) = 1$ and $(a_0, p^2) = p$ for some prime integer $p$, then the only factors of $a(\lambda)$ in $J[\lambda]$ are of degree $n$ or 0.*

Suppose that $a(\lambda) = b(\lambda)c(\lambda)$ in $J[\lambda]$, where

$$b(\lambda) = b_0 + \cdots + b_r\lambda^r$$

and

$$c(\lambda) = c_0 + \cdots + c_m\lambda^m.$$

Then

$$\begin{aligned} a_0 &= b_0c_0, \\ a_1 &= b_0c_1 + b_1c_0, \\ &\;\;\vdots \\ a_n &= b_rc_m \qquad \text{with } r + m = n. \end{aligned}$$

Since $p$ divides $a_0$ but $p^2$ does not, we see that one of the constant terms is divisible by $p$ and the other is not. We choose to write $(p, c_0) = 1$, whereas $b_0 \equiv 0 \bmod p$. On the other end of the scale we have both $b_r$ and $c_m$ prime to $p$, since $a_n$ is prime to $p$:

$$(a_n, p) = (b_r, p) = (c_m, p) = 1.$$

Now consider the integers $b_0, b_1, \cdots, b_r$; $b_0$ is divisible by $p$ but $b_r$ is not. Hence there is an integer $k$, $0 < k \leqslant r$, such that $(b_k, p) = 1$ but $b_i \equiv 0 \bmod p$ for $0 \leqslant i < k$.

Then as in the last proof we consider the coefficient of $\lambda^k$ in the product $b(\lambda)c(\lambda)$:

$$a_k = \sum b_i c_j \qquad \text{with } i + j = k,$$

or

$$a_k = b_0 c_k + \cdots + b_k c_0.$$

Now in the summation every term except $b_k c_0$ involves $b_i$ with $i < k$, so that every term except the last is divisible by $p$; the term $b_k c_0$ is prime to $p$ since $(b_k, p) = (c_0, p) = 1$. This naturally means that $(a_k, p) = 1$, and since the only component of $a(\lambda)$ which is prime to $p$ is $a_n$, we conclude that

$$k = n.$$

Since $k \leqslant r$ and $r$, the degree of $b(\lambda)$, is less than or equal to $n$, we have

$$k = n, \qquad k \leqslant r, \qquad r \leqslant n.$$

Hence $r = n$ and $m = 0$, so that the only factors of $a(\lambda)$ in $J[\lambda]$ (and by Theorem 8.14, in $R[\lambda]$) are of degree $n$ or 0.

From this result we are able to detect a considerable collection of irreducible elements of $R[\lambda]$ of all degrees. Such elements as

$$\lambda^2 + 2\lambda + 2,\ \lambda^3 + 2\lambda^2 + 2\lambda + 2,\ \lambda^{100} + 3\lambda + 3, \text{ and } \lambda^{10} - 15\lambda^2 + 135$$

are irreducible over $R$ by Eisenstein's criterion.

To find whether or not an element of $J[\lambda]$ possesses linear factors is a problem which can be solved in a finite number of steps. This procedure is a consequence of the relation between linear factors and zeros of $a(\lambda)$.

THEOREM 8.16. *If $b\lambda + c$, $(b, c) = 1$, is a factor of $a(\lambda) = a_0 + \cdots + a_n\lambda^n$ in $J[\lambda]$, then the integer $c$ is a factor of the integer $a_0$ and the integer $b$ is a factor of the integer $a_n$.*

We know that $\lambda - (-c/b)$ is a factor of $a(\lambda)$ in $F[\lambda]$ if and only if $-c/b$ is a zero of $a(\lambda)$. Thus if $b\lambda + c$ is a factor of $a(\lambda)$ in $J[\lambda]$, we have

$$0 = a_0 + a_1(-c/b) + \cdots + a_n(-c/b)^n$$

or

$$0 = a_0 b^n - a_1 c b^{n-1} + \cdots + a_n(-c)^n.$$

Now we can write this as

$$a_0 b^n = \big(a_1 b^{n-1} + \cdots + a_n(-c)^{n-1}\big)c,$$

and since $(b, c) = 1$ we must conclude that $c$ is a factor of $a_0$. Similarly the equation

$$-a_n(-c)^n = (a_0 b^{n-1} - a_1 c b^{n-2} + \cdots)b$$

implies that $b$ is a factor of $a_n$.

*Example* 2. Show that the polynomial $\lambda^2 + 2\lambda + 4$ is irreducible over $R$.

If this element reduces in $R[\lambda]$, then it has a linear factor $b\lambda + c$ in $J[\lambda]$. The only choices for $b$ are 1 and $-1$, and the only choices for $c$ are factors of 4: $1, -1, 2, -2, 4, -4$. Then the *possible* rational zeros of $a(\lambda) = \lambda^2 + 2\lambda + 4$ are $1, -1, 2, -2, 4$, and $-4$. A little computing shows that

$$a(1) = 7,\ a(-1) = 3,\ a(2) = 12,\ a(-2) = 4,\ a(4) = 28, \text{ and } a(-4) = 12.$$

Hence $a(\lambda)$ has no rational zeros and is therefore irreducible.

*Note:* This example shows that the criterion for irreducibility which was proved sufficient in Eisenstein's Theorem is not necessary. Here the prime 2 divides $a_0$ and $a_1$ and $(2, a_2) = 1$, but 4 divides $a_0$.

*Example* 3. Find primes $p$ and $q$ such that the polynomial $\lambda^2 + 3\lambda - pq$ is irreducible in $R[\lambda]$.

The only possible rational zeros of this polynomial are $\pm p$, $\pm q$, and $\pm pq$. If $p$ is a zero, then we have

$$p^2 + 3p = pq$$

so that

$$p + 3 = q.$$

This can only happen if $p = 2$ and $q = 5$.

If $-p$ is a zero, then

$$p^2 - 3p = -pq$$

and

$$p + q = 3.$$

Since this cannot happen we conclude that any two primes whose product is not 10 make this polynomial irreducible in $R[\lambda]$.

*Example* 4. Verify that $\lambda^4 - 10\lambda^2 + 1$ is irreducible over $R$.

Obviously this polynomial has no rational zero since neither 1 nor $-1$ is a zero. Hence if it is reducible it is the product of two second degree polynomials from $J[\lambda]$,

$$\lambda^4 - 10\lambda^2 + 1 = (\lambda^2 + a\lambda + b)(\lambda^2 + c\lambda + d).$$

Expanding and comparing components we get the equations, in $J$,

$$\begin{aligned} a + c &= 0, \\ b + ac + d &= -10, \\ bc + ad &= 0, \\ bd &= 1. \end{aligned}$$

These imply that $c = -a$ and $b = d = \pm 1$, so the second equation becomes

$$\pm 1 - a^2 \pm 1 = -10$$

or

$$a^2 = 10 \pm 2,$$

and since there is no integer whose square is 8 or 12, we conclude that there are no integers satisfying these conditions. Hence the polynomial $\lambda^4 - 10\lambda^2 + 1$ is irreducible in $R[\lambda]$.

## Exercise 8.4

**1.** Check for linear factors in $R[\lambda]$:

(*a*) $(1/2)\lambda^3 + (3/2)\lambda^2 + 4\lambda + 6$.

(*b*) $3\lambda^3 - (1/2)\lambda^2 - 2\lambda - (1/2)$.

(*c*) $6\lambda^4 + 2\lambda^3 - (20/3)\lambda^2 - (20/3)\lambda + (16/3)$.

(*d*) $8\lambda^5 + 4\lambda^4 - 30\lambda^3 - 25\lambda^2 + 7\lambda + 6$.

**2.** Factor the above polynomials.

**3.** Let $a(\lambda) = b(\lambda)c(\lambda)$ in $J[\lambda]$, where

$$b(\lambda) = p + 2p\lambda + 3p\lambda^2 + p\lambda^3 + 4\lambda^4 + 6\lambda^5 + 4\lambda^6$$

and

$$c(\lambda) = 2p + p\lambda + 2p\lambda^2 + \lambda^3 - \lambda^4 + 2\lambda^5,$$

$p$ a prime larger than 3. Show that the coefficient of $\lambda^7$ in $a(\lambda)$ is relatively prime to $p$.

**4.** Decompose the element $2\lambda^4 - 10\lambda^2 + 12$ in $R[\lambda]$ as indicated in Theorem 8.10.

**5.** How many different linear factors has the polynomial $\lambda^3 + 9\lambda^2 + 9\lambda + 8$ in $R[\lambda]$? How are they related?

**6.** Can an element of $F[\lambda]$ be reducible in $F[\lambda]$ but irreducible in a subdomain? Consider the polynomial $\lambda^{10} - 10\lambda^2 + 1$ of $Re[\lambda]$ which is contained in the subdomain $R[\lambda]$.

**7.** If $m$ is an integer such that $2\lambda^2 - m\lambda + 9$ is irreducible in $R[\lambda]$, what can you say about $m$?

**8.** Let $a(\lambda)$ be a polynomial of degree $n - 1$ in $R[\lambda]$, and let $r_1, \cdots, r_n$ be $n$ distinct elements of $R$. Show that $a(\lambda)$ is equal to the polynomial

$$b_1(\lambda - r_2)\cdots(\lambda - r_n) + b_2(\lambda - r_1)(\lambda - r_3)\cdots(\lambda - r_n) + \cdots + b_n(\lambda - r_1)\cdots(\lambda - r_{n-1}),$$

where

$$b_i = a(r_i)(r_i - r_i)^{-1}\cdots(r_{i-1} - r_i)^{-1}(r_{i+1} - r_i)^{-1}\cdots(r^n - r_i)^{-1}.$$

This is sometimes called Lagrange's Interpolation Formula. Is it valid in $F[\lambda]$? Illustrate by finding $a(\lambda)$ of degree 2 in $R[\lambda]$ if $a(-1) = 2$, $a(0) = 1$, and $a(1) = 3$.

**9.** If $a(\lambda)$ is a factor of $b(\lambda)$ in $J[\lambda]$, then the integer $a(n)$ is a factor of the integer $b(n)$ for every $n$ in $J$. Use this to show that the polynomial $a(\lambda) = \lambda^4 - 10\lambda^2 + 1$ is irreducible over $R$ in the following way: $a(0) = 1$, $a(1) = -8$, and $a(-1) = -8$, so, if $b(\lambda)$ is a factor of $a(\lambda)$, then $b(0)$ is a factor of 1, $b(1)$ is a factor of $-8$, and $b(-1)$ is a factor of $-8$. Use the Lagrange Interpolation Formula to find all $b(\lambda)$ of degree 2 satisfying these conditions, and show that none is a factor of $a(\lambda)$. Generalize.

**10.** Generalize Eisenstein's Theorem by showing that, if $a(\lambda)$ is an element of $J[\lambda]$ such that $(a_n, p) = (a_k, p) = 1$, whereas $(a_{k-1}, p) = \cdots = (a_1, p) = (a_0, p^2) = p$ for some prime $p$, then $a(\lambda)$ has an irreducible factor of degree $k$ or larger.

**11.** Let $a(\lambda) = a_0 + a_1\lambda + \cdots + a_n\lambda^n$ be an element of $R[\lambda]$. The *formal derivative*, $D(a(\lambda))$, of $a(\lambda)$ is defined to be the polynomial $D(a(\lambda)) = a_1 + 2a_2\lambda + \cdots + na_n\lambda^{n-1}$. Show that $D(b(\lambda)c(\lambda)) = b(\lambda)\,D(c(\lambda)) + c(\lambda)\,D(b(\lambda))$. Illustrate by computing the derivative of $\lambda^4 - 1$ in two ways.

**12.** A zero $r$ of $a(\lambda)$ is said to have multiplicity $m$ if and only if $(\lambda - r)^m$ is a factor of $a(\lambda)$ but $(\lambda - r)^{m+1}$ is *not* a factor of $a(\lambda)$. Show that $a(\lambda)$ has no multiple roots in $R$ or any extension of $R$ if and only if $(a(\lambda), D(a(\lambda))) = 1$ in $R$.

**13.** Find the G.C.F. of $a(\lambda) = \lambda^5 - 2\lambda^4 - 8\lambda^3 + 16\lambda^2 + 16\lambda - 32$ and its derivative. Factor $a(\lambda)$ into linear factors.

**14.** Define the formal derivative of an element $a(\lambda)$ of $F[\lambda]$. Compute the derivative of $a(\lambda) = \lambda^7 - 1$ where $F = J/(7)$, and factor $\lambda^7 - 1$ into linear factors. Compare with Problem 12. (Note that $(a + b)^p = a^p + b^p$ in an integral domain of characteristic $p$.)

**15.** If $a(\lambda)$ from $R[\lambda]$ has multiple zeros as an element of $Re[\lambda]$, does $a(\lambda)$ factor in $R[\lambda]$? Why?

## 8.5 Ideals and Extensions

Now we turn our attention to the ideals of $F[\lambda]$ and the quotient rings of $F[\lambda]$ over these ideals. These new systems are very intimately related to the factorization problem for elements of $F[\lambda]$ as we shall see.

THEOREM 8.17. *If $T$ is an ideal of $F[\lambda]$, then $T$ contains an element $a(\lambda)$ such that every element of $T$ is of the form $a(\lambda)q(\lambda)$ for some $q(\lambda)$ in $F[\lambda]$.*

If $T$ contains only the element $z$, then the result is obviously true, so consider the case where $T$ contains nonzero elements. The set $D(T)$ of degrees of the nonzero elements of $T$ contains a least nonnegative integer $n$, by the Well-Ordering Theorem. Then $T$ contains a monic polynomial of degree $n$ (for if $2\lambda^2 + 1$ is in $T$ of $R[\lambda]$, then $\lambda^2 + \frac{1}{2} = (\frac{1}{2})(2\lambda^2 + 1)$ is in $T$), and we shall show that this element $a(\lambda)$ has the stated property. As in the proof of Theorem 8.11 we select an arbitrary element $b(\lambda)$ of $T$ and apply the Divisor Theorem to get

$$b(\lambda) = a(\lambda)q(\lambda) + r(\lambda), \qquad \text{with } r(\lambda) < a(\lambda).$$

Since

$$r(\lambda) = b(\lambda) - q(\lambda)a(\lambda)$$

is in $T$, an ideal, then $r(\lambda)$ can have no degree and hence is $z$. For otherwise $r(\lambda)$ is a nonzero element of $T$ with degree less than $n$, and, since $n$ is the least element of $D(T)$, this is impossible. Hence

$$b(\lambda) = a(\lambda)q(\lambda),$$

and the theorem is proved.

Since it is quite easy to show that the set of all multiples of a monic polynomial $a(\lambda)$ of $F[\lambda]$ is an ideal of $F[\lambda]$, we see that there is a one-to-one correspondence between nonzero ideals of $F[\lambda]$ and monic polynomials of $F[\lambda]$.

*Corollary* 8.17.1. The mapping

$$a(\lambda) \to (a(\lambda)) = \{a(\lambda)q(\lambda) : q(\lambda) \text{ in } F[\lambda]\}$$

is a one-to-one mapping from the set of monic polynomials of $F[\lambda]$ onto the set of nonzero ideals of $F[\lambda]$.

This follows from the fact that, if $a(\lambda)$ is a monic polynomial of minimal degree $n$ of the ideal $T$, then $a(\lambda)$ is the only monic polynomial of degree $n$. Suppose $b(\lambda)$ is a monic element of $T$ of degree $n$. By the above theorem there is an element $q(\lambda)$ in $F[\lambda]$ such that

$$b(\lambda) = q(\lambda)a(\lambda).$$

Since $\deg(a(\lambda)) = \deg(b(\lambda))$ we see that $q$ is a constant, and by checking the leading coefficients we conclude that $q = e$ and

$$a(\lambda) = b(\lambda).$$

Hence the mapping is one-to-one, and we can identify the ideal $T$ as $T = (a(\lambda))$.

This correspondence enables us to analyze the quotient ring $F[\lambda]/(a(\lambda))$ in terms of the factors of $a(\lambda)$. This is entirely analogous with the analysis of the ideals and homomorphic images of $J$. First of all, the cosets of $T = (a(\lambda))$ are determined completely by the remainders upon division by $a(\lambda)$.

THEOREM 8.18. *The elements $b(\lambda)$ and $c(\lambda)$ are in the same coset of $T = (a(\lambda))$ in $F[\lambda]$ if and only if they leave the same remainder when divided by $a(\lambda)$.*

Suppose

$$b(\lambda) = q_1(\lambda)a(\lambda) + r(\lambda)$$

and

$$c(\lambda) = q_2(\lambda)a(\lambda) + r(\lambda).$$

Then

$$b(\lambda) - c(\lambda) = (q_1(\lambda) - q_2(\lambda))a(\lambda)$$

so that $b(\lambda) - c(\lambda)$ is in $T$. Thus $b(\lambda)$ is in the coset $c(\lambda) + T$, and since the cosets coincide if they overlap, we conclude that

$$b(\lambda) + T = c(\lambda) + T.$$

Conversely, suppose $b(\lambda) + T = c(\lambda) + T$. Then $T$ contains an element $q(\lambda)a(\lambda)$ such that

$$b(\lambda) = c(\lambda) + q(\lambda)a(\lambda).$$

Dividing $a(\lambda)$ into $c(\lambda)$ yields

$$c(\lambda) = q_2(\lambda)a(\lambda) + r(\lambda), \qquad r(\lambda) < a(\lambda),$$

so that

$$b(\lambda) = q_2(\lambda)a(\lambda) + r(\lambda) + q(\lambda)a(\lambda)$$

or

$$b(\lambda) = (q_2(\lambda) + q(\lambda))a(\lambda) + r(\lambda), \qquad r(\lambda) < a(\lambda).$$

Thus $b(\lambda)$ has the same remainder as $c(\lambda)$.

*Example* 1. If $F = J/(2)$ and $T = (\lambda^2 + \lambda + 1)$, then the distinct cosets of $T$ in $F[\lambda]$ are the sets $0 + T$, $1 + T$, $\lambda + T$, and $\lambda + 1 + T$ since the elements $0, 1, \lambda,$ and $\lambda + 1$ are precisely the remainders possible upon division by $\lambda^2 + \lambda + 1$ in $F[\lambda]$.

We note that $\lambda^2 + \lambda + 1$ is in $0 + T$, $\lambda^2$ is in $\lambda + 1 + T$, $\lambda^3$ is in $1 + T$, and $\lambda^3 + 1$ is in $0 + T$. The operation tables for the quotient ring $F[\lambda]/(\lambda^2 + \lambda + 1)$ are as shown. We see, for example, that $(\lambda + T)(\lambda + T) = \lambda^2 + T = \lambda + 1 + T$.

| $+$ | $0 + T$ | $1 + T$ | $\lambda + T$ | $\lambda + 1 + T$ |
|---|---|---|---|---|
| $0 + T$ | $0 + T$ | $1 + T$ | $\lambda + T$ | $\lambda + 1 + T$ |
| $1 + T$ | $1 + T$ | $0 + T$ | $\lambda + 1 + T$ | $\lambda + T$ |
| $\lambda + T$ | $\lambda + T$ | $\lambda + 1 + T$ | $0 + T$ | $1 + T$ |
| $\lambda + 1 + T$ | $\lambda + 1 + T$ | $\lambda + T$ | $1 + T$ | $0 + T$ |

| $\cdot$ | $0 + T$ | $1 + T$ | $\lambda + T$ | $\lambda + 1 + T$ |
|---|---|---|---|---|
| $0 + T$ | $0 + T$ | $0 + T$ | $0 + T$ | $0 + T$ |
| $1 + T$ | $0 + T$ | $1 + T$ | $\lambda + T$ | $\lambda + 1 + T$ |
| $\lambda + T$ | $0 + T$ | $\lambda + T$ | $\lambda + 1 + T$ | $1 + T$ |
| $\lambda + 1 + T$ | $0 + T$ | $\lambda + 1 + T$ | $1 + T$ | $\lambda + T$ |

What kind of ring is $F[\lambda]/(a(\lambda))$? Since it is a homomorphic image of an integral domain $F[\lambda]$, it is certainly a commutative ring with an identity when $T = (a(\lambda))$ is a proper ideal. Moreover, it is an extension of the field $F$.

THEOREM 8.19. *If $T = (a(\lambda))$ is a proper ideal of $F[\lambda]$, then the elements $r + T$ of $F[\lambda]/T$, where $r$ is in $F$, form a field isomorphic with $F$, and the natural mapping*

$$r \to r + T, \qquad \text{all } r \text{ in } F,$$

*is an isomorphism.*

Since $T$ is a proper ideal we know that $\deg (a(\lambda)) > 0$. Hence every element $r$ of $F$ occurs as a remainder relative to division by $a(\lambda)$, so that by Theorem 8.18 the cosets $r + T$, as $r$ ranges over $F$, are all distinct. Thus the mapping is one-to-one. If $r$ and $s$ are two elements of $F$, then

$$r \to r + T, \qquad s \to s + T,$$
$$r + s \to (r + s) + T = (r + T) + (s + T),$$

and

$$rs \to rs + T = (r + T)(s + T).$$

This means that the set $\{r + T: r \text{ in } F\}$ is a subring of $F[\lambda]/T$ which is isomorphic with $F$ and hence is a field.

*Example* 2. The elements $0 + T$ and $1 + T$ of Example 1 form a field isomorphic with $J/(2)$ as we can see directly by checking the operation tables:

| $+$ | $0 + T$ | $1 + T$ |
|---|---|---|
| $0 + T$ | $0 + T$ | $1 + T$ |
| $1 + T$ | $1 + T$ | $0 + T$ |

| $\cdot$ | $0 + T$ | $1 + T$ |
|---|---|---|
| $0 + T$ | $0 + T$ | $0 + T$ |
| $1 + T$ | $0 + T$ | $1 + T$ |

So far we have only made use of the degree of $a(\lambda)$. Now we will talk about its factors.

THEOREM 8.20. *The quotient ring* $F[\lambda]/(a(\lambda))$ *is a field if and only if* $a(\lambda)$ *is an irreducible element of* $F[\lambda]$.

Suppose $a(\lambda)$ is irreducible. Then we must show that each element of $F[\lambda]/(a(\lambda))$ except $z + T$ has a multiplicative inverse. To do this we use the theory of the G.C.F. in $F[\lambda]$. Consider the coset $b(\lambda) + T \neq T = (a(\lambda))$. Then $b(\lambda)$ is not in $T$ and hence does not have $a(\lambda)$ as a factor. Since the only monic factors of $a(\lambda)$ are $e$ and $a(\lambda)$, $a(\lambda)$ being irreducible, this means that $e$ is the G.C.F. of $a(\lambda)$ and $b(\lambda)$. Hence $F[\lambda]$ contains polynomials $f(\lambda)$ and $g(\lambda)$ such that

$$e = a(\lambda)f(\lambda) + b(\lambda)g(\lambda).$$

Switching to cosets of $T$ this means that

$$e + T = b(\lambda)g(\lambda) + T = (b(\lambda) + T)(g(\lambda) + T).$$

Therefore $g(\lambda) + T$ is the multiplicative inverse of $b(\lambda) + T$ in $F[\lambda]/T$ since $e + T$ is certainly the multiplicative identity.

On the other hand, if $a(\lambda)$ factors as

$$a(\lambda) = c(\lambda)d(\lambda) \text{ in } F[\lambda],$$

where deg $(c(\lambda))$ and deg $(d(\lambda))$ are both less than deg $(a(\lambda))$, then the product of the two cosets $c(\lambda) + T$ and $d(\lambda) + T$ is

$$(c(\lambda) + T)(d(\lambda) + T) = a(\lambda) + T = z + T = T.$$

Since the cosets $c(\lambda) + T$ and $d(\lambda) + T$ are both different from $z + T$ this means that the quotient ring has divisors of zero.

*Example* 3. By inspecting the polynomial $\lambda^2 + \lambda + 1$ of Example 1 we conclude that the system $F[\lambda]/(\lambda^2 + \lambda + 1)$ of Example 1 is a field containing four elements. This field contains (in the sense of isomorphism) the field $J/(2)$ as a subfield. On the other hand the polynomial $\lambda^2 + \lambda$ is reducible in $F[\lambda]$ when $F = J/(2)$, and the system $F[\lambda]/(\lambda^2 + \lambda)$ is a ring of four elements with divisors of zero. In particular we have, for $S = (\lambda^2 + \lambda)$,

$$(\lambda + S)(\lambda + 1 + S) = \lambda^2 + \lambda + S = 0 + S$$

in this system.

DEFINITION 8.7. If $m(\lambda)$ is an irreducible element of $F[\lambda]$, then the field $F[\lambda]/m(\lambda)$ is an *algebraic extension* of $F$. If every irreducible $m(\lambda)$ is of degree one, then $F$ is an *algebraically closed* field.

Obviously an algebraically closed field is one which cannot be extended to a larger field by this method. According to the so-called *Fundamental Theorem of Algebra*, the complex field $C$ is an algebraically closed field. Every polynomial in $C[\lambda]$ factors as a product of linear factors, so that an irreducible element of $C[\lambda]$ is of degree one. Then $C[\lambda]/T$, $T = (\lambda - c)$, is just $C$ again (i.e., the quotient ring is isomorphic with $C$).

Many other fields, such as $R$, can be extended algebraically, and these extensions provide not only new examples of fields but also a new way of studying polynomials. We are now coming into what is generally accepted as the modern theory of equations. This is the Galois theory of fields, which was invented by the mathematicians E. Galois and N. H. Abel. No attempt is made here to develop this beautiful, abstract interplay of fields and groups, but we will try to reveal the basic ideas which should be of interest to all educated persons.

Now if we extend the rational field relative to the irreducible polynomial $a(\lambda) = \lambda^2 - 2$, then what can we say about the polynomial domain of $R_1 = R[\lambda]/(\lambda^2 - 2)$? First we consider the problem of notation. The symbol $r$ for an element of $R$ is adopted as the symbol for the coset to which $r$ belongs; that is, we choose to identify corresponding elements (Theorem 8.19) by the simpler symbol. Then, if we invent a simple symbol for the coset $\lambda + T$, where $T = (\lambda^2 - 2)$, we should have a relatively simple system of notation for the elements of $R_1$. Now we note that

$$(\lambda + T)(\lambda + T) = \lambda^2 + T = 2 + T,$$

and since we have already decided to denote $2 + T$ by 2, this means that $\lambda + T$ is an element of $R_1$ such that

$$(\lambda + T)^2 = 2.$$

So we choose to denote $\lambda + T$ by the classical symbol $\sqrt{2}$,

$$\lambda + T = \sqrt{2}.$$

(More will be said in justification of this later.)

Since the remainders possible upon division of elements of $R[\lambda]$ are of the form $a + b\lambda$, $a$ and $b$ in $R$, we see from Theorem 8.18 that the elements of $R_1 = R[\lambda]/(\lambda^2 - 2)$ are now expressible in the form

$$a + b\sqrt{2}.$$

This expression is unique since each coset of $T = (\lambda^2 - 2)$ contains exactly one remainder of the form $a + b\lambda$.

Consider the polynomial domain of $R_1$. The indeterminate of *this* domain is now denoted as (0, 1), so we again label it as $\lambda$ and the domain as $R_1[\lambda]$. Since $R_1$ contains $R$ as a subfield we see that by identifying isomorphic systems we have $R[\lambda]$ as a subdomain of $R_1[\lambda]$. So we have extended $R[\lambda]$ to $R_1[\lambda]$.

Now we look at the polynomial $\lambda^2 - 2$ as an element of $R_1[\lambda]$. In $R[\lambda]$ this polynomial is irreducible, but in $R_1[\lambda]$ we have

$$\lambda^2 - 2 = (\lambda + \sqrt{2})(\lambda - \sqrt{2}).$$

More generally, let $m(\lambda)$ be an irreducible polynomial of degree $n$ in $F[\lambda]$,

$$m(\lambda) = a_0 + a_1\lambda + \cdots + a_n\lambda^n.$$

Then the distinct cosets of $T = \big(m(\lambda)\big)$ are represented uniquely by the remainders

$$b_0 + b_1\lambda + \cdots + b_{n-1}\lambda^{n-1}$$

with $b_i$ in $F$. If we coin the symbol $x$ for the coset $\lambda + T$ and identify the cosets $b_i + T$, $b_i$ in $F$, with $b_i$, then the elements of $F[\lambda]/T$ are uniquely expressible as

$$b_0 + b_1x + \cdots + b_{n-1}x^{n-1}.$$

Moreover $x$ has the property that

$$a_0 + a_1x + \cdots + a_nx^n = z$$

in $F_1 = F[\lambda]/\big(m(\lambda)\big)$. So the element

$$m(\lambda) = a_0 + a_1\lambda + \cdots + a_n\lambda^n$$

of the polynomial domain $F_1[\lambda]$ is reducible in this extension of $F[\lambda]$ since it has a zero, namely $x$, in $F_1$. Hence $\lambda - x$ is a factor of $m(\lambda)$ in $F_1[\lambda]$. Of course $m(\lambda)$ can still have irreducible factors of degree greater than one.

*Example* 4. Extend $R$ relative to $\lambda^3 - 2$, and consider the factorization of $\lambda^3 - 2$ in the extended domain.

As in the discussion above we adopt a classical symbol $\sqrt[3]{2}$ for the coset $\lambda + (\lambda^3 - 2)$. Then the elements of $R_1 = R[\lambda]/(\lambda^3 - 2)$ are expressible uniquely in the form

$$a + b\sqrt[3]{2} + c\sqrt[3]{4}$$

with $a$, $b$, and $c$ in $R$. In $R_1[\lambda]$ we see that $\lambda^3 - 2$ factors as

$$\lambda^3 - 2 = (\lambda - \sqrt[3]{2})(\lambda^2 + \sqrt[3]{2}\lambda + \sqrt[3]{4}),$$

and we shall show that the second degree factor is irreducible over $R_1$.

If it were reducible it would have a zero, $r$, in $R_1$ and

$$r^2 + \sqrt[3]{2}r + \sqrt[3]{4} = 0.$$

Completing the square we have

$$(2r - \sqrt[3]{2})^2 = -\sqrt[3]{4}.$$

But no number exists in $R_1$ whose square is $-\sqrt[3]{4}$, for, if

$$(a + b\sqrt[3]{2} + c\sqrt[3]{4})^2 = -\sqrt[3]{4},$$

then expansion yields

$$(a^2 + 4bc) + (2c^2 + 2ab)\sqrt[3]{2} + (b^2 + 2ac)\sqrt[3]{4} = -\sqrt[3]{4}.$$

The uniqueness of the expression for elements of $R_1$ leads to these equations in $R$:

$$\begin{aligned} a^2 + 4bc &= 0 \\ c^2 + ab &= 0 \\ b^2 + 2ac &= -1. \end{aligned}$$

From the first two equations we see that $c$ and $a$ have the opposite sign of $b$. Hence $b^2 + 2ac$ is nonnegative and *cannot* equal $-1$. Therefore the polynomial

$$b(\lambda) = \lambda^2 + \lambda\sqrt[3]{2} + \sqrt[3]{4}$$

is irreducible over $R_1$.

If we extend $R_1$, however, to $R_2 = R_1[\lambda]/(b(\lambda))$, then we have a field such that in $R_2[\lambda]$ the original polynomial $\lambda^3 - 2$ factors into linear factors.

It is quite evident that for any polynomial $m(\lambda)$ of degree $n$ in $F[\lambda]$ we can extend $F$ to a field $F^*$ in at most $n - 1$ steps so that $m(\lambda)$ factors completely into linear factors in $F^*[\lambda]$.

THEOREM 8.21. *If $m(\lambda)$ is an element of degree $n$ in $F[\lambda]$, then there exists a field $F^*$ obtainable by at most $n - 1$ algebraic extensions such that $m(\lambda)$ in $F^*[\lambda]$ is expressible as a product of linear factors.*

The proof is by induction on $n$, and we need only consider the case when $m(\lambda)$ is irreducible in $F[\lambda]$. Then $m(\lambda)$ reduces in $F_1[\lambda]$, where $F_1 = F[\lambda]/(m(\lambda))$, and we apply the induction hypothesis to the factors of $m(\lambda)$.

*Example* 5. Extend $R$ so that $m(\lambda) = \lambda^4 - 5\lambda^2 + 6$ can be factored completely.

Since $m(\lambda) = (\lambda^2 - 2)(\lambda^2 - 3)$ we extend $R$ to $R_1 = R[\lambda]/(\lambda^2 - 2)$ and $R_1$ to $R_2 = R_1[\lambda]/(\lambda^2 - 3)$. The elements of $R_1$ are of the form

$$a + b\sqrt{2}, \qquad a \text{ and } b \text{ in } R,$$

and the elements of $R_2$ are of the form

$$(a + b\sqrt{2}) + (c + d\sqrt{2})\sqrt{3}, \qquad a, b, c, \text{ and } d \text{ in } R,$$

or

$$a + b\sqrt{2} + c\sqrt{3} + d\sqrt{6}.$$

Clearly $m(\lambda)$ factors in $R_2[\lambda]$ as

$$(\lambda - \sqrt{2})(\lambda + \sqrt{2})(\lambda - \sqrt{3})(\lambda + \sqrt{3}).$$

## Exercise 8.5

**1.** What can you say about the ideal of $R[\lambda]$ which contains $\lambda^2 - 3\lambda + 2$ and $\lambda^2 + 2\lambda + 1$?

**2.** Find an irreducible polynomial $m(\lambda)$ of degree 2 in $F[\lambda]$ when $F = J/(3)$, and construct the operation tables for $F_1 = F[\lambda]/(m(\lambda))$. Factor $m(\lambda)$ in $F_1[\lambda]$.

**3.** Describe the principal features of $R_1 = R[\lambda]/(m(\lambda))$ when (see Problem 1 of Section 8.4)

(*a*) $m(\lambda) = \lambda^3 + 3\lambda^2 + 8\lambda + 12$.
(*b*) $m(\lambda) = \lambda^3 - (\frac{1}{6})\lambda^2 - (\frac{2}{3})\lambda - (1/6)$.

**4.** Let $R_1 = R[\lambda]/(\lambda^2 - 2)$. Show that $\lambda^4 - 10\lambda^2 + 1$ is reducible in $R_1[\lambda]$.

5. Describe the quotient rings of $F[\lambda]$ for $F = J/(2)$ and

(a) $m(\lambda) = \lambda + 1.$
(b) $m(\lambda) = \lambda^2 + 1.$
(c) $m(\lambda) = \lambda^3 + \lambda + 1.$

6. Show that $\lambda^2 - 3$ is irreducible in $R_1[\lambda]$, where $R_1 = R[\lambda]/(\lambda^2 - 2)$.

7. Show that, if $R_3 = R[\lambda]/(\lambda^2 - 3)$ and $R_4 = R_3[\lambda]/(\lambda^2 - 2)$, then $R_4$ is isomorphic with $R_2$ in Example 5.

8. In $J[\lambda]$ let $a(\lambda) = 2\lambda + 2$ and $b(\lambda) = \lambda^2 + 2\lambda + 2$. Form the set $T = \{a(\lambda)f(\lambda) + b(\lambda)g(\lambda): f(\lambda)$ and $g(\lambda)$ in $J[\lambda]\}$. Show that $T$ is an ideal of $J[\lambda]$. Show further that Theorem 8.17 is *not* true for this ideal.

9. Let $(s(\lambda))$ and $(b(\lambda))$ be two ideals of $F[\lambda]$. Describe the intersection. How is it related to the G.C.F. $(a(\lambda), b(\lambda))$?

10. Show that the ideal $(a(\lambda))$ contains the ideal $(b(\lambda))$ in $F[\lambda]$ if and only if $a(\lambda)$ is a factor of $b(\lambda)$.

11. Show that, if $S$ and $T$ are two ideals of $F[\lambda]$, then $ST = \{s(\lambda)t(\lambda)$: $s(\lambda)$ in $S$, $t(\lambda)$ in $T\}$ is an ideal also.

12. Prove that the monic polynomial $m(\lambda)$ of $F[\lambda]$ is irreducible if and only if the ideal $(m(\lambda))$ is contained in no other proper ideal of $F[\lambda]$. (See Problem 10.)

13. Rewrite Theorem 8.10, using ideals. (See Problem 12.)

14. Show that $m(\lambda) = \lambda^4 - 10\lambda^2 + 1$ is reducible in the domain $R_2[\lambda]$ of Example 5. Compare $R_2$ with the field $R[\lambda]/(\lambda^4 - 10\lambda^2 + 1)$.

15. Show that the field $R_1 = R[\lambda]/(\lambda^2 - 2)$ is isomorphic with a subfield of the real field.

16. Describe the quotient ring $F[\lambda]/(\lambda^2 + 1)$ when $F$ is the real field. How does it compare with $C$, the complex field?

17. Describe the quotient ring $J[\lambda]/(2\lambda - 1) = J_1$. What happens to the element $2\lambda - 1$ in $J_1[\lambda]$?

18. In the field $R[\lambda]/(\lambda^4 - 10\lambda^2 + 1)$ show that the square of the coset $(\frac{1}{2})(\lambda^3 - 9\lambda) + T$ equals $2 + T$, where $T = (\lambda^4 - 10\lambda^2 + 1)$, that the square of $(\frac{1}{2})(11\lambda - \lambda^3) + T$ is $3 + T$, and that the square of $(\frac{1}{2})(\lambda^2 - 5) + T$ is $6 + T$. Compare with Problem 14.

19. Show that, if $\lambda^2 + p\lambda + q$ is an irreducible element of $R[\lambda]$, then $r = (p^2/4) - q$ is an element such that $R[\lambda]/(\lambda^2 + p\lambda + q)$ is isomorphic with $R[\lambda]/(\lambda^2 - r)$. Illustrate for $p = q = 1$.

20. Show that the field $R_2$ of Example 5 contains two subfields $S_1$ and $S_2$ such that $S_1$ is isomorphic with $R[\lambda^2 - 2)$ and $S_2$ is isomorphic with $R[\lambda]/(\lambda^2 - 3)$. Show that $S_1 \cap S_2 = R$.

## 8.6 Root Fields and Splitting Fields

Now we know that for a given polynomial $m(\lambda)$ of $F[\lambda]$ it is possible to extend $F$ by means of a finite series of algebraic extensions to a field $F_1$ such that in $F_1[\lambda]$ the element $m(\lambda)$ is expressible as a product of first degree polynomials. This procedure is not unique, however. Consider the following example.

*Example* 1. Show that the polynomial $\lambda^2 - 2$ is reducible in $R_1[\lambda]$, where $R_1 = R[\lambda]/T$ and $T = (\lambda^4 - 10\lambda^2 + 1)$.

Consider the coset $(\lambda^3 - 9\lambda) + T$, an element of $R_1$. If we denote it by $t$, then

$$t^2 = (\lambda^6 - 18\lambda^4 + 81\lambda^2) + T.$$

Now back in $R[\lambda]$ we divide $\lambda^4 - 10\lambda^2 + 1$ into the polynomial $\lambda^6 - 18\lambda^4 + 81\lambda^2$ and get the equation

$$\lambda^6 - 18\lambda^4 + 81\lambda^2 = (\lambda^4 - 10\lambda^2 + 1)(\lambda^2 - 8) + 8.$$

Hence in $R_1$ we have

$$t^2 = 8 + T,$$

which we agree to write as

$$t^2 = 8.$$

Therefore $(\frac{1}{2})t$ is a zero of $\lambda^2 - 2$, and so $\lambda^2 - 2$ reduces in $R_1[\lambda]$. Since $\lambda^2 - 2$ also reduces in $R_2[\lambda]$, where $R_2 = R[\lambda]/(\lambda^2 - 2)$, this indicates that there are different algebraic extensions for the same $m(\lambda)$ which lead to fields over which $m(\lambda)$ reduces completely.

DEFINITION 8.8. If the polynomial $m(\lambda)$ of $F[\lambda]$ factors into linear factors in $F[\lambda]$, then $F$ is a *root field* of $m(\lambda)$. If, moreover, no proper subfield of $F$ is a root field of $m(\lambda)$, then $F$ is a *splitting field* for $m(\lambda)$.

This means that a splitting field for $m(\lambda)$ is in effect a "smallest" root field of the polynomial, and this idea enables us to prove that a polynomial has a splitting field.

THEOREM 8.22. *A polynomial $m(\lambda)$ from $F[\lambda]$ possesses a splitting field.*

First of all we replace the field $F$ by a root field $F_1$. This is accomplished, as we saw in the previous section, through at most $n - 1$ algebraic extensions, where $n$ is the degree of $m(\lambda)$. Then from the field $F_1$ we take the collection $K$ of all subfields (not necessarily proper) of $F_1$ which are root fields of $m(\lambda)$. The set $K$ of fields is not empty since $F_1$ is in $K$, so we can form $F_0$, the intersection of all elements of $K$. We shall show that $F_0$ is a splitting field for $m(\lambda)$.

To begin with $F_0$ is a field since the intersection of any nonempty collection of subfields of a field is a field. If $a$ and $b$ are in $F_0$, then $a$ and $b$ are in every element of $K$. Since the elements of $K$ are subfields of $F_1$ this means that $a \pm b$, $ab$, and $a^{-1}$, if $a \neq z$, are all in $F_0$. So $F_0$ is a field.

Now consider the factorization

$$m(\lambda) = a_n(\lambda - r_1)\cdots(\lambda - r_n)$$

in $F_1[\lambda]$. Since this factorization is unique in $F_1[\lambda]$, by Theorem 8.13, we know that in the subdomain of $F_1[\lambda]$ which is the polynomial domain of a subfield $F_i$, $F_i$ a root field of $m(\lambda)$, this is also the complete factorization of $m(\lambda)$ into monic linear factors. Hence the above factorization of $m(\lambda)$ is valid in the polynomial domain of each element of $K$, and so we conclude that it is valid in $F_0[\lambda]$. So $F_0$ is a root field of $m(\lambda)$.

If $F_0$ contains a subfield $F'$ which is also a root field of $m(\lambda)$, then $F'$, being a subfield of $F_1$ also, is in $K$. But $F_0$ is the smallest element of $K$ in that it is contained in every element of $K$, so that $F_0 \subseteq F'$. Thus we see that $F_0 = F'$ and so conclude that $F_0$ is a splitting field for $m(\lambda)$.

The purpose in singling out this particular root field is to bring a type of uniqueness into the picture.

THEOREM 8.23. *The splitting field for $m(\lambda)$ is unique up to an isomorphism.*

A stronger statement could hardly be made.

We shall *not* prove this very basic and very important theorem since we have not yet developed the machinery for doing so. (A rather simple proof is given in the monograph, *Galois Theory*, by E. Artin.)

However, use was, in effect, made of this result in the previous section when the symbol $\sqrt{2}$ was adopted to denote the coset $\lambda + (\lambda^2 - 2)$ in $R[\lambda]/(\lambda^2 - 2)$. Without proving the theorem we can discuss this particular situation more thoroughly.

*Example* 2. Compare the fields $R_1 = R[\lambda]/(\lambda^2 - 2)$ and $R_2 = \{a + b\sqrt{2}$: $a$ and $b$ in $R\}$.

Here $R_2$ is intended to specify a particular subfield of the real field $Re$. We can show that these two fields are isomorphic by using the remainder representatives for the cosets of $T = (\lambda^2 - 2)$. Then a typical element of $R_1$ is expressible as

$$a + b\lambda + T, \qquad a \text{ and } b \text{ in } R,$$

and the obvious mapping to consider is

$$a + b\sqrt{2} \rightarrow a + b\lambda + T$$

for each $a$ and $b$ in $R$. Now

$$(a + b\sqrt{2}) + (c + d\sqrt{2}) = (a + c) + (b + d)\sqrt{2}$$

and

$$(a + b\sqrt{2})(c + d\sqrt{2}) = (ac + 2bd) + (ad + bc)\sqrt{2}$$

whereas

$$(a + b\lambda + T) + (c + d\lambda + T) = (a + c) + (b + d)\lambda + T$$

and

$$(a + b\lambda + T)(c + d\lambda + T) = (ac + (ad + bc)\lambda + bd\lambda^2) + T.$$

Reduction of the polynomial of degree two modulo $\lambda^2 - 2$ yields the product

$$(ac + 2bd) + (ad + bc)\lambda + T.$$

So we see that the mapping is a homomorphism. Since $a + b\lambda + T = T$ if and only if $a = b = 0$ we conclude that the kernel of the homomorphism is (0), and so the mapping is an isomorphism.

Now the field $R_1$ is a splitting field for $\lambda^2 - 2$ since a splitting field for $\lambda^2 - 2$ necessarily contains the components 1 and $-2$ of $\lambda^2 - 2$. This means that a splitting field must contain $R$, which is generated by 1 and the arithmetic operations of addition, subtraction, multiplication, and division.

Thus $R$ is the *component* or *coefficient field* of $\lambda^2 - 2$, that is, it is the smallest field containing the coefficients 1 and $-2$. Since a subfield of $R_1$ which is to be a splitting field of $\lambda^2 - 2$ must also contain a zero of $\lambda^2 - 2$, say $\sqrt{2}$ (as we can again designate $\lambda + T$), then $R_1$, the set of all $a + b\sqrt{2}$, is the splitting field of $\lambda^2 - 2$.

*Example* 3. Determine the splitting field of the polynomial $\lambda^2 - 4$ of $R[\lambda]$.
Since the coefficient field $R$ of $\lambda^2 - 4$ is also a root field of the polynomial we conclude that $R$ is the splitting field of $\lambda^2 - 4$.

*Example* 4. Find the splitting field of the polynomial $m(\lambda) = \lambda^3 - 2$ of $R[\lambda]$.

The splitting field $F$ of this polynomial must contain $R$ and the zero $\sqrt[3]{2}$. Thus $F$ must contain all elements of the form

$$a + b\sqrt[3]{2} + c\sqrt[3]{4}.$$

(See Example 4 of Section 8.5.) These elements form the field (or one isomorphic with) $R_1 = R[\lambda]/(\lambda^3 - 2)$. However, the element $\lambda^3 - 2$ does not factor completely in $R_1[\lambda]$ since the polynomial

$$m_1(\lambda) = \lambda^2 + \sqrt[3]{2}\lambda + \sqrt[3]{4}$$

is irreducible in $R_1[\lambda]$ as we saw in Section 8.5. Therefore $F$ must contain a zero of $m_1(\lambda)$, so extending $R_1$ to $R_2 = R_1[\lambda]/(m_1(\lambda))$ we find the element $t$ in $R_2$ such that

$$m_1(t) = t^2 + \sqrt[3]{2}t + \sqrt[3]{4} = 0.$$

Then $m(\lambda)$ factors in $R_2[\lambda]$ as

$$m(\lambda) = (\lambda - \sqrt[3]{2})(\lambda - t)(\lambda + t + \sqrt[3]{2}).$$

So the splitting field $F$ contains the element $t$ and hence all elements of the form

$$a + b\sqrt[3]{2} + c\sqrt[3]{4} + dt + f\sqrt[3]{2}t + g\sqrt[3]{4}t,$$

where $a, b, c, d, f$, and $g$ are in $R$. But these are just the elements of $R_2$; remember that the distinct elements of $R_2$ are the cosets of $S = (m_1(\lambda))$ which are identified by the different remainders

$$m + n\lambda + S = m + nt,$$

where $m$ and $n$ are elements of $R_1$. Because of the nature of $m$ and $n$ we get the above expression for elements of $R_2$.

Note that different polynomials can have the same splitting field. Certainly all polynomials of degree one in $R[\lambda]$ have the same splitting field, namely, $R$. There are other examples, too.

*Example* 5. Show that $\lambda^2 + 2\lambda - 1$ is irreducible over $R$ and has the same splitting field as $\lambda^2 - 2$.

In $R_1 = R[\lambda]/(\lambda^2 - 2)$ we see that $\lambda^2 + 2\lambda - 1$ factors completely as

$$\lambda^2 + 2\lambda - 1 = (\lambda + 1 - \sqrt{2})(\lambda + 1 + \sqrt{2}),$$

and because of the nature of the components of the linear factors (and the unique factorization theorem) we know that $\lambda^2 + 2\lambda - 1$ is irreducible in $R[\lambda]$. Now a subfield $F$ of $R_1$ which is a root field of $\lambda^2 + 2\lambda - 1$ must contain in addition to the rationals the two zeros or roots,

$$-1 + \sqrt{2} \quad \text{and} \quad -1 - \sqrt{2}.$$

Hence $F$ must contain

$$\sqrt{2} = (\tfrac{1}{2})(-1 + \sqrt{2} - (-1 - \sqrt{2}))$$

so that $F = R_1$, the splitting field of $\lambda^2 - 2$.

## Exercise 8.6

**1.** Describe the splitting field of the element $\lambda^2 - 3$ from $R[\lambda]$ and compare it with the splitting field of $\lambda^2 + 4\lambda + 1$.

**2.** Compare the splitting field of $\lambda^2 + \lambda + 1$ with that of $\lambda^2 + 3\lambda + 3$, elements of $R[\lambda]$. (Note that, if $r$ is an element of $F$, then $(r + 1)^2 + (r + 1) + 1 = r^2 + 3r + 3$.)

**3.** Compare the splitting fields of the elements $\lambda^3 + \lambda + 1$ and $\lambda^3 + \lambda^2 + 1$ of $F[\lambda]$, $F = J/(2)$. Show that, if $t$ denotes the coset $\lambda + T$, $T = (\lambda^3 + \lambda + 1)$, then in $F_1[\lambda]$, where $F_1 = F[\lambda]/T$, we have

$$\lambda^3 + \lambda + 1 = (\lambda + t)(\lambda^2 + t\lambda + t^2 + 1).$$

**4.** Factor the polynomial $\lambda^2 + \lambda + 1$ in the domain $F_1[\lambda]$ when $F_1 = F[\lambda]/(\lambda^2 + \lambda + 1)$ and $F = J/(2)$.

**5.** Factor the element $\lambda^3 + 3\lambda + 1$ in the domain $R_1[\lambda]$ when $R_1 = R[\lambda]/(\lambda^3 + 3\lambda + 1)$.

**6.** Find the inverses of the following elements in the splitting field of the element $\lambda^2 - p$ of $R[\lambda]$:

| | | |
|---|---|---|
| (*a*) | $1 - 2\sqrt{3}$, | $p = 3$. |
| (*b*) | $(1/2) + (1/3)\sqrt{7}$, | $p = 7$ |
| (*c*) | $\sqrt{11}$, | $p = 11$. |

**7.** Find the inverse of the element $1 - 2\sqrt[3]{2} + \sqrt[3]{4}$ in the field $R[\lambda]/(\lambda^3 - 2)$.

**8.** Find an irreducible polynomial $m(\lambda)$ of degree three in $F[\lambda]$ for $F = J/(5)$, and factor $m(\lambda)$ in $F_1[\lambda]$, $F_1 = F[\lambda]/(m(\lambda))$.

**9.** Describe the splitting field of the polynomial $\lambda^3 + 2$ from $F[\lambda]$, $F = J/(7)$, and describe the zeros of $\lambda^3 + 2$. (Note that, if $t^3 + 2 = 0$, then $(2t)^3 + 2 = 0$.)

**10.** Prove that, if $a(\lambda)$ is a factor of $m(\lambda)$ in $F[\lambda]$, then the splitting field of $m(\lambda)$ contains a subfield which is the splitting field of $a(\lambda)$.

**11.** Let $m(\lambda) = a(\lambda)b(\lambda)$ in $R[\lambda]$, where $(a(\lambda), b(\lambda)) = e$, and let $F_0$ be the splitting field of $m(\lambda)$. Show that $F_0$ contains exactly one subfield $F_1$ which is the splitting field of $a(\lambda)$ and exactly one subfield $F_2$ which is the splitting field of $b(\lambda)$. Show also that $F_1 \cap F_2$ is the coefficient field $R$.

**12.** Show that an irreducible element $m(\lambda)$ of $R[\lambda]$ of degree $n$ has $n$ distinct zeros in its splitting field $F$. (Extend the definition of the *formal derivative* to $F[\lambda]$ and compare $m(\lambda)$ and $m'(\lambda) = D(m(\lambda))$.)

**13.** What irreducible polynomials of $R[\lambda]$ have the following zeros?

(*a*) $(1/2) + (1/2)\sqrt[3]{7}$.

(*b*) $1 + \sqrt{2} - \sqrt{3}$.

(*c*) $1 + \sqrt{2} + \sqrt{6}$.

**14.** Describe the ring $F[\lambda]/(m(\lambda))$ by defining congruence modulo $m(\lambda)$. Compare with $J/(m)$.

**15.** Let $F_1$ be the splitting field of the polynomial $m(\lambda)$ of $R[\lambda]$, and let $r$ be a zero of $m(\lambda)$ in $F_1$. Show that there exists a monic irreducible polynomial $a(\lambda)$ in $R[\lambda]$ which has $r$ as a zero. Show also that $a(\lambda)$ is a factor of $m(\lambda)$ in $R[\lambda]$. (Form the set $T = \{b(\lambda)\colon b(\lambda) \text{ in } R[\lambda] \text{ and } b(r) = 0\}$. Then $T$ is the ideal $(a(\lambda))$.)

## 8.7 Automorphisms and Galois Groups

In this section we investigate a somewhat indirect way of studying fields and, correspondingly, of studying polynomials. Roughly speaking this involves determining what might be called the symmetry of the field. This concept of symmetry is reflected by the automorphisms of the field.

DEFINITION 8.9. Let $F_1$ be a subfield of the field $F$. Then the set of all automorphisms of $F$ which do not change the elements of $F_1$ is denoted by $A(F/F_1)$.

We recall that an automorphism $A$ of the field $F$ is a one-to-one mapping $A$ of $F$ onto itself such that addition and multiplication are preserved. In two notations

$$A(a + b) = A(a) + A(b), \quad \text{or} \quad (a + b)A = aA + bA,$$

and

$$A(ab) = A(a)A(b), \quad \text{or} \quad (ab)A = (aA)(bA),$$

for every $a$ and $b$ in $F$. From our study of isomorphisms and homomorphisms we know that an automorphism has these properties:

$$A(e) = e$$
$$A(z) = z$$
$$A(-a) = -A(a), \qquad \text{any } a \text{ in } F,$$

and

$$A(a^{-1}) = (A(a))^{-1}, \qquad a \neq z \text{ in } F.$$

*Example* 1. Let $F = \{a + b\sqrt{2}\colon a \text{ and } b \text{ in } R\}$, and determine an element of $A(F/R)$.

Define

$$A\colon a + b\sqrt{2} \to a - b\sqrt{2}.$$

Then for two elements $a + b\sqrt{2}$ and $c + d\sqrt{2}$ of $F$ we have

$$\begin{aligned} A((a + b\sqrt{2}) + (c + d\sqrt{2})) &= (a + c) - (b + d)\sqrt{2} \\ &= A(a + b\sqrt{2}) + A(c + d\sqrt{2}) \end{aligned}$$

and

$$\begin{aligned} A((a + b\sqrt{2})(c + d\sqrt{2})) &= (ac + 2bd) - (ad + bc)\sqrt{2} \\ &= (A(a + b\sqrt{2}))(A(c + d\sqrt{2})). \end{aligned}$$

Since $a - b\sqrt{2}$ equals 0 if and only if $a = b = 0$ we conclude that this is a one-to-one mapping of $F$ onto $F$ which preserves the operations. Furthermore, if $r$ is in $R$, then

$$r = r + 0\sqrt{2}$$

so that

$$A(r) = r - 0\sqrt{2} = r,$$

and $A$ fixes the elements of $R$.

By the *product* of two automorphisms $\boldsymbol{A}$ and $\boldsymbol{B}$ of the field $F$ we mean the composite function $\boldsymbol{AB}$,

$$\boldsymbol{AB}: f \to (f\boldsymbol{A})\boldsymbol{B} = \boldsymbol{B}(\boldsymbol{A}(f)), \text{ for each } f \text{ in } F.$$

From our earlier studies of one-to-one mappings and permutations we know that $\boldsymbol{AB}$ is certainly a one-to-one mapping of $F$ onto $F$. It is also an automorphism of $F$ since

$$(f + g)\boldsymbol{AB} = ((f + g)\boldsymbol{A})\boldsymbol{B} = (f\boldsymbol{A} + g\boldsymbol{A})\boldsymbol{B} = (f\boldsymbol{A})\boldsymbol{B} + (g\boldsymbol{A})\boldsymbol{B}$$

shows that

$$(f + g)\boldsymbol{AB} = f\boldsymbol{AB} + g\boldsymbol{AB}$$

whereas

$$(fg)\boldsymbol{AB} = ((fg)\boldsymbol{A})\boldsymbol{B} = ((f\boldsymbol{A})(g\boldsymbol{A}))\boldsymbol{B} = (f\boldsymbol{A})\boldsymbol{B}(g\boldsymbol{A})\boldsymbol{B}$$

so that

$$(fg)\boldsymbol{AB} = (f\boldsymbol{AB})(g\boldsymbol{AB}).$$

THEOREM 8.24. *The collection $A(F)$ of all automorphisms of $F$ is a group under function composition. Moreover, $A(F/F_1)$ is a subgroup of $A(F)$.*

To show that $A(F)$ is a group we need to show that the identity mapping $\boldsymbol{E}$,

$$\boldsymbol{E}: f \to f, \qquad \text{all } f \text{ in } F,$$

is an automorphism, which is an obvious conclusion, and that each automorphism $\boldsymbol{A}$ in $A(F)$ has an inverse $\boldsymbol{A}^{-1}$ in $A(F)$. To define the inverse $\boldsymbol{A}^{-1}$ of $\boldsymbol{A}$ we note that each element $a$ of $F$ is expressible uniquely as

$$a = b\boldsymbol{A} = \boldsymbol{A}(b)$$

for some $b$ in $F$ since $A$ is a one-to-one mapping and so pairs off an image and a preimage uniquely. Then we define $A^{-1}$ as

$$A^{-1}: a = bA \to b \qquad \text{for each } a \text{ in } F.$$

So

$$a(A^{-1}A) = (aA^{-1})A = bA = a, \qquad \text{each } a \text{ in } F,$$

and

$$b(AA^{-1}) = (bA)A^{-1} = aA^{-1} = b, \qquad \text{each } b \text{ in } F.$$

Hence

$$AA^{-1} = A^{-1}A = E.$$

Moreover $A^{-1}$ is in $A(F)$, for, if $a = bA$ and $f = gA$, then

$$\begin{aligned}(a + f)A^{-1} &= (bA + gA)A^{-1} = (b + g)AA^{-1} = b + g,\\ &= aA^{-1} + fA^{-1},\end{aligned}$$

and

$$\begin{aligned}(af)A^{-1} &= ((bA)(gA))A^{-1} = ((bg)A)A^{-1} = bg,\\ &= (aA^{-1})(fA^{-1}).\end{aligned}$$

Thus we conclude that $A(F)$ is a group.

To show that $A(F/F_1)$ is a subgroup of $A(F)$ we take two elements $A$ and $B$ of $A(F/F_1)$. By definition of $A(F/F_1)$ we know that

$$hA = h = hB \qquad \text{for each } h \text{ in } F_1.$$

Therefore,

$$hAB = (hA)B = h, \qquad \text{for each } h \text{ in } F_1,$$

and we see that $AB$ is in $A(F/F_1)$. Also, consider $A^{-1}$ when $A$ is in $A(F/F_1)$. By the definition above, $A^{-1}$ maps $a$ onto $b$ where $b$ is the element mapped onto $a$ by $A$. If $h$ is in $F_1$, then

$$hA = h$$

so that

$$hA^{-1} = h$$

also. Thus $A^{-1}$ is in $A(F/F_1)$, and we conclude that it is a subgroup of $A(F)$.

DEFINITION 8.10. The group $A(F/F_1)$ is the *automorphism group of $F$ relative to $F_1$*.

*Example* 2. The group $A(F/R)$, where $F$ is the field $R[\lambda]/(\lambda^2 - 2)$ is of order two.

The elements of $F$ are expressible uniquely in the form $a + b\sqrt{2}$, $a$ and $b$ in $R$. Hence, if $A$ is an element of $A(F/R)$, then the effect of $A$ on $a + b\sqrt{2}$ is completely determined by its effect on $\sqrt{2}$. For $A$ must leave $a$ and $b$ of $R$ unchanged, so that

$$\begin{aligned}(a + b\sqrt{2})A &= aA + (bA)(\sqrt{2}A)\\ &= a + b(\sqrt{2}A).\end{aligned}$$

Now we know that

$$(\sqrt{2})^2 = 2,$$

and applying $A$ to this equation yields

$$((\sqrt{2})(\sqrt{2}))A = 2A$$

or

$$(\sqrt{2}A)(\sqrt{2}A) = 2.$$

Thus $\sqrt{2}A$ is a zero of $\lambda^2 - 2$ and so is either $\sqrt{2}$ or $-\sqrt{2}$. Therefore $A(F/R)$ consists of two automorphisms:

$$E\colon a + b\sqrt{2} \rightarrow a + b\sqrt{2}$$

and

$$A\colon a + b\sqrt{2} \rightarrow a - b\sqrt{2}.$$

The operation table of $A(F/R)$ is quite elementary.

| $\cdot$ | $E$ | $A$ |
|---|---|---|
| $E$ | $E$ | $A$ |
| $A$ | $A$ | $E$ |

This simple example illustrates a very basic relation between automorphisms and zeros of polynomials. That relationship is the key to the whole discussion.

THEOREM 8.25. *If $m(\lambda)$ is an element of $F_1[\lambda]$, where $F_1$ is a subfield of $F$, and if the element $r$ of $F$ is a zero of $m(\lambda)$, then for each automorphism $A$ in $A(F/F_1)$ the image $rA$ of $r$ is also a zero of $m(\lambda)$.*

The argument is quite simple.

$$m(\lambda) = a_0 + a_1\lambda + \cdots + a_n\lambda^n \qquad \text{with } a_i \text{ in } F_1,$$

and

$$m(r) = z = a_0 + a_1 r + \cdots + a_n r^n.$$

Now we apply $A$ from $A(F/F_1)$ to this equation, remembering that $A$ fixes the elements of $F_1$ and that $A$ preserves the operations of $F$. Thus we have

$$z = zA = a_0 + a_1(rA) + \cdots + a_n(rA)^n,$$

an equation that implies

$$m(rA) = z.$$

So we see that the image $rA$ is a zero of $m(\lambda)$ also.

This idea is known to many students through the statement, "*The complex conjugate of a complex zero of a real polynomial is also a zero of the polynomial.*" This is based on the fact that the mapping

$$A\colon a + bi \rightarrow a - bi, \qquad a \text{ and } b \text{ real numbers,}$$

of the complex field $C = Re[\lambda]/(\lambda^2 + 1)$ is an element of $A(C/Re)$. The proof is almost identical with that of Example 1. Thus a fragment of the principle is known widely.

The association between the polynomial $m(\lambda)$, its splitting field $F$, and the automorphism group $A(F/F_0)$ forms the basis for the Galois theory. Roughly stated, in this theory the problem of studying the zeros of $m(\lambda)$ is replaced by or converted into the problem of studying $F$, and this is accomplished to some extent by studying the groups $A(F/F_0)$ for subfields $F_0$ of $F$. Although we are not developing the Galois theory in this book we will demonstrate the tremendous theoretical power of this technique by using it to resolve the classical problems of doubling a cube and trisecting an angle through ruler-and-compass constructions. Toward this end we extend the concept embodied in Example 2 to a general quadratic extension.

DEFINITION 8.11. The field $F_0$ is the *coefficient field* of the polynomial $m(\lambda)$ if and only if $m(\lambda)$ is in the polynomial domain of $F_0$ but not in the polynomial domain of any subfield of $F_0$. Then $A(F/F_0)$, where $F$ is the splitting field of $m(\lambda)$, is the *Galois group* of $m(\lambda)$.

In Example 2 we see that $R$ is the coefficient field of $m(\lambda) = \lambda^2 - 2$, that $F = \{a + b\sqrt{2}: a \text{ and } b \text{ in } R\}$ is the splitting field, and that $A(F/R)$ is the group of order two consisting of the two automorphisms,

$$E: a + b\sqrt{2} \to a + b\sqrt{2}$$

and

$$A: a + b\sqrt{2} \to a - b\sqrt{2}.$$

THEOREM 8.26. *If $m(\lambda)$ is an irreducible polynomial of degree two in $F[\lambda]$, where $F$ is a field of characteristic not 2, then the group $A(F_1/F)$, $F_1 = F[\lambda]/(m(\lambda))$, is of order two and the only elements of $F_1$ which are fixed by both automorphisms in $A(F_1/F)$ are the elements of $F$.*

Consider the polynomial $m(\lambda)$,

$$m(\lambda) = a\lambda^2 + b\lambda + c$$

over $F_1$. We know that $m(\lambda)$ has a zero, $x$, in $F_1$, so that in $F_1$

$$ax^2 + bx + c = z.$$

This can be written

$$x^2 + a^{-1}bx = -a^{-1}c$$

or

$$x^2 + a^{-1}bx + (1/4)(a^{-1}b)^2 = (1/4)(a^{-1}b)^2 - a^{-1}c,$$

so that

$$(2ax + b)^2 = b^2 - 4ac.$$

Again we have used a process known to most high school students. Note how essential it is that the characteristic of $F$ be different from two.

From this formal manipulation we conclude that the polynomial

$$m_1(\lambda) = \lambda^2 - r,$$

where

$$r = b^2 - 4ac,$$

of $F[\lambda]$ has a zero, namely $2ax + b$, in $F_1$. Also the element $2ax + b$ is not in $F$ since $2a$ and $b$ are but $x$ is not. Thus $m_1(\lambda)$ is an irreducible polynomial of degree two from $F[\lambda]$, and certainly

$$F_1 \supseteq F[\lambda]/(m_1(\lambda)) = F_2$$

(in an isomorphic way) since every element of $F_2$ is of the form

$$h + kx_1, \qquad h \text{ and } k \text{ in } F,$$

where $x_1$ is a zero of $m_1(\lambda)$,

$$x_1 = 2ax + b.$$

However, this last equation can be solved for $x$,

$$x = (2a)^{-1}(x_1 - b),$$

so that each element of $F_1$,

$$m + nx \qquad \text{where } m \text{ and } n \text{ are in } F,$$

is expressible as

$$m + nx = (m - n(2a)^{-1}b) + n(2a)^{-1}x_1.$$

Thus $F_2 \supseteq F_1$, and we conclude that

$$F_1 = F[\lambda]/(\lambda^2 - r).$$

The element $x_1$, a zero of $\lambda^2 - r$, can be thought of as a square root of $r$. Then we proceed exactly as in Example 2 and show that the elements of $A(F_1/F)$ are precisely

$$\boldsymbol{E}\colon h + kx_1 \to h + kx_1$$

and

$$\boldsymbol{A}\colon h + kx_1 \to h - kx_1.$$

Now suppose the element $m + nx_1$ of $F_1$ is left unchanged by all the elements of $A(F_1/F)$. Then we have

$$(m + nx_1)\boldsymbol{A} = m - nx_1 = m + nx_1,$$

so that

$$2nx_1 = z$$

and

$$n = z(2x_1)^{-1} = z.$$

Thus $m + nx_1 = m$, an element of $F$, and we conclude that the only elements of $F_1$ which are unchanged by both elements of $A(F_1/F)$ are the elements of $F$.

*Example* 3. Determine the group $A(F/R)$, where $F = R[\lambda]/(\lambda^2 + 4\lambda + 2)$.

The polynomial is irreducible over $R$ since neither 1, 2, $-1$, nor $-2$ is a zero. In the field $F$ it has a zero $x$, and from

$$x^2 + 4x + 2 = 0$$

we get the equation

$$x^2 + 4x + 4 = 2$$

and

$$(x + 2)^2 = 2.$$

Thus

$$x + 2 = \sqrt{2} \quad \text{or} \quad -\sqrt{2},$$

and

$$F = R[\lambda]/(\lambda^2 - 2).$$

Then the Galois group of

$$m(\lambda) = \lambda^2 + 4\lambda + 2$$

is precisely the group of order two which was determined in Example 2.

In general the Galois group of a polynomial of degree $n$ over the coefficient field $F_0$ is a finite group whose order is less than or equal to $n!$, and the only elements of the splitting field which are left unchanged by all the automorphisms in the Galois group are the elements of $F_0$ *provided* the characteristic of $F_0$ does not divide $n$.

## Exercise 8.7

**1.** Describe the Galois group of $m(\lambda) = \lambda^2 + \lambda + 1$ over $R$.
**2.** Describe the Galois group of $m(\lambda) = \lambda^2 + 2\lambda + 1$ over $R$.
**3.** Describe the Galois group of $m(\lambda) = \lambda^2 + \lambda + 1$ over $J/(3)$.
**4.** Describe the Galois group of $m(\lambda) = \lambda^2 + 2\lambda + 2$ over $J/(3)$.
**5.** Denote the four elements of $F_1 = F[\lambda]/(\lambda^2 + \lambda + 1)$, where $F = J/(2)$, by 0, 1, $x$, and $x + 1$. Here $x$ is the coset $\lambda + T$ and is a zero of $\lambda^2 + \lambda + 1$. Show that the mapping $A = \{(0, 0), (1, 1), (x, x + 1), (x + 1, x)\}$ is an automorphism of $F_1$. What is the Galois group of $m(\lambda) = \lambda^2 + \lambda + 1$?
**6.** Let $A$ be an automorphism of the field $F$. Show that the set $F_A = \{x: x \text{ in } F \text{ and } xA = x\}$ is a subfield of $F$.
**7.** Extend the automorphism $A$ of the field $F$ to an automorphism $A^*$ of $F[\lambda]$ by defining $\lambda A^* = \lambda$. Discuss $A^*$ for the field and automorphism of Example 2.

**8.** Locate the $n$ complex numbers $r_m = \cos\theta + i\sin\theta$, where $\theta = 2\pi m/n$ and $m = 0, 1, \cdots, n-1$, on the unit circle in the complex plane. Show that these are the zeros of $\lambda^n - 1$, and discuss the effect of an automorphism $A$ of the field $C$

**Figure 8.1**

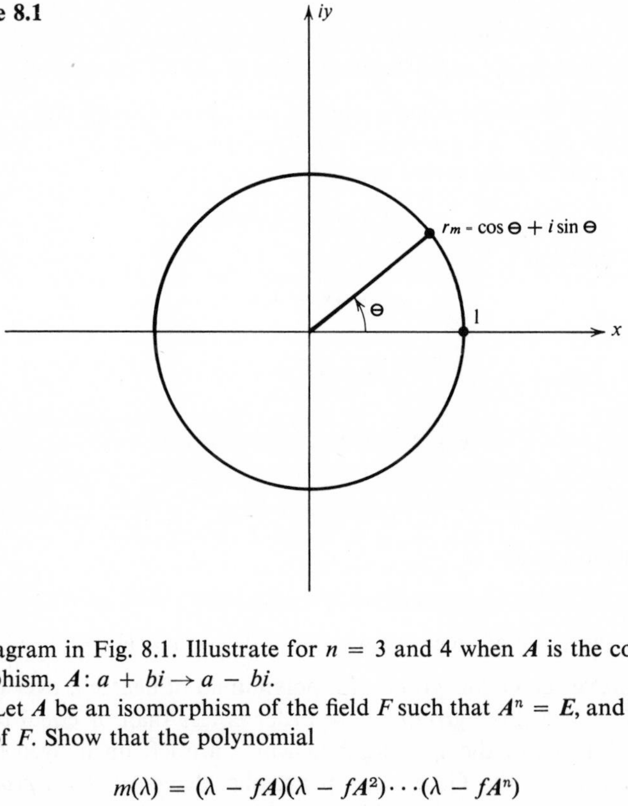


on the diagram in Fig. 8.1. Illustrate for $n = 3$ and 4 when $A$ is the conjugation automorphism, $A: a + bi \to a - bi$.

**9.** Let $A$ be an isomorphism of the field $F$ such that $A^n = E$, and let $f$ be an element of $F$. Show that the polynomial

$$m(\lambda) = (\lambda - fA)(\lambda - fA^2)\cdots(\lambda - fA^n)$$

is in the domain of $F_A$. (See Problem 6.)

**10.** Let $m(\lambda)$ be an irreducible polynomial of degree three over $F$. Show that $A(F_1/F)$ contains only $E$ if $F_1 = F[\lambda]/(m(\lambda))$ is not a root field of $m(\lambda)$. What if $m(\lambda)$ has degree four?

**11.** Show that, if $a + b\sqrt{p}$, $a$ and $b$ in $R$, is a zero of $m(\lambda)$, a polynomial in $R[\lambda]$, then $a - b\sqrt{p}$ is a zero also, by considering the G.C.F. of $m(\lambda)$ and $\lambda^2 - 2a\lambda + a^2 - pb^2$ in $R[\lambda]$.

**12.** Show that the prime fields $R$ and $J/(p)$ have automorphism groups of order one.

**13.** Let $F_1$ be a subfield of $F$ containing $F_0$, and show that the set of all elements of $A(F/F_0)$ which leave the elements of $F_1$ unchanged is a subgroup of $A(F/F_0)$.

**14.** Show that the automorphism groups $A(F)$ and $A(F_1)$ are isomorphic if the fields $F$ and $F_1$ are isomorphic. By considering the fields $R[\lambda]/(\lambda^2 - 2)$ and $R[\lambda]/(\lambda^2 - 3)$ show that the converse is not true.

**15.** The polynomial $m(\lambda) = \lambda^4 + 4\lambda^2 + 2$ is irreducible over $R$. Show that the field $F = R[\lambda]/(m(\lambda))$ has four automorphisms which are determined by their effect on $x$, the coset $\lambda + (m(\lambda))$:

$$E: x \to x,$$
$$A: x \to -x,$$
$$B: x \to x^3 + 3x,$$
$$C: x \to -x^3 - 3x.$$

(Consider the polynomial

$$(\lambda - x)(\lambda + x)(\lambda - x^3 - 3x)(\lambda + x^3 + 3x)$$

in $F[\lambda]$.)

**16.** Factor the polynomial $\lambda^4 + 3\lambda^2 + 9$ over $F = R[\lambda]/(\lambda^4 + 3\lambda^2 + 9)$. What are the possible automorphisms of $F$?

**17.** What are the possible automorphisms of the splitting field of $\lambda^3 - 2$ over $R$?

## 8.8 An Application to Geometry

Two famous classical Euclidean geometry problems are as follows:

(1) Construct a cube whose volume is twice the volume of a given cube.

(2) Trisect a given plane angle.

Now the tools permissible in completing those problems are the straight-edge (*not* a ruler with measurements marked on it) and the compass. We shall show that in general these problems are unsolvable with the permitted equipment.

Naturally the problems must be transformed from geometrical problems into algebraic problems, and so must the permissible constructions. This change-over from geometry to algebra is familiar to the student from his study of analytic geometry so we shall touch lightly upon it here. (See W. W. Sawyer's *A Concrete Approach to Abstract Algebra.*) The permissible constructions correspond to the simple algebraic operations of addition, subtraction, multiplication, and division as well as the more complex unary operation of square root extraction. Thus from a given subfield $F$ of the real field we are permitted to "construct" new numbers by using any finite sequence of the above five operations. So from the field $R$ we build such numbers as $\sqrt{3}$, $\sqrt{1 + \sqrt{3}}$, $\sqrt{2} + 1/\sqrt{7}$, etc.

The problem of doubling a cube by straight-edge-and-compass constructions changes to the algebraic problem of "constructing" a zero of the polynomial

$$\lambda^3 - 2$$

from the field $R$ by means of a finite sequence of the above five operations applied to a finite collection of rational numbers. This cubic problem corresponds to the formula for the volume of a cube.

The trisection problem also comes down to the problem of "constructing" a zero of an irreducible cubic of $R[\lambda]$. Now a standard trigonometric identity is

$$0 = 4\cos^3 A - 3\cos A - \cos 3A$$

where $A$ is the measure of an angle. Thus when $A = 60°$ we have

$$4x^3 - 3x - 1/2 = 0$$

or

$$(2x)^3 - 3(2x) - 1 = 0,$$

where $2x = 2\cos 20°$. If the angle whose measure is 60° can be trisected by straight-edge-and-compass constructions, then the number $2x = 2\cos 20°$

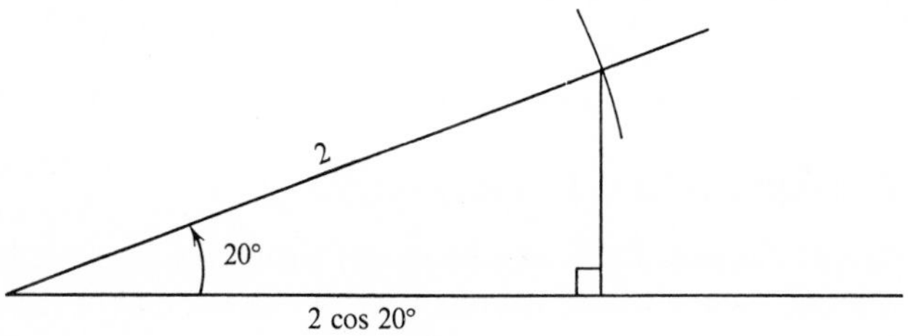


**Figure 8.2**

is also constructable as Fig. 8.2 indicates. This corresponds to the algebraic construction of a zero of the polynomial

$$\lambda^3 - 3\lambda - 1$$

which is obviously irreducible over $R$ since neither 1 nor $-1$ is a zero.

Now we replace the algebraic constructions by quadratic field extensions. Suppose we start with the rational field $R$. If in attempting to construct a certain number we extract the square root of 2, then thereafter we are working in $R[\lambda]/(\lambda^2 - 2)$. In constructing the number $-1 + \sqrt{2}$ we stay in $R[\lambda]/(\lambda^2 - 2) = F_1$, but if we construct $\sqrt{-1 + \sqrt{2}}$ then we have moved on into the field $F_2 = F_1[\lambda]/(\lambda^2 + 1 - \sqrt{2})$. For there is no number $a + b\sqrt{2}$ in $F_1$ such that

$$(a + b\sqrt{2})^2 = -1 + \sqrt{2}$$

since

$$a^2 + 2b^2 = -1$$

is impossible in $R$. Thus we are faced with the problem of determining whether a zero of either of the elements $\lambda^3 - 2$ or $\lambda^3 - 3\lambda - 1$ of $R[\lambda]$ can lie in a field which can be reached through a finite sequence of quadratic extensions.

Let $m(\lambda)$ be an irreducible polynomial of degree three from the domain of $R$, and suppose a field $F$ containing a zero of $m(\lambda)$ can be reached through a finite sequence of quadratic extensions starting from $R$. Then we consider a shortest such sequence,

$$F_0 = R, F_1 = R[\lambda]/(m_1(\lambda)), \cdots, F_n = F_{n-1}[\lambda]/(m_n(\lambda)),$$

where $m_i(\lambda)$ is an irreducible polynomial of degree two in $F_{i-1}[\lambda]$, $i = 1, 2, \cdots, n$. Thus $m(\lambda)$ has a zero in $F = F_n$ but *not* in $F_i$ for $i < n$. We shall show that this is impossible.

THEOREM 8.27. *A zero of an irreducible cubic polynomial from $R[\lambda]$ lies in no field which is obtainable through a finite series of quadratic extensions from $R$.*

Consider the automorphism group $A(F_n/F_{n-1})$. From the work in Section 8.7 we know three very important facts:

(1) $F_n = \{a + b\sqrt{c}$: $a, b, c$ in $F_{n-1}$ and $\lambda^2 - c$ irreducible in $F_{n-1}[\lambda]\}$.

(2) $A(F_n/F_{n-1})$ contains two elements, the identity mapping $\boldsymbol{E}$ and the mapping $\boldsymbol{A}$,

$$\boldsymbol{A}: a + b\sqrt{c} \rightarrow a - b\sqrt{c}.$$

(3) The only elements of $F_n$ which are left unchanged by $\boldsymbol{A}$ are the elements of $F_{n-1}$.

Now let $r$ be a zero of $m(\lambda)$ in $F_n$. Since $r$ is not in $F_{n-1}$ because of the minimality of the sequence of extensions, we know that

$$r = a + b\sqrt{c} \qquad \text{with } b \neq 0.$$

Thus

$$r\boldsymbol{A} = a - b\sqrt{c},$$

and since the coefficients of $m(\lambda)$ are in $R$ we know that $r\boldsymbol{A}$ is also a zero of $m(\lambda)$ by Theorem 8.25. From this we conclude that the product

$$p(\lambda) = (\lambda - r)(\lambda - r\boldsymbol{A})$$

is a factor of $m(\lambda)$ in $F_n[\lambda]$.

We examine $p(\lambda)$ more closely:

$$\begin{aligned} p(\lambda) &= (\lambda - a - b\sqrt{c})(\lambda - a + b\sqrt{c}) \\ &= \lambda^2 - 2a\lambda + a^2 - b^2c. \end{aligned}$$

Since $a$, $b$, and $c$ are in $F_{n-1}$ we see that $p(\lambda)$ is an element of $F_{n-1}[\lambda]$. But this means that the cubic polynomial $m(\lambda)$ is *reducible* in $F_{n-1}[\lambda]$ and hence has a zero in $F_{n-1}$. As this contradicts the selection of $F_n$ we have proved the theorem.

*Corollary* 8.27.1. Zeros of the polynomials $\lambda^3 - 2$ and $\lambda^3 - 3\lambda - 1$ are not obtainable through a finite sequence of quadratic extensions from $R$.

This follows since the two polynomials are obviously irreducible over $R$.

From the idea of a sequence of quadratic extensions we move to that of radical extensions.

DEFINITION 8.12. The field $F$ is a *radical extension* of $R$ if and only if

$$F = F_n = F_{n-1}[\lambda]/(m_n(\lambda)), \cdots, F_1 = R[\lambda]/(m_1(\lambda)),$$

where $m_i(\lambda)$ is an irreducible polynomial in $F_{i-1}[\lambda]$ of the form $\lambda^r - c$. An element $m(\lambda)$ of $R[\lambda]$ is *solvable by radicals* if and only if the splitting field of $m(\lambda)$ lies in a radical extension of $R$.

The interest in radical extensions stems from the centuries of efforts to generalize the quadratic formula to find a formula for the zeros of polynomials of higher degree. These efforts culminated in the brilliant achievement of Abel and Galois who proved that $m(\lambda)$ is solvable by radicals if and only if the Galois group of $m(\lambda)$ is a solvable group (i.e., has composition factors of prime order). Further discussion of this outstanding intellectual accomplishment would lead us into complexities that we choose not to deal with here.

## Exercise 8.8

**1.** How was the Well-Ordering Theorem used in the proof of Theorem 8.27?

**2.** Describe a straight-edge and compass construction of

$$\sqrt{3};\ -1 + \sqrt{3};\ \sqrt{-1 + \sqrt{3}}.$$

**3.** Is the following permissible in straight-edge constructions? Mark three points $A$, $B$, and $C$ on a straight-edge so that $B$ is the midpoint of $AC$; put $A$ on the $y$-axis and $C$ on the $x$-axis and trace out a curve with $B$. See Fig. 8.3.

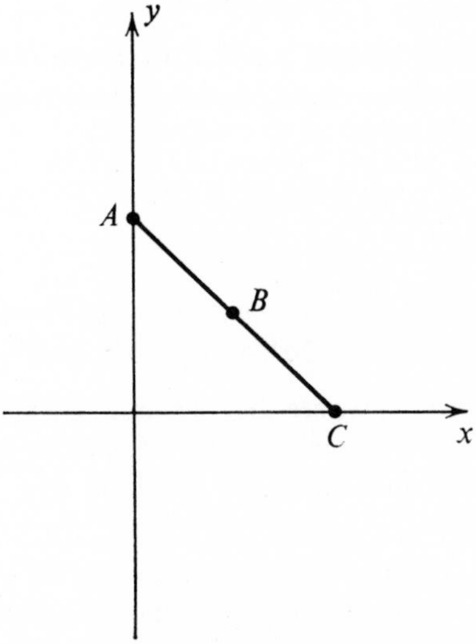


**Figure 8.3**

**4.** What kind of curve is traced out by $B$ in Problem 3?

**5.** Read Section C, "On Roots and Radicals," of Chapter II in *Number, the Language of Science* by T. Dantzig. Describe the evolution of the straight-edge-and-compass problem.

**6.** Why will the argument of Theorem 8.27 not work for any but cubic polynomials?

**7.** Let $m(\lambda)$ be an irreducible cubic polynomial in $F[\lambda]$. Show that, if $F_1$ is an extension of $F$ such that $m(\lambda)$ has a zero in $F_1$, then $F_1$ contains a subfield isomorphic with $F[\lambda]/(m(\lambda))$.

**8.** From the rough description of the Abel-Galois Theorem on solvability by radicals, what do you conclude about the Galois groups of such polynomials of $R[\lambda]$ as $\lambda^2 - p$, $\lambda^3 - p$, $\lambda^n - 1$, etc.?

**9.** The smallest symmetric group which is not solvable is $S_5$, the symmetric group on five elements. What connection does this have, apparently, with attempts to find a formula involving radicals for the zeros of a quintic polynomial?

**10.** Write a two-page essay describing the interrelations of polynomials, algebraic extensions, and automorphisms.

## 8.9 Transcendental Extensions and Partial Fractions

An integral domain can always be extended to a field, its *field of quotients*, by the method used to form the rational numbers from the integers. Since the student can (and should) read through that Section of Chapter 2 in which $R$ is formed from $J$, we will not discuss the general method. Instead we shall investigate the field of quotients of the polynomial domain of the field $F$. This field, which we denote by $F(\lambda)$, is called a *transcendental extension* of $F$, and we see that it involves a two-step process, $F$ to $F[\lambda]$ to $F(\lambda)$.

Let $D$ be the domain $F[\lambda]$ and $D^*$ the set of nonzero elements of $D$, and form the Cartesian product $D \times D^*$. Then $D \times D^*$ consists of the ordered pairs $(m(\lambda)/n(\lambda))$, where $n(\lambda) \neq z$. Abstracting from the definition of $R$ we define an equivalence relation on $D \times D^*$:

$$(p(\lambda)/q(\lambda))\mathbf{Q}(r(\lambda)/s(\lambda))$$

if and only if

$$p(\lambda)s(\lambda) = q(\lambda)r(\lambda).$$

THEOREM 8.28. *The relation* $\mathbf{Q}$ *is an equivalence relation on* $D \times D^*$.

Obviously $\mathbf{Q}$ is reflexive and symmetric, so consider the problem of transitivity. If $(p(\lambda)/q(\lambda))\mathbf{Q}(r(\lambda)/s(\lambda))$ and $(r(\lambda)/s(\lambda))\mathbf{Q}(t(\lambda)/v(\lambda))$, then we have the equations

$$p(\lambda)s(\lambda) = q(\lambda)r(\lambda)$$

and

$$r(\lambda)v(\lambda) = s(\lambda)t(\lambda).$$

Multiplying the first equation by $v(\lambda) \neq z$ and the second by $q(\lambda) \neq z$ we get

$$p(\lambda)s(\lambda)v(\lambda) = q(\lambda)r(\lambda)v(\lambda) = q(\lambda)s(\lambda)t(\lambda).$$

Since $s(\lambda) \neq z$ we apply the Cancellation Law to

$$p(\lambda)s(\lambda)v(\lambda) = q(\lambda)s(\lambda)t(\lambda)$$

and get

$$p(\lambda)v(\lambda) = q(\lambda)t(\lambda).$$

Hence

$$(p(\lambda)/q(\lambda))\mathbf{Q}(t(\lambda)/v(\lambda)).$$

The equivalence class containing the pair $(p(\lambda)/q(\lambda))$ is denoted by $p(\lambda)/q(\lambda)$ and is called a *rational form* in $\lambda$ over $F$. The collection of all rational forms in $\lambda$ over $F$ is denoted by $F(\lambda)$, and $F(\lambda)$ is made into a field by defining addition and multiplication in the usual way for fractions.

*Addition.*

$$p(\lambda)/q(\lambda) + r(\lambda)/s(\lambda) = (p(\lambda)s(\lambda) + q(\lambda)r(\lambda))/q(\lambda)s(\lambda).$$

*Multiplication.*

$$p(\lambda)/q(\lambda) \cdot r(\lambda)/s(\lambda) = p(\lambda)r(\lambda)/q(\lambda)s(\lambda).$$

It is necessary to show that addition and multiplication are well-defined, and this is done in the same way, formally, as in the case of $R$.

THEOREM 8.29. *The system* $\{F(\lambda), +, \cdot\}$ *is a field which is an extension of* $F$.

The proof that $F(\lambda)$ is a field is identical with the proof that $R$ is a field, except that we are now working with fractions $p(\lambda)/q(\lambda)$ instead of $p/q$ with $p$ and $q$ in $J$. Since there is little sense in repeating the same formal procedure we shall assume that $F(\lambda)$ is a field and get on to other matters.

The elements $p(\lambda)/q(\lambda)$ of $F(\lambda)$ with the denominator $q(\lambda)$ equal to the multiplicative identity $e$ of $F$ and $F[\lambda]$ form a subdomain of $F(\lambda)$ which is isomorphic with $F[\lambda]$. Here the correspondence is given by

$$p(\lambda)/e \leftrightarrow p(\lambda),$$

and it preserves the operations since

$$p(\lambda)/e + r(\lambda)/e = (p(\lambda) + r(\lambda))/e$$

and

$$p(\lambda)/e \cdot r(\lambda)/e = p(\lambda)r(\lambda)/e.$$

Thus $F(\lambda)$ is an extension of $F[\lambda]$ which is an extension of $F$, and so $F(\lambda)$ is an extension of $F$. We shall accordingly make no distinction between the form $p(\lambda)/e$ and the polynomial $p(\lambda)$.

*Example* 1. Add and multiply the elements $(\lambda^2 + 1)/(\lambda + 1)$ and $(\lambda^2 - 1)/(\lambda^2 + \lambda)$ in $R(\lambda)$.

By applying the definitions in a routine way we have

$$(\lambda^2 + 1)/(\lambda + 1) + (\lambda^2 - 1)/(\lambda^2 + \lambda) = (\lambda^4 + 2\lambda^3 + 2\lambda^2 - 1)/(\lambda^3 + 2\lambda^2 + \lambda)$$

and

$$(\lambda^2 + 1)/(\lambda + 1) \cdot (\lambda^2 - 1)/(\lambda^2 + \lambda) = (\lambda^4 - 1)/(\lambda^3 + 2\lambda^2 + \lambda).$$

These answers are certainly correct, but just as we usually write $\frac{1}{2}$ instead of $\frac{2}{4}$, it is customary to choose representatives of the classes (i.e., the rational forms) which are relatively prime. This process is the familiar *reduction to simplest terms* and is based on the theory of the G.C.F. in $F[\lambda]$ and the fact that, if

$$p(\lambda) = r(\lambda)m(\lambda)$$

and

$$q(\lambda) = s(\lambda)m(\lambda)$$

then

$$p(\lambda)/q(\lambda) = r(\lambda)/s(\lambda).$$

(For certainly the pairs $(p(\lambda)/q(\lambda))$ and $(r(\lambda)/s(\lambda))$ are equivalent.)

From these observations we conclude that the above elements and arithmetic can be written as

$$(\lambda^2 - 1)/(\lambda^2 + \lambda) = (\lambda - 1)/\lambda,$$
$$(\lambda^2 + 1)/(\lambda + 1) + (\lambda^2 - 1)(\lambda^2 + \lambda) = (\lambda^3 + \lambda^2 + \lambda - 1)/(\lambda^2 + \lambda),$$

and

$$(\lambda^2 + 1)/(\lambda + 1) \cdot (\lambda^2 - 1)/(\lambda^2 + \lambda) = (\lambda^3 - \lambda^2 + \lambda - 1)/(\lambda^2 + \lambda).$$

If we bring the Divisor Theorem of $F[\lambda]$ into play we can effect a further reduction of an element $p(\lambda)/q(\lambda)$ when $q(\lambda) < p(\lambda)$.

THEOREM 8.30. *An element $p(\lambda)/q(\lambda)$ of $F(\lambda)$ is expressible uniquely in the orm*

$$p(\lambda)/q(\lambda) = m(\lambda) + r(\lambda)/q(\lambda)$$

*where $m(\lambda)$ is a polynomial and $r(\lambda) < q(\lambda)$.*

From the Divisor Theorem we know that the polynomial $p(\lambda)$ is expressible uniquely as

$$p(\lambda) = m(\lambda)q(\lambda) + r(\lambda), \qquad r(\lambda) < q(\lambda),$$

so that $p(\lambda)/q(\lambda)$ is expressible uniquely as

$$p(\lambda)/q(\lambda) = m(\lambda) + r(\lambda)/q(\lambda), \qquad r(\lambda) < q(\lambda).$$

In other words, this is just a restatement of the Divisor Theorem.

The process of long division provides us with a simple routine for finding $m(\lambda)$ and $r(\lambda)$. The form $(\lambda^2 + 1)/(\lambda + 1)$ reduces to

$$(\lambda^2 + 1)(\lambda + 1) = (\lambda - 1) + 2(\lambda + 1)$$

since

$$\begin{array}{r|lll}
 & \lambda & - 1 & \\
\hline
\lambda + 1 & \lambda^2 & & + 1 \\
 & \lambda^2 + \lambda & & \\
\cline{2-2}
 & & -\lambda & \\
 & & -\lambda & - 1 \\
\cline{3-4}
 & & & 2
\end{array}$$

Now there exists a further decomposition of the proper fraction $r(\lambda)/q(\lambda)$ based upon the factorization of $q(\lambda)$ into irreducible factors in $F[\lambda]$. This decomposition is known as the *partial fraction decomposition*, and it is frequently used in Calculus courses with little explanation. The development of the decomposition is made in two parts.

*Lemma* 8.3. If $r(\lambda) < q(\lambda)$ and $q(\lambda) = q_1(\lambda)q_2(\lambda)$, where $(q_1(\lambda), q_2(\lambda)) = e$, then the rational form $r(\lambda)/q(\lambda)$ is expressible uniquely as

$$r(\lambda)/q(\lambda) = r_1(\lambda)/q_1(\lambda) + r_2(\lambda)/q_2(\lambda),$$

where $r_i(\lambda) < q_i(\lambda)$, $i = 1$ and 2.

Since the G.C.F. of $q_1(\lambda)$ and $q_2(\lambda)$ is $e$ we know there exist polynomials $p_1(\lambda)$ and $p_2(\lambda)$ in $F[\lambda]$ such that

$$e = p_1(\lambda)q_1(\lambda) + p_2(\lambda)q_2(\lambda).$$

Multiplying by $r(\lambda)/q(\lambda)$ yields

$$r(\lambda)/q(\lambda) = r(\lambda)p_1(\lambda)/q_2(\lambda) + r(\lambda)p_2(\lambda)/q_1(\lambda),$$

and by using Theorem 8.30 we obtain

$$r(\lambda)/q(\lambda) = s_2(\lambda) + r_2(\lambda)/q_2(\lambda) + s_1(\lambda) + r_1(\lambda)/q_1(\lambda).$$

This comes from dividing $q_2(\lambda)$ into $r(\lambda)p_1(\lambda)$ so that

$$r(\lambda)p_1(\lambda) = s_2(\lambda)q_2(\lambda) + r_2(\lambda),$$

and so forth. The division process leaves remainders such that $r_i(\lambda) < q_i(\lambda)$.

Now we shall show that

$$s_1(\lambda) + s_2(\lambda) = z.$$

Multiplying the last equation for $r(\lambda)/q(\lambda)$ by $q(\lambda)$ yields an equation in $F[\lambda]$, effectively:

$$r(\lambda) = \big(s_1(\lambda) + s_2(\lambda)\big)q(\lambda) + r_1(\lambda)q_2(\lambda) + r_2(\lambda)q_1(\lambda).$$

We rewrite this as

$$\big(s_1(\lambda) + s_2(\lambda)\big)q(\lambda) = r(\lambda) - r_1(\lambda)q_2(\lambda) - r_2(\lambda)q_1(\lambda),$$

and consider degrees of the polynomials. If

$$s_1(\lambda) + s_2(\lambda) \neq z,$$

then the left side has degree as least as large as deg $\big(q(\lambda)\big)$, but the right side has degree less than deg $\big(q(\lambda)\big)$ since

$$r(\lambda) < q(\lambda), \qquad r_1(\lambda)q_2(\lambda) < q_1(\lambda)q_2(\lambda) = q(\lambda),$$

and

$$r_2(\lambda)q_1(\lambda) < q_2(\lambda)q_1(\lambda) = q(\lambda).$$

Since this is impossible we conclude that $s_1(\lambda) + s_2(\lambda)$ has no degree, so that

$$s_1(\lambda) + s_2(\lambda) = z$$

and

$$r(\lambda)/q(\lambda) = r_1(\lambda)/q_1(\lambda) + r_2(\lambda)q_2(\lambda),$$

with $r_i(\lambda) < q_i(\lambda)$.

The uniqueness of the $r_i(\lambda)$ is proved by a degree argument also. If

$$r_1(\lambda)/q_1(\lambda) + r_2(\lambda)/q_2(\lambda) = t_1(\lambda)/q_1(\lambda) + t_2(\lambda)/q_2(\lambda),$$

with $t_i(\lambda) < q_i(\lambda)$, then multiplying by $q(\lambda)$ leads to the equation

$$(r_1(\lambda) - t_1(\lambda))q_2(\lambda) = (t_2(\lambda) - r_2(\lambda))q_1(\lambda).$$

Since $q_1(\lambda)$ and $q_2(\lambda)$ are relatively prime this means that $q_1(\lambda)$ is a factor of $r_1(\lambda) - t_1(\lambda)$, and from the relations

$$r_1(\lambda) < q_1(\lambda) \qquad \text{and} \qquad t_1(\lambda) < q_1(\lambda)$$

we know that

$$(r_1(\lambda) - t_1(\lambda)) < q_1(\lambda).$$

Hence the only way that $r_1(\lambda) - t_1(\lambda)$ can have $q_1(\lambda)$ as a factor is for the difference to be zero. Thus we conclude that

$$r_i(\lambda) = t_i(\lambda)$$

and the uniqueness is established.

*Example* 2. Decompose $2\lambda/(\lambda^2 - 1)$ in $R(\lambda)$.

Since $\lambda^2 - 1 = (\lambda + 1)(\lambda - 1)$ we check the factors and get

$$1 = (\tfrac{1}{2})(\lambda + 1) + (-\tfrac{1}{2})(\lambda - 1).$$

Multiplying by $2\lambda/(\lambda^2 - 1)$ we get

$$2\lambda/(\lambda^2 - 1) = \lambda/(\lambda - 1) + (-\lambda)/(\lambda + 1),$$

and since

$$\lambda = 1(\lambda - 1) + 1,$$

and

$$-\lambda = -1(\lambda + 1) + 1,$$

this can be written

$$2\lambda/(\lambda^2 - 1) = 1 + 1/(\lambda - 1) - 1 + 1/(\lambda + 1).$$

Hence our rational form is expressible as

$$2\lambda/(\lambda^2 - 1) = 1/(\lambda - 1) + 1/(\lambda + 1).$$

Relative to powers of a polynomial we have a similar decomposition.

*Lemma* 8.4. If $r(\lambda) < q(\lambda)$ and if $q(\lambda) = (m(\lambda))^n$, then there are $n$ polynomials $r_1(\lambda), \cdots, r_n(\lambda)$, $r_i(\lambda) < m(\lambda)$, such that

$$r(\lambda)/q(\lambda) = r_1(\lambda)/m(\lambda) + \cdots + r_n(\lambda)/(m(\lambda))^n.$$

Furthermore the $r_i(\lambda)$ are unique and $r_n(\lambda) \neq z$ if $r(\lambda)$ and $m(\lambda)$ are relatively prime.

This is basically an extension of the Divisor Theorem. As in the development of the radial representation for integers we write

$$r(\lambda) = q_n(\lambda)m(\lambda) + r_n(\lambda),$$

with $z < r_n(\lambda) < m(\lambda)$ and $q_n(\lambda) < (m(\lambda))^{n-1}$,

$$q_n(\lambda) = q_{n-1}(\lambda)m(\lambda) + r_{n-1}(\lambda),$$

with $r_{n-1}(\lambda) < m(\lambda)$, and $q_{n-1}(\lambda) < (m(\lambda))^{n-2}$, etc., until finally we have

$$q_3(\lambda) = q_2(\lambda)m(\lambda) + r_2(\lambda),$$

$r_2(\lambda) < m(\lambda)$, and $q_2(\lambda) < m(\lambda)$.

Labeling $q_2(\lambda)$ as $r_1(\lambda)$ we can collapse this set of equations to obtain

$$r(\lambda) = r_1(\lambda)(m(\lambda))^{n-1} + \cdots + r_{n-1}(\lambda)m(\lambda) + r_n(\lambda).$$

Dividing by $(m(\lambda))^n$ yields

$$r(\lambda)/q(\lambda) = r_1(\lambda)/m(\lambda) + \cdots + r_n(\lambda)/(m(\lambda))^n$$

with $r_n(\lambda) \neq z$. This exposes the idea of the proof; the proof naturally is by induction.

The uniqueness again is proved by considering degrees. If

$$r(\lambda)/q(\lambda) = s_1(\lambda)/m(\lambda) + \cdots + s_n(\lambda)/(m(\lambda))^n$$

with $s_i(q) < m(\lambda)$, then as a result we have

$$z = (r_1(\lambda) - s_1(\lambda))(m(\lambda))^{n-1} + \cdots + (r_n(\lambda) - s_n(\lambda)).$$

Since $z$ has no degree, such an equation is possible if and only if

$$r_1(\lambda) - s_1(\lambda) = r_2(\lambda) - s_2(\lambda) = \cdots = r_n(\lambda) - s_n(\lambda) = z.$$

Hence $r_i = s_i$ for $i = 1, \cdots, n$, and the expansion is unique.

*Example* 3. Expand $\lambda^5/(\lambda^2 + 1)^3$ in $R(\lambda)$.

We proceed as indicated above:

$$\lambda^5 = (\lambda^2 + 1)(\lambda^3 - \lambda) + \lambda$$

and

$$\lambda^3 - \lambda = (\lambda^2 + 1)(\lambda) + (-2\lambda).$$

Substitution yields

$$\lambda^5 = (\lambda^2 + 1)((\lambda^2 + 1)(\lambda) + (-2)) + \lambda$$

so that

$$\lambda^5 = \lambda(\lambda^2 + 1)^2 - 2\lambda(\lambda^2 + 1) + \lambda.$$

Thus

$$\lambda^5/(\lambda^2 + 1)^3 = \lambda/(\lambda^2 + 1) - 2\lambda/(\lambda^2 + 1) + \lambda/(\lambda^2 + 1)^3$$

is the desired expansion.

THEOREM 8.31. *If $p(\lambda)/q(\lambda)$ is an element of $F(\lambda)$, and if $q(\lambda)$ factors in $F[\lambda]$ as*

$$q(\lambda) = (q_1(\lambda))^{n_1} \cdots (q_v(\lambda))^{n_v},$$

*where the $q_i(\lambda)$ are the distinct irreducible factors of $q(\lambda)$, then $p(\lambda)/q(\lambda)$ decomposes uniquely as*

$$p(\lambda)/q(\lambda) = p_0 + \sum r_{ij}(\lambda)/(q_i(\lambda))^j,$$

*where $r_{ij}(\lambda) < q_i(\lambda)$.*

This is the *partial fraction decomposition* of a rational form. It is proved rather simply (although the notation is a trifle complex) by using the preceding results and mathematical induction. We shall illustrate the process instead.

*Example* 4. Find the partial fraction decomposition of $\lambda^8/(\lambda^6 + \lambda^4 - \lambda^2 - 1)$ in $R(\lambda)$.

First we divide the denominator into the numerator:

$$\lambda^8/(\lambda^6 + \lambda^4 - \lambda^2 - \lambda) = \lambda^2 - 1 + (2\lambda^4 - 1)/(\lambda^6 + \lambda^4 - \lambda^2 - 1).$$

Then we factor the denominator:

$$\lambda^6 + \lambda^4 - \lambda^2 - 1 = (\lambda^2 - 1)(\lambda^2 + 1)^2,$$

and since $1 = (\lambda^2 - 1, \lambda^4 + 2\lambda^2 + 1)$ we have

$$1 = (\tfrac{1}{4})(\lambda^4 + 2\lambda^2 + 1) - (\tfrac{1}{4})(\lambda^2 + 3)(\lambda^2 - 1)$$

so that

$$(2\lambda^4 - 1)/(\lambda^2 - 1)(\lambda^4 + 2\lambda^2 + 1) = (\tfrac{1}{4})(2\lambda^4 - 1)/(\lambda^2 - 1) \\ - (\tfrac{1}{4})(\lambda^2 + 3)(2\lambda^4 - 1)/(\lambda^4 + 2\lambda^2 + 1).$$

Simplified this is

$$(2\lambda^4 - 1)/(\lambda^2 - 1)(\lambda^4 + 2\lambda^2 + 1) = (\tfrac{1}{4})/(\lambda^2 - 1) + (\tfrac{1}{4})/(7\lambda^2 + 5)/(\lambda^2 + 1)^2.$$

Now

$$(\tfrac{1}{4})/(\lambda^2 - 1) = (\tfrac{1}{8})/(\lambda - 1) - (\tfrac{1}{8})/(\lambda + 1),$$

and, since

$$7\lambda^2 + 5 = 7(\lambda^2 + 1) - 2,$$

we see that

$$(\tfrac{1}{4})(7\lambda^2 + 5)/(\lambda^2 + 1)^2 = (\tfrac{7}{4})/(\lambda^2 + 1) - (\tfrac{1}{2})/(\lambda^2 + 1)^2.$$

Thus we conclude that

$$\lambda^8/(\lambda^6 + \lambda^4 - \lambda^2 - 1) = \lambda^2 - 1 + \tfrac{1}{8}(\lambda - 1) - \tfrac{1}{8}(\lambda + 1) \\ + \tfrac{7}{4}(\lambda^2 + 1) - \tfrac{1}{2}(\lambda^2 + 1)^2.$$

The main difficulty is the splitting of the proper fraction, and a method known as the *method of undetermined coefficients* is sometimes useful. We will demonstrate this method on the form $(2\lambda^4 - 1)/(\lambda^6 + \lambda^4 - \lambda^2 - 1)$. From Theorem 8.31 we know that this rational form decomposes as the sum

$$r_1(\lambda)/(\lambda - 1) + r_2(\lambda)/(\lambda + 1) + r_3(\lambda)/(\lambda^2 + 1) + r_4(\lambda)/(\lambda^2 + 1)^2$$

where $r_1(\lambda) < \lambda - 1$, $r_2(\lambda) < \lambda + 1$, $r_3(\lambda) < \lambda^2 + 1$, and $r_4(\lambda) < \lambda^2 + 1$.

Thus $r_1(\lambda)$ and $r_2(\lambda)$ are constants $a$ and $b$, respectively, whereas $r_3(\lambda)$ and $r_4(\lambda)$ are of the general form $c\lambda + d$ and $g\lambda + h$, respectively. Then multiplying the equation for the rational form $(2\lambda^4 - 1)/(\lambda^6 + \lambda^4 - \lambda^2 - 1)$ we get the following equation in $R[\lambda]$:

$$2\lambda^4 - 1 = a(\lambda + 1)(\lambda^2 + 1)^2 + b(\lambda - 1)(\lambda^2 + 1)^2 + (c\lambda + d)(\lambda^4 - 1) + (g\lambda + h)(\lambda^2 - 1).$$

Now we recall that polynomials in $F[\lambda]$ are equal if and only if their components (i.e., coefficients of like powers of $\lambda$) are equal. Thus the unknown coefficients must satisfy these equations:

For $\lambda^5$: $0 = a + b + c;$
For $\lambda^4$: $2 = a - b + d;$
For $\lambda^3$: $0 = 2a + 2b + g;$
For $\lambda^2$: $0 = 2a - 2b + h;$
For $\lambda$: $0 = a + b - c - g;$
For 1: $-1 = a - b - d - h.$

We can solve these, getting

$$a = \tfrac{1}{8}, \quad b = -\tfrac{1}{8}, \quad c = 0, \quad d = \tfrac{7}{4}, \quad g = 0, \quad h = -\tfrac{1}{2},$$

and these check with the above answers.

## Exercise 8.9

**1.** Decompose the following elements of $R(\lambda)$ into partial fractions by two methods:

(*a*) $(\lambda^3 - 1)/(\lambda^2 - 1)$.
(*b*) $\lambda^5/(\lambda^4 + 1)$.
(*c*) $(\lambda^5 + \lambda^4 + \lambda^3 + \lambda^2 + \lambda + 1)/(\lambda^{12} - 1)$.
(*d*) $(\lambda^2 + \lambda - 2)/(\lambda^2 - 1)$.

**2.** Decompose $\lambda/(\lambda^2 - 2)$ of $F(\lambda)$, where $F$ is the field $R[\lambda]/(\lambda^2 - 2)$.

**3.** Decompose $1/(\lambda - 1)^2(\lambda^2 + 1)$ in the transcendental extension of $J/(3)$.

**4.** Let $F = J/(p)$. Show that $F(\lambda)$ is an infinite field of characteristic $p$.

**5.** Show that, if $p(\lambda)$ and $q(\lambda)$ are relatively prime monic elements of $F[\lambda]$, then $(p(\lambda)/q(\lambda))$ is the only pair of such elements in the set $p(\lambda)/q(\lambda)$.

**6.** Is there a proper subfield of $F(\lambda)$ which contains the subdomain $F[\lambda]$? Explain.

**7.** Show that the mapping $T$ of $R(\lambda)$ onto itself defined by

$$T: \lambda \to 1/(2\lambda)$$

and

$$T: r \to r \qquad \text{for } r \text{ in } R$$

is an automorphism of $R(\lambda)$. The image of $1 + \lambda$ is $1 + 1/(2\lambda)$ and the image of $1/(\lambda + 1)$ is $2\lambda/(\lambda + 1)$. Calculate the images of $1 - 1/\lambda$, $1/(\lambda^2 + 1)$, $\lambda - 1/\lambda$.

**8.** Show that the mapping $T$ of $R(\lambda)$ onto itself defined by

$$T: \lambda \to (a\lambda + b)/(c\lambda + d), \qquad \text{where } ad \neq bc,$$

and

$$T: r \to r, \qquad \text{for } r \text{ in } R,$$

is an automorphism of $R(\lambda)$.

**9.** Show that the inverse of the mapping $T$ of Problem 8 is the mapping $T'$ defined by

$$T': \lambda \to (-d\lambda + b)/(c\lambda - a)$$

and

$$T': r \to r.$$

Where does the restriction $ad \neq bc$ come into use?

**10.** The real number $\pi$ is said to be *transcendental* since it is the zero of no polynomial over $R$ (see *Irrational Numbers* by I. Niven). Show that the set $R(\pi)$ of all real numbers of the form

$$(a_0 + a_1\pi + \cdots + a_n\pi^n)/(b_0 + \cdots + b_m\pi^m),$$

where the $a_i$ and $b_j$ are in $R$, is a subfield of $Re$ isomorphic with $R(\lambda)$.

**11.** Why is it important to prove the uniqueness of the partial fraction decomposition or of other similar expressions?

**12.** What can you say about the "mapping" of $F(\lambda)$ onto $F$ obtained by specializing $\lambda$ to $a$ of $F$? Can it be made into a mapping by sending $p(a)/q(a)$ onto $z$ when $q(a) = z$?

**13.** Can a field always be extended to a "larger" field? Explain.

## 8.10 Suggested Reading

*Articles*

Dickson, L. E., "Why it is impossible to trisect an angle or to construct a regular polygon of 7 or 9 sides by ruler and compass," *Math. Teacher* **14** (1921), 217–223.

——— "Constructions with ruler and compasses," *Monographs on Topics of Modern Mathematics* (Edited by J. W. A. Young, Dover Publications, New York, 1955; 353–388.

Vaughn, H., "On the irrationality of roots," *Amer. Math. Monthly* **67** (1960), 576–578.

*Books*

Artin, E., *Galois Theory*, Notre Dame Mathematics Lecture 2, Notre Dame, Indiana, 1944.

Coolidge, J. L., *A History of Geometrical Methods*, Oxford University Press, New York, 1940.

Dantzig, T., *Number, the Language of Science*, Doubleday & Co. (Anchor Books), New York, 1956.

McCoy, N. H., *Rings and Ideals*, Carus Monograph 8, Mathematical Association of America, Buffalo, 1948.

Niven, I., *Irrational Numbers*, Carus Monograph 11, John Wiley & Sons, New York, 1956.

Sawyer, W. W., *A Concrete Approach to Abstract Algebra*, W. H. Freeman & Co., San Francisco, 1959.

# 9

# Quadratic Domains

IN THE DISCUSSION about factorization of integers into a product of primes we implied that there exist integral domains in which composites are expressible as the products of two different sets of primes. In this chapter we encounter such a domain, and then we show that, by introducing *ideal numbers*, the concept of unique factorization is re-established.

A quadratic domain is a certain subsystem of a subfield of the complex field determined by a quadratic polynomial $m(\lambda)$ with rational coefficients. Thus there are many different quadratic domains. Factorization into primes is unique in some but not unique in others. From a study of ideals we obtain, in addition to a unique factorization theorem for ideals of a quadratic domain, a criterion which distinguishes between these two types of quadratic domains: factorization into primes is unique in a quadratic domain if and only if all of its ideals are principal ideals. The problem of determining the prime ideals is studied by using the famous Quadratic Reciprocity Theorem.

## 9.1 Quadratic Fields and Integers

Extensions of the rational field obtained by using irreducible polynomials of degree two with rational coefficients were encountered in the previous chapter. However, these quadratic extensions can be described in a rather more intuitive and elementary way by treating them as subfields of the complex field. In this way each quadratic field can be shown quite easily to be a set $\{r + s\sqrt{m}\colon r \text{ and } s \text{ in } R\}$ determined by an integer $m$ which has the property that $R$ contains no element whose square is $m$.

DEFINITION 9.1. If $m$ is an element of $J$ such that $R$ contains no element whose square equals $m$, then the set $QF(m) = \{r + s\sqrt{m}\colon r \text{ and } s \text{ in } R\}$ is a *quadratic extension* of $R$ relative to $m$.

It is evident that we can reduce $m$ to a square-free integer since

$$r + s\sqrt{8} = r + 2s\sqrt{2}$$

and

$$r + s\sqrt{2} = r + (s/2)\sqrt{8},$$

so hereafter $m$ will always be taken as a square-free integer from $J$.

Now it is a simple exercise to show that $QF(m)$ is a subfield of the complex field. If $r$, $s$, $t$, and $u$ are elements of $R$, then

$$(r + s\sqrt{m}) \pm (t + u\sqrt{m}) = (r \pm t) + (s + u)\sqrt{m}$$

and

$$(r + s\sqrt{m})(t + u\sqrt{m}) = (rt + sum) + (ru + st)\sqrt{m},$$

so that $QF(m)$ is a subring of the complex field $C$. So we must show that each nonzero element of $QF(m)$ has a multiplicative inverse in $QF(m)$.

What does a nonzero element of $QF(m)$ look like? Working backwards we see from

$$r + s\sqrt{m} = 0$$

that

$$r = -s\sqrt{m}$$

and

$$r^2 = s^2m,$$

so that, if $s \neq 0$, then

$$m = r^2/s^2 = (r/s)^2,$$

contradicting the choice of $m$. Thus

$$r + s\sqrt{m} = 0$$

if and only if

$$r = s = 0.$$

This argument also shows that

$$r + s\sqrt{m} \neq 0$$

if and only if

$$r^2 - s^2m \neq 0.$$

Then if $r + s\sqrt{m} \neq 0$ the element

$$\big(r/(r^2 - s^2m)\big) - \big(s/(r^2 - s^2m)\big)\sqrt{m}$$

is the multiplicative inverse of $r + s\sqrt{m}$ since their product is

$$(r^2 - s^2m)/(r^2 - s^2m) = 1.$$

THEOREM 9.1. *The set $QF(m)$ is a subfield of the complex field $C$ for each square-free element $m$ of $J$. Moreover $QF(m_1) = QF(m_2)$ implies $m_1 = m_2$.*

If $QF(m_1) = QF(m_2)$, then $R$ contains elements $r$ and $s$ such that

$$\sqrt{m_1} = r + s\sqrt{m_2}.$$

Then

$$m_1 = (r^2 + s^2m_2) + 2rs\sqrt{m_2}.$$

Certainly $s$ cannot be zero since then

$$\sqrt{m_1} = r,$$

contrary to choice of $m_1$. And if $r \neq 0$ we see that

$$\sqrt{m_2} = (m_1 - r^2 - s^2m_2)/2rs$$

is an element of $R$, contrary to the choice of $m_2$. Hence $r = 0$ and

$$s = p/q \neq 0,$$

where $p$ and $q$ are relatively prime elements of $J$. Therefore

$$q^2m_1 = p^2m_2,$$

which means, since $m_1$ and $m_2$ are square-free and $(p, q) = 1$, that

$$p^2 = q^2 = 1,$$

and so

$$m_1 = m_2.$$

These quadratic fields $QF(m)$ are clearly associated with the polynomials

$$\lambda^2 - m$$

which are irreducible in $J[\lambda]$ in that the zeros of $\lambda^2 - m$ are the elements $\sqrt{m}$ and $-\sqrt{m}$ from $QF(m)$. Actually every irreducible polynomial of degree two from $J[\lambda]$ (and from $R[\lambda]$ also) is associated with just one $QF(m)$ in exactly this same way.

THEOREM 9.2. *If*

$$m(\lambda) = a\lambda^2 + b\lambda + c$$

*is an irreducible element from $J[\lambda]$, then the zeros of $m(\lambda)$ lie in $QF(m)$ where $m$ is the square-free factor of $b^2 - 4ac$.*

The proof of this is familiar to most students since it rests on the *quadratic formula*. The two zeros of $m(\lambda)$ are

$$x_1 = (-b + \sqrt{b^2 - 4ac})/2a$$

and

$$x_2 = (-b - \sqrt{b^2 - 4ac})/2a,$$

and since the *discriminant* reduces as

$$b^2 - 4ac = d^2m, \qquad d > 1 \text{ in } J,$$

we see that $x_1$ and $x_2$ are in $QF(m)$,

$$x = (-b/2a) \pm (d/2a)\sqrt{m}.$$

In fact the elements of $QF(m)$ can be expressed in terms of either zero. From the equation

$$x = (-b + d\sqrt{m})/2a$$

we get

$$\sqrt{m} = (2ax + b)/d$$

so that

$$r + s\sqrt{m} = r_1 + s_1x$$

where

$$r_1 = r + sb/d$$

and

$$s_1 = 2sa/d, \qquad r \text{ and } s \text{ in } R.$$

Thus we can say that each irreducible quadratic polynomial $m(\lambda)$ from $J[\lambda]$ determines exactly one quadratic field $QF(m)$, where $m$ is the square-free factor of the discriminant of $m(\lambda)$.

*Example* 1. Illustrate the above discussion with the polynomial

$$\lambda^2 + \lambda - 1/2.$$

We lift this polynomial into $J[\lambda]$ by multiplying by 2, so that

$$m(\lambda) = 2\lambda^2 + 2\lambda - 1.$$

The discriminant of $m(\lambda)$ is

$$4 - 4(2)(-1) = 12.$$

Hence $m = 3$ and the zeros of $m(\lambda)$ are the elements

$$x_1 = (-2 + \sqrt{12})/2 = -1 + \sqrt{3}$$

and

$$x_2 = -1 - \sqrt{3}$$

from $QF(3)$. Note that

$$\sqrt{3} = 1 + x_1 \qquad (\text{and } -1 - x_2)$$

so that each element of $QF(3)$ can be written in the form $r + sx_i$, $r$ and $s$ in $R$.

We intend to select certain elements from $QF(m)$ and designate them as quadratic integers relative to $m$. The question is, how can we select these in a way which will justify both the adjectives, "quadratic" and "integral"? First we consider a criterion for the elements of $J$.

The elements of $J$ are precisely the elements of $R$ which are zeros of *monic* polynomials of degree *one* from $J[\lambda]$. (This is set forth not as a useful or noteworthy criterion for $J$ but as one which can be generalized.)

Every element $r = p/q$, $p$ and $q$ in $J$, from $R$ is the zero of a first degree polynomial from $J[\lambda]$ since $r$ is the zero of

$$q\lambda - p,$$

so that the restriction to monic polynomials distinguishes elements of $J$ from the other elements of $R$.

Now we note that every element $r + s\sqrt{m}$ from $QF(m)$ is a zero of some polynomial from $J[m]$ since it is clearly a zero of the polynomial

$$(\lambda - r - s\sqrt{m})(\lambda - r + s\sqrt{m}) = \lambda^2 - 2r\lambda + r^2 - s^2m$$

which can be lifted into $J[\lambda]$ by multiplying by a suitable element of $J$. Then by analogy with the above we define the integers of $QF(m)$ as follows.

DEFINITION 9.2. An element of the field $QF(m)$ is a *quadratic integer* if and only if it is a zero of a monic polynomial of degree two from $J[\lambda]$. The set of quadratic integers of $QF(m)$ is denoted by $QD(m)$.

It is easy to see that an element $r$ of $R$ is in $QD(m)$ if and only if $r$ is in $J$. Suppose $r$ is a zero of

$$\lambda^2 + b\lambda + c, \qquad b \text{ and } c \text{ in } J.$$

Then by Gauss's Lemma (Section 8.4) this polynomial factors over $J$ and so has its zeros in $J$.

On the other hand, if $n$ is in $J$, then $n$ is a zero of

$$\lambda^2 - 2n\lambda + n^2 = (\lambda - n)^2.$$

Thus we conclude that $R \cap QD(m) = J$. The elements of $J$ are hereafter called *rational integers.*

THEOREM 9.3. *An element $r$ of $R$ is in $QD(m)$ if and only if $r$ is in $J$.*

Now one might make the reasonable conjecture that $s + t\sqrt{m}$ is in $QD(m)$ if and only if $s$ and $t$ are in $J$. But this is not quite correct. Consider the element

$$\tfrac{1}{2} + (\tfrac{1}{2})\sqrt{5};$$

it is a zero of the polynomial $\lambda^2 - \lambda - 1$ since

$$(\tfrac{1}{2})^2(1 + \sqrt{5})^2 - \tfrac{1}{2} - (1/2)\sqrt{5} - 1 = 0.$$

Hence the element $\frac{1}{2} + (1/2)\sqrt{5}$ is in $QD(5)$.

The general story is told by the following result.

THEOREM 9.4. *If $m \equiv 2$ or $3$ modulo 4, then $QD(m) = \{a + b\sqrt{m}$: a and b in $J\}$. If $m \equiv 1$ modulo 4, then $QD(m)$ consists of the elements $a + b\sqrt{m}$, where a and b either are in J or are both halves of odd rational integers.*

Let $a + b\sqrt{m}$ be an element of $QD(m)$ with $b \neq 0$. If $a + b\sqrt{m}$ is a zero of a monic quadratic

$$m(\lambda) = \lambda^2 - c\lambda + d, \qquad c \text{ and } d \text{ in } J,$$

then $a - b\sqrt{m}$ is also a zero of $m(\lambda)$ by the quadratic formula, and

$$m(\lambda) = (\lambda - a - b\sqrt{m})(\lambda - a + b\sqrt{m}).$$

Hence the rationals $2a$ and $a^2 - b^2m$ are integers,

$$2a = c \qquad \text{and} \qquad a^2 - b^2m = d.$$

Now we do a bit of squaring and manipulating to get

$$4a^2 = c^2 = 4b^2m + 4d$$

and

$$c^2 - 4d = 4b^2m.$$

Hence $4b^2m$ is in $J$, so that the square of the denominator of $2b$ is a factor of $m$. But $m$ is square-free, so we conclude that $2b$ is in $J$.

Denote $2b$ by $f$; then the last equation above can be rewritten as

$$4d = c^2 - mf^2.$$

This can be written as a congruence,

$$c^2 \equiv mf^2 \bmod 4.$$

*Case* 1. If $m \equiv 2$ or 3 modulo 4, then the congruence

$$c^2 \equiv mf^2 \bmod 4$$

is satisfied if and only if $c$ and $f$ are both even integers. Hence $a = c/2$ and $b = f/2$ are elements of $J$.

*Case* 2. If $m \equiv 1 \bmod 4$ the congruence

$$c^2 \equiv mf^2 \bmod 4$$

is satisfied in $J$ if and only if $c$ and $f$ are either both even or both odd. Therefore $a$ and $b$ are both either integers or halves of odd integers.

It is quite evident that $a + b\sqrt{m}$ is in $QD(m)$ when $a$ and $b$ are in $J$, so consider the case when $m \equiv 1 \bmod 4$ and $a$ and $b$ are halves of odd integers,

$$m = 1 + 4k, \quad 2a = 2r + 1, \quad 2b = 2s + 1, \qquad r, k, \text{ and } s \text{ in } J.$$

Then $2a = c$ is in $J$ and

$$a^2 - b^2m = r^2 + r + \tfrac{1}{4} - 4ks^2 - 4ks - k - s^2 - s - \tfrac{1}{4}$$

is also in $J$. Hence $a + b\sqrt{m}$ is in $QD(m)$.

*Example* 2. Show that $\frac{3}{2} - (7/2)\sqrt{-3}$ is an element of $QD(-3)$.
Form the polynomial

$$\lambda^2 - 3 + 39 = (\lambda - 3/2 + (7/2)\sqrt{-3})(\lambda - 3/2 - (7/2)\sqrt{-3}).$$

Since it is in $J[\lambda]$ we see that the element in question is in $QD(-3)$.

Thus far in working with an element $a + b\sqrt{m}$ of $QD(m)$ we have frequently used the element $a - b\sqrt{m}$ and the rational integer $a^2 - b^2m$. Since these elements seem to be important associates of $a + b\sqrt{m}$ we give them special names.

DEFINITION 9.3. If $x = a + b\sqrt{m}$, $a$ and $b$ in $R$, is an element of $QF(m)$, then

$$\bar{x} = a - b\sqrt{m}$$

is the *conjugate* of $x$ and

$$N(x) = a^2 - b^2m$$

is the *norm* of $x$.

The concept of conjugation in $QF(m)$ is identical with that of automorphism, as we know from the proof of Theorem 8.26.

THEOREM 9.5. *If $v$ and $w$ are elements of $QF(m)$, then*

(i) $N(vw) = N(v)N(w)$;
(ii) $N(v) = v\bar{v}$;
(iii) $\bar{\bar{v}} = v$.

To prove (i) we take

$$v = a + b\sqrt{m} \qquad \text{and} \qquad w = c + d\sqrt{m}.$$

Then

$$vw = (ac + bdm) + (ad + bc)\sqrt{m}$$

so that

$$N(vw) = (ac + bdm)^2 - (ad + bc)^2m.$$

This is readily verified to be equal to

$$N(v)N(w) = (a^2 - b^2m)(c^2 - d^2m).$$

The rest of the theorem is left as an exercise.

THEOREM 9.6. *If $x$ is in $QD(m)$, then $\bar{x}$ is in $QD(m)$ also, and $N(x)$ is in $J$.*

If $x = a + b\sqrt{m}$ is in $QD(m)$, then by the criterion furnished by Theorem 9.4 we can see immediately that $\bar{x} = a - b\sqrt{m}$ is in $QD(m)$. And the fact that $a^2 - b^2m = N(x)$ is in $J$ was verified at the end of the proof of Theorem 9.4.

Although we labeled $QD(m)$ as a domain we have not proved this to be the case. We do so by showing $QD(m)$ to be a subring of $QF(m)$ with an identity.

THEOREM 9.7. *$QD(m)$ is an integral domain.*

Let $a + b\sqrt{m}$ and $c + d\sqrt{m}$ be elements of $QD(m)$, $a$, $b$, $c$, and $d$ in $R$. Then consider

$$v = (a + b\sqrt{m}) + (c + d\sqrt{m}) = (a + c) + (b + d)\sqrt{m}$$

and

$$w = (a + b\sqrt{m})(c + d\sqrt{m}) = (ac + bdm) + (ad + bc)\sqrt{m}.$$

Now the elements $2a$, $2b$, $2c$, $2d$, $N(a + b\sqrt{m})$, and $N(c + d\sqrt{m})$ are all in $J$. Hence the polynomials

$$\begin{aligned}&(\lambda - v)(\lambda - \bar{v})\\&\quad = \lambda^2 - 2(a + c)\lambda + (a^2 - b^2m) + (c^2 - d^2m) + (2ac - 2bdm)\end{aligned}$$

and

$$(\lambda - w)(\lambda - \bar{w}) = \lambda^2 - 2(ac + bdm)\lambda + N(w)$$

have coefficients from $J$. (Note that

$$N(w) = N(a + b\sqrt{m})N(c + d\sqrt{m}).)$$

Since $v$ and $w$ are zeros of these monic quadratics from $J[\lambda]$ we conclude that $QD(m)$ is a subring of $QF(m)$. Since it obviously contains 1 we know that $QD(m)$ is an integral domain.

*Example* 3. Find some elements $x$ of $QD(2)$ such that $N(x) = 1$.

Since $2 \not\equiv 1 \bmod 4$ we know that $x$ is of the form $x = a + b\sqrt{2}$ with $a$ and $b$ in $J$. Then

$$N(x) = a^2 - 2b^2 = 1$$

when

$$\begin{aligned}x &= 1 \quad\text{or}\quad -1,\\x &= 3 + 2\sqrt{2}, \quad -3 + 2\sqrt{2}, \quad 3 - 2\sqrt{2}, \quad\text{or}\quad -3 - 2\sqrt{2},\\x &= 17 + 12\sqrt{2}, \quad -17 + 12\sqrt{2}, \quad\text{etc.}\end{aligned}$$

In fact if $N(a + b\sqrt{2}) = 1$, $a$ and $b$ in $J$, then

$$N((4b^2 + 1) + 2ab\sqrt{2}) = 1$$

also.

## Exercise 9.1

1. Find $m$ such that $QF(m)$ is determined by
   - (*a*) $m(\lambda) = \lambda^2 - \lambda - 1/2.$
   - (*b*) $m(\lambda) = 2\lambda^2 - 3\lambda + 4.$
   - (*c*) $m(\lambda) = \lambda^2 + \lambda + 17.$

**2.** For what values of $k$ does the quadratic $\lambda^2 + k\lambda - 7$ determine a $QF(m)$, $-17 < k < 20$?

**3.** Find three nonrational quadratic integers from each of the fields of Problem 1, and determine the monic quadratic polynomials of which they are zeros.

**4.** Compute the sums and products of the following quadratic integers and find their quadratic polynomials:

(*a*) $1 + \sqrt{-1}$ and $2 - \sqrt{-1}$.
(*b*) $1 + \sqrt{5}$ and $1/2 - (3/2)\sqrt{5}$.
(*c*) $1/2 + (1/2)\sqrt{-3}$ and $-1/2 + (7/2)\sqrt{-3}$.

**5.** Prove that $c^2 \equiv 2f^2 \bmod 4$ if and only if $c$ and $f$ are even in $J$.

**6.** Prove that $c^2 - 3f^2$ is divisible by 4 in $J$ if and only if $c$ and $f$ are even.

**7.** Show that conjugation is an automorphism of $QD(m)$.

**8.** What can you say about $m_1$ and $m_2$ if $QD(m_1)$ is isomorphic with $QD(m_2)$?

**9.** Determine the norms and conjugates of the elements in Problem 4.

**10.** Complete the proof of Theorem 9.4.

**11.** Show that $QD(2)$ contains infinitely many elements having norm 1.

**12.** Show that $QD(m)$ contains only finitely many elements of norm 1 if $m$ is negative.

**13.** Verify that $x$ in $QF(m)$ equals 0 if and only if $N(x) = 0$.

**14.** Prove that $x \neq 0$ in $QF(m)$ has $\bar{x}/N(x)$ as its multiplicative inverse.

**15.** Show that an element $x$ of $QD(m)$ has an inverse in $QD(m)$ if and only if $N(x) = 1$ or $-1$.

**16.** Show that each element of $QD(5)$ is expressible uniquely in the form $au + bv$, where $a$ and $b$ are in $J$, $u = 4 + \sqrt{5}$, and $v = (11/2) + (3/2)\sqrt{5}$.

**17.** Determine all of the subfields of $QF(m)$.

**18.** Let $v$ and $w$ be two elements of $QF(m)$. Show that $\overline{(vw)} = \bar{v}\bar{w}$.

**19.** If $x$ is in $QF(m)$ and $N(x)$ is in $J$, is $x$ in $QD(m)$?

## 9.2 Factorization in Quadratic Domains

The concept of factor of an integer leads to a classification of the elements of $QD(m)$ according to their factors. In this manner we extend the idea of the familiar classification of the rational integers to obtain a classification of the elements of $QD(m)$.

DEFINITION 9.4. Let $x$ and $w$ be nonzero elements of $QD(m)$.

(1) $x$ is a *factor* of $w$ if and only if $QD(m)$ contains an element $v$ such that $w = xv$. Then $w$ is a *multiple* of $x$.

(2) $x$ is a *unit* if and only if $x$ is a factor of 1.

(3) $w$ is a *prime* if and only if the equation $w = xv$ implies that exactly one of the two elements $x$ and $v$ is a unit.

(4) $w$ is a *composite* if and only if $w = xv$ where neither $x$ nor $v$ is a unit.

Now all discussion and work with this classification in $QD(m)$ hinges on the relationship with the norm. The norm provides a homomorphism of the multiplicative semigroup of $QD(m)$ into the multiplicative semigroup of $J$ and thereby enables us to use the properties of $J$ to study $QD(m)$.

THEOREM 9.8. *The element $x$ of $QD(m)$ is a unit if and only if $N(x) = 1$ or $-1$.*

If $xv = 1$ in $QD(m)$, then since

$$N(xv) = N(x)N(v) \qquad \text{and} \qquad N(1) = 1$$

we see that

$$N(x)N(v) = 1.$$

Since the norms of elements of $QD(m)$ are in $J$ this equation means that $N(x) = 1$ or $-1$.

Conversely, consider an element in $QF(m)$

$$a + b\sqrt{m}, \qquad a \text{ and } b \text{ in } R.$$

From

$$(a + b\sqrt{m})(a - b\sqrt{m}) = a^2 - b^2m = N(a + b\sqrt{m})$$

we see that, if $a + b\sqrt{m} \neq 0$, then

$$(a + b\sqrt{m})^{-1} = (a - b\sqrt{m})(1/N(a + b\sqrt{m})).$$

Now if $a + b\sqrt{m}$ is in $QD(m)$ and $N(a + b\sqrt{m}) = 1$ or $-1$, then it is obvious that

$$(a + b\sqrt{m})^{-1} = a - b\sqrt{m} \qquad \text{or} \qquad -a + b\sqrt{m}$$

is in $QD(m)$ also. Hence an element $x$ of $QD(m)$ is a unit if $N(x) = 1$ or $-1$.

In developing the factorization theorems for the positive rational integers we used the very important fact that, if

$$a = bc$$

and $b$ and $c$ are greater than 1, then

$$b < a \qquad \text{and} \qquad c < a.$$

This enabled us to use induction arguments in proving theorems about factorization in $J$. Fortunately we have a similar result for the elements of $QD(m)$.

THEOREM 9.9. *If $w = xv$ in $QD(m)$ and neither $x$ nor $v$ is a unit, then*

$$|N(x)| < |N(w)|.$$

From

$$N(w) = N(xv) = N(x)N(v)$$

and the fact that neither $N(x)$ nor $N(v)$ is 1 in absolute value, we conclude that the absolute value of $N(x)$ (and of $N(v)$ also) is less than the absolute value of $N(w)$.

*Example* 1. Show that in $QD(-1)$ the element $1 + i$ is a prime but 2 is not a prime. (Here $i$ denotes $\sqrt{-1}$.)

The norm of $1 + i$ is $1^2 - (-1)1^2 = 2$. Since the only rational integral factors of 2 have absolute values 1 or 2 we conclude from Theorem 9.8 that $1 + i$ (and $1 - i$) are primes. And since

$$(1 + i)(1 - i) = 2$$

we see that 2 is a composite in $QD(-1)$. Note that

$$N(2) = (2 + 0i)(2 - 0i) = 4,$$

so that

$$N(2) = 4 = 2(2) = N(1 + i)N(1 - i).$$

This example shows that the classification of elements in $QD(m)$ should not be considered as an extension of the classification in $J$ since the primes in $J$ are not necessarily primes in $QD(m)$. In fact the theory of quadratic integers (and other more general integers) was developed partially as an aid to the study of rational integers through the introduction of *additional* decompositions of the rational integers.

*Example* 2. The elements 3, $2 + \sqrt{-5}$, and $2 - \sqrt{-5}$ are primes of $QD(-5)$.

The argument is somewhat like the one used in Example 1. Each of these three quadratic integers has norm 9, so, if we can show that no element of $QD(-5)$ has norm 3, then from Theorems 9.5 and 9.8 we can conclude that the numbers are primes. Suppose $a + b\sqrt{-5}$ is an element of $QD(-5)$ with norm 3. Then $a$ and $b$ are in $J$ (since $-5 \equiv 3 \bmod 4$) and

$$N(a + b\sqrt{-5}) = a^2 + 5b^2 = 3.$$

Clearly there are no elements in $J$ with this property, so we see that the elements 3, $2 + \sqrt{-5}$, and $2 - \sqrt{-5}$ are primes of $QD(-5)$.

*Example* 3. Show that the element 9 of $QD(-5)$ can be written as a product of primes in two different ways.

From Example 2 we know that

$$9 = (3)(3) = (2 + \sqrt{-5})(2 - \sqrt{-5}),$$

yielding two different factorizations into primes. Now when we say that the two primes 3 and $2 + \sqrt{-5}$ are different we mean that not only are they unequal but neither is a unit times the other.

DEFINITION 9.5. Two elements $x$ and $v$ of $QD(m)$ are *associates* if $QD(m)$ contains a unit $u$ such that $x = uv$.

In $QD(-1)$ the primes $1 + i$ and $-1 + i = i(1 + i)$ are associates since $N(i) = 1$.

In $QD(-5)$ the only units are 1 and $-1$ since

$$N(a + b\sqrt{-5}) = a^2 + 5b^2 = 1 \quad \text{or} \quad -1$$

implies that $a = 1$ or $-1$ and $b = 0$. Hence the primes 3, $2 + \sqrt{-5}$, and $2 - \sqrt{-5}$ are not only different but neither is an associate of either of the others.

Even though this example shows that a factorization into primes may not be unique, we can use Theorem 9.9 and the properties of the rational integers to prove that each quadratic composite is expressible as a product of primes in at least *one* way.

THEOREM 9.10. *A composite of $QD(m)$ can be expressed as the product of a finite collection of primes of $QD(m)$.*

The proof is quite elementary. If $w$ is a composite in $QD(m)$, then

$$w = xv, \qquad x \text{ and } v \text{ not units.}$$

Therefore

$$|N(w)| > |N(x)| > 1$$

and

$$|N(w)| > |N(v)| > 1,$$

so either $x$ and/or $v$ are primes or composites of smaller absolute norm than that of $w$. Then the factorizations of $x$ and $v$ (which follow by the induction hypothesis) provide a factorization for $w$ as the product of a finite collection of primes.

The domain $QD(-5)$ provides an example of a quadratic domain in which factorization into primes is *not unique*. The following example shows that $QD(-5)$ fails to possess another property we proved for $J$.

*Example* 4. Show that not every ideal of $QD(-5)$ is principal.

We recall that an ideal $T$ of a ring $S$ is *principal* if and only if $T$ contains an element $x$ such that every element of $T$ is expressible as $xs$ or $sx$ for some $s$ in $S$.

Now consider the set $W$ of all elements of $QD(-5)$ of the form

$$3x + (2 + \sqrt{-5})v,$$

for some $x$ and $v$ in $QD(-5)$. It is easy to show that $W$ is an ideal of the domain $QD(-5)$, so suppose $W$ is a principal ideal $(w)$. Since

$$3 = 3 \cdot 1 + (2 + \sqrt{-5})0$$

and

$$2 + \sqrt{-5} = 3 \cdot 0 + (2 + \sqrt{-5})1$$

are in $W$ we see that $w$ must be a common factor of these two primes. Hence $w$ is either 1 or $-1$, and since $w$ is in $W$ we have in either case elements $x$ and $v$ in $QD(-5)$ such that

$$1 = 3x + (2 + \sqrt{-5})v.$$

Multiplying this equation by $2 - \sqrt{-5}$ yields

$$2 - \sqrt{-5} = 3x(2 - \sqrt{-5}) + 9v = 3((2 - \sqrt{-5})x + 3v)$$

which means that 3 is a factor of $2 - \sqrt{-5}$. But $2 - \sqrt{-5}$ has exactly four distinct factors:

$$-1, 1, 2 - \sqrt{-5}, \quad \text{and} \quad -2 + \sqrt{-5}.$$

Hence the prime 3 is not a factor of $2 - \sqrt{-5}$, and the contradiction shows that $W$ is not principal.

This example suggests that the factorization of the elements in $QD(m)$ is closely associated with the nature of the ideals of $QD(m)$, and we will prove that the factorization into primes in $QD(m)$ is unique up to units if and only if the ideals of $QD(m)$ are principal. Moreover we shall investigate a semigroup $K(m)$ whose elements are the ideals of $QD(m)$ and develop a unique factorization theorem for $K(m)$. Then the structure of $K(m)$ is related to the structure of $QD(m)$.

## Exercise 9.2

**1.** If $x$ and $v$ are elements of $QD(m)$ such that $N(x)$ is a factor of $N(v)$, does this mean that $x$ is a factor of $v$? Consider 3 and $2 + \sqrt{-5}$ in $QD(-5)$.

**2.** Find all of the units of $QD(-1)$, $QD(-2)$, and $QD(-3)$. (Note that $-3 \equiv 1 \bmod 4$.)

**3.** Show that $x \neq 0$ in $QD(m)$ has positive norm if $m$ is negative.

**4.** Find three nonrational primes in $QD(m)$, and explain why they are primes, when (*a*) $m = 2$; (*b*) $m = -2$; (*c*) $m = 5$.

(*Hint:* Check elements whose norms are primes or squares of primes in $J$.)

**5.** Show that $1 + 2\sqrt{-5}$, $1 - 2\sqrt{-5}$, $4 + \sqrt{-5}$, and $4 - \sqrt{-5}$ are primes in $QD(-5)$. Factor 21 in this domain, in every possible way.

**6.** Show that the set $\{7x + (4 + \sqrt{-5})v$: all $x$ and $v$ in $QD(-5)\}$ is a nonprincipal ideal of $QD(-5)$.

**7.** Show that $1 + \sqrt{-14}$ is a prime in $QD(-14)$. Find all prime factorizations of 15 in this domain, after first finding all the units.

**8.** Show that 7 is a prime in $QD(-1)$, and find all of its associates. Find two other rational primes which are primes in $QD(-1)$.

**9.** Determine a rational prime which is not a prime in $QD(m)$: (*a*) When $m = 2$; (*b*) when $m = -2$; (*c*) when $m = -7$; (*d*) when $m = 11$.

**10.** Are there infinitely many nonassociated primes in $QD(m)$? (Consider the norms.)

**11.** Define the relation E on $QD(m)$ by $x\mathrm{E}v$ if and only if $x$ is an associate of $v$. Show that E is an equivalence relation on $QD(m)$. Describe the corresponding partition of $QD(-1)$; of $QD(2)$.

**12.** Show that $(\frac{1}{2}) + (1/2)\sqrt{5}$ is a unit of $QD(5)$ and that $5 + 2\sqrt{5}$ is a prime.

**13.** How many units has $QD(5)$?

**14.** Factor 65 into primes in $QD(-1)$. How many nonassociated such factorings are there?

**15.** Show that the quotient ring $QD(-5)/W$, where $W$ is the ideal of Example 4, is isomorphic with $J/(3)$. (Show that $W$ has three distinct cosets, $0 + W$, $1 + W$, and $2 + W$.)

**16.** Prove that a unit $u$ of $QD(m)$ is a factor of every element of the domain.

## 9.3 Gaussian Integers

The domain $QD(-1)$ is the *Gaussian* domain, or the domain of *Gaussian integers*. (This quadratic domain was studied by Gauss in his number theoretic investigations.) We shall see that $QD(-1)$ is a unique factorization domain and that all of the ideals of this domain are principal. The development of these properties depends upon the following Divisor Theorem.

THEOREM 9.11. *If $x$ and $v$ are elements of $QD(-1)$ and $v \neq 0$, then $QD(-1)$ contains elements $q$ and $r$ such that*

$$x = qv + r \qquad \text{with } N(r) < N(v).$$

We drop into the field $QF(-1)$ and pick out the multiplicative inverse $v^{-1}$ of $v$. Then consider the product $xv^{-1}$; it is an element of $QF(-1)$ and so is of the form

$$xv^{-1} = m + n\sqrt{-1} = m + ni$$

where $m$ and $n$ are in $R$. Now in $R$ the fractions $m$ and $n$ are expressible as

$$m = m_1 + r_1 \qquad \text{and} \qquad n = n_1 + r_2$$

where $m_1$ and $n_1$ are in $J$ and $r_1$ and $r_2$ are fractions less than or equal to $\frac{1}{2}$ in absolute value. (This of course is a consequence of the Divisor Theorem for $J$.) Thus we have the equation

$$xv^{-1} = (m_1 + n_1 i) + (r_1 + r_2 i),$$

and multiplying by $v$ yields

$$x = qv + r$$

where

$$q = m_1 + n_1 i$$

and

$$r = v(r_1 + r_2 i).$$

Since $x$, $q$, and $v$ are in $QD(-1)$ we see that this equation implies that $r$ is in $QD(-1)$ also. (Everything we have done so far can be done in any $QD(m)$.)

Now we wish to show that $N(r) < N(v)$. To do this we consider $N(r_1 + r_2 i)$:

$$N(r_1 + r_2 i) = r_1^2 - mr_2^2 = r_1^2 + r_2^2,$$

and this sum is no larger than 1/2 since $r_1^2$ and $r_2^2$ are bound by 1/4. Thus

$$N(r) = N(v)N(r_1 + r_2 i) \leqslant N(v)(\tfrac{1}{2}) < N(v),$$

and the theorem is proved.

*Corollary* 9.11.1. The quotient $q$ and the remainder $r$ are not in general unique.

Take $x = 5 + 7i$ and $v = 4 + 4i$. Then we can verify easily that

$$x = (1)v + (1 + 3i) = (2)v + (-3 - i).$$

Since

$$N(v) = 32$$

and

$$N(1 + 3i) = N(-3 - i) = 10,$$

we see there are two different pairs of $q$ and $r$ which satisfy the requirements.

Nevertheless the proof of the theorem spells out a particular way for constructing one quotient and one remainder. Thus we have established a method of long division in $QD(-1)$.

*Example* 1. Find the quotient and remainder for $x = 15i$ and $v = -3 + 2i$.

The inverse of $v$ is obtained by using the norm and conjugate:

$$v^{-1} = \bar{v}/N(v) = (1/13)(-3 - 2i).$$

Then

$$xv^{-1} = (30/13) - (45/13)i,$$

and reducing the rationals yields

$$xv^{-1} = (2 - 3i) + ((4/13) - (6/13)i).$$

Multiplying by $v$ yields

$$x = (2 - 3i)v + 2i$$

and we see that

$$N(2i) = 4 < N(v) = 13.$$

*Example* 2. Find a second $q$ and $r$ for the $x$ and $v$ of Example 1.

$$\begin{aligned} x &= (2 - 3i)v + 2i + v - v \\ &= (3 - 3i)v + 3, \end{aligned}$$

and since $N(3) = 9 < 13$, we see that $q = 3 - 3i$ and $r = 3$ satisfy the theorem.

DEFINITION 9.6. Let $x$ and $v$ be nonzero elements of $QD(m)$. If $w$ is an integer such that (1) $w$ is a factor of $x$ and a factor of $v$ (i.e., a *common factor* of $x$ and $v$), and (2) $w$ is a multiple of every common factor of $x$ and $v$ in $QD(m)$, then $w$ is a *greatest common factor* (G.C.F.) of $x$ and $v$.

From our study of factorization in $J$ and in $F[\lambda]$ we know that an important feature for a G.C.F. to have is linear expressibility. We can show that a G.C.F. $w$ exists for each pair of elements $x$ and $v$ in $QD(-1)$ and that the domain contains elements $s$ and $t$ such that

$$w = xs + vt.$$

This comes as a corollary of the following result on ideals of the Gaussian domain.

THEOREM 9.12. *Each ideal of the Gaussian domain is principal.*

Let $T$ be a nontrivial ideal of $QD(-1)$. Then $T$ contains a nonzero element and its norm is a positive integer. Thus the set $N(T)$ of the norms of all nonzero elements of $T$ is a nonempty set of positive elements of $J$. Choose $w$ as an element of $T$ whose norm is a minimal element of $N(T)$. We shall use the Divisor Theorem to show that every element $x$ of $T$ is a multiple of $w$.

Since $w \neq 0$ we can apply Theorem 9.11 to $w$ and $x$, obtaining

$$x = qw + r \qquad \text{with } N(r) < N(w).$$

From

$$r = x - qw$$

and the fact that $x$ and $w$ (hence $qw$) are in $T$ we see that $r$ is in $T$. If $r$ were different from zero we would have an element of $T$ whose norm was positive but less than $N(w)$, contradicting the choice of $w$. Hence we conclude that $r = 0$ and

$$x = qw.$$

Thus $T$ is the principal ideal generated by $w$,

$$T = (w).$$

*Corollary* 9.12.1. Two nonzero elements $x$ and $v$ of $QD(-1)$ possess a G.C.F. $w$ which is expressible in the linear form

$$w = xs + vt$$

for some $s$ and $t$ in $QD(-1)$.

Form the set $T = \{xs + vt\colon s \text{ and } t \text{ in } QD(-1)\}$. As we know, this is an ideal of $QD(-1)$ so that by the theorem $T = (w)$. Now we will show that $w$ is a G.C.F. of $x$ and $v$. Since

$$x = x(1) + v(0)$$

and

$$v = x(0) + v(1)$$

we know from the theorem above that $w$ is a common factor of $x$ and $v$.

On the other hand, since

$$w = xs + vt$$

for some $s$ and $t$ in $QD(-1)$, we see from the Associative and Distributive Laws that a common factor of $x$ and $v$ is a factor of $w$. Hence $w$ is a G.C.F. of $x$ and $v$ and we write

$$(w) = (x, v),$$

which means that the ideal generated by $x$ and $v$ is the principal ideal $(w)$.

*Corollary* 9.12.2. The G.C.F. of $x$ and $v$ is unique up to a unit in $QD(-1)$.

Suppose $w$ and $w_1$ are both G.C.F.'s of $x$ and $v$. Then $w$ is a factor of $w_1$ and $w_1$ is a factor of $w$:

$$w_1 = aw \qquad \text{and} \qquad w = bw_1.$$

Therefore a little substitution yields

$$w = abw$$

and taking norms we have

$$N(w) = N(a)N(b)N(w).$$

Since $w \neq 0$ this enables us to conclude that

$$N(a)N(b) = 1$$

and that $a$ and $b$ are units of $QD(-1)$. Thus $w$ is unique up to a unit.

Using exactly the same arguments as we used in working with $J$ and $F[\lambda]$ we can prove:

(1) If $x$, $b$, and $c$ are nonzero elements of $QD(-1)$, if $x$ is a factor of $bc$ and if the G.C.F. of $x$ and $b$ is 1 (or any unit), then $x$ is a factor of $c$.

(2) If the prime $p$ of $QD(-1)$ is a factor of the product $q_1q_2\cdots q_n$, where each $q_i$ is a prime in $QD(-1)$, then $p$ equals one of the $q_i$ multiplied by the appropriate unit.

The proof of the first statement follows from the equation

$$c = xsc + btc$$

which comes from

$$1 = xs + bt,$$

a consequence of the fact that $1 = (x, b)$. The second statement is the key statement proved in the proof of unique factorization.

THEOREM 9.13. *A factorization of a composite Gaussian integer $x$ as a product of a finite set of primes in $QD(-1)$ is unique up to a unit.*

The proof is by induction on $N(x)$, so suppose the composites with lower norm are uniquely factorable into primes. Consider

$$x = p_1 p_2 \cdots p_r = q_1 q_2 \cdots q_n$$

where the $p$'s and $q$'s are primes. Then $p_1$ is a factor of

$$q_1(q_2 \cdots q_n),$$

and, since $p_1$ is a prime, either $p_1$ is a factor of $q_1$ or $p_1$ is a factor of $q_2 \cdots q_n$. Since

$$N(q_2 \cdots q_n) = N(x)/N(q_1) < N(x)$$

we see that, if $p_1$ is a factor of $q_2 \cdots q_n$, then $p_1$ is a unit times one of the $q_i$. Thus in either case statement (2) above is proved.

Now we cancel (remember that $QD(-1)$ is a domain) $p_1$ from both sides of

$$p_1 p_2 \cdots p_r = q_1 q_2 \cdots q_n,$$

obtaining a Gaussian integer with norm less that $N(x)$. Applying the induction hypothesis we see that $r - 1 = n - 1$ and $p_2, \cdots, p_r$ are just $q$'s relabeled and multiplied by appropriate units. In this manner the theorem is proved by mathematical induction.

From this result and a theorem on sums of squares in $J$ (Chapter 4) we can describe the Gaussian primes. First we show that they are closely tied up with the rational primes.

THEOREM 9.14. *A Gaussian prime is a factor of a rational prime.*

Let $x$ be a Gaussian prime. Then $x$ is a factor of some positive elements of $J$ since

$$N(x) = x\bar{x}$$

is a positive rational integer. By the Well-Ordering Theorem there is a minimal positive element $n$ of $J$ which is a multiple (in $QD(-1)$) of $x$. Then we see from the unique factorization in the Gaussian domain that $n$ is a rational prime. For suppose

$$n = n_1 n_2, \qquad 1 < n_1 \leqslant n_2 < n \text{ in } J;$$

since $n$, $n_1$, and $n_2$ are in $QD(-1)$ and since $x$ is a Gaussian prime factor of $n$ we see that $x$ is a factor of either $n_1$ or $n_2$. But this contradicts the choice of $n$. Hence $n$ is a rational prime.

This means that the study of Gaussian primes is an extension of the study of rational primes. So let us look at the rational primes as Gaussian integers.

THEOREM 9.15. *Let $p$ be a rational prime:*

(*a*) *If $p \equiv 3 \bmod 4$, then $p$ is a Gaussian prime.*

(*b*) *If $p \equiv 1 \bmod 4$, then $p$ is the product of a conjugate pair of Gaussian primes.*

(*c*) *If $p = 2$, then $(1 + i)(1 - i) = i(1 - i)^2$ are the factorizations into primes.*

If $x$ is a Gaussian prime factor of $p$, then

$$p = xv$$

for some $v$ in $QD(-1)$. Therefore

$$p^2 = N(p) = N(x)N(v).$$

Since the only factors of $p^2$ in $J$ which are larger than 1 are $p$ and $p^2$, we have two cases: $N(x) = p$ and $N(x) = p^2$.

*Case* 1. If $N(x) = p^2$, then $N(v) = 1$ so that $v$ is a unit. Therefore $p$ is a prime in $QD(-1)$.

*Case* 2. If $N(x) = p$, we write

$$x = m + ni, \qquad m \text{ and } n \text{ in } J,$$

so that

$$N(x) = p = (m + ni)(m - ni) = m^2 + n^2.$$

From our work in Chapter 4 on sums of squares we know that an odd prime is expressible as a sum of squares in $J$ if and only if it is congruent with 1 modulo 4. Thus $N(x) = p$ and $p$ odd imply that

$$p \equiv 1 \bmod 4.$$

On the other hand, if

$$p \equiv 1 \bmod 4,$$

then by our work on sums of squares,

$$p = m^2 + n^2, \qquad m \text{ and } n \text{ in } J,$$

so that $p$ factors in $QD(-1)$ as

$$p = (m + ni)(m - ni).$$

Thus parts (*a*) and (*b*) of the theorem are proved. Part (*c*) is left for the student to verify.

*Example* 3. List five nonrational Gaussian primes.

From the rational primes 5, 13, and 17 we obtain the Gaussian primes $2 + i$, $2 - i$, $3 + 2i$, $3 - 2i$, $4 + i$, and $4 - i$.

We note that a Gaussian prime $x$ can only divide one prime $p$ from $J$ since $N(x)$ is a factor of $p^2$.

## Exercise 9.3

**1.** For $x = 23 - 2i$ and $v = 13i$ find $q$ and $r$ in $QD(-1)$ such that $x = qv + r$ with $N(r) < N(v)$. Find another such pair.

**2.** Show that $q = 1 + 2i$ and $r = 1 + i$ serve as quotient and remainder when $x = -1 + 5i$ and $v = 2$. Now divide $r$ into $v$. Compare this with the Euclidean algorithm in $J$. Find a G.C.F. of $-1 + 5i$ and 2.

**3.** How many different G.C.F.'s can two Gaussian integers have? Why?

**4.** Find a G.C.F. $w$ of $x = 1 - 18i$ and $v = 5i$ by the Euclidean algorithm. Show that $N(w)$ is *not* the G.C.F. of $N(x)$ and $N(v)$ in $J$. Express $w$ in the form $w = xs + vt$.

**5.** Factor 130 completely in $QD(-1)$.

**6.** Find all Gaussian primes $x$ with $N(x) < 30$.

**7.** Prove that the set $T$ in the proof of Corollary 9.12.1 is an ideal.

**8.** Show $3 + 2i$, $-3 - 2i$, $-2 + 3i$, $2 - 3i$, $3 - 2i$, $-3 + 2i$, $-2 - 3i$, and $2 + 3i$ are all factors of 13 in $QD(-1)$. How are these factors related?

**9.** Factor $3 - i$, $1 + 7i$, and $1 - 5i$ in $QD(-1)$.

**10.** The method used to prove the Divisor Theorem in $QD(-1)$ can also be used to prove such a theorem for $QD(m)$ when $m = -2$, 2, or 3. Prove this statement. What can you conclude about factorization in those domains?

**11.** By altering slightly the proof of Theorem 9.11, it is possible to prove the Divisor Theorem for certain other domains. Show that $QD(-3)$ is a unique factorization domain. (Note that $-3 \equiv 1 \bmod 4$.)

**12.** Show that, if $x$ is a prime in $QD(m)$ and if factorization into primes is unique in $QD(m)$, then $x$ is a factor of exactly one rational prime.

**13.** Verify that $\sqrt{3}$ and $\sqrt{3} - 1$ are primes in the domain $QD(3)$. Show also that $\sqrt{3} + 1$ and $\sqrt{3} - 1$ are associates.

**14.** Comment on the fact that in $QD(-3)$ the integer 13 factors as

$$13 = (7/2 + (1/2)\sqrt{-3})(7/2 - (1/2)\sqrt{-3})$$

and

$$13 = (1 + 2\sqrt{-3})(1 - 2\sqrt{-3}).$$

**15.** Prove that, if every ideal of the domain $QD(m)$ is principal, then each pair of nonzero elements $x$ and $v$ has a G.C.F. $w$ such that $w = xs + vt$ for some $s$ and $t$ in $QD(m)$. Sketch a development of the unique factorization property in this domain.

**16.** Factor the integers $-5$, $2 - \sqrt{2}$, and $3 + 9\sqrt{2}$ in $QD(2)$.

**17.** In $QD(-5)$ the integer $w = 1$ is a G.C.F. of $x = 3$ and $v = 2 + \sqrt{-5}$. Show that $w$ cannot be expressed in the form

$$w = xs + vt, \qquad s \text{ and } t \text{ in } QD(-5).$$

## 9.4 Ideals and Integral Bases

Our discoveries about the differences between the ideals of $QD(-5)$ and those of $QD(-1)$ suggest that an investigation of the ideals of quadratic domains might reveal characterizing features of the domain with the unique factorization property. Such an investigation requires a better understanding of the elements in an ideal, and to obtain this information we develop the idea of integral basis or $J$-basis.

DEFINITION 9.7. The elements $u$ and $v$ of the ideal $T$ of $QD(m)$ form a *$J$-basis* for $T$ if and only if each element of $T$ is expressible uniquely in the form

$$hu + nv, \qquad h \text{ and } n \text{ in } J.$$

Now we know that the domain $QD(m)$ has a $J$-basis if $m \not\equiv 1 \bmod 4$. Other than that our information on $J$-bases is rather slight. So we show first that every quadratic domain has a $J$-basis.

THEOREM 9.16. *The integers* 1 *and* $\theta$ *form a $J$-basis for* $QD(m)$ *where* $\theta = \sqrt{m}$, *when* $m \not\equiv 1 \bmod 4$, *and* $\theta = (1/2) + (1/2)\sqrt{m}$, *when* $m \equiv 1 \bmod 4$.

To prove this we need only to handle the case $m \equiv 1 \bmod 4$. Such a domain has two classes of elements: the class of elements of the form $a + b\sqrt{m}$, where $a$ and $b$ are in $J$, and the class of elements of the form $c + d\sqrt{m}$, where $c$ and $d$ are halves of odd integers of $J$. Now

$$\begin{aligned} a + b\sqrt{m} &= (a - b) + (2b)\left((\tfrac{1}{2}) + (\tfrac{1}{2})\sqrt{m}\right) \\ &= (a - b)1 + (2b)\theta, \end{aligned}$$

so that an element of the first class can be expressed in the form

$$h1 + n\theta \qquad \text{with } h \text{ and } n \text{ in } J.$$

So consider an element $c + d\sqrt{m}$ from the second class. Since $c$ and $d$ are odd we can write

$$c = 2g + 1 \qquad \text{and} \qquad d = 2h + 1, \qquad g \text{ and } h \text{ in } J,$$

so that

$$\begin{aligned} c + d\sqrt{m} &= (g - h) + (2h + 1)\left((1/2) + (1/2)\sqrt{m}\right) \\ &= (g - h)1 + (2h + 1)\theta. \end{aligned}$$

Hence every element of $QD(m)$, $m \equiv 1 \bmod 4$, is expressible in the form

$$h1 + n\theta, \qquad h \text{ and } n \text{ in } J.$$

To show that such expressions are unique we consider

$$h1 + n\theta = r1 + s\theta, \qquad h, n, r, s \text{ in } J.$$

Then

$$h - r = (s - n)\theta = (s - n)/2 + \left((s - n)/2\right)\sqrt{m}.$$

Since

$$a + b\sqrt{m} = c + d\sqrt{m}, \qquad a, b, c, \text{ and } d \text{ in } R,$$

when and only when $a = c$ and $b = d$, the equation

$$2(h - n) + 0\sqrt{m} = (s - n) + (s - n)\sqrt{m}$$

implies that

$$2(h - r) = s - n$$

and

$$0 = s - n.$$

Hence $s = n$ and $h = r$, and the expressions $h1 + n\theta = h + n\theta$ for the elements of $QD(m)$ are unique.

*Example* 1. Write $1 + \sqrt{5}$ and $(3/2) + (7/2)\sqrt{5}$ in terms of 1 and $\theta$. Using the method in the proof we have

$$1 - \sqrt{5} = 2 - 2\theta = 1 - (-1) + 2(-1)\theta,$$

and

$$(3/2) + (7/2)\sqrt{5} = (2g + 1)/2 + ((2h + 1)/2)\sqrt{5}$$

with $g = 1$ and $h = 3$, so that

$$(3/2) + (7/2)\sqrt{5} = -2 + 7\theta.$$

In terms of this $J$-basis for $QD(m)$ we can describe a very useful $J$-basis, called the *minimal basis*, for a nontrivial ideal $T$ of $QD(m)$.

THEOREM 9.17. *A nontrivial ideal $T$ of $QD(m)$ has a $J$-basis $u$ and $v$ where*

$$u = rs \qquad \text{and} \qquad v = r(t + \theta)$$

*with $r$ and $s$ positive elements of $J$ and $t$ a rational integer, $0 \leqslant t < s$, such that*

$$t^2 + t \equiv (m - 1)/4 \bmod s \qquad \text{if } m \equiv 1 \bmod 4$$

*and*

$$t^2 \equiv m \bmod s \text{ otherwise.}$$

First we select the rational integer $u$ as the least positive rational integer in $T$. Since $T \neq (0)$ it is obvious that $T$ contains positive rational integers. Then we show in the usual way that $u$ is a factor of every rational integer $n$ in $T$. By the Divisor Theorem for $J$ we have

$$n = qu + r, \qquad 0 \leqslant r < u,$$

and since

$$r = n - qu$$

is in $T$, the minimality of $u$ implies that $r = 0$. Thus

$$n = qu.$$

To select $v$ we consider all of the elements of $T$ reduced relative to $u$. That is, if $a + b\theta$ is an element of $T$ with $a$ and $b$ in $J$, then we reduce $a$ and $b$ modulo $u$,

$$a \equiv c \bmod u, \qquad 0 \leqslant c < u,$$

and

$$b \equiv d \bmod u, \qquad 0 \leqslant d < u,$$

and consider the element $c + d\theta$. This is certainly a permissible reduction since all multiples of $u$ are in $T$. There are two situations to consider.

(1) If all elements of $T$ reduce to zero modulo $u$, then we have

$$a + b\theta = gu + hu\theta, \qquad g \text{ and } h \text{ in } J,$$

for every element $a + b\theta$ in $T$. Thus we can take

$$v = u\theta, \quad r = u, \quad s = 1, \quad \text{and } t = 0,$$

and all of the requirements of the theorem are met.

(2) If not all of the elements of $T$ reduce to zero modulo $u$, then there exists an element

$$v = h + r\theta$$

in $T$ with $0 \leqslant h < u$, $0 < r < u$, and $r$ minimal among all the positive rational coefficients of $\theta$ among the elements of $T$. (Note that $r$ is selected the same way in both cases.) Thus $T$ cannot contain another element

$$a + b\theta, \qquad a \text{ and } b \text{ in } J,$$

with $0 < b < r$, for subtracting this element from $v$ would yield an element contradicting the choice of $u$.

Now we prove that $r$ is a factor of $u$. By the Divisor Theorem for $J$ we can write

$$u = rs + k, \qquad 0 \leqslant k < r.$$

Then

$$u\theta = rs\theta + k\theta,$$
$$sv = hs + rs\theta,$$

and

$$u\theta - sv = -hs + k\theta$$

are elements of $T$. Since $h$, $s$, and $k$ are in $J$, and since $0 \leqslant k < r$, we must conclude from the minimality of $r$ that

$$k = 0.$$

Hence

$$u = rs,$$

and $s$ is certainly positive since $u$ and $r$ are positive.

Essentially the same argument is used to prove that $r$ is a factor of $h$, although here we must distinguish between the two different expressions for $\theta$.

*Case* 1. Suppose $m \equiv 1 \bmod 4$ and

$$\theta = 1/2 + (1/2)\sqrt{m}.$$

Multiplying $v$ by $\theta$ yields the element

$$v\theta = h\theta + r\theta^2 = (h + r)\theta + r(m - 1)/4$$

since

$$\theta^2 = (1/4)(1 + \sqrt{m})^2 = (1/4)(m - 1) + \theta.$$

In $J$ we write

$$h = tr + n, \qquad 0 \leqslant n < r,$$

so that the element $v\theta$ of $T$ can be written as

$$v\theta = r(t + 1)\theta + n\theta + r(m - 1)/4.$$

Since the element

$$(t + 1)v = h(t + 1) + r(t + 1)\theta$$

is in $T$ also, then we have in $T$ the difference

$$v\theta - v(t + 1) = \big(r(m - 1)/4 - h(t + 1)\big) + n\theta.$$

Because of the minimality of $r$ this equation means that

$$n = 0 \qquad \text{and} \qquad h = tr.$$

We also conclude from this last equation that

$$r(m - 1)/4 - h(t + 1) = r(m - 1)/4 - rt^2 - rt$$

is a rational element of $T$. Hence it is a multiple of $u = rs$ in $J$. Therefore

$$rt^2 + rt \equiv r(m - 1)/4 \bmod rs$$

or

$$t^2 + t \equiv (m - 1)/4 \bmod s.$$

*Case* 2. If $m \not\equiv 1 \bmod 4$, then

$$v\theta = h\theta + mr$$

since

$$\theta^2 = m.$$

From

$$h = tr + n, \qquad 0 \leqslant n < r,$$

in $J$ we get

$$v\theta = tr\theta + n\theta + rm,$$

and subtracting

$$vt = ht + tr\theta$$

yields

$$v\theta - vt = rm - ht + n\theta,$$

an element of $T$. The minimality of $r$ implies that $n = 0$ as above so that

$$h = tr.$$

Then

$$v\theta - vt = rm - rt^2$$

is a rational element of $T$. Hence

$$rm \equiv rt^2 \bmod rs$$

and

$$m \equiv t^2 \bmod s.$$

Before completing the proof (we still have to show that the elements $u$ and $v$ form a $J$-basis for $T$) let us look at an example which illustrates the above.

*Example* 2. Let $T$ be the ideal $\{(5 + 7\theta)x + (8 - 5\theta)w\colon x \text{ and } w \text{ in } QD(-5)\}$, and find the minimal basis for $T$.

Taking $x = a + b\theta$ and $w = c + d\theta$ we obtain the following expression for a typical element $x$ of $T$:

$$x = (5a - 35b + 8c + 25d) + (7a + 5b + 8d - 5c)\theta$$

This element is in $J$ if and only if

$$7a + 5b + 8d - 5c = 0,$$

and from this equation we know that

$$c = (1/5)(7a + 5b + 8d)$$

*and* that

$$7a + 8d \equiv 0 \text{ modulo } 5.$$

Now

$$7a + 8d \equiv 2a - 2d \bmod 5,$$

and $2(a - d)$ is a multiple of 5 if and only if $a - d = 5k$ in $J$. Applying this information to $x$ in $J$ yields

$$x = 5a - 35b + (8/5)(7a + 5b + 8d) + 25d$$

or

$$x = 81a/5 - 27b + 189d/5$$

or

$$x = 81(d + 5k)/5 - 27b + 189d/5$$

or

$$x = 54d + 81k - 27b.$$

Thus $x$ in $J$ is a multiple of 27, and 27 is in $T$ as we see by setting

$$a = d = 0, \quad b = -1, \quad \text{and} \quad c = -1.$$

The smallest positive coefficient of $\theta$ is clearly 1, which is obtained by taking

$$a = -1, \quad b = c = 0, \quad \text{and} \quad d = 1.$$

Thus we have

$$u = 27 \quad \text{and} \quad v = 20 + \theta,$$

so that

$$r = 1, \quad s = 27, \quad \text{and} \quad t = 20.$$

Moreover,

$$(20)^2 = 400 \equiv -5 \bmod 27$$

since

$$405 = 27(15).$$

Now to complete the proof of the theorem. We must show that, if $a + b\theta$, $a$ and $b$ in $J$, is an element of $T$, then there exists a unique pair of rational integers $c$ and $d$ such that

$$a + b\theta = cu + dv.$$

We continue by using the Divisor Theorem in $J$. Now in $J$

$$b = rd + e, \quad 0 \leqslant e < r,$$

so that in $T$ we have

$$a + b\theta = a + (rd\theta + e\theta).$$

Since

$$r\theta = v - rt$$

we know that

$$rd\theta = dv - drt.$$

Hence

$$a + b\theta = dv + (a - drt) + e\theta$$

in $T$, and since $dv$ is in $T$ we have in $T$

$$a + b\theta - dv = (a - drt) + e\theta$$

with

$$0 \leqslant e < r.$$

The choice of $r$ clearly implies

$$e = 0$$

so that

$$b = rd.$$

Since the rational integer

$$a - drt = a + b\theta - dv$$

is in $T$ it is a multiple of $u$ in $J$,

$$a - drt = cu, \qquad c \text{ in } J.$$

Thus

$$cu = a + b\theta - dv$$

or

$$a + b\theta = cu + dv.$$

Finally we note that since $u$ is a rational integer the representation

$$a + b\theta = cu + dv, \qquad c \text{ and } d \text{ in } J,$$

must be unique. For

$$cu + dv = c_1u + d_1v, \qquad c_1 \text{ and } d_1 \text{ in } J,$$

implies that

$$(c - c_1)u = (d_1 - d)v,$$

and a rational integer cannot equal a nonrational integer in $QD(m)$.

*Example* 3. Find the minimal basis for $T = (7 + 3i, 4 - 5i)$ in $QD(-1)$. By considering norms we find that 58 and 41 are in $T$. Then

$$17 = 58 - 41, \qquad 7 = 41 - 2(17),$$

and

$$1 = 6(7) - 41$$

are in $T$. Hence

$$u = 1.$$

Reducing the coefficients of elements in $T$ modulo 1 obviously leaves only the remainder 0. Thus we take $v = \theta$, and so $T$ has the minimal basis $u = 1$, $v = \theta$. Moreover $T = QD(-1)$.

## Exercise 9.4

**1.** Find the minimal basis for each of the following ideals:

(*a*) $T = \{(5 + 2\theta)x + (9 + 3\theta)v\colon x \text{ and } v \text{ in } QD(-5)\}$.

(*b*) $T = (\theta)$ in $QD(-5)$.

(*c*) $T = \{3x + (4 + \sqrt{13})v\colon x \text{ and } v \text{ in } QD(13)\}$.

(*d*) $T = \{13x + (18 - 12\theta)v\colon x \text{ and } v \text{ in } QD(-14)\}$.

(*e*) $T = \{7x + (1 - 2\theta)v\colon x \text{ and } v \text{ in } QD(-5)\}$.

**2.** Show that the minimal basis for a nonzero ideal of $QD(m)$ is unique.

**3.** Describe the equivalence relation modulo the rational integer $u$ which was used to select the element $v$ of the minimal basis for $T$.

**4.** Prove that a subset $M$ of the domain $QD(m)$ is an ideal if and only if $pq + rs$ is in $M$ for all $p$ and $r$ in $M$ and $q$ and $s$ in $QD(m)$.

**5.** Show that, if $m$, $t$, $s$, and $n$ are elements of $J$ such that $m \not\equiv 1 \bmod 4$ and $t^2 - m = sn$, then $s$ and $n$ cannot both be even if $m$ is square-free.

**6.** Let $T$ be the principal ideal $(x)$, $x \neq 0$. Show that the elements $x$ and $x\theta$ form a $J$-basis for $T$. When is this the minimal basis for $T$? (See Problem 1(*b*).)

**7.** Show that an ideal can have several $J$-bases in $QD(m)$.

**8.** Let $S$ and $T$ be two ideals of $QD(m)$. Describe the rational elements of $S \cap T$.

**9.** Let $S$ and $T$ be two ideals of $QD(m)$ with $S$ a subset of $T$. Compare the minimal basis of $S$ with the minimal basis of $T$.

**10.** Denote by $\overline{T}$ the set of all conjugates in $QD(m)$ of the elements of the ideal $T$. Show that $\overline{T}$ is an ideal also. Compare the minimal bases of $T$ and $\overline{T}$.

**11.** Do the norms of the elements of an ideal $T$ form an ideal in $J$? Explain.

**12.** Describe in terms of the minimal basis the $x \neq 0$ in an ideal $T$ which have minimal norms. (Are these norms in $T$?)

**13.** Justify the statement "Each ideal $T$ of $QD(m)$ is close to being principal since $T$ is generated by not more than two elements of $T$."

## 9.5 The Semigroup of Ideals

Denote by $K(m)$ the set of all nonzero ideals of the quadratic domain $QD(m)$. Our plan is to make $K(m)$ into a "multiplicative" semigroup which effectively extends the multiplicative semigroup of $QD(m)$ sufficiently to permit unique factorization into primes. To define this multiplication of ideals we must, however, use both of the binary operations of $QD(m)$.

THEOREM 9.18. *If $S$ and $T$ are elements of $K(m)$, then the set $ST$ consisting of all elements of the form $st$, $s$ in $S$ and $t$ in $T$, together with the sums of finite collections of such products, is an ideal of $QD(m)$.*

Quite clearly the sum of any two elements of the set $ST$ is in $ST$ since a finite collection joined with a finite collection yields a collection still finite. And subtraction is no problem since $st$ in $ST$ implies that $-(st) = (-s)t = s(-t)$ is in $ST$ also since $s$ in $S$ implies that $-s$ is in $S$. Similarly, if $x$ is in $QD(m)$ and $st$ is in $ST$, then

$$x(st) = (xs)t = (st)x = s(tx)$$

is also in $ST$ since $s$ in $S$ implies that $xs$ is in $S$. Thus $x$ times any element of $ST$ is a sum of elements from $ST$ and so is in $ST$, and we conclude that $ST$ is an ideal of $QD(m)$ when $S$ and $T$ are.

DEFINITION 9.8. The *product* of two elements $S$ and $T$ of $K(m)$ is defined to be the ideal $ST$.

Clearly this is a binary operation on $K(m)$ since $ST$ is a nonzero ideal when $S$ and $T$ are nonzero ideals. For $st$ is a nonzero element of $ST$ when $s$ and $t$ are nonzero elements of $S$ and $T$, respectively.

THEOREM 9.19. *The set $K(m)$ is a commutative semigroup with an identity element relative to multiplication.*

Let $S$, $T$, and $W$ be elements of $K(m)$. The Distributive Law for $QD(m)$ enables us to conclude that the ideal $S(TW)$ consists of the elements

$$s(tw), \qquad s \text{ in } S,\ t \text{ in } T, \text{ and } w \text{ in } W,$$

and finite summations of such elements. Similarly the ideal $(ST)W$ consists of the elements

$$(st)w, \qquad s \text{ in } S,\ t \text{ in } T, \text{ and } w \text{ in } W,$$

and finite summations of such elements. Since

$$s(tw) = (st)w \qquad \text{in } QD(m)$$

we conclude that

$$S(TW) = (ST)W.$$

Hence $K(m)$ is a semigroup.

The commutativity is a consequence of the Commutative Law for Multiplication in $QD(m)$ since

$$tw = wt$$

implies

$$TW = WT.$$

And the principal ideal (1) is the identity element for $K(m)$.

In our investigation of the ideals of $J$ we saw that the product of two ideals was contained in both of the ideals; for example,

$$(2)(5) = (10)$$

and the set of all multiples of 10 in $J$ is a subset of both (2) and (5). This result extends to $K(m)$.

THEOREM 9.20. *If $T$ and $W$ are two elements of $K(m)$, then $TW \subseteq T \cap W$.*

For the elements of $TW$ are determined by the products

$$tw, \qquad t \text{ in } T \text{ and } w \text{ in } W,$$

and by the multiplicative absorption property of ideals the element $tw$ is in both $T$ and $W$. (The absorption property states that the product of any element of the ideal $S$ of $QD(m)$ with any element of $QD(m)$ is in $S$.) Since $tw$ is in both $T$ and $W$ we conclude that

$$TW \subseteq T \cap W.$$

*Corollary* 9.20.1. If $T$ and $W$ are two ideals of $QD(m)$ whose only common element is zero, then at least one of the ideals is the zero ideal.

If $T$ and $W$ are in $K(m)$, then $TW$, and consequently $T \cap W$, are in $K(m)$. Since $K(m)$ consists of nonzero ideals only, the result follows.

Now we wish to bring the very powerful tool we developed in the previous section, the basis theorem for ideals, into play. To do this we introduce the idea of *conjugate ideal.*

DEFINITION 9.9. The set $\overline{T}$ consisting of the conjugates of the elements of the ideal $T$ is called the *conjugate* of $T$.

It is easy to show that $\overline{T}$ is an ideal of $QD(m)$ also since conjugation is an automorphism of the domain. If $\bar{s}$ and $\bar{t}$ are elements of $\overline{T}$ and $\bar{x}$ is an arbitrary element of $QD(m)$, then

$$\bar{s} + \bar{t} = \overline{(s + t)},$$
$$\bar{s}\bar{t} = \overline{(st)},$$

and

$$\bar{x}\bar{t} = \overline{(xt)},$$

and since $s + t$, $st$, and $xt$ are in $T$ these prove that $\overline{T}$ is an ideal.

THEOREM 9.21. *The conjugate of an ideal in $QD(m)$ is also an ideal.*

In treating the elements of $QF(m)$ we defined the norm of an element $x$ to be the product of $x$ and its conjugate. So we define the norm of an ideal analogously.

DEFINITION 9.10. The *norm* of an element $T$ of $K(m)$ is the element $T\overline{T} = N(T)$.

What kind of ideal is the norm of $T$? It certainly contains all of the norms of the elements of $T$, and it naturally contains nonrational integers also. But when we consider the minimal basis of $T$ we are able to show that the norm of $T$ is a principal ideal. In fact we can show more than that.

THEOREM 9.22. *If $u = rs$ and $v = r(t + \theta)$ is the minimal basis for the ideal $\overline{T}$, then $T\overline{T} = (r^2s)$.*

We shall work through the details only for the case $m \not\equiv 1 \bmod 4$. Then an arbitrary element $w$ of the ideal $T\overline{T}$ is expressible in the form

$$w = a(r^2s^2) + b\big(r^2s(t + \theta)\big) + c\big(r^2s(t - \theta)\big) + dr^2(t^2 - m)$$

where $a$, $b$, $c$, and $d$ are elements of $J$. For an element $x$ of $T$ is expressible as

$$x = hrs + kr(t + \theta), \qquad h \text{ and } k \text{ in } J,$$

and an element $\bar{z}$ of $\overline{T}$ is expressible as

$$\bar{z} = nrs + pr(t - \theta), \qquad n \text{ and } p \text{ in } J,$$

since

$$\bar{u} = \overline{(rs)} = rs$$

and

$$\bar{v} = \big(\overline{r(t + \theta)}\big) = r(t - \theta) = r(t - \sqrt{m}).$$

Multiplication of these representative elements yields an element of the form described for $w$ above. Because of the Distributive Law the sum of a finite collection of such products is again expressible in the form of $w$, so that we see that $w$ is a typical element of $T\overline{T}$.

Since $m \not\equiv 1 \bmod 4$ we know that not only is $\bar{\theta} = -\theta$ (a fact used above) but

$$t^2 - m \equiv 0 \bmod s.$$

Thus each of the four terms of the expression for $w$ has the factor $r^2 s$, and we see that $w$ is an element of the principal ideal $(r^2 s)$ of $QD(m)$. Hence

$$T\overline{T} \subseteq (r^2 s).$$

Now we must show that a multiple of $r^2 s$ is in $T\overline{T}$. First we consider the congruence $t^2 \equiv m \bmod s$. This implies that in $J$

$$t^2 - m = sn,$$

and we know that $s$ and $n$ are not both even. For $sn$ to be divisible by 4 implies that either $m \equiv 1 \bmod 4$ or $m \equiv 0 \bmod 4$ since

$$t^2 \equiv 1 \quad \text{or} \quad 0 \bmod 4.$$

Since $m$ is by hypothesis square-free and not congruent with 1 mod 4 we conclude that the G.C.F. of $s$ and $n$ is not even. Hence the G.C.F. of $s$, $2t$, and $n$, which we denote by $g$, is an odd rational integer. Since $g$ is a factor of both $s$ and $n$ we see that

$$m \equiv t^2 \bmod sn$$

implies

$$m \equiv 0 \bmod g^2.$$

From the hypothesis that $m$ is square-free we conclude that

$$g = 1.$$

From our theory of the G.C.F. in $J$ we know that $J$ contains elements $e, f$, and $j$ such that

$$1 = es + 2ft + jn.$$

Multiplying by $r^2 s$ yields

$$r^2 s = er^2 s^2 + 2fr^2 st + jr^2(t^2 - m),$$

and by adding and subtracting the element $fr^2 s\theta$, we obtain the expression

$$r^2 s = er^2 s^2 + f\big(r^2 s(t + \theta)\big) + f\big(r^2 s(t - \theta)\big) + jr^2(t^2 - m).$$

This means that $r^2 s$ is in $T\overline{T}$ so that

$$(r^2 s) \subseteq T\overline{T}.$$

Therefore

$$T\overline{T} = (r^2 s).$$

*Example* 1. Verify that the norm of the ideal $T$ having minimal basis 3 and $1 + \sqrt{-5}$ is (3).

Since $\overline{3} = 3$ and $\overline{(1 + \sqrt{-5})} = 1 - \sqrt{-5}$, an element $w$ of $T\overline{T} = N(T)$ is of the form

$$w = 9a + 3b(1 - \sqrt{-5}) + 3c(1 + \sqrt{-5}) + 6d,$$

$a$, $b$, $c$, and $d$ in $J$, as we can see easily by multiplying typical elements of $T$ and $\overline{T}$ together. For example

$$(6 + 2(1 + \sqrt{-5}))(9 + (1 - \sqrt{-5})) = 54 + 6(1 - \sqrt{-5}) + 18(1 + \sqrt{-5}) + 12.$$

Clearly $w$ is a multiple of 3, and so

$$T\overline{T} \subseteq (3).$$

On the other hand $w$ can be rewritten as

$$w = 9a + 6b + 6d + 3(c - b)(1 + \sqrt{-5}).$$

Then for $a = 1$, $b = -1$, $c = 1$, and $d = 0$, we get $w = 3$. Hence 3 is in $T\overline{T}$ and

$$(3) \subseteq T\overline{T}.$$

One point perhaps requires a bit of additional explanation here. The element

$$w = ar^2s^2 + br^2s(t + \theta) + cr^2s(t - \theta) + dr^2(t^2 - m)$$

is in $N(T) = T\overline{T}$ for any elements $a$, $b$, $c$, and $d$ of $J$ since the elements

$$ar^2s^2 = (ars)rs,$$
$$br^2s(t + \theta) = (brs)\big(r(t + \theta)\big),$$
$$cr^2s(t - \theta) = (crs)\big(r(t - \theta)\big),$$

and

$$dr^2(t^2 - m) = \big(dr(t + \theta)\big)\big(r(t - \theta)\big)$$

are all elements of $T\overline{T}$.

From this result we obtain the very important conclusion that $K(m)$ is a *cancellation semigroup*.

THEOREM 9.23. *If $S$, $T$, and $W$ are elements of $K(m)$ such that*

$$ST = WT,$$

then

$$S = W.$$

We multiply the equation

$$ST = WT$$

by $\overline{T}$, obtaining

$$SN(T) = WN(T).$$

The ideal $N(T)$ is principal with generator $n$ so that every element $x$ of $SN(T)$ is of the form

$$x = sn, \quad s \text{ in } S.$$

For each element of $SN(T)$ is a finite summation of products of the form

$$s_1(zn) = (s_1 z)n = s_2 n$$

for $s_1$ in $S$ and $z$ in $QD(m)$. By the Distributive Law $n$ can be factored out and $x$ written as

$$x = sn.$$

Also it is obvious from the definition of $SN(T)$ that for each $s$ in $S$, $sn$ is in $SN(T)$.

Now the element $x$ of $SN(T)$ is also in $WN(T)$, so by the same reasoning we have

$$x = wn, \qquad w \text{ in } W.$$

From

$$x = sn = wn$$

we conclude that $s = w$ and

$$S \subseteq W.$$

Reversing the role of $S$ and $W$ leads to the relation

$$W \subseteq S,$$

and so we see that $S = W$.

## Exercise 9.5

**1.** Find the norm of each of the ideals of Problem 1 in Section 9.4.

**2.** Show that the element $T$ of $K(m)$ is the identity of $K(m)$ if and only if $T\overline{T} = (1)$.

**3.** What can you say about the minimal basis of $T$ if $N(T) = (n)$ and $n$ is square-free?

**4.** Show that, if $S$ and $T$ are elements of $K(m)$, then $\overline{ST} = \overline{S}\overline{T}$. Find an automorphism of $K(m)$.

**5.** Let $S$ and $T$ be elements of $K(m)$. Show that $N(ST) = N(S)N(T)$.

**6.** Show that the mapping $F\colon T \to n$, where $(n) = N(T)$, is a homomorphism from the semigroup $K(m)$ into the multiplicative semigroup of positive elements of $J$. (The element $n$ is sometimes called the *norm* of $T$.)

**7.** Prove that the norm of $T = (a)$, $a$ in $J$, is $(a^2)$. Compare with the norm of $a$.

**8.** Use the Cancellation Theorem to show that the identity (1) is the only idempotent element of $K(m)$.

**9.** Prove that the norm of the principal ideal $(x)$ is $(x\bar{x})$ and $N((x)) = (N(x))$. (Note that, if $T = (x)$, then $\overline{T} = (\bar{x})$.)

**10.** Show that the nonzero ideals of $QD(m)$ form a semigroup relative to set intersection.

**11.** Show that the two different ideals (2) and $(2, 1 + \sqrt{3})$ of $QD(3)$ have the same norm.

**12.** Find a bound for the number of $T$ in $K(m)$ with norm $(n)$, where $n$ is a positive rational integer. (Check the possibilities for $r$, $s$, and $t$ in the minimal bases and find an upper bound.)

**13.** Find all ideals $T$ in $QD(3)$ with $N(T)$ equal to (1), (2), (3), or (4) by considering the minimal basis for $T$.

**14.** Prove that every element of the ideal $ST$ is of the form $sx$, $s$ in $S$, if $S$ and $T$ are ideals of $QD(m)$ and $T = (x)$. Does this mean that $ST$ is a principal ideal? Explain.

**15.** What elements of $K(m)$ are equal to their norms? Explain.

**16.** Let $T$ be an element of $K(m)$ with norm $(n)$. Show that the quotient ring $QD(m)/T$ has not more than $n$ elements.

## 9.6 Factorization of Ideals

The concept of factorization in $K(m)$ is based on the familiar idea of factor.

DEFINITION 9.11. If $S$ and $T$ are two elements of $K(m)$, then $S$ is a *factor* of $T$ if and only if $K(m)$ contains an element $W$ such that $T = SW$.

It is a simple matter to show that the principal ideal (3) is a factor of the principal ideal (6) in $QD(m)$, and it is done by verifying that

$$(6) = (2)(3).$$

Let $6x$ be an arbitrary element of (6); then surely

$$6x = 2 \cdot 3x$$

so that $6x$ is contained in (2)(3) and

$$(6) \subseteq (2)(3).$$

Similarly, if $2r$ and $3s$ are arbitrary elements from (2) and (3), respectively, then

$$2r \cdot 3s = 6rs$$

is an element of (6). Hence

$$(6) \supseteq (2)(3)$$

so that we conclude that (2) and (3) are both factors of (6).

*Example* 1. The principal ideals (2) and (3) are factors of (6) in $QD(m)$.

This example suggests an important correspondence between factors and set inclusion. Note that the ideals which are factors of an ideal $T$ also *contain* $T$. It is actually a fact that an ideal which contains $T$ is also a factor of $T$. (Checking the ideals of $J$ we see that this is also true in that domain.)

THEOREM 9.24. *Let $S$ and $T$ be ideals of $QD(m)$. Then $S$ is a factor of $T$ if and only if $S \supseteq T$.*

If $S$ is a factor of $T$, then $T = SW$ and we saw earlier that $T \subseteq S \cap W \subseteq S$. So consider the converse. We must prove that, if $S \supseteq T$, then $QD(m)$ contains an ideal $W$ such that $T = SW$.

Now multiply $T$ and $S$ by $\bar{S}$, the conjugate of $S$. Then we have from $T \subseteq S$ the inclusion

$$T\bar{S} \subseteq (n) = N(S) = S\bar{S},$$

so that every element of $T\bar{S}$ is of the form

$$wn, \qquad \text{for some } w \text{ in } QD(m).$$

We define $W$ to be the set of all elements $w$ in $QD(m)$ such that $wn$ is in $T\bar{S}$. The set $W$ is an ideal of $QD(m)$, for, if $w_1$ and $w_2$ are in $W$ and $x_1$ and $x_2$ are in $QD(m)$, then

$$(x_1w_1 + x_2w_2)n = x_1w_1n + x_2w_2n$$

is an element of the ideal $T\bar{S}$ since $w_1n$ and $w_2n$ are in that ideal. Hence $x_1w_1 + x_2w_2$ is in $W$ and $W$ is an ideal.

From the form of the elements of $T\bar{S}$ we know that

$$T\bar{S} = W(n) = WS\bar{S}.$$

Since $\bar{S}$ can be assumed to differ from (0) as the whole problem is trivial when $S = \bar{S} = (0)$, we can apply the Cancellation Law. Thus we get

$$T = WS,$$

and the theorem is proved.

This result means that the problem of factoring an element $T$ of $K(m)$ is equivalent to the problem of finding the ideals of $QD(m)$ which contain $T$.

*Example* 2. Find the factors of the principal ideal (3) in $QD(-5)$.

If $S$ is a factor of (3), then $S$ is an ideal of $QD(-5)$ containing (3). Now $S$ is determined by its minimal basis $u = rs$ and $v = r(t + \theta)$ where $r$, $s$, and $t$ are rational integers. If $(3) \subset S$, then surely 3 is in $S$, and we conclude that $u$ is a factor of 3 in $J$ from the manner in which $u$ was chosen. Then there are three cases to consider.

*Case* 1. $r = 1$ and $s = 3$. This means that $v = t + \theta$ where $0 \leqslant t < 3$ and

$$t^2 \equiv -5 \bmod 3,$$

and the congruence and inequality are satisfied only by the rational integers $t = 1$ or 2. Hence there are two distinct ideals determined in this case, and these are denoted by $(3, 1 + \theta)$ and $(3, 2 + \theta)$.

*Case* 2. $r = 3$ and $s = 1$. In this case $v = 3(t + \theta)$ where $0 \leqslant t < 1$, so that $v = 3\theta$. The ideal whose minimal basis consists of $u = 3$ and $v = 3\theta$ is precisely the principal ideal (3).

*Case* 3. $u = rs = 1$. In this case $u = 1$ and $v = \theta$ so that we have the improper ideal $(1) = QD(-5)$.

Thus we see that (3) has exactly four factors, the two obvious factors (1) and (3) and the ideals $(3, 1 + \theta)$ and $(3, 2 + \theta)$. Using the nontrivial factors yields the factorization

$$(3) = (3, 2 + \theta)(3, 1 + \theta).$$

Note that the ideal $(3, 2 + \theta)$ is the conjugate of $(3, 1 + \theta)$ since

$$2 + \theta = 3 + (-1)(1 - \theta)$$

whereas

$$1 - \theta = 3 + (-1)(2 + \theta)$$

implying that

$$(3, 2 + \theta) = \overline{(3, 1 + \theta)}.$$

This method of using the minimal basis of a nonzero ideal enables us to prove that an element of $K(m)$ has only a finite number of factors.

*Lemma* 9.1. The positive rational integer $n$ is contained in at most $n^3$ elements of $K(m)$.

If the ideal $T$ contains $n$, then the element $u$ of the minimal basis of $T$ is a factor of $n$. Since $u = rs$, where $r$ and $s$ are positive elements of $J$, this restricts $r$ and $s$ to the range 1 to $n$ in $J$. Furthermore, the second element of the basis,

$$v(t + \theta), \qquad 0 \leqslant t < s \text{ in } J,$$

is restricted since $t$ must lie in the range 0 to $n - 1$. Thus there are not more than $n^3$ different minimal bases possible so that there cannot be more than $n^3$ ideals in $QD(m)$ which contain $n$.

THEOREM 9.25. *An element $T$ of $K(m)$ has a finite number of factors.*

$T$ is in $K(m)$ if and only if it is a nonzero ideal of $QD(m)$. Since a nonzero ideal contains positive elements of $J$ the theorem follows from the lemma.

As in the classification of the elements of $QD(m)$ we define an element $T$ of $K(m)$ to be:

(1) A *unit* if and only if $T$ is a factor of the identity element of $K(m)$.

(2) A *prime* if and only if the only factors of $T$ are $T$ and units, $T$ not a unit.

(3) A *composite* if it is neither a unit nor a prime.

From the inclusion criterion for factors we see immediately that the only unit in $K(m)$ is the principal ideal $(1) = QD(m)$ since no other ideal of $QD(m)$ contains $QD(m)$. This means that an ideal $T$ of $QD(m)$ is a prime in $K(m)$ if and only if $T$ is a *maximal* ideal of $QD(m)$, one which is a proper ideal contained in no other proper ideal.

THEOREM 9.26. *The primes of $K(m)$ are the maximal ideals of $QD(m)$.*

From Theorem 9.25 we see that $K(m)$ contains prime elements and that every element $T$ of $K(m)$ except (1) is expressible in the form

$$T = P_1 P_2 \cdots P_n$$

where the $P_i$ are primes. For consider the factors of $T \neq (1)$. If there are only two of these, $T$ and (1), then $T$ is a prime. Otherwise there is an ideal $T_1$ such that

$$T \subset T_1 \subset (1).$$

Consider the factors of $T_1$; since these are ideals of $QD(m)$ containing $T_1$ they are also factors of $T$. Hence we are faced with a smaller collection of factors so that after a finite number of steps we must arrive at a prime factor of $T$ (i.e., a maximal ideal of $QD(m)$ which contains $T$). This is the heuristic reasoning behind the following result.

THEOREM 9.27. *Each element except* (1) *in $K(m)$ is expressible as $P_1 P_2 \cdots P_n$, where the $P_i$ are primes in $K(m)$.*

The formal proof involves induction, and the induction is on $f(T)$, the number of factors of $T \neq (1)$ in $K(m)$. If $f(T) = 2$ (when the only factors are (1) and $T$), then $t$ is a prime and already "factored," so suppose $f(T) > 2$. Then $T$ has a factor $T_1$,

$$T \subset T_1 \subset (1)$$

and

$$T = T_1 T_2.$$

Since $K(m)$ is a cancellation semigroup we see that

$$T \subset T_2 \subset (1).$$

Thus $T_1$ and $T_2$ are contained in fewer ideals of $QD(m)$ than $T$ is (since neither is contained in $T$) so that

$$f(T_1) < f(T) \qquad \text{and} \qquad f(T_2) < f(T).$$

Applying the induction hypothesis to $T_1$ and $T_2$ yields the desired factorization of $T$.

*Example* 3. Find all of the factors of the ideal $T$ having the minimal basis $u = 6$ and $v = 4 + 2\theta$ in $QD(7)$.

The positive factors of 6 in $J$ are 6, 3, 2, and 1 so we have four cases to consider, apparently. Moreover, if $rs$ and $r(t + \theta)$ form the minimal basis of an ideal containing $T$, then we know from the way that the element $r(t + \theta)$ is selected that $r$, the coefficient of $\theta$, must be no larger than 2.

(1) $rs = 6$, $s = 3$, and $r = 2$. This yields two ideals, $(6, 2(2 + \theta))$ and $(6, 2(1 + \theta))$, since the congruence $t^2 \equiv 7 \bmod 3$ has two solutions mod 3. The ideal $(6, 2 + 2\theta)$ does not contain $T$.

(2) $rs = 3$, $s = 3$, and $r = 1$. Here again there are two ideals, $(3, 1 + \theta)$ and $(3, 2 + \theta)$, for the same reason as above. The ideal $(3, 2 + \theta)$ contains $T$; the other does not.

(3) $rs = 2$, $s = 2$, and $r = 1$. There is one such ideal, $(2, 2 + \theta)$, and it contains $T$. Note than the congruence $t^2 \equiv 7 \bmod 2$ has only one solution mod 2.

(4) If $s = 1$, then the resulting ideal is (6), (3), (2), and (1). Of these only (2) and (1) contain $T$.

## Exercise 9.6

**1.** Determine all of the factors of the ideal (*a*) generated by 5 in $QD(-5)$; (*b*) generated by 5 in $QD(3)$; (*c*) generated by 5 in $QD(-3)$.

**2.** Find all factors of the ideal of $QD(14)$ generated by 13 and $18 - 12\theta$. (Find the minimal basis first.)

**3.** Find all the prime factors of the ideal of $QD(-5)$ generated by 6 and $4 + 2\theta$.

**4.** Find all the ideals of $QD(-5)$ which contain $\theta$.

**5.** Determine the ideals of $QD(19)$ having norm (6).

**6.** Show that (7) is the square of a prime in $K(14)$.

**7.** Show that (2) is a prime ideal in $QD(13)$.

**8.** Let $S$ and $T$ be ideals of $QD(m)$. Show that the set

$$\{s + t\colon s \text{ in } S \text{ and } t \text{ in } T\}$$

is an ideal of $QD(m)$.

**9.** Find two primes in $K(5)$.

**10.** Compare the factorizations of 9 in $QD(-5)$ with the factorization of (9) in $K(-5)$.

**11.** Find the norms of the primes which appear in the preceding problems.

**12.** Describe and illustrate the relation between factors of $n$ in $J$ and ideal factors of $(n)$ in $J$.

**13.** Let $A$ and $B$ be two ideals of $QD(m)$. If we were to proceed by analogy with the ideals and elements of $J$, what should we call $A \cap B$? (Note that, in $J$, $(6) \cap (4) = (12)$.)

**14.** Describe the primes of $K(-1)$. (What is true of ideals in the Gaussian domain?)

## 9.7 Unique Factorization and Primes

Again the question of uniqueness must be considered. This time we can prove that the representation of an element of $K(m)$ as a product of primes is unique, and the procedure is rather like the others we have studied since it is based on the idea of greatest common factor (although the concept should probably be called the "smallest" common factor here).

DEFINITION 9.12. An element $T$ of $K(m)$ is a *common factor* of $A$ and $B$ in $K(m)$ if and only if it is a factor of both. And a common factor $D$ of $A$ and $B$ in $K(m)$ is a *greatest common factor* of $A$ and $B$ if and only if every common factor of $A$ and $B$ is a factor of $D$.

We use the inclusion criterion for factors to prove that each pair of elements from $K(m)$ has a unique G.C.F. in $K(m)$. This means that we plan to show that $D$ is the smallest ideal of $QD(m)$ which contains the ideals $A$ and $B$. (Notice again how the idea of order is inverted in passing from elements of $J$ to ideals of $J$: 10 is larger than 5 but the ideal (10) is contained in the ideal (5).)

THEOREM 9.28. *If $A$ and $B$ are elements of $K(m)$, then the set $(A, B) = \{a + b$: $a$ in $A$, $b$ in $B\}$ is the unique G.C.F. of $A$ and $B$.*

First we must show that $(A, B)$ is an ideal of $QD(m)$. Let $a_1 + b_1$ and $a_2 + b_2$ be two elements of $(A, B)$ and $x$ and $w$ be two elements of $QD(m)$; then

$$x(a_1 + b_1) + w(a_2 + b_2) = (xa_1 + wa_2) + (xb_1 + wb_2).$$

This sum is in $(A, B)$ since $xa_1 + wa_2$ and $xb_1 + wb_2$ are in $A$ and $B$, respectively, as $A$ and $B$ are ideals. Thus $(A, B)$ is an ideal of $QD(m)$.

The second step involves showing that $(A, B)$ is a common factor of $A$ and $B$. This follows from the inclusion criterion for a factor since the equations

$$a = a + 0 \qquad \text{and} \qquad b = 0 + b$$

imply that $A \subseteq (A, B)$ and $B \subseteq (A, B)$. (Remember that 0 is in all ideals.)

Finally we show that $(A, B)$ is contained in each common factor $T$ of $A$ and $B$. For, if $T$ is a factor of both $A$ and $B$, then $T$ contains both $A$ and $B$. Thus $T$ contains the elements

$$a + b, \qquad a \text{ in } A,\ b \text{ in } B,$$

since $T$ is closed under addition, and we conclude that $(A, B) \subseteq T$. Hence $T$ is a factor of $(A, B)$, and we have shown that $(A, B)$ is a G.C.F. of $A$ and $B$.

This last step suffices to prove that the G.C.F. is unique, for, if $W$ were also a G.C.F. of $A$ and $B$, then the last argument implies

$$(A, B) \subseteq W \qquad \textit{and} \qquad W \subseteq (A, B).$$

So $W = (A, B)$, and the G.C.F. is unique.

*Example* 1. Integrate this concept of G.C.F. with the idea of G.C.F. in $J$.

Let $d$ be the G.C.F. of the two positive elements $a$ and $b$ of $J$. Since $d$ is a factor of both $a$ and $b$ we know that

$$a = a_1 d \qquad \text{and} \qquad b = b_1 d.$$

Hence the ideal $(d)$ in $J$ contains the ideals $(a)$ and $(b)$. Moreover $(d)$ is the smallest ideal of $J$ which contains both $(a)$ and $(b)$ for, if $(f)$ contains $(a)$ and $(b)$, then

$$a = ff_1 \qquad \text{and} \qquad b = ff_2.$$

But every common factor of $a$ and $b$ is a factor of $d$, so that

$$d = ff_3.$$

This means that $(d)$ is contained in the ideal $(f)$. Furthermore the ideal $(d)$ can be described as the set of all sums

$$a'' + b'', \qquad a'' \text{ in } (a),\ b'' \text{ in } (b).$$

Thus the theorem above is abstracted from a certain way of describing the arithmetic of $J$.

DEFINITION 9.13. The elements $A$ and $B$ of $K(m)$ are *relatively prime* if and only if $(A, B) = (1)$.

*Corollary* 9.28.1. The elements $A$ and $B$ of $K(m)$ are *relatively prime* if and only if $A$ and $B$ contain elements $a$ and $b$, respectively, such that

$$1 = a + b.$$

This result, which is an immediate consequence of the definition of $(A, B)$ and the theorem, provides the key to proving the uniqueness of the factorization into primes in $K(m)$.

THEOREM 9.29. *If $A$, $B$, and $T$ are elements of $K(m)$ such that $A$ is a factor of $BT$ and $A$ and $B$ are relatively prime, then $A$ is a factor of $T$.*

Since $(A, B) = (1)$ we know that $A$ and $B$ contain elements $a$ and $b$, respectively, such that

$$a + b = 1.$$

Then for any element $t$ of $T$, we obtain

$$t = at + bt$$

by multiplying by $t$. Now we bring the inclusion criterion for a factor into play. The element $bt$ is in $BT$ and hence in $A$, which is a factor of (i.e., contains) $BT$. Also $at$ is in $A$ since any multiple of an element of $A$ is in $A$. Therefore

$$t = at + bt$$

is in $A$, implying that

$$T \subseteq A.$$

Thus $A$ is a factor of $T$.

The uniqueness of the factorization in Theorem 9.27 can be proved rather easily now, but let us consider some examples before going on to that.

*Example* 2. Find the G.C.F. of the ideals (3) and $(1 + \theta)$ in $QD(-5)$. Every element of the G.C.F. is of the form

$$3x + (1 + \theta)w,$$

$x$ and $w$ in $QD(-5)$. Since 6 is the smallest positive rational integer in the principal ideal $(1 + \theta)$ we see that $u = 3$ and $v = 1 + \theta$ is the minimal basis of the G.C.F. Hence we have determined the G.C.F.,

$$((3), (1 + \theta)) = (3, 1 + \theta).$$

*Example* 3. Find the G.C.F. of the ideals $(3, 1 + \theta)$ and $(3, 2 + \theta)$ in $QD(-5)$.

We see immediately that

$$1 = 2 + \theta + (-1 - \theta)$$

so that the G.C.F. is (1) and the two ideals are relatively prime. These are, as we saw earlier, the two prime factors of the principal ideal (3).

*Corollary* 9.29.1. If $P$ and $Q$ are primes of $K(m)$, then either $P = Q$ or $(P, Q) = (1)$.

If $P$ is a prime, then the only ideals of $QD(m)$ which contain $P$ are $P$ and (1). If $Q \neq P$, then naturally $(P, Q)$ contains $P$ properly since it also contains $Q$. Thus $Q \neq P$ implies that $(P, Q) = (1)$.

Now the proof of the unique factorization property for $K(m)$ is identical with the proof of that property for the rational integers, except that the induction is on the number of factors.

THEOREM 9.30. *The expression for an element $A \neq (1)$ of $K(m)$ as a product of primes,*

$$A = P_1P_2 \cdots P_n,$$

*is unique.*

We proceed by induction of $f(A)$ as in the proof of Theorem 9.27. If $f(A) = 2$, then $A$ is a prime and nothing more needs to be said. So suppose $f(A) = t > 2$ and that all elements of $K(m)$ with fewer factors are uniquely factorable into primes. Consider

$$A = P_1P_2 \cdots P_n = Q_1Q_2 \cdots Q_r,$$

where all of $P_i$ and $Q_j$ are primes in $K(m)$. Comparing $P_1$ and $Q_1$ we conclude that either $P_1 = Q_1$ or $(P_1, Q_1) = (1)$. In the second case we know by the previous theorem that $P_1$ is a factor of the product $B = Q_2 \cdots Q_r$, and applying the induction hypothesis to $B$ we conclude that $P_1$ must equal one of the prime factors $Q_i$ of $B$. Thus we see that in both cases $P_1$ equals one of the primes $Q_j$, and, relabeling the elements if necessary, we take $P_1 = Q_1$. Now we use the fact that $K(m)$ is a cancellation semigroup and conclude from

$$A = P_1P_2 \cdots P_n = P_1Q_2 \cdots Q_r = Q_1Q_2 \cdots Q_r$$

that

$$P_2 \cdots P_n = Q_2 \cdots Q_r.$$

Bringing the induction hypothesis into play again enables us to conclude that the two factorizations are identical (except for arrangement of factors). This completes the induction and proves the theorem.

An important consequence of this theory is that we can now relate the primes of $K(m)$ with the primes of $J$.

THEOREM 9.31. *If $P$ is a prime in $K(m)$, then $N(P) = (p)$ or $(p^2)$ where $p$ is a rational prime.*

By theorem 9.22 $N(P) = (n)$ where $n$ is a positive element of $J$. From the factorization of $n$ in $J$ we have in $K(m)$ the factorization

$$N(P) = P\bar{P} = (p_1)(p_2)\cdots(p_j),$$
$$p_i \text{ prime in } J.$$

Since $P$ is a prime ideal this equation implies that $P$ is a factor of one of the principal ideals $(p_i) = (p)$, and so there exists $Q$ in $K(m)$ such that

$$PQ = (p).$$

Taking norms we obtain the equation

$$(n)(q) = N(P)N(Q) = (p^2)$$

which shows that $n$ divides $p^2$ in $J$. From this we conclude that $n$, which is greater than 1, is either $p$ or $p^2$, and the theorem is proved.

Now can we work backwards along this relationship between the primes of $K(m)$ and the primes of $J$? In particular, can we find the primes of $K(m)$ from the primes of $J$? Consider the prime $p$ from $J$, and form the ideal $(p)$ in $K(m)$. The ideal $(p)$ may be a prime of $K(m)$, in which case it is a prime whose norm is $(p^2)$. However, $(p)$ is not always a prime in $K(m)$, so let us investigate the minimal basis of an ideal $T$ which contains $(p)$.

The minimal basis $u = rs$ and $v = r(t + \theta)$ of $T$ is such that $rs$ is a factor of $p$ in $J$. If $r = p$, then $s = 1$ and $t = 0$ so that $T = (p)$, so we check the other possibility. If $r = 1$, then $s = p$ and $t$ is a solution of the congruence

$$t^2 \equiv m \bmod p \qquad \text{if } m \not\equiv 1 \bmod 4$$

and of the congruence

$$t^2 + t \equiv (1/4)(m - 1) \bmod p \qquad \text{if } m \equiv 1 \bmod 4.$$

If the appropriate congruence has a solution in $J$, then it has exactly two solutions of the required size. Labeling these as $t_1$ and $t_2$ we see that $(p)$ has exactly two proper factors,

$$P_1 = (p, t_1 + \theta) \qquad \text{and} \qquad P_2 = (p, t_2 + \theta).$$

These both have norm $(p)$ and are primes in $K(m)$ since $(p)$ has no other factors except $(p)$ and $(1)$. Thus we conclude that the determination of the primes in $K(m)$ depends upon solving the appropriate congruence above.

THEOREM 9.32. *If $p$ is a prime of $J$, then $(p)$ is a prime of $K(m)$ if the congruence*

$$t^2 \equiv m \bmod p \qquad (\textit{if } m \not\equiv 1 \bmod 4)$$

*or*

$$t^2 + t \equiv (1/4)(m - 1) \bmod p \qquad (\textit{if } m \equiv 1 \bmod 4)$$

*has no solution in $J$, whereas $(p)$ has the two prime factors $P_1 = (p, t_1 + \theta)$ and $P_2 = (p, t_2 + \theta)$ if $t_1$ and $t_2$ are the two solutions of the appropriate congruence. Moreover every prime of $K(m)$ is obtainable in this way.*

The first sentence is a consequence of the above discussion. The second follows from the previous theorem, really, for, if the norm of the prime ideal $P$ is $(p^2)$, then in the minimal basis of $P$ $rs$ equals $p$ and $r = p$ so that $s = 1$, $t = 0$, and

$$P = (p, p\theta) = (p).$$

But, if $N(P) = (p)$, then $rs = p$, $r = 1$, $s = p$, and $P = (p, t + \theta)$ where $t$ is a solution of the appropriate congruence.

*Example* 4. Determine three primes of $K(3)$.

We shall work from the three primes 2, 3, and 5 of $J$ and consider congruences.

(1) The congruence

$$t^2 \equiv 3 \bmod 2$$

has two solutions (i.e., the polynomial $\lambda^2 - 1$ factors as $(\lambda - 1)^2$ over $J/(2)$) so that (2) factors as

$$(2) = (2, 1 + \theta)(2, 1 + \theta).$$

$(2, 1 + \theta)$ is a prime of $K(3)$ and is in fact the principal ideal $(1 + \theta)$.

(2) The congruence

$$t^2 \equiv 3 \bmod 3$$

is obviously solvable, and $(3) = (\theta)(\theta)$ so that $(\theta)$ is a prime ideal of $K(3)$.

(3) The congruence

$$t^2 \equiv 3 \bmod 5$$

has no solution in $J$ so that (5) is a prime ideal in $K(3)$.

## Exercise 9.7

**1.** Find $(A, B)$ in $K(-5)$ for $A = (3)$ and $B = (2 - \theta)$.

**2.** Find $(A, B)$ in $K(14)$ for $A = (13)$ and $B = (18 - 12\theta)$.

**3.** Find $(A, B)$ in $K(-5)$ for $A = (2 - \theta)$ and $B = (1 + \theta)$.

**4.** Let $A$, $B$, and $C$ be three elements of $K(m)$. Show that $(A, (B, C)) = ((A, B), C)$. Show that $K(m)$ is a commutative semigroup with identity relative to the binary operation defined by the concept of G.C.F.

**5.** Find three primes of $K(m)$ for (*a*) $m = 2$; (*b*) $m = 5$; (*c*) $m = 6$; (*d*) $m = -2$.

**6.** Compare the criterion for primes in $K(-1)$ with that for Gaussian primes. (Check the development of the sum of two squares theory in Chapter 4.)

**7.** Show that $A \cap B$ is a reasonable L.C.M. for the nonzero ideals of $QD(m)$.

**8.** Prove that the element $P$ of $K(m)$ is a prime if and only if its conjugate $\bar{P}$ is a prime.

**9.** What is the relation between the rational integer $t$ satisfying the conditions

$$t^2 \equiv m \bmod p \quad \text{and} \quad 0 \leqslant t < p,$$

and the polynomial $\lambda^2 - m$ of the polynomial domain $F[\lambda]$, $F = J/(p)$?

**10.** Show that the mapping

$$G: x \to (x), \quad x \text{ in } QD(m),$$

is a homomorphism of the multiplicative semigroup of $QD(m)$ onto the subsemigroup of $K(m)$ of principal ideals. What elements of $QD(m)$ map onto (1)?

## 9.8 Quadratic Residues

The problem of determining whether $(p)$ is a prime of $K(m)$ reduces, as we saw in the last section, to the problem of determining whether a certain second degree polynomial is reducible over $J/(p)$. Of course $p$ substitutions (or less) suffice to settle this problem but such a process is extremely laborious for large primes $p$. Now there happens to exist a truly amazing arithmetic device for testing a quadratic element of $(J/(p))[\lambda]$ for reducibility over $J/(p)$, and we shall discuss that method now.

Working over the field $J/(p)$ we need only consider monic polynomials, and when $p$ is an odd prime an even greater restriction can be effected.

THEOREM 9.33. *The polynomial*

$$m(\lambda) = \lambda^2 + by + c$$

*over $J/(p)$, $p$ an odd prime, has a zero in $J/(p)$ if and only if the polynomial*

$$h(\lambda) = \lambda^2 - (b^2 - 4c)$$

*has a zero in $J/(p)$.*

This is based on the familiar process of completing the square. If $r$ is a zero of $m(\lambda)$, then

$$r^2 + br = -c,$$
$$4r^2 + 4br + b^2 = b^2 - 4c,$$

and

$$(2r + b)^2 = b^2 - 4ac$$

so that $2r + b$ is a zero in $J/(p)$ of $h(\lambda)$. Reversing the procedure (and here is where we need $p$ to be odd) we see that, if $s$ is a zero of $h(\lambda)$ from $J/(p)$, then solving the equation

$$2r + b = s$$

for $r$ yields a solution in $J/(p)$ for $m(\lambda)$.

Now we shall concentrate our attention on the *pure quadratic* $\lambda^2 - d$ from $J[\lambda]$ and attempt to determine whether it has a zero modulo $p$ where $p$ is an odd prime.

DEFINITION 9.14. The element $d$ of $J$ is a *quadratic residue* modulo $m$ if and only if:

(i) $d$ and $m$ are relatively prime in $J$.
(ii) $\lambda^2 - d$ has a zero modulo $m$.

We are interested only in the case where $m$ is an odd prime $p$ but the general theory exists and is well developed (see *Elementary Number Theory* by Uspensky and Heaslet).

*Example* 1. Determine whether 7 is a quadratic residue of 11.

Obviously 7 and 11 are relatively prime in $J$ so we need only determine whether $\lambda^2 - 7$ has a zero in $J/(11)$. Checking the numbers $1^2 - 7, 2^2 - 7, \cdots,$ $10^2 - 7$ modulo 11 we see that $\lambda^2 - 7$ does not have a zero in $J/(11)$. Hence 7 is not a quadratic residue mod 11.

There are quadratic residues for each odd prime (1, 3, 4, 5, and 9 are the quadratic residues modulo 11 between 0 and 11), and we count the number of these modulo the prime.

THEOREM 9.34. *Exactly one-half of the* $p - 1$ *integers* $1, 2, \cdots, p - 1$ *are quadratic residues modulo the odd prime* $p$.

Consider the polynomial $\lambda^{p-1} - 1$ over the field $J/(p)$. By the Fermat-Euler Theorem we know that each of the elements $1, 2, \cdots, p - 1$ of $J/(p)$ is a zero of this polynomial. This means that the $p - 1$ nonzero elements of $J/(p)$ are all powers of one of the elements of $J/(p)$, for suppose $k$ is the largest number of distinct nonzero elements of $J/(p)$ which can be written as powers of one element of $J/(p)$. Then all $p - 1$ nonzero elements of $J/(p)$ are zeros of the polynomial $\lambda^k - 1$, and since a polynomial over a field has no more zeros than its degree, we see that the $p - 1$ elements $1, 2, \cdots, p - 1$ of $J/(p)$ can be expressed as powers of an element $x$ of $J/(p)$. Clearly, then, the even powers of $x$ are the quadratic residues modulo $p$.

*Example* 2. Find the quadratic residues modulo 11.

What element $x$ of $J/(11)$ has the property that $x, x^2, x^3, \cdots, x^{10}$ are the ten nonzero elements of $J/(11)$? Certainly $x = 2$ will do the trick since in $J/(11)$

$$2^2 = 4,\ 2^3 = 8,\ 2^4 = 5,\ 2^5 = 10,\ 2^6 = 9,\ 2^7 = 7,\ 2^8 = 3,\ 2^9 = 6, \text{ and } 2^{10} = 1.$$

Reading from this list we see that 4, 5, 9, 3, and 1 are the quadratic residues mod 11 between 0 and 11.

THEOREM 9.35. *The integer* $r$ *is a quadratic residue* mod $p$, $p$ *an odd prime if and only if* $r$ *is a zero* mod $p$ *of the polynomial* $\lambda^t - 1$, *where* $t = (1/2)(p - 1)$.

If $r$ is a quadratic residue mod $p$, then there is an integer $w$ such that

$$w^2 \equiv r \bmod p.$$

Thus

$$r^t \equiv w^{p-1} \equiv 1 \bmod p$$

and $r$ is a zero mod $p$ of the polynomial $\lambda^t - 1$.

Conversely suppose $r$ is a zero mod $p$ of the polynomial $\lambda^t - 1$. We shall prove that $r$ is a quadratic residue mod $p$ by showing that $r$ is congruent with an even power of the generator $x$ from the previous theorem. For suppose

$$r \equiv x^{2n+1} \bmod p.$$

Then

$$r^t \equiv 1 \equiv x^{2nt+t} \bmod p,$$

and since

$$2nt + t = n(p - 1) + t$$

we get

$$x^{(p-1)n+t} \equiv x^t \equiv 1 \bmod p,$$

which contradicts the fact that $x$ is a generator of the set of nonzero elements of $J/(p)$. Hence

$$r \equiv x^{2n} \bmod p$$

so that $x^n$ is a zero mod $p$ of $\lambda^2 - r$, and we see that $r$ is a quadratic residue modulo $p$.

Now we come to the counterpart of the discriminant for quadratic polynomials. This involves a certain mapping from a subset of $J \times J$ into $J$, and this function is defined in terms of the Legendre symbol.

DEFINITION 9.15. If $r$ is an element of $J$ and $p$ is an odd prime, then the *Legendre symbol* $(r/p)$ is defined to be (i) 1 if $r$ is a quadratic residue mod $p$, (ii) 0 if $r \equiv 0 \bmod p$, and (iii) $-1$ otherwise.

This symbol defines a mapping from $J \times P_1$, where $P_1$ is the set of odd primes of $J$, onto the set $\{1, 0, -1\}$. Our aim is to find an easy way of evaluating the Legendre symbol since such a process would clearly tell us whether or not a certain quadratic polynomial has a zero mod $p$.

*Example* 3. Evaluate $(-1/11)$, $(5/11)$, and $(10/3)$.

The polynomial $\lambda^2 + 1$ has a zero mod 11 if and only if $\lambda^2 - 10$ has a zero mod 11 since

$$-1 \equiv 10 \bmod 11.$$

Thus $(-1/11) = (10/11) = -1$ since we know that 10 is not a quadratic residue mod 11. From Example 2 we know that 5 is a quadratic residue mod 11, and so

$$(5/11) = 1.$$

Finally $(10/3) = (1/3)$ since $\lambda^2 - 10$ has a zero mod 3 if and only if $\lambda^2 - 1$ has a zero mod 3 as

$$10 \equiv 1 \bmod 3.$$

Obviously $\lambda^2 - 1$ does have a zero mod 3, and so $(10/3) = (1/3) = 1$.

THEOREM 9.36. *Let $r$ and $s$ be rational integers and $p$ be an odd prime. Then*

(i) $$(r/p) = (s/p) \quad \textit{if } r \equiv s \bmod p,$$

*and*

(ii) $$(rs/p) = (r/p)(s/p).$$

To prove (i) we note that, if $r \equiv s \bmod p$, then $(r/p) = (s/p)$ since $\lambda^2 - r$ has a zero mod $p$ if and only if $\lambda^2 - s$ has a zero mod $p$.

To prove (ii) we go back to the proofs of Theorems 9.34 and 9.35. If $r$ and $s$, reduced modulo $p$, are both relatively prime to $p$, then $r$ and $s$ are powers of the generating element $x$,

$$r \equiv x^m \bmod p$$

and

$$s \equiv x^n \bmod p.$$

Thus

$$rs \equiv x^{n+m} \bmod p.$$

Now

$$(rs/p) = 1$$

implies that $n + m$ is even, which means that $m$ and $n$ are both either even or odd, so that

$$(r/p) = (s/p) = 1 \text{ or } -1$$

and

$$(rs/p) = (r/p)(s/p) = 1.$$

Similarly, if $(rs/p) = -1$, then $n + m$ is odd and exactly one of $n$ and $m$ is even so that

$$(rs/p) = (r/p)(s/p) = -1.$$

Finally, if $rs$ is divisible by $p$, then either $r$ or $s$ is divisible by $p$, and conversely. So, in all cases

$$(rs/p) = (r/p)(s/p).$$

*Corollary* 9.36.1. If $(a, p) = 1$, then $(a^2/p) = 1$.

These results are useful in evaluating the Legendre symbol, but the principal simplifications stem from the following amazing theorems due to Legendre and Gauss.

THEOREM 9.37. $(2/p) = (-1)^n$ *where* $8n = p^2 - 1$.

THEOREM 9.38 (THE QUADRATIC RECIPROCITY LAW). *If $p$ and $q$ are distinct odd primes, then*

$$(p/q)(q/p) = (-1)^{nm}$$

*where* $2n = p - 1$ *and* $2m = q - 1$.

Proofs of these theorems can be found in the books listed at the end of this chapter or in the article by D. H. Lehmer. We shall *not* discuss the proofs here. Instead we will work out some simple examples.

*Example* 4. Determine whether $\lambda^2 + 11$ has a zero modulo 23 by evaluating $(-11/23)$.

Now

$$-11 \equiv 12 \bmod 23$$

so that

$$(-11/23) = (12/23).$$

Factoring 12 leads to

$$(12/23) = (4/23)(3/23) = (3/23)$$

since

$$(4/23) = 1.$$

By the Quadratic Reciprocity Law,

$$(3/23)(23/3) = (-1)^6 = 1,$$

so that

$$(3/23) = (3/23)(23/3)(23/3) = (23/3).$$

Since

$$23 \equiv 2 \bmod 3$$

we know that

$$(23/3) = (2/3),$$

and since

$$(2/3) = (-1)^1 = -1$$

by Theorem 9.37, we conclude that

$$(-11/23) = (12/23) = (3/23) = (2/3) = -1.$$

Thus the polynomial $\lambda^2 + 11$ has no zero in $J/(23)$.

*Example* 5. Determine whether the principal ideal (29) of $QD(53)$ is a prime of $K(53)$.

Since $53 \equiv 1 \bmod 4$ we know that (29) is prime if and only if the congruence

$$t^2 + t \equiv (1/4)(m - 1) \bmod 29$$

has no solution. Now the polynomial $\lambda^2 + \lambda - 13$ has a zero mod 29 if and only if the polynomial

$$\lambda^2 - (b^2 - 4c) = \lambda^2 - 53$$

has a zero mod 29 by Theorem 9.33, and this can be checked out by using the Legendre symbol. We see that

$$(53/29) = (24/29) = (4/29)(2/29)(3/29),$$

and since

$$(4/29) = 1,$$
$$(2/29) = (-1)^{105} = -1,$$

and

$$(3/29) = (3/29)(29/3)(29/2) = (-1)^{14}(29/3)$$
$$= (2/3) = -1,$$

we conclude that

$$(53/29) = 1(-1)(-1) = 1.$$

Therefore $\lambda^2 + \lambda - 13$ has a zero mod 29, and although we do not know this zero we do know that the ideal (29) is not a prime in $K(53)$. To determine the factorization of (29) we fall back on the substitution process and find that

$$(6)^2 + 6 - 13 = 29$$

and

$$(-7)^2 - 7 - 13 = 29.$$

Thus (29) factors into primes in $K(53)$ as

$$(29) = (29, 6 + \theta)(29, 22 + \theta).$$

*Example* 6. Describe all odd primes $p$ such that $(3/p) = 1$.
Now

$$(3/p) = (p/3)(-1)^n$$

where $2n = p - 1$, and

$$(p/3) = \text{either } (1/3) \quad \text{or} \quad (2/3).$$

Since $(1/3) = 1$ and $(2/3) = -1$

whereas

$$(-1)^n = 1 \qquad \text{if } p \equiv 1 \bmod 4$$

and

$$(-1)^n = -1 \qquad \text{if } p \equiv 3 \bmod 4,$$

we see that $(3/p) = 1$ if and only if either

$$p \equiv 1 \bmod 3 \qquad \text{and} \qquad p \equiv 1 \bmod 4$$

or

$$p \equiv 2 \bmod 3 \qquad \text{and} \qquad p \equiv 3 \bmod 4.$$

Then we conclude that 3 is a quadratic residue mod $p$ if and only if $p \equiv 1$ or 11 mod 12.

## Exercise 9.8

**1.** Determine the quadratic residues mod $p$ for $p = 7$ and $p = 13$ by finding in each case an element $x$ such that the nonzero elements of $J/(p)$ are given by $x, x^2, \cdots, x^{p-1}$.

**2.** Factor the polynomial $\lambda^{p-1} - 1$ over $J/(p)$ for $p = 7$ and 13.

**3.** Show that $\lambda^2 + 15$ has a zero mod 23 by evaluating $(-15/23)$. Find the zeros mod 23.

**4.** Evaluate the following: (59/131), (365/877), (783/863), and (−477/547).

**5.** Determine if (73) is a prime of $K(m)$ when (*a*) $m = 17$; (*b*) $m = -17$; (*c*) $m = 29$; (*d*) $m = 35$.

**6.** Determine all primes $p$ such that 2 is a quadratic residue mod $p$.

**7.** Show that $-1$ is a quadratic residue of the odd prime $p$ if and only if $p \equiv 1 \bmod 4$. (See Chapter 4.)

**8.** Analyze the equation $(5/p) = (p/5)$, and show that 5 is a quadratic residue modulo the odd prime $p$ if and only if $p$ is of the form $10k + 1$ or $10k - 1$.

**9.** Show that the polynomial $\lambda^2 - 15$ has zeros mod $p$ for $p = 7, 11, 17, 43$, and 61.

**10.** Check for zeros mod 997 of $\lambda^2 - 231$.

**11.** Let $m$ be a positive, square-free rational integer and prove that $a$ is a quadratic residue modulo $m$ if and only if $a$ is a quadratic residue modulo each prime divisor of $m$. (Use the Chinese Remainder Theorem.)

**12.** Illustrate Problem 11 by determining all of the quadratic residues modulo 6; modulo 10; modulo 15.

**13.** Show that the result of Example 6 can be used to check for primes in $J$ as follows: If $n = k^2 - 3$ and 3 is not a factor of $n$, then $n$ is a prime if $n$ is not divisible by any prime $q$ of the form $12r + 1$ or $12r - 1$. Thus 61 is a prime since 11, 13, 23, 37, 47, and 59 are not factors of 61.

**14.** Show that the polynomial $\lambda^2 + b\lambda + c$ has a zero modulo the odd prime $p$ if and only if $((b^2 - 4c)/p)$ is 1 or 0.

**15.** What can you say about the zeros mod $p$ of the following polynomials?

(*a*) $\lambda^2 - 3\lambda + 4$ and $p = 23$.
(*b*) $7\lambda^2 - 3\lambda + 11$ and $p = 19$.
(*c*) $\lambda^2 + 11\lambda - 13$ and $p = 227$.

## 9.9 Principal Ideal Domains

Our object in this section is to prove that the factorization of a composite element of $QD(m)$ into primes is unique (up to units and arrangement) if and only if the ideals of $QD(m)$ are all principal ideals. But first we list a few simple results about principal ideals.

THEOREM 9.39. *If $a$ and $b$ are elements of $QD(m)$, then:*

*(1) $(a) = (b)$ if and only if $a = eb$, $e$ a unit.*
*(2) $(a)(b) = (ab)$.*

To prove the first statement suppose $a = eb$ where $e$ is a unit. Now for any $x$ in $QD(m)$ we have

$$xa = xeb$$

so that

$$(a) \subseteq (b).$$

Since $e$ is a unit it has an inverse $e^{-1}$ in $QD(m)$ so that

$$e^{-1}a = e^{-1}eb = 1b = b.$$

The same argument as used above shows that

$$(b) \subseteq (a).$$

Hence $(a) = (b)$.

For the converse suppose $(a) = (b)$. Then $QD(m)$ contains elements $c$ and $d$ such that

$$a = cb \qquad \text{and} \qquad b = da.$$

Combining these yields

$$a = cda,$$

so that, if $a \neq 0$, then

$$cd = 1$$

and $c$ and $d$ are units. Of course if either $a$ or $b$ equals 0 then both do and the result is trivially true.

The second statement is a consequence of the Distributive Law. An arbitrary element of $(ab)$ is of the form $xab$ for some $x$ in $QD(m)$ and since $xa$ is in $(a)$ we see that

$$(ab) \subseteq (a)(b).$$

On the other hand, taking $xa$ from $(a)$ and $zb$ from $(b)$ we have $xazb$ in $(a)(b)$. Clearly $xazb$ is in $(ab)$ so that sums of such elements are in $(ab)$ also. Thus

$$(a)(b) \subseteq (ab)$$

and we conclude that $(ab) = (a)(b)$.

THEOREM 9.40. *If every ideal of $QD(m)$ is principal, then $QD(m)$ has the unique factorization property.*

Let $x$ be a composite element of $QD(m)$. We know already that $x$ is expressible as

$$x = p_1 p_2 \cdots p_n$$

where the $p_i$ are primes in $QD(m)$, and we can write the principal ideal $(x)$ as

$$(x) = (p_1)(p_2)\cdots(p_n).$$

The important conclusion that we can draw from the fact that ideals in $QD(m)$ are principal is that the principal ideals $(p_i)$ are prime in $K(m)$. For, if

$$(p) = AB, \qquad A \text{ and } B \text{ in } K(m),$$

then $A$ and $B$ are principal ideals,

$$A = (a) \qquad \text{and} \qquad B = (b),$$

so that

$$(p) = (a)(b) = (ab)$$

and

$$p = eab$$

where $e$ is a unit in $QD(m)$. Since $p$ is a prime in $QD(m)$ this means that $a$ or $b$ is a unit and $(p)$ is a prime in $K(m)$.

So suppose $x$ factors as

$$x = q_1q_2\cdots q_r$$

where the $q_i$ are primes of $QD(m)$. Then in $K(m)$ we have

$$(x) = (p_1)(p_2)\cdots(p_n) = (q_1)(q_2)\cdots(q_r)$$

and the principal ideals $(p_i)$ and $(q_j)$ are primes in $K(m)$. Since factorization into primes in $K(m)$ is unique we conclude that $r = n$ and, relabeling where required,

$$(p_1) = (q_1), (p_2) = (q_2), \cdots, (p_n) = (q_n).$$

Consequently the factorization of $x$ into primes is unique up to units.

The converse is also true and is proved in similar fashion.

THEOREM 9.41. *If factorization into primes in $QD(m)$ is unique (up to units), then every ideal of $QD(m)$ is a principal ideal.*

Because of the factorization theorem for $K(m)$ and Theorem 9.39 it is only necessary to prove that the prime ideals of $QD(m)$ are principal, so denote by $P$ a prime ideal of $QD(m)$. We select an element $x \neq 0$ from $P$ and express $x$ in the form

$$x = p_1p_2\cdots p_n$$

where the $p_i$ are primes of $QD(m)$. This is possible since $P$ is not the unit ideal (1). Now we switch again to principal ideals so that

$$(x) = (p_1)(p_2)\cdots(p_n),$$

and this time the ideals $(p_i)$ are again primes of $K(m)$. For suppose $p$ is a prime in $QD(m)$ and

$$(p) = AB, \qquad A \text{ and } B \text{ ideals.}$$

Then if neither $A$ nor $B$ equals $(p)$ there exists an element $a$ in $A$ and an element $b$ in $B$ such that neither has $p$ as a factor. However, the product $ab$ is in $(p)$ and so does have $p$ as a factor. This contradicts the unique factorization property of $QD(m)$, which implies that the factorization of $ab$ into primes is the unique factorization obtained by factoring the two factors $a$ and $b$. Hence the supposition that $(p)$ is *not* a prime ideal leads to a contradiction of the unique factorization property of $QD(m)$, and so we see that $(p)$ must be a prime ideal.

Now we consider the factorization of the ideal $(x)$,

$$(x) = (p_1)\cdots(p_n).$$

We know that the ideals $(p_i)$ are prime ideals, and by the unique factorization theorem for $K(m)$ we know also that these are the only prime factors of $(x)$.

But $(x)$ has the prime $P$ as a factor since $x$ lies in the ideal $P$, implying that

$$P \supseteq (x).$$

Therefore $P$ equals one of the principal ideals $(p_i)$, and we conclude that $P$ is a principal ideal.

*Example* 1. Show that factorization into primes in $QD(10)$ is not unique.

A little elementary arithmetic shows us that the ideal (2) is prime in this domain since

$$t^2 \equiv 10 \bmod 2$$

has the solution 0. Then we move on to (3) and find that

$$t^2 \equiv 10 \bmod 3$$

is solvable so that

$$(3) = (3, 1 + \theta)(3, 2 + \theta).$$

Now we can show that the prime ideal $(3, 1 + \theta)$ is not principal, for suppose

$$(3, 1 + \theta) = (a + b\theta)$$

where $a$ and $b$ are in $J$. Then there must exist rational integers $c$ and $d$ such that

$$(a + b\theta)(c + d\theta) = 3,$$

and using norms we have

$$(a^2 - 10b^2)(c^2 - 10d^2) = 9.$$

Now this means that

$$a^2 - 10b^2 = 3 \quad \text{or} \quad -3$$

since otherwise we have

$$(a + b\theta) = (1) \quad \text{or} \quad (3),$$

according to whether

$$a^2 - 10b^2 \qquad \text{or} \qquad c^2 - 10d^2$$

is 1 or $-1$. Consider the equation

$$a^2 - 10b^2 = 3 \quad \text{or} \quad -3$$

modulo 5; then

$$a^2 \equiv 3 \quad \text{or} \quad 2$$

mod 5. But for any $a$ in $J$,

$$a \equiv 0, 1, 2, -1, \quad \text{or} \quad -2$$

mod 5 so that

$$a^2 \equiv 0, 1, 4, 1, \quad \text{or} \quad 4$$

mod 5. Hence $a$ and $b$ do not exist in $J$ such that $(a + b\theta) = (3, 1 + \theta)$ in $QD(10)$.

Note that in $QD(10)$ the integer 9 factors as

$$9 = 3 \cdot 3 = (\theta - 1)(\theta + 1).$$

## Exercise 9.9

**1.** Show that the ideal (17) has a prime ideal divisor in $QD(15)$ which is not principal, by the method of the example in this section.

**2.** Find an element of $QD(15)$ which can be factored into primes in two different ways.

**3.** Let the rational prime $p$ be such that $(p)$ factors as $(p, t_1 + \theta)(p, t_2 + \theta)$ in $K(m)$. Show that, if $m \not\equiv 1 \bmod 4$ and $(p/q) = -1$ for some rational prime factor $q$ of $m$, then $QD(m)$ is not a unique factorization domain. (*Note:* If $p$ is a multiple of $a + b\theta$, then taking norms yields the result $a^2 - mb^2 = p$. Consider modulo $q$.)

**4.** Find five different $QD(m)$ in which the ideals are not all principal.

**5.** In each of the domains of Problem 5 find an element which has two different factorizations into primes.

**6.** Show that the quotient ring $QD(m)/P$ of $QD(m)$ over the ideal $P$ is a field if and only if $P$ is a prime ideal. How many elements are in the quotient ring?

**7.** An ideal $T$ of a commutative ring $S$ is said to be *prime* if $ab$ in $T$ implies that $a$ and/or $b$ is in $T$. Compare this definition with the definition of prime ideal used in this chapter.

**8.** Let $D$ be an integral domain. Show that, if there is a mapping $N$ from $D$ to $J$ such that

(1) $$N(x) = 0 \quad \text{if } x \text{ is zero in } D,$$
(2) $$N(x) > 0 \quad \text{if } x \text{ is not zero in } D,$$

and

(3) $$N(ab) = N(a)N(b),$$

then $D$ has the unique factorization property.

**9.** Let $D = J[\lambda]$ and define

$$N(m(\lambda)) = 0 \qquad \text{if } m(\lambda) = 0,$$
$$N(m(\lambda)) = 10^n \qquad \text{where } n = \deg(m(\lambda)).$$

Show that this mapping satisfies the requirements of Problem 8. Show also that the ideal $T$ generated by the two elements $2\lambda + 2$ and $\lambda^2 - 1$ is *not* a principal ideal in this domain.

## 9.10 Remarks

Most of the material in this chapter can be developed for domains determined by irreducible monic polynomials of higher degree than two over $J$. Such domains are called *algebraic domains*, and their elements are called *algebraic integers*. The development is considerably more involved although the general procedure is about the same. Such treatments can be found in some of the books listed in the reading list.

Other generalizations or partial generalizations of these results exist. Integral quaternions and quaternion ideals have been studied, particularly in connection with the problem of representing a rational integer as a sum of four squares (cf. MacDuffee, pp. 259–268). More exotic generalizations have been invented in other skew fields and noncommutative rings. The difficulties presented by such efforts will be more evident after we have investigated the basic model for noncommutative rings, the total matric ring, in a later chapter.

## 9.11 Suggested Reading

*Article*

Lehmer, D. H., "Low energy proof of the Quadratic Reciprocity Law," *Amer. Math. Monthly*, **64** (1957), 103–106.

*Books*

MacDuffee, C. C., *Introduction to Abstract Algebra*, John Wiley & Sons, New York, 1940.

Niven, J., and H. S. Zuckerman, *An Introduction to the Theory of Numbers*, John Wiley & Sons, New York, 1960.

Pollard, H., *Theory of Algebraic Numbers*, Carus Monograph 9, John Wiley & Sons, New York, 1950.

Stewart, B. M., *Theory of Numbers*, 2nd ed., The Macmillan Co., New York, 1964.

Uspensky, J. V., and M. H. Heaslet, *Elementary Number Theory*, McGraw-Hill Book Co., New York, 1939.

# 10

# Modular Systems

THE MODULAR SYSTEMS (i.e., the rings $J/(m)$ and their extensions) have been growing in importance in recent years. Once considered to be primarily curiosities, these systems are of great interest to many people today for at least two reasons. The modular systems form a veritable gold mine for the teachers of the so-called "new mathematics" in the elementary and secondary schools, and many a science project features such an abstract number system. And in the vast domain of applied mathematics the modular systems, forming a basic component of finite combinatorial mathematics, have been attracting interest also. For a discussion of some applications of these systems the reader is referred to the monograph, *Analysis and Design of Experiments* by H. B. Mann.

In this chapter we investigate the problem of finding the zeros of the polynomials over $J/(m)$ by considering the elements of $J[\lambda]$ modulo $m$. (This material is often referred to as the Theory of Congruences.) Associated with the study of zeros of polynomials is the study of irreducible polynomials, and we determine all of the irreducible polynomials over $J/(p)$ by classifying all of the finite fields and showing that they are the splitting fields of irreducible polynomials over $J/(p)$. We also find the automorphism groups of these fields, the Galois fields.

## 10.1 The Polynomial Ring of $J/(m)$

The element

$$f(\lambda) = a'_0 + a'_1\lambda + \cdots + a'_n\lambda^n$$

of the polynomial ring $S[\lambda]$ with $S = J/(m)$ is the ordered set

$$(a'_0, a'_1, \cdots, a'_n)$$

of elements from $J/(m)$ with $a'_n$ different from zero in $J/(m)$. Instead of working directly with such elements we shall deal with polynomials from $J[\lambda]$ and reduce them relative to the principal ideal $(m)$ of $J[\lambda]$. Thus instead of treating the polynomial

$$1' + 2'\lambda + 2'\lambda^2$$

with components in $J/(4)$ we shall deal with the polynomial

$$1 + 2\lambda + 2\lambda^2$$

with components in $J$ and reduce this relative to the ideal (4) of $J[\lambda]$. Our basis for this switch is the "natural" isomorphism between $J[\lambda]/(m)$ and $(J/(m))[\lambda]$.

THEOREM 10.1. *The mapping* $\boldsymbol{K}$,

$$\boldsymbol{K}\colon a_0 + \cdots + a_n\lambda^n + (m) \to a'_0 + \cdots + a'_n\lambda^n,$$

*where* $a_i$ *is in* $J$ *and* $a'_i = a_i + (m)$ *in* $J/(m)$, *is an isomorphism from* $J[\lambda]/(m)$ *onto the polynomial ring of* $J/(m)$.

We make no distinction between the indeterminates of the two systems $J[\lambda]$ and $(J/(m))[\lambda]$ since the symbols are primarily conveniences anyway. Technically

$$\lambda = (0, 1) \qquad \text{in } J[\lambda]$$

and

$$\lambda = (0', 1') \qquad \text{in } (J/(m))[\lambda],$$

where $0'$ and $1'$ denote the residue classes of $J$ modulo $m$. Moreover we will be reducing the elements of $J[\lambda]$ relative to the principal ideal $(m)$.

The elements of $J[\lambda]/(m)$ are represented uniquely by the remainders left when dividing by the positive integer $m$ which is of degree zero. These remainders are clearly of the form

$$a'_0 + a'_1\lambda + \cdots + a'_n\lambda^n$$

where the $a'_i$ are the least residues modulo $m$. In other words the cosets of $(m)$ in $J[\lambda]$ are represented uniquely by the ordered sets

$$(a'_0, a'_1, \cdots, a'_n)$$

where the $a'_i$ are the representatives of the cosets (i.e., residue classes) of $(m)$ in $J$. This establishes the one-to-one property of $\boldsymbol{K}$, and the definitions of addition and multiplication in $J[\lambda]/(m)$, which are given in terms of these representatives, show that the mapping preserves the arithmetic of the systems.

*Example* 1. Discuss the element

$$f(\lambda) = 3 + 14\lambda + 11\lambda^2 - 10\lambda^3$$

as an element of $J[\lambda]/(6)$ and as an element of $(J/(6))[\lambda]$.

Actually the polynomial $f(\lambda)$ is in neither of these systems since it is in $J[\lambda]$. However, in terms of cosets of the ideal (6) in $J[\lambda]$ it lies in the coset

$$f(\lambda) + (6) = 3 + 2\lambda + 5\lambda^2 + 2\lambda^3 + (6)$$

since

$$f(\lambda) = 3 + 2\lambda + 5\lambda^2 + 2\lambda^3 + 6(2\lambda + \lambda^2 - 2\lambda^3).$$

And in $J$ the elements 3, 14, 11, and $-10$ are representatives of the congruence classes $3 + (6)$, $14 + (6)$, $11 + (6)$, and $-10 + (6)$. These classes are usually represented by 3, 2, 5, and 2, respectively, so that $f(\lambda)$ represents the element

$$(3 + (6), 2 + (6), 5 + (6), 2 + (6))$$

of $(J/(6))[\lambda]$, an element which can also be written as

$$3' + 2'\lambda + 5'\lambda^2 + 2'\lambda^3.$$

Then to study the zeros of a polynomial over $J/(m)$ we consider a polynomial $f(\lambda)$ from $J[\lambda]$ and determine the elements $r$ of $J$ such that

$$f(r) \equiv 0 \bmod m.$$

For surely the residue class $r'$ determined by $r$ modulo $m$ is a zero of $f(\lambda)$, as an element of $(J/(m))[\lambda]$, if and only if

$$f(r') = 0' \qquad \text{in } J/(m),$$

and this happens if and only if $f(\lambda)$, as a representative of a coset of $(m)$ in $J[\lambda]$, specializes onto a multiple of $m$ when $\lambda$ is replaced by $r$.

*Example* 2. Find the zeros of the polynomial $2' + 2'\lambda + 3'\lambda^2$ over $J/(4)$. The elements of $J/(4)$ are $0'$, $1'$, $2'$, and $3'$ and direct substitution yields

$$\begin{aligned} 0'&: 2' + 0' + 0' = 2', \\ 1'&: 2' + 2' + 3' = 3', \\ 2'&: 2' + 0' + 2' = 0', \\ 3'&: 2' + 2' + 3' = 3', \end{aligned}$$

and we conclude that $2'$ is the only zero of this polynomial from $J/(6)$. Now consider the polynomial

$$f(\lambda) = 2 + 2\lambda + 3\lambda^2.$$

Then

$$f(0) = 2,$$
$$f(1) = 7,$$
$$f(2) = 18,$$

and

$$f(3) = 33.$$

Furthermore,

$$f(a + 6b) = f(a) + (6)$$

since the mapping

$$H: a \to a + (m), \qquad a \text{ in } J,$$

is a homomorphism from $J$ onto $J/(6)$. So we conclude that the residue class of 2 modulo 6 is the zero of $f(\lambda)$ modulo 6 (i.e., considered as a polynomial over $J/(6)$).

*Example* 3. Find the zeros modulo 10 of the polynomial

$$217 + 39\lambda + 72\lambda^2 - 30\lambda^3.$$

Replacing this polynomial from $J[\lambda]$ by the "simplest" representative of the coset of the ideal (6) to which it belongs we obtain the polynomial

$$f_1(\lambda) = 7 + 9\lambda + 2\lambda^2.$$

However, for the purposes of substitution the representative

$$f(\lambda) = -3 - \lambda + 2\lambda^2$$

is a better one to handle. Then

$$f(0) = -3,\ f(1) = -2,\ f(2) = 3,\ f(3) = 12,\ f(4) = 25,\ f(5) = 42,$$
$$f(-4) = 33,\ f(-3) = 18,\ f(-2) = 7,\ f(-1) = 0,$$

and we conclude that the residue class of $-1$ (which also includes 9) is the zero modulo 10 of the original polynomial. Note that the representative of least *absolute* value is often a more convenient representative of a congruence class to select in this type of work.

THEOREM 10.2. *The element $r'$ of the ring $J/(m)$ is a zero of the polynomial*

$$f(\lambda) = (a'_0, a'_1, \cdots, a'_n)$$

*from $(J/(m))[\lambda]$ if and only if in $J$ the integer*

$$a_0 + a_1 r + \cdots + a_n r^n \equiv 0 \bmod m.$$

By the definition of a zero of a polynomial we know that

$$f(r') = a'_0 + a'_1 r' + \cdots + a'_n (r')^n = 0'$$

if and only if $r'$ is a zero of $f(\lambda)$. Because of the homomorphism from $J$ onto $J/(m)$ this is equivalent to the condition

$$a_0 + a_1 r + \cdots + a_n r^n \equiv 0 \bmod m.$$

Hereafter we shall work with elements of $J[\lambda]$ and elements of $J$ and reduce them relative to the modulus $m$ in a manner which seems convenient.

Now the problem of determining the zeros modulo $m$ of the polynomial $f(\lambda)$ with rational integral coefficients is in a sense a completely solvable problem. We select apparently convenient representatives from each of the $m$ residue classes, substitute in $f(\lambda)$, and reduce the resulting element of $J$ modulo $m$. Thus in a finite number of steps all of the zeros modulo $m$ can be determined. However, since $m$ can be arbitrarily large it is important to introduce some short cuts.

THEOREM 10.3. *If $q$ is a rational integral divisor of $m$, then $r$ is a zero* modulo *$q$ of $f(\lambda)$ if it is a zero* modulo *$m$ of $f(\lambda)$.*

In other words, if an element of $J$ has the factor $m$, then it also has the factor $q$. Thus if $f(r)$ is not a multiple of $q$ it cannot be a multiple of $m$.

*Example* 4. Show that $\lambda^2 + \lambda + 1$ has no zeros in $J/(6)$.

Consider this polynomial modulo 2. Since neither 0 nor 1 is a zero mod 2 of this polynomial we conclude from the above result that the polynomial has no zeros modulo 6.

This certainly serves to shorten the work when a factor $q$ of $m$ is found such that $f(\lambda)$ has no zeros modulo $q$. The obvious factors of $m$ to check first are the prime factors, so the zeros of a polynomial over $J/(p)$ are considered in the next section.

*Example* 5. Check the polynomial

$$f(\lambda) = 2\lambda^2 + 19\lambda - 13$$

for zeros modulo 10.

First we consider the polynomial modulo 2. Since $f(\lambda)$ reduces here to $\lambda + 1$ we see that $f(\lambda)$ has one zero mod 2, namely 1. (That is, if $r$ is an odd integer, then $f(r)$ is even.) Then we consider $f(\lambda)$ modulo 5 and find that it reduces to

$$g(\lambda) = 2\lambda^2 + 4\lambda + 2 = 2(\lambda + 1)^2$$

so that 4 is the only zero mod 5 of $f(\lambda)$. (That is, if $r$ is an integer of the form $5k + 4$, then $f(r)$ is a multiple of 5.)

Is it possible to obtain a zero mod 10 for $f(\lambda)$ from this information? Well, consider the two linear congruences

$$x \equiv 1 \bmod 2 \qquad \text{and} \qquad x \equiv 4 \bmod 5.$$

By the Chinese Remainder Theorem there is a unique integer $x$ modulo 10 satisfying these conditions, as we see that

$$f(x) \equiv f(1) \equiv 0 \bmod 2$$

and

$$f(x) \equiv f(4) \equiv 0 \bmod 5.$$

Since $f(x)$ is a multiple of both 2 and 5 we conclude that $x$ is a zero modulo 10 of $f(\lambda)$. This process is quite general and will be discussed later. In the meantime the student should review the section of Chapter 3 in which the Chinese Remainder Theorem is developed.

## Exercise 10.1

**1.** Discuss the polynomial

$$f(\lambda) = 2 + 7\lambda + 31\lambda^2 - 16\lambda^3$$

as an element of $J[\lambda]/(m)$ when (*a*) $m = 7$; (*b*) $m = 8$; (*c*) $m = 10$.

**2.** Discuss the polynomial

$$f(\lambda) = 13 - 6\lambda + 32\lambda^2 - 70\lambda^3$$

as an element of $(J/(m))[\lambda]$ when (*a*) $m = 7$; (*b*) $m = 8$; (*c*) $m = 10$.

**3.** Find the zeros mod $m$ of

$$f(\lambda) = 77 + 39\lambda - 78\lambda^2 + 19\lambda^3$$

when (*a*) $m = 3$; (*b*) $m = 4$; (*c*) $m = 5$; (*d*) $m = 6$.

**4.** Show that the polynomial

$$f(\lambda) = 1 + 101\lambda + 1001\lambda^{1000}$$

has no zeros modulo 998. Does $f(\lambda)$ have a zero in $J/(m)$ when $m$ is even?

**5.** Let $r$ be a zero mod $m$ of $f(\lambda)$. Show that in $J[\lambda]$

$$f(\lambda) = (\lambda - r)q(\lambda) + k$$

where $k \equiv 0 \bmod m$.

**6.** Divide $\lambda + 1$ into the polynomial $f(\lambda)$ of Example 3. What do you conclude about the zeros mod 10 of the quotient?

**7.** When does the polynomial $f(\lambda) = a\lambda + b$ have a zero mod $m$?

**8.** Find the zeros mod 5 and mod 7 of the polynomial

$$f(\lambda) = \lambda^3 + 3\lambda^2 + 31\lambda + 23$$

and determine the zeros mod 35 of $f(\lambda)$.

**9.** The zeros mod 25 of the polynomial

$$f(\lambda) = \lambda^3 + 3\lambda^2 + \lambda + 3$$

are 2, 7, 12, 17, 18, and 22. Find the zeros mod 50 of this polynomial.

**10.** Find a homomorphism of $J[\lambda]$ onto $(J/(m))[\lambda]$, and describe it as an extension of the natural homomorphism from $J$ onto $J/(m)$.

**11.** Take $f(\lambda)$ as an arbitrary element of $J[\lambda]$ and $r$ as an arbitrary element of $J$. Define $f_1(\lambda)$ to be the polynomial over $J/(m)$ whose components are the residue classes mod $m$ of the corresponding components of $f(\lambda)$, and let $r'$ denote the residue class mod $m$ to which $r$ belongs. Show that using function composition

$$\boldsymbol{HG_1 = GH}$$

where $\boldsymbol{G}$, $\boldsymbol{G_1}$, and $\boldsymbol{H}$ are the mappings

$$\boldsymbol{G}: f(\lambda) \to f(r), \qquad f(\lambda) \text{ in } J[\lambda],$$
$$\boldsymbol{G_1}: f_1(\lambda) \to f_1(r'), \qquad f_1(\lambda) \text{ in } (J/(m))[\lambda],$$

and

$$\boldsymbol{H}: f(\lambda) \to f_1(\lambda), \qquad f(\lambda) \text{ in } J[\lambda].$$

In other words verify that it is possible to travel from $f(\lambda)$ to $f_1(r')$ by either of the two paths in the diagram shown in Fig. 10.1.

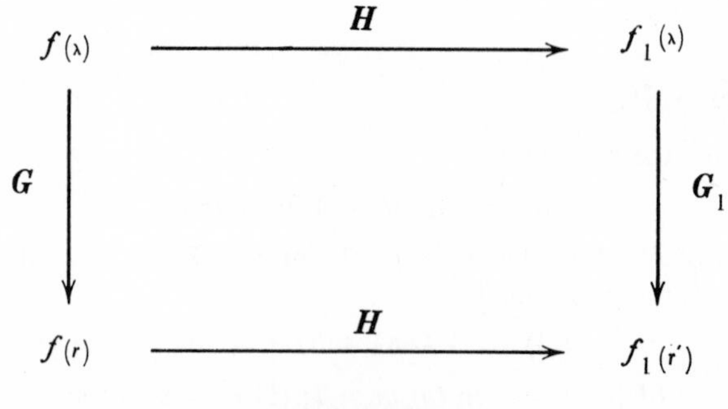


**Figure 10.1**

**12.** Can a polynomial $f(\lambda)$ have more than $n$ zeros mod $m$ where $n$ is the degree of $f(\lambda)$? (See Problem 9.) If so, what must be true of $m$?

## 10.2 Zeros Modulo a Prime

The problem of determining the zeros modulo a prime $p$ of the polynomial $f(\lambda)$ is somewhat simpler than the corresponding problem for composite moduli. In the first place we are dealing essentially with an element from the integral domain $(J/(p))[\lambda]$ so that our knowledge of such polynomial domains can be used.

THEOREM 10.4. *If $f(\lambda)$ as an element with components in $J/(p)$ has degree $n$, then $f(\lambda)$ cannot have more than $n$ zeros modulo $p$.*

This is just a restatement of the well-known result on the zeros of an element from the polynomial domain of a field.

Of course we can also use the theorems on which this is based.

THEOREM 10.5. *If $f(\lambda)$ is a monic polynomial of degree $n$ over $J$ and $r$ is in $J$, then there exists a monic polynomial $g(\lambda)$ of degree $n - 1$ over $J$ such that*

$$f(\lambda) = (\lambda - r)g(\lambda) + k, \qquad k \text{ in } J.$$

*Corollary* 10.5.1. The integer $r$ is a zero mod $p$ of $f(\lambda)$ if and only if

$$k \equiv 0 \bmod p.$$

*Corollary* 10.5.2. If $r$ and $r_1$ are zeros mod $p$ of $f(\lambda)$ and if

$$r \not\equiv r_1 \bmod p,$$

then $r_1$ is a zero mod $p$ of $g(\lambda)$.

The theorem is a simple consequence of the Divisor Theorem for $J[\lambda]$, and the first corollary follows easily by substitution (and is true if $p$ is replaced by any positive integer). The second corollary follows by substitution and the fact that $J/(p)$ is a field. Hence in $J/(p)$

$$f(r_1) = (r_1 - r)g(r_1) = 0$$

implies that

$$g(r_1) = 0$$

since

$$r_1 - r \neq 0 \qquad \text{in } J/(p).$$

*Example* 1. Find the zeros modulo 5 of the polynomial $2\lambda^3 + 11\lambda^2 - 8$. Reduced modulo 5 this becomes

$$2\lambda^3 + \lambda^2 + 2,$$

and we make it monic modulo 5 by multiplying by 3, the multiplicative inverse of 2 modulo 5. Thus we obtain

$$f(\lambda) = \lambda^3 + 3\lambda^2 + 1.$$

Now $f(1) = 5$ in $J$ so that 1 is a zero modulo 5, and we divide $\lambda - 1$ into $f(\lambda)$:

$$f(\lambda) = (\lambda - 1)(\lambda^2 + 4\lambda + 4) + 5.$$

So

$$g(\lambda) = \lambda^2 + 4\lambda + 4$$

and $k = 5$ is surely a multiple of 5. $g(\lambda)$ factors easily (we could use the quadratic formula also since $(2, 5) = 1$) and

$$g(\lambda) = (\lambda + 2)^2.$$

Thus the polynomial $2\lambda^3 + 11\lambda^2 - 8$ has two zeros modulo 5, namely 1 and 3.

There is also another reduction theorem which is sometimes useful in shortening the task of finding zeros modulo $p$, and it is based on the Little Theorem of Fermat and the Divisor Theorem in $J[\lambda]$.

THEOREM 10.6. *If $f(\lambda)$ is a monic polynomial of degree $n$ over $J$, then the zeros modulo $p$ of $f(\lambda)$ are precisely the zeros modulo $p$ of the polynomial $h(\lambda)$ where*

$$f(\lambda) = g(\lambda)(\lambda^p - \lambda) + h(\lambda)$$

*and* $\deg\big(h(\lambda)\big) < p$ or $h(\lambda) = 0$.

The unique polynomials $g(\lambda)$ and $h(\lambda)$ from $J[\lambda]$ come as a result of the Divisor Theorem, and since every element of $J/(p)$ is a zero of $\lambda^p - \lambda$ we see that

$$f(r) \equiv h(r) \bmod p$$

for every $r$ in $J$.

*Example* 2. Find the zeros modulo 5 of the polynomial $2 + \lambda^5 + 2\lambda^7$. Dividing $\lambda^5 - \lambda$ into this polynomial we obtain

$$h(\lambda) = 2\lambda^2 + \lambda + 4.$$

Multiplying by 3 and reducing modulo 5 we get the polynomial

$$\lambda^2 + 3\lambda + 2 = (\lambda + 2)(\lambda + 1),$$

and so the zeros modulo 5 of the element $2\lambda^7 + \lambda^5 + 2$ are 3 and 4 (or $-1$ and $-2$ since any representative of a residue class mod 5 identifies that class).

*Corollary* 10.6.1. The element $f(\lambda)$ of $F[\lambda]$, $F = J/(p)$, has no zeros in $J/(p)$ if and only if $f(\lambda)$ and $\lambda^p - \lambda$ are relatively prime in $F[\lambda]$.

This hinges upon the fact that the polynomial $\lambda^p - \lambda$ of $F[\lambda]$ has each of the $p$ elements of $J/(p)$ as a zero. Hence

$$\lambda^p - \lambda = \lambda(\lambda - 1)\cdots(\lambda - p + 1)$$

in $F[\lambda]$ so that it is quite clear that $f(\lambda)$ can have no zeros in $J/(p)$ if and only if $f(\lambda)$ and $\lambda^p - \lambda$ are relatively prime in $F[\lambda]$.

Switching back to the polynomial domain of $J$ we pose a little problem.

*Problem.* If $f(\lambda)$ is a polynomial of degree $n$ over $J$, determine the number of primes $p$ such that $f(\lambda)$ has a zero modulo $p$. (Clearly $n$ must be positive before a problem exists.)

*Solution.* There are infinitely many such primes. For suppose

$$f(\lambda) = a_0 + a_1\lambda + \cdots + a_n\lambda^n, \qquad n > 0,$$

has zeros modulo only the $m$ primes $p_1, \cdots, p_m$. We can show that this leads to an impossible situation.

Form the integer

$$a = a_0 p_1 \cdots p_m;$$

then for an arbitrary $c$ in $J$ we have

$$f(ac) = a_0 g(c)$$

where

$$g(\lambda) = 1 + b_1\lambda + \cdots + b_n\lambda^n$$

and

$$b_i \equiv 0 \bmod p_1 p_2 \cdots p_m.$$

Thus for any integer $c$, $g(\lambda)$ is a polynomial such that

$$g(c) \equiv 1 \bmod p_i, \qquad i = 1, 2, \cdots, m,$$

and we see that $g(\lambda)$ has no zeros modulo any of the $m$ primes $p_1, \cdots, p_m$. From this we conclude that $g(\lambda)$ has no zeros modulo any prime $p$, for, if $r$ is an integer such that

$$g(r) \equiv 0 \bmod p,$$

then

$$f(ar) = a_0 g(r) \equiv 0 \bmod p,$$

and we see that $p$ must be one of the primes $p_1, \cdots, p_m$. Since these have already been ruled out we know that $g(\lambda)$ has no zeros modulo any prime in $J$.

Now a polynomial of positive degree with such a property cannot exist, for this condition implies that

$$g(c) = 1 \quad \text{or} \quad -1$$

for every $c$ in $J$. Why is this? Well, if

$$g(c) = m,$$

where $m$ has a prime factor $p$, then $c$ is a zero mod $p$ of $g(\lambda)$. Thus if $g(\lambda)$ has no zeros modulo any prime, then $m$ cannot have any prime factors, and 1 and $-1$ are the only such elements of $J$. But consider the polynomial

$$h(\lambda) = (g(\lambda))^2 - 1;$$

it is of degree $2n$ but has *every* element of $J$ as a zero. This is impossible, and we have proved the solution statement correct.

## Exercise 10.2

**1.** Find the zeros modulo $p$ of

$$f(\lambda) = \lambda^3 + 3\lambda^2 + 29\lambda + 23$$

when (*a*) $p = 3$; (*b*) $p = 5$; (*c*) $p = 7$; (*d*) $p = 11$.

**2.** Find the zeros mod 3 of the polynomial $2\lambda^4 + \lambda^3 + \lambda + 4$.

**3.** Factor the polynomial $\lambda^3 + \lambda + 16$ as an element of $(J/(2))[\lambda]$.

**4.** Find all of the zeros in $J/(3)$ of $\lambda^9 - \lambda$. Factor the polynomial over $J/(3)$.

**5.** Show that the polynomial $f(\lambda) = \lambda^3 + \lambda^2 + \lambda + 1$ has zeros modulo 2 and modulo 3. Form the polynomial $g(\lambda)$ used in the problem at the end of the section.

**6.** Find the zeros mod 7 of $3\lambda^3 - 6\lambda^2 + 5\lambda - 3$.

**7.** Find the zeros mod 13 of $\lambda^4 + 11$.

**8.** Find the zeros mod 11 of $2\lambda^4 + 8\lambda + 9$.

**9.** Find the zeros mod 5 of $3\lambda^3 + 239\lambda^2 + 5\lambda + 242$.

**10.** Show that, for any prime $p$ of the form $8k + 1$, the polynomial $\lambda^4 + 1$ has four zeros modulo $p$. (Consider $\lambda^{8k} - 1$ and its factors.)

**11.** Show that $f(\lambda) = \lambda^2 + 1$ has a zero mod $p$ if and only if $p$ is a prime of the form $4k + 1$. (See Chapter 4.)

**12.** Combine Problem 11 and the problem of this section to get a proof that $J$ contains infinitely many primes of the form $4k + 1$.

**13.** By considering $\lambda^p - \lambda$ prove that

$$(p - 1)! \equiv -1 \bmod p.$$

**14.** Let $f(\lambda) = a\lambda^2 + b\lambda + c$ and show that $f(\lambda)$ has a zero modulo the odd prime $p$ if and only if the polynomial $\lambda^2 - (b^2 - 4ac)$ has a zero mod $p$. (Read the section on quadratic residues in the preceding chapter.)

**15.** Use Problem 14 to determine if:

(*a*) $3\lambda^2 + 8\lambda - 6$ has a zero mod 13.
(*b*) $5\lambda^2 + 7\lambda + 15$ has a zero mod 11.
(*c*) $\lambda^2 - 10\lambda - 7$ has a zero mod 17.

## 10.3 Zeros Modulo a Prime Power

If $q = p^n$, where $p$ is a prime and $n > 1$, then we know from Theorem 10.3 that a polynomial $f(\lambda)$ has a zero modulo $p^{n-1}$ if it has a zero modulo $q$. In this section we shall study the converse question: Can a zero modulo $q$ be constructed from a zero modulo $p^{n-1}$ for $f(\lambda)$? We will develop a step-up procedure for lifting a zero mod $p^{n-1}$ of $f(\lambda)$ up to a zero mod $p^n$ of $f(\lambda)$ when such a zero mod $p^n$ exists. This method is based on the concept of the formal derivative.

DEFINITION 10.1. If $f(\lambda)$ is a polynomial over $J$,

$$f(\lambda) = a_0 + a_1\lambda + \cdots + a_n\lambda^n,$$

then the *formal derivative* of $f(\lambda)$ is the polynomial

$$Df(\lambda) = a_1 + 2a_2\lambda + \cdots + na_n\lambda^{n-1}.$$

This concept (mentioned earlier for polynomials over $R$) can be defined for any polynomial ring.

*Lemma* 10.1. If $g(\lambda) = (\lambda - a)f(\lambda)$ in $J[\lambda]$, then

$$\boldsymbol{D}g(\lambda) = f(\lambda) + (\lambda - a)\boldsymbol{D}f(\lambda).$$

More general statements about the formal derivative of a product can be proved, but this simple statement is sufficient for our aims.

Denote $f(\lambda)$ as

$$f(\lambda) = a_0 + a_1\lambda + \cdots + a_n\lambda^n;$$

then

$$\begin{aligned} g(\lambda) &= (\lambda - a)f(\lambda), \\ &= -aa_0 + (a_0 - aa_1)\lambda + \cdots + (a_{n-1} - aa_n)\lambda^n + a_n\lambda^{n+1}. \end{aligned}$$

Therefore

$$\boldsymbol{D}g(\lambda) = (a_0 - aa_1) + 2(a_1 - aa_2)\lambda + \cdots + n(a_{n-1} - aa_n)\lambda^{n-1} + (n + 1)a_n\lambda^n,$$

and

$$\boldsymbol{D}f(\lambda) = a_1 + 2a_2\lambda + \cdots + na_n\lambda^{n-1}.$$

Then

$$(\lambda - a)\boldsymbol{D}f(\lambda) = -aa_1 + (a_1 - 2aa_2)\lambda + \cdots + na_n\lambda^n,$$

and adding $f(\lambda)$ to this yields

$$\boldsymbol{D}g(\lambda) = f(\lambda) + (\lambda - a)\boldsymbol{D}f(\lambda).$$

*Example* 1. Find the derivative of

$$g(\lambda) = (\lambda - 2)(\lambda^3 + \lambda + 2)$$

two ways.

(1) $g(\lambda) = -4 + \lambda^2 - 2\lambda^3 + y^4$ so that

$$\boldsymbol{D}g(\lambda) = 2\lambda - 6\lambda^2 + 4\lambda^3.$$

(2) Set $f(\lambda) = 2 + \lambda + \lambda^3$. Then

$$\begin{aligned} \boldsymbol{D}f(\lambda) &= 1 + 3\lambda^2 \\ (\lambda - 2)\boldsymbol{D}f(\lambda) &= -2 + \lambda - 6\lambda^2 + 3\lambda^3 \end{aligned}$$

so that

$$f(\lambda) + (\lambda - 2)\boldsymbol{D}f(\lambda) = 2\lambda - 6\lambda^2 + 4\lambda^3.$$

Now we use Lemma 10.1 to derive *Taylor's expansion* for an element of $J[\lambda]$. (Note that $\boldsymbol{D}^2f(\lambda) = \boldsymbol{D}(\boldsymbol{D}f(\lambda))$ and so forth for repeated differentiations.)

THEOREM 10.7. *If $g(\lambda)$ is an element of degree $n$ from the polynomial domain of $J$, then*

$$g(\lambda) = g(a) + b_1(\lambda - a) + b_2(\lambda - a)^2 + \cdots + b_n(\lambda - a)^n$$

*where $a$ is in $J$ and*

$$b_m = \boldsymbol{D}^m g(a)/m!, \qquad m = 1, 2, \cdots, n.$$

This is in reality an extension of the Remainder Theorem, which states that

$$g(\lambda) = (\lambda - a)f(\lambda) + g(a).$$

Since the degree of the quotient $f(\lambda)$ is $n - 1$ we apply the induction hypothesis to get

$$f(\lambda) = f(a) + (\lambda - a)\boldsymbol{D}f(a) + \cdots + (\lambda - a)\boldsymbol{D}^{n-1}f(a)/(n - 1)!.$$

Then we use the lemma above repeatedly to get

$$\begin{aligned}
\boldsymbol{D}g(\lambda) &= f(\lambda) + (\lambda - a)\boldsymbol{D}f(\lambda),\\
\boldsymbol{D}^2g(\lambda) &= \boldsymbol{D}f(\lambda) + \boldsymbol{D}f(\lambda) + (\lambda - a)\boldsymbol{D}^2f(\lambda),\\
\boldsymbol{D}^3g(\lambda) &= 3\boldsymbol{D}^2f(\lambda) + (\lambda - a)\boldsymbol{D}^3f(\lambda),\\
\boldsymbol{D}^4g(\lambda) &= 4\boldsymbol{D}^3f(\lambda) + (\lambda - a)\boldsymbol{D}^4f(\lambda),\\
&\vdots\\
\boldsymbol{D}^ng(\lambda) &= n\boldsymbol{D}^{n-1}f(\lambda).
\end{aligned}$$

(Note that $\boldsymbol{D}^nf(\lambda) = 0$ since $f(\lambda)$ is of degree $n - 1$.) Therefore, substituting $a$ for $\lambda$, we get

$$\begin{aligned}
\boldsymbol{D}g(a) &= f(a),\\
\boldsymbol{D}^2g(a) &= 2\boldsymbol{D}f(a),\\
\boldsymbol{D}^3g(a) &= 3\boldsymbol{D}^2f(a),\\
\boldsymbol{D}^4g(a) &= 4\boldsymbol{D}^3f(a),\\
&\vdots\\
\boldsymbol{D}^ng(a) &= n\boldsymbol{D}^{n-1}f(a),
\end{aligned}$$

so that collapsing all of this information back into

$$g(\lambda) = (\lambda - a)f(\lambda) + g(a)$$

yields

$$g(\lambda) = g(a) + (\lambda - a)\big(\boldsymbol{D}g(a) + (\lambda - a)\boldsymbol{D}^2g(a)/2 + \cdots + (\lambda - a)^{n-1}\boldsymbol{D}^ng(a)/n!\big)$$

or

$$g(\lambda) = g(a) + b_1(\lambda - a) + b_2(\lambda - a)^2 + \cdots + b_n(\lambda - a)^n,$$

where the $b_m$ are the prescribed elements of $J$.

Of course the expansion does not depend upon the concept of formal differentiation for its existence here, but the derivative provides a convenient method for computing the coefficients in the expansion.

*Example* 2. Find the expansion of $\lambda^3 - 1 = f(\lambda)$ in powers of $\lambda + 1$.

(1) $\boldsymbol{D}f(\lambda) = 3\lambda^2$, $\boldsymbol{D}^2f(\lambda) = 6\lambda$, and $\boldsymbol{D}^3f(\lambda) = 6$. Evaluating these for $a = -1$ we get

$$\lambda^3 + 1 = -2 + 3(\lambda + 1) - 3(\lambda + 1)^2 + (\lambda + 1)^3.$$

(2) Dividing $\lambda + 1$ into $\lambda^3 - 1$ yields

$$\lambda^3 - 1 = (\lambda + 1)(\lambda^2 - \lambda + 1) - 2,$$

dividing $\lambda + 1$ into $\lambda^2 - \lambda + 1$ yields

$$\lambda^2 - \lambda + 1 = (\lambda + 1)(\lambda - 2) + 3,$$

and dividing $\lambda + 1$ into $\lambda - 2$ yields

$$\lambda - 2 = (\lambda + 1) - 3.$$

Working back up the stack we get

$$\lambda^2 - \lambda + 1 = (\lambda + 1)^2 - 3(\lambda + 1) + 3$$

and

$$\lambda^3 - 1 = (\lambda + 1)^3 - 3(\lambda + 1)^2 + 3(\lambda + 1) - 2.$$

Using Taylor's expansion for a polynomial we are able to prove the following *step-up theorem.*

THEOREM 10.8. *Let $f(\lambda)$ be a polynomial over J. If r is a zero* mod $p^n$ *of $f(\lambda)$, then it is expressible as*

$$r = s + tp^{n-1},$$

*where*

$$f(s) = kp^{n-1}$$

*and*

$$k + t\boldsymbol{D}f(s) \equiv 0 \bmod p.$$

From this theorem we see that a zero mod $p^n$ of $f(\lambda)$ is obtained by combining a zero mod $p^{n-1}$ of $f(\lambda)$ with a zero mod $p$ of a linear polynomial. Thus a zero mod $p^n$, when it exists, is a stepped-up version of a zero mod $p^{n-1}$ of $f(\lambda)$.

To prove the theorem we take $r$, a zero mod $p^n$ of $f(\lambda)$, and write it as

$$r = s + tp^{n-1}, \qquad 0 \leqslant s < p^{n-1}.$$

Writing $f(\lambda)$ in powers of $\lambda - s$,

$$f(\lambda) = f(s) + (\lambda - s)\boldsymbol{D}f(s) + \cdots + (\lambda - s)^n\boldsymbol{D}^n f(s)/n!,$$

we see that

$$f(r) = f(s + tp^{n-1}) = f(s) + tp^{n-1}\boldsymbol{D}f(s) + wp^n$$

for some integer $w$ since

$$(s + tp^{n-1} - s)^m \equiv 0 \bmod p^n \qquad \text{for } m > 1.$$

Therefore we have the two congruences,

$$f(s) \equiv 0 \bmod p^{n-1}$$

and

$$f(s) + tp^{n-1}\boldsymbol{D}f(s) \equiv 0 \bmod p^n$$

since

$$f(r) \equiv 0 \bmod p^n.$$

From

$$f(s) \equiv 0 \bmod p^{n-1}$$

we get

$$f(s) = kp^{n-1}$$

so that the congruence

$$f(s) + tp^{n-1}Df(s) \equiv 0 \bmod p^n$$

becomes

$$kp^{n-1} + tp^{n-1}Df(s) \equiv 0 \bmod p^n.$$

Hence dividing by $p^{n-1}$ yields

$$k + tDf(s) \equiv 0 \bmod p.$$

The converse of the theorem is true also since the steps are reversible. Let $s$ be a zero mod $p^{n-1}$ of $f(\lambda)$, and let $t$ be an element of $J$ such that

$$k + tDf(s) \equiv 0 \bmod p,$$

where

$$k = f(s)/p^{n-1}.$$

Then the element

$$r = s + tp^{n-1}$$

is a zero mod $p^n$ of $f(\lambda)$ as the above expansion of $f(\lambda)$ in powers of $\lambda - s$ shows.

THEOREM 10.9. *If $s$ is a zero* mod $p^{n-1}$ *of $f(\lambda)$, if $t$ is a zero* mod $p$ *of the linear polynomial $f(s)/p^{n-1} + \lambda Df(s)$, then $r = s + tp^{n-1}$ is a zero* mod $p^n$ *of $f(\lambda)$.*

*Example* 3. Find the zeros mod 25 of

$$f(\lambda) = \lambda^3 + 3\lambda^2 + \lambda + 3.$$

First we find the zeros mod 5 of $f(\lambda)$ by substitution: $f(1) = 8$, $f(-1) = 4$, $f(2) = 25$, $f(-2) = 5$. Thus 2 and $-2$ are the zeros mod 5 of $f(\lambda)$, and we will try to step them up to zeros mod 25 of $f(\lambda)$.

(1) For $s = 2$ we have $Df(s) = 25$ since

$$Df(\lambda) = 3\lambda^2 + 6\lambda + 1.$$

Then the linear polynomial

$$f(s)/p^{n-1} + \lambda Df(s)$$

has five solutions for $s = 2$ and $p = 5$ since modulo 5 this polynomial reduces to the polynomial

$$5 + 25\lambda \equiv 0 \bmod 5$$

which has, trivially, the solutions 0, 1, 2, 3, and 4 modulo 5. Giving $t$ these values we get five distinct zeros modulo 25 for $f(\lambda)$:

$$2 + 0 = 2, \quad 2 + 1 \cdot 5 = 7, \quad 2 + 2 \cdot 5 = 12, \quad 2 + 3 \cdot 5 = 17,$$

and

$$2 + 4 \cdot 5 = 22.$$

(2) For $s = -2$ we have $f(-2) = 5$ and $Df(-2) = 1$. This time the linear polynomial

$$f(s)/p^{n-1} + \lambda Df(s)$$

is not so trivial, being $1 + \lambda$. It has the one solution 4 mod 5 so that $s = -2$ steps up to $r = -2 + 4(5) = 18$.

Because of Theorem 10.8 we conclude that the classes determined by 2, 7, 12, 17, 18, and 22, are all of the zeros mod 25 of $f(\lambda)$.

However, the student should not jump to the erroneous conclusion that each zero mod $p^{n-1}$ of $f(\lambda)$ can be stepped up to a zero mod $p^n$ of $f(\lambda)$. This is far from being true.

*Example* 4. Determine the zeros modulo 9 of the polynomial

$$f(\lambda) = \lambda^2 + \lambda + 1.$$

It is easy to see that $f(\lambda)$ has exactly one zero modulo 3, namely $s = 1$. We compute

$$Df(\lambda) = 2\lambda^2 + 1,$$
$$f(1) = 3, \quad Df(1) = 3, \quad \text{and} \quad k = f(1)/3 = 1.$$

Thus to step $s = 1$ up to a zero modulo 9 we need a zero modulo 3 of

$$f(s)/p^{n-1} + \lambda Df(s) = 1 + 3\lambda.$$

Since $1 + 3\lambda$ has no zeros modulo 3 we conclude that the step-up process cannot be performed. Hence $f(\lambda) = \lambda^2 + \lambda + 1$ has no zeros modulo 9.

From Example 3 we see that a polynomial over a ring with divisors of zero (in this case $J/(25)$) can have more than $n$ zeros, where $n$ is the degree of the polynomial.

THEOREM 10.10. *An element $f(\lambda)$ in the polynomial ring of a ring with divisors of zero can have more than n zeros, where $n = \deg\big(f(\lambda)\big)$.*

Some interesting bounds on the number of zeros mod $m$ a polynomial $f(\lambda)$ can have, have been obtained. See Chapter III of *Introduction to Number Theory* by T. Nagell.

## Exercise 10.3

1. Find the derivatives of the following in two ways:
   (*a*) $g(\lambda) = (\lambda - 7)(2\lambda^2 + 3\lambda - 10)$.
   (*b*) $g(\lambda) = (\lambda + 2)(\lambda^3 + \lambda^2 + \lambda + 1)$.
2. Expand the polynomial

$$f(\lambda) = \lambda^4 + \lambda + 1$$

in two ways in powers of (*a*) $\lambda - 1$; (*b*) $\lambda + 3$; (*c*) $\lambda + 2$.

3. Try to step 2 and 7, zeros mod 25 of

$$f(\lambda) = \lambda^3 + 3\lambda^2 + \lambda + 3,$$

up to zeros mod 125.

**4.** Find the zeros mod 25 of $f(\lambda) = \lambda^4 - 1$.

**5.** Find the zeros mod 49 of $f(\lambda) = 3\lambda^3 - 6\lambda^2 + 5\lambda - 3$.

**6.** Find the zeros mod $(13)^3$ of $f(\lambda) = \lambda^4 + 11$.

**7.** Find the zeros mod 121 of $f(\lambda) = 2\lambda^4 + 8\lambda + 9$.

**8.** Find the zeros modulo 27, modulo 81, and modulo 243 of $f(\lambda) = \lambda^3 + 3\lambda + 9$.

**9.** Prove that the elements $b_m$, $m = 1, \cdots, n$, are elements of $J$.

**10.** Develop the Taylor expansion for an element $f(\lambda)$ of the polynomial ring of a commutative ring $S$ with identity.

**11.** Show that, if $f(\lambda)$ has $m$ distinct zeros modulo $p^{n-1}$, then it cannot have more than $pm$ zeros modulo $p^n$. Use this and the basic bound on the number of zeros of a polynomial over a field to obtain an upper bound on the number of zeros mod $p^n$ of the polynomial $f(\lambda)$.

**12.** Define the formal derivative of a polynomial in the polynomial ring of the commutative ring $S$ with identity 1. Extend Lemma 10.1 to this ring.

**13.** Prove

$$D(f(\lambda)g(\lambda)) = f(\lambda)Dg(\lambda) + g(\lambda)Df(\lambda)$$

and

$$D(f(\lambda) + g(\lambda)) = Df(\lambda) + Dg(\lambda).$$

**14.** What is formal differentiation anyway, a mapping, a relation, a binary operation, or what? (Consider the set $\{(f(\lambda), Df(\lambda)): f(\lambda) \text{ in } J[\lambda]\}$.)

**15.** Let $H$ and $K$ be two mappings of the commutative ring $S$ onto itself such that

$$\begin{aligned} H&: rs \to rH(s) + sH(r), \\ H&: r + s \to H(r) + H(s), \\ K&: rs \to rK(s) + sK(r), \\ K&: r + s \to K(r) + K(s). \end{aligned}$$

Show that the mapping $L = HK - KH$ has the same property. (*Note:* The image of $s$ relative to $L$ is $L(s) = H(K(s)) - K(H(s))$.)

## 10.4 Zeros Modulo a Composite

If the composite $m$ is a power of a single prime $p$, then we already know how to find all of the zeros modulo $m$ of a polynomial $f(\lambda)$ by lifting up the zeros mod $p$ to zeros mod $p^2$, etc. In this section we complete our discussion of zeros modulo a composite by proving and illustrating the following basic result.

THEOREM 10.11. *Let $m = m_1 m_2$ where $m_1$ and $m_2$ are positive, relatively prime integers. If $r_i$ is a zero* mod $m_i$ *of $f(\lambda)$ and if $r$ is the unique integer* mod $m$ *such that*

$$r \equiv r_i \bmod m_i, \qquad i = 1 \text{ and } 2,$$

*then $r$ is a solution* mod $m$ *of $f(\lambda)$.*

We know from the Chinese Remainder Theorem that since $(m_1, m_2) = 1$ there is a unique integer $r$ modulo $m = m_1m_2$ such that

$$r \equiv r_1 \bmod m_1$$

and

$$r \equiv r_2 \bmod m_2.$$

Considering $f(r)$ modulo $m_1$ we see that

$$f(r) \equiv f(r_1) \equiv 0 \bmod m_1;$$

similarly

$$f(r) \equiv f(r_2) \equiv 0 \bmod m_2.$$

Thus $f(r)$ is a multiple of both $m_1$ and $m_2$, and since $(m_1, m_2) = 1$ this means that $f(r)$ is a multiple of $m$. Hence $r$ is a zero modulo $m$ of $f(\lambda)$.

*Example* 1. Find a zero modulo 50 of the polynomial

$$f(\lambda) = \lambda^3 + 3\lambda^2 + \lambda + 3.$$

Earlier we found the zeros mod 25 of $f(\lambda)$ to be 2, 7, 12, 17, 18, and 22, and it is easy to see that 1 is the only zero mod 2 of $f(\lambda)$. Thus we are able to construct six zeros modulo 50 from the resulting six pairs:

(1) $r \equiv 1 \bmod 2$ and $r \equiv 2 \bmod 25$ imply

$$r \equiv 27 \bmod 50;$$

(2) $r \equiv 1 \bmod 2$ and $r \equiv 7 \bmod 25$ imply

$$r \equiv 7 \bmod 50;$$

(3) $r \equiv 1 \bmod 2$ and $r \equiv 12 \bmod 25$ imply

$$r \equiv 37 \bmod 50;$$

(4) $r \equiv 1 \bmod 2$ and $r \equiv 17 \bmod 25$ imply

$$r \equiv 17 \bmod 50;$$

(5) $r \equiv 1 \bmod 2$ and $r \equiv 18 \bmod 25$ imply

$$r \equiv 43 \bmod 50;$$

(6) $r \equiv 1 \bmod 2$ and $r \equiv 22 \bmod 25$ imply

$$r \equiv 47 \bmod 50.$$

The numbers are so simple here that the values of $r$ can be found very quickly by trial and error. However, a straightforward routine for finding $r$ modulo $m$ is given in Chapter 3 in the section on linear congruences.

An obvious question to ask at this point is whether all zeros modulo $m$ of $f(\lambda)$ are obtainable in this way. The answer is positive and is supplied by Theorem 10.3. If $r$ is a zero modulo $m = m_1m_2$ of $f(\lambda)$, then

$$f(r) \equiv 0 \bmod m$$

implies

$$f(r) \equiv 0 \bmod m_1$$

and

$$f(r) \equiv 0 \bmod m_2,$$

and surely $r$ can be reduced modulo the factors to yield

$$r \equiv r_1 \bmod m_1 \qquad \text{and} \qquad r \equiv r_2 \bmod m_2.$$

Thus

$$f(r) \equiv f(r_1) \bmod m_1$$

and

$$f(r) \equiv f(r_2) \bmod m_2,$$

so that $r$ reduces to zeros $r_1$ and $r_2$ of $f(\lambda)$ modulo $m_1$ and $m_2$, respectively. Moreover since $(m_1, m_2) = 1$ we know that distinct zeros modulo $m$ of $f(\lambda)$ reduce to *distinct pairs* of zeros modulo $m_1$ and $m_2$. For, if $r$ and $s$ are zeros modulo $m$ of $f(\lambda)$ such that

$$r \equiv s \equiv r_1 \bmod m_1$$

and

$$r \equiv s \equiv r_2 \bmod m_2,$$

then certainly we must have

$$r \equiv s \bmod m.$$

Thus $r$ and $s$ are the same zeros modulo $m$ of $f(\lambda)$ in that they determine the same residue class modulo $m$. (In other words $r'$ and $s'$ are equal in $J/(m)$.) This is the basis for the next result on the number of zeros modulo $m$.

THEOREM 10.12. *If $f(\lambda)$ has $n_1$ zeros modulo $m_1$ and $n_2$ zeros modulo $m_2$, where $(m_1, m_2) = 1$, then $f(\lambda)$ has $n_1n_2$ zeros modulo $m$.*

By the preceding argument we know that each zero mod $m$ of $f(\lambda)$ is obtained from a pair of zeros, one modulo $m_1$ and the other modulo $m_2$, of $f(\lambda)$. Furthermore we know that all such pairs give rise to zeros mod $m$ of $f(\lambda)$. Counting the number of such pairs we conclude that $f(\lambda)$ has $n_1n_2$ zeros mod $m$.

*Example* 2. Find the zeros modulo 350 of the polynomial

$$f(\lambda) = \lambda^3 + 3\lambda^2 + \lambda + 3.$$

Checking $f(\lambda)$ for zeros mod 7 we see that $f(\lambda)$ has exactly one zero modulo 7, namely 4, since

$$f(\lambda) = (\lambda + 3)(\lambda^2 + 1)$$

and $\lambda^2 + 1$ is irreducible over $J/(7)$. Therefore we conclude from the results of Example 1 that $f(\lambda)$ has six zeros modulo 350. We shall now find one of these by finding $r$ such that

$$r \equiv 4 \bmod 7 \qquad \text{and} \qquad r \equiv 47 \bmod 50.$$

Then

$$r = 4 + 7p = 47 + 50q$$

for some $p$ and $q$ in $J$, and

$$47 - 4 = 43 = 7p - 50q.$$

Now we see that

$$1 = -7(7) + 1(50)$$

so that

$$43 = 7(43(-7)) - 50(-43)$$

by multiplying by 43. Thus we can take

$$p = -7(43) = -301$$

and

$$q = -43,$$

and so

$$r = 4 + 7p = 4 - 2107 = 47 + 50q = -2103.$$

Reducing this modulo 350 yields the simpler representative $-3$ for this residue class, which is a zero mod 350 of $f(\lambda)$.

*Example* 3. Establish an upper bound for the number of zeros modulo 1225 of $f(\lambda) = \lambda^5 + 100\lambda^2 + 99$.

First we factor 1225 as

$$1225 = 5^2 7^2.$$

Over $J/(5)$ $f(\lambda)$ has at most 5 zeros so that it has at most 25 zeros modulo 25 since each zero mod $p$ can be stepped up to at most $p$ zeros mod $p^2$. Similarly $f(\lambda)$ has at most 5 zeros mod 7 and at most 35 zeros mod 49. Hence $f(\lambda)$ has not more than $875 = 25(35)$ zeros modulo 1225.

## Exercise 10.4

**1.** Find the remaining zeros modulo 350 in Example 2.

**2.** Find the zeros mod 100 of $f(\lambda) = \lambda^4 - 1$ (see Problem 4, Section 10.3).

**3.** Find the zeros mod 245 of $f(\lambda) = 3\lambda^3 - 6\lambda^2 + 5\lambda - 3$ (see Problem 5, Section 10.3).

**4.** Find the zeros mod $4(13)^3$ of $f(\lambda) = \lambda^4 + 11$ (see Problem 6, Section 10.3).

**5.** Find the zeros mod 847 of $f(\lambda) = 2\lambda^4 + 8\lambda + 9$ (see Problem 7, Section 10.3).

**6.** Find the zeros mod 490 of $f(\lambda) = \lambda^3 + 477$.

**7.** The polynomial $f(\lambda) = \lambda^3 + 3\lambda^2 + \lambda + 3$ has six zeros in $J/(50)$ as we saw in Example 1. What does this mean about the factorization of $f(\lambda)$ in $S[\lambda]$, where $S = J/(50)$? Write out some different factorizations of $f(\lambda)$ over $S$.

**8.** Develop an upper bound for the number of zeros in $J/(4900)$ of a polynomial $f(\lambda)$ of degree six. Generalize.

## 10.5 Galois Fields

The complementary problem to the finding of the zeros of the polynomial $f(\lambda)$ in $J/(p)$ is the problem of determining the irreducible polynomials over $J/(p)$. We know that an irreducible polynomial $m(\lambda)$ in the domain $F[\lambda]$ of the field $F$ determines a field, namely $F[\lambda]/(m(\lambda))$, which is an extension of $F$. Moreover, if $F$ is a finite field, then so is $F[\lambda]/(m(\lambda))$. Therefore if we could find all finite fields which contain $F$ (or a subfield isomorphic with $F$), then we would have, in a sense, found all of the irreducible polynomials of $F[\lambda]$. Thus we change the problem of studying the irreducible polynomials of $(J/(p))[\lambda]$ to the problem of determining all of the finite fields of characteristic $p$.

THEOREM 10.13. *If $F$ is a finite field, then $F$ contains $p^n$ elements, where $p$ is the characteristic of $F$.*

In Chapter 7 we proved that a finite integral domain has characteristic a prime, so that we know $F$ has characteristic $p$ for some prime $p$. Now consider $F$ as an additive group: It is finite and Abelian and every element, except zero of course, has additive order $p$. Using the theory of finite Abelian groups we conclude that $F$ contains $p^n$ elements, for some positive integer $n$. For if the order of $F$ is divisible by any other prime $p_1$ then by the Sylow Theorem $F$ must contain some elements whose additive orders are $p_1$. Since this is not possible we know that $F$ contains $p^n$ elements.

*Corollary* 10.13.1. $F$ is an extension of $J/(p)$.

It was noted in discussing the characteristic that an integral domain of characteristic $p$ contains a subsystem generated by its multiplicative identity which is isomorphic with $J/(p)$. Hence $F$ contains $J/(p)$ in the sense of isomorphism so that $F$ is an extension of $J/(p)$.

*Example* 1. Show that finite fields other than the fields $J/(p)$ exist.

This is done easily by exhibiting an irreducible polynomial of degree two or higher from the polynomial domain of some $J/(p)$. Surely $\lambda^2 + \lambda + 1$ is irreducible over $J/(2)$ so that $(J/(2))[\lambda]/(\lambda^2 + \lambda + 1)$ is a field of four elements which can be identified by the possible remainders 0, 1, $\lambda$, and $\lambda + 1$. The operation tables of this field are as shown.

| $+$ | $0$ | $1$ | $\lambda$ | $\lambda+1$ |
|---|---|---|---|---|
| $0$ | $0$ | $1$ | $\lambda$ | $\lambda+1$ |
| $1$ | $1$ | $0$ | $\lambda+1$ | $\lambda$ |
| $\lambda$ | $\lambda$ | $\lambda+1$ | $0$ | $1$ |
| $\lambda+1$ | $\lambda+1$ | $\lambda$ | $1$ | $0$ |

| $\cdot$ | $0$ | $1$ | $\lambda$ | $\lambda+1$ |
|---|---|---|---|---|
| $0$ | $0$ | $0$ | $0$ | $0$ |
| $1$ | $0$ | $1$ | $\lambda$ | $\lambda+1$ |
| $\lambda$ | $0$ | $\lambda$ | $\lambda+1$ | $1$ |
| $\lambda+1$ | $0$ | $\lambda+1$ | $1$ | $\lambda$ |

Now we turn our attention to the multiplicative group $F'$ of nonzero elements from $F$. Since the order of $F$ is $q = p^n$ we know that the multiplicative group $F'$ contains $q - 1$ elements.

THEOREM 10.14. *Every element of the field F of $q = p^n$ elements is a zero of the polynomial*

$$f(\lambda) = \lambda^q - \lambda$$

*from* $F[\lambda]$.

Let $x$ be an element of $F'$. Then the order of $x$, the minimal positive integer $m$ such that

$$x^m = 1 \qquad \text{in } F',$$

is a factor of $q - 1$, the order of $F'$, since $m$ is the order of the subgroup of $F'$ generated by $x$ (see Chapter 6). Since $m$ is a factor of $q - 1$, say

$$q - 1 = km,$$

then certainly

$$x^q = x^{1+km} = x(x^m)^k = x,$$

so that $x$ is a zero of $\lambda^q - \lambda$.

*Corollary* 10.14.1. The multiplicative group $F'$ of the nonzero elements of the finite field $F$ of order $q = p^n$ is a cyclic group.

Denote by $r$ the largest of the multiplicative orders of the elements of $F'$. Then $F'$ contains an element $u$ such that

$$u^r = 1$$

but no lower power of $u$ equals 1. Now we claim that, if $x$ is any element of $F'$, then

$$x^r = 1.$$

For otherwise $F'$ contains an element $t$ whose order $k$ is a prime power which does not divide $r$. Then the order of $ut$ is greater than $r$, which contradicts the choice of $r$. (See the sections on finite Abelian groups in Chapter 6.) Thus every element of $F'$ is a zero of the polynomial

$$\lambda^r - 1,$$

and since this polynomial has at most $r$ zeros in a field we know that

$$q - 1 \leqslant r.$$

On the other hand we know from the theorem above that

$$r \leqslant q - 1.$$

Thus $r = q - 1$ and the elements of $F'$ are precisely the powers

$$u, u^2, \cdots, u^r = 1,$$

and $F'$ is cyclic.

*Example* 2. Find a generator of the group $F'$ in Example 1.

The nonzero elements of Example 1 form a group of order three. We see that both $\lambda$ and $\lambda + 1$ serve as generators since

$$\lambda^2 = \lambda + 1, \qquad \lambda^3 = 1,$$

and

$$(\lambda + 1)^2 = \lambda, \qquad (\lambda + 1)^3 = 1.$$

Theorem 10.14 is the key to classifying the finite fields since it suggests that we work with the polynomials of the form $\lambda^q - \lambda$, $q = p^n$, over $J/(p)$ and investigate their splitting fields. It turns out that for each prime $p$ and each positive integer $n$ there is exactly one (in the sense of isomorphism) finite field of order $q = p^n$, and it is the splitting field of the polynomial $\lambda^q - \lambda$.

DEFINITION 10.2. The *Galois Field* $GF(p^n)$, where $p$ is a prime and $n$ is a positive integer, is the splitting field of the polynomial $f(\lambda) = \lambda^q - \lambda, q = p^n$, of $\big(J/(p)\big)[\lambda]$.

When $n = 1$ we know from the Little Theorem of Fermat that $GF(p)$ is the field $J/(p)$ since each of the $p$ elements of $J/(p)$ is a zero of the polynomial

$$\lambda^p - \lambda.$$

The general situation follows the same pattern.

THEOREM 10.15. *The Galois field* $GF(p^n)$ *contains* $p^n = q$ *elements.*

First we wish to show that $GF(p^n)$ has at least $q$ elements, and this requires showing that $f(\lambda) = \lambda^q - \lambda$ has $q$ distinct zeros in $GF(p^n)$. This is accomplished by using the formal derivative on the polynomial $f(\lambda)$ in the polynomial domain of $GF(p^n)$. For, if

$$f(\lambda) = \lambda^q - \lambda = (\lambda - t)g(\lambda)$$

and $t$ is a zero of $g(\lambda)$ also, then

$$\boldsymbol{D}\big((\lambda - t)g(\lambda)\big) = g(\lambda) + (\lambda - t)\boldsymbol{D}g(\lambda) = \boldsymbol{D}f(\lambda)$$

has $t$ as a zero. But

$$\boldsymbol{D}f(\lambda) = q\lambda^{q-1} - 1 = -1$$

since

$$q = p^n \equiv 0 \text{ modulo } p,$$

and the polynomial $\boldsymbol{D}f(\lambda) = -1$ has no zeros. Hence the splitting field of

$$f(\lambda) = \lambda^q - \lambda$$

must contain at least $q = p^n$ elements since there are $q$ different zeros of $f(\lambda)$.

Denote these $q$ zeros by

$$a_1 = 0, a_2 = 1, \cdots, a_q.$$

From

$$a_i^q = a_i \quad \text{and} \quad a_m^q = a_m \text{ in } GF(p^n)$$

we get

$$(a_i a_m)^q = a_i^q a_m^q = a_i a_m$$

and

$$(a_i + a_m)^q = a_i^q + a_m^q = a_i + a_m.$$

(Here we again use the fact that

$$q = p^n \equiv 0 \bmod p.)$$

Furthermore, if $a_i \neq 0$, then

$$a_i^q = a_i$$

implies

$$(a_i^{-1})^q = a_i^{-q} = a_i^{-1}.$$

Thus we see that the $q$ zeros of $f(\lambda)$ form a field $F$, and since $f(\lambda)$ factors into linear factors in $F[\lambda]$,

$$f(\lambda) = (\lambda - a_1)(\lambda - a_2)\cdots(\lambda - a_q),$$

we conclude that $F$ is a root field of $f(\lambda)$. But the splitting field $GF(p^n)$ of $f(\lambda)$ is the smallest root field of $f(\lambda)$, so from

$$F \subseteq GF(p^n)$$

we conclude that

$$F = GF(p^n).$$

Thus $GF(p^n)$ contains $p^n$ elements.

*Corollary* 10.15.1. For each prime $p$ and each positive integer $n$ there exists a field $F$ of $p^n$ elements, and $F$ is isomorphic with $GF(p^n)$.

The existence of $F$ is a consequence of the fact that the splitting field of

$$f(\lambda) = \lambda^q - \lambda$$

exists and contains $q = p^n$ elements. And $F$ is isomorphic with $GF(p^n)$ since the splitting field of a polynomial is unique up to an isomorphism.

*Example* 3. Find the Galois field $GF(9)$.

Since $GF(9)$ is in the sense of isomorphism the only field of order nine we find an irreducible polynomial

$$m(\lambda) = \lambda^2 + 1$$

of degree two over $J/(3) = F$. Then the field $F_1 = F[\lambda]/(m(\lambda))$ is the field $GF(9)$. Denote the coset $\lambda + (m(\lambda))$ by $x$; then the elements of $F_1$ can be written as

$$0, 1, 2, x, 2x, x + 1, 2x + 1, x + 2, 2x + 2.$$

Since $x$ is a zero of $m(\lambda)$ we have

$$x^2 = -1,$$

and using this we compute

$$(x+1)^2 = 2x, \quad (x+1)^3 = 2x+1, \quad (x+1)^4 = 2, (x+1)^5 = 2x+2,$$
$$(x+1)^6 = x, \quad (x+1)^7 = x+2, \quad \text{and} \quad (x+1)^8 = 1.$$

Thus we see that the element $x + 1$ is a generator of the multiplicative group of nonzero elements of $F_1$. From these computations we conclude that

$$((x+1)^k)^9 = ((x+1)^9)^k = (x+1)^k$$

for $k = 1, 2, \cdots, 8$, so that the nine elements of $F_1$ are zeros of

$$f(\lambda) = \lambda^9 - \lambda.$$

Hence $f(\lambda)$ splits completely over $F_1$ so that $F_1$ is a splitting field of $f(\lambda)$. Thus $F_1$ and $GF(9)$ are isomorphic.

## Exercise 10.5

**1.** Construct the operation tables for the field $F_1$ of Example 3.

**2.** Show that $\lambda^2 + \lambda + 2$ is irreducible over $F = J/(3)$, and construct the operation tables of $F_2 = F[\lambda]/(\lambda^2 + \lambda + 2)$. Denote the coset containing $\lambda$ by $t$.

**3.** Show that $\lambda^2 + 2\lambda + 2$ is irreducible over $F = J/(3)$, and construct the operation tables of $F_3 = F[\lambda]/(\lambda^2 + 2\lambda + 2)$. Denote the coset containing $\lambda$ by $w$.

**4.** Show that in the polynomial domain of $J/(3)$ the polynomial $\lambda^9 - \lambda$ factors as

$$\lambda(\lambda - 1)(\lambda + 1)(\lambda^2 + 1)(\lambda^2 + \lambda + 2)(\lambda^2 + 2\lambda + 2).$$

**5.** In the field $F_1$ (Problem 1) show that $x + 1$ is a zero of $\lambda^2 + \lambda + 2$ and that $2x + 1$ is the other zero of this polynomial. On the other hand show that $2t + 1$ from $F_2$ (Problem 2) is a zero of the polynomial $\lambda^2 + 1$.

**6.** Show that $x + 2$ from the field $F_1$ (Problem 1) is a zero of $\lambda^2 + 2\lambda + 2$, and the element $w + 1$ in $F_3$ is a zero of $\lambda^2 + 1$.

**7.** By checking and comparing the tables obtained in Problems 1, 2, and 3 show that the three fields $F_1$, $F_2$, and $F_3$ are isomorphic.

**8.** Find generators of the multiplicative groups of the fields $F_1$, $F_2$, and $F_3$.

**9.** Let $m(\lambda)$ be an irreducible polynomial of degree $n$ in $F[\lambda]$, where $F = J/(p)$. By considering the G.C.F. of $m(\lambda)$ and $\lambda^q - \lambda$, $q = p^n$, show that $m(\lambda)$ is a factor of $\lambda^q - \lambda$ in $F[\lambda]$. (Note that $F[\lambda]/(m(\lambda))$ is a field of order $q$.)

**10.** By considering $\lambda^{25} - \lambda$ show that $F[\lambda]$ contains exactly ten monic irreducible polynomials of degree two when $F = J/(5)$.

**11.** Show that $\lambda^2 + 1$ is a factor of $\lambda^{81} - \lambda$ in the polynomial domain of $J/(3)$. What does this show about the degrees of the nonlinear factors of $\lambda^q - \lambda$ when $q = p^n$? (Note that $\lambda^8 - 1 = (\lambda^2 + 1)(\lambda^6 - \lambda^4 + \lambda^2 - 1)$.)

**12.** Let $S$ be a commutative ring of characteristic $p$. Show that, if $a$ and $b$ are elements of $S$ and $q = p^n$, then

$$(a + b)^q = a^q + b^q.$$

Use induction on $n$.

## 10.6 Automorphisms of a Galois Field

Since an automorphism of $GF(p^n)$ leaves the zero element unchanged we need only to look at the nonzero elements when investigating automorphisms of $GF(p^n)$. Already we know that these elements form a multiplicative group which is cyclic of order $p^n - 1$. Now we look at the properties of the generators of this cyclic group since an automorphism of $GF(p^n)$ will also be an automorphism of this cyclic group and so map generators onto generators.

THEOREM 10.16. *Let $w$ denote a generator of the multiplicative group of nonzero elements of $GF(p^n)$. Then, when $n > 1$, $w$ is a zero of an irreducible polynomial $m(\lambda)$ of degree $n$ from the polynomial domain of $GF(p)$.*

Form the $p^n$ elements of $GF(p^n)$ of the form

$$a_0 + a_1w + \cdots + a_{n-1}w^{n-1} + w^n$$

where the $a_i$ are in $GF(p)$. Since there are $p$ choices for each $a_i$ there are certainly $p^n$ such expressions, and we can show that no two of them are equal. For suppose two such elements are equal. By subtracting one from the other we get an equation

$$b_0 + b_1w + \cdots + b_rw^r = 0$$

where $r < n$, $b_r \neq 0$, and the $b_i$ are in $GF(p)$. This equation can be solved for $w^r$:

$$w^r = c_0 + c_1w + \cdots + c_mw^m$$

where $m < n - 1$ and the $c_i$ are in $GF(p)$. But such an equation implies that $GF(p^n)$ contains not more than $p^{n-1}$ elements since it means that all powers of $w$ can be expressed in the form

$$d_0 + d_1w + \cdots + d_mw^m,$$

where the $d_i$ are in $GF(p)$, and there are only $p^{m+1}$ choices for the coefficients $d_i$. But this contradicts the fact that $GF(p^n)$ contains $p^n$ distinct elements, so that we have proved that the $p^n$ expressions

$$a_0 + a_1w + \cdots + a_{n-1}w^{n-1} + w^n$$

are all distinct. This means that $w$ is a zero of some polynomial $m(\lambda)$ of degree $n$ over $GF(p)$ since one of these expressions equals zero.

Furthermore the argument above shows that $m(\lambda)$ is irreducible over $GF(p)$. For, if

$$m(\lambda) = g(\lambda)h(\lambda),$$

then $w$ is a zero of one of these, and we again obtain the equation

$$w^r = c_0 + c_1w + \cdots + c_mw^m$$

where $n > r > m$ and the $c_i$ are in $GF(p)$. Since this equation leads to a contradiction of the number of distinct elements in $GF(p^n)$ we conclude that $m(\lambda)$ is irreducible over $GF(p)$.

*Example* 1. In Example 3 of the previous section the field $GF(9)$ was discussed. There we took $GF(9)$ as the field $F[\lambda]/(\lambda^2 + 1)$ where $F = J/(3)$. In that example $x$ denoted the coset of the ideal $(\lambda^2 + 1)$ which contained $\lambda$, and we saw that $x + 1$ was a generator of the multiplicative group of nonzero elements of $GF(9)$. Taking $w$ as $x + 1$ we see that $w$ is a zero of

$$m(\lambda) = \lambda^2 + \lambda + 2$$

since

$$w^2 = 2x, \qquad w = x + 1,$$

and

$$2x + x + 1 + 2 = 0$$

in $GF(9)$. The nine elements of $GF(9)$ can be written as

$$\begin{aligned} 0 &= 2 + w + w^2, & 1 &= 0 + w + w^2, \\ 2 &= 1 + w + w^2, & w &= 2 + 2w + w^2, \\ w + 1 &= 0 + 2w + w^2, & w + 2 &= 1 + 2w + w^2, \\ 2w &= 2 + 0w + w^2, & 2w + 1 &= 0 + 0w + w^2, \end{aligned}$$

and

$$2w + 2 = 1 + 0w + w^2.$$

These are the $p^n = 9$ expressions used in the proof of Theorem 10.16.

Note that this example illustrates the fact that not every zero of an irreducible polynomial of degree $n$ over $GF(p)$ is a generator of the multiplicative group of nonzero elements of $GF(p^n)$. For the element $x$ above is a zero of $\lambda^2 + 1$ which is certainly irreducible over $GF(3)$, but the powers of $x$ are

$$x^2 = -1 = 2, \quad x^3 = 2x, \quad x^4 = 1, \quad x^5 = x, \quad x^6 = 2, \quad x^7 = 2x, \quad \text{and} \quad x^8 = 1.$$

Thus $x$ generates a proper subgroup of the multiplicative group.

What about the other zeros of the irreducible polynomial $m(\lambda)$ which has the generator $w$ as a zero? Are they generators of the multiplicative group of nonzero elements of $GF(p^n)$ also? The answer is positive, but to prove it we need the following extension of the binomial expansion.

*Lemma* 10.2. If $a_1, \cdots, a_m$ are elements in a commutative ring of characteristic $p$, then for $q = p^n$,

$$(a_1 + \cdots + a_m)^q = a_1{}^q + \cdots + a_m{}^q.$$

The proof involves a double extension of the binomial expansion

$$(a + b)^p = a^p + b^p.$$

First,

$$(a + b)^q = ((a + b)^r)^p, \qquad \text{where } r = p^{n-1},$$

so, by the induction hypothesis,

$$(a + b)^r = a^r + b^r,$$

and

$$(a^r + b^r)^p = a^{rp} + b^{rp}.$$

Hence

$$(a + b)^q = a^q + b^q.$$

Now consider the expression

$$(a_1 + a_2 + \cdots + a_m)^q = (a_1 + (a_2 + \cdots + a_m))^q.$$

By the above

$$(a_1 + (a_2 + \cdots + a_m))^q = a_1{}^q + (a_2 + \cdots + a_m)^q,$$

and applying the second induction hypothesis to the second term on the right we get

$$(a_1 + a_2 + \cdots + a_m)^q = a_1{}^q + a_2{}^q + \cdots + a_m{}^q,$$

completing the second induction. This proves the lemma.

THEOREM 10.17. *If $w$ is a generator of the multiplicative group of nonzero elements of $GF(p^n)$, $n > 1$,* then the zeros *of the monic irreducible polynomial $m(\lambda)$ over $GF(p)$ which has $w$ as a zero are $w, w^p, \cdots, w^t$, where $t = p^{n-1}$.*

From the fact that $w$ is a zero of

$$m(\lambda) = a_0 + a_1\lambda + \cdots + \lambda^n$$

we get the equation

$$0 = a_0 + a_1 w + \cdots + w^n.$$

Raising zero to the $p^{\text{th}}$ power yields

$$\begin{aligned} 0^p = 0 &= (a_0 + a_1 w + \cdots + w^n)^p \\ &= a_0{}^p + a_1{}^p w^p + \cdots + (w^p)^n. \end{aligned}$$

Using the Little Theorem of Fermat we can replace $a_i{}^p$ by $a_i$ in $GF(p)$, obtaining

$$0 = a_0 + a_1 w^p + \cdots + (w^p)^n.$$

Hence $w^p$ is a zero of $m(\lambda)$. Continuing this process proves the theorem.

Not only are the $n$ elements $w^k$, $k = 1, p, p^2, \cdots, p^{n-1}$, the $n$ zeros of $m(\lambda)$, but they are all generators of the cyclic group of nonzero elements of $GF(p^n)$ (although there are still other generators in general). This follows easily from the fact that the cyclic group generated by $w$ is of order $p^n - 1$, an integer relatively prime to powers of $p$.

THEOREM 10.18. *If $w$ generates the cyclic group of nonzero elements of $GF(p^n)$, then $w^k$ is also a generator when $k = 1, p, p^2, \cdots$, or $p^{n-1}$.*

Note that

$$1 = (k, p^n - 1).$$

If

$$(w^k)^m = 1, \qquad m > 0,$$

then $km$ is a multiple of $p^n - 1$, and since $k$ is relatively prime to $p^n - 1$ this means that $m$ is a multiple of $p^n - 1$. Thus $w^k$ generates a subgroup $H$ of order at least $p^n - 1$, and since this is the order of the whole group of nonzero elements we conclude that $w^k$ is a generator of that group.

*Example* 2. Show that $w^3$ is a generator of the multiplicative group in Example 1.

Rewriting the computations of Example 4 in the previous section we have

$$w,\ w^2 = 2w + 1,\quad w^3 = 2w + 2,\quad w^4 = 2,\quad w^5 = 2w,\quad w^6 = w + 2,$$
$$w^7 = w + 1, \quad \text{and} \quad w^8 = 1.$$

From these calculations we obtain

$$w^3 = 2w + 2,\quad w^6 = w + 2,\quad w^9 = w,\quad w^{12} = w^4 = 2,\quad w^{15} = w^7 = w + 1,$$
$$w^{18} = w^2 = 2w + 1,\quad w^{21} = w^5 = 2w, \quad \text{and} \quad w^{24} = (w^8)^3 = 1.$$

Thus $w^3$ is a generator of this group of order eight, as are $w^5$ and $w^7$ also.

Now we can determine the automorphism group of $GF(p^n)$.

THEOREM 10.19. *The automorphism group $AGF(p^n)$ of $GF(p^n)$ is a cyclic group of order $n$.*

Let $A$ be an automorphism of $GF(p^n)$. Since it fixes 1 it also fixes $2 = 1 + 1, 3 = 2 + 1$, etc., so that the elements of $GF(p)$ are all fixed by $A$. Using this we see that a generator $w$ of the multiplicative group of nonzero elements of $GF(p^n)$ is mapped onto a zero of $m(\lambda)$, where $m(\lambda)$ is the irreducible polynomial of degree $n$ over $GF(p)$,

$$m(\lambda) = a_0 + a_1\lambda + \cdots + \lambda^n,$$

which has $w$ as a zero. For

$$0 = a_0 + a_1 w + \cdots + w^n$$

acted upon by $A$ becomes

$$0A = 0 = a_0 + a_1(wA) + \cdots + (wA)^n$$

since $A$ preserves the arithmetic of $GF(p^n)$ and leaves the elements of $GF(p)$ unchanged. Thus $wA$ is a zero of $m(\lambda)$ also, so that by Theorem 10.17,

$$wA = w^k$$

where $k$ is some power of $p$. This means that we can identify the automorphisms of $GF(p^n)$ by looking at the $n$ elements

$$w, w^p, \cdots, w^{p^{n-1}},$$

since each automorphism is identified completely by its effect on the generator

$w$. Since the only possible images of $w$ are the $n$ elements $w^k$ for $k = 1, p, \cdots, p^{n-1}$ we know then that the automorphism group $AGF(p^n)$ contains at most $n$ elements.

On the other hand, using Lemma 10.2 we see easily that $AGF(p^n)$ contains at least $n$ elements since the mapping

$$A_m: x \to x^r, \qquad r = p^m, \ x \text{ in } GF(p^n),$$

is an automorphism of $GF(p^n)$. If $x$ and $v$ are two elements of $GF(p^n)$, then

$$(x + v)^r = x^r + v^r$$

by the lemma, and certainly

$$(xv)^r = x^r v^r.$$

Thus $A_m$ preserves the arithmetic of $GF(p^n)$, and since

$$x^r = 0$$

if and only if $x = 0$, this means that $A_m$ is an automorphism of $GF(p^n)$. The $n$ mappings $A_1, A_2, \cdots, A_{n-1}$, and $A_n = E$, the identity mapping, are all different since each of them sends $w$ onto a different zero of $m(\lambda)$. So we conclude that the group $AGF(p^n)$ is of order $n$ and contains exactly the elements $A_1, A_2, \cdots, A_n$. Furthermore we see that

$$A_1^2 = A_2$$

since

$$xA_1^2 = (xA_1)A_1 = x^p A_1 = (x^p)^p = x^{p^2} = xA_2,$$

that

$$A_1^3 = A_3, \qquad A_1^4 = A_4, \qquad \text{etc.}$$

Hence the automorphism group of $GF(p^n)$ is a cyclic group of order $n$.

*Corollary* 10.19.1. The elements of $GF(p)$ are the only elements of $GF(p^n)$ which are left unchanged by all automorphisms of $GF(p^n)$.

If $x$ is left fixed by every element of $AGF(p^n)$, then it is certainly left unchanged by $A_1$. Hence

$$xA_1 = x^p = x,$$

so that

$$x^p - x = 0.$$

Thus $x$ is a zero of the polynomial $\lambda^p - \lambda$, and the $p$ zeros of that polynomial make up the field $GF(p)$.

*Example* 3. Find the automorphism group of $GF(9)$.

Using the notation of Examples 1 and 2 we see that $GF(9)$ has two distinct automorphisms which are determined by the two possible images of $w$, namely

$w$ and $w^3$. The identity mapping sends $w$ onto $w$, so let us consider the mapping $A$ which sends $w$ onto $w^3$. Then we have the following:

$$\begin{aligned} wA &= w^3 = 2w + 2, \\ (w + 1)A &= wA + 1 = 2w, \\ (w + 2)A &= wA + 2 = 2w + 1, \\ (2w)A &= 2(wA) = w + 1, \\ (2w + 1)A &= 2(wA) + 1 = w + 2, \\ (2w + 2)A &= 2(wA) + 2 = w. \end{aligned}$$

The elements 0, 1, and 2 are fixed by $A$.

Checking a few arithmetic calculations we have:

(1) $w(2w + 1) = 2w + 2;$

$$(wA)((2w + 1)A) = (2w + 2)(w + 2) = w = (2w + 2)A.$$

(2) $2w + (2w + 2) = w + 2;$

$$(2w)A + (2w + 2)A = w + 1 + w = 2w + 1 = (w + 2)A.$$

The group $AGF(9)$ is a cyclic group of order two and contains the elements $E$ and $A$.

## Exercise 10.6

**1.** Factor $\lambda^8 - \lambda$ over $GF(2)$, find the two irreducible cubics, extend $GF(2)$ to $GF(8)$, and find all of the generators of the multiplicative group of nonzero elements of $GF(8)$.

**2.** Select a generator $w$ from Problem 1, and form the polynomial

$$m(\lambda) = (\lambda - w)(\lambda - w^2)(\lambda - w^4).$$

Show that $m(\lambda)$ is one of the two irreducible cubics found in Problem 1.

**3.** Find the automorphism group of $GF(8)$.

**4.** Find all irreducible factors of $\lambda^{15} - 1$ over $GF(2)$. (Note that a quartic can be reducible even if it has no linear factors.) Find a generator $w$ of the multiplicative group of nonzero elements of $GF(16)$, and describe the elements of $GF(16)$ in terms of powers of $w$.

**5.** Show that the set of elements of $GF(16)$ which are left fixed by the automorphism $A_2$,

$$A_2: x \to x^4, \qquad x \text{ in } GF(16),$$

is a subfield of $GF(16)$ which is isomorphic with $GF(4)$.

**6.** Continue the calculations of Example 3 with the following:

(*a*) $2w(w + 1)(w + 2)$.

(*b*) $(w + 1)(2w + 1) + (2w)(w + 2)$.

**7.** Prove that $GF(p^m)$ is isomorphic with a subfield of $GF(p^n)$ if and only if $m$ is a factor of $n$. (Consider the polynomials $\lambda^m - \lambda$ and $\lambda^n - \lambda$ over $GF(p)$.)

**8.** Prove that a cyclic group of order $n$ contains a cyclic subgroup of index $m$ if and only if $m$ is a factor of $n$.

**9.** Relate Problems 7 and 8 by showing that, if $B$ is the subgroup of index $m$ in the group $AGF(p^n)$, then the set of elements in $GF(p^n)$ fixed by the automorphisms in $B$ is a subfield of $GF(p^n)$ which is isomorphic with $GF(p^m)$.

**10.** If $n$ is a prime what can be said about the number of subfields of $GF(p^n)$? (Look at the subgroups of $AGF(p^n)$.)

**11.** An irreducible polynomial $f(\lambda)$ of $F[\lambda]$ of degree $m$, where $F = GF(p^n)$, is said to *belong to the exponent* $r$ if and only if $r$ is the least positive integer such that $f(\lambda)$ is a factor of $\lambda^r - 1$ in $F[\lambda]$. Prove that $f(\lambda)$ belongs to $r$ if and only if every zero of $f(\lambda)$ has multiplicative order $r$, in which case $r$ is a factor of $p^{nm} - 1$.

## 10.7 Suggested Reading

*Articles*

Golomb, M., "Combinatorial proof of Fermat's Little Theorem," *Amer. Math. Monthly*, **63** (1956), 718.

Wall, D. D., "Fibonacci series mod *m*," *Amer. Math. Monthly*, **67** (1960), 525–532.

*Books*

Albert, A., *Fundamental Concepts of Higher Algebra*, University of Chicago Press, Chicago, 1956.

Mann, H. B., *Analysis and Design of Experiments*, Dover Publications, New York, 1951.

Nagell, T., *Introduction to Number Theory*, John Wiley & Sons, New York, 1951.

Niven, J., and H. Zuckerman, *An Introduction to the Theory of Numbers*, John Wiley & Sons, New York, 1960.

Stewart, B. M., *Theory of Numbers*, 2nd ed., The Macmillan Co., New York, 1964.

# 11

# Modules and Vector Spaces

In this chapter we digress from the study of rings to introduce a new type of algebraic system, the module, and in particular a variety of module called the vector space. The concept is of considerable importance and use since it links various abstract algebraic systems with that intuitive, visual, and familiar subject, coordinate geometry. This connection enables the geometry to be generalized and abstracted by using the knowledge of the various algebraic systems, and from the algebraic viewpoint this geometric tie-up leads to suggested procedures, problems, conjectures, etc., which in turn can lead to a better understanding of the algebraic systems. Although we naturally make some use of this interplay, our investigation is restricted to the development of little more than enough material to provide for the study of a new type of ring in the following chapters. Thus the chapter can be considered as, effectively, a continuation of our study of rings.

## 11.1 Definitions and Examples

Most students today encounter the classic example of a module in their elementary physics classes. There a vector quantity is presented as a "directed number" and these elements are used in the study of force, velocity, acceleration, etc. Such a quantity is presented geometrically as a line segment in a plane (or in three-space) with an arrowhead indicating direction and the length, according to some scale, representing the magnitude. The totality of such directed line segments, or vectors, in a plane emanating from a fixed point $O$ (the origin) form a plane vector space. Here two vectors are added according to the parallelogram rule (Fig. 11.1).

It is quite easy to see that the resulting algebraic system is an Abelian group, especially by using the methods of analytic geometry. In this analysis of the plane relative to a fixed pair of perpendicular axes through $O$ and an arbitrary unit, each vector $\mathbf{v}$ is assigned a unique pair of real numbers which are called the components of **v**. These numbers are precisely the coordinates of the arrowhead of the vector (Fig. 11.2).

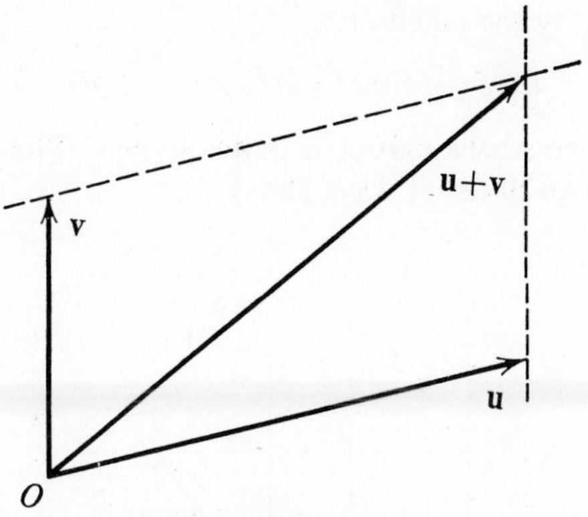


**Figure 11.1**

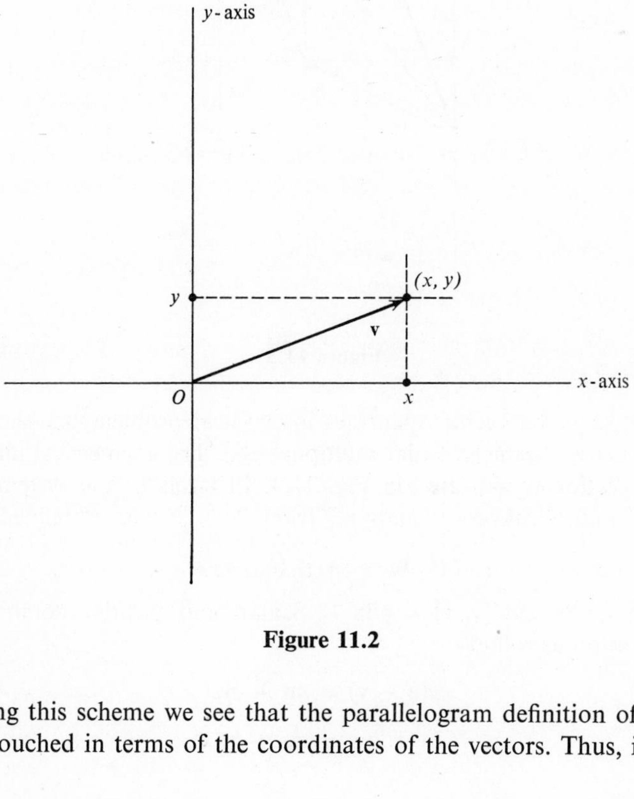


**Figure 11.2**

Using this scheme we see that the parallelogram definition of addition can be couched in terms of the coordinates of the vectors. Thus, if **u** and **v** are coordinatized as $(x_1, y_1)$ and $(x_2, y_2)$, respectively, then $\mathbf{u} + \mathbf{v}$ is the vector with coordinates $(x_1 + x_2, y_1 + y_2)$ (Fig. 11.3).

Thus in considering a plane vector space and vector addition we are effectively studying the Abelian group $(V, +)$ where $V = Re \times Re$ and addition is defined by the equation

$$(a, b) + (c, d) = (a + c, b + d).$$

That this system is an Abelian group is quite obvious. (Note that the addition symbol is used in two different ways here.)

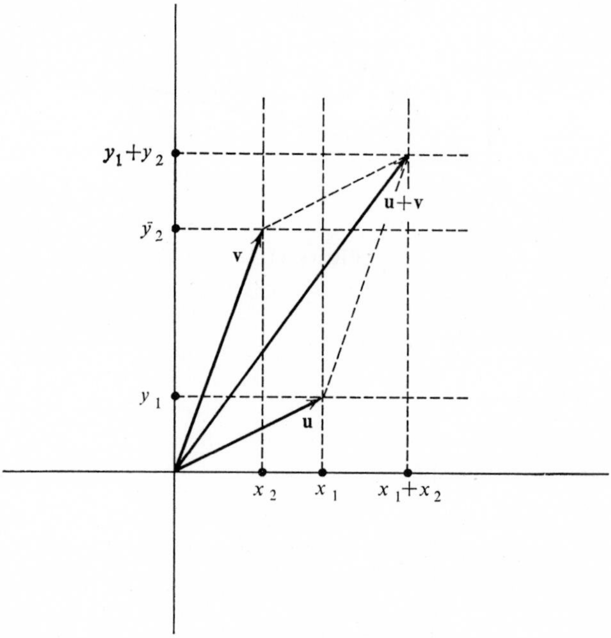


**Figure 11.3**

In dealing with vector quantities in physical problems another binary operation is used, namely, scalar multiplication. The geometrical illustration of this operation is indicated in Fig. 11.4. In terms of the system $(V, +)$ this scalar multiplication is a mapping from $Re \times V$ onto $V$ defined by

$$(k, \mathbf{v}) \rightarrow k\mathbf{v} = (kx, ky)$$

for each $k$ in $Re$ and $(x, y) = \mathbf{v}$ in $V$. Scalar multiplication combines with vector addition as follows:

(11.1) $$a(\mathbf{u} + \mathbf{v}) = a\mathbf{u} + a\mathbf{v},$$

(11.2) $$(a + b)\mathbf{u} = a\mathbf{u} + b\mathbf{u},$$

(11.3) $$(ab)\mathbf{u} = a(b\mathbf{u}),$$

and

(11.4) $$1\mathbf{u} = \mathbf{u},$$

for real numbers $a$ and $b$ and vectors $\mathbf{u}$ and $\mathbf{v}$.

Actually we have made considerable use of just such an intertwining of an Abelian group with a ring in our earlier investigations of groups and

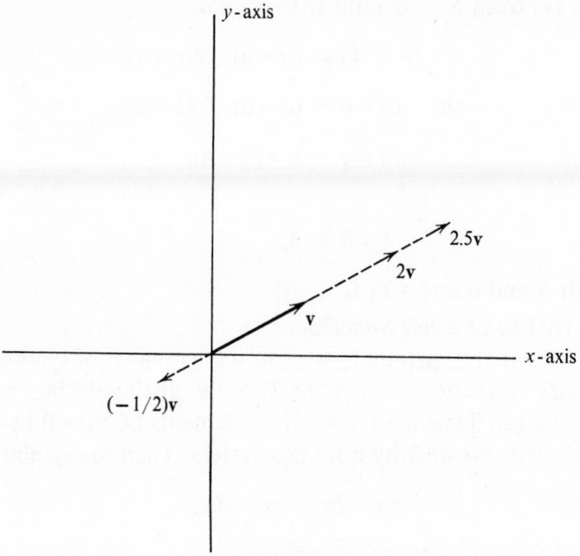


**Figure 11.4**

rings. That intertwining was based on the Associative Law and "exponentiation," and related an Abelian group $(G, \oplus)$ with the ring $J$. If $\mathbf{g}$ is in $G$ and $n$ is in $J$, then the scalar multiplication $(*)$ was defined by

$$n * \mathbf{g} = \mathbf{g} \oplus \mathbf{g} \oplus \cdots \oplus \mathbf{g}, \qquad n \text{ times}, \ n > 0,$$
$$n * 0 = \mathbf{z}, \text{ the zero of } G,$$

and

$$n * \mathbf{g} = (-n) * (-\mathbf{g}) \qquad \text{when } n < 0.$$

Here again the four binary operations (addition in $G$, symbolized by $\oplus$, addition and multiplication in $J$, and scalar multiplication) are related closely:

(11.5) $$a * (\mathbf{u} \oplus \mathbf{v}) = (a * \mathbf{u}) \oplus (a * \mathbf{v}),$$

(11.6) $$(a + b) * \mathbf{u} = (a * \mathbf{u}) \oplus (b * \mathbf{u}),$$

(11.7) $$(ab) * \mathbf{u} = a * (b * \mathbf{u}),$$

and

(11.8) $$1 * \mathbf{u} = \mathbf{u},$$

for integers $a$ and $b$ and elements $\mathbf{u}$ and $\mathbf{v}$ of $G$. (Compare with the properties of the plane vector space above.) These properties were discussed and used in Chapters 6 and 7.

Abstracting from these two familiar examples we define a module as a combination of an Abelian group and a ring.

DEFINITION 11.1. An Abelian group $(G, \oplus)$ is a *left module* over the ring $(S, +, \cdot)$ with identity 1 if and only if there exists a mapping called *scalar multiplication* $(*)$ from $S \times G$ onto $G$ such that

(11.5) $$a * (\mathbf{u} \oplus \mathbf{v}) = (a * \mathbf{u}) \oplus (a * \mathbf{v}),$$

(11.6) $$(a + b) * \mathbf{u} = (a * \mathbf{u}) \oplus (b * \mathbf{u}),$$

(11.7) $$(ab) * \mathbf{u} = a * (b * \mathbf{u}),$$

and

(11.8) $$1 * \mathbf{u} = \mathbf{u},$$

for $a$ and $b$ in $S$ and $\mathbf{u}$ and $\mathbf{v}$ in $G$.

$G$ is referred to as a *left S-module*.

It is convenient and customary to reduce the number of symbols denoting the four binary operations above to two by distinguishing between the elements of $G$ and $S$. Thus the scalars (i.e., elements of $S$) will be denoted by italics and the elements of $G$ by bold face letters. Then the symbols

$$a\mathbf{u}, \quad b\mathbf{v}, \quad c\mathbf{x}, \quad d\mathbf{w},$$

can only stand for scalar products, whereas

$$\mathbf{u} + \mathbf{v}, \qquad \mathbf{v} + \mathbf{w}, \qquad \mathbf{u} + \mathbf{x}$$

must denote sums in $G$ and cannot be confused with

$$a + b, \qquad c + d, \qquad e + k,$$

which are sums in $S$. Then the axioms above take the forms

(11.1) $$a(\mathbf{u} + \mathbf{v}) = a\mathbf{u} + a\mathbf{v},$$

(11.2) $$(a + b)\mathbf{u} = a\mathbf{u} + b\mathbf{u},$$

(11.3) $$(ab)\mathbf{u} = a(b\mathbf{u}),$$

and

(11.4) $$1\mathbf{u} = \mathbf{u}.$$

Note that $a + \mathbf{x}$ and $\mathbf{xy}$ are undefined.

*Example* 1. An additively written Abelian group $G$ is a left $J$-module by our discussions of associativity, exponentiation, and scalar multiplication.

*Example* 2. The additive group of $S[\lambda]$ for a ring $S$ with identity is a left $S$-module. Here the scalar multiplication is given by

$$a(b_0 + b_1\lambda + \cdots + b_n\lambda^n) = ab_0 + ab_1\lambda + \cdots + ab_n\lambda^n$$

for $a$ in $S$.

Since $S[\lambda]$ is an extension of $S$ this example is a special case of the following.

*Example* 3. If the ring $T$ is an extension of the ring $S$ with identity 1 and if 1 is the multiplicative identity of $T$ also, then the additive group of $T$ is a left $S$-module. Here the scalar multiplication is just the multiplication of $T$ and the properties 11.1, 11.2, and 11.3 follow from the usual Distributive and Associative Laws.

This situation can be essentially reversed in some very important instances.

*Example* 4. The additive group of the ideal $(m)$ of $J$ is a left $J$-module. Here again the scalar multiplication is just the multiplication of $J$.

In fact the additive group of any ideal of a ring $S$ with identity forms a left $S$-module. Indeed the additive groups of some subrings of $S$ which are not ideals also form left $S$-modules, and this leads to the concept of left ideal which will be discussed later.

In all of the examples considered thus far the adjective "left" has been of little significance, and in fact we shall soon dispose of it completely. However, the distinction is an important one, especially when $S$ is a non-commutative ring, so in the work that follows the scalar multiplication is understood to be on the left unless explicit instructions to the contrary are given. (A corresponding treatment of *right* $S$-modules can be carried out, but since the resulting theory is completely dual to that for left $S$-modules we shall not bother discussing the concept here. There exists also a theory of *two-sided* $S$-modules, which stems from the concept of ideal in $S$, but this is a more advanced topic which we do not treat.)

These examples indicate that any general theory of modules would have to include development of both a theory of Abelian groups and a theory of rings with identity elements. *Since we are attempting only to introduce some of the basic concepts we shall restrict our attention to special types of modules.*

DEFINITION 11.2. A *vector space* over a field $F$ is a left $F$-module.

The following notation is used for vector spaces. $V(F)$ denotes an abstract vector space over the field $F$, $V$ is the space, $\mathbf{u}, \mathbf{v}, \mathbf{w}, \cdots$, are the *vectors* or elements of $V$, and $a, b, c, \cdots$, are the *scalars* or elements of $F$.

There are many examples of vector spaces, but for reasons that will become clearer in later sections the following is of considerable importance in our work.

*Example* 5. Denote by $C_n(F)$ the set of all ordered sets of $n$ elements of the field $F$, where $n$ is an arbitrary but fixed positive integer. These $n$-tuples (or mappings from the first $n$ positive integers onto $F$) are denoted by

$$\mathbf{v} = (v_1, v_2, \cdots, v_n).$$

Vector addition and scalar multiplication are defined by abstracting from the discussion at the start of this section; if

$$\mathbf{u} = (u_1, \cdots, u_n) \quad \text{and} \quad \mathbf{v} = (v_1, \cdots, v_n),$$

then

$$\mathbf{u} + \mathbf{v} = (u_1 + v_1, \cdots, u_n + v_n)$$

and

$$a\mathbf{v} = (av_1, \cdots, av_n)$$

for $a$ in $F$. This vector space is referred to as the *coordinate $n$-space* of $F$.

When $F$ is the real field and $n = 2$, then this is the first space discussed in this section.

We conclude with a simple but basic result which relates certain key elements of the ring $S$ and the $S$-module $G$.

THEOREM 11.1. *If* $\mathbf{z}$ *is the identity of the S-module G and* $-\mathbf{v}$ *is the inverse of* $\mathbf{v}$, *then*

(i) $$0\mathbf{v} = \mathbf{z} \quad \textit{for each } \mathbf{v} \textit{ in } G;$$
(ii) $$(-1)\mathbf{v} = -\mathbf{v} \quad \textit{for each } \mathbf{v} \textit{ in } G;$$

*and*

(iii) $$a\mathbf{z} = \mathbf{z} \quad \textit{for each } a \textit{ in } S.$$

To prove (i) we write

$$\mathbf{v} = 1\mathbf{v} = (1 + 0)\mathbf{v} = 1\mathbf{v} + 0\mathbf{v} = \mathbf{v} + 0\mathbf{v}.$$

Adding $-\mathbf{v}$ yields

$$\mathbf{z} = -\mathbf{v} + \mathbf{v} = -\mathbf{v} + \mathbf{v} + 0\mathbf{v} = \mathbf{z} + 0\mathbf{v} = 0\mathbf{v}.$$

To prove (ii) we write

$$\mathbf{z} = 0\mathbf{v} = \big(1 + (-1)\big)\mathbf{v} = 1\mathbf{v} + (-1)\mathbf{v}.$$

Adding $-\mathbf{v}$ yields

$$-\mathbf{v} = -\mathbf{v} + \mathbf{z} = -\mathbf{v} + \mathbf{v} + (-1)\mathbf{v} = (-1)\mathbf{v}.$$

The proof of (iii) is left as an exercise

## Exercise 11.1

**1.** Using the ordered pair technique show that the vectors in the plane form an Abelian group.

**2.** Draw a diagram illustrating the Associative Law for addition of plane vectors. Prove the Associative Law geometrically.

**3.** Show that, if **u** and **v** are two plane vectors from $O$ which do not lie entirely on a single line through $O$, then each vector **w** is expressible uniquely in the form

$$\mathbf{w} = a\mathbf{u} + b\mathbf{v}.$$

Associate this with the coordinatization of the plane.

**4.** Let $G$ be the set $J \times J$. Interpret the elements of $G$ as plane vectors and thereby obtain a geometrical illustration of a $J$-module.

**5.** Consider the collection of all segments of great circles on a sphere which emanate from a fixed point $O$. Can this be made into an $S$-module for some ring $S$? Explain. Can it be projected onto a plane vector space?

**6.** Describe addition of vector quantities in three-space.

**7.** Is there any physical reason for studying spaces of "dimension" greater than three?

**8.** Write out all of the axioms for a vector space $V(F)$.

**9.** Show that $C_n(F)$ satisfies each of the requirements listed in Problem 8.

**10.** Define a right $S$-module, and give two examples.

**11.** Show that the set $P_n(F)$ of all polynomials from $F[\lambda]$ of degree less than $n$ or no degree form a vector space relative to the operations of Example 2. How does it compare with $C_n(F)$?

**12.** Prove (iii) of Theorem 11.1.

**13.** Let $M(F)$ be the set of all functions from the field $F$ to $F$. Let $H$ and $K$ be two such functions and define $H + K$ and $aH$ by their images:

$$(H + K)(f) = H(f) + K(f)$$

and

$$(aH)(f) = aH(f) \qquad \text{for all } a \text{ and } f \text{ in } F.$$

Show that $M$ is a vector space over $F$.

**14.** Let $M_b(F)$ be the set of all elements $H$ from $M(F)$ in Problem 13 such that

$$H(b) = 0.$$

Show that $M_b(F)$ is a vector space over $F$ relative to the operations defined above.

**15.** Show that the additive group of the domain $F[\lambda]$ is a left $F[\lambda]$-module when the *scalar multiplication* is defined by using the formal derivative: If $f(\lambda)$ and $g(\lambda)$ are in $F[\lambda]$, $f(\lambda) = a_0 + a_1\lambda + \cdots + a_n\lambda^n$, then

$$f(\lambda) * g(\lambda) = a_0 g(\lambda) + a_1 Dg(\lambda) + \cdots + a_n D^n g(\lambda).$$

**16.** Let $G$ be an $S$-module. Show that the mapping which is called scalar multiplication describes a homomorphism $H_a$ of $G$ onto a subgroup of itself for each $a$ in $S$,

$$H_a\colon \mathbf{v} \to a\mathbf{v}.$$

Use this idea to generalize the concept of module to non-Abelian groups.

**17.** Show that the complex field $C = Re[\lambda]/(\lambda^2 + 1)$ is a vector space of "dimension" two over $Re$. (See Problem 3.)

**18.** Show that a quadratic extension of the rational field $R$ is a vector space of "dimension" two over $R$.

**19.** Let $G$ be an $S$-module, where $S$ is an integral domain, and let $a$ and $\mathbf{x}$ be elements of $S$ and $G$, respectively. Show that

$$a\mathbf{x} = \mathbf{z},$$

where $\mathbf{z}$ is the zero of $G$, if and only if $a = 0$ and/or $\mathbf{x} = \mathbf{z}$.

## 11.2 Subspaces

As the student should expect, the study of modules and vector spaces involves the investigation of subsystems and homomorphisms. This is again the generalized number theoretic approach to the study of the structure of an algebraic system which we have illustrated earlier in our analysis of other systems. Roughly speaking the subsystems are the "factors" of the whole system.

DEFINITION 11.3. A nonempty subset $M$ of the $S$-module $G$ is a *submodule* if and only if the element

$$a\mathbf{u} + b\mathbf{v}$$

is in $M$ for each $a$ and $b$ in $S$ and $\mathbf{u}$ and $\mathbf{v}$ in $G$.

It is quite easy to see that a submodule $M$ of the left $S$-module $G$ is also a left $S$-module. Since

$$\mathbf{u} + \mathbf{v} = 1\mathbf{u} + 1\mathbf{v},$$

for $\mathbf{u}$ and $\mathbf{v}$ in $M$, we see that the binary operation (which is written as addition) of $G$ induces a binary operation on $M$, and this operation is associative and commutative by inheritance from $G$. Moreover the equations

$$-\mathbf{u} = (-1)\mathbf{u} + 0\mathbf{v}$$

and

$$\mathbf{z} = (-1)\mathbf{u} + 1\mathbf{u} = 0\mathbf{u}$$

show that $-\mathbf{u}$ and $\mathbf{z}$ are in $M$ when $\mathbf{u}$ is in $M$. Hence $(M, +)$ is a group, a subgroup of $(G, +)$. Since the properties of scalar multiplication are also inherited by $M$ we conclude that $M$ is a left $S$-module.

THEOREM 11.2. *A submodule $M$ of the left $S$-module $G$ is also a left $S$-module.*

*Example* 1. Let $M$ be the set of all elements $(a_1, a_2, a_3)$ of $C_3(R)$ with $a_1 = 0$. Since

$$a(0, a_2, a_3) + b(0, b_2, b_3) = (0, c_2, c_3)$$

with

$$c_i = aa_i + bb_i, \qquad i = 1 \text{ and } 2,$$

we conclude that $M$ is a submodule of $C_3(R)$. Since $C_3(R)$ is a vector space the set $M$ is called a subspace.

DEFINITION 11.4. A submodule $M$ of a vector space $V(F)$ is a *subspace*.

*Example* 2. Let $(G, +)$ be an Abelian group; then $G$ is a $J$-module (as we saw earlier) and each subgroup $M$ of $G$ is a submodule of the $J$-module $G$. For, if **u** and **v** are in $M$ and $a$ and $b$ are positive integers, then

$$a\mathbf{u} + b\mathbf{v} = (\mathbf{u} + \cdots + \mathbf{u}) + (\mathbf{v} + \cdots + \mathbf{v})$$

where $(\mathbf{u} + \cdots + \mathbf{u})$ and $(\mathbf{v} + \cdots + \mathbf{v})$ denote the sum of $a$ **u**'s and the sum of $b$ **v**'s, respectively. Obviously these are in $M$, and we see from this that $M$ is a submodule.

*Example* 3. Let $M$ be an ideal of the ring $S$ with identity. Now the additive group $(S, +)$ can be interpreted as a left $S$-module since the requisite properties follow from the Associative and Distributive Laws for $S$. Then the elements of $M$ form a submodule of $(S, +)$ since

$$a\mathbf{u} + b\mathbf{v}$$

is surely in $M$ when $a$ and $b$ are in $S$ and **u** and **v** are in $M$.

Now that we have some idea of what a subspace (or a submodule) is, we pose a problem which will be the subject of our investigations in the ensuing sections of this chapter.

*Problem.* Determine some or all of the subspaces of the vector space $V(F)$.

The problem is stated only for vector spaces since the counterpart for modules is considerably more difficult. As a matter of fact we will restrict our attention to just a certain type of vector space.

As a first step in the investigation of this problem we describe two methods for obtaining a subspace of the vector space $V(F)$.

*Method* 1: Building a subspace from a nonempty collection $T$ of vectors of $V(F)$. This method is a very simple one, basically. We select finitely many elements from $T$, say $\mathbf{t}_1, \mathbf{t}_2, \cdots, \mathbf{t}_m$, and $m$ elements $a_1, \cdots, a_m$ from $F$, and form

$$\mathbf{t} = a_1\mathbf{t}_1 + a_2\mathbf{t}_2 + \cdots + a_m\mathbf{t}_m.$$

If **t** is in $T$, nothing more needs to be done, but if **t** is not in $T$, then we enlarge $T$ to include this element.

DEFINITION 11.5. The element **t** is a *linear combination* of elements from $T$. The collection of all linear combinations of elements from $T$ is denoted by $(T)$.

For example, if the set $T$ of a vector space $V(F)$ with $F = J/(3)$ consists of two vectors, $\mathbf{t}_1$ and $\mathbf{t}_2$, then the set $(T)$ consists of

$$\mathbf{z} \text{ (the zero vector)}, \mathbf{t}_1, 2\mathbf{t}_1, \mathbf{t}_2, 2\mathbf{t}_2, \mathbf{t}_1 + \mathbf{t}_2,$$
$$2\mathbf{t}_1 + \mathbf{t}_2, \mathbf{t}_1 + 2\mathbf{t}_2, \text{ and } 2\mathbf{t}_1 + 2\mathbf{t}_2.$$

These are not necessarily all distinct.

If $T$ is an infinite set, then $(T)$ consists of all linear combinations involving a single vector, all linear combinations involving two vectors, all linear combinations involving three vectors, etc. From the definition we see that a linear combination of vectors always involves just a finite collection of vectors.

THEOREM 11.3. *If $T$ is a nonempty subset of $V(F)$, then $(T)$ is a subspace of $V(F)$.*

Let $\mathbf{u}$ and $\mathbf{v}$ be two vectors from $(T)$. Then by the definition of $(T)$ we know that $\mathbf{u}$ and $\mathbf{v}$ are linear combinations of elements from $T$,

$$\mathbf{u} = a_1\mathbf{t}_1 + \cdots + a_m\mathbf{t}_m$$

and

$$\mathbf{v} = b_1\mathbf{t}'_1 + \cdots + b_n\mathbf{t}'_n$$

where the $a_i$ and $b_i$ are in $F$ and the $\mathbf{t}_i$ and $\mathbf{t}'_i$ are vectors from $T$. Certainly

$$a\mathbf{u} + b\mathbf{v} = aa_1\mathbf{t}_1 + \cdots + aa_m\mathbf{t}_m + bb_1\mathbf{t}'_1 + \cdots + bb_n\mathbf{t}'_n,$$

where $a$ and $b$ are in $F$, is also a linear combination of elements from $T$. Hence $a\mathbf{u} + b\mathbf{v}$ is in $(T)$ so that $(T)$ is a subspace of $V(F)$.

DEFINITION 11.6. A subspace $U$ of the vector space $V(F)$ is *spanned* by the set $T$ of vectors from $V(F)$ if and only if $U = (T)$. Sometimes we say that $T$ *generates* $U$.

Of course each subspace $U$ of $V(F)$ has at least one spanning or generating set, namely the set $U$. More important, however, are the minimal generating sets, and these are studied in the next section.

*Method* 2: Building subspaces from subspaces of $V(F)$. From our studies of other algebraic systems we should expect subspaces to intersect in subspaces, and that is indeed what happens. Moreover we can combine two subspaces to build a larger space (and basically we are back to the first method).

THEOREM 11.4. *If $K$ is a nonempty class of subspaces of $V(F)$, then $I(K)$, the set of elements of $V(F)$ which are common to all of the subspaces in $K$ is a subspace of $V(F)$.*

Let $\mathbf{u}$ and $\mathbf{v}$ be in $I(K)$ and $a$ and $b$ be in $F$. Then $\mathbf{u}$, $\mathbf{v}$, and hence $a\mathbf{u} + b\mathbf{v}$ are all elements of each element of $K$. That is, if $U$ is in $K$, then $\mathbf{u}$ and $\mathbf{v}$ are in $U$ so that $a\mathbf{u} + b\mathbf{v}$ is also in $U$ since it is a subspace of $V(F)$. Therefore $a\mathbf{u} + b\mathbf{v}$ is in every subspace in $K$ so that $a\mathbf{u} + b\mathbf{v}$ is in $I(K)$. Thus we see that $I(K)$ is a subspace of $V(F)$. (Note that $I(K)$ is not empty since every subspace of $V(F)$ contains the zero vector $\mathbf{z}$.)

*Example* 4. Let $V(F)$ be the familiar three-dimensional real vector space of vectors emanating from the origin $O$. Then any two planes through $O$ correspond to subspaces of $V(F)$, and their intersection is (in general) a line through the origin. The vectors in this line form a subspace just as the vectors in a plane through $O$ determine a subspace.

THEOREM 11.5. *If $U$ and $W$ are subspaces of $V(F)$, then the set*

$$U + W = \{\mathbf{u} + \mathbf{w}: \mathbf{u} \text{ in } U, \mathbf{w} \text{ in } W\}$$

*is a subspace of $V(F)$.*

The subspace $U + W$ is called the *sum* of $U$ and $W$ and is easily seen to be the subspace spanned by the set union of $U$ and $W$. To show that $U + W$ is a subspace we note that, if $\mathbf{u}$ and $\mathbf{v}$ are in $U + W$, then

$$\mathbf{u} = \mathbf{u}_1 + \mathbf{w}_1 \quad \text{and} \quad \mathbf{v} = \mathbf{u}_2 + \mathbf{w}_2$$

where $\mathbf{u}_i$ is in $U$ and $\mathbf{w}_i$ is in $W$. Then

$$a\mathbf{u} + b\mathbf{v} = (a\mathbf{u}_1 + b\mathbf{u}_1) + (a\mathbf{w}_1 + b\mathbf{w}_2),$$

and this is in $U + W$ since

$$a\mathbf{u}_1 + b\mathbf{u}_2$$

is in $U$ and

$$a\mathbf{w}_1 + b\mathbf{w}_2$$

is in $W$.

This definition of the sum of two spaces can obviously be extended to enable a finite collection of subspaces to be summed. What is not so obvious is that the concept can be extended to an infinite collection of subspaces of $V(F)$.

DEFINITION 11.7. If $K$ is a collection of subspaces of the space $V(F)$, then the *sum* of subspaces in $K$ is defined to be the subspace spanned by the set union of the elements of $K$ and is denoted by $\Sigma(K)$.

*Example* 5. Let $V(F)$ be the polynomial domain of $F$ considered as a left $F$-module. Denote by $F\lambda^n$ the set of all polynomials of the form $a\lambda^n$,

$$F\lambda^n = \{a\lambda^n: a \text{ in } F\}.$$

This set is quite obviously a subspace of $V(F)$ for each positive integer $n$ since

$$a\lambda^n + b\lambda^n = (a + b)\lambda^n,$$

so take $K$ to be the collection of all $F\lambda^n$ with $n$ even. Then the subspace $\Sigma(K)$ is the collection of all polynomials of the form

$$a_2\lambda^2 + a_4\lambda^4 + \cdots + a_{2m}\lambda^{2m}.$$

Note also that the subspace consisting of all polynomials of degree less than $n$ or of no degree can be written as

$$F + F\lambda + \cdots + F\lambda^{n-1}.$$

As in the discussions of other subsystems a *proper* subspace of $V(F)$ is a subspace $U \neq V(F)$, and the set $(\mathbf{z})$ is the *trivial* subspace of $V(F)$.

In certain specific spaces or types of spaces there are many, many other ways for singling out subspaces, and more are being discovered every day.

A very common method for distinguishing subspaces of the coordinate $n$-space $C_n(F)$ involves a system of linear equations. If $(a_1, \cdots, a_n)$ and $(b_1, \cdots, b_n)$ are two vectors of $C_n(F)$, then the set of all vectors

$$\mathbf{v} = (x_1, \cdots, x_n)$$

such that

$$a_1x_1 + a_2x_2 + \cdots + a_nx_n = 0$$

and

$$b_1x_1 + b_2x_2 + \cdots + b_nx_n = 0,$$

form a subspace of $C_n(F)$. This subspace is the subspace of $C_n(F)$ *orthogonal* to the subspace spanned by $(a_1, \cdots, a_n)$ and $(b_1, \cdots, b_n)$.

*Example* 6. Find the subspace of $C_3(R)$ which is orthogonal to the subspace spanned by (1, 1, 2) and (2, 2, 3).

From the equations

$$x_1 + x_2 + 2x_3 = 0$$

and

$$2x_1 + 2x_2 + 3x_3 = 0$$

we conclude that

$$2(x_1 + x_2 + 2x_3) - (2x_1 + 2x_2 + 3x_3) = x_3 = 0.$$

Then

$$x_1 + x_2 = 0$$

and

$$2x_1 + 2x_2 = 0$$

imply that $x_1 = -x_2$, so that the orthogonal subspace consists of the vectors of the form

$$(-x_2, x_2, 0),$$

where $x_2$ is an arbitrary element of $R$. Since

$$a(-c, c, 0) + b(-d, d, 0) = (-(ac + bd), ac + bd, 0)$$

we see that this collection is indeed a subspace of $C_3(R)$.

If we switched to the real field instead of the rational field $R$ we could describe this situation geometrically. The two vectors (1, 1, 2) and (2, 2, 3) determine a plane through the origin, and the orthogonal subspace consists of the vectors on the line through the origin which is perpendicular to this plane.

## Exercise 11.2

**1.** Find two different, proper, nontrivial subspaces $U$ and $W$ of $C_3(R)$, and describe the sets $U \cap W$, $U + W$, and $U \cup W$.

**2.** Show that the following pairs of vectors from $C_3(R)$ span the same subspace:

$$\begin{aligned} \mathbf{u}_1 &= (1, 0, 0) \quad \text{and} \quad \mathbf{v}_1 = (1, 1, 0); \\ \mathbf{u}_2 &= (4, 4, 0) \quad \text{and} \quad \mathbf{v}_2 = (2, -1, 0); \\ \mathbf{u}_3 &= (0, 4, 0) \quad \text{and} \quad \mathbf{v}_3 = (3, 2, 0). \end{aligned}$$

(Show that $\mathbf{u}_1$ and $\mathbf{v}_1$ are in $(\{\mathbf{u}_2, \mathbf{v}_2\})$, etc.)

**3.** Show that the two nonzero vectors $(a_1, a_2)$ and $(b_1, b_2)$ of $C_2(F)$ each span the same subspace if and only if $a_1b_2 - a_2b_1 = 0$.

**4.** Let $V(F)$ be the polynomial domain of $F$. Is the set consisting of zero and all of the polynomials of even degree a subspace of $V(F)$? Explain.

**5.** Let $U$ be the set of all differentiable functions in the space $V(Re)$ of all continuous mappings of $Re$ to $Re$. (Here the functions are added coordinate-wise so that for functions $\mathbf{u}$ and $\mathbf{v}$,

$$(a\mathbf{u} + b\mathbf{v})(c) = a\mathbf{u}(c) + b\mathbf{v}(c),$$

$a$, $b$, and $c$ real numbers.) Is $U$ a subspace?

**6.** Which of the following subsets of $C_n(F)$ are subspaces?

(*a*) All $(a_1, \cdots, a_n)$ with $a_1 = 1$.
(*b*) All $(a_1, \cdots, a_n)$ with $a_n \neq 0$.
(*c*) All $(a_1, \cdots, a_n)$ with $a_1 + a_2 + \cdots + a_n = 0$.
(*d*) All $(a_1, \cdots, a_n)$ with $a_1 = a_2 = \cdots = a_n$.
(*e*) All $(a_1, \cdots, a_n)$ with $a_1 + a_2 + \cdots + a_n \neq 0$.

**7.** Determine all of the subspaces of $C_2(J/(3))$.

**8.** Determine all of the subspaces of $C_3(J/(2))$.

**9.** In $C_3(J/(3))$ find all of the vectors in the subspace spanned by (1, 2, 1) and (2, 2, 1).

**10.** Describe the subspace of $C_3(Re)$ which is orthogonal to the subspace spanned by (1, 1.9999, 0) and (−2.733111, 14, 0). Describe geometrically.

**11.** Describe the subspace of $C_3(F)$, where $F$ is the complex field, which is orthogonal to the subspace spanned by $(i, 1, 0)$ and (0, 0, 1). Find the intersection of the two subspaces and compare with the results of Problem 10.

**12.** How are the subspaces $U$ and $W$ of $V(F)$ related if $U + W =$ the union of $U$ and $W$?

**13.** Show that, if $U$ and $W$ are subspaces of $V(F)$, then $\mathbf{v}$ in $U + W$ is uniquely expressible as $\mathbf{v} = \mathbf{u} + \mathbf{w}$ with $\mathbf{u}$ in $U$ and $\mathbf{w}$ in $W$ if and only if $U \cap W = \{\mathbf{z}\}$.

**14.** Prove that $U + W = (U \cup W)$ when $U$ and $W$ are subspaces of $V(F)$.

**15.** Prove that the subspace spanned by the $n$ vectors $\mathbf{v}_1, \cdots, \mathbf{v}_n$ of $V(F)$ is precisely the intersection of all of the subspaces of $V(F)$ which contain these vectors.

**16.** Let $U$ and $W$ be two subspaces of $V(F)$. Show that $U + W$ equals the intersection of all of the subspaces of $V(F)$ which contain both $U$ and $W$.

**17.** After working Problems 15 and 16 compare Method 1 and Method 2.

**18.** Is there anything in this section which cannot be extended to left $S$-modules? Explain.

**19.** Describe the algebraic system formed by the subsets of $V(F)$ and the binary operations of set intersection and subspace addition.

## 11.3 Linear Independence and Bases

In the previous section the concept of spanning or generating set of a subspace $U$ of $V(F)$ was defined. This concept combines with the idea of the sum of subspaces so that we can say that every subspace $U \neq \{\mathbf{z}\}$ in $V(F)$ is the sum of a collection of minimal subspaces of $V(F)$.

DEFINITION 11.8. A subspace $W \neq \{\mathbf{z}\}$ of $V(F)$ is *minimal* if and only if it contains no subspaces of $V(F)$ except $W$ and $\{\mathbf{z}\}$.

A minimal subspace of $V(F)$ is easily described. It is precisely the set of all scalar multiples of a single nonzero vector $\mathbf{v}$ of $V(F)$ and is denoted as $(\mathbf{v})$. This is the counterpart here of the cyclic subgroup in group theory and the principal ideal in ideal theory. The geometric example of a minimal subspace is a line through the origin.

THEOREM 11.6. *A nonzero subspace $U$ of $V(F)$ is the sum of a collection of minimal subspaces.*

Let $T$ be a generating set of $U$, and form the minimal subspace $(\mathbf{t})$ for each $\mathbf{t} \neq \mathbf{z}$ in $T$. Then $U$ is the sum of these minimal subspaces. To prove this we note that, since $\mathbf{t}$ is in $T$, which is a subset of $U$, certainly $(\mathbf{t})$ is a subset of $U$. Thus the sum of all the subspaces is in $U$ since it (the sum) consists of linear combinations of the $\mathbf{t}$'s. But since $U = (T)$ we know that each element of $U$ is a linear combination of the $\mathbf{t}$'s. Thus $U$ equals the sum of the minimal subspaces generated by the individual elements of a spanning set for $U$.

Now a subspace in general has many different spanning sets. The plane vector space, for example, is spanned by any collection of two or more vectors which do not lie in the same line through the origin. Thus there is no possibility that this decomposition of a subspace into the sum of a collection of minimal subspaces is at all unique. However, when the subspace $U$ is spanned by a *finite* set of vectors we are able to show that the *number* of minimal subspaces which sum to $U$ in an irredundant way is unique.

Heuristically we proceed as follows to pick out an irredundant collection of minimal subspaces which sum to $U$, when $U$ is spanned by the $n$ vectors $\mathbf{u}_1, \cdots, \mathbf{u}_n$. First we consider the subspace $(\mathbf{v}_1)$ with $\mathbf{v}_1 = \mathbf{u}_1 \neq \mathbf{z}$. This consists of all vectors of the form $a_1 v_1$ for $a_1$ in $F$ and is obviously a minimal subspace since a subspace $W \neq (\mathbf{z})$ which contains $b\mathbf{v}_1$ must also contain

$$b^{-1}(b\mathbf{v}_1) = 1\mathbf{v}_1 = \mathbf{v}_1.$$

Now, if $(\mathbf{v}_1) \neq U$, then one of the $n - 1$ vectors $\mathbf{u}_2, \cdots, \mathbf{u}_n$ is not in $(\mathbf{v}_1)$, for, if all of the spanning vectors are in $(\mathbf{v}_1)$, then all of their linear combinations are in $(\mathbf{v}_1)$ also. This could only happen if $(\mathbf{v}_1) = U$.

We select from the $\mathbf{u}_i$ and label as $\mathbf{v}_2$ an element not in $(\mathbf{v}_1)$ and form the subspace

$$(\mathbf{v}_1) + (\mathbf{v}_2).$$

The elements of this subspace are linear combinations of $\mathbf{v}_1$ and $\mathbf{v}_2$ and so are in $U$. Thus $(\mathbf{v}_1) + (\mathbf{v}_2) \subseteq U$.

If $U \neq (\mathbf{v}_1) + (\mathbf{v}_2)$ we select another vector from the vectors of the spanning set which are not in $(\mathbf{v}_1) + (\mathbf{v}_2)$, label it as $\mathbf{v}_3$, and form the subspace

$$(\mathbf{v}_1) + (\mathbf{v}_2) + (\mathbf{v}_3) \subseteq U.$$

Continuing in this way we eventually obtain $m$ vectors $\mathbf{v}_1, \mathbf{v}_2, \cdots, \mathbf{v}_m$ such that

$$(\mathbf{v}_1) + (\mathbf{v}_2) + \cdots + (\mathbf{v}_m) = U$$

and $m \leqslant n$.

But what about the "irredundancy" we mentioned earlier? Well, each vector $\mathbf{u}$ of $U$ is now representable *uniquely* in the form

$$\mathbf{u} = a_1\mathbf{v}_1 + \cdots + a_m\mathbf{v}_m$$

with $a_i$ in $F$ (and obviously every such linear combination is in $U$). For, if $\mathbf{u}$ were expressible as

$$\mathbf{u} = b_1\mathbf{v}_1 + \cdots + b_m\mathbf{v}_m, \qquad b_i \text{ in } F,$$

with the $b_i$ different from the $a_i$ for some $i$, then, subtracting, we get

$$\mathbf{z} = (a_1 - b_1)\mathbf{v}_1 + \cdots + (a_m - b_m)\mathbf{v}_m$$

or

$$\mathbf{z} = c_1\mathbf{v}_1 + \cdots + c_m\mathbf{v}_m, \qquad c_i \text{ in } F.$$

Then, if $r$ is the largest subscript, $1 \leqslant r \leqslant m$, such that $c_r \neq 0$, we have

$$c_r\mathbf{v}_r = -c_1\mathbf{v}_1 - \cdots - c_{r-1}\mathbf{v}_{r-1}.$$

But this equation means that the vector

$$\mathbf{v}_r = c_r^{-1}(c_r\mathbf{v}_r)$$

is in the subspace

$$(\mathbf{v}_1) + (\mathbf{v}_2) + \cdots + (\mathbf{v}_{r-1}),$$

which contradicts the way the elements $\mathbf{v}_i$ were selected. Hence the elements of $U$ can be expressed in a unique fashion as linear combinations of the $m$ generators $\mathbf{v}_1, \cdots, \mathbf{v}_m$.

For a more formal development we restate this idea of irredundancy in terms of vectors and then proceed with an induction proof.

DEFINITION 11.9. The $m$ vectors $\mathbf{v}_1, \cdots, \mathbf{v}_m$ of a vector space $V(F)$ are *linearly independent* (and form a *linearly independent set*) if and only if the equation

$$a_1\mathbf{v}_1 + \cdots + a_m\mathbf{v}_m = \mathbf{z}$$

implies that $a_1 = a_2 = \cdots = a_m = 0$ in $F$. Vectors which are not linearly independent are said to be *linearly dependent*.

This concept is easily seen to be equivalent to the idea of irredundancy discussed above.

THEOREM 11.7. *If the subspace $U \neq (\mathbf{z})$ of $V(F)$ is spanned by the $m$ linearly independent vectors $\mathbf{v}_1, \cdots, \mathbf{v}_m$, then each vector $\mathbf{u}$ of $U$ is uniquely expressible in the form*

$$\mathbf{u} = a_1\mathbf{v}_1 + \cdots + a_m\mathbf{v}_m, \qquad a_i \text{ in } F.$$

*Conversely if each element of U is expressible uniquely in terms of m vectors* $\mathbf{v}_1, \cdots, \mathbf{v}_m$, *then these m vectors are linearly independent.*

If the vectors $\mathbf{v}_1, \cdots, \mathbf{v}_m$ are linearly independent, then the two equations

$$\mathbf{u} = a_1\mathbf{v}_1 + \cdots + a_m\mathbf{v}_m$$

and

$$\mathbf{u} = b_1\mathbf{v}_1 + \cdots + b_m\mathbf{v}_m$$

lead to the equation

$$\mathbf{z} = \mathbf{u} - \mathbf{u} = (a_1 - b_1)\mathbf{v}_1 + \cdots + (a_m - b_m)\mathbf{v}_m,$$

which implies that

$$0 = a_1 - b_1 = a_2 - b_2 = \cdots = a_m - b_m.$$

Hence the expression for $\mathbf{u}$ in terms of the $\mathbf{v}_i$ is unique.

Conversely if each element of $U$ is uniquely expressible in terms of the $m$ vectors $\mathbf{v}_1, \cdots, \mathbf{v}_m$, then these vectors are certainly linearly independent. For the equation

$$\mathbf{z} = 0\mathbf{v}_1 + \cdots + 0\mathbf{v}_m,$$

and the uniqueness of this representation enable us to conclude from

$$a_1\mathbf{v}_1 + \cdots + a_m\mathbf{v}_m = \mathbf{z}$$

that

$$a_1 = a_2 = \cdots = a_m = 0 \qquad \text{in } F.$$

THEOREM 11.8. *If the subspace* $U \neq (\mathbf{z})$ *of* $V(F)$ *is spanned by the vectors* $\mathbf{u}_1, \cdots, \mathbf{u}_n$, *then U is spanned by a linearly independent subset of these n vectors.*

If $n = 1$, then $U$ is precisely the minimal subspace $(\mathbf{v}_1)$, so we proceed by induction on $n$. Let $U'$ be the subspace spanned by $\mathbf{u}_2, \cdots, \boldsymbol{u}_n$. Then the induction hypothesis enables us to conclude that $U'$ is spanned by a linearly independent subset $\{\mathbf{v}_2, \cdots, \mathbf{v}_m\}$ of these. Now we look at the set of vectors $\{\mathbf{u}_1, \mathbf{v}_2, \cdots, \mathbf{v}_m\}$. This set spans $U$, for each element $\mathbf{u}$ of $U$ is a linear combination of the $n$ vectors $\mathbf{u}_1, \mathbf{u}_2, \cdots, \mathbf{u}_n$, and, since each $\mathbf{u}_i$ for $i = 2, \cdots, n$ is a linear combination of the vectors $\mathbf{v}_2, \cdots, \mathbf{v}_m$, we see that $\mathbf{u}$ is a linear combination of $\mathbf{u}_1, \mathbf{v}_2, \cdots, \mathbf{v}_m$ by substituting.

If the $m$ vectors $\mathbf{u}_1, \mathbf{v}_2, \cdots, \mathbf{v}_m$ are linearly independent then nothing more needs to be done. But if they are dependent, then there is an equation

$$b_1\mathbf{u}_1 + b_2\mathbf{v}_2 + \cdots + b_m\mathbf{v}_m = \mathbf{z}$$

with not all of the $b_i$ equal to zero. In particular $b_1 \neq 0$ for otherwise we would have a contradiction of the linear independence of the $\mathbf{v}_2, \cdots, \mathbf{v}_m$. Since $b_1 \neq 0$ we can solve this equation for $\mathbf{u}_1$,

$$\mathbf{u}_1 = -b_1^{-1}b_2\mathbf{v}_2 - \cdots - b_1^{-1}b_m\mathbf{v}_m,$$

and this means that the linearly independent vectors $\mathbf{v}_2, \cdots, \mathbf{v}_m$ span the subspace $U$. Thus in either case $U$ is spanned by a linearly independent subset of the $n$ generating vectors $\mathbf{u}_1, \cdots, \mathbf{u}_n$.

This is precisely the same idea which was discussed earlier, viz., if $U$ is the sum of a collection of $n$ minimal subspaces, then $U$ is the irredundant sum of a subcollection of $m$ of these minimal subspaces, $m \leqslant n$. Now we wish to show that the positive integer $m$ is unique.

THEOREM 11.9. *If the subspace $U$ of $V(F)$ is spanned by the $m$ linearly independent vectors $\mathbf{v}_1, \cdots, \mathbf{v}_m$, then no linearly independent set of vectors of $U$ can contain more than $m$ vectors.*

Let the $r$ vectors $\mathbf{w}_1, \cdots, \mathbf{w}_r$ be linearly independent vectors from $U$, and consider the $m + 1$ vectors $\mathbf{w}_1, \mathbf{v}_1, \mathbf{v}_2, \cdots, \mathbf{v}_m$. Since $\mathbf{w}_1$ is expressible in terms of the $\mathbf{v}_i$ (as is every vector of $U$) we have the relation

$$\mathbf{w}_1 = a_1\mathbf{v}_1 + \cdots + a_m\mathbf{v}_m.$$

Since $\mathbf{w} \neq \mathbf{z}$ (no vector of a linearly independent set of vectors can be the zero vector) we see that the $a_i$ are not all zero. So suppose $a_1 \neq 0$. (This involves no loss of generality since we can relabel the vectors if necessary.) Then we can solve for $\mathbf{v}_1$ in terms of $\mathbf{w}_1, \mathbf{v}_2, \cdots, \mathbf{v}_m$,

$$\mathbf{v}_1 = a_1^{-1}\mathbf{w}_1 - a_1^{-1}a_2\mathbf{v}_2 - \cdots - a_1^{-1}a_m\mathbf{v}_m,$$

and from this we conclude that the $m$ vectors $\mathbf{w}_1, \mathbf{v}_2, \cdots, \mathbf{v}_m$ span $U$ since this equation permits us to replace $\mathbf{v}_1$ by a combination of $\mathbf{w}_1, \mathbf{v}_2, \cdots, \mathbf{v}_m$. Moreover the $m$ vectors $\mathbf{w}_1, \mathbf{v}_2, \cdots, \mathbf{v}_m$ are linearly independent since an equation

$$b_1\mathbf{w}_1 + b_2\mathbf{v}_2 + \cdots + b_m\mathbf{v}_m = \mathbf{z}$$

with the $b_i$ not all zero leads to contradictions.

(1) If $b_1 \neq 0$, then $\mathbf{w}_1$ is expressible as a linear combination of the $m - 1$ vectors $\mathbf{v}_2, \cdots, \mathbf{v}_m$, which contradicts the *unique* expression above for $\mathbf{w}_1$ in terms of the $m$ vectors $\mathbf{v}_1, \mathbf{v}_2, \cdots, \mathbf{v}_m$.

(2) If $b_1 = 0$, then we have, adding $0\mathbf{v}_1$,

$$0\mathbf{v}_1 + \mathbf{z} = \mathbf{z} = 0\mathbf{v}_1 + b_2\mathbf{v}_2 + \cdots + b_m\mathbf{v}_m$$

with the $b_i$ not all zero, which contradicts the independence of the $m$ vectors $\mathbf{v}_1, \cdots, \mathbf{v}_m$.

Thus we conclude that the $m$ vectors $\mathbf{w}_1, \mathbf{v}_2, \cdots, \mathbf{v}_m$ are linearly independent and span $U$.

Now we repeat essentially the same process with the vector $\mathbf{w}_2$ and the linearly independent set $\mathbf{w}_1, \mathbf{v}_2, \cdots, \mathbf{v}_m$ which spans $U$. Since $\mathbf{w}_2$ is in $U$ there exist scalars $c_1, \cdots, c_m$ such that

$$\mathbf{w}_2 = c_1\mathbf{w}_1 + c_2\mathbf{v}_2 + \cdots + c_m\mathbf{v}_m,$$

and the $c_i$ are not all zero since $\mathbf{w}_2 \neq \mathbf{z}$. Moreover, and this is a very important point which did not occur in the previous step, the scalars $c_2, \cdots, c_m$ cannot all be zero since that would mean that $c_1 \neq 0$ and

$$\mathbf{z} = -1\mathbf{w}_2 + c_1\mathbf{w}_1 + 0\mathbf{w}_3 + \cdots + 0\mathbf{w}_n,$$

contradicting the linear independence of the $r$ vectors $\mathbf{w}_1, \cdots, \mathbf{w}_r$. Thus some scalar from $c_2, \cdots, c_m$ must be nonzero, and we take this to be $c_2$ (relabeling if necessary). Then we can solve for $\mathbf{v}_2$,

$$\mathbf{v}_2 = c_2^{-1}\mathbf{w}_2 - c_2^{-1}c_1\mathbf{w}_1 - c_2^{-1}c_3\mathbf{v}_3 - \cdots - c_2^{-1}c_m\mathbf{v}_m,$$

and from this we deduce that the $m$ vectors $\mathbf{w}_1, \mathbf{w}_2, \mathbf{v}_3, \cdots, \mathbf{v}_m$ span the subspace $U$. Also these vectors are linearly independent since an equation

$$b_1\mathbf{w}_1 + b_2\mathbf{w}_2 + b_3\mathbf{v}_3 + \cdots + b_m\mathbf{v}_m = \mathbf{z}$$

with the $b_i$ not all zero leads to contradictions.

(1) If $b_2 \neq 0$, then $\mathbf{w}_2$ is expressible in terms of the $m - 1$ vectors $\mathbf{w}_1, \mathbf{v}_3, \cdots, \mathbf{v}_m$, which contradicts the above unique expression for $\mathbf{w}_2$ in terms of $\mathbf{w}_1, \mathbf{v}_2, \cdots, \mathbf{v}_m$.

(2) If $b_2 = 0$, then we have, adding $0\mathbf{v}_2$,

$$\mathbf{z} = 0\mathbf{v}_2 + \mathbf{z} = b_1\mathbf{w}_1 + 0\mathbf{v}_2 + b_3\mathbf{v}_3 + \cdots + b_m\mathbf{v}_m$$

with the $b_i$ not all zero, which contradicts the linear independence of $\mathbf{w}_1, \mathbf{v}_2, \cdots, \mathbf{v}_m$.

We can repeat this procedure to replace $\mathbf{v}_3$ (relabeling if necessary) by $\mathbf{w}_3$ and obtain the linearly independent spanning set $\mathbf{w}_1, \mathbf{w}_2, \mathbf{w}_3, \mathbf{v}_4, \cdots, \mathbf{v}_m$. In fact for $r$ no larger than $m$ we can replace $r$ of the $\mathbf{v}$'s (labeling them as $\mathbf{v}_1, \mathbf{v}_2, \cdots, \mathbf{v}_r$ for the sake of simplicity) by the $r$ $\mathbf{w}$'s to obtain the linearly independent spanning set for $U$,

$$\mathbf{w}_1, \mathbf{w}_2, \cdots, \mathbf{w}_r, \qquad \mathbf{v}_{r+1}, \cdots, \mathbf{v}_m.$$

However, if $r$ is larger than $m$, we arrive at the following contradictory situation: the $m$ spanning vectors $\mathbf{v}_1, \cdots, \mathbf{v}_m$ are replaced by the $m$ vectors $\mathbf{w}_1, \cdots, \mathbf{w}_m$, which also span $U$. Then $\mathbf{w}_{m+1}$ is expressible as a linear combination of the $m$ vectors $\mathbf{w}_1, \cdots, \mathbf{w}_m$,

$$\mathbf{w}_{m+1} = d_1\mathbf{w}_1 + \cdots + d_m\mathbf{w}_m,$$

and the $d_i$ are not all zero since $\mathbf{w}_{m+1} \neq \mathbf{z}$. But this means that

$$\mathbf{z} = d_1\mathbf{w}_1 + \cdots + d_m\mathbf{w}_m - 1\mathbf{w}_{m+1} + \cdots + 0\mathbf{w}_r,$$

which contradicts the linear independence of the $r$ vectors $\mathbf{w}_1, \cdots, \mathbf{w}_r$. Hence we conclude that $r$ cannot be larger than $m$.

*Corollary* 11.9.1. If $U \neq (\mathbf{z})$ is a finitely generated subspace of $V(F)$, then any linearly independent subset of vectors in $U$ can be embedded in a linearly independent generating set for $U$.

Let $\mathbf{w}_1, \cdots, \mathbf{w}_n$ be linearly independent in $U$. We know that $U$ has a linearly independent spanning set $\{\mathbf{v}_1, \cdots, \mathbf{v}_m\}$, and by the above argument $n$ of the v's can be replaced by the w's to obtain a linearly independent generating set for $U$ which includes $\mathbf{w}_1, \cdots, \mathbf{w}_n$.

*Corollary* 11.9.2. If $\{\mathbf{v}_1, \cdots, \mathbf{v}_m\}$ and $\{\mathbf{w}_1, \cdots, \mathbf{w}_n\}$ are two linearly independent spanning sets for the subspace $U$ of $V(F)$, then $m = n$.

Since $U$ has the linearly independent spanning set $\mathbf{v}_1, \cdots, \mathbf{v}_m$ we know from the theorem above that no linearly independent subset of $U$ can contain more than $m$ vectors. Hence $n$ is no larger than $m$. And since $U$ is spanned by the $n$ independent vectors $\mathbf{v}_1, \cdots, \mathbf{v}_n$ we know that $m$ is no larger than $n$. Thus $n = m$.

DEFINITION 11.10. A linearly independent spanning set of the subspace $U$ of $V(F)$ is a *basis* of $U$.

THEOREM 11.10. *If $U$ is a finitely generated nonzero subspace of $V(F)$, then $U$ has a finite basis $\{\mathbf{v}_1, \cdots, \mathbf{v}_m\}$ and all the bases of $U$ contain exactly $m$ elements.*

This is just a reformulation of the preceding results.

*Example* 1. Show that the space $C_4(F)$ has a basis of 4 elements.

Write $\mathbf{v}_1 = (1, 0, 0, 0)$, $\mathbf{v}_2 = (0, 1, 0, 0)$, $\mathbf{v}_3 = (0, 0, 1, 0)$, and $\mathbf{v}_4 = (0, 0, 0, 1)$. Then for an arbitrary element $\mathbf{v} = (a_1, a_2, a_3, a_4)$ of $C_4(F)$ we can write

$$\mathbf{v} = a_1\mathbf{v}_1 + a_2\mathbf{v}_2 + a_3\mathbf{v}_3 + a_4\mathbf{v}_4.$$

Hence the four vectors $\mathbf{v}_1$, $\mathbf{v}_2$, $\mathbf{v}_3$, $\mathbf{v}_4$ span $C_4(F)$. To show that they are linearly independent, suppose that

$$a_1\mathbf{v}_1 + a_2\mathbf{v}_2 + a_3\mathbf{v}_3 + a_4\mathbf{v}_4 = \mathbf{z} = (0, 0, 0, 0).$$

Then

$$(a_1, a_2, a_3, a_4) = (0, 0, 0, 0)$$

which means that

$$a_1 = a_2 = a_3 = a_4 = 0,$$

and so the $\mathbf{v}_i$ are linearly independent.

*Example* 2. Show that the vectors $\mathbf{w}_1 = (1, 1, 1, 1)$, $\mathbf{w}_2 = (1, -1, -1, 1)$, and $\mathbf{w}_3 = (1, 2, 2, 1)$ of $C_4(R)$ are linearly dependent.

We wish to show that there are nonzero scalars $a_1$, $a_2$, and $a_3$ such that

$$a_1\mathbf{w}_1 + a_2\mathbf{w}_2 + a_3\mathbf{w}_3 = \mathbf{z} = (0, 0, 0, 0).$$

Checking components we see that $a_1$, $a_2$, and $a_3$ must satisfy the two distinct equations

$$a_1 - a_2 + 2a_3 = 0$$

and

$$a_1 + a_2 + a_3 = 0.$$

Clearly $a_1 = 3$, $a_2 = -1$, and $a_3 = -2$ satisfy these conditions so that the vectors are dependent. Any two of these vectors form a basis for the subspace spanned by the three.

## Exercise 11.3

**1.** Let $\mathbf{v}$ be a nonzero vector of $V(F)$, and show that $(\mathbf{v}) = \{a\mathbf{v}: a \text{ in } F\}$ is a minimal subspace of $V(F)$. Show by example that this result is not true in general for left $S$-modules. (Consider the additive group of integers as a $J$-module.)

**2.** Find a smallest set of minimal subspaces of $C_4(R)$ which sum to the subspace $U$ spanned by the vectors:

(*a*) $(-1, -2, -3, 0)$, $(6, 0, 2, 4)$, $(2, 4, 2, 4)$, $(3, 5, 3, 1)$.
(*b*) $(1, 1, 1, 1)$, $(1, 2, 1, 2)$, $(2, 1, 2, 1)$, $(1, 0, -2, 0)$.
(*c*) $(1, 0, 0, 0)$, $(2, -1, 1, -1)$, $(1, 1, -1, 1)$, $(2, -2, 2, -2)$.

(Reread the discussion following Theorem 11.6.)

**3.** Let $U$ denote the subspace of $C_4(R)$ spanned by $\mathbf{v}_1 = (1, 0, 0, 0)$, $\mathbf{v}_2 = (0, 1, 0, 0)$, and $\mathbf{v}_3 = (0, 0, 0, 1)$. Show that $U$ has a basis which includes the two vectors $\mathbf{w}_1 = (2, 3, 0, -1000)$ and $\mathbf{w}_2 = (101, 102, 0, 103)$. (Use the replacement procedure of Corollary 11.9.1)

**4.** Find a basis for $C_n(F)$.

**5.** Show that $n + k$ vectors in $C_n\ (F)$ are linearly dependent when $k$ is positive.

**6.** Show that a linearly independent set of vectors cannot contain the zero vector.

**7.** Let the subspace $U$ of $V(F)$ have the basis $\{\mathbf{v}_1, \mathbf{v}_2, \mathbf{v}_3\}$. Show that the three vectors

$$\begin{aligned} \mathbf{w}_1 &= \mathbf{v}_1 + \mathbf{v}_2 + \mathbf{v}_3, \\ \mathbf{w}_2 &= \phantom{\mathbf{v}_1 + {}} \mathbf{v}_2 + \mathbf{v}_3, \\ \mathbf{w}_3 &= \phantom{\mathbf{v}_1 + \mathbf{v}_2 + {}} \mathbf{v}_3, \end{aligned}$$

form a basis for $U$ also. Compare this with the fact that the three vectors $(1, 1, 1)$, $(0, 1, 1)$, and $(0, 0, 1)$ form a basis of $C_3(F)$.

**8.** Show that any three vectors not in the same plane form a basis for the real three-dimensional vector space.

**9.** Let $\mathbf{v}$ be a vector of $V(F)$ which is not in the subspace $U$. Show that, if $\{\mathbf{v}_1, \cdots, \mathbf{v}_m\}$ is a basis for $U$, then the $m + 1$ vectors $\mathbf{v}, \mathbf{v}_1, \cdots, \mathbf{v}_m$ are linearly independent. Illustrate geometrically.

**10.** If the subspace $U$ of $C_6(J/(5))$ has a basis of three elements, then how many vectors does $U$ contain? What is the answer when $U$ has a basis of $m$ elements in $C_n(J/(p))$?

**11.** Consider the real field as a vector space over $R$ and show that $1$, $\sqrt{2}$, $\sqrt{3}$, and $\sqrt{6}$ are linearly independent "vectors." Compare this with the coset representation of the field $R[\lambda]/(\lambda^4 - 10\lambda^2 + 1)$.

**12.** Prove that every nonempty subset of a linearly independent set of vectors from $V(F)$ is also linearly independent. State the negative of this theorem.

**13.** An infinite set of vectors from $V(F)$ is linearly independent if and only if every finite nonempty subset is linearly independent. Extend Problem 12 to this case.

**14.** Show that the "vectors" $1, \lambda, \lambda^2, \lambda^3, \lambda^4$, etc., of the $F$-space $F[\lambda]$ are linearly independent.

**15.** Show that the results of this section extend to $S$-modules when $S$ is a sfield.

**16.** Let $U$ be a subspace of $V(F)$ with a basis of $n$ elements. Show that each proper nonzero subspace of $U$ has a basis with fewer than $n$ elements.

## 11.4 Dimension and Isomorphism

The role of $V(F)$ in the preceding section was very minor since our attention was on the finitely generated subspace $U$. Obviously, then, to carry these results over to $V(F)$ we must assume that it is finitely generated, and we do this by restricting our attention to finite dimensional vector spaces. This concept is based on the work of the previous section.

DEFINITION 11.11. The vector space $V(F)$ has *finite dimension* if and only if it possesses a finite spanning set. The *dimension* of $V(F)$, denoted by dim $(V)$, is the number of elements in a basis of $V(F)$. $V(F)$ is *infinite dimensional* if and only if it is not finite dimensional.

If $V(F)$ is the trivial space consisting of the zero vector only, then we say it has dimension 0. However, we are primarily interested in spaces of positive dimension $n$, and we know from our earlier results that this concept is uniquely defined for each finitely generated space. To indicate that the space $V(F)$ has dimension $n$ we write $V_n(F)$.

The results in the previous section enable us to write down the following facts about $V_n(F)$.

(1) $V_n(F)$ contains $n$ linearly independent elements $\mathbf{v}_1, \cdots, \mathbf{v}_n$ such that each element $\mathbf{v}$ of $V_n(F)$ is expressible uniquely as

$$\mathbf{v} = a_1\mathbf{v}_1 + \cdots + a_n\mathbf{v}_n, \qquad a_i \text{ in } F.$$

These vectors form a basis for $V_n(F)$.

(2) If the $m$ vectors $\mathbf{w}_1, \cdots, \mathbf{w}_m$ of $V_n(F)$ are linearly independent, then $m$ is no larger than $n$ and $V_n(F)$ has a basis which includes the $\mathbf{w}_i$.

(3) Any $n$ linearly independent vectors of $V_n(F)$ form a basis for $V_n(F)$.

(4) If the $n$ vectors $\mathbf{w}_1, \cdots, \mathbf{w}_n$ of $V_n(F)$ generate $V_n(F)$, then they are linearly independent.

What else can we find out about $V_n(F)$? Presumably one purpose in narrowing our attention down to finite dimensional spaces was to isolate a type of module in which we could determine all of the submodules. Thus we should devote some attention to the subspaces of $V_n(F)$.

THEOREM 11.11. *A proper subspace $U$ of $V_n(F)$ has dimension $m$ less than $n$.*

If $U$ has finite dimension $m$, then by property (2) above we know that $m$ is less than $n$. Hence we need only to show that $U$ is finite dimensional, and this is rather trivial. If $U = (\mathbf{z})$, then $U$ has dimension 0, so suppose $U \neq (\mathbf{z})$. Then $U$ contains a nonzero vector $\mathbf{u}_1$, which all by itself forms a linearly independent subset of $U$. Thus $U$ contains linearly independent sets of vectors, so we consider the number of elements in each such set. This collection of positive integers is bounded by $n$ (property (2)) and so contains a maximal element $m$. Therefore $U$ contains a linearly independent set of vectors $\mathbf{u}_1, \mathbf{u}_2, \cdots, \mathbf{u}_m$ and these span $U$; for, if $\mathbf{u}$ from $U$ is not a linear combination of $\mathbf{u}_1, \cdots, \mathbf{u}_m$, then the $m + 1$ vectors $\mathbf{u}, \mathbf{u}_1, \cdots, \mathbf{u}_m$ are linearly independent, contradicting the maximality of $m$. So we see that $U$ has dimension $m$.

As an application of this we can prove the following result which relates the dimensions of the sum and intersection of two subspaces of $V_n(F)$.

THEOREM 11.12. *If $U$ and $W$ are subspaces of $V_n(F)$, then*

$$\dim (U + W) + \dim (U \cap W) = \dim (U) + \dim (W).$$

We note that $U \cap W$ is a subspace of both $U$ and $W$ whereas $U$, $W$, and $U \cap W$ are all subspaces of $U + W$. So $U \cap W$ has a basis $\mathbf{v}_1, \cdots, \mathbf{v}_k$ which can be extended to a basis of $U$ (by property (2)) by incorporating $i$ additional vectors: $\mathbf{v}_1, \cdots, \mathbf{v}_k; \mathbf{u}_1, \cdots, \mathbf{u}_i$. Similarly this basis of $U \cap W$ can be extended to a basis of $W$ by incorporating $j$ additional vectors:

$$\mathbf{v}_1, \cdots, \mathbf{v}_k; \qquad \mathbf{w}_1, \cdots, \mathbf{w}_j.$$

Thus

$$\dim (U \cap W) = k, \qquad \dim (U) = k + i,$$

and

$$\dim (W) = k + j.$$

Now we claim that the $k + i + j$ vectors

$$\mathbf{v}_1, \cdots, \mathbf{v}_k; \qquad \mathbf{u}_1, \cdots, \mathbf{u}_i; \qquad \mathbf{w}_1, \cdots, \mathbf{w}_j$$

form a basis for $U + W$ so that

$$\dim (U + W) = k + i + j.$$

Suppose these vectors are dependent; then we would have

$$\mathbf{z} = a_1\mathbf{v}_1 + \cdots + a_k\mathbf{v}_k + b_1\mathbf{u}_1 + \cdots + b_i\mathbf{u}_i + c_1\mathbf{w}_1 + \cdots + c_j\mathbf{w}_j.$$

But such a relation implies one of the following.

(*a*) Some $\mathbf{u}_r$ is in $W$, which contradicts the choice of the $\mathbf{u}_r$.
(*b*) Some $\mathbf{w}_r$ is in $U$, which contradicts the choice of the $\mathbf{w}_r$.
or
(*c*) There is a linear relation among the basis elements of $U \cap W$, of $U$, or of $W$, contradicting the idea of a basis.

So we conclude that the $k + i + j$ vectors are linearly independent. Since they are easily seen to span $U + W$ we conclude that the theorem is true.

Geometrically interpreted this theorem implies that two planes through the origin intersect in a line (dimension one) or a plane (dimension 2).

*Example* 1. In $C_3(R)$ the subspace $U$ consists of all vectors of the form $(a_1, 0, a_3)$ and $W$ is spanned by (1, 2, 1) and (3, 1, 2). Find $U \cap W$ and $U + W$.

$U$ has a basis $\mathbf{u}_1 = (1, 0, 0)$ and $\mathbf{u}_2 = (0, 0, 1)$, and $W$ has a basis $\mathbf{w}_1 = (1, 2, 1)$ and $\mathbf{w}_2 = (3, 1, 2)$. Then, if $\mathbf{v}$ is in the intersection we have

$$\mathbf{v} = (a_1, a_2, a_3) = b_1\mathbf{u}_1 + b_2\mathbf{u}_2 = c_1\mathbf{w}_1 + c_2\mathbf{w}_2.$$

Equating components yields the scalar equations

$$a_1 = b_1 = c_1 + 3c_2,$$
$$a_2 = 0 = 2c_1 + c_2,$$

and

$$a_3 = b_3 = c_1 + 2c_2.$$

From the second we see that

$$c_2 = -2c_1,$$

and substitution leads to

$$a_1 = b_1 = -5c_1$$

and

$$a_3 = b_3 = -3c_1.$$

Hence

$$\mathbf{v} = c_1(-5, 0, -3)$$

so that $U \cap W$ is spanned by the vector $\mathbf{v}_1 = (5, 0, 3)$. Then $\mathbf{v}_1$ and $\mathbf{u}_1$ span $U$ and $\mathbf{v}_1$ and $\mathbf{w}_1$ span $W$. Finally $\mathbf{v}_1$, $\mathbf{u}_1$, and $\mathbf{w}_1$ span $C_3(F)$ since they are linearly independent. For suppose

$$a\mathbf{v}_1 + b\mathbf{u}_1 + c\mathbf{w}_1 = \mathbf{z} = (0, 0, 0);$$

then we have the scalar equations

$$5a + b + c = 0$$
$$0a + 0b + 2c = 0$$
$$3a + 0b + c = 0.$$

The second yields $c = 0$, which together with the third implies $a = 0$, and clearly

$$a = b = c = 0.$$

Now to study the subspaces of $V_n(F)$ we can use a basis for $V_n(F)$, and this we know is a set of $n$ vectors $\mathbf{v}_1, \cdots, \mathbf{v}_n$ of $V_n(F)$ such that each vector $\mathbf{v}$ of the space is expressible uniquely as

$$\mathbf{v} = a_1\mathbf{v}_1 + \cdots + a_n\mathbf{v}_n.$$

Because of this uniqueness the vector $\mathbf{v}$ is determined completely by two things, the basis $\{\mathbf{v}_1, \cdots, \mathbf{v}_n\}$ and the ordered set of scalars $(a_1, \cdots, a_n)$. Thus we see that this basis establishes a one-to-one correspondence between the elements of $V_n(F)$,

$$\mathbf{v} = a_1\mathbf{v}_1 + \cdots + a_n\mathbf{v}_n,$$

and the elements of $C_n(F)$,

$$(a_1, \cdots, a_n).$$

(And a different basis for $V_n(F)$ would establish a different correspondence.) Since this is precisely the correspondence between plane vectors and ordered pairs of real numbers which was described at the beginning of the chapter, the student should not be surprised to learn that this correspondence is an isomorphism.

DEFINITION 11.12. A one-to-one mapping $\boldsymbol{H}$ from a vector space $V(F)$ onto a vector space $U(F)$ is an *isomorphism* if and only if

$$(a\mathbf{v} + b\mathbf{w})\boldsymbol{H} = a(\mathbf{v}\boldsymbol{H}) + b(\mathbf{w}\boldsymbol{H}),$$

for $a$ and $b$ in $F$ and $\mathbf{v}$ and $\mathbf{w}$ in $V(F)$.

Here $\mathbf{v}\boldsymbol{H}$ denotes the image in $U(F)$ of $\mathbf{v}$ under the mapping $\boldsymbol{H}$. We see that $\boldsymbol{H}$ is compatible with the addition and scalar multiplication of $V(F)$ and $U(F)$; the corresponding binary operations are denoted by the same symbols.

THEOREM 11.13. *Each basis* $\{\mathbf{v}_1, \cdots, \mathbf{v}_n\}$ of $V_n(F)$ *determines an isomorphism* $\boldsymbol{H}$ *of* $V_n(F)$ *with* $C_n(F)$ *which is given by*

$$(a_1\mathbf{v}_1 + \cdots + a_n\mathbf{v}_n)\boldsymbol{H} = (a_1, \cdots, a_n).$$

As we noted above this mapping is one-to-one onto because of the uniqueness of the expression for a vector in terms of a basis. That $\boldsymbol{H}$ is compatible with the binary operations is easily shown. Let

$$\mathbf{u} = a_1\mathbf{v}_1 + \cdots + a_n\mathbf{v}_n \quad \text{and} \quad \mathbf{v} = b_1\mathbf{v}_1 + \cdots + b_m\mathbf{v}_m;$$

then

$$a\mathbf{u} + b\mathbf{v} = (aa_1 + bb_1)\mathbf{v}_1 + \cdots + (aa_n + bb_n)\mathbf{v}_n$$

so that

$$\begin{aligned}(a\mathbf{u} + b\mathbf{v})\boldsymbol{H} &= (aa_1 + bb_1, \cdots, aa_n + bb_n)\\ &= a(a_1, a_2, \cdots, a_n) + b(b_1, b_2, \cdots, b_n).\end{aligned}$$

Hence for $a$ and $b$ in $F$ and $\mathbf{u}$ and $\mathbf{v}$ in $V_n(F)$ we have

$$(a\mathbf{u} + b\mathbf{v})\boldsymbol{H} = a(\mathbf{u}\boldsymbol{H}) + b(\mathbf{v}\boldsymbol{H})$$

since

$$\mathbf{u}\boldsymbol{H} = (a_1, a_2, \cdots, a_n)$$

and

$$\mathbf{v}\boldsymbol{H} = (b_1, b_2, \cdots, b_n).$$

Basically this isomorphism depends on relating the arbitrary basis $\{\mathbf{v}_1, \cdots, \mathbf{v}_n\}$ of $V_n(F)$ with the very special, so-called *canonical basis* of $C_n(F)$ which consists of the $n$ vectors

$$\mathbf{e}_1 = (1, 0, \cdots, 0), \quad \mathbf{e}_2 = (0, 1, 0, \cdots, 0), \cdots, \\ \mathbf{e}_n(0, \cdots, 0, 1).$$

In particular we have

$$\mathbf{v}_i\boldsymbol{H} = \mathbf{e}_i.$$

This theorem certainly does not mean that $C_n(F)$ is *the* $n$-dimensional vector space over $F$ (although this impression is sometimes given by careless expositors). It does mean, however, that we can find all of the subspaces of $V_n(F)$ by finding the subspaces of $C_n(F)$.

THEOREM 11.14. *Let $\boldsymbol{H}$ be an isomorphism from $V(F)$ onto $U(F)$. If $V'$ is a subspace of $V(F)$, then $V'' = \{\mathbf{v}\boldsymbol{H}\colon \mathbf{v} \text{ in } V'\}$ is a subspace of $U(F)$, and, conversely, if $U'$ is a subspace of $U(F)$, then $U'' = \{\mathbf{v}\colon \mathbf{v}\boldsymbol{H} \text{ is in } U'\}$ is a subspace of $V(F)$.*

We shall prove only the first part of the theorem. Let $\mathbf{u}'$ and $\mathbf{v}'$ be two elements of $V''$; then $V'$ contains unique elements $\mathbf{u}$ and $\mathbf{v}$ such that $\mathbf{u}' = \mathbf{u}\boldsymbol{H}$ and $\mathbf{v}' = \mathbf{v}\boldsymbol{H}$. Then $a\mathbf{u} + b\mathbf{v}$ is also in $V'$ since $V'$ is a subspace, so that

$$(a\mathbf{u} + b\mathbf{v})\boldsymbol{H} = a\mathbf{u}' + b\mathbf{v}'$$

is in $V''$. Hence $V''$ is a subspace of $U(F)$.

The second part is proved similarly.

*Example* 2. Let $\mathbf{v}_1$, $\mathbf{v}_2$, and $\mathbf{v}_3$ form a basis for $V_3(R)$, and find a basis for the subspace $U$ spanned by the three vectors

$$\mathbf{u}_1 = \mathbf{v}_1 - 2\mathbf{v}_2 + 3\mathbf{v}_3, \quad \mathbf{u}_2 = 2\mathbf{v}_1 + 3\mathbf{v}_2 + 2\mathbf{v}_3, \quad \text{and} \quad \mathbf{u}_3 = 7\mathbf{v}_1 + 13\mathbf{v}_3.$$

We switch over to $C_3(R)$ via $\boldsymbol{H}$, replacing $\mathbf{v}_1$, $\mathbf{v}_2$, and $\mathbf{v}_3$ by the canonical basis of $C_3(R)$. Then we wish to find a basis for the subspace $U'$ spanned by $(1, -2, 3)$, $(2, 3, 2)$, and $(7, 0, 13)$. Since the first two are obviously linearly independent we can take them as at least a part of a basis for $U'$. Then we check to see if $(7, 0, 13)$ is dependent on these by considering

$$(7, 0, 13) = a(1, -2, 3) + b(2, 3, 2).$$

Checking components we get

$$\begin{aligned} 7 &= a + 2b \\ 0 &= -2a + 3b \\ 13 &= 3a + 2b; \end{aligned}$$

solving, we find that $b = 2$ and $a = 3$. Thus $U'$ has the basis $(1, -2, 3)$ and $(2, 3, 2)$ so that $\mathbf{u}_1$ and $\mathbf{u}_2$ form a basis for $U$.

Here we have used the fact that linearly independent sets of vectors correspond to linearly independent sets of vectors under an isomorphism. This is an easily proved theorem.

In the next section we will determine all of the subspaces of $C_n(F)$. This is done by formalizing the method of elimination commonly used for solving systems of linear equations. Using such a device we obtain a unique basis for each subspace of $C_n(F)$, and this naturally describes all of the subspaces of $C_n(F)$. Once we know these we effectively know all of the subspaces of $V_n(F)$.

## Exercise 11.4

**1.** Classify all of the vector spaces mentioned in the set of problems in Exercise 11.1 by dimension; in Exercise 11.2; in Exercise 11.3.

**2.** By considering various collections of the canonical basis vectors for $C_n(F)$ show that $C_n(F)$ has a subspace of every possible dimension less than $n$.

**3.** Show that $C_5(F)$ contains at least ten subspaces of dimension three; at least ten of dimension two; at least five of dimension one. Generalize.

**4.** Illustrate Theorem 11.12 in $C_4(J/(3))$.

**5.** Describe how the three alternatives arise in the last part of the proof of Theorem 11.12.

**6.** Let $\boldsymbol{H}$ be an isomorphism from $V(F)$ onto $U(F)$. Show that $\boldsymbol{H}$ maps the zero vector of $V(F)$ onto the zero vector of $U(F)$. (Remember that $\mathbf{z} = 0\mathbf{v}$.)

**7.** Let $\boldsymbol{H}$ be an isomorphism from $V(F)$ onto $U(F)$. Show that the $n$ vectors $\mathbf{v}_1, \cdots, \mathbf{v}_n$ of $V(F)$ are linearly independent if and only if the $n$ vectors $\mathbf{v}_1\boldsymbol{H}, \cdots, \mathbf{v}_n\boldsymbol{H}$ of $U(F)$ are linearly independent. (Note that the equation $a_1\mathbf{v}_1 + \cdots + a_n\mathbf{v}_n = \mathbf{z}$ maps onto the equation $a_1\mathbf{v}\boldsymbol{H} + \cdots + a_n\mathbf{v}_n\boldsymbol{H} = \mathbf{z}\boldsymbol{H}$.)

**8.** Show that the mapping $\boldsymbol{H}$,

$$\boldsymbol{H}: (a_1, a_2) \to (a_2, a_1),$$

is an isomorphism of $C_2(F)$ onto itself.

**9.** Show that the mapping $\boldsymbol{H}_k$,

$$\boldsymbol{H}_k: (a_1, a_2, a_3) \to (a_1, a_2, ka_3),$$

where $k$ is an arbitrary but fixed nonzero element of $F$, is an isomorphism of $C_3(F)$ onto itself.

**10.** Show that the mapping $\boldsymbol{H}$,

$$\boldsymbol{H}: (a_1, a_2, a_3) \to (a_1, a_2 + 9a_1, a_3)$$

is an isomorphism of $C_3(R)$ onto itself.

**11.** Show that two different bases of $V_n(F)$, say $\{\mathbf{v}_1, \cdots, \mathbf{v}_n\}$ and $\{\mathbf{u}_1, \cdots, \mathbf{u}_n\}$, define an isomorphism $\boldsymbol{H}$ of $V_n(F)$ onto itself with

$$(a_1\mathbf{v}_1 + \cdots + a_n\mathbf{v}_n)\boldsymbol{H} = a_1(\mathbf{v}_1\boldsymbol{H}) + \cdots + a_n(\mathbf{v}_n\boldsymbol{H}) = a_1\mathbf{u}_1 + \cdots + a_n\mathbf{u}_n.$$

**12.** Can an isomorphism between two $n$-dimensional vector spaces be described as a matching of bases? Explain. (See Problem 11.)

**13.** Let $\{V\}$ be a collection of finite dimensional vector spaces over the field $F$. Describe an equivalence relation on this set.

**14.** If the field $F$ is considered as a vector space over a subfield $F_0$, then the dimension of this vector space over $F_0$ is called the *degree* of $F$ over $F_0$ and is denoted by $[F:F_0]$. Find the degree of $R[\lambda]/(\lambda^3 + 1)$ over $R$. Find the degree of $R[\lambda]/(\lambda^2 - 2)$ over $R$.

**15.** Let $F_1$, $F_2$, and $F_3$ be fields with $F_1$ a subfield of $F_2$ and $F_2$ a subfield of $F_3$. Show that $[F_3:F_1] = [F_3:F_2][F_2:F_1]$. Illustrate with $F_1 = R$, $F_2 = R[\lambda]/(\lambda^2 - 2)$, and $F_3 = F_2[\lambda]/(\lambda^2 - 3)$.

**16.** If $R$ is extended $n$ times by means of irreducible quadratic polynomials to $F$, then $[F:R] = 2^n$. Show that $F$ contains no subfield obtained by extending $R$ by means of an irreducible cubic. What does this imply about the problem of doubling a cube by means of straight-edge and compass constructions?

**17.** Let the subspace $U$ of $C_4(R)$ have basis $\{(1, 0, 0, 0), (0, 1, 0, 0)\}$. Find two different subspaces $V$ and $W$ of $C_4(R)$ of dimension two such that

$$C_4(R) = U + V = U + W.$$

**18.** If $G$ is a left $S$-module what (if any) of the preceding theory breaks down when $S$ is a division ring? An integral domain? A ring with zero divisors?

## 11.5 Row Echelon Form

Our intention now is to describe all of the subspaces of $C_n(F)$ by determining a unique (i.e., canonical) basis for each subspace. In doing this we shall develop a program for reducing any finite set of spanning vectors of a subspace $U$ of $C_n(F)$ to the canonical basis of $U$. Our program or routine (which is not itself unique) is based on the familiar elimination method for solving a set of linear equations.

When we write down a set of vectors from $C_n(F)$, say $\mathbf{v}_1, \cdots, \mathbf{v}_m$, we are ordering them by listing or counting them. Since each vector of $C_n(F)$ is itself an ordered set of $n$ elements from $F$ we are really dealing with a *doubly ordered set* of elements when we consider the $m$ vectors $\mathbf{v}_1, \cdots, \mathbf{v}_m$. Since the ordering of the $n$ components of the vectors of $C_n(F)$ is horizontally written from left to right we can write the second ordering vertically, from top to bottom.

$$\begin{pmatrix} a_{11} & a_{12} & \cdots & a_{1n} \\ a_{21} & a_{22} & \cdots & a_{2n} \\ \vdots & & & \\ a_{m1} & a_{m2} & \cdots & a_{mn} \end{pmatrix}$$

This doubly ordered set of $mn$ elements from $F$ is called an *$m$-by-$n$ array* over $F$ (and it can be defined more formally as a function from $J_m \times J_n$ onto $F$, where $J_r$ denotes the first $r$ positive integers).

The double ordering of this array, which we denote by $A$, is fully indicated by the *double subscripts* attached to the elements of $A$. The first subscript on $a_{rs}$, the $r$ or *row subscript*, describes the vertical ordering, and the second subscript, the $s$ or *column subscript*, describes the horizontal ordering. Then the element $a_{12}$ lies in the first row and second column, whereas $a_{32}$ lies in the third row and second column. (Strictly speaking a comma should separate the two subscripts so that $a_{12}$ could not be misinterpreted as the twelfth component in a vector from $C_{13}(F)$. However, the context of the usage renders this cumbersome precaution unnecessary in general.)

Thus we see that a collection of $m$ vectors

$$\begin{aligned} \mathbf{v}_1 &= (a_{11}, \cdots, a_{1n}), \\ \mathbf{v}_2 &= (a_{21}, \cdots, a_{2n}), \\ &\vdots \\ \mathbf{v}_m &= (a_{m1}, \cdots, a_{mn}), \end{aligned}$$

from $C_n(F)$ can be stacked up to give an $m$-by-$n$ array $A$ over $F$:

$$A = \begin{pmatrix} a_{11} & \cdots & a_{1n} \\ a_{21} & \cdots & a_{2n} \\ \vdots & & \\ a_{m1} & \cdots & a_{mn} \end{pmatrix} = (a_{rs}).$$

Conversely an $m$-by-$n$ array $A$ over $F$ can be sliced into $m$ rows of $n$ components each, thus yielding $m$ vectors from $C_n(F)$. These $m$ vectors are the *row vectors* of $A$, the subspace $V(A)$ of $C_n(F)$ spanned by these row vectors is the *row space* of $A$, and the dimension of $V(A)$ is the *row rank* of $A$.

Now to obtain a unique basis for a subspace of $C_n(F)$ spanned by the $m$ vectors $\mathbf{v}_1, \cdots, \mathbf{v}_m$ we stack these vectors to form an $m$-by-$n$ array $A$ over $F$ and reduce $A$ to a unique form by means of the following simple operations.

DEFINITION 11.13. The *elementary row operations* on an $m$-by-$n$ array $A$ are the mappings of the set $F(m, n)$ of all $m$-by-$n$ arrays over $F$ onto itself defined by:

(1) $\boldsymbol{I}(i, j)$: interchange of row $i$ and row $j$.
(2) $\boldsymbol{M}(i, k)$: multiply row $i$ by $k \neq 0$ in $F$.
(3) $\boldsymbol{E}(i; k, j)$: add to row $i$ the scalar product of $k$ and row $j$.

*Example* 1. If $A$ is the 3-by-4 array over $R$,

$$A = \begin{pmatrix} 1 & 2 & 3 & 4 \\ 5 & 6 & 7 & 8 \\ 9 & 8 & 7 & 6 \end{pmatrix},$$

then

(1) $\boldsymbol{I}(1, 2)$ applied to $A$ yields the array

$$\boldsymbol{I}(1, 2)A = \begin{pmatrix} 5 & 6 & 7 & 8 \\ 1 & 2 & 3 & 4 \\ 9 & 8 & 7 & 6 \end{pmatrix};$$

(2) $\boldsymbol{M}(2, -1)$ applied to $A$ yields the array

$$\boldsymbol{M}(2, -1)A = \begin{pmatrix} 1 & 2 & 3 & 4 \\ -5 & -6 & -7 & -8 \\ 9 & 8 & 7 & 6 \end{pmatrix};$$

(3) $\boldsymbol{E}(3; -9, 1)$ applied to $A$ yields the array

$$\boldsymbol{E}(3; -9, 1)A = \begin{pmatrix} 1 & 2 & 3 & 4 \\ 5 & 6 & 7 & 8 \\ 0 & -10 & -20 & -30 \end{pmatrix}.$$

This last example illustrates a key use of the elementary operations, the introduction of zeros into the arrays.

A very important feature of these row operations is that they are reversible.

THEOREM 11.15. *If $A$ is an $m$-by-$n$ array over $F$, then*

$$\text{(1)} \qquad \boldsymbol{I}(j, i)(\boldsymbol{I}(i, j)A) = A;$$
$$\text{(2)} \qquad \boldsymbol{M}(i, k^{-1})(\boldsymbol{M}(i, k)A) = A;$$
$$\text{(3)} \qquad \boldsymbol{E}(i; -k, j)(\boldsymbol{E}(i; k, j)A) = A,$$

*for all allowable $i$, $j$, and $k$.*

For example, using the array of Example 1,

$$\boldsymbol{I}(2, 1)(\boldsymbol{I}(1, 2)A) = \boldsymbol{I}(2, 1)\begin{pmatrix} 5 & 6 & 7 & 8 \\ 1 & 2 & 3 & 4 \\ 9 & 8 & 7 & 6 \end{pmatrix} = A.$$

In other words the two mappings $\boldsymbol{I}(2, 1)$ and $\boldsymbol{I}(1, 2)$ combine by function composition to yield the identity mapping on the set of all 3-by-4 arrays over $R$.

*Corollary* 11.15.1. If the $m$-by-$n$ array $B$ is obtained from the $m$-by-$n$ array $A$ by means of an elementary row operation $\boldsymbol{E}$, then $V(A) = V(B)$.

Since $B = \boldsymbol{E}A$ we see that each element of $V(B)$, the row space of $B$, is a linear combination over $F$ of the row vectors of $A$. For each row of $B$ is either a multiple of a row of $A$, or a linear combination of two rows of $A$. Thus

$$V(B) \subseteq V(A).$$

However, by the theorem above there is an elementary row operation $\boldsymbol{E}'$ such that

$$A = \boldsymbol{E}'(\boldsymbol{E}A) = \boldsymbol{E}'B,$$

so that by the same argument we have $V(A) \subseteq V(B)$. Hence $V(A) = V(B)$.

This result can obviously be extended from one elementary row operation to any finite collection of elementary row operations.

*Corollary* 11.15.2. If $A$ and $B$ are two $m$-by-$n$ arrays over $F$ such that one is obtainable from the other through a finite collection of elementary row operations, then $V(A) = V(B)$.

*Corollary* 11.15.3. The row rank of an array is unchanged by the elementary row operations.

What use can we make of these results? Consider the following example.

*Example* 2. Let $A$ be the 3-by-3 array over $R$,

$$A = \begin{pmatrix} 1 & 2 & 3 \\ 4 & 5 & 6 \\ 6 & 5 & 6 \end{pmatrix}.$$

Then,

$$A_1 = \boldsymbol{E}(2;\ -4,\ 1)A = \begin{pmatrix} 1 & 2 & 3 \\ 0 & -3 & -6 \\ 6 & 5 & 6 \end{pmatrix};$$

$$A_2 = \boldsymbol{E}(3;\ -6,\ 1)A_1 = \begin{pmatrix} 1 & 2 & 3 \\ 0 & -3 & -6 \\ 0 & -7 & -12 \end{pmatrix};$$

$$A_3 = \boldsymbol{M}(2,\ -\tfrac{1}{3})A_2 = \begin{pmatrix} 1 & 2 & 3 \\ 0 & 1 & 2 \\ 0 & -7 & -12 \end{pmatrix};$$

$$A_4 = \boldsymbol{E}(3;\ 7,\ 2)A_3 = \begin{pmatrix} 1 & 2 & 3 \\ 0 & 1 & 2 \\ 0 & 0 & 2 \end{pmatrix};$$

$$A_5 = \boldsymbol{M}(3,\ \tfrac{1}{2})A_4 = \begin{pmatrix} 1 & 2 & 3 \\ 0 & 1 & 2 \\ 0 & 0 & 1 \end{pmatrix};$$

$$A_6 = \boldsymbol{E}(2;\ -2,\ 3)A_5 = \begin{pmatrix} 1 & 2 & 3 \\ 0 & 1 & 0 \\ 0 & 0 & 1 \end{pmatrix};$$

$$A_7 = \boldsymbol{E}(1;\ -3,\ 3)(\boldsymbol{E}(1;\ -2,\ 2)A_6) = \begin{pmatrix} 1 & 0 & 0 \\ 0 & 1 & 0 \\ 0 & 0 & 1 \end{pmatrix}.$$

Thus we see that the row space of $A$ is $C_3(R)$, and this means that the three vectors $\mathbf{v}_1 = (1, 2, 3)$, $\mathbf{v}_2 = (4, 5, 6)$, $\mathbf{v}_3 = (6, 5, 6)$ are linearly independent. In fact we have displayed above *eight* different bases for the space $C_3(R)$.

Now we wish to devise a program which will lead in a finite number of applications of elementary row operations to an array $A$ over $F$, to a canonical or unique basis for the row space $V(A)$. The process we are going to describe permits the reduction of $A$ to its *reduced row echelon form* in not more than $nm$ applications of elementary row operations when $A$ is an $m$-by-$n$ array over $F$. In practice the number of steps is usually substantially less than $nm$.

The idea is to reduce the array $A$ as nearly as possible to an array made up of the canonical vectors. Since the stacking of this basis illustrated by the array $A_7$ of Example 2 is an easily remembered one, with the 1's running in echelon down the diagonal, we select this form as an ideal (which is rarely attained). Thus we decide to try to get a one in the upper left corner, and we look at the first column of $A$. If

$$a_{11} = a_{21} = \cdots = a_{n1} = 0,$$

then there is absolutely no way (or need) of getting a one into the one-one position. However, if there is a nonzero element in the first column, then we can shift it into the one-one position by an interchange of rows (one operation). In this new array the element $k$ in the one-one position can be changed into a 1 by multiplying the first row by $1/k$ (another elementary operation). Finally the rest of the elements in column one can be reduced to zeros by adding suitable multiples of row one to the other $m - 1$ rows (possibly $m - 1$ more steps, but not more than $m - 2$ steps if the first interchange had to be made). Thus in at most $m$ steps the $m$-by-$n$ array $A$ has been replaced by an array whose first column looks like this

$$\begin{pmatrix} a & \cdots \\ 0 & \\ 0 & \\ \vdots & \\ 0 & \end{pmatrix},$$

where $a$ is either 0 or 1.

We move on to column two and repeat *exactly* the same procedure provided *all* of the elements in column one are zeros. If all of the elements in columns one and two are zeros we move on to column three and repeat exactly the same procedure. Unless all components of $A$ are zero we eventually obtain (in at most $m$ applications of the appropriate elementary row operations) an array $A_1$ with a 1 in the first row and only zeros below and to the left of it (provided there are any elements to the left of it). This completes phase 1 of the reduction.

Phase 2 involves getting a 1 in the second row, without altering the 1 or the 0's described in phase 1, so that the element immediately above this 1, the elements to the left of this 1, and the elements below this 1 are all zero. If we delete row one and apply phase 1 to the $(m - 1)$-by-$n$ array remaining we can get the 1 and the zeros to the left and below it in at most $m - 1$ steps. Then one more step (back in $A_1$) reduces the element immediately above this 1 in row two to 0. Hence in at most $m$ steps we complete phase 2.

Continuing this process (or by induction) we see that by means of at most $mn$ elementary row operations the $m$-by-$n$ array $A$ can be reduced to an array of the following form.

DEFINITION 11.14. An $m$-by-$n$ array $B$ is in *reduced row echelon form* if and only if the following conditions hold:

(1) Either all of the elements of a row are 0 or the leftmost nonzero element is 1.

(2) If $b_{rs} \neq 0$ in $B$ and $r \neq 1$, then row $r - 1$ contains a nonzero element to the left of column $s$.

(3) If $b_{rs} = 1$ is the leftmost 1 in row $r$, then all other elements of column $s$ are 0.

*Example* 3. The following are in reduced row echelon form:

$$\begin{pmatrix} 1 & 2 & 3 \\ 0 & 0 & 0 \\ 0 & 0 & 0 \end{pmatrix}; \quad \begin{pmatrix} 1 & 0 & 0 \\ 0 & 1 & 2 \\ 0 & 0 & 0 \end{pmatrix}; \quad \begin{pmatrix} 0 & 0 & 1 & 0 \\ 0 & 0 & 0 & 1 \\ 0 & 0 & 0 & 0 \end{pmatrix};$$

$$\begin{pmatrix} 1 & -1 & 1 & 0 \\ 0 & 0 & 0 & 1 \\ 0 & 0 & 0 & 0 \end{pmatrix}; \quad \begin{pmatrix} 1 & 2 & 10 & 0 & -0 & 0 \\ 0 & 0 & 0 & 1 & -1 & 0 \\ 0 & 0 & 0 & 0 & 0 & 1 \end{pmatrix}.$$

The discussion preceding the definition shows that every array over $F$ can be changed into an array in reduced row echelon form in a finite number of steps. Moreover an effective algorithm or routine is described there.

THEOREM 11.16. *An m-by-n array over F can be altered to an array in reduced row echelon form by means of not more than mn elementary row operations.*

*Example* 4. Reduce to reduced row echelon form the array

$$A = \begin{pmatrix} 0 & 4 & 6 & 5 \\ \frac{1}{2} & 1 & \frac{3}{2} & 2 \\ 2 & 2 & 3 & 4 \end{pmatrix}.$$

$$A_1 = \boldsymbol{I}(1, 2)A = \begin{pmatrix} \frac{1}{2} & 1 & \frac{3}{2} & 2 \\ 0 & 4 & 6 & 5 \\ 2 & 2 & 3 & 4 \end{pmatrix};$$

$$A_2 = \boldsymbol{M}(1, 2)A_1 = \begin{pmatrix} 1 & 2 & 3 & 4 \\ 0 & 4 & 6 & 5 \\ 2 & 2 & 3 & 4 \end{pmatrix};$$

$$A_3 = \boldsymbol{E}(3; -2, 1)A_2 = \begin{pmatrix} 1 & 2 & 3 & 4 \\ 0 & 4 & 6 & 5 \\ 0 & -2 & -3 & -4 \end{pmatrix};$$

$$A_4 = \boldsymbol{M}(2, \tfrac{1}{4})A_3 = \begin{pmatrix} 1 & 2 & 3 & 4 \\ 0 & 1 & \frac{3}{2} & \frac{5}{4} \\ 0 & -2 & -3 & -4 \end{pmatrix};$$

$$A_5 = \boldsymbol{E}(1; -2, 2)(\boldsymbol{E}(3; 2, 2)A_4) = \begin{pmatrix} 1 & 0 & 0 & -1 \\ 0 & 1 & \frac{3}{2} & 5/4 \\ 0 & 0 & 0 & 1 \end{pmatrix};$$

$$A_6 = \boldsymbol{E}(1; 1, 3)(\boldsymbol{E}(2; -\tfrac{5}{4}, 3)A_5) = \begin{pmatrix} 1 & 0 & 0 & 0 \\ 0 & 1 & 3/2 & 0 \\ 0 & 0 & 0 & 1 \end{pmatrix}.$$

The array $A_6$ is in reduced row echelon form.

## Exercise 11.5

**1.** Exhibit five vectors from the row space of the array $A$ over $R$,

$$A = \begin{pmatrix} 1 & 2 & 2 & 1 \\ 3 & 4 & 1 & 1 \\ 4 & 4 & -2 & 0 \end{pmatrix}.$$

**2.** How many different 4-by-3 arrays can be concocted from the four vectors (1, 2, 1), (3, 4, 3), (7, 8, 9), and (1, −2, 11) of $C_3(R)$? How are their row spaces related? Why?

**3.** Consider a column from an $m$-by-$n$ array over $F$. Is it an ordered set? How is it related to $C_m(F)$?

**4.** Show that an elementary row operation applied to an array $A$ yields an isomorphism of the row space $V(A)$ onto itself.

**5.** If $A$ is the 3-by-4 array over $R$ of Problem 1, compute (*a*) $\boldsymbol{I}(2, 3)A$; (*b*) $\boldsymbol{I}(1, 3)A$; (*c*) $\boldsymbol{M}(3, -2)A$; (*d*) $\boldsymbol{E}(3; -7, 1)A$; (*e*) $\boldsymbol{E}(1; -6, 2)A$.

**6.** Change each of the following 3-by-3 arrays over $R$ to reduced row echelon form:

$$\begin{pmatrix} 1 & 2 & 3 \\ 2 & 3 & 0 \\ 0 & 1 & 2 \end{pmatrix}; \quad \begin{pmatrix} 6 & -1 & -9 \\ -4 & 2 & 6 \\ 2 & -1 & -1 \end{pmatrix}; \quad \begin{pmatrix} 5 & 3 & 8 \\ 3 & 1 & 4 \\ -1 & 3 & 2 \end{pmatrix}; \quad \begin{pmatrix} -1 & 5 & 6 \\ 1 & 3 & 2 \\ 0 & 1 & 1 \end{pmatrix}:$$

and

$$\begin{pmatrix} 4 & 4 & 0 \\ 1 & 2 & 3 \\ 2 & 8 & 6 \end{pmatrix}.$$

**7.** Is an $m$-by-$n$ array consisting only of zeros in reduced row echelon form? Explain.

**8.** If an $m$-by-$n$ array $A$ is in reduced row echelon form and $m$ exceeds $n$, then what can be said about the bottom $m - n$ rows of $A$?

**9.** What does the word "echelon" mean? Justify its use here.

**10.** Solve the three linear equations

$$x + 2y + 4z = 3,$$
$$2x + 2y + 4z = 3,$$

and

$$4y + 5z = 6,$$

by elimination, and compare the procedure with the reduction of the array

$$A = \begin{pmatrix} 1 & 2 & 4 & 3 \\ 2 & 2 & 4 & 3 \\ 0 & 4 & 5 & 6 \end{pmatrix}$$

to reduced row echelon form. Work over $R$.

**11.** Describe the reduced row echelon form of an $m$-by-$n$ array if its row space is $C_n(F)$.

**12.** Show that the row rank of the $m$-by-$n$ array $A$ equals the number of leftmost 1's in the rows of the reduced row echelon form of $A$.

**13.** Use the elementary row operations to define an equivalence relation on the set $F(m, n)$ of all $m$-by-$n$ arrays over $F$.

**14.** Describe all possible 2-by-3 arrays over $J/(2)$ which are in reduced row echelon form.

## 11.6 Uniqueness

When we change an array $A$ into reduced row echelon form by means of elementary row operations we are effectively selecting a very special basis for the row space of $A$. In the first place the number of leftmost 1's (the echelon of 1's) in a reduced row echelon form array is the row rank of the array. This number is also the number of nonzero rows in the array in reduced row echelon since by definition a nonzero row has a leftmost 1. Thus the row rank of the array is certainly no greater than the number of leftmost 1's. On the other hand the column in which a leftmost 1 lies contains nothing else but zeros by part (3) of Definition 11.14. Hence no row with a leftmost 1 can be written as a linear combination of the other rows in an array in reduced row echelon form since 1 is certainly not equal to a linear combination of zeros.

THEOREM 11.17. *If the m-by-n array A over F is in reduced row echelon form, then the number of leftmost* 1*'s in A is the dimension of* $V(A)$, *the row space of A.*

If we look at the array $A$ over $R$,

$$A = \begin{pmatrix} 0 & 1 & 0 & -99 \\ 0 & 0 & 1 & 12 \\ 0 & 0 & 0 & 0 \end{pmatrix},$$

we see that $A$ is in reduced row echelon form. Looking at the zeros above and/or below the echelon 1's we see that the two nonzero rows are clearly linear independent.

Thus we see that in changing an array $A$ to reduced row echelon form $B$ we are in reality selecting a basis for $V(A)$, namely, the nonzero rows of $B$, which is as much like the canonical basis of $C_n(F)$ as any we can find. Now from its definition the canonical basis for $C_n(F)$ is unique, so we should ask whether this special basis for $V(A)$ is unique. This question is answered positively by showing that, if two $m$-by-$n$ arrays over $F$ in reduced row echelon form have equal row spaces, then the arrays are themselves equal. (Note that two $m$-by-$n$ arrays, as doubly ordered sets, are equal if and only if all of the corresponding components are equal in $F$; i.e., $a_{rs} = b_{rs}$ for each $r = 1, \cdots, m$ and each $s = 1, \cdots, n$.)

THEOREM 11.18. *Let $A$ be two $m$-by-$n$ arrays over $F$, both in reduced row echelon form. Then $V(A) = V(B)$ if and only if $A = B$.*

If $A = B$, then trivially $V(A) = V(B)$ since the two row spaces are spanned by exactly the same vectors, so we need only to study the converse proposition. In this case our hypothesis states that $A$ and $B$ are $m$-by-$n$ arrays in reduced row echelon form such that $V(A) = V(B)$, and we wish to prove that $A = B$. This we do by assuming that $A \neq B$ and developing a contradictory situation.

If $A$ and $B$ are *not* equal, then there is a maximal positive integer $k$ not larger than $m$ such that row $k$ of $A$ differs from row $k$ of $B$. Then if we denote the rows of $A$ as $\mathbf{v}_1, \cdots, \mathbf{v}_m$ and the rows of $B$ as $\mathbf{u}_1, \cdots, \mathbf{u}_m$, this integer $k$ is such that, when $k \neq m$,

$$\mathbf{v}_i = \mathbf{u}_i$$

when $m \geqslant i > k$. In other words we are working up from the bottom of the two arrays and we stop when we first reach the level (the $k$th row) where $A$ and $B$ are not the same.

Now we compare $\mathbf{v}_k$ and $\mathbf{u}_k$; since they are not equal, at least one of them is different from $\mathbf{z}$, the zero vector of $C_n(F)$. Therefore there is a leftmost 1 in one of these vectors so that we know there exists a positive integer $p$, not larger than $n$, with the following properties:

(1) $a_{kp}$ and $b_{kp}$ are not both zero.

(2) All components in the vectors $\mathbf{v}_k$ and $\mathbf{u}_k$ which are to the left of column (or position) $p$ equal zero.

(Note that the second condition is to be ignored if $p = 1$.)

Thus we look at the two vectors

$$\mathbf{v}_k = (a_{k1}, a_{k2}, \cdots, a_{kn})$$

and

$$\mathbf{u}_k = (b_{k1}, b_{k2}, \cdots, b_{kn})$$

and label the leftmost nonzero column as column $p$. Since at least one of the $p$th components is nonzero we can assume, as a notational convenience, that

$$a_{kp} = 1.$$

(Remember that $A$ and $B$ are in reduced row echelon form.)

Consider, then, the vector $\mathbf{u}_k$; since it is in $V(A) = V(B)$ we know that it can be written as a linear combination of the row vectors of $A$,

$$\mathbf{u}_k = \sum_{i=1}^{m} c_i \mathbf{v}_i$$

with $c_1, \cdots, c_m$ in $F$. Since $\mathbf{v}_i = \mathbf{u}_i$ when $i$ is larger than $k$ we can form the following vector equation from the preceding equation:

$$\mathbf{u} = \mathbf{u}_k - \sum_{i=k+1}^{m} c_i \mathbf{u}_i = \sum_{i=1}^{k} c_i \mathbf{v}_i.$$

Thus the vector $\mathbf{u}$ is expressed in two different ways. From the first expression for $\mathbf{u}$ in terms of $\mathbf{u}_k, \cdots, \mathbf{u}_m$ we conclude that $\mathbf{u}$ has *no nonzero* components left of position $p$ since none of the vectors $\mathbf{u}_k, \cdots, \mathbf{u}_m$ do. Then we look at the second expression for $\mathbf{u}$,

$$\mathbf{u} = c_1\mathbf{v}_1 + \cdots + c_k\mathbf{v}_k.$$

Since $\mathbf{v}_k$ has 1 as its $p$th component, we know from part (2) of Definition 11.14 that $\mathbf{v}_{k-1}, \cdots, \mathbf{v}_1$ all have leftmost 1's farther left than column $p$. Because of the isolation of these leftmost 1's as the only nonzero elements in their columns, we conclude from the above-determined nature of $\mathbf{u}$ that

$$c_1 = c_2 = \cdots = c_{k-1} = 0.$$

Thus

$$\mathbf{u} = c_k\mathbf{v}_k.$$

To understand this argument better look at the following array:

$$\begin{pmatrix} 1 & 0 & 0 & 7 & 0 \\ 0 & 1 & 0 & 2 & 0 \\ 0 & 0 & 1 & 3 & 0 \\ 0 & 0 & 0 & 0 & 1 \end{pmatrix}.$$

If the vector $\mathbf{u} = (0, 0, 0, a, b)$ were expressed as a linear combination of the four rows of this array,

$$\mathbf{u} = c_1\mathbf{v}_1 + c_2\mathbf{v}_2 + c_3\mathbf{v}_3 + c_4\mathbf{v}_4,$$

we see by looking at the leftmost three components that

$$c_1 = c_2 = c_3 = 0.$$

Consider now the equation

$$\mathbf{u} = c_k\mathbf{v}_k = \mathbf{u}_k - (c_{k+1}\mathbf{u}_{k+1} + \cdots + c_m\mathbf{u}_m).$$

Since $V(A) = V(B)$ we know by the preceding theorem that the row rank of $A$ equals the number of nonzero rows in $A$ (which is in reduced row echelon form) which equals the row rank of $B$ which equals the number of nonzero rows of $B$. From $\mathbf{v}_k \neq \mathbf{z}$ we know that the array $B$ must have at least $k$ nonzero rows, reading down from the top. Hence

$$\mathbf{u}_k \neq \mathbf{z},$$

so that in the preceding equation

$$\mathbf{u} \neq \mathbf{z} \quad \text{and} \quad c_k = 1.$$

This implies that the $m - k$ vectors $c_i\mathbf{u}_i$, $i = k + 1, \cdots, m$, are not all zero, so among these we choose a nonzero vector as $c_t\mathbf{u}_t$. In particular this means that

$$c_t \neq 0 \quad \text{and} \quad \mathbf{u}_t \neq \mathbf{z}.$$

Since $\mathbf{u}_t$ is not a row of zeros it has a leftmost 1, say in column $q$. Then all other elements of column $q$ in array $B$ are zero. But the vectors $\mathbf{u}_t$ and $\mathbf{v}_t$ are equal since $t$ is larger than $k$, so we see that all elements of column $q$ of $A$, except the element in row $t$, are also zero. In particular this means that the element of

$$\mathbf{u} = c_k\mathbf{v}_k$$

in column $q$ is zero. But this yields the equation

$$c_t = 0$$

since from the equation

$$\mathbf{u} = \mathbf{u}_k - c_{k+1}\mathbf{u}_{k+1} - \cdots - \mathbf{u}_m c_m$$

we know that the element in column $q$ is $-c_t$. Thus we have the impossible situation where

$$c_t \neq 0 \qquad \textit{and} \qquad c_t = 0.$$

This contradiction proves the theorem.

*Example* 1. Determine all of the two-dimensional subspaces of $C_3(J/(2))$. A two-dimensional subspace $V$ has a basis of two vectors which we can stack up to yield a 2-by-3 array $A$. Then $V = V(A)$, the row space of $A$, and changing $A$ to an array in reduced row echelon form yields a unique basis for $V$. Thus if we list all possible 2-by-3 arrays of row rank two in reduced row echelon form over $J/(2)$, we describe all of the two-dimensional subspaces of $C_3(J/(2))$. First we locate the leftmost or echelon 1's; these can lie in columns 1 and 2, 1 and 3, or 2 and 3. Then we allow for all possible variations in the column which does *not* contain a leftmost 1. From these observations we conclude that the following arrays are the ones we seek:

$$\begin{pmatrix}1 & 0 & 0\\ 0 & 1 & 0\end{pmatrix}, \begin{pmatrix}1 & 0 & 1\\ 0 & 1 & 0\end{pmatrix}, \begin{pmatrix}1 & 0 & 1\\ 0 & 1 & 1\end{pmatrix}, \begin{pmatrix}1 & 0 & 0\\ 0 & 1 & 1\end{pmatrix},$$

$$\begin{pmatrix}1 & 0 & 0\\ 0 & 0 & 1\end{pmatrix}, \begin{pmatrix}1 & 1 & 0\\ 0 & 0 & 1\end{pmatrix}, \begin{pmatrix}0 & 1 & 0\\ 0 & 0 & 1\end{pmatrix}.$$

Thus the space $C_3(J/(2))$ has seven distinct two-dimensional subspaces.

Definition 11.15. A basis for a subspace $V$ of $C_n(F)$ is a *canonical basis* for $V$ if and only if the basis can be stacked up to yield an array in reduced row echelon form.

*Corollary* 11.18.1. Each subspace $V$ of $C_n(F)$ has a unique canonical basis.

From Theorem 11.16 we know that $V$ has a canonical basis which can be obtained by stacking up an arbitrary basis of $V$ to form an $m$-by-$n$ array $A$ and changing it to the reduced row echelon form $B$. Unstacking $B$ provides a canonical basis for $V$, and this basis is unique since $B$ is unique by Theorem 11.18.

Since all of the subspaces of $C_n(F)$ have dimension less than or equal to $n$ we can describe in a unique fashion all of the subspaces of $C_n(F)$ by listing or describing all of the different $n$-by-$n$ arrays over $F$ which are in reduced row echelon form. (Any zero rows which appear can be ignored when the array is unstacked to provide the canonical basis of a subspace.) Thus we have in a sense specified all of the subspaces of $V_n(F)$ since $V_n(F)$ is isomorphic with $C_n(F)$.

## Exercise 11.6

**1.** Let $V$ be the subspace of $C_3(R)$ spanned by $\mathbf{v}_1 = (1, 2, 3)$, $\mathbf{v}_2 = (-4, 2, -2)$, and $\mathbf{v}_3 = (4, 0, 4)$. Find the canonical basis of $V$.

**2.** Let $\mathbf{v}_1 = (0, 1, 0, 0, 3, 7)$, $\mathbf{v}_2 = (0, 0, 1, 0, 9, 2)$, and $\mathbf{v}_3 = (0, 0, 0, 1, 5, -1)$ be vectors in $C_6(R)$. Show that $\mathbf{v} = (0, 7, 9, 0, 5, 6) = c_1\mathbf{v}_1 + c_2\mathbf{v}_2 + c_3\mathbf{v}_3$ certainly implies that $c_3 = 0$.

**3.** Show that the three vectors of Problem 2 form the canonical basis of a subspace of $C_6(R)$.

**4.** How many subspaces of dimension 2 has a three-dimensional space over $J/(2)$? (See Example 1.)

**5.** Determine the number of subspaces of $V_3(J/(2))$.

**6.** List the canonical bases for five different subspaces of dimension 3 in $C_4(R)$.

**7.** Test the following sets of vectors to see if they are linearly independent or not:

(*a*) $(3, 1, 11)$, $(-2, 7, 8)$, $(7, -1, 19)$ in $C_3(R)$.
(*b*) $(3i, i, 11i)$, $(2, -7, -8)$, $(7 + 7i, -1 - i, 19 + 19i)$ in $C_3(C)$.
(*c*) $(0, 2, 1, 4)$, $(2, 2, 4, 0)$, $(4, 2, 3, 4)$ in $C_4(J/(5))$.

**8.** Determine the number of subspaces of dimension 2 in $C_5(J/(7))$.

**9.** If an $m$-by-$n$ array $A$ over $F$ is increased to an $m$-by-$(n + k)$ array $B$ by attaching $k$ additional columns to $A$, show that the row rank of $B$ is at least as large as the row rank of $A$.

**10.** Let $V$ be an $m$-dimensional subspace of $C_n(F)$ with canonical basis $\{\mathbf{v}_1, \cdots, \mathbf{v}_m\}$. In the canonical basis $\{\mathbf{e}_1, \cdots, \mathbf{e}_n\}$ of $C_n(F)$ eliminate those $\mathbf{e}_i$ whose leftmost 1 is in the same column as a leftmost 1 of one of the $\mathbf{v}_i$. Show that the remaining $\mathbf{e}_j$ form the canonical basis of a subspace $U$ such that $U + V = C_n(F)$ and $U \cap V = (\mathbf{z})$. Illustrate, using the vectors of Problem 3.

**11.** Let $U$ and $V$ be subspaces of $C_n(F)$ generated by the sets of vectors $\{\mathbf{v}_1, \cdots, \mathbf{v}_m\}$ and $\{\mathbf{u}_1, \cdots, \mathbf{u}_k\}$, respectively. Show how one can tell by examining the canonical bases of $U$ and $V$ whether $U \subset V$, $U = V$, or $V \subset U$.

## 11.7 Systems of Linear Equations

One problem always encountered in elementary mathematics courses is that of "solving a system of linear equations." This problem involves answering the following questions:

(1) If $\mathbf{v}_1, \cdots, \mathbf{v}_m$ are $m$ elements of $C_n(F)$, does $C_n(F)$ contain a vector $\mathbf{u}$ of the form

$$\mathbf{u} = (x_1, \cdots, x_{n-1}, -1)$$

such that

$$\sum_{i=1}^{n-1} a_{ji}x_i = a_{jn},$$

for $j = 1, 2, \cdots, m$, where

$$\mathbf{v}_j = (a_{j1}, \cdots, a_{jn})?$$

(2) If the answer to question (1) is positive, what is $\mathbf{u}$?

Answering these questions is known as solving a system of $m$ linear equations in $n - 1$ unknowns $x_1, \cdots, x_{n-1}$. The standard "answer" to the problem is furnished by an algorithm which produces a vector $\mathbf{u}$ if it exists or an impossibility if no such vector $\mathbf{u}$ exists. This algorithm is just the one used in the previous sections to change an array to reduced row echelon form.

Looking at the set of equations above we see that, if $\mathbf{v} = (a_1, \cdots, a_n)$ is in the subspace $V$ spanned by the $m$ vectors, then

$$a_1x_1 + \cdots + a_{n-1}x_{n-1} = a_n$$

since this is just a linear combination of the $m$ equations. Conversely, if $\{\mathbf{u}_1, \cdots, \mathbf{u}_k\}$ is a basis for the subspace $V$ generated in $C_n(F)$ by the vectors $\mathbf{v}_1, \cdots, \mathbf{v}_m$, then, if

$$\mathbf{u} = (x_1, x_2, \cdots, x_{n-1}, -1)$$

is a vector such that

$$\sum_{i=1}^{n-1} b_{ji}x_i = b_{jn},$$

for $j = 1, 2, \cdots, k$, where

$$\mathbf{u}_j = (b_{j1}, \cdots, b_{jn}),$$

we see that this vector $\mathbf{u}$ satisfies the original set of equations since the vectors $\mathbf{v}_1, \cdots, \mathbf{v}_m$ of $V$ are just linear combinations of these basis vectors. Thus we can simplify the original set of $m$ equations without altering the solutions (if solutions exist at all). This simplification is effected by choosing as the basis $\{\mathbf{u}_1, \cdots, \mathbf{u}_k\}$ of $V$ its canonical basis.

*Example* 1. Solve the following system in $R$:

$$\begin{aligned} 1x_1 + 1x_2 + 1x_3 + 0x_4 &= 8, \\ 1x_1 + 1x_2 + 0x_3 - 2x_4 &= -12, \\ 1x_1 + 0x_2 + 1x_3 + 1x_4 &= 14, \\ 0x_1 + 1x_2 + 1x_3 + 1x_4 &= 14. \end{aligned}$$

The 4-by-5 array

$$A = \begin{pmatrix} 1 & 1 & 1 & 0 & 8 \\ 1 & 1 & 0 & -2 & -12 \\ 1 & 0 & 1 & 1 & 14 \\ 0 & 1 & 1 & 1 & 14 \end{pmatrix}$$

is called *the array of the system* and its row space $V(A)$ is the subspace $V$ of $C_5(R)$ mentioned above. Changing $A$ to reduced row echelon form yields

$$B = \begin{pmatrix} 1 & 0 & 0 & -1 & -6 \\ 0 & 1 & 0 & -1 & -6 \\ 0 & 0 & 1 & 2 & 20 \\ 0 & 0 & 0 & 0 & 0 \end{pmatrix}$$

and we have the much simpler system

$$\begin{aligned} x_1 - x_4 &= -6, \\ x_2 - x_4 &= -6, \\ x_3 - 2x_4 &= 20, \end{aligned}$$

and

$$0x_4 = 0$$

to consider. The last equation obviously puts no restrictions on $x_4$ so that taking an arbitrary value $t$ for $x_4$ yields the solution vector $\mathbf{u} = (t - 6, t - 6, 2t + 20, t, -1)$ in $C_5(R)$. Then for the various values of $t$ we get all of the solutions of the original system.

This illustrates how the process reveals the solutions when they exist. But what happens if no solutions exist?

*Example* 2. Solve over $R$ the system

$$\begin{aligned} x_1 + x_2 + x_3 &= 6 \\ x_1 + x_2 - 2x_4 &= -12, \\ -x_2 + x_4 &= 6 \\ x_2 + x_3 + x_4 &= 14. \end{aligned}$$

The array of this system is

$$A = \begin{pmatrix} 1 & 1 & 1 & 0 & 6 \\ 1 & 1 & 0 & -2 & -12 \\ 0 & -1 & 0 & 1 & 6 \\ 0 & 1 & 1 & 1 & 14 \end{pmatrix}$$

which reduces to

$$B = \begin{pmatrix} 1 & 0 & 0 & -1 & 0 \\ 0 & 1 & 0 & -1 & 0 \\ 0 & 0 & 1 & 2 & 0 \\ 0 & 0 & 0 & 0 & 1 \end{pmatrix}.$$

Then the original system of equations can be replaced by the following system

$$\begin{aligned} x_1 - x_4 &= 0, \\ x_2 - x_4 &= 0, \\ x_3 + 2x_4 &= 0, \\ 0x_4 &= 1. \end{aligned}$$

Since the last equation is an impossibility in $R$ we conclude that this system has no solution. (Such a system is sometimes called *inconsistent*.)

## Exercise 11.7

**1.** Write out the array of the following linear system over $R$:

$$x_1 + x_2 - x_3 = 3, \quad x_1 - 3x_2 + 2x_3 = 1, \quad 2x_1 - 2x_2 + x_3 = 4.$$

Transform the array of the system into an array in reduced row echelon form. Solve the simplified system.

**2.** Solve the following system (by the method of this section) over $R$:

$$\begin{aligned} x_1 + x_2 + x_3 &= 12, & x_1 + x_3 + x_4 &= 14, \\ x_1 + x_2 + x_4 &= 8, & x_2 + x_3 + x_4 &= 14, \end{aligned}$$

**3.** Solve the following system over $R$:

$$\begin{aligned} x_1 + x_2 + x_3 + x_4 &= 1, & -x_1 + x_3 + 2x_4 &= 1, \\ 3x_1 + 2x_2 - x_4 &= 1, & x_1 + x_2 + 2x_3 + 2x_4 &= 1, \end{aligned}$$

**4.** Solve over $J/(3)$:

$$\begin{aligned} 2x_1 + x_2 + x_3 + x_4 &= 2, & x_1 + 2x_2 + x_3 + 2x_4 &= 0, \\ x_1 + x_2 + x_3 + 2x_4 &= 1, & 2x_2 + x_3 &= 2. \end{aligned}$$

**5.** Show that the system of

$$\begin{aligned} 3x_1 - 2x_2 + 4x_3 &= 13, \\ 7x_1 + 8x_2 - 5x_3 + 6 &= 0, \\ 2x_1 + 5x_2 - 3x_3 + 9 &= 0 \end{aligned}$$

has no solution over $R$.

**6.** Describe how the method of this section could be used to solve a linear system with the aid of an electronic computer.

**7.** Can the method of this section be used to solve a linear system without explicitly writing any arrays? Explain.

**8.** The *inner product* of two vectors $\mathbf{v} = (a_1, \cdots, a_n)$ and $\mathbf{u} = (b_1, \cdots, b_n)$ of $C_n(F)$ is defined to be $(\mathbf{u}, \mathbf{v}) = a_1b_1 + \cdots + a_nb_n$. Find as many properties of this binary operation on $C_n(F)$ as you can. (Is it commutative, associative, distributive over addition, etc.?)

**9.** Let $U$ be a subspace of $C_n(F)$, and define $U$ to be the collection of all $\mathbf{v}$ in $C_n(F)$ such that $(\mathbf{u}, \mathbf{v}) = 0$ for every $u$ in $U$. Show that $U$ is a subspace of $C_n(F)$. ($U$ is the *orthogonal complement* of $U$ in $C_n(F)$.)

**10.** Find the orthogonal complement (Problem 9) of the subspace $U$ of $C_5(R)$ spanned by the three vectors $\mathbf{u}_1 = (1, 1, 1, 1, 1)$, $\mathbf{u}_2 = (1, 2, 3, 4, 5)$, and $\mathbf{u}_3 = (5, 4, 3, 2, 1)$. (Find the canonical basis for $U$.)

**11.** How are $\dim(U)$ and $\dim(U)$ related in $C_n(F)$?

**12.** Interpret the inner product in $C_3(Re)$ geometrically. What is the orthogonal complement of a line through the origin?

**13.** Consider the $m$ linear *homogeneous* equations:

$$\begin{aligned} a_{11}x_1 + \cdots + a_{1n}x_n &= 0 \\ \vdots \qquad\qquad & \quad \vdots \\ a_{m1}x_1 + \cdots + a_{mn}x_n &= 0. \end{aligned}$$

Show that, if the $m$-by-$n$ array $A = (a_{rs})$ has row rank $k$, then the "solution space" of all $(x_1, \cdots, x_n)$ in $C_n(F)$ has dimension $n - k$. (Transform $A$ to reduced row echelon form, and then write down the resulting linear homogeneous equations. Check Problem 9.)

**14.** Find the canonical basis for the subspace of solutions of the following homogeneous systems over $R$:

(*a*) $x_1 + 2x_2 + 3x_3 = 0$, $2x_1 + 3x_2 + x_1 = 0$.
(*b*) $x_1 - 2x_2 + x_3 = 0$, $x_1 + 3x_2 + x_3 = 0$, $2x_1 - x_2 + 2x_3 = 0$.

## 11.8 Column Rank

Up to this point we have treated a doubly ordered set or array as a stack of vectors. Thus a 3-by-4 array over $F$ was considered to be a stack of three vectors from $C_4(F)$. Now it is quite clear that we can slice this 3-by-4 array vertically and treat it as an ordered collection of four vectors from $C_3(F)$, where the vectors from $C_3(F)$ are written as columns instead of rows.

*Example* 1. The array

$$A = \begin{pmatrix} 1 & 2 & 3 & 4 \\ 5 & 6 & 7 & 8 \\ 8 & 7 & 6 & 5 \end{pmatrix}$$

can be considered as the ordered set of row vectors $\mathbf{v}_1 = (1, 2, 3, 4)$, $\mathbf{v}_2 = (5, 6, 7, 8)$, and $\mathbf{v}_3 = (8, 7, 6, 5)$ from $C_4(F)$, or as the ordered set of column vectors

$$\mathbf{u}_1 = \begin{pmatrix} 1 \\ 5 \\ 8 \end{pmatrix}, \quad \mathbf{u}_2 = \begin{pmatrix} 2 \\ 6 \\ 7 \end{pmatrix}, \quad \mathbf{u}_3 = \begin{pmatrix} 3 \\ 7 \\ 8 \end{pmatrix}, \quad \text{and} \quad \mathbf{u}_4 = \begin{pmatrix} 4 \\ 8 \\ 5 \end{pmatrix}$$

from $C_3(F)$.

This somewhat different view of the array $A$ suggests that we should consider the column space and column rank of $A$ by describing and investigating elementary column operations. We do this by effectively reducing the situation to one which has already been handled.

DEFINITION 11.16. The $n$-by-$m$ array $A^T$ obtained from the $m$-by-$n$ array $A$ by writing the $r$th row of $A$ as the $r$th column of $A^T$ is called the *transpose* of $A$. If $A = (a_{rs})$, then $A^T = (b_{rs})$ with $b_{rs} = a_{sr}$.

If

$$A = \begin{pmatrix} 1 & 2 & 3 & 4 \\ 5 & 6 & 7 & 8 \end{pmatrix},$$

then

$$A^T = \begin{pmatrix} 1 & 5 \\ 2 & 6 \\ 3 & 7 \\ 4 & 8 \end{pmatrix}.$$

DEFINITION 11.17. The *column rank* of $A$ is the row rank of $A^T$. The array $A$ is in *reduced column echelon form* if and only if $A^T$ is in reduced row echelon form.

*Example* 2. The following arrays

$$A = \begin{pmatrix} 1 & 0 & 0 \\ 0 & 1 & 0 \\ 2 & 2 & 0 \end{pmatrix} \quad \text{and} \quad B = \begin{pmatrix} 1 & 0 & 0 \\ 2 & 0 & 0 \\ 0 & 1 & 0 \\ 0 & 0 & 1 \end{pmatrix}$$

are in reduced column echelon form since their transposes

$$A^T = \begin{pmatrix} 1 & 0 & 2 \\ 0 & 1 & 2 \\ 0 & 0 & 0 \end{pmatrix} \quad \text{and} \quad B^T = \begin{pmatrix} 1 & 2 & 0 & 0 \\ 0 & 0 & 1 & 0 \\ 0 & 0 & 0 & 1 \end{pmatrix}$$

are in reduced row echelon form.

The row rank of $A^T$ is 2 so that the column rank of $A$ is 2. Similarly the column rank of $B$ is 3.

The *elementary column operations* are quite obviously the counterparts of the elementary row operations:

(1) The interchange of two columns.

(2) The multiplication of a column by a nonzero scalar.

(3) The addition of a scalar multiple of one column to another column.

Since these are the counterparts of the elementary row operations it is quite evident that when applied to an array $A$ they do not affect the column rank (or dimension of the column space) of $A$.

Now, however, we consider another question: How are the row rank and column rank of $A$ related? We shall show them to be equal, and for this we need to verify that an elementary column operation on $A$ changes $A$ into an array $B$ with the same row rank as $A$. (In general the row space of $A$ *differs* from the row space of $B$; we wish only to show them isomorphic.)

THEOREM 11.19. *If the array $B$ is obtained from the array $A$ by means of an elementary column operation, then $A$ and $B$ have the same row rank.*

Since such operations are clearly reversible it is only necessary to prove that the row rank of $B$ is not less than the row rank of $A$. We shall do this only for the most complicated type of column operation.

Suppose $c$ times column $i$ is added to column $j$ of $A$ to get $B$, and suppose $i < j$. Then we can show that, if every collection of $k$ rows of $B$ is linearly dependent, so is every collection of $k$ rows of $A$. (Thus if $B$ has row rank $k - 1$, the row rank of $A$ is no larger than $k - 1$.) Consider a typical row of $A$,

$$\mathbf{v}_r = (a_{r1}, \cdots, a_{ri}, \cdots, a_{rj}, \cdots, a_{rn});$$

then the corresponding row of $B$ is

$$\mathbf{u}_r = \mathbf{v}_r + ca_{ri}\mathbf{e}_j,$$

where $\mathbf{e}_j$ is the $j$th vector of the canonical basis of $C_n(F)$.

Then a relationship among $k$ row vectors of $B$ would be expressible in the form

$$\sum_r d_r\mathbf{u}_r = \sum_r d_r\mathbf{u}_r + c\sum_r d_r a_{ri}\mathbf{e}_j = z.$$

We look at the components of this equation:

$$\begin{array}{ll}
\text{Component } 1: & \sum_r d_r a_{r1} = 0, \\
\vdots & \vdots \\
\text{Component } i: & \sum_r d_r a_{ri} = 0, \\
\vdots & \vdots \\
\text{Component } j: & \sum_r d_r(a_{rj} + ca_{ri}) = 0, \\
\vdots & \vdots \\
\text{Component } n: & \sum_r d_r a_{rn} = 0.
\end{array}$$

Clearly the expressions for components $i$ and $j$ lead to the conclusion that

$$\sum_r d_r a_{rj} = 0.$$

Hence we have the same linear relationship among the corresponding $k$ row vectors of $A$:

$$\sum_r d_r\mathbf{v}_r = \mathbf{z}.$$

This effectively proves the theorem for this type of elementary column operation. The other two types are easier to deal with so we leave them for the student to practice on.

As a consequence of this result we can prove that the row rank of $A$ equals the column rank of $A$ by considering the case when $A$ is in reduced column echelon form (since changing $A$ to this form does not affect the row rank). First we write out the explicit description of the reduced column echelon form of an array.

THEOREM 11.20. *An array $A$ of column rank $r$ is in reduced column echelon form if and only if:*

(1) *Columns* $1, 2, \cdots, r$ *are the nonzero columns of* $A$.

(2) *The uppermost nonzero element in each column is* 1, *and the other elements in the* row *in which it appears are all zeros.*

(3) *If the uppermost* 1 *in column $i$ appears in row $j$, then $a_{rs} = 0$ for $r < j$ and $s > i$.*

This is just a description of the transpose of an array in reduced row echelon form.

From this description of an array $A$ in reduced column echelon form we see that, if $A$ has column rank $r$, then the row space of $A$ is spanned by $r$ canonical basis vectors $\mathbf{e}_i$, and so $A$ has row rank $r$. This observation suffices to prove the next statement.

THEOREM 11.21. *The row rank of an array $A$ equals the column rank of $A$.*

Consequently we speak hereafter of the *rank* of $A$.

*Example* 3. Reduce the following array $A$ over $R$ to reduced column echelon form $B$, and write each row of $B$ as linear combinations of the first $r$ (for rank) rows of $B$:

$$A = \begin{pmatrix} 1 & -2 & 1 \\ 1 & 3 & 1 \\ 2 & -1 & 2 \end{pmatrix}.$$

Add 2 times column one to column two and $-1$ times column one to column three, yielding

$$A_1 = \begin{pmatrix} 1 & 0 & 0 \\ 1 & 5 & 0 \\ 2 & 3 & 0 \end{pmatrix}.$$

Now multiply column two (of $A_1$) by $\frac{1}{5}$, and then add $-1$ times the new column two to column one, yielding

$$B = \begin{pmatrix} 1 & 0 & 0 \\ 0 & 1 & 0 \\ \frac{7}{5} & \frac{3}{5} & 0 \end{pmatrix}.$$

This array is in reduced column echelon form, and obviously

$$(\tfrac{7}{5}, \tfrac{3}{5}, 0) = \tfrac{7}{5}(1, 0, 0) + \tfrac{3}{5}(0, 1, 0).$$

The rank of $A$ is two. Note that the top two rows of $B$ are the canonical basis vectors $\mathbf{e}_1$ and $\mathbf{e}_2$ of $C_3(R)$.

## Exercise 11.8

**1.** Give three examples of 3-by-5 arrays over $R$ which are in reduced column echelon form.

**2.** Give two examples of 3-by-4 arrays over $R$ which are in both reduced row and column form.

**3.** Transform the five arrays of Problem 6, Exercise 11.5, into reduced column echelon form.

**4.** By using column and row operations intermixed the rank of an array can often be found quite quickly. Illustrate.

**5.** Complete the proof of Theorem 11.19.

**6.** Define two $m$-by-$n$ arrays $A$ and $B$ over $F$ to be *equivalent* if and only if $B$ can be obtained from $A$ by means of a finite sequence of elementary row and column operations. Show that this is an equivalence relation on the set of all $m$-by-$n$ arrays over $F$. Show that two such arrays are equivalent if and only if they have the same rank. Devise the "simplest" representative for each equivalence class (see Problem 2).

## 11.9 Suggested Reading

*Articles*

Ackerson, R. H., "A note on vector spaces," *Amer. Math. Monthly*, **62** (1955), 721–722.

Flanders, H., "Methods of proof in linear algebra," *Amer. Math. Monthly*, **63** (1956), 1–15.

MacDuffee, C. C., "What is a matrix?" *Amer. Math. Monthly*, **50** (1943), 360–365.

Murase, Itiro, "Remark on rank of a matrix," *Amer. Math. Monthly*, **67** (1960), 176–177.

Wong, W. J., "Modules over principal ideal domains," *Amer. Math. Monthly*, **69** (1962), 398–400.

*Books*

Finkbeiner, D. T., *Introduction to Matrices and Linear Transformations*, W. H. Freeman & Co., San Francisco, 1960.

Halmos, P. R., *Finite Dimensional Vector Spaces*, Princeton University Press, Princeton, N.J., 1942.

MacDuffee, C. C., *Vectors and Matrices*, Carus Monograph 7, Mathematical Association of America, Menasha, Wis., 1943.

Sawyer, W. W., *A Concrete Approach to Abstract Algebra*, W. H. Freeman & Co., San Francisco, 1959.

# 12

# Linear Transformations and Matrices

As we have seen in our study of groups and rings (both abstract and specific) a useful and important concept in the investigation of algebraic systems is that of homomorphism. In this chapter we begin the study of the homomorphisms of vector spaces, especially finite dimensional vector spaces. For finite dimensional vector spaces we are able to describe all the homomorphisms in a manner quite similar to that used in the previous chapter to describe all the subspaces of an $n$-dimensional vector space.

These homomorphisms, known commonly as linear transformations, can often be represented by doubly ordered sets of scalars which are usually referred to as matrices. The theory of linear transformations and matrices has been widely used throughout mathematics and the physical sciences and is today being used in many other areas of intellectual activity (such as game theory, linear programming, biometrics, econometrics, etc.). From an algebraic viewpoint the theory contributes models and methods, as well as problems, to the continuing study of mathematical systems.

For the most part our attention is devoted to the homomorphisms of a vector space onto itself (endomorphisms). This restriction (which involves little loss of generality because of certain isomorphisms) permits us to form a ring from the linear transformations on a vector space. Thus we arrive at a very rich and significant corner of ring theory.

Many of the results in this and the next chapter regarding matrices and linear transformations on finite dimensional vector spaces can be extended in some degree to the corresponding mappings of infinite dimensional vector spaces and of general $S$-modules. These topics are treated in advanced books dealing with functional analysis and with the abstract theory of rings (e.g., *Introduction to Functional Analysis*, by A. E. Taylor, and *Lectures in Abstract Algebra*, volumes I and II, by N. Jacobson).

## 12.1 Homomorphisms and Linear Transformations

In the preceding chapter the concept of isomorphism of vector spaces was discussed and used. An isomorphism, as we remember from our study of other algebraic systems, is just a special case of the more general concept of homomorphism, and the definition of homomorphism can be obtained easily from that of isomorphism by simply omitting the restriction, one-to-one. A homomorphic image of a system is rather like a shadow or a cross section of the system (and anyone who is familiar with blueprints and their uses in engineering work knows that such images can be quite informative).

DEFINITION 12.1.   The mapping $A$ from vector space $V(F)$ to vector space $W(F)$ is a *homomorphism* or *linear transformation* from $V(F)$ to $W(F)$ if and only if $\qquad A(\alpha \vec{x} + \beta \vec{\omega}) = \alpha A(\vec{x}) + \beta A(\vec{\omega})$

$$V \qquad (a\mathbf{u} + b\mathbf{v})A = a(\mathbf{u}A) + b(\mathbf{v}A) \qquad \omega$$

for any $a$ and $b$ in $F$ and any $\mathbf{u}$ and $\mathbf{v}$ in $V$.

Here we are using the same symbolism for the corresponding binary operations of both spaces, so that in $V(F)$ we write

$$V \qquad a\mathbf{u} + b\mathbf{v}$$

whereas in $W(F)$ we write    $W$ *results*

$$a(\mathbf{u}A) + b(\mathbf{v}A).$$

The *image* of the vector $\mathbf{u}$ under the mapping is denoted by $\mathbf{u}A$ so that we are employing the *right-hand function notation* in this chapter (unless stated otherwise in an example).

Since linear transformations are mappings the equality of two linear transformations has been dealt with already.

THEOREM 12.1.   *Two linear transformations $A$ and $B$ from $V(F)$ to $W(F)$ are equal if and only if $\mathbf{v}A = \mathbf{v}B$ for every $\mathbf{v}$ in $V$.*

We recall that the mappings $A$ and $B$ are subsets of the product set $V \times W$ with the property that each element $\mathbf{v}$ of $V$ appears exactly once as the first element in an ordered pair element of each subset. The theorem therefore is just a restatement of set equality for these subsets.

As a result of this theorem we can describe a linear transformation $A$ from $V(F)$ to $W(F)$ by describing the image $\mathbf{v}A$ of each $\mathbf{v}$ in $V$. Naturally the mapping which is thus uniquely defined must be shown to be compatible with the binary operations of the vector spaces involved.

*Example* 1.   Let $c$ be an arbitrary but fixed element of the field $F$. The mapping $A_c$ from $V(F)$ to $V(F)$ defined by the image

$$\mathbf{v}A_c = c\mathbf{v}, \qquad \mathbf{v} \text{ in } V,$$

is a linear transformation since

$$\begin{aligned} c(a\mathbf{u} + b\mathbf{v}) &= c(a\mathbf{u}) + c(b\mathbf{v}) \\ &= (ca)\mathbf{u} + (cb)\mathbf{v} \\ &= (ac)\mathbf{u} + (bc)\mathbf{v} \\ &= a(c\mathbf{u}) + b(c\mathbf{v}) \\ &= a(\mathbf{u}A_c) + b(\mathbf{v}A_c). \end{aligned}$$

$A_c$ is the *scalar linear transformation* from $V(F)$ to $V(F)$ determined by the scalar $c$. This mapping is easily seen to be an automorphism of $V(F)$ except when $c = 0$.

*Example* 2. Consider the additive group of $R[\lambda]$ as a vector space $V(R)$. Then a familiar linear transformation from $V(R)$ to $V(R)$ is provided by the formal derivative $\boldsymbol{D}$,

$$\boldsymbol{D}p(\lambda) = a_1 + 2a_2\lambda + \cdots + na_n\lambda^{n-1}$$

when

$$p(\lambda) = a_0 + a_1\lambda + \cdots + a_n\lambda^n.$$

(Here we use the more common *left* operator notation for $\boldsymbol{D}$.) This linear transformation is *not* an automorphism since it maps all of the elements of $R$ onto 0.

*Example* 3. The mapping $A$ from $C_2(Re)$ to $C_2(Re)$ described by

$$(a_1, a_2)A = (a_2, a_1)$$

is a linear transformation of the plane vector space which is frequently used as a test for symmetry.

*Example* 4. A linear transformation often used in the study of plane analytic geometry is a "rotation about the origin." Such a mapping $A$ from $C_2(Re)$ to $C_2(Re)$ is defined for the fixed real number $c$ as

$$(a_1, a_2)A = (b_1, b_2)$$

where

$$b_1 = a_1 \cos c - a_2 \sin c$$

and

$$b_2 = a_1 \sin c + a_2 \cos c.$$

This mapping describes the effect of rotating a vector $(a_1, a_2)$ counterclockwise about the origin through an angle whose radian measure is $c$. (Alternatively, $A$ can be thought of as a mapping which rotates the reference system of axes clockwise through an angle whose radian measure is $-c$.)

*Example* 5. In solid analytic geometry collections of points are frequently studied by "projecting" them onto one of the coordinate planes. This corresponds to a linear transformation $A$ from $C_3(Re)$ to $C_3(Re)$ defined by

$$(a_1, a_2, a_3)A = (a_1, a_2, 0)$$

for all $(a_1, a_2, a_3)$ in $C_3(Re)$. If

$$\mathbf{u} = (a_1, a_2, a_3) \quad \text{and} \quad \mathbf{v} = (b_1, b_2, b_3),$$

then

$$\begin{aligned} (a\mathbf{u} + b\mathbf{v})A &= (aa_1 + bb_1, aa_2 + bb_2, 0) \\ &= a(\mathbf{u}A) + b(\mathbf{v}A), \end{aligned}$$

so that $A$ is indeed a linear transformation.

In this last example we note that the image vectors $(a_1, a_2, 0)$ form a subspace which is isomorphic with $C_2(Re)$. Moreover the vectors of $C_3(Re)$ which are mapped onto $\mathbf{z} = (0, 0, 0)$, namely the vectors $(0, 0, a_3)$, form a subspace of $C_3(Re)$. We see rather easily that this is always the case.

THEOREM 12.2. *Let $A$ be a linear transformation from $V(F)$ to $W(F)$. Then the set*

$$VA = \{\mathbf{v}A : \mathbf{v} \text{ in } V\}$$

*is a subspace of $W(F)$, and the set*

$$N_A = \{\mathbf{v} : \mathbf{v}A = \mathbf{z}, \mathbf{v} \textit{ in } V, \mathbf{z} \textit{ in } W\}$$

*is a subspace of $V(F)$.*

Let $\mathbf{u}A$ and $\mathbf{v}A$ be two elements from $VA$. Then for $a$ and $b$ in $F$,

$$a(\mathbf{u}A) + b(\mathbf{v}A) = (a\mathbf{u} + b\mathbf{v})A$$

so that $a(\mathbf{u}A) + b(\mathbf{v}A)$ is in $\mathbf{V}A$. Hence $\mathbf{V}A$ is a subspace of $W(F)$.

Let $\mathbf{u}$ and $\mathbf{v}$ be elements of $N_A$; then

$$\mathbf{u}A = \mathbf{v}A = \mathbf{z}$$

so that

$$a(\mathbf{u}A) + b(\mathbf{v}A) = a\mathbf{z} + b\mathbf{z} = \mathbf{z}.$$

Therefore

$$(a\mathbf{u} + b\mathbf{v})A = a(\mathbf{u}A) + b(\mathbf{v}A) = \mathbf{z}$$

and we see that $a\mathbf{u} + b\mathbf{v}$ is in $N_A$. Hence $N_A$ is a subspace of $V(F)$.

DEFINITION 12.2. The subspace $VA$ of $W(F)$ is the *image space* (or *range space*) of the linear transformation $A$. The subspace $N_A$ of $V(F)$ is the *null space* (or *kernel*) of the linear transformation $A$.

If $VA = W(F)$, then we say that $A$ is a mapping from $V$ *onto* $W$. If $VA \neq W(F)$, then we say that $A$ is a mapping *into* $W$. And if we wish to allow for either of these possibilities we speak of $A$ as a linear transformation from $V(F)$ *to* $W(F)$. However, we can always say that $A$ is a mapping from $V$ onto $VA$, the *image space*.

THEOREM 12.3. *The linear transformation $A$ from $V(F)$ onto $VA$ is an isomorphism if and only if $N_A$, the null space, consists of the zero vector only.*

$A$ is an isomorphism if and only if $A$ is one-to-one. If $A$ is an isomorphism from $V(F)$ onto $VA$, then $N_A$ can contain only one element, and since the only subspace of $V$ containing a single element is $(\mathbf{z})$ we conclude that $N_A = (\mathbf{z})$. Conversely, suppose $N_A = (\mathbf{z})$ and let

$$\mathbf{u}A = \mathbf{v}A$$

in $VA$. Then

$$(\mathbf{u} - \mathbf{v})A = \mathbf{z} \qquad \text{in } VA$$

so that $\mathbf{u} - \mathbf{v}$ belongs to $N_A$ in $V(F)$. Therefore

$$\mathbf{u} = \mathbf{v}$$

and the mapping $A$ is one-to-one. So $A$ is an isomorphism from $V(F)$ onto $VA$.

In the next section we will see that, when $\dim\big(V(F)\big) = n$, then

$$\dim(N_A) + \dim(VA) = n.$$

## Exercise 12.1

**1.** Describe the effect of $A_c$ (Example 1) on $C_2(Re)$ when $c = 2$; when $c = \frac{1}{2}$; when $c = -1$. Illustrate geometrically.

**2.** How does the adjective "linear" arise in describing a homomorphism $A$ from $V(F)$ to $W(F)$? (Consider the condition $(a\mathbf{u} + b\mathbf{v})A = a(\mathbf{u}A) + b(\mathbf{v}A)$.)

**3.** Determine the null space and the image space of each of the examples in this section. Are any of the homomorphisms isomorphisms?

**4.** Show that $D$ in Example 2 is a linear transformation.

**5.** Draw geometric illustrations of Examples 3, 4, and 5.

**6.** What kind of symmetry does the linear transformation of Example 3 provide a test for? Describe the linear transformations involved in other such tests.

**7.** Show that the mapping $A$ from $R[\lambda]$ to $R[\lambda]$ defined by

$$(a_0 + a_1\lambda + \cdots + a_n\lambda^n)A = a_0 + a_1\lambda^2 + \cdots + a_n\lambda^{2n}$$

is a linear transformation of the system as a vector space over $R$. Describe $N_A$ and $VA$.

**8.** Generalize Theorem 12.2 as follows:

(*a*) If $A$ is a linear transformation from $V(F)$ to $W(F)$ and if $U$ is a subspace of $V$, then $UA = \{\mathbf{u}A : \mathbf{u} \text{ in } U\}$ is a subspace of $W$.

(*b*) If $A$ is a linear transformation from $V(F)$ to $W(F)$ and if $W'$ is a subspace of $W$, then the set

$$\{\mathbf{v} : \mathbf{v} \text{ in } V \text{ and } \mathbf{v}A \text{ in } W'\}$$

is a subspace of $V$, called the *preimage* of $W'$.

Illustrate using the space and mapping of Example 2.

**9.** Let $A$ be a linear transformation from $V(F)$ to $W(F)$. Generalize the linearity condition of the definition to show that $A$ takes any linear combination of vectors $\mathbf{v}_1, \cdots, \mathbf{v}_n$ of $V$ onto the same linear combination of vectors $\mathbf{v}_1A, \cdots, \mathbf{v}_nA$ in $W$.

**10.** Let $A$ be the linear transformation from $C_2(R)$ to $C_2(R)$ which maps $(1, 2)$ onto $(3, 4)$ and $(5, 6)$ onto $(7, 8)$. Determine $(a_1, a_2)A$.
(*Ans.* $(\frac{1}{2})(-4a_1 + 5a_2, -6a_1 + 7a_2)$.)

**11.** Show that a linear transformation $A$ maps a linearly dependent set of vectors in $V(F)$ onto a linearly dependent set in $VA$. From this deduce the fact that $\dim(VA)$ is never larger than $\dim\big(V(F)\big)$ by proving that a linearly independent set of vectors in $VA$ is the image of a linearly independent set of vectors in $V$.

**12.** An *S-homomorphism* from left $S$-module $G$ to left $S$-module $H$ is defined by the same linearity condition that we used in Definition 12.1. Give an example of a $J$-homomorphism from $J[\lambda]$ to $J[\lambda]$ (see Problem 7).

**13.** To generalize the linear transformation of Example 1 to an $S$-homomorphism when $S$ is noncommutative we must assume what about $c$?

## 12.2 Bases and Matrices

When we match the linearity of a linear transformation with the linear properties of a spanning set we see that a linear transformation $A$ from $V(F)$ to $W(F)$ is determined completely by the effect of $A$ on a spanning set for $V$.

THEOREM 12.4. *Let $A$ be a linear transformation from $V(F)$ to $W(F)$. Then $A$ is completely determined by its effect on a spanning set for $V(F)$.*

This is certainly a corollary of Theorem 12.1 and the idea of a spanning set. By that theorem the mapping $A$ is determined completely when the image $\mathbf{v}A$ of every $\mathbf{v}$ in $V$ is known. Then if

$$\mathbf{v} = a_1\mathbf{v}_1 + \cdots + a_n\mathbf{v}_n$$

we see by extending the linearity property of $A$ through an induction argument that

$$\mathbf{v}A = a_1(\mathbf{v}_1A) + \cdots + a_n(\mathbf{v}_nA).$$

Hence $\mathbf{v}A$ is known from the images $\mathbf{v}_iA$.

Now when we have one of those very special generating sets, a basis, then we can work backward along this line of argument and invent linear transformations.

THEOREM 12.5. *Let $\mathbf{v}_1, \cdots, \mathbf{v}_n$ form a basis for $V_n(F)$ and let $\mathbf{w}_1, \cdots, \mathbf{w}_n$ be $n$ arbitrary vectors from $W(F)$. There is a unique linear transformation $A$ from $V_n(F)$ to $W(F)$ such that*

$$\mathbf{v}_iA = \mathbf{w}_i, \qquad i = 1, \cdots, n.$$

The mapping $A$ is defined quite simply by specifying that

$$\mathbf{v}_iA = \mathbf{w}_i, \qquad i = 1, \cdots, n,$$

and then extending this to all elements in $V$ by using linearity. Each element $\mathbf{v}$ of $V(F)$ is *uniquely* expressible as

$$\mathbf{v} = a_1\mathbf{v}_1 + \cdots + a_n\mathbf{v}_n,$$

so we define

$$\mathbf{v}A = a_1\mathbf{w}_1 + \cdots + a_n\mathbf{w}_n.$$

It is quite trivial to show that the mapping $A$ so defined by linearity over all of $V$ is a linear transformation. If

$$\mathbf{u} = b_1\mathbf{v}_1 + \cdots + b_n\mathbf{v}_n$$

then

$$a\mathbf{u} + b\mathbf{v} = (ab_1 + ba_1)\mathbf{v}_1 + \cdots + (ab_n + ba_n)\mathbf{v}_n$$

so that

$$\begin{aligned}(a\mathbf{u} + b\mathbf{v})A &= (ab_1 + ba_1)\mathbf{w} + \cdots + (ab_n + ba_n)\mathbf{w}_n, \\ &= a(\mathbf{u}A) + b(\mathbf{v}A).\end{aligned}$$

Of course if $A$ is given as a linear transformation from $V_n(F)$ to $W(F)$ such that

$$\mathbf{v}_iA = \mathbf{w}_i, \qquad i = 1, \cdots, n,$$

then we know from the linearity of $A$ that, if

$$\mathbf{v} = a_1\mathbf{v}_1 + \cdots + a_n\mathbf{v}_n$$

in $V(F)$, then

$$\mathbf{v}A = a_1(\mathbf{v}_1A) + \cdots + a_n(\mathbf{v}_nA).$$

Thus the mapping defined above through linearity is the only linear transformation from $V_n(F)$ to $W(F)$ which sends $\mathbf{v}_i$ onto $\mathbf{w}_i$ for $i = 1, \cdots, n$.

From these two theorems we see that *every* linear transformation from $V_n(F)$ to $W(F)$ is determined by a basis $\{\mathbf{v}_1, \cdots, \mathbf{v}_n\}$ of $V_n(F)$ and a set of $n$ elements $\mathbf{w}_1, \cdots, \mathbf{w}_n$ in $W(F)$. For through linearity a linear transformation $A$ from $V_n(F)$ to $W(F)$ is determined by the $n$ images $\mathbf{v}_iA = \mathbf{w}_i$. And conversely $n$ elements in $W$ and linearity over $F$ determine a linear transformation from $V_n(F)$ to $W$.

THEOREM 12.6. *If $A$ is a linear transformation from $V_n(F)$ to $W(F)$, then* dim $(VA)$ *is no larger than $n$.*

Let $\mathbf{v}_1, \cdots, \mathbf{v}_n$ form a basis for $V_n(F)$. Then their images $\mathbf{v}_1A, \cdots, \mathbf{v}_nA$ span $VA$ since $\mathbf{v}$ in $V$ is expressible as

$$\mathbf{v} = a_1\mathbf{v}_1 + \cdots + a_n\mathbf{v}_n$$

so that

$$\mathbf{v}A = a_1\mathbf{v}_1A + \cdots + a_n\mathbf{v}_nA.$$

Since the dimension of $VA$ is the number of elements in a minimal spanning set (unless $VA = (\mathbf{z})$ in which case it has dimension 0) we conclude that dim $(VA)$ is bounded by $n$.

This does not mean that the space $W(F)$ has dimension no larger than $n$. In fact $W(F)$ need not have finite dimension.

*Example* 1. Select $\mathbf{w}_1, \cdots, \mathbf{w}_n$ as $n$ arbitrary polynomials in $R[\lambda]$. Then the mapping $A$ from $C_n(R)$ to $R[\lambda]$, defined by linearity from

$$\mathbf{e}_i A = \mathbf{w}_i, \qquad i = 1, \cdots, n,$$

where $\mathbf{e}_1, \cdots, \mathbf{e}_n$ is the canonical basis of $C_n(R)$, is a linear transformation from an $n$-dimensional space into an infinite dimensional space.

The above procedure shows us how to get *one* linear transformation from $V_n(F)$ to $W(F)$ out of one collection of $n$ vectors $\mathbf{w}_1, \cdots, \mathbf{w}_n$ from $W(F)$. Now let us consider an arbitrary but finite set of vectors from $W$. We select a maximal linearly independent set $\{\mathbf{w}_1, \cdots, \mathbf{w}_m\}$ from this collection (relabeling if and when convenient). These $m$ vectors form a basis for the subspace $W_m(F)$ spanned by the original finite collection. How can we describe a linear transformation $A$ from $V_n(F)$ to $W_m(F)$ in terms of the basis vectors $\mathbf{v}_1, \cdots, \mathbf{v}_n$ of $V_n$ and the basis vectors $\mathbf{w}_1, \cdots, \mathbf{w}_m$ of $W_m$?

Consider the images

$$\mathbf{v}_1 A, \cdots, \mathbf{v}_n A;$$

as elements of $W_m$ they are uniquely expressible in terms of the vectors $\mathbf{w}_1, \cdots, \mathbf{w}_m$:

$$\begin{aligned}
\mathbf{v}_1 A &= a_{11}\mathbf{w}_1 + \cdots + a_{1m}\mathbf{w}_m, \\
\mathbf{v}_2 A &= a_{21}\mathbf{w}_1 + \cdots + a_{2m}\mathbf{w}_m, \\
&\vdots \\
\mathbf{v}_n A &= a_{n1}\mathbf{w}_1 + \cdots + a_{nm}\mathbf{w}_m.
\end{aligned}$$

Since $A$ is uniquely determined by the images $\mathbf{v}_i A$, which are uniquely determined by the scalars $a_{ij}$, we see that $A$ is uniquely determined by the array $(a_{rs})$, which has $n$ rows and $m$ columns.

DEFINITION 12.3. The $n$-by-$m$ array $(a_{rs})$ associated above with the linear transformation $A$ is the *matrix of A* relative to the bases $\{\mathbf{v}_1, \cdots, \mathbf{v}_n\}$ for $V_n$ and $\{\mathbf{w}_1, \cdots, \mathbf{w}_m\}$ for $W_m$.

We raise the obvious question of whether an arbitrary $n$-by-$m$ array $(b_{rs})$ over $F$ is the matrix of some linear transformation $\boldsymbol{B}$ from $V_n(F)$ to $W_m(F)$, relative to the given bases. By using the preceding theorems we can show that the answer to this is positive. The $n$-by-$m$ array $(b_{rs})$ assigns exactly one vector of $W_m$ to each basis vector $\mathbf{v}_i$ of $V_n$, so that the equations

$$\begin{aligned}
\mathbf{v}_1 \boldsymbol{B} &= b_{11}\mathbf{w}_1 + \cdots + b_{1m}\mathbf{w}_m, \\
&\vdots \\
\mathbf{v}_n \boldsymbol{B} &= b_{n1}\mathbf{w}_1 + \cdots + b_{nm}\mathbf{w}_m,
\end{aligned}$$

together with linearity, define a unique linear transformation $\boldsymbol{B}$ from $V_n$ to $W_m$. *For this reason no distinction is made hereafter between an array and a matrix.*

THEOREM 12.7. *A basis* $\{\mathbf{v}_1, \cdots, \mathbf{v}_n\}$ *for* $V_n(F)$ *and a basis* $\{\mathbf{w}_1, \cdots, \mathbf{w}_m\}$ *for* $W_m(F)$ *establish a one-to-one correspondence between the linear transformations from* $V_n$ *to* $W_m$ *and the n-by-m matrices over F.*

By this result we could actually list all of the linear transformations from $V_3(F)$ to $V_2(F)$ where $F = J/(2)$. Since a 3-by-2 array contains six positions and since there are two choices for each position we see that there are $2^6$ different homomorphisms from $V_3(J/(2))$ to $V_2(J/(2))$. We will not bother to write them out.

This tie-up between linear transformations and arrays can be strengthened even more.

THEOREM 12.8. *If the n-by-m matrix* $(a_{rs})$ *corresponds to the linear transformation A from* $V_n(F)$ *to* $W_m(F)$, *then* $V_nA$ *is isomorphic with the row space of* $(a_{rs})$.

The correspondence between $A$ and $(a_{rs})$ is spelled out by the equations

$$\begin{aligned} \mathbf{v}_1A &= a_{11}\mathbf{w}_1 + \cdots + a_{1m}\mathbf{w}_m, \\ &\vdots \\ \mathbf{v}_nA &= a_{n1}\mathbf{w}_1 + \cdots + a_{nm}\mathbf{w}_m. \end{aligned}$$

The $n$ vectors $\mathbf{v}_1A, \cdots, \mathbf{v}_nA$ span $V_nA$, and the $n$ row vectors

$$(a_{i1}, \cdots, a_{im}), \qquad i = 1, 2, \cdots, n$$

of $(a_{rs})$ span the row space of that array. The relation

$$(\mathbf{v}_iA)\boldsymbol{B} = (a_{i1}, \cdots, a_{im}), \qquad i = 1, 2, \cdots, n,$$

establishes a homomorphism $\boldsymbol{B}$ from $V_nA$ to the row space of $(a_{rs})$, through linearity, and this homomorphism is an isomorphism since the null space of $\boldsymbol{B}$ is the zero space of $W_m$. For suppose

$$(b_1\mathbf{v}_1A + \cdots + b_n\mathbf{v}_nA)\boldsymbol{B} = (0, \cdots, 0);$$

then

$$\begin{aligned} b_1(a_{11}\mathbf{w}_1 &+ \cdots + a_{1m}\mathbf{w}_m) + \cdots + b_n(a_{n1}\mathbf{w}_1 + \cdots + a_n\mathbf{w}_m) \\ &= (b_1a_{11} + \cdots + b_na_{n1})\mathbf{w}_1 + \cdots + (b_1a_{1m} + \cdots + b_na_{nm})\mathbf{w}_m \end{aligned}$$

maps onto $(0, \cdots, 0)$, implying that

$$b_1a_{1i} + \cdots + b_na_{ni} = 0$$

for $i = 1, 2, \cdots, m$. Hence the vector

$$b_1\mathbf{v}_1A + \cdots + b_n\mathbf{v}_nA = \mathbf{z} \qquad \text{in } V_nA.$$

*Corollary* 12.8.1. The dimension of $V_nA$ equals the rank of $(a_{rs})$. Isomorphic spaces have the same dimension.

Because of this result the dimension of $V_nA$ is often called the *rank* of $A$. Then $A$ and its matrix have the same rank.

*Example* 2. Let the linear transformation $A$ from $C_3(R)$ to $C_3(R)$ be determined by the canonical basis and the array

$$\begin{pmatrix} 1 & 2 & 1 \\ 2 & 2 & 2 \\ 0 & -2 & 0 \end{pmatrix}.$$

Describe $N_A$ and the image space.

Checking the discussion preceding Theorem 12.7 we see that the effect of $A$ on the basis vectors is given by the rows of the array:

$$\mathbf{e}_1A = 1\mathbf{e}_1 + 2\mathbf{e}_2 + 1\mathbf{e}_3 = (1, 2, 1),$$
$$\mathbf{e}_2A = 2\mathbf{e}_1 + 2\mathbf{e}_2 + 1\mathbf{e}_3 = (2, 2, 2),$$

and

$$\mathbf{e}_3A = 0\mathbf{e}_1 - 2\mathbf{e}_2 + 0\mathbf{e}_3 = (0, -2, 0).$$

In this particular example the row space of the array is not just isomorphic with the image space, it *is* the image space, and $C_n(R)A$ has the canonical basis

$$\mathbf{w}_1 = (1, 0, 1) \quad \text{and} \quad \mathbf{w}_2 = (0, 1, 0).$$

This is seen by changing the array to reduced row echelon form.

The null space $N_A$ consists of vectors $(x_1, x_2, x_3)$ such that $(x_1, x_2, x_3)A = (0, 0, 0)$. This means that

$$x_1\mathbf{e}_1A + x_2\mathbf{e}_2A + x_3\mathbf{e}_3A = (0, 0, 0),$$

or, switching to components,

$$\begin{aligned} 1x_1 + 2x_2 + 0x_3 &= 0, \\ 2x_1 + 2x_2 - 2x_3 &= 0, \\ 1x_1 + 2x_2 + 0x_3 &= 0. \end{aligned}$$

Since the array has been transposed in this new system of equations we see that the method of elimination of solving for $x_1$, $x_2$, and $x_3$ is essentially that of reducing the array to reduced column echelon form. Carrying this out we get

$$\begin{aligned} x_1 - 2x_3 &= 0, \\ x_2 + x_3 &= 0, \\ 0x_3 &= 0, \end{aligned}$$

so that $N_A$ consists of all vectors of the form $(2x_3, -x_3, x_3)$. That is, $N_A$ is the subspace spanned by the vector $(2, -1, 1)$, and so we see that

$$\dim (N_A) + \dim \big(C_3(R)A\big) = 3.$$

If we wish to find the image of a vector such as $(1, 2, 5)$ we need only to evaluate

$$1\mathbf{e}_1A + 2\mathbf{e}_2A + 5\mathbf{e}_3A = (5, -4, 5).$$

And to find what vectors, if any, are mapped onto some vector, such as $(2, 3, 2)$, we solve for $x_1$, $x_2$, and $x_3$ such that

$$x_1\mathbf{e}_1A + x_2\mathbf{e}_2A + x_3\mathbf{e}_3A = (2, 3, 2).$$

This reduces to solving the system

$$\begin{aligned} x_1 + 2x_2 &= 2, \\ 2x_1 + 2x_2 - 2x_3 &= 3, \\ x_1 + 2x_2 &= 2. \end{aligned}$$

We wish to emphasize that the correspondence between an $n$-by-$m$ array over $F$ and a linear transformation from $V_n(F)$ to $W_m(F)$ is specified entirely by the bases selected for these spaces. Relative to one choice of bases the linear transformation $A$ corresponds to an array $(a_{rs})$, but relative to a different choice of bases $A$ generally corresponds to a different array. More will be said about this in a later section.

*Example* 3. Find matrices for the linear transformation $A$ from $C_3(R)$ to $C_2(R)$ which sends (1, 1, 1) onto (1, 1), (1, 2, 1) onto (1, 2), and (1, 1, 2) onto (1, 2), and (1, 1, 2) onto (2, 2).

Using the methods developed in the previous chapter we check and see that $\mathbf{v}_1 = (1, 1, 1)$, $\mathbf{v}_2 = (1, 2, 1)$, and $\mathbf{v}_3 = (1, 1, 2)$ form a basis for $C_3(R)$, and $\mathbf{w}_1 = (1, 1)$ and $\mathbf{w}_2 = (1, 2)$ form a basis for $C_2(R)$. Then

$$\mathbf{v}_1A = 1\mathbf{w}_1 + 0\mathbf{w}_2,$$
$$\mathbf{v}_2A = 0\mathbf{w}_1 + 1\mathbf{w}_2,$$

and

$$\mathbf{v}_3A = 2\mathbf{w}_1 + 0\mathbf{w}_2,$$

so that *relative to this choice of bases*, $A$ is described by the 3-by-2 array

$$\begin{pmatrix} 1 & 0 \\ 0 & 1 \\ 2 & 0 \end{pmatrix}.$$

However, if we select the canonical basis $\mathbf{e}_1, \mathbf{e}_2, \mathbf{e}_3$ for $C_3(R)$ while retaining the above basis for $C_2(R)$, then we get a different description of $A$. To find this new array we have to determine the effect of $A$ on $\mathbf{e}_1$, $\mathbf{e}_2$, and $\mathbf{e}_3$, and to do this we write these vectors in terms of $\mathbf{v}_1$, $\mathbf{v}_2$, and $\mathbf{v}_3$:

$$\mathbf{e}_1 = a_1\mathbf{v}_1 + a_2\mathbf{v}_2 + a_3\mathbf{v}_3$$

implies, switching to components (the usual procedure in working with coordinate spaces), that

$$1 = a_1 + a_2 + a_3,$$
$$0 = a_1 + 2a_2 + a_3,$$
$$0 = a_1 + a_2 + 2a_3.$$

From these we conclude that

$$a_1 = 3, \qquad a_2 = -1, \qquad \text{and} \qquad a_3 = -1,$$

and that

$$\mathbf{e}_1 = 3\mathbf{v}_1 - \mathbf{v}_2 - \mathbf{v}_3.$$

Similarly we determine that

$$\mathbf{e}_2 = \mathbf{v}_2 - \mathbf{v}_1 \qquad \text{and} \qquad \mathbf{e}_3 = \mathbf{v}_3 - \mathbf{v}_1,$$

so that

$$\mathbf{e}_1A = 3\mathbf{w}_1 - \mathbf{w}_2 - 2\mathbf{w}_1 = 1\mathbf{w}_1 - 1\mathbf{w}_2,$$
$$\mathbf{e}_2A = -1\mathbf{w}_1 + 1\mathbf{w}_2,$$

and

$$\mathbf{e}_3A = -1\mathbf{w}_1 + 2\mathbf{w}_1 = 1\mathbf{w}_1 + 0\mathbf{w}_2.$$

Hence, relative to this new choice of bases $A$ corresponds to the matrix

$$\begin{pmatrix} 1 & -1 \\ -1 & 1 \\ 1 & 0 \end{pmatrix}.$$

## Exercise 12.2

**1.** Let the linear transformation $A$ from $C_3(R)$ to $C_2(R)$ be determined by the canonical bases of those spaces and the 3-by-2 array

$$\begin{pmatrix} 1 & 2 \\ 3 & 2 \\ 2 & 1 \end{pmatrix}.$$

Find the images $(1, -1, 7)A$, $(0, -2, 8)A$, and $(1, 1, 1)A$.

**2.** In the preceding problem find three vectors of $C_3(R)$ which map onto $(2, 2)$.

**3.** Find the null space of the linear transformation of Problem 1.

**4.** In Example 2 find all vectors which map onto $(2, 3, 2)$.

**5.** Using the canonical basis for $C_2(Re)$ find the matrix describing the rotation of 30 degrees counterclockwise about the origin.

**6.** Find matrices describing the linear transformations of Examples 3 and 5 in the preceding section. How many possible answers are there?

**7.** Discuss the number of linear transformations from $C_n(J/(p))$ to $C_m(J/(p))$.

**8.** The linear transformation $A$ from $C_2(R)$ to $C_2(R)$ sends $(1, 2)$ and $(3, 4)$ onto $(-1, 0)$ and $(0, 3)$, respectively. Find two different matrices describing $A$, using the canonical basis in one case.

**9.** The linear transformation $A$ from $C_3(R)$ to $C_2(R)$ sends $\mathbf{v}_1 = (1, 2, 3)$ onto $\mathbf{w}_1 = (1, 2)$, $\mathbf{v}_2 = (2, 2, 3)$ onto $\mathbf{w}_2 = (2, 1)$, and $\mathbf{v}_3 = (-1, 1, 1)$ onto $\mathbf{w}_3 = (3, 3)$. Find two different descriptions (i.e., matrices) of $A$.

**10.** Let $A$ be a linear transformation from $V_n(F)$ to $W(F)$. Show that

$$\dim (N_A) + \dim (V_nA) = n.$$

(Select a basis $\{\mathbf{u}_1, \cdots, \mathbf{u}_k\}$ for $N_A$ and extend it to a basis $\{\mathbf{u}_1, \cdots, \mathbf{u}_k; \mathbf{v}_1, \cdots, \mathbf{v}_g\}$ for $V_n$. Then $\mathbf{v}_1A, \cdots, \mathbf{v}_gA$ form a basis for $V_nA$.)

**11.** Let the $n$-by-$m$ array $(a_{rs})$ correspond to the linear transformation $A$ from $V_n(F)$ to $W_m(F)$. Show that $N_A$ is isomorphic with the subspace of $C_n(F)$ which is orthogonal with the column space of $(a_{rs})$. (See Example 2.)

**12.** Complete Example 2.

**13.** Let $A$ be an automorphism of a quadratic field

$$F = \{a + b\sqrt{m}: a \text{ and } b \text{ in } R\}.$$

Consider $F$ as a vector space over $R$ and find a matrix describing $A$. Do this for all automorphisms of $F$.

**14.** The Galois field $GF(p^2)$ is a vector space of dimension $p$ over $GF(p) = J/(p)$, and an automorphism of this field is a linear transformation of it as a vector space. Find matric descriptions of the automorphisms of $GF(4)$; of $GF(8)$.

## 12.3 Addition

Up to this point we have been considering *individual* linear transformations. Now we raise our sights a bit and look at the set $L(V(F); W(F))$ of all linear transformations from $V(F)$ to $W(F)$. If we can make this collection into an algebraic system of a type already known to us, then we will be able to utilize the theory developed earlier. Moreover the discovery and development of a new example or variety of examples of an abstract system often lead to an extension of the general theory by suggesting new avenues of approach and new problems.

Since the basic binary operations of the vector spaces $V(F)$ and $W(F)$ are addition and scalar multiplication we should naturally attempt to extend these to the set $\boldsymbol{L}(V(F); W(F))$. And since linear transformations, by Theorem 12.1, are determined by the images which they map vectors onto we use these images to define addition and scalar multiplication in $\boldsymbol{L}(V; W)$.

*Addition.* Let $\boldsymbol{A}$ and $\boldsymbol{B}$ be two linear transformations from $V(F)$ to $W(F)$. Then the sum $\boldsymbol{A} + \boldsymbol{B}$ is defined to be the mapping from $V$ to $W$ determined by the images

$$\mathbf{v}(\boldsymbol{A} + \boldsymbol{B}) = \mathbf{v}\boldsymbol{A} + \mathbf{v}\boldsymbol{B}, \qquad \text{all } \mathbf{v} \text{ in } V.$$

This brings in yet another use of the symbol $+$, but it seems fairly safe to do this since the variation in symbols and the explicit indications for the elements in $F$, $V$, $W$, and $\boldsymbol{L}(V; W)$ serve to show which addition is actually being used.

THEOREM 12.9. *The mapping $\boldsymbol{A} + \boldsymbol{B}$ is a linear transformation from $V(F)$ to $W(F)$.*

Let $a$ and $b$ be elements of $F$ and $\mathbf{u}$ and $\mathbf{v}$ be vectors from $V$. Then

$$(a\mathbf{u} + b\mathbf{v})(\boldsymbol{A} + \boldsymbol{B}) = (a\mathbf{u} + b\mathbf{v})\boldsymbol{A} + (a\mathbf{u} + b\mathbf{v})\boldsymbol{B}$$

by the definition of $\boldsymbol{A} + \boldsymbol{B}$, and since

$$(a\mathbf{u} + b\mathbf{v})\boldsymbol{A} = a(\mathbf{u}\boldsymbol{A}) + b(\mathbf{v}\boldsymbol{A})$$

and

$$(a\mathbf{u} + b\mathbf{v})\boldsymbol{B} = a(\mathbf{u}\boldsymbol{B}) + b(\mathbf{v}\boldsymbol{B})$$

we see that

$$(a\mathbf{u} + b\mathbf{v})(\boldsymbol{A} + \boldsymbol{B}) = a(\mathbf{u}\boldsymbol{A}) + b(\mathbf{v}\boldsymbol{A}) + a(\mathbf{u}\boldsymbol{B}) + b(\mathbf{v}\boldsymbol{B}).$$

Working in $W(F)$ and using the properties of a vector space we see that

$$\begin{aligned} a(\mathbf{u}\boldsymbol{A}) + b(\mathbf{v}\boldsymbol{A}) &+ a(\mathbf{u}\boldsymbol{B}) + b(\mathbf{v}\boldsymbol{B}) \\ &= a(\mathbf{u}\boldsymbol{A}) + a(\mathbf{u}\boldsymbol{B}) + b(\mathbf{v}\boldsymbol{A}) + b(\mathbf{v}\boldsymbol{B}), \\ &= a(\mathbf{u}\boldsymbol{A} + \mathbf{u}\boldsymbol{B}) + b(\mathbf{v}\boldsymbol{A} + \mathbf{v}\boldsymbol{B}). \end{aligned}$$

By definition we have

$$\mathbf{u}\boldsymbol{A} + \mathbf{u}\boldsymbol{B} = \mathbf{u}(\boldsymbol{A} + \boldsymbol{B}) \qquad \text{and} \qquad \mathbf{v}\boldsymbol{A} + \mathbf{v}\boldsymbol{B} = \mathbf{v}(\boldsymbol{A} + \boldsymbol{B}),$$

and assembling these facts we see that

$$(a\mathbf{u} + b\mathbf{v})(\boldsymbol{A} + \boldsymbol{B}) = a(\mathbf{u}(\boldsymbol{A} + \boldsymbol{B})) + b(\mathbf{v}(\boldsymbol{A} + \boldsymbol{B})).$$

Hence $\boldsymbol{A} + \boldsymbol{B}$ is a linear transformation from $V(F)$ to $W(F)$.

Since addition in $\mathbf{L}(V; W)$ is based on the addition in the Abelian group $W$ we should expect the system formed by $\mathbf{L}(V; W)$ and this binary operation to be quite nice. Consider the following equations:

$$\begin{aligned}(12.1)\qquad \mathbf{v}(\mathbf{A} + (\mathbf{B} + \mathbf{C})) &= \mathbf{v}\mathbf{A} + \mathbf{v}(\mathbf{B} + \mathbf{C}),\\ &= \mathbf{v}\mathbf{A} + (\mathbf{v}\mathbf{B} + \mathbf{v}\mathbf{C}) = (\mathbf{v}\mathbf{A} + \mathbf{v}\mathbf{B}) + \mathbf{v}\mathbf{C},\\ &= \mathbf{v}((\mathbf{A} + \mathbf{B}) + \mathbf{C}),\end{aligned}$$

for $\mathbf{v}$ in $V$ and $\mathbf{A}$, $\mathbf{B}$, and $\mathbf{C}$ in $\mathbf{L}(V; W)$;

$$\begin{aligned}(12.2)\qquad \mathbf{v}(\mathbf{A} + \mathbf{B}) &= \mathbf{v}\mathbf{A} + \mathbf{v}\mathbf{B} = \mathbf{v}\mathbf{B} + \mathbf{v}\mathbf{A},\\ &= \mathbf{v}(\mathbf{B} + \mathbf{A}),\end{aligned}$$

for $\mathbf{v}$ in $V$ and $\mathbf{A} + \mathbf{B}$ in $\mathbf{L}(V; W)$.

From these we conclude that $\mathbf{L}(V; W)$ forms a commutative semigroup relative to addition. In fact much more can be said.

THEOREM 12.10. *The system* $\{\mathbf{L}(V; W), +\}$ *is an Abelian group.*

Consider the mapping $\mathbf{Z}$ defined by

$$\mathbf{v}\mathbf{Z} = \mathbf{z}, \qquad \text{all } \mathbf{v} \text{ in } V,$$

where $\mathbf{z}$ denotes the zero of $W$. From

$$(a\mathbf{u} + b\mathbf{v})\mathbf{Z} = a(\mathbf{u}\mathbf{Z}) + b(\mathbf{v}\mathbf{Z}) = a\mathbf{z} + b\mathbf{z} = \mathbf{z}$$

we conclude that $\mathbf{Z}$ is in $\mathbf{L}(V; W)$, and it follows easily that $\mathbf{Z}$ is the additive identity of $\mathbf{L}(V; W)$ since

$$\mathbf{v}(\mathbf{A} + \mathbf{Z}) = \mathbf{v}\mathbf{A} + \mathbf{v}\mathbf{Z} = \mathbf{v}\mathbf{A} + \mathbf{z} = \mathbf{v}\mathbf{A}.$$

Moreover the mapping $-\mathbf{A}$ from $V$ to $W$ defined by

$$\mathbf{v}(-\mathbf{A}) = -\mathbf{v}\mathbf{A}, \qquad \text{all } \mathbf{v} \text{ in } V,$$

is an element of $\mathbf{L}(V; W)$, and

$$\mathbf{A} + (-\mathbf{A}) = -\mathbf{A} + \mathbf{A} = \mathbf{Z}$$

since

$$\mathbf{v}(\mathbf{A} + (-\mathbf{A})) = \mathbf{v}\mathbf{A} - \mathbf{v}\mathbf{A} = \mathbf{z} \qquad \text{for all } \mathbf{v} \text{ in } V.$$

So we see that the system $\{\mathbf{L}(V; W), +\}$ is an Abelian group.

*Scalar Multiplication.* If $a$ is an element from $F$ and $\mathbf{A}$ is a linear transformation from $V(F)$ to $W(F)$, then $a\mathbf{A}$, the *scalar multiple*, is the mapping from $V$ to $W$ defined by the images

$$\mathbf{v}(a\mathbf{A}) = (a\mathbf{v})\mathbf{A} = a(\mathbf{v}\mathbf{A}), \qquad \text{all } \mathbf{v} \text{ in } V.$$

$(\alpha A)(\vec{x}) = A(\alpha\vec{x}) = \alpha A(\vec{x})$

The idea here is to make $\mathbf{L}(V; W)$ into a vector space over $F$, and the following equations show that this is accomplished.

(12.3)
$$\begin{aligned}(b\mathbf{u} + c\mathbf{v})(aA) &= \big(a(b\mathbf{u} + c\mathbf{v})\big)A,\\ &= a\big((b\mathbf{u} + c\mathbf{v})A\big) = a\big(b(\mathbf{u}A) + c(\mathbf{v}A)\big),\\ &= ba(\mathbf{u}A) + ca(\mathbf{v}A) = b\big(\mathbf{u}(aA)\big) + c\big(\mathbf{v}(aA)\big),\end{aligned}$$

for $a$, $b$, $c$ in $F$, $\mathbf{v}$ in $V$, and $A$ in $\mathbf{L}(V; W)$. Hence $aA$ is in $\mathbf{L}(V; W)$.

(12.4)
$$\begin{aligned}\mathbf{v}\big((a + b)A\big) &= (a + b)\mathbf{v}A = a(\mathbf{v}A) + b(\mathbf{v}A),\\ &= \mathbf{v}(aA + bA),\end{aligned}$$

for $a$ and $b$ in $F$, $\mathbf{v}$ in $V$, and $A$ in $\mathbf{L}(V; W)$.

(12.5)
$$\begin{aligned}\mathbf{v}\big(a(A + \mathbf{B})\big) &= (a\mathbf{v})(A + \mathbf{B}),\\ &= (a\mathbf{v})A + (a\mathbf{v})\mathbf{B},\\ &= \mathbf{v}(aA) + \mathbf{v}(a\mathbf{B}),\\ &= \mathbf{v}(aA + a\mathbf{B}),\end{aligned}$$

for $a$ in $F$, $\mathbf{v}$ in $V$, and $A$ and $\mathbf{B}$ in $\mathbf{L}(V; W)$.

(12.6)
$$\begin{aligned}\mathbf{v}\big((ab)A\big) &= \big((ab)\mathbf{v}\big)A = \big(a(b\mathbf{v})\big)A = a\big((b\mathbf{v})A\big),\\ &= a\big(\mathbf{v}(bA)\big) = \mathbf{v}\big(a(bA)\big)\end{aligned}$$

for $a$ and $b$ in $F$, $\mathbf{v}$ in $V$, and $A$ in $\mathbf{L}(V; W)$.

(12.7)
$$\mathbf{v}(1A) = 1(\mathbf{v}A) = \mathbf{v}A$$

for $\mathbf{v}$ in $V$ and $A$ in $\mathbf{L}(V; W)$.

THEOREM 12.11. *The system consisting of the set $\mathbf{L}(V; W)$ of all linear transformations from $V(F)$ to $W(F)$ and of the binary operations of addition and scalar multiplication, defined above, is a vector space over $F$.*

Theorem 12.10 shows that $(\mathbf{L}, +)$ is an Abelian group, and equation (12.3) shows that $aA$ is in $\mathbf{L}(V; W)$ and hence that scalar multiplication is a mapping from $F \times \mathbf{L}$ to $\mathbf{L}$. From equations (12.4) through (12.7) we conclude that

(12.8)
$$(a + b)A = aA + bA,$$

(12.9)
$$a(A + \mathbf{B}) = aA + a\mathbf{B},$$

(12.10)
$$(ab)A = a(bA),$$

(12.11)
$$1A = A,$$

for $a$ and $b$ in $F$ and $A$ and $\mathbf{B}$ in $\mathbf{L}(V; W)$. Hence this system, which we denote simply by $\mathbf{L}(V; W)$, is a vector space over $F$.

We can get a better description of what is happening by restricting our attention to finite dimensional vector spaces $V_n(F)$ and $W_m(F)$, selecting arbitrary but fixed bases for these spaces, and looking at the $n$-by-$m$ matrices which correspond to the elements of $\mathbf{L}(V; W)$. For convenience we take $n = 3$ and $m = 3$ and the sets $\{\mathbf{v}_1, \mathbf{v}_2, \mathbf{v}_3\}$ and $\{\mathbf{w}_1, \mathbf{w}_2, \mathbf{w}_3\}$ as bases for $V_3$

and $W_3$, respectively. Then two linear transformations $\boldsymbol{A}$ and $\boldsymbol{B}$ are determined by their effect on $\mathbf{v}_1$, $\mathbf{v}_2$, and $\mathbf{v}_3$:

$$\begin{aligned}\mathbf{v}_1\boldsymbol{A} &= a_{11}\mathbf{w}_1 + a_{12}\mathbf{w}_2 + a_{13}\mathbf{w}_3,\\ \mathbf{v}_2\boldsymbol{A} &= a_{21}\mathbf{w}_1 + a_{22}\mathbf{w}_2 + a_{23}\mathbf{w}_3,\\ \mathbf{v}_3\boldsymbol{A} &= a_{31}\mathbf{w}_1 + a_{32}\mathbf{w}_2 + a_{33}\mathbf{w}_3;\end{aligned}$$

and, more concisely,

$$\mathbf{v}_i\boldsymbol{B} = b_{i1}\mathbf{w}_1 + b_{i2}\mathbf{w}_2 + b_{i3}\mathbf{w}_3$$

for $i = 1, 2, 3$. Thus $\boldsymbol{A}$ and $\boldsymbol{B}$ are described by the 3-by-3 matrices

$$(a_{rs}) = \begin{pmatrix} a_{11} & a_{12} & a_{13}\\ a_{21} & a_{22} & a_{23}\\ a_{31} & a_{32} & a_{33}\end{pmatrix}$$

and $(b_{rs})$, respectively. The effect of $\boldsymbol{A} + \boldsymbol{B}$ on the basis vectors $\mathbf{v}_i$ is quite obvious:

$$\begin{aligned}\mathbf{v}_i(\boldsymbol{A} + \boldsymbol{B}) &= \mathbf{v}_i\boldsymbol{A} + \mathbf{v}_i\boldsymbol{B},\\ &= (a_{i1}\mathbf{w}_1 + a_{i2}\mathbf{w}_2 + a_{i3}\mathbf{w}_3) + (b_{i1}\mathbf{w}_1 + b_{i2}\mathbf{w}_2 + b_{i3}\mathbf{w}_3),\\ &= (a_{i1} + b_{i1})\mathbf{w}_1 + (a_{i2} + b_{i2})\mathbf{w}_2 + (a_{i3} + b_{i3})\mathbf{w}_3,\end{aligned}$$

for $i = 1$, 2, and 3. Hence the matrix of $\boldsymbol{A} + \boldsymbol{B}$ is

$$\begin{pmatrix} a_{11} + b_{11} & a_{12} + b_{12} & a_{13} + b_{13}\\ a_{21} + b_{21} & a_{22} + b_{22} & a_{23} + b_{23}\\ a_{31} + b_{31} & a_{32} + b_{32} & a_{33} + b_{33}\end{pmatrix},$$

which is clearly obtainable by adding the corresponding components of the matrices $(a_{rs})$ and $(b_{rs})$. Also, since

$$\begin{aligned}\mathbf{v}_i(a\boldsymbol{A}) = a(\mathbf{v}_i\boldsymbol{A}) &= a(a_{i1}\mathbf{w}_1 + a_{i2}\mathbf{w}_2 + a_{i3}\mathbf{w}_3),\\ &= aa_{i1}\mathbf{w}_1 + aa_{i2}\mathbf{w}_2 + aa_{i3}\mathbf{w}_3,\end{aligned}$$

for $i = 1$, 2, and 3, we see that the matrix of $a\boldsymbol{A}$ is

$$\begin{pmatrix} aa_{11} & aa_{12} & aa_{13}\\ aa_{21} & aa_{22} & aa_{23}\\ aa_{31} & aa_{32} & aa_{33}\end{pmatrix}.$$

Thus the previous results for the vector space $\boldsymbol{L}(V; W)$ and the correspondence between linear transformations and matrices enable us to make $F(n, m)$, the set of all $n$-by-$m$ matrices over $F$, into a vector space over $F$.

*Addition.* The *sum* of two elements from $F(n, m)$ is obtained by adding the corresponding components, so that

$$(a_{rs}) + (b_{rs}) = (a_{rs} + b_{rs}).$$

*Scalar Multiplication.* The product of $a$ in $F$ and $(a_{rs})$ in $F(n, m)$ is defined to be the matrix $(b_{rs})$ where

$$b_{rs} = aa_{rs}$$

for $r = 1, \cdots, n$ and $s = 1, \cdots, m$.

These definitions are chosen so that the natural one-to-one correspondence, relative to a particular basis for $V_n(F)$ and a particular basis for $W_m(F)$, which was discussed in the preceding section, is compatible with the addition and scalar multiplication in $\mathbf{L}(V_n; W_m)$ and $F(n, m)$. Consequently the system consisting of $F(n, m)$ and the two binary operations defined above is a vector space over $F$ since it is an isomorphic image of the vector space $\mathbf{L}(V_n; W_m)$.

THEOREM 12.12. *The system consisting of all n-by-m matrices over the field F is a vector space of dimension nm over F relative to componentwise addition and scalar multiplication.*

The isomorphism discussed above shows that $F(n, m)$ is a vector space, but the theorem follows quite easily from looking at the coordinate vector space $C_{nm}(F)$ of dimension $nm$. We break a vector of this space into $n$ ordered pieces of $m$ components each by counting (from left to right) the first $m$ components, the next $m$ components, etc. Then we stack these up in an orderly fashion and thereby obtain an element of $F(n, m)$. Since the procedure is reversible we see that the system $\{F(n, m), +, \cdot\}$ is just $C_{nm}(F)$ written in a folded style.

*Example* 1. We illustrate the above by looking at $C_6(R)$.

From an arbitrary element

$$\mathbf{v} = (a_1, a_2, a_3, a_4, a_5, a_6)$$

of this space we form the 3-by-2 array

$$\begin{pmatrix} a_1 & a_2 \\ a_3 & a_4 \\ a_5 & a_6 \end{pmatrix}$$

so that by letting these two elements correspond we obtain an isomorphism between $C_6(R)$ and $R(3, 2)$. The vector $\mathbf{v}$ can also be broken and stacked to yield the 2-by-3 array

$$\begin{pmatrix} a_1 & a_2 & a_3 \\ a_4 & a_5 & a_6 \end{pmatrix}$$

so that $C_6(R)$ is also isomorphic with $R(2, 3)$.

For particular elements

$$\mathbf{u} = (1, 0, 2, 3, -1, 5) \quad \text{and} \quad \mathbf{v} = (2, 3, -1, -1, 2, -2)$$

of $C_6(R)$ we have

$$\begin{aligned} 2\mathbf{u} &= (2, 0, 4, 6, -2, 10), \\ -1\mathbf{v} &= (-2, -3, 1, 1, -2, 2). \end{aligned}$$

and

$$2\mathbf{u} + (-1)\mathbf{v} = (0, -3, 5, 7, -4, 12).$$

Written in terms of 3-by-2 matrices this simple arithmetic becomes

$$A = \begin{pmatrix} 1 & 0 \\ 2 & 3 \\ -1 & 5 \end{pmatrix}, \qquad B = \begin{pmatrix} 2 & 3 \\ -1 & -1 \\ 2 & -2 \end{pmatrix},$$

$$2A = \begin{pmatrix} 2 & 0 \\ 4 & 6 \\ -2 & 10 \end{pmatrix}, \qquad -1B = \begin{pmatrix} -2 & -3 \\ 1 & 1 \\ -2 & 2 \end{pmatrix},$$

and

$$2A + (-1)B = \begin{pmatrix} 0 & -3 \\ 5 & 7 \\ -4 & 12 \end{pmatrix}.$$

*Example* 2. Describe a simple basis for the vector space $F(n, m)$.

Take the canonical basis for $C_{nm}(F)$ and rewrite it as a basis for $F(n, m)$. This yields the basis, which we will call the *canonical basis* of $F(n, m)$, denoted by $E_{11}, \cdots, E_{1m}, \cdots, E_{nm}$ where $E_{ij}$ is the $n$-by-$m$ matrix with 1 in the $(i, j)$-position and zeros everywhere else. These matrices are sometimes called *matric units.* In $R(2, 2)$ the four matric units are

$$E_{11} = \begin{pmatrix} 1 & 0 \\ 0 & 0 \end{pmatrix}, \quad E_{12} = \begin{pmatrix} 0 & 1 \\ 0 & 0 \end{pmatrix}, \quad E_{21} = \begin{pmatrix} 0 & 0 \\ 1 & 0 \end{pmatrix},$$

and

$$E_{22} = \begin{pmatrix} 0 & 0 \\ 0 & 1 \end{pmatrix}.$$

## Exercise 12.3

**1.** Let $A$ be a rotation of the plane vector space through an angle of 120 degrees about the origin and $B$ a rotation of 30 degrees. Describe $A + B$ and illustrate geometrically.

**2.** Let $A$ be the linear transformation of Problem 1 and describe $2A$, $-A$, $-3A$, and $(\frac{1}{3})A$.

**3.** Show that the vector space $L(V_n(F); V_n(F))$ has dimension $n^2$ over $F$ and contains a subspace isomorphic with $V_n(F)$.

**4.** Show that the $m$ matric units $E_{i1}, \cdots, E_{im}$ of $F(n, m)$ span a subspace $U_i$ of dimension $m$. Show furthermore that the space $F(n, m)$ is expressible as the sum

$$U_1 + U_2 + \cdots + U_n,$$

and that this sum is irredundant in that each element $A$ of $F(n, m)$ is uniquely expressible as

$$A = A_1 + A_2 + \cdots + A_n$$

with $A_i$ in $U_i$.

**5.** Illustrate Problem 4 with $R(3, 4)$.

**6.** Find the rank of the matrices $A$, $B$, and $A + B$ when $A$ and $B$ are the following elements of $R(3, 3)$:

$$A = \begin{pmatrix} 2 & 0 & -1 \\ -2 & 1 & 1 \\ 1 & 5 & 2 \end{pmatrix} \quad \text{and} \quad B = \begin{pmatrix} -1 & 1 & 2 \\ 2 & 1 & 4 \\ 3 & 0 & 1 \end{pmatrix}.$$

**7.** Let $A$ and $B$ be two $n$-by-$m$ matrices. Prove that the rank of $A + B$ never exceeds the rank of $A$ plus the rank of $B$. Show by example that the rank of $A + B$ can be zero.

**8.** Let $\mathbf{A}$ and $\mathbf{B}$ be linear transformations from $V(F)$ to $W(F)$. Show that the image space $V(\mathbf{A} + \mathbf{B})$ is contained in the sum $V\mathbf{A} + V\mathbf{B}$ but that in general $V(\mathbf{A} + \mathbf{B}) \neq V\mathbf{A} + V\mathbf{B}$. (What happens when $\mathbf{B} = -\mathbf{A}$?)

**9.** Find the null spaces of the linear transformations from $C_3(R)$ to $C_3(R)$ which correspond, relative to the canonical basis, to the matrices of Problem 6.

**10.** Let $\mathbf{A}$ and $\mathbf{B}$ be linear transformations from $V_n(F)$ to $V_n(F)$. Prove that the dimension of the null space of $\mathbf{A} + \mathbf{B}$ is at least as large as

$$\dim (N_{\mathbf{A}}) + \dim (N_{\mathbf{B}}) - n.$$

(Use Problem 7, the relation between $N_A$ and $V_nA$, and the correspondence between matrices and linear transformations.) Illustrate with Problem 9.

**11.** A linear transformation from $V(F)$ to $F$ (considered as a vector space over $F$) is a *linear functional*, and the vector space $\mathbf{L}(V(F); F)$ is the *dual space* of $V(F)$. Show that $\mathbf{L}(V_n(F); F)$ is isomorphic with $C_n(F)$ by using a matric description of $\mathbf{L}(V_n(F); F)$.

## 12.4 Multiplication

In many of our previous dealings with functions (or mappings) we were able to use function composition to form new mappings. Thus if $\mathbf{A}$ is a mapping from set $U$ to set $V$ and if $\mathbf{B}$ is a mapping from set $V$ to set $W$, then the *composite mapping* $\mathbf{AB}$ from set $U$ to set $W$ is defined by the images

$$\mathbf{u}(\mathbf{AB}) = (u\mathbf{A})\mathbf{B}, \qquad \text{all } \mathbf{u} \text{ in } U.$$

Naturally we should consider the question of whether or not the composite of two linear transformations is a linear transformation, and it is quite easy to verify that this "product" is a linear transformation.

THEOREM 12.13. *If $\mathbf{A}$ belongs to $\mathbf{L}(U(F); V(F))$ and $\mathbf{B}$ belongs to $\mathbf{L}(V(F); W(F))$, then the product defined by the images*

$$\mathbf{u}(\mathbf{AB}) = (\mathbf{u}\mathbf{A})\mathbf{B}, \qquad \text{all } \mathbf{u} \text{ in } U(F),$$

*is an element of $\mathbf{L}(U(F); W(F))$.*

We know that the composite $\mathbf{AB}$ is a mapping from $U$ to $W$ so all we need to show is that it is linear. Let $\mathbf{u}$ and $\mathbf{v}$ be two elements of $U(F)$ and $a$ and $b$ be in $F$. Then

$$(a\mathbf{u} + b\mathbf{v})(\boldsymbol{AB}) = \big((a\mathbf{u} + b\mathbf{v})\boldsymbol{A}\big)\boldsymbol{B}$$

by definition,

$$(a\mathbf{u} + b\mathbf{v})\boldsymbol{A} = a(\mathbf{u}\boldsymbol{A}) + b(\mathbf{v}\boldsymbol{A})$$

since $\boldsymbol{A}$ is linear,

$$\big(a(\mathbf{u}\boldsymbol{A}) + b(\mathbf{v}\boldsymbol{A})\big)\boldsymbol{B} = a\big((\mathbf{u}\boldsymbol{A})\boldsymbol{B}\big) + b\big((\mathbf{v}\boldsymbol{A})\boldsymbol{B}\big)$$

since $\boldsymbol{B}$ is linear, and

$$(\mathbf{u}\boldsymbol{A})\boldsymbol{B} = \mathbf{u}(\boldsymbol{AB}) \qquad \text{and} \qquad (\mathbf{v}\boldsymbol{A})\boldsymbol{B} = \mathbf{v}(\boldsymbol{AB})$$

by definition, so that

$$(a\mathbf{u} + b\mathbf{v})(\boldsymbol{AB}) = a\big(\mathbf{u}(\boldsymbol{AB})\big) + b\big(\mathbf{v}(\boldsymbol{AB})\big).$$

Hence $\boldsymbol{AB}$ is a linear transformation from $U(F)$ to $W(F)$.

Note that in general the product $\boldsymbol{BA}$ is not defined even though $\boldsymbol{AB}$ is.

*Example* 1. Let $U(F)$ be $C_3(Re)$, $V(F)$ be $C_2(Re)$, and $W(F) = C_1(Re)$. Then, if $\boldsymbol{A}$ projects $(a_1, a_2, a_3)$ onto $(a_1, a_2)$ and $\boldsymbol{B}$ projects $(a_1, a_2)$ onto $a_1$, $\boldsymbol{AB}$ projects $(a_1, a_2, a_3)$ directly onto $a_1$ (see Fig. 12.1).

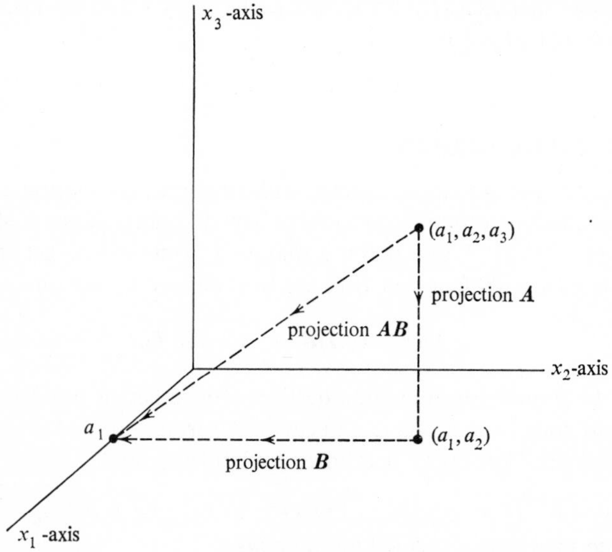


**Figure 12.1**

By restricting our attention to finite dimensional vector spaces this concept of multiplication of certain linear transformations enables us to define the product of certain matrices. For the sake of simplicity we take $U(F)$,

$V(F)$, and $W(F)$ to have dimension 3, 3, and 2, respectively. If $\{\mathbf{u}_1, \mathbf{u}_2, \mathbf{u}_3\}$, $\{\mathbf{v}_1, \mathbf{v}_2, \mathbf{v}_3\}$, and $\{\mathbf{w}_1, \mathbf{w}_2\}$ are bases for $U$, $V$, and $W$, respectively, and if $\boldsymbol{A}$ and $\boldsymbol{B}$ are in $\boldsymbol{L}(U; V)$ and $\boldsymbol{L}(V; W)$, respectively, we can describe $\boldsymbol{A}$, $\boldsymbol{B}$, and $\boldsymbol{AB}$ with matrices.

From

$$\mathbf{u}_i\boldsymbol{A} = a_{i1}\mathbf{v}_1 + a_{i2}\mathbf{v}_2 + a_{i3}\mathbf{v}_3, \qquad i = 1, 2, \text{ and } 3,$$

and

$$\mathbf{v}_i\boldsymbol{B} = b_{i1}\mathbf{w}_1 + b_{i2}\mathbf{w}_2 \qquad \text{for } i = 1, 2, \text{ and } 3,$$

we see that

$$\begin{aligned}\mathbf{u}_1\boldsymbol{AB} &= a_{11}\mathbf{v}_1\boldsymbol{B} + a_{12}\mathbf{v}_2\boldsymbol{B} + a_{13}\mathbf{v}_3\boldsymbol{B}\\ &= a_{11}(b_{11}\mathbf{w}_1 + b_{12}\mathbf{w}_2) + a_{12}(b_{21}\mathbf{w}_1 + b_{22}\mathbf{w}_2) + a_{13}(b_{31}\mathbf{w}_1 + b_{32}\mathbf{w}_2),\\ &= (a_{11}b_{11} + a_{12}b_{21} + a_{13}b_{31})\mathbf{w}_1 + (a_{11}b_{12} + a_{12}b_{22} + a_{13}b_{32})\mathbf{w}_2.\end{aligned}$$

In the same way we get

$$\mathbf{u}_2\boldsymbol{AB} = (a_{21}b_{11} + a_{22}b_{21} + a_{23}b_{31})\mathbf{w}_1 + (a_{21}b_{12} + a_{22}b_{22} + a_{23}b_{32})\mathbf{w}_2$$

and

$$\mathbf{u}_3\boldsymbol{AB} = (a_{31}b_{11} + a_{32}b_{21} + a_{33}b_{31})\mathbf{w}_1 + (a_{31}b_{12} + a_{32}b_{22} + a_{33}b_{31})\mathbf{w}_2,$$

and the matrices corresponding to $\boldsymbol{A}$, $\boldsymbol{B}$, and $\boldsymbol{AB}$ are

$$A = \begin{pmatrix} a_{11} & a_{12} & a_{13}\\ a_{21} & a_{22} & a_{23}\\ a_{31} & a_{32} & a_{33}\end{pmatrix},$$

$$B = \begin{pmatrix} b_{11} & b_{12}\\ b_{21} & b_{22}\\ b_{31} & b_{32}\end{pmatrix},$$

and

$$C = \begin{pmatrix} a_{11}b_{11} + a_{12}b_{21} + a_{13}b_{31} & a_{11}b_{12} + a_{12}b_{22} + a_{13}b_{32}\\ a_{21}b_{11} + a_{22}b_{21} + a_{23}b_{31} & a_{21}b_{12} + a_{22}b_{22} + a_{23}b_{32}\\ a_{31}b_{11} + a_{32}b_{21} + a_{33}b_{31} & a_{31}b_{12} + a_{32}b_{22} + a_{33}b_{32}\end{pmatrix}.$$

So how can we "multiply" $A$ and $B$ to get $C$? First we note the following facts:

(1) Elements from row 1 of $A$ appear only in row 1 of $C$, and similarly for rows 2 and 3.

(2) Elements from column 1 of $B$ appear only in column 1 of $C$, and similarly for column 2.

Thus it appears that row $i$ of matrix $A$ is combined with column $j$ of matrix $B$ to produce the $(i, j)$-element of matrix $C$. Closer inspection reveals that, for example, row 2 of $A$ and column 1 of $B$,

$$(a_{21}, a_{22}, a_{23}) \qquad \text{and} \qquad \begin{pmatrix} b_{11} \\ b_{21} \\ b_{31} \end{pmatrix},$$

respectively, combine to yield the scalar

$$a_{21}b_{11} + a_{22}b_{21} + a_{23}b_{31}$$

which is the element in row 2 and column 1 of $C$.

*Matric Multiplication.* The *product* of the $n$-by-$m$ matrix $(a_{rs})$ from $F(n, m)$ and the $m$-by-$t$ matrix $(b_{rs})$ from $F(m, t)$ is the $n$-by-$t$ matrix $(c_{rs})$ from $F(n, t)$ with

$$c_{rs} = \sum_{i=1}^{m} a_{ri}b_{is}$$

for $r = 1, \cdots, n$ and $s = 1, \cdots, t$. If $(a_{rs})$, $(b_{rs})$, and $(c_{rs})$ are denoted by $A$, $B$, and $C$, respectively, then we write

$$AB = C.$$

This definition is abstracted from the preceding discussion and is made so that the matrix $C$, which corresponds to the composite linear transformation $\boldsymbol{AB}$, is precisely the product of the matrices $A$ and $B$ which correspond to $\boldsymbol{A}$ and $\boldsymbol{B}$.

In the definition above we see that the component

$$c_{rs} = a_{r1}b_{1s} + a_{r2}b_{2s} + \cdots + a_{rm}b_{ms}$$

of $AB = C$ is determined by row $r$ of the left factor $A$, namely

$$(a_{r1}, a_{r2}, \cdots, a_{rm}),$$

and column $s$ of the right factor $B$, namely

$$\begin{pmatrix} b_{1s} \\ b_{2s} \\ \vdots \end{pmatrix}.$$

In fact the multiplication of $A$ and $B$ depends entirely upon a rule for combining two vectors of the coordinate space $C_m(F)$, one written as a row vector and the other as a column vector:

$$(a_1, \cdots, a_m)\begin{pmatrix} b_1 \\ \vdots \\ b_m \end{pmatrix} = a_1b_1 + \cdots + a_mb_m.$$

(This scalar is called the *inner product* of the two vectors involved; it can be interpreted as the matric product of a 1-by-$m$ matrix and an $m$-by-1 matrix.)

*Example* 2. Multiply the following matrices over the rational field:

$$A = \begin{pmatrix} 1 & 2 & -1 \\ 7 & -3 & 4 \end{pmatrix} \quad \text{and} \quad B = \begin{pmatrix} 5 & -8 \\ 9 & -10 \end{pmatrix}.$$

Since the number of columns in the left factor must equal the number of rows in the right factor, the only product which can be formed from these matrices is

$$BA = \begin{pmatrix} 5\cdot 1 - 8\cdot 7 & 5\cdot 2 + 8\cdot 3 & -5\cdot 1 - 8\cdot 4 \\ 9\cdot 1 - 10\cdot 7 & 9\cdot 2 + 10\cdot 3 & -9\cdot 1 - 10\cdot 4 \end{pmatrix},$$

$$= \begin{pmatrix} -51 & 34 & -37 \\ -63 & 48 & -49 \end{pmatrix}.$$

We loosen the ties between linear transformations and matrices somewhat, and indicate an important aspect of matric theory, by pointing out that the very nice properties of the field $F$ are not utilized in the definition of matric multiplication. In fact we need only to have the products of certain components in $A$ with certain components in $B$ defined and the sums of certain of these products defined. Thus, if $A$ and $B$ are doubly ordered sets of elements,

$$A = (a_{rs}) \quad \text{and} \quad B = (b_{rs}),$$

such that the elements

$$c_{rs} = \sum_i a_{ri}b_{is}$$

are defined, then the product $AB = (c_{rs})$ is defined.

*Example* 3. Describe the product $B_1A_1$ of the two matrices

$$A_1 = (a_1, a_2) \quad \text{and} \quad B_1 = \begin{pmatrix} b_1 \\ b_2 \end{pmatrix}$$

where

$$a_1 = \begin{pmatrix} 1 & 2 \\ 7 & -3 \end{pmatrix}, \quad a_2 = \begin{pmatrix} -1 \\ 4 \end{pmatrix}, \quad b_1 = (5, -8),$$

and

$$b_2 = (9, -10).$$

The product $B_1A_1$ is defined since the matric products $b_1a_1$, $b_1a_2$, $b_2a_1$, and $b_2a_2$ are all defined. This is basically the same arithmetic problem as Example 2 and serves to illustrate the *method of partitioned matrices* wherein "large" matrices are broken or partitioned into doubly ordered sets of "smaller" matrices.

Much of the theory of matrices over a field $F$ extends quite readily to matrices over a ring $S$ (i.e., doubly ordered sets of elements from $S$), and some portions of the theory can be extended even more. This allows some of the methods which we will discuss in the next sections and chapter to be quite useful in situations involving finite (and sometimes infinite) doubly ordered sets.

Getting back to matrices over the field $F$ we again emphasize the association between the product of matrices and the product of linear transformations.

THEOREM 12.14. *If $\mathbf{A}$ and $\mathbf{B}$ are linear transformations from $\mathbf{L}(V_n(F); V_m(F))$ and $\mathbf{L}(V_m(F); V_t(F))$, respectively, and if $A$ and $B$ are the n-by-m and m-by-t matrices associated with these mappings by fixed bases of the spaces, then the product $AB$ corresponds to the product mapping $\mathbf{AB}$.*

The preceding discussion when $n = 3$, $m = 3$, and $t = 2$ was completely indicative of the general situation. For the bases $(\mathbf{u}_1, \cdots, \mathbf{u}_n\}$ of $V_n$, $\{\mathbf{v}_1, \cdots, \mathbf{v}_m\}$ of $V_m$, and $\{\mathbf{w}_1, \cdots, \mathbf{w}_t\}$ *of* $V_t$ we have

$$\mathbf{u}_i\mathbf{A} = a_{i1}\mathbf{v}_1 + \cdots + a_{im}\mathbf{v}_m, \quad i = 1, \cdots, n,$$
$$\mathbf{v}_i\mathbf{B} = b_{i1}\mathbf{w}_1 + \cdots + b_{it}\mathbf{w}_t, \quad i = 1, \cdots, m,$$

and

$$\mathbf{u}_i\mathbf{AB} = c_{i1}\mathbf{w}_1 + \cdots + c_{it}\mathbf{w}_t, \quad i = 1, \cdots, n,$$

where

$$c_{rs} = \sum_{i=1}^{m} a_{ri}b_{is}.$$

Then

$$A = (a_{rs}), \qquad B = (b_{rs})$$

and

$$AB = (c_{rs}).$$

In fact the theorem is true since we defined the product $AB$ by working backwards from the desired conclusion.

*Example* 4. Define "product" of two elements of $C_n(F)$, using the idea of matric product and of transpose.

If $\mathbf{u} = (a_1, \cdots, a_n)$ and $\mathbf{v} = (b_1, \cdots, b_n)$, writing the elements of $C_n(F)$ as row vectors or 1-by-$n$ matrices, there are two "products" which can be defined easily. The first was mentioned earlier:

(1) $\mathbf{u} \bigcirc \mathbf{v} = \mathbf{u}\mathbf{v}^T = a_1b_1 + \cdots + a_nb_n$.
(2) $\mathbf{u} * \mathbf{v} = \mathbf{u}^T\mathbf{v}$.

The first is a mapping from $V \times V$ to $F$ (where $V$ denotes $C_n(F)$) and the second is a mapping from $V \times V$ to $F(n, n)$, the set of $n$-by-$n$ matrices over $F$. The first "product" is the *inner product* (sometimes called the *scalar* product) of two coordinate vectors. Note that the transpose of the 1-by-$n$ array $\mathbf{v} = (b_1, \cdots, b_n)$ is the $n$-by-1 array

$$\mathbf{v}^T = \begin{pmatrix} b_1 \\ \vdots \\ b_n \end{pmatrix}.$$

## Exercise 12.4

**1.** Let $A$ and $B$ be the linear transformations from $V(F) = F[\lambda]$ to $V(F)$ defined by the following and linearity:

$$\lambda^n A = \lambda^{2n}, \qquad \text{all positive } n,$$
$$\lambda^n B = (-\lambda)^n, \qquad \text{all positive } n.$$

Describe $AB$ and $BA$. Illustrate by computing the images of

$$p(\lambda) = 1 + 2\lambda + 3\lambda^2 - 4\lambda^3.$$

**2.** If $A$ and $B$ are from $L(U; V)$ and $L(V; W)$, respectively, show that $N_A$ is a subspace of the null space $N_{AB}$.

**3.** Illustrate geometrically the result of a rotation of the vector space $C_2(Re)$ through an angle of 30 degrees followed by a dilation of 2 (i.e., a doubling in length).

**4.** Write out the matrices associated with the linear transformations of Problem 3, and check the appropriate matric product.

**5.** What happens to the composite linear transformation of Problem 3 when the order in which the transformations are made is reversed? How do $AB$ and $BA$ from Problem 1 compare?

**6.** If $B$ is the linear transformation of Problem 1, describe $B^2 = BB$, $B^3 = BB^2$, and $B^4 = BB^3$.

**7.** If $A$ is the rotation of Problem 3 describe the linear transformation $A^{13}$.

**8.** Compute all of the "products" described in Example 4 when **u** and **v** are selected in all possible ways from the canonical basis vectors of $C_3(R)$.

**9.** Compute $AB$, $A^2$, and $A^3$ for the following matrices over $R$:

$$A = \begin{pmatrix} 0 & 1 & 0 \\ 0 & 0 & 1 \\ 1 & 0 & 0 \end{pmatrix} \quad \text{and} \quad B = \begin{pmatrix} 1 & 2 \\ 3 & 4 \\ 5 & 6 \end{pmatrix}.$$

**10.** Compute $BB^T$ and $AA^T$ for the matrices of Problem 9.

**11.** Work Problems 9 and 10 with the elements of the matrices interpreted as being in $J/(7)$; in $J/(8)$.

**12.** Calculate the number of arithmetical computations necessary to multiply two $n$-by-$n$ matrices over $F$ together.

**13.** Describe how the method of partitioning matrices into matrices whose components are smaller matrices can be used to enable a computing machine of relatively small storage capacity to multiply two large matrices. (The products of the smaller matrices could be stored on tape or cards and then fed back into the machine at the appropriate time.)

**14.** Form two 2-by-2 matrices $A$ and $B$ whose components are 2-by-2 matrices over $R$. Compute the product $AB$ in two ways.

**15.** Write out matrices describing Example 1.

**16.** Let $C$ be the linear transformation from $V(R) = R[\lambda]$ to $V(R)$ defined by linearity and the following

$$\lambda^n C = \lambda^{n+1} + (-\lambda)^{n+1}, \qquad n = 1, 2, \cdots.$$

Show that $C^2$ is a linear functional, mapping $R[\lambda]$ onto $R$.

**17.** Determine all 2-by-2 matrices $B$ over $R$ such that

$$AB = BA \qquad \text{when} \qquad A = \begin{pmatrix} 1 & 2 \\ 0 & 2 \end{pmatrix}.$$

**18.** Determine $a$ and $b$ in $R$ such that

$$A^2 = A \qquad \text{when} \qquad A = \begin{pmatrix} 2 & a \\ 2 & b \end{pmatrix}.$$

**19.** The infinite collection of polynomials $1, \lambda, \lambda^2, \lambda^3, \lambda^4, \cdots$, of $R[\lambda]$ form a basis for $R[\lambda]$ as an $R$-space since it has no linearly dependent finite subset. Describe "infinite dimensional" matrices which reflect the effects of linear transformations $\mathbf{A}$ and $\mathbf{B}$ from problem 1 and $\mathbf{C}$ from Problem 16.

**20.** Define the products of the matrices in Problem 19 as a generalization of the regular matric multiplication. Illustrate by carrying out the multiplications. What would be the difficulty in handling such matrices in general?

## 12.5 Rings of Linear Transformations and of Matrices

The composition of linear transformations discussed previously is not in general a binary operation on $\mathbf{L}(V(F); W(F))$. If $\mathbf{A}$ and $\mathbf{B}$ are elements from $\mathbf{L}(V; W)$, then the product $\mathbf{AB}$ is defined if and only if the image space $V\mathbf{A}$ is a subspace of $V$. For the image

$$\mathbf{v}\mathbf{AB} = (\mathbf{v}\mathbf{A})\mathbf{B}, \qquad \mathbf{v} \text{ in } V,$$

is defined if and only if $V\mathbf{A}$ is a subspace of $V$. Thus if we wish to study an algebraic system whose elements are linear transformations and which has the binary operation suggested by function composition, then we must look to the set $\mathbf{L}(V; V)$. Hereafter the set $\mathbf{L}(V(F); V(F))$ of all linear transformations from $V(F)$ to $V(F)$ is denoted by $\mathbf{L}(V(F))$, the *set of linear transformations on* $V(F)$.

THEOREM 12.15. *The system consisting of* $\mathbf{L}(V(F))$ *and the binary operations of addition and multiplication defined by the images*

$$\mathbf{v}(\mathbf{A} + \mathbf{B}) = \mathbf{v}\mathbf{A} + \mathbf{v}\mathbf{B} \qquad \text{and} \qquad \mathbf{v}(\mathbf{AB}) = (\mathbf{v}\mathbf{A})\mathbf{B},$$

*for all* $\mathbf{v}$ *in* $V$ *and* $\mathbf{A}$ *and* $\mathbf{B}$ *in* $\mathbf{L}(V(F))$, *is a ring with identity.*

This ring, denoted by $\mathbf{L}(V)$ or $\mathbf{L}(V(F))$, is the *ring of linear transformations* on $V(F)$. To show that it is a ring we note first that we have proved already that $(\mathbf{L}(V), +)$ is an Abelian group. Thus we need only to check the multiplication.

(1) Multiplication is associative. If $\mathbf{A}$, $\mathbf{B}$, and $\mathbf{C}$ are in $\mathbf{L}(V)$, then

$$\mathbf{v}(\mathbf{A}(\mathbf{BC})) = (\mathbf{v}\mathbf{A})(\mathbf{BC}) = ((\mathbf{v}\mathbf{A})\mathbf{B})\mathbf{C}$$

and

$$\mathbf{v}((\mathbf{AB})\mathbf{C}) = (\mathbf{v}\mathbf{AB})\mathbf{C} = ((\mathbf{v}\mathbf{A})\mathbf{B})\mathbf{C},$$

so that

$$\mathbf{v}(A(BC)) = \mathbf{v}((AB)C)$$

for every $\mathbf{v}$ in $V$. Since the images determine the mapping we conclude that

$$A(BC) = (AB)C.$$

(2) Multiplication is distributive over addition. If $\boldsymbol{A}$, $\boldsymbol{B}$, and $\boldsymbol{C}$ are in $\boldsymbol{L}(V)$, then

$$\begin{aligned} \mathbf{v}(A(B + C)) &= (\mathbf{v}A)(B + C), \\ &= (\mathbf{v}A)B + (\mathbf{v}A)C = \mathbf{v}(AB) + \mathbf{v}(AC), \\ &= \mathbf{v}(AB + AC), \end{aligned}$$

for every $\mathbf{v}$ in $V$. Therefore

$$A(B + C) = AB + AC.$$

Similarly,

$$\begin{aligned} \mathbf{v}((B + C)A) &= (\mathbf{v}(B + C))A, \\ &= (\mathbf{v}B + \mathbf{v}C)A = (\mathbf{v}B)A + (\mathbf{v}C)A, \\ &= \mathbf{v}(BA) + \mathbf{v}(CA) = \mathbf{v}(BA + CA), \end{aligned}$$

for every $\mathbf{v}$ in $V$ so that

$$(B + C)A = BA + CA.$$

The identity mapping $\boldsymbol{I}$ defined by

$$\mathbf{v}I = \mathbf{v}, \qquad \text{all } \mathbf{v} \text{ in } V,$$

is in $\boldsymbol{L}(V(F))$ since

$$\begin{aligned} (a\mathbf{u} + b\mathbf{v})I &= a\mathbf{u} + b\mathbf{v}, \\ &= a(\mathbf{u}I) + b(\mathbf{v}I), \end{aligned}$$

for $a$ and $b$ in $F$ and $\mathbf{u}$ and $\mathbf{v}$ in $V(F)$. And

$$AI = IA = A$$

for $A$ in $\boldsymbol{L}(V)$ since

$$\mathbf{v}(AI) = (\mathbf{v}A)I = \mathbf{v}A$$

and

$$\mathbf{v}(IA) = (\mathbf{v}I)A = \mathbf{v}A.$$

Thus we see that $\boldsymbol{L}(V(F))$ is a ring with identity.

*Example* 1. In the ring $\boldsymbol{L}(V_2(R))$, let $\boldsymbol{A}$ and $\boldsymbol{B}$ be identified by their effect on a basis $\{\mathbf{v}_1\ \mathbf{v}_2\}$:

$$\begin{aligned} \mathbf{v}_1A &= \mathbf{v}_2 \quad \text{and} \quad \mathbf{v}_2A = \mathbf{v}_2, \\ \mathbf{v}_1B &= \mathbf{v}_1 \quad \text{and} \quad \mathbf{v}_2B = \mathbf{v}_1. \end{aligned}$$

Then the products $\boldsymbol{AB}$ and $\boldsymbol{BA}$ are identified by the images

$$\mathbf{v}_1\boldsymbol{AB} = \mathbf{v}_1 \quad \text{and} \quad \mathbf{v}_2\boldsymbol{AB} = \mathbf{v}_1,$$
$$\mathbf{v}_1\boldsymbol{BA} = \mathbf{v}_2 \quad \text{and} \quad \mathbf{v}_2\boldsymbol{BA} = \mathbf{v}_2.$$

Thus we have

$$\boldsymbol{AB} = \boldsymbol{B} \quad \text{and} \quad \boldsymbol{BA} = \boldsymbol{A},$$

so that since $\boldsymbol{A} \neq \boldsymbol{B}$ we conclude

$$\boldsymbol{AB} \neq \boldsymbol{BA}.$$

Hence the ring $\boldsymbol{L}(V_2(R))$ is noncommutative.

If we define the linear transformation $\boldsymbol{C}$ of $V_2(R)$ by

$$\mathbf{v}_1\boldsymbol{C} = \mathbf{z} \quad \text{and} \quad \mathbf{v}_2\boldsymbol{C} = \mathbf{v}_1 - \mathbf{v}_2$$

then we see that

$$\mathbf{v}_1\boldsymbol{AC} = \mathbf{v}_1 - \mathbf{v}_2 \quad \text{and} \quad \mathbf{v}_2\boldsymbol{AC} = \mathbf{v}_1 - \mathbf{v}_2$$

and

$$\mathbf{v}_1\boldsymbol{CA} = \mathbf{z} \quad \text{and} \quad \mathbf{v}_2\boldsymbol{CA} = \mathbf{z}.$$

Therefore

$$\boldsymbol{A} \neq \boldsymbol{Z}, \quad \boldsymbol{C} \neq \boldsymbol{Z}, \quad \text{and} \quad \boldsymbol{AC} \neq \boldsymbol{Z},$$

but

$$\boldsymbol{CA} = \boldsymbol{Z},$$

where $\boldsymbol{Z}$ is the zero element of $\boldsymbol{L}(V_2(R))$, so we see that this noncommutative ring has one-sided (nonzero) divisors of zero.

*Example* 2. Let $\boldsymbol{A}$ and $\boldsymbol{B}$ be elements of $\boldsymbol{L}(V_3(R))$ which, relative to the basis $\{\mathbf{v}_1, \mathbf{v}_2, \mathbf{v}_3\}$, are defined by

$$\mathbf{v}_1\boldsymbol{A} = \mathbf{v}_3, \quad \mathbf{v}_2\boldsymbol{A} = \mathbf{v}_2 + \mathbf{v}_3, \quad \text{and} \quad \mathbf{v}_3\boldsymbol{A} = \mathbf{v}_1 + \mathbf{v}_2 + \mathbf{v}_3,$$

and

$$\mathbf{v}_1\boldsymbol{B} = -\mathbf{v}_2 + \mathbf{v}_3, \quad \mathbf{v}_2\boldsymbol{B} = -\mathbf{v}_1 + \mathbf{v}_2, \quad \text{and} \quad \mathbf{v}_3\boldsymbol{B} = \mathbf{v}_1.$$

Then

$$\mathbf{v}_1\boldsymbol{AB} = \mathbf{v}_3\boldsymbol{B} = \mathbf{v}_1, \qquad \mathbf{v}_2\boldsymbol{AB} = (\mathbf{v}_2 + \mathbf{v}_3)\boldsymbol{B} = \mathbf{v}_2,$$

and

$$\mathbf{v}_3\boldsymbol{AB} = (\mathbf{v}_1 + \mathbf{v}_2 + \mathbf{v}_3)\boldsymbol{B} = -\mathbf{v}_2 + \mathbf{v}_3 - \mathbf{v}_1 + \mathbf{v}_2 = \mathbf{v}_3$$

so that

$$\boldsymbol{AB} = \boldsymbol{I}.$$

Also,

$$\mathbf{v}_1\boldsymbol{BA} = (-\mathbf{v}_2 + \mathbf{v}_3)\boldsymbol{A} = -\mathbf{v}_2 - \mathbf{v}_3 + \mathbf{v}_1 + \mathbf{v}_2 + \mathbf{v}_3 = \mathbf{v}_1,$$
$$\mathbf{v}_2\boldsymbol{BA} = (-\mathbf{v}_1 + \mathbf{v}_2)\boldsymbol{A} = -\mathbf{v}_3 + \mathbf{v}_2 + \mathbf{v}_3 = \mathbf{v}_2,$$

and

$$\mathbf{v}_3\boldsymbol{BA} = \mathbf{v}_1\boldsymbol{A} = \mathbf{v}_3$$

so that

$$\boldsymbol{BA} = \boldsymbol{I}.$$

Thus $\boldsymbol{A}$ and $\boldsymbol{B}$ have left and right inverses in the ring of linear transformations on $V_3(R)$.

These examples certainly indicate that these rings are quite a bit more complicated than any ring we have investigated heretofore. As a matter of fact these rings serve as models for the study of general abstract rings.

THEOREM 12.16. *If $A$ and $B$ are in $\mathbf{L}(V(F))$, then*

(1) $$N_A \subseteq N_{AB};$$

(2) $$VB \supseteq VAB.$$

The first statement follows from the fact that a linear transformation maps the zero vector $\mathbf{z}$ onto $\mathbf{z}$. So if $\mathbf{v}$ is in $N_A$, then (by definition of null space)

$$\mathbf{v}A = \mathbf{z} \quad \text{and} \quad \mathbf{v}AB = (\mathbf{v}A)B = \mathbf{z},$$

implying that $\mathbf{v}$ is in $N_{AB}$.

Since $VA$ is a subspace of $V$ we see from

$$\mathbf{v}AB = (\mathbf{v}A)B$$

that $(VA)B = VAB$ is a subspace of $VB$.

*Corollary* 12.16.1. If $A$ is in $\mathbf{L}(V(F))$, then

$$V \supseteq VA \supseteq VA^2 \supseteq \cdots \supseteq VA^n \supseteq \cdots.$$

This follows by induction on part (2) of Theorem 12.16.

*Example* 3. Let $V(F) = F[\lambda]$, and define $A$ by linearity and the images

$$\lambda^n A = \lambda^{2n} \qquad \text{for } n = 1, 2, \cdots.$$

Then we see that

$$V \supset VA \supset VA^2 \supset VA^3 \supset \cdots$$

is an infinite chain of proper subspaces. The elements of $VA^m$ are all of the polynomials over $F$ in $\lambda^k$, where $k = 2^m$, and for $p(\lambda) = 1 + \lambda + \lambda^2$ we have

$$\begin{aligned} p(\lambda)A &= 1 + \lambda^2 + \lambda^4, \\ p(\lambda)A^2 &= 1 + \lambda^4 + \lambda^8, \\ p(\lambda)A^3 &= 1 + \lambda^8 + \lambda^{16}, \qquad \text{etc.} \end{aligned}$$

As a consequence of Theorem 12.14 and Theorem 12.15 we know that the set $F_n$ of all $n$-by-$n$ matrices over $F$ is a ring relative to matric addition and matric multiplication. For a fixed but arbitrary basis of $V_n(F)$ the one-to-one correspondence so determined is an isomorphism from $\mathbf{L}(V_n(F))$ onto the ring $F_n$.

THEOREM 12.17. *The algebraic system consisting of $F_n$, the n-by-n matrices over the field F, and matric addition and matric multiplication, is a ring which is an isomorphic image of $\mathbf{L}(V_n(F))$.*

The ring $F_n$ is the *complete* (or *total*) *matric ring of order n* over $F$.

More generally the set $S_n$ of all $n$-by-$n$ matrices (arrays or doubly ordered sets) with components in the ring $S$ is also a ring, the *complete matric ring of order n over S*. We will not attempt to give a general proof of this fact since we will be dealing principally with matrices over fields. The following computation indicates the general procedure, however.

Let $A = (a_{rs})$, $B = (b_{rs})$, and $C = (c_{rs})$ be three elements from $S_n$. Then the element in the $(r, s)$-position of $(AB)C$ is of the form

$$\sum_{i=1}^{n}\left(\sum_{j=1}^{n} a_{rj}b_{ji}\right)c_{is},$$

and the element in the $(r, s)$-position of $A(BC)$ is of the form

$$\sum_{j=1}^{n} a_{rj}\left(\sum_{i=1}^{n} b_{ji}c_{is}\right).$$

The Distributive and Associative Laws of $S$ enable us to conclude that these two elements are equal. So we see that

$$(AB)C = A(BC)$$

in $S_n$.

THEOREM 12.18. *The set $S_n$ of all n-by-n matrices over the ring S is a ring relative to the binary operations of matric addition and matric multiplication.*

The remainder of the proof is omitted, but not because it is difficult. Rather it is one of those proofs which when given in full detail are distracting rather than convincing. The student should be able to satisfy himself of its validity without too much trouble.

THEOREM 12.19. *The ring $S_n$ has an identity element if S has an identity element.*

Denote the identity element of $S$ for addition by 0 and for multiplication by 1. Then the $n$-by-$n$ matrix

$$I_n = (c_{rs}),$$

with $c_{rs} = 1$ when $r = s$, and $c_{rs} = 0$ when $r \neq s$, is the multiplicative identity of $S_n$. For suppose $A = (a_{rs})$; then

$$AI_n = (b_{rs})$$

with $b_{rs} = a_{r1}c_{1s} + a_{r2}c_{2s} + \cdots + a_{rn}c_{ns}$, so that

$$b_{rs} = a_{rs} \qquad \text{and} \qquad AI_n = A.$$

In the same manner we show that

$$I_nA = A,$$

and therefore $I_n$ is the multiplicative identity of $S_n$.

As a matter of fact the converse of this theorem is true. Let the ring $S_n$ have the identity element $B$ such that

$$A = BA = AB \qquad \text{for each } A \text{ in } S_n.$$

Now we form a very special element $A$ of $S_n$ as follows:

$$A = (a_{rs})$$

where $a_{11}$ is an arbitrary nonzero element of $S$ and all other components of $A$ are zero. Then, writing $B = (b_{rs})$, we have upon forming $AB$ and looking at the (1, 1)-component,

$$a_{11} = a_{11}b_{11} + 0b_{21} + \cdots + 0b_{n1}.$$

Hence

$$a_{11} = a_{11}b_{11}$$

is $S$ so that $b_{11}$ is a right identity in $S$ for the arbitrary element $a_{11}$ of $S$. Forming $BA$ we see upon checking the (1, 1)-position that

$$a_{11} = b_{11}a_{11} + b_{12}0 + \cdots + b_{1n}0 = b_{11}a_{11}.$$

Hence $b_{11}$ is the multiplicative identity of $S$.

THEOREM 12.20. *If matric ring $S_n$ over the ring $S$ has a multiplicative identity, then $S$ must have a multiplicative identity.*

*Example* 4. Describe the elements of $R_2$, the ring of all 2-by-2 matrices over the rational field, which commute with every element of $R_2$.

Let $A = (a_{rs})$ be a 2-by-2 matrix which commutes with every element of $R_2$. Then $A$ commutes with the four special matrices of $R_2$, the matric units $E_{11}$. $E_{12}$, $E_{21}$, and $E_{22}$. From the equations

$$E_{11}A = \begin{pmatrix} 1 & 0 \\ 0 & 0 \end{pmatrix}\begin{pmatrix} a_{11} & a_{12} \\ a_{21} & a_{22} \end{pmatrix} = \begin{pmatrix} a_{11} & a_{12} \\ 0 & 0 \end{pmatrix} = AE_{11} = \begin{pmatrix} a_{11} & 0 \\ a_{21} & 0 \end{pmatrix}$$

we conclude that

$$a_{12} = a_{21} = 0.$$

Hence $A$ is a *diagonal* matrix of the form

$$A = \begin{pmatrix} a_{11} & 0 \\ 0 & a_{22} \end{pmatrix}$$

From the equations

$$E_{12}A = \begin{pmatrix} 0 & 1 \\ 0 & 0 \end{pmatrix}\begin{pmatrix} a_{11} & 0 \\ 0 & a_{22} \end{pmatrix} = \begin{pmatrix} 0 & a_{22} \\ 0 & 0 \end{pmatrix} = AE_{12} = \begin{pmatrix} 0 & a_{11} \\ 0 & 0 \end{pmatrix}$$

we see that

$$a_{11} = a_{22} = k.$$

Thus

$$A = \begin{pmatrix} k & 0 \\ 0 & k \end{pmatrix} = kI_2 = k(E_{11} + E_{22}).$$

Such matrices are called *scalar matrices*, and it is easily verified that the scalar matrices of $R_2$ commute with all elements of $R_2$.

## Exercise 12.5

**1.** For $V(R) = R[\lambda]$ show that the mapping $\boldsymbol{E}$ defined by linearity and

$$\lambda^n \boldsymbol{E} = (\lambda + 1)^n, \qquad n = 1, 2, \cdots,$$

is in $\boldsymbol{L}(V(R))$. Describe the linear transformations $\boldsymbol{E}^2$; $\boldsymbol{E}^m$; $\boldsymbol{E} - \boldsymbol{I}$; $\boldsymbol{E}^m - \boldsymbol{I}$; $\boldsymbol{ED}$; $\boldsymbol{DE}$. ($\boldsymbol{D}$ denotes the formal derivation mapping.)

**2.** Describe a multiplicative inverse for the linear transformation $\boldsymbol{E}$ of Problem 1. Can you define a multiplicative inverse for $\boldsymbol{D}$?

**3.** For the element $a$ of $R$ let $\boldsymbol{E}_a$ be the mapping from $V(R) = R[\lambda]$ to $V(R)$ defined by linearity and

$$\lambda^n \boldsymbol{E}_a = (\lambda - a)^n, \qquad n = 1, 2, \cdots.$$

Show that $\boldsymbol{E}_a$ lies in $\boldsymbol{L}(V)$, and compare $\boldsymbol{E}_a - \boldsymbol{I}$ with $a\boldsymbol{D}$.

**4.** For the elements $A$ and $B$ of $R_3$,

$$A = \begin{pmatrix} 2 & 0 & -1 \\ -2 & 1 & 1 \\ 1 & 5 & 2 \end{pmatrix} \quad \text{and} \quad B = \begin{pmatrix} -1 & -1 & 2 \\ 2 & 1 & 4 \\ 3 & 0 & 1 \end{pmatrix},$$

compute $A^2 + A - I_2$; $AB$; $BA$; and $B^2$.

**5.** Write out a matric description of Example 1.

**6.** Write out a matric description of Example 2.

**7.** For the following 2-by-2 matrices with components in $J$ check the Distributive and Associative Laws:

$$A = \begin{pmatrix} 2 & 0 \\ -2 & 1 \end{pmatrix}, \quad B = \begin{pmatrix} 1 & 1 \\ 5 & 2 \end{pmatrix}, \quad \text{and} \quad C = \begin{pmatrix} 1 & 4 \\ 0 & -1 \end{pmatrix}.$$

**8.** Using the canonical basis for $C_2(Re)$ write out the matric description of the following linear transformations: $\boldsymbol{A}$, a rotation about the origin through an angle whose measure is $a$; $\boldsymbol{B}$, a rotation through an angle $b$; and $\boldsymbol{AB}$. Let $A$ and $B$ be the matrices corresponding to $\boldsymbol{A}$ and $\boldsymbol{B}$. How does the product $AB$ compare with the matrix of $\boldsymbol{AB}$?

**9.** Show that the collection of all 2-by-2 matrices of the form

$$\begin{pmatrix} \cos a & -\sin a \\ \sin a & \cos a \end{pmatrix}, \qquad a \text{ in } Re,$$

is a group relative to matric multiplication. (See Problem 8.)

**10.** Prove that the scalar matrices of $F_n$ form a subring of $F_n$ which is isomorphic with $F$. Is a similar result true for $S_n$?

**11.** Show that the product of two diagonal matrices from $R_3$ is also diagonal. Is this true in general?

**12.** Establish an isomorphism between $R_4$ and $S_2$ when $S = R_2$. Illustrate.

**13.** For the matrices $A$ and $B$ of Problem 7 compute $A^T B^T$ and compare with $(AB)^T$ and $(BA)^T$, where $A^T$ is the transpose of $A$ as defined in Chapter 11. What do you conjecture? Test your conjecture on the matrices of Problem 4.

**14.** Let $A$ and $B$ be elements of $F_n$ and define a new "product" of $A$ and $B$ by

$$A \bigcirc B = AB^T.$$

Describe in terms of the rows of $A$ and the rows of $B$. Show by example that this binary operation on $F_n$ is not in general associative. (See Problem 13.)

**15.** Let $V_4(R)$ be the vector space over $R$ of all polynomials over $R$ of degree less than 4 or of no degree. Describe by a matrix $D$ the formal derivative $\mathbf{D}$ and show that $D^4 = Z$, where $Z$ is the zero matrix (i.e., all components are zero).

**16.** Show that $C(A)$, the set of all elements $\mathbf{B}$ of $\mathbf{L}(V(F))$ such that $\mathbf{AB} = \mathbf{BA}$, is a subring of $\mathbf{L}(V(F))$. $C(A)$ is called the *centralizer* of $\mathbf{A}$.

**17.** Find the centralizer of the following element $A$ of $F_3$ when $F = J/(5)$:

$$A = \begin{pmatrix} 1 & 0 & 0 \\ 0 & 2 & 0 \\ 0 & 0 & 3 \end{pmatrix}.$$

(See Example 4 and Problem 16.)

**18.** Show that the mapping $\mathbf{K}$ from the complex field onto a subring of 2-by-2 matrices over the real field given by

$$\mathbf{K}: a + bi \rightarrow \begin{pmatrix} a & 0 \\ 0 & a \end{pmatrix} + \begin{pmatrix} 0 & -b \\ b & 0 \end{pmatrix},$$

$a$ and $b$ in $Re$, is an isomorphism.

**19.** Calculate $AB$ and $BA$ when $A$ and $B$ are the following 2-by-2 matrices over $R[\lambda]$:

$$A = \begin{pmatrix} \lambda & \lambda^2 + 1 \\ -2 & 7\lambda \end{pmatrix} \quad \text{and} \quad B = \begin{pmatrix} \lambda & -2 \\ \lambda^2 & -2\lambda \end{pmatrix}.$$

**20.** Let $\mathbf{A}$, $\mathbf{B}$, and $\mathbf{C}$ be mappings from $V(F)$ to $V(F)$. Using the definitions of addition and multiplication for $\mathbf{L}(V(F))$ show that: (1) $\mathbf{A}(\mathbf{B} + \mathbf{C}) = \mathbf{AB} + \mathbf{AC}$; (2) $(\mathbf{B} + \mathbf{C})\mathbf{A}$ does not in general equal $\mathbf{BA} + \mathbf{CA}$ unless $\mathbf{A}$ is a linear transformation. (See the article, "Near-rings," by Berman and Silverman.)

## 12.6 Nonsingular Matrices

Let $\mathbf{A}$ be an element of $\mathbf{L}(V_n(F))$. Then from Theorem 12.3 we know that $\mathbf{A}$ is an isomorphism from $V_n$ onto $V_n$ (an automorphism of $V_n$) if and only if the null space of $\mathbf{A}$ is the zero space of $V_n$. In that case the rank of $\mathbf{A}$ or the dimension of $V_n\mathbf{A}$ is also $n$ and the row space of a matrix representing $\mathbf{A}$ relative to a particular basis of $V_n$ is the coordinate space $C_n(F)$.

THEOREM 12.21. *If the element* $\mathbf{A}$ *of* $\mathbf{L}(V_n(F))$ *has the zero subspace of* $V_n(F)$ *as its null space, then* $\mathbf{L}(V_n(F))$ *contains an element* $\mathbf{B}$ *such that* $\mathbf{AB} = \mathbf{I}$.

Let $\mathbf{v}_1, \cdots, \mathbf{v}_n$ form a basis for $V_n(F)$. Then the $n$ images $\mathbf{v}_1\mathbf{A}, \cdots, \mathbf{v}_n\mathbf{A}$ form a basis for $V_n(F)$ also. For, if

$$a_1(\mathbf{v}_1\mathbf{A}) + \cdots + a_n(\mathbf{v}_n\mathbf{A}) = \mathbf{z},$$

then

$$(a_1\mathbf{v}_1 + \cdots + a_n\mathbf{v}_n)\mathbf{A} = \mathbf{z},$$

implying that

$$a_1\mathbf{v}_1 + \cdots + a_n\mathbf{v}_n = \mathbf{z}$$

since the null space of $\boldsymbol{A}$ is $(\mathbf{z})$. From the linear independence of the $\mathbf{v}_i$ we conclude that

$$a_1 \cdots = a_n = 0$$

so that the vectors $\mathbf{v}_1\boldsymbol{A}, \cdots, \mathbf{v}_n\boldsymbol{A}$ are linearly independent. Now we define a linear transformation $\boldsymbol{B}$ on $V_n(F)$ by using these two bases and linearity:

$$(\mathbf{v}_1\boldsymbol{A})\boldsymbol{B} = \mathbf{v}_1, \cdots, (\mathbf{v}_n\boldsymbol{A})\boldsymbol{B} = \mathbf{v}_n.$$

From the equations

$$\begin{aligned}(b_1\mathbf{v}_1 + \cdots + b_n\mathbf{v}_n)\boldsymbol{AB} &= (b_1\mathbf{v}_1\boldsymbol{A} + \cdots + b_n\mathbf{v}_n\boldsymbol{A})\boldsymbol{B},\\ &= b_1\mathbf{v}_1 + \cdots + b_n\mathbf{v}_n,\end{aligned}$$

we conclude that

$$\boldsymbol{AB} = \boldsymbol{I}.$$

*Corollary* 12.21.1. The rank of $\boldsymbol{B}$ equals the rank of $\boldsymbol{A}$ which equals $n$.

This is a restatement of the fact that both $\boldsymbol{A}$ and $\boldsymbol{B}$ map a basis for $V_n(F)$ onto a basis for $V_n(F)$.

*Corollary* 12.21.2. The null space of $\boldsymbol{B}$ is the zero subspace $(\mathbf{z})$ of $V_n(F)$.

Let $\mathbf{v}$ belong to the null space of $\boldsymbol{B}$. Since $\mathbf{v}_1\boldsymbol{A}, \cdots, \mathbf{v}_n\boldsymbol{A}$ form a basis for $V_n$ there are scalars $b_1, \cdots, b_n$ such that

$$\mathbf{v} = b_1(\mathbf{v}_1\boldsymbol{A}) + \cdots + b_n(\mathbf{v}_n\boldsymbol{A}).$$

Then

$$\mathbf{v}\boldsymbol{A} = \mathbf{z}$$

implies that

$$(b_1\mathbf{v}_1\boldsymbol{A} + \cdots + b_n\mathbf{v}_n\boldsymbol{A})\boldsymbol{B} = b_1\mathbf{v}_1 + \cdots + b_n\mathbf{v}_n = \mathbf{z},$$

and since the $\mathbf{v}_i$ are linearly independent,

$$b_1 = \cdots = b_n = 0.$$

Hence

$$\mathbf{v} = 0(\mathbf{v}_1\boldsymbol{A}) + \cdots + 0(\mathbf{v}_n\boldsymbol{A}) = \mathbf{z}.$$

From the corollaries we see that Theorem 12.21 can also be applied to $\boldsymbol{B}$, so that $\boldsymbol{L}(V_n(F))$ contains an element $\boldsymbol{C}$ such that

$$\boldsymbol{BC} = \boldsymbol{I}.$$

Therefore, from the Associative Law,

$$\boldsymbol{A}(\boldsymbol{BC}) = (\boldsymbol{AB})\boldsymbol{C}$$

and

$$\boldsymbol{A} = \boldsymbol{AI} = \boldsymbol{A}(\boldsymbol{BC}) = (\boldsymbol{AB})\boldsymbol{C} = \boldsymbol{IC} = \boldsymbol{C}.$$

*Corollary* 12.21.3. An element $\boldsymbol{A}$ of $\boldsymbol{L}(V_n(F))$ of rank $n$ has a (two-sided) inverse $\boldsymbol{B}$ in $\boldsymbol{L}(V_n(F))$,

$$\boldsymbol{AB} = \boldsymbol{BA} = \boldsymbol{I}.$$

Now we switch over and consider the matric ring $F_n$.

DEFINITION 12.4. An element $A$ from $F_n$ is *nonsingular* if and only if $F_n$ contains an element $B$ such that

$$AB = BA = I_n.$$

The element $B$ is called the *inverse* of $A$, and we write $B = A^{-1}$.

We know from our knowledge of rings that when an element of a ring possesses a multiplicative inverse, then that inverse is unique. Thus we speak of *the* inverse.

Since our definition above is quite obviously drawn from the discussion of linear transformations we can write the last corollary in terms of matrices.

*Corollary* 12.21.4. The matrix $A$ of $F_n$ which corresponds to the element $\boldsymbol{A}$ from $\boldsymbol{L}(V_n(F))$, relative to a certain basis for $V_n(F)$, is nonsingular if $\boldsymbol{A}$ has rank $n$.

For if $\boldsymbol{A}$ has rank $n$, then $\boldsymbol{B}$ exists such that

$$\boldsymbol{AB} = \boldsymbol{BA} = \boldsymbol{I}.$$

Using the isomorphism between $F_n$ and $\boldsymbol{L}(V_n(F))$ determined by an arbitrary basis of $V_n(F)$ we see that the matrix $B$ which corresponds to $\boldsymbol{B}$ is such that

$$AB = BA = I_n,$$

$I_n$ being the diagonal matrix of 1's which corresponds to $\boldsymbol{I}$. Thus $A$ is nonsingular.

We can use the close relationship between $F_n$ and $\boldsymbol{L}(V_n(F))$ to characterize nonsingularity in terms of the rank of a matrix.

THEOREM 12.22. *The matrix $A$ of $F_n$ is nonsingular if and only if it has rank $n$.*

If $A$ has rank $n$, then its row space is precisely $C_n(F)$. Selecting an arbitrary basis for $V_n(F)$ of vectors $\mathbf{v}_1, \cdots, \mathbf{v}_n$ we define a linear transformation $\boldsymbol{A}$ on $V_n(F)$ by using the rows of $A$:

$$\mathbf{v}_i\boldsymbol{A} = a_{i1}\mathbf{v}_1 + \cdots + a_{in}\mathbf{v}_n, \qquad i = 1, \cdots, n.$$

Then $A$ is the matrix of $\boldsymbol{A}$, and by Corollary 12.8.1 the dimension of $V_n\boldsymbol{A}$ equals the dimension of $C_n(F)$, the row space of $A$, which is $n$. Hence

$$V_n\boldsymbol{A} = V_n$$

so that $\boldsymbol{A}$ has rank $n$. By Corollary 12.21.4 we see that $A$ is nonsingular.

Conversely, suppose $A$ is nonsingular. Then it has an inverse $B$ such that

$$AB = BA = I_n.$$

If $A = (a_{rs})$, $B = (b_{rs})$, and the vectors $\mathbf{v}_1, \cdots, \mathbf{v}_n$ form a basis for $V_n(F)$, then we define linear transformations $\boldsymbol{A}$ and $\boldsymbol{B}$ by

$$\mathbf{v}_i\boldsymbol{A} = a_{i1}\mathbf{v}_1 + \cdots + a_{in}\mathbf{v}_n, \qquad i = 1, \cdots, n,$$

and

$$\mathbf{v}_i\boldsymbol{B} = b_{i1}\mathbf{v}_1 + \cdots + b_{in}\mathbf{v}_n, \qquad i = 1, \cdots, n.$$

Since

$$AB = I_n$$

we have from the isomorphism between $F_n$ and $\boldsymbol{L}(V_n(F))$,

$$\boldsymbol{AB} = \boldsymbol{I}.$$

Therefore

$$\mathbf{v}_i(\boldsymbol{AB}) = (\mathbf{v}_i\boldsymbol{A})\boldsymbol{B} = \mathbf{v}_i$$

for $i = 1, \cdots, n$, and from this we see that

$$V_n\boldsymbol{A} = V_n.$$

For, if

$$c_1(\mathbf{v}_1\boldsymbol{A}) + \cdots + c_n(\mathbf{v}_n\boldsymbol{A}) = \mathbf{z}$$

in $V_n\boldsymbol{A}$, then applying $\boldsymbol{B}$ to this yields

$$(c_1\mathbf{v}_1\boldsymbol{A} + \cdots + c_n\mathbf{v}_n\boldsymbol{A})\boldsymbol{B} = \mathbf{z}\boldsymbol{B} = \mathbf{z}$$

or

$$c_1\mathbf{v}_1 + \cdots + c_n\mathbf{v}_n = \mathbf{z}.$$

Thus

$$c_1 = \cdots = c_n = 0,$$

the $n$ vectors

$$\mathbf{v}_1\boldsymbol{A}, \cdots, \mathbf{v}_n\boldsymbol{A}$$

are linearly independent, and $\dim(V_n\boldsymbol{A}) = n$. Then from Corollary 12.8.1 we conclude that the rank of the matrix $A$ is $n$.

*Corollary* 12.22.1. The inverse of a matrix $A$ of $F_n$ is nonsingular and of rank $n$.

If $B$ is the inverse of $A$ then the equation

$$AB = BA = I_n$$

shows that $A$ is the inverse of $B$. Thus $B$ is nonsingular and of rank $n$.

This characterization of the concept of nonsingularity or invertibility in terms of rank enables us to use the methods from the previous chapter to determine whether or not an element $A$ of $F_n$ has an inverse.

*Example* 1. Determine whether the following element of $R_3$ has an inverse:

$$A = \begin{pmatrix} -1 & -1 & 2 \\ 2 & 1 & 4 \\ 3 & 0 & 1 \end{pmatrix}.$$

Using elementary row operations we change the array to its reduced row echelon form, viz.,

$$\begin{pmatrix} 1 & 0 & 0 \\ 0 & 1 & 0 \\ 0 & 0 & 1 \end{pmatrix}.$$

Hence $A$ is of rank 3 and so has an inverse.

In the next chapter we shall develop a simple program for finding the inverse by using these same elementary row operations.

*Example* 2. Find the inverse of the following element from $R_2$:

$$A = \begin{pmatrix} 1 & 2 \\ 1 & -1 \end{pmatrix}.$$

Obviously the rank of this matrix is 2, so we write

$$B = \begin{pmatrix} a & b \\ c & d \end{pmatrix}$$

and

$$AB = \begin{pmatrix} a + 2c & b + 2d \\ a - c & b - d \end{pmatrix} = \begin{pmatrix} 1 & 0 \\ 0 & 1 \end{pmatrix} = I_2.$$

Then checking the components of these matrices we get the following four equations:

$$\begin{aligned} a + 2c &= 1, \\ b + 2d &= 0, \\ a - c &= 0, \\ b - d &= 1. \end{aligned}$$

Solving these yields $a = \frac{1}{3}$, $b = \frac{2}{3}$, $c = \frac{1}{3}$, and $d = -\frac{1}{3}$. We check these calculations by evaluating $BA$:

$$\begin{pmatrix} \frac{1}{3} & \frac{2}{3} \\ \frac{1}{3} & -\frac{1}{3} \end{pmatrix} \begin{pmatrix} 1 & 2 \\ 1 & -1 \end{pmatrix} = \begin{pmatrix} 1 & 0 \\ 0 & 1 \end{pmatrix}.$$

## Exercise 12.6

**1.** Describe the linear transformation $\boldsymbol{B}$ on $C_2(Re)$ such that $\boldsymbol{AB} = \boldsymbol{I}$ when:

(i) $\boldsymbol{A}$ sends $(a_1, a_2)$ onto $(a_1, a_2)\boldsymbol{A} = (a_1 \cos b - a_2 \sin b, a_1 \sin b + a_2 \cos b)$.
(ii) $\boldsymbol{A}$ sends $(a_1, a_2)$ onto $(a_1, a_2)\boldsymbol{A} = (aa_1, aa_2)$, $a \neq 0$.
(iii) $\boldsymbol{A}$ sends $(a_1, a_2)$ onto $(a_1, a_2)\boldsymbol{A} = (a(a_1 \cos b - a_2 \sin b),$
$a(a_1, \sin b + a_2 \cos b))$, $a \neq 0$.

**2.** Describe the transformations of Problem 1 by matrices $A$ and $B$, relative to the canonical basis of $C_2(Re)$, and check that $AB = BA = I_2$.

**3.** Determine the matrices $A$ and $B$ of $\boldsymbol{A}$ and $\boldsymbol{B}$ in Problem 1(iii) relative to the basis $\mathbf{v}_1 = (1, 1)$ and $\mathbf{v}_2 = (-1, 1)$ when $b$ is 30 degrees and $a = 2$. Compute $AB$ and $BA$. Illustrate geometrically.

**4.** Determine the rank of the element $A$ of $L(V_3(R))$ if the images of the basis vectors $\mathbf{v}_1$, $\mathbf{v}_2$, $\mathbf{v}_3$ of $V_3(R)$ are

$$\mathbf{v}_1A = 3\mathbf{v}_1 + 2\mathbf{v}_2 - \mathbf{v}_3,$$
$$\mathbf{v}_2A = -2\mathbf{v}_1 + 5\mathbf{v}_2 + 3\mathbf{v}_3,$$

and

$$\mathbf{v}_3A = \mathbf{v}_1 + 7\mathbf{v}_2 + 2\mathbf{v}_3.$$

(Check the matrix of $A$.)

**5.** Decide whether the following element of $R_3$ is nonsingular:

$$A = \begin{pmatrix} -3 & -2 & 1 \\ 7 & 11 & 0 \\ 4 & 9 & 1 \end{pmatrix}.$$

**6.** If $A$ is a linear transformation on $V_4(R)$ of rank 4, if $\mathbf{v}_1$, $\mathbf{v}_2$, $\mathbf{v}_3$, and $\mathbf{v}_4$ form a basis for $V_4$, and if

$$\mathbf{v}_1A = 10\mathbf{v}_1 + 2\mathbf{v}_2 - 2\mathbf{v}_3 + 2\mathbf{v}_4,$$
$$\mathbf{v}_2A = 7\mathbf{v}_1 + 2\mathbf{v}_2 - \mathbf{v}_3 + \mathbf{v}_4,$$

and

$$\mathbf{v}_3A = -4\mathbf{v}_1 + 4\mathbf{v}_2 + 4\mathbf{v}_3 - 4\mathbf{v}_4,$$

then find a possible description of $\mathbf{v}_4A$.

**7.** Find the inverse of the following element of $R_2$:

$$A = \begin{pmatrix} 1 & 2 \\ 3 & -1 \end{pmatrix}.$$

**8.** Consider the matrix of Problem 7 over $J/(5)$ and find its inverse.

**9.** Find the inverse over $R$ of the matrix

$$B = \begin{pmatrix} 1 & 1 & 1 \\ 0 & 1 & 1 \\ 0 & 0 & 1 \end{pmatrix}.$$

**10.** Let $A$ and $B$ be two nonsingular elements of $F_n$. Show that $AB$ is nonsingular by computing the products $(AB)(B^{-1}A^{-1})$ and $(B^{-1}A^{-1})(AB)$. What kind of system does the set of nonsingular matrices from $F_n$ and matric multiplication form?

**11.** Show that $(AB)^{-1} = B^{-1}A^{-1}$. (See Problem 10.)

**12.** Let $A$ be the linear transformation on $V(F) = F[\lambda]$ defined by linearity and the images

$$\lambda^n A = \lambda^{2n}, \qquad n = 1, 2, \cdots.$$

Show that the null space of $A$ is the zero subspace of $V$ but that $VA \neq V$. What prevents this from happening in finite dimensional cases?

## 12.7 Change of Basis

From our discussion of an element $A$ of $L(V_n(F))$ of rank $n$ we know that the $n$ vectors $\mathbf{v}_1A, \cdots, v_nA$ of $V_n$ form a basis whenever the vectors $\mathbf{v}_1, \cdots, \mathbf{v}_n$ form a basis for $V_n$. Thus the application of $A$ to $V_n$ can be viewed as a change of basis for $V_n$. Conversely, if the $n$ vectors $\mathbf{v}_1, \cdots, \mathbf{v}_n$ and the $n$ vectors $\mathbf{w}_1, \cdots, \mathbf{w}_n$ form bases for $V_n(F)$, then the linear transformation $\boldsymbol{C}$ on $V_n(F)$ defined by linearity and the images

$$\mathbf{v}_i\boldsymbol{C} = \mathbf{w}_i, \qquad i = 1, \cdots, n,$$

is clearly of rank $n$ since $V_n\boldsymbol{C} = V_n$. This means that we can speak interchangeably of changing a basis of $V_n(F)$ and applying an element of rank $n$ from $\boldsymbol{L}(V_n(F))$ to $V_n(F)$.

Throughout this chapter we have made considerable use of the isomorphism between $F_n$ and $\boldsymbol{L}(V_n(F))$ which is established through an arbitrary basis $\{\mathbf{v}_1, \cdots, \mathbf{v}_n\}$ for $V_n(F)$. What happens to this correspondence when another basis for $V_n(F)$ is selected? In other words, if the matrix $A$ corresponds to the linear transformation $\boldsymbol{A}$ relative to the basis $\{\mathbf{v}_1, \cdots, \mathbf{v}_n\}$ and the matrix $A_1$ corresponds to $\boldsymbol{A}$ relative to the basis $\{\mathbf{w}_1, \cdots, \mathbf{w}_n\}$ of $V_n(F)$, how are the two matrices $A$ and $A_1$ related? Well, we know that changing the basis corresponds to applying a linear transformation $\boldsymbol{C}$ of rank $n$ to $V_n(F)$, where $\boldsymbol{C}$ is defined by

$$\mathbf{v}_i\boldsymbol{C} = \mathbf{w}_i, \qquad i = 1, \cdots, n.$$

Furthermore, with the two bases for $V_n(F)$ we can associate a third matrix $D$ with $\boldsymbol{A}$, where $D$ describes the mapping $\boldsymbol{A}$ from space $V_n$ with basis $\{\mathbf{w}_1, \cdots, \mathbf{w}_n\}$ to space $V_n$ with basis $\{\mathbf{v}_1, \cdots, \mathbf{v}_n\}$. We shall compute $D$ in two different ways.

From

$$\begin{aligned} \mathbf{v}_i\boldsymbol{A} &= a_{i1}\mathbf{v}_1 + \cdots + a_{in}\mathbf{v}_n, && i = 1, \cdots, n, \\ \mathbf{w}_i\boldsymbol{A} &= b_{i1}\mathbf{w}_1 + \cdots + b_{in}\mathbf{w}_n, && i = 1, \cdots, n, \\ \mathbf{v}_i\boldsymbol{C} &= \mathbf{w}_i = c_{i1}\mathbf{v}_1 + \cdots + c_{in}\mathbf{v}_n, && i = 1, \cdots, n, \end{aligned}$$

and

$$\mathbf{w}_i\boldsymbol{A} = d_{i1}\mathbf{v}_1 + \cdots + d_{in}\mathbf{v}_n, \qquad i = 1, \cdots, n,$$

we see that

$$A = (a_{rs}), \qquad A_1 = (b_{rs}), \qquad C = (c_{rs}),$$

and

$$D = (d_{rs}).$$

Then the image $\mathbf{w}_i\boldsymbol{A}$ of $\mathbf{w}_i$ can be obtained in two different ways in terms of the $\mathbf{v}_i$ by using $\boldsymbol{A}$ and $\boldsymbol{C}$:

*Method* 1. Replace $\mathbf{w}_i$ by $\mathbf{v}_i\boldsymbol{C}$. Then

$$\begin{aligned} \mathbf{w}_i\boldsymbol{A} &= (\mathbf{v}_i\boldsymbol{C})\boldsymbol{A} = (c_{i1}\mathbf{v}_1 + \cdots + c_{in}\mathbf{v}_n)\boldsymbol{A}, \\ &= \sum_{j=1}^{n} c_{ij}(\mathbf{v}_j\boldsymbol{A}), \\ &= \sum_{j=1}^{n} c_{ij} \sum_{k=1}^{n} a_{jk}\mathbf{v}_k. \end{aligned}$$

Thus $\mathbf{w}_i A$ is expressible in terms of the $\mathbf{v}$'s as

$$\mathbf{w}_i A = \left(\sum_{j=1}^{n} c_{ij}a_{j1}\right)\mathbf{v}_1 + \cdots + \left(\sum_{j=1}^{n} c_{ij}a_{jn}\right)\mathbf{v}_n.$$

*Method* 2. This time we find $\mathbf{w}_i A$ in terms of the $\mathbf{w}$'s first, and then express the $\mathbf{w}$'s in terms of the $\mathbf{v}$'s. So

$$\begin{aligned}\mathbf{w}_i A &= b_{i1}\mathbf{w}_1 + \cdots + b_{in}\mathbf{w}_n,\\ &= b_{i1}\left(\sum_{k=1}^{n} c_{1k}\mathbf{v}_k\right) + \cdots + b_{in}\left(\sum_{k=1}^{n} c_{nk}\mathbf{v}_k\right)\end{aligned}$$

when the $\mathbf{w}$'s are expressed in terms of the $\mathbf{v}$'s. Rearranging these terms to find the coefficients of the $\mathbf{v}$'s we have

$$\mathbf{w}_i A = \left(\sum_{j=1}^{n} b_{ij}c_{j1}\right)\mathbf{v}_1 + \cdots + \left(\sum_{j=1}^{n} b_{ij}c_{jn}\right)\mathbf{v}_n.$$

Comparing these two expressions for the images of the $\mathbf{w}$'s under $A$ we conclude from the uniqueness of the matrix $D$ (relative to the particular bases) that

$$d_{rs} = \sum_{j=1}^{n} c_{rj}a_{js} = \sum_{j=1}^{n} b_{rj}c_{js}.$$

Looking at the definition of matric multiplication we see that this equation implies

$$D = CA = A_1C,$$

or, since $C$ is nonsingular,

$$A_1 = CAC^{-1}.$$

This proves the next statement.

THEOREM 12.23. *If $A$ and $A_1$ are the matrices which correspond to the element $A$ of $\mathbf{L}(V_n(F))$ relative to the bases $\{\mathbf{v}_1, \cdots, \mathbf{v}_n\}$ and $\{\mathbf{w}_1, \cdots, \mathbf{w}_n\}$, respectively, of $V_n(F)$, then there exists a nonsingular matrix $C$ in $F_n$ such that*

$$A_1 = CAC^{-1}.$$

*Moreover $C$ is the matrix, relative to the $\mathbf{v}$'s, of the linear transformation $\mathbf{C}$ defined by $\mathbf{v}_i\mathbf{C} = \mathbf{w}_i$ for $i = 1, \cdots, n$.*

Now we shall illustrate our proof with an example.

*Example* 1. Let $A$ be the linear transformation on the real plane which can be described as the projection on the $x$-axis. Then the point $(a_1, a_2)$ maps onto $(a_1, 0)$ and

$$(a_1, a_2)A = (a_1, 0).$$

Relative to the canonical basis of $C_2(Re)$ the element $A$ corresponds to the matrix

$$A = \begin{pmatrix} 1 & 0 \\ 0 & 0 \end{pmatrix}$$

since

$$\mathbf{e}_1A = (1, 0)A = (1, 0) = 1\mathbf{e}_1 + 0\mathbf{e}_2$$

and

$$\mathbf{e}_2A = (0, 1)A = (0, 0) = 0\mathbf{e}_1 + 0\mathbf{e}_2.$$

Relative to the basis $\mathbf{w}_1 = (1, 1)$ and $\mathbf{w}_2 = (-1, 1)$ the linear transformation $\mathbf{A}$ is described by the matrix

$$A_1 = \begin{pmatrix} \tfrac{1}{2} & -\tfrac{1}{2} \\ -\tfrac{1}{2} & \tfrac{1}{2} \end{pmatrix}$$

since

$$\mathbf{w}_1A = (1, 0) = (\tfrac{1}{2})\mathbf{w}_1 = (\tfrac{1}{2})\mathbf{w}_2$$

and

$$\mathbf{w}_2A = (-1, 0) = (-\tfrac{1}{2})\mathbf{w}_1 + (\tfrac{1}{2})\mathbf{w}_2.$$

Now the matrix $C$ of the theorem is the matrix, relative to the canonical basis, of the linear transformation $\mathbf{C}$ defined by

$$\mathbf{e}_1C = \mathbf{w}_1 \qquad \text{and} \qquad \mathbf{e}_2C = \mathbf{w}_2.$$

Expressing $\mathbf{w}_1$ and $\mathbf{w}_2$ in terms of $\mathbf{e}_1$ and $\mathbf{e}_2$ we get

$$\mathbf{e}_1C = (1, 1) = 1\mathbf{e}_1 + 1\mathbf{e}_2$$

and

$$\mathbf{e}_2C = (-1, 1) = -1\mathbf{e}_1 + 1\mathbf{e}_2.$$

Hence

$$C = \begin{pmatrix} 1 & 1 \\ -1 & 1 \end{pmatrix},$$

and we compute the products $CA$ and $A_1C$:

$$\begin{pmatrix} 1 & 1 \\ -1 & 1 \end{pmatrix}\begin{pmatrix} 1 & 0 \\ 0 & 0 \end{pmatrix} = \begin{pmatrix} 1 & 0 \\ -1 & 0 \end{pmatrix} = CA,$$

$$\begin{pmatrix} \tfrac{1}{2} & -\tfrac{1}{2} \\ -\tfrac{1}{2} & \tfrac{1}{2} \end{pmatrix}\begin{pmatrix} 1 & 1 \\ -1 & 1 \end{pmatrix} = \begin{pmatrix} 1 & 0 \\ -1 & 0 \end{pmatrix} = A_1C.$$

We see that $CA = A_1C$.

The converse of the theorem is true also.

THEOREM 12.24. *If $A$, $B$, and $C$ are elements of $F_n$ such that $C$ is nonsingular and*

$$CA = BC,$$

*then $A$ and $B$ correspond to the same element $\mathbf{A}$ of $\mathbf{L}(V_n(F))$ relative to the appropriate bases for $V_n(F)$.*

To prove this we do little more than reverse the procedure used in proving the previous theorem. First we use $A$ and an arbitrary basis $\{\mathbf{v}_1, \cdots, \mathbf{v}_n\}$ for $V_n$ to define $\boldsymbol{A}$ so that, if $A = (a_{rs})$, then

$$\mathbf{v}_i\boldsymbol{A} = a_{i1}\mathbf{v}_1 + \cdots + a_{in}\mathbf{v}_n, \qquad i = 1, \cdots, n.$$

Now we obtain the basis $\{\mathbf{w}_1, \cdots, \mathbf{w}_n\}$ by using the nonsingular matrix $C = (c_{rs})$:

$$\mathbf{w}_i = \mathbf{v}_i\boldsymbol{C} = c_{i1}\mathbf{v}_1 + \cdots + c_{in}\mathbf{v}_n, \qquad i = 1, \cdots, n.$$

The vectors $\mathbf{w}_1, \cdots, \mathbf{w}_n$ form a basis for $V_n$ since $C$ is nonsingular. Now by the previous theorem the linear transformation $\boldsymbol{A}$ is represented, relative to this new basis of $\mathbf{w}$'s, by the matrix $A_1$, where

$$A_1 = CAC^{-1}.$$

But by hypothesis

$$B = CAC^{-1},$$

so we see that

$$A_1 = B.$$

Thus $A$ and $B$ both describe the mapping $\boldsymbol{A}$, relative to the appropriate bases for $V_n(F)$.

DEFINITION 12.5. Two matrices $A$ and $B$ of $F_n$ are *similar* if and only if there exists a nonsingular $C$ in $F_n$ such that $B = CAC^{-1}$.

The concept of similarity is discussed at some length in the next chapter.

If we go back and consider an $n$-by-$m$ matrix $A$ which corresponds to the linear transformation $\boldsymbol{A}$ from $V_n(F)$ to $W_m(F)$ relative to certain bases of these spaces we get a completely analogous result. In this case there are *two* bases to be changed, that of $V_n(F)$ and that of $W_m(F)$. Let $\{\mathbf{v}_1, \cdots, \mathbf{v}_n\}$ and $\{\mathbf{v}_1\boldsymbol{C}, \cdots, \mathbf{v}_n\boldsymbol{C}\}$ be two bases of $V_n(F)$ and $\{\mathbf{w}_1, \cdots, \mathbf{w}_m\}$ and $\{\mathbf{w}_1\boldsymbol{H}, \cdots, \mathbf{w}_m\boldsymbol{H}\}$ are two bases of $W_m(F)$.

($\boldsymbol{C}$ and $\boldsymbol{H}$ are elements from $\boldsymbol{L}(V_n(F))$ and $\boldsymbol{L}(W_m(F))$ of rank $n$ and $m$, respectively.) Then the linear transformation $\boldsymbol{A}$ is described in terms of the various bases as follows:

$$\begin{aligned} \mathbf{v}_i\boldsymbol{A} &= a_{i1}\mathbf{w}_1 + \cdots + a_{im}\mathbf{w}_m, && i = 1, \cdots, n, \\ (\mathbf{v}_i\boldsymbol{C})\boldsymbol{A} &= b_{i1}(\mathbf{w}_1\boldsymbol{H}) + \cdots + b_{im}(\mathbf{w}_m\boldsymbol{H}), && i = 1, \cdots, n, \end{aligned}$$

and

$$(\mathbf{v}_i\boldsymbol{C})\boldsymbol{A} = d_{i1}\mathbf{w}_1 + \cdots + d_{im}\mathbf{w}_m, \qquad i = 1, \cdots, n.$$

The transformation $\boldsymbol{C}$ is described by

$$\mathbf{v}_i\boldsymbol{C} = c_{i1}\mathbf{v}_1 + \cdots + c_{in}\mathbf{v}_n, \qquad i = 1, \cdots, n,$$

and $\boldsymbol{H}$ from $\boldsymbol{L}(W_m(F))$ is described by

$$\mathbf{w}_i\boldsymbol{H} = h_{i1}\mathbf{w}_1 + \cdots + h_{im}\mathbf{w}_m, \qquad i = 1, \cdots, m.$$

Now we determine two other formulations for the scalars $d_{rs}$.

*Method* 1. Replace $\mathbf{v}_i C$ by its expression in terms of the $\mathbf{v}$'s.

$$(\mathbf{v}_i C)A = (c_{i1}\mathbf{v}_1 + \cdots + c_{in}\mathbf{v}_n)A = \sum_{j=1}^{n} c_{ij}\mathbf{v}_j A,$$
$$= \sum_{j=1}^{n} c_{ij}(a_{j1}\mathbf{w}_1 + \cdots + a_{jm}\mathbf{w}_m),$$
$$= \sum_{j=1}^{n} c_{ij}\left(\sum_{k=1}^{m} a_{jk}\mathbf{w}_k\right).$$

Thus each $(\mathbf{v}_i C)A$ is expressible in terms of the $\mathbf{w}$'s as

$$(\mathbf{v}_i C)A = \left(\sum_{j=1}^{n} c_{ij}a_{j1}\right)\mathbf{w}_1 + \cdots + \left(\sum_{j=1}^{n} c_{ij}a_{jm}\right)\mathbf{w}_m.$$

*Method* 2. This time we express $(\mathbf{v}_i C)A$ in terms of $\mathbf{w}_j H$ first.

$$(\mathbf{v}_i C)A = b_{i1}(\mathbf{w}_1 H) + \cdots + b_{im}(\mathbf{w}_m H) = \sum_{j=1}^{m} b_{ij}\mathbf{w}_j H,$$
$$= \sum_{j=1}^{m} b_{ij}(h_{j1}\mathbf{w}_1 + \cdots + h_{jm}\mathbf{w}_m),$$
$$= \sum_{j=1}^{m} b_{ij}\left(\sum_{k=1}^{m} h_{jk}\mathbf{w}_k\right).$$

So each $(\mathbf{v}_i C)A$ is expressible in terms of the $\mathbf{w}$'s as

$$(\mathbf{v}_i C)A = \left(\sum_{j=1}^{m} b_{ij}h_{j1}\right)\mathbf{w}_1 + \cdots + \left(\sum_{j=1}^{m} b_{ij}h_{jm}\right)\mathbf{w}_m.$$

Comparing these expressions we get

$$d_{rs} = \sum_{j=1}^{n} c_{rj}a_{js} = \sum_{j=1}^{m} b_{rj}h_{js}$$

for $r = 1, \cdots, n$ and $s = 1, \cdots, m$. In terms of the $n$-by-$m$ matrices $D = (d_{rs})$, $A = (a_{rs})$, and $B = (b_{rs})$, the $n$-by-$n$ matrix $C = (c_{rs})$, and the $m$-by-$m$ matrix $H = (h_{rs})$, we have

$$D = CA = BH \qquad \text{and} \qquad B = CAH^{-1}.$$

Since $C$ and $H$ are nonsingular matrices we have proved one part of the following theorem.

THEOREM 12.25. *Two $n$-by-$m$ matrices $A$ and $B$ over $F$ correspond to the same element $A$ of $\mathbf{L}(V_n(F);\ W_m(F))$ relative to the appropriate bases for $V_n(F)$ and $W_m(F)$ if and only if $F_n$ and $F_m$ contain nonsingular elements $C$ and $H$, respectively, such that*

$$CA = BH.$$

The remainder of the proof is very much like the proof of Theorem 12.24 so we shall not bother writing it out.

DEFINITION 12.6. The $n$-by-$m$ matrices $A$ and $B$ over $F$ are *equivalent* if and only if $F_n$ and $F_m$ contain nonsingular matrices $C$ and $D$ respectively, such that $CAD = B$.

The concept of equivalence of matrices is considered in the next chapter. We show there that two $n$-by-$m$ matrices are equivalent if and only if they have the same rank. Basically this is due to the fact that all vector spaces over $F$ of dimension $r$ are isomorphic.

## Exercise 12.7

**1.** Let $A$ be the linear transformation on $C_2(R)$ such that the matrix of $A$ relative to the canonical basis is

$$A = \begin{pmatrix} 1 & 2 \\ 3 & 4 \end{pmatrix}.$$

Find the matrix $B$ of $A$ relative to the basis $\mathbf{w}_1 = (1, 1)$, $\mathbf{w}_2 = (-1, 1)$ in two ways.

**2.** Let $A$ be the projection of $C_3(Re)$ onto $C_2(Re)$ given by $(a_1, a_2, a_3)A = (a_2, a_3)$. Find the matrix $A$ of $A$ relative to the canonical bases of the two systems, and then find the matrix $B$ of $A$ relative to the basis $\mathbf{v}_1 = (1, 1, 1)$, $\mathbf{v}_2 = (0, 1, 1)$, and $\mathbf{v}_3 = (0, 0, 1)$ for $C_3(Re)$ and the basis $\mathbf{w}_1 = (1, 1)$ and $\mathbf{w}_2 = (-1, 1)$ for $C_2(Re)$ in two ways.

**3.** Show that similarity of matrices defines an equivalence relation on $F_n$.

**4.** Show that equivalence of matrices defines an equivalence relation on the set $F(n, m)$ of all $n$-by-$m$ matrices over $F$.

**5.** Show that the sum of two nonsingular matrices can be singular.

**6.** Show that two elements of $F_n$ are certainly equivalent if they are similar.

**7.** Prove that all nonsingular matrices of $F_n$ are equivalent with the identity matrix $I_n$ and hence with each other. (Note that, if $A$ is nonsingular, then $A^{-1}AI_n = I_n$.)

**8.** Compare the result in Problem 7 with the fact that all vector spaces of dimension $n$ over $F$ are isomorphic.

**9.** Show that, if $A$ and $B$ are similar matrices, then they have the same rank.

**10.** Prove that the converse of Problem 9 is false by considering the matric equation

$$\begin{pmatrix} 1 & 0 \\ 0 & 1 \end{pmatrix}\begin{pmatrix} a & b \\ c & d \end{pmatrix} = \begin{pmatrix} a & b \\ c & d \end{pmatrix}\begin{pmatrix} 1 & 1 \\ 0 & 1 \end{pmatrix}$$

and showing that $a$, $b$, $c$, and $d$ do not exist in $R$ such that the resulting matrix is nonsingular.

## 12.8 Ideals and Algebras

Thus far little has been said about the subrings of $F_n$ (or of $L(V_n(F))$) and nothing has been said about those very important subrings, the ideals. We recall that the subring $T$ of a ring $S$ is an ideal if and only if the products $at$ and $ta$ are in $T$ whenever $t$ is in $T$ and $a$ is in $S$.

THEOREM 12.26. *The only ideals of the complete matric ring $F_n$ are the zero ideal $\{Z\}$ and the entire ring $F_n$.*

Let $T$ be an ideal of $F_n$ different from the zero subring $\{Z\}$. Then $T$ contains an element $A \neq Z$ so that the matrix $A = (a_{rs})$ has a component, say $a_{11}$, which is not equal to 0 in $F$. We multiply the following matrices:

$$E_{11}(bI_n)AE_{11}$$

where $ba_{11} = 1$, $bI_n$ is a scalar matrix, and $E_{11}$ is the indicated unit matrix. Because of all the 0's in $E_{11}$ this product, which is in $T$, equals $E_{11}$.

*Example* 1. Suppose $A$ is the following matrix from $R_2$:

$$A = \begin{pmatrix} 2 & 3 \\ 4 & 5 \end{pmatrix}.$$

Then

$$E_{11}((1/2)I_2)AE_{11} = \begin{pmatrix} 1 & 0 \\ 0 & 0 \end{pmatrix}\begin{pmatrix} \frac{1}{2} & 0 \\ 0 & \frac{1}{2} \end{pmatrix}\begin{pmatrix} 2 & 3 \\ 4 & 5 \end{pmatrix}\begin{pmatrix} 1 & 0 \\ 0 & 0 \end{pmatrix} = E_{11}.$$

Of course if the nonzero component of $A$ were $a_{ij}$ we would consider the product

$$E_{ii}(bI_n)AE_{jj}, \qquad \text{where } ba_{ij} = 1,$$

and conclude that it equals $E_{ij}$. In any case, if $T \neq \{Z\}$ is an ideal of $F_n$, then $T$ contains a matric unit $E_{ij}$.

From the equations

$$E_{rs} = E_{ri}E_{ij}E_{js}, \qquad r = 1, \cdots, n \quad \text{and} \quad s = 1, \cdots, n,$$

we conclude that $T \neq \{Z\}$ contains all $n^2$ matric units of $F_n$. Hence $T \neq \{Z\}$ contains all elements of $F_n$ and $T = F_n$, proving the theorem.

*Corollary* 12.26.1. The ring $L(V_n(F))$ of all linear transformations on $V_n(F)$ has no nontrivial ideals.

This follows from the isomorphism between $F_n$ and $L(V_n(F))$.

From the structural view of rings this result classifies the complete matric rings over a field as basic building units in ring theory, along with fields, sfields and complete matric rings over sfields. This does *not* mean that every ring is constructed in some unique way from just these basic systems, but there is a sizable class of rings which are so constructed.

DEFINITION 12.7. An *algebra* (or *linear algebra*) over the field $F$ is a system $M$ with the following properties:

(1) $M$ is a vector space over $F$.
(2) $M$ is a multiplicative semigroup.
(3) Multiplication in $M$ is bilinear in that

$$\mathbf{u}(a\mathbf{v} + b\mathbf{w}) = a\mathbf{uv} + b\mathbf{uw}$$

and

$$(a\mathbf{v} + b\mathbf{w})\mathbf{u} = a\mathbf{vu} + b\mathbf{wu}$$

for $a$ and $b$ in $F$ and $\mathbf{u}$, $\mathbf{v}$, and $\mathbf{w}$ in $M$.

The *dimension* of $M$ is the dimension of $M$ as a vector space.

We note that there are three cases of multiplication and two cases of addition involved here. In an algebra we have the field product, $ab$; the scalar product, $a\mathbf{v}$; the ring product (in $M$), $\mathbf{uv}$; the field sum, $a + b$; and the vector sum, $\mathbf{u} + \mathbf{v}$.

*Example* 2. The ring $F_n$ is an algebra of dimension $n^2$ over $F$.

The fact that $F_n$ is a vector space of dimension $n^2$ over $F$ was noted previously when we discussed addition. And we know that $F_n$ is a semigroup relative to matric multiplication. So consider the bilinearity; it follows from the Distributive Laws and the fact that scalar matrices commute with every element of $F_n$.

*Example* 3. The ring $\mathbf{L}(V_n(F))$ is an algebra of dimension $n^2$ over $F$.

This follows from the isomorphism between $F_n$ and $\mathbf{L}(V_n(F))$, but look at the argument for bilinearity:

$$\begin{aligned}\mathbf{v}(\boldsymbol{A}(a\boldsymbol{B} + b\boldsymbol{C})) &= (\mathbf{v}\boldsymbol{A})(a\boldsymbol{B} + b\boldsymbol{C}),\\ &= (\mathbf{v}\boldsymbol{A})(a\boldsymbol{B}) + (\mathbf{v}\boldsymbol{A})(b\boldsymbol{C}),\\ &= a(\mathbf{v}\boldsymbol{A})\boldsymbol{B} + b(\mathbf{v}\boldsymbol{A})\boldsymbol{C},\\ &= a(\mathbf{v}\boldsymbol{AB}) + b(\mathbf{v}\boldsymbol{AC}),\\ &= \mathbf{v}(a\boldsymbol{AB}) + \mathbf{v}(b\boldsymbol{AC}),\\ &= \mathbf{v}(a\boldsymbol{AB} + b\boldsymbol{AC}),\end{aligned}$$

for $\mathbf{v}$ in $V_n(F)$ and $\boldsymbol{A}$, $\boldsymbol{B}$, and $\boldsymbol{C}$ in $\mathbf{L}(V_n(F))$.

*Example* 4. The ring $\mathbf{L}(V(F))$ is an algebra over $F$.

Everything except the bilinearity was proved in previous sections, and the argument in Example 3 makes no use of dimension. Hence $\mathbf{L}(V(F))$ is an algebra over $F$.

The close relation between algebras and the rings of linear transformations is indicated by the following analogue of Cayley's Theorem for groups.

THEOREM 12.27. *If $M$ is an algebra over $F$, then the mapping $\boldsymbol{K}$ defined by*

$$\mathbf{v}\boldsymbol{K} = \boldsymbol{A}_{\mathbf{v}}$$

*for each $\mathbf{v}$ in $M$, where $\boldsymbol{A}_{\mathbf{v}}$ is the linear transformation of $V(F) = M$ given by*

$$\mathbf{u}\boldsymbol{A}_{\mathbf{v}} = \mathbf{uv}, \qquad \text{all } \mathbf{u} \text{ in } V(F),$$

*is a homomorphism from $M$ to $\mathbf{L}(V(F))$. If $M$ has a multiplicative identity, then $\boldsymbol{K}$ is an isomorphism.*

First, we see that $\boldsymbol{A}_{\mathbf{v}}$ is a linear transformation on $M$ (treated as our vector space $V(F)$) due to the bilinearity of multiplication in $M$:

$$\begin{aligned}(a\mathbf{u} + b\mathbf{w})\boldsymbol{A}_{\mathbf{v}} &= (a\mathbf{u} + b\mathbf{w})\mathbf{v} = a\mathbf{uv} + b\mathbf{wv},\\ &= a(\mathbf{u}\boldsymbol{A}_{\mathbf{v}}) + b(\mathbf{w}\boldsymbol{A}_{\mathbf{v}})\end{aligned}$$

for $a$ and $b$ in $F$ and $\mathbf{u}$, $\mathbf{v}$, and $\mathbf{w}$ in $M$. Also we see that $\boldsymbol{A}_{\mathbf{v}} \neq \boldsymbol{A}_{\mathbf{u}}$ if $\mathbf{u} \neq \mathbf{v}$ when $M$ has a multiplicative identity $\mathbf{e}$ since the images of $\mathbf{e}$ are

$$\mathbf{e}\boldsymbol{A}_{\mathbf{v}} = \mathbf{ev} = \mathbf{v} \qquad \text{and} \qquad \mathbf{e}\boldsymbol{A}_{\mathbf{u}} = \mathbf{eu} = \mathbf{u}.$$

To prove that $K$ is a homomorphism we must show that the three basic binary operations of $M$ and $L(V(F))$ are compatible:

(1) $$(\mathbf{u} + \mathbf{v})K = \mathbf{u}K + \mathbf{v}K.$$
(2) $$(a\mathbf{u})K = a(\mathbf{u}K).$$
(3) $$(\mathbf{u}\mathbf{v})K = (\mathbf{u}K)(\mathbf{v}K).$$

We consider them in order given.

(1) $(\mathbf{u} + \mathbf{v})K = A_{\mathbf{w}}$ where $\mathbf{w} = \mathbf{u} + \mathbf{v}$. For $\mathbf{x}$ in $M$ we have the image

$$\begin{aligned}\mathbf{x}A_{\mathbf{w}} &= \mathbf{x}\mathbf{w} = \mathbf{x}(\mathbf{u} + \mathbf{v}) = \mathbf{x}\mathbf{u} + \mathbf{x}\mathbf{v},\\ &= \mathbf{x}A_{\mathbf{u}} + \mathbf{x}A_{\mathbf{v}} = \mathbf{x}(A_{\mathbf{u}} + A_{\mathbf{v}}).\end{aligned}$$

Since linear transformations are determined by their images we conclude that

$$A_{\mathbf{w}} = A_{\mathbf{u}} + A_{\mathbf{v}} = \mathbf{u}K + \mathbf{v}K = (\mathbf{u} + \mathbf{v})K.$$

(2) $(a\mathbf{u})K = A_{\mathbf{w}}$ where $\mathbf{w} = a\mathbf{u}$. Consider the image of $\mathbf{x}$, $\mathbf{x}$ in $M$:

$$\begin{aligned}\mathbf{x}A_{\mathbf{w}} &= \mathbf{x}\mathbf{w} = \mathbf{x}(a\mathbf{u}) = a\mathbf{u}\mathbf{x} = a(\mathbf{u}\mathbf{x}),\\ &= a(\mathbf{x}A_{\mathbf{u}}) = \mathbf{x}(aA_{\mathbf{u}}).\end{aligned}$$

Since $\mathbf{x}$ is arbitrary this implies

$$A_{\mathbf{w}} = aA_{\mathbf{u}} = a(\mathbf{u}K).$$

(3) $(\mathbf{u}\mathbf{v})K = A_{\mathbf{w}}$ where $\mathbf{w} = \mathbf{u}\mathbf{v}$. Considering the image $\mathbf{x}$ of $M$ under this linear transformation we see that

$$\begin{aligned}\mathbf{x}A_{\mathbf{w}} &= \mathbf{x}\mathbf{w} = \mathbf{x}(\mathbf{u}\mathbf{v}) = (\mathbf{x}\mathbf{u})\mathbf{v},\\ &= (\mathbf{x}\mathbf{u})A_{\mathbf{v}} = (\mathbf{x}A_{\mathbf{u}})A_{\mathbf{v}} = \mathbf{x}(A_{\mathbf{u}}A_{\mathbf{v}}).\end{aligned}$$

Therefore

$$A_{\mathbf{w}} = A_{\mathbf{u}}A_{\mathbf{v}} = (\mathbf{u}K)(\mathbf{v}K).$$

From these we conclude that $K$ is a homomorphism from $M$ to $L(V(F))$. If $M$ has an identity, then distinct elements of $M$ go onto distinct linear transformations so that $M$ is isomorphic with a subring of $L(V(F))$.

*Corollary* 12.27.1. An $n$-dimensional algebra $M$ over $F$ with a multiplicative identity is isomorphic with a subring of $F_n$.

This is a result of the theorem above and the isomorphism between $F_n$ and $L(V_n(F))$. The subring of $F_n$ which is obtained in this fashion is the *right regular representation* of $M$.

(Using left multiplications defined by

$$\mathbf{u}B_{\mathbf{v}} = \mathbf{v}\mathbf{u}, \qquad \mathbf{u} \text{ in } M,$$

for a fixed $\mathbf{v}$ in $M$, yields the *left regular representation* which is anti-isomorphic with $M$ since, for $\mathbf{w} = \mathbf{u}\mathbf{v}$,

$$\begin{aligned}\mathbf{x}A_{\mathbf{w}} &= (\mathbf{u}\mathbf{v})\mathbf{x} = \mathbf{u}(\mathbf{v}\mathbf{x}) = (\mathbf{v}\mathbf{x})A_{\mathbf{u}},\\ &= (\mathbf{x}A_{\mathbf{v}})A_{\mathbf{u}} = \mathbf{x}(A_{\mathbf{v}}A_{\mathbf{u}}).\end{aligned}$$

This means that $A_{\mathbf{w}} = A_{\mathbf{v}}A_{\mathbf{u}}$.)

*Example* 5. To exhibit the matrices of the right regular representation of the algebra $M$ of dimension $n$ over $F$ we select a basis $\{\mathbf{v}_1, \cdots, \mathbf{v}_n\}$ for $M$ as a vector space. Then we multiply each basis vector on the right by all basis vectors and express the products in terms of the $\mathbf{v}$'s.

Take $M$ to be the quadratic field consisting of all real numbers of the form

$$a + b\sqrt{2}, \qquad a \text{ and } b \text{ in } R.$$

Then $M$ has the basis $\mathbf{v}_1 = 1$ and $\mathbf{v}_2 = \sqrt{2}$. Form the products

$$1 \cdot 1 = 1 + 0\sqrt{2},$$
$$\sqrt{2} \cdot 1 = 0 + \sqrt{2},$$
$$1\sqrt{2} = 0 + \sqrt{2},$$

and

$$\sqrt{2}\sqrt{2} = 2 + 0\sqrt{2}.$$

From the first two we get the matrix

$$I_2 = \begin{pmatrix} 1 & 0 \\ 0 & 1 \end{pmatrix}$$

which corresponds to 1. From the second pair we get

$$A = \begin{pmatrix} 0 & 1 \\ 2 & 0 \end{pmatrix}$$

which corresponds to $\sqrt{2}$. Then we have the matric description of $a + b\sqrt{2}$ as

$$\begin{pmatrix} a & b \\ 2b & a \end{pmatrix}.$$

Note that $A^2 = 2I_2$.

A finite dimensional linear algebra is called *semisimple* if it contains no ideal except the zero ideal which consists entirely of nilpotent elements. (We recall that an element $r$ of a ring $S$ is *nilpotent* if

$$r^n = 0$$

for some positive integer $n$.) The theory of semisimple rings (the *Wedderburn structure theory*) is rather well-developed. For example, if $M$ is a semisimple algebra of dimension $m$ over the complex field $C$, then $M$ can be expressed irredundantly as

$$M = M_1 + M_2 + \cdots + M_r$$

where the $M_r$ are ideals of $M$ which are isomorphic with complete matric rings over $C$.

## Exercise 12.8

**1.** Let $M$ be all of the elements of $R_2$ of the form

$$\begin{pmatrix} a & b \\ 0 & c \end{pmatrix}$$

Show that $M$ is a subring of $R_2$. Show that the set $N$ of all elements of $M$ of the form

$$\begin{pmatrix} 0 & b \\ 0 & 0 \end{pmatrix}$$

is an ideal of $M$ of nilpotent elements.

**2.** Show that the domain $F[\lambda]$ is a linear algebra over $F$.

**3.** Find the right regular representation of the complex field by 2-by-2 matrices over the real field.

**4.** Show that, in the right regular representation of the algebra of quaternions over $R$, the basis elements 1, $i$, $j$, and $k$ correspond to the following 4-by-4 matrices:

$$I_4,\ A_i = \begin{pmatrix} 0 & 1 & 0 & 0 \\ -1 & 0 & 0 & 0 \\ 0 & 0 & 0 & -1 \\ 0 & 0 & 1 & 0 \end{pmatrix}, \qquad A_j = \begin{pmatrix} 0 & 0 & 1 & 0 \\ 0 & 0 & 0 & 1 \\ -1 & 0 & 0 & 0 \\ 0 & -1 & 0 & 0 \end{pmatrix},$$

and

$$A_k = \begin{pmatrix} 0 & 0 & 0 & 1 \\ 0 & 0 & -1 & 0 \\ 0 & 1 & 0 & 0 \\ -1 & 0 & 0 & 0 \end{pmatrix},$$

respectively. These matrices are sometimes used to define the quaternions. Check the products $A_iA_j$ and $A_jA_i$.

**5.** Find the right regular representation of the field $F = R[\lambda]/(\lambda^3 - 2)$ by 3-by-3 matrices over $R$. (Take the coset representatives 1, $\lambda$, and $\lambda^2$ as a basis for the algebra $F$.)

**6.** Write out the following products of matric units from $R_3$: $E_{11}E_{11}$, $E_{11}E_{12}$, $E_{11}E_{13}$, $E_{11}E_{21}$, $E_{11}E_{31}$, $E_{21}E_{11}$, $E_{31}E_{11}$.

**7.** Show that the set $S$ of all elements of $F_n$ with only zeros in their first rows is a subring of $F_n$. Show also that $SF_n = S$, where $SF_n = \{AB\colon A \text{ in } S \text{ and } B \text{ in } F_n\}$.

**8.** Let $N$ be the set of all matrices $A = (a_{rs})$ in $F_n$ such that $a_{rs} = 0$ if $r$ is equal or greater than $s$. Show that $N$ is an algebra of dimension $(\frac{1}{2})(n^2 - n)$ over $F$. Show also that the $n$th power of every element in $N$ is the zero matrix.

**9.** Show that the product of *any n* elements of $N$ (Problem 8) is the zero matrix.

**10.** Use the right regular representation to embed the algebra $R_2$ in $R_4$. (Take matric units as the basis elements for $R_2$.)

**11.** Describe all algebras of dimension 2.

## 12.9 Suggested Reading

*Articles*

Berman, G., and R. J. Silverman, "Near-rings," *Amer. Math. Monthly* **66** (1959), 22–33.

Charnes, A., and W. W. Cooper, "Linear Programming," *Sci. American* **191** (Aug. 1954), 21–23.

Dubisch, R., "The Wedderburn structure theorems," *Amer. Math. Monthly* **54** (1947), 253–259.

Leavitt, W., "Matrices as mappings," *Amer. Math. Monthly* **59** (1952), 219–222; *ibid.* **60** (1953), 75–79.

MacDuffee, C. C., "What is a matrix?" *Amer. Math. Monthly* **50** (1943), 360–365.

Robinson, D. W., "On the generalized inverse of a linear transformation," *Amer. Math. Monthly* **69** (1962), 412–416.

Taussky, O., "Commutativity in finite matrices," *Amer. Math. Monthly* **64** (1957) 229–235.

*Books*

Dubisch, R., *The Nature of Number*, Ronald Press Co., New York, 1952.

Finkbeiner, D., *Introduction to Matrices and Linear Transformations*, W. H. Freeman & Co., San Francisco, 1960.

Halmos, P., *Finite Dimensional Vector Spaces*, D. Van Nostrand Co., Princeton, N.J., 1958.

Thrall, R., and L. Tornheim, *Vector Spaces and Matrices*, John Wiley & Sons, New York, 1957.

# 13

# Elementary Theory of Matrices

In our study of the ordinary integer we developed the idea of a factorization into primes, and this idea was extended to the elements of other rings such as polynomial domains and quadratic domains. We were able to show that these expressions for elements were unique (up to units) in general although in dealing with algebraic integers it was necessary to introduce ideal numbers. In this chapter we investigate some of the basic factorization theorems for an element of a matric ring (usually over a field).

The study of factorizations in a matric ring is complicated by a number of items. Since matrices do not in general commute (relative to multiplication, of course) the order in which factors appear in a product is of great significance. There is no obvious model of a noncommutative ring to use in the study of matric ring, so suggestions for various factorizations of matrices arise through different views and uses of matrices. (The ones we discuss are mainly suggested by the effect of a change of basis for $V_n$ and $W_n$ on the relation between $F_n$ and $L(V_n(F);\ W_n(F))$.) Furthermore the matric ring $S_n$ has divisors of zero (when $n$ exceeds 1) whether $S$ has such elements or not, and in fact every matrix which is not a unit is a divisor of zero.

The concept of factorization in a matric ring is necessarily rather different from the factorizations we have studied previously. For example we shall prove that an element $A$ of $F_n$ is expressible as a product

$$A = BH,$$

where $B$ is nonsingular (a unit) in $F_n$ and $H$ is in reduced row echelon form. Furthermore this factorization is unique up to a unit in that if

$$A = B'H'$$

where $B'$ is a unit and $H'$ is in reduced row echelon form, then $H = H'$.

This can be looked at in the following way also. If an equivalence relation is defined on a matric ring through its units, then select a unique (i.e., canonical) representative of each equivalence class in the resulting partition. We shall say more about this idea at the end of the chapter.

## 13.1 Special Types of Matrices

A variety of special types of matrices have cropped up at various points in our work in the previous chapters. Since our work in this chapter utilizes these and some others, we start by compiling a list with examples and elementary properties of some of the basic classes of elements in the ring $F_n$.

(1) The *identity matrix* of $F_n$, which we will generally indicate by $I$ unless we wish to emphasize the fact that it is an $n$-by-$n$ matrix by writing $I_n$, is the matrix $(a_{rs})$ with

$$a_{rs} = 1 \qquad \text{if } r = s,$$

and zero otherwise. Then

$$AI = IA = A$$

for every $A$ in $F_n$.

(2) The *scalar matrices* of $F_n$ are scalar multiples of $I$. The matrix $(a_{rs})$ is scalar if and only if

$$a_{rs} = 0 \qquad \text{when } r \neq s$$

and

$$a_{11} = \cdots = a_{nn} = a.$$

Then of course

$$(a_{rs}) = aI.$$

The scalar matrices of $F_n$ form a subring which is isomorphic with $F$, the correspondence being

$$a \leftrightarrow aI, \qquad \text{each } a \text{ in } F.$$

(3) The *diagonal matrices* of $F_n$ are somewhat more complicated than scalar matrices, but the scalar matrices are special examples of diagonal matrices. The matrix $(a_{rs})$ is diagonal if and only if

$$a_{rs} = 0 \qquad \text{when } r \neq s.$$

*Example* 1. The following elements of $R_2$ are diagonal but not scalar:

$$A = \begin{pmatrix} 1 & 0 \\ 0 & 2 \end{pmatrix} \qquad \text{and} \qquad B = \begin{pmatrix} -2 & 0 \\ 0 & 0 \end{pmatrix}.$$

The diagonal elements of $F_n$ form a subring $DF_n$ which is a commutative ring with identity and divisors of zero (when $n$ exceeds 1). To show this we note that the sum of two diagonal matrices is clearly diagonal since the addition is made by adding corresponding components. Consider the product

$$C = AB$$

when $A = (a_{rs})$ and $B = (b_{rs})$ are diagonal. Then $C = (c_{rs})$ with

$$c_{rs} = \sum_{i=1}^{n} a_{ri}b_{is} = a_{rr}b_{rs}$$

which equals zero if $r \neq s$. Hence $C$ is diagonal also.

(4) The *matric units* $E_{ij}$ of $F_n$ are the $n^2$ elements which make up the "simplest" basis for $F_n$ considered as a vector space over $F$. $E_{ij}$ has 1 as its $(i, j)$-component and zero elsewhere.

$$I = E_{11} + E_{22} + \cdots + E_{nn};$$

$$E_{ij}E_{hk} = \begin{cases} E_{ik} & \text{if } h = j \\ Z & \text{if } h \neq j. \end{cases}$$

The elements $E_{11}, E_{22}, \cdots, E_{nn}$ are in the subring of diagonal matrices, and they are clearly divisors of zero. Moreover they form a basis for the subring $DF_n$ of diagonal rings considered as a vector space over $F$.

*Example* 2.

$$\begin{pmatrix} 2 & 0 \\ 0 & 3 \end{pmatrix} = 2E_{11} + 3E_{22}.$$

(5) The *triangular matrices* form a larger subclass of $F_n$. The matrix $(a_{rs})$ is (upper) *triangular* if and only if

$$a_{rs} = 0 \qquad \text{when } r > s.$$

(*Note*: This says nothing about the component $a_{rs}$ when $r \leqslant s$.)

Let $A = (a_{rs})$ and $B = (b_{rs})$ be two triangular matrices of $F_n$, and consider

$$C = (c_{rs}) = AB.$$

Then

$$c_{rs} = \sum_{i=1}^{n} a_{ri}b_{is},$$

and if $r$ exceeds $s$ we have the following situation:

$$a_{r1} = \cdots = a_{r,r-1} = 0$$

and

$$b_{rs} = b_{r+1,s} = \cdots = b_{ns} = 0.$$

Hence each factor in the sum expressing $c_{rs}$ is zero when $r$ exceeds $s$ so that

$$c_{rs} = 0 \qquad \text{when } r > s$$

and $C$ is triangular.

From this it is easy to show that the triangular matrices in $F_n$ form a ring $TF_n$ which, as a vector space over $F$, has the basis $E_{11}, E_{12}, \cdots, E_{1n}, E_{21}, \cdots, E_{2n}, \cdots, E_{nn}$.

(6) The matrix $A$ of $F_n$ is *nilpotent* of *index m* if and only if

$$A^m = Z$$

but

$$A^{m-1} \neq Z \qquad (m \text{ larger than } 1).$$

The matric units $E_{ij}$. $i \neq j$, are all nilpotent of index 2. The matrix $A = (a_{rs})$ with

$$a_{rs} = 0 \qquad \text{when } r \geqslant s,$$

is nilpotent of index no larger than $n$. (Such a matrix is called *strictly triangular*.)

(7) The matrix $A$ is *idempotent* if and only if $A^2 = A \neq Z$.

The $n$ matric units $E_{ii}$ are all idempotent as is $E_{11} + E_{12}$.

(8) The *nonsingular matrices* are the units of $F_n$. The matrix $A$ is nonsingular if and only if matrix $B$ exists in $F_n$ such that

$$AB = BA = I.$$

The matrix $B$ is called the inverse of $A$ and denoted by $A^{-1}$. The matrix $A^{-1}$ is unique and nonsingular (when it exists). The matrix $A^{-1}$ exists if and only if $A$ has rank $n$ (as we proved in the previous chapter).

The nonsingular matrices of $F_n$ do not form a subring (even when $Z$ is included) since the sum of two nonsingular matrices is not in general nonsingular:

$$\begin{pmatrix} 1 & 0 \\ 0 & 1 \end{pmatrix} + \begin{pmatrix} 0 & 1 \\ 1 & 0 \end{pmatrix} = \begin{pmatrix} 1 & 1 \\ 1 & 1 \end{pmatrix}.$$

The set of all nonsingular matrices in $F_n$ is, however, a group relative to matric multiplication as we see easily from

$$(AB)(B^{-1}A^{-1}) = I = (B^{-1}A^{-1})(AB).$$

This is called the *general* (or full) *linear group* of degree $n$ over $F$, $GLF(n)$.

An element of $F_n$ having rank less than $n$ is called *singular*, and we shall see that the product $AB$ of two elements in $F_n$ is nonsingular if and only if $A$ and $B$ are both nonsingular.

(9) An *elementary matrix* of $F_n$ is one which is obtainable from the identity matrix by applying either an elementary row or an elementary column operation to $I$. The elementary matrices are of three types:

(*a*) The interchange of two rows (or two columns) of $I$ produces a matrix whose technical description is

$$I_{ij} = I - E_{ii} - E_{jj} + E_{ij} + E_{ji}.$$

This elementary matrix can be obtained by interchanging row $i$ and row $j$ (or column $i$ and column $j$) of $I$. In $F_3$, $I_{23}$ has the following appearance:

$$I_{23} = \begin{pmatrix} 1 & 0 & 0 \\ 0 & 0 & 1 \\ 0 & 1 & 0 \end{pmatrix}.$$

(*b*) The multiplication of row $i$ (or column $i$) of $I$ by the scalar $k \neq 0$ produces the elementary matrix

$$M_i(k) = I + (k - 1)E_{ii}.$$

In $F_3$ the matrix $M_3(7)$ has the appearance

$$M_3(7) = \begin{pmatrix} 1 & 0 & 0 \\ 0 & 1 & 0 \\ 0 & 0 & 7 \end{pmatrix}.$$

(*c*) The addition of $k$ times row $i$ to row $j$, $i \neq j$ (or of $k$ times column $j$ to column $i$) produces from $I$ the matrix

$$A_{ij}(k) = I + kE_{ji}.$$

If $F_3$ the matrix $A_{13}(9)$ looks like the following:

$$A_{13}(9) = \begin{pmatrix} 1 & 0 & 0 \\ 0 & 1 & 0 \\ 9 & 0 & 1 \end{pmatrix}.$$

THEOREM 13.1. *An elementary matrix of $F_n$ is nonsingular, and its inverse is also an elementary matrix.*

An elementary matrix is obtained from $I$ by an elementary row operation which, as we know, does not alter the row rank. Since $I$ has rank $n$ we see that an elementary matrix has rank $n$ and so is nonsingular.

(i) The inverse of $I_{ij}$ is $I_{ij}$. Consider

$$(I - E_{ii} - E_{jj} + E_{ij} + E_{ji})^2 = A;$$

using the Distributive Law we get

$$A = I$$

so that

$$(I_{ij})^{-1} = I_{ij}.$$

(ii) The inverse of $M_i(k)$ is $M_i(k^{-1})$ since

$$(I + (k - 1)E_{ii})(I + (k^{-1} - 1)E_{ii}) = I.$$

(iii) The inverse of $A_{ij}(k)$ is $A_{ij}(-k)$ since

$$(I + kE_{ji})(I - kE_{ji}) = I$$

when $j \neq i$.

(10) A *bordered matrix* is an element of $F_n$ which is obtainable from a matrix with fewer rows and/or columns by tacking on a sufficient number of rows and/or columns of zeros at the bottom and/or right side.

*Example* 3. The following matrix $A$ is obtainable by bordering the matrix $B$:

$$A = \begin{pmatrix} 1 & 2 & 3 & 0 \\ 4 & 5 & 6 & 0 \\ 0 & 0 & 0 & 0 \\ 0 & 0 & 0 & 0 \end{pmatrix} \quad \text{and} \quad B = \begin{pmatrix} 1 & 2 & 3 \\ 4 & 5 & 6 \end{pmatrix}.$$

The purpose in introducing this idea is to include (to a large extent) the study of rectangular matrices in the study of square matrices. We note, for example, that, if $C$ and $D$ are $n$-by-$m$ and $m$-by-$t$ matrices with $n$ larger than $m$ and $t$, then the $n$-by-$n$ bordered matrices $C_1$ and $D_1$ can be formed,

$$C_1 = (C, \quad Z_1) \quad \text{and} \quad D_1 = \begin{pmatrix} D & Z_3 \\ Z_2 & Z_4 \end{pmatrix},$$

where $Z_1$, $Z_2$, $Z_3$, and $Z_4$ are $n$-by-$(n - m)$, $(n - m)$-by-$t$, $m$-by-$(n - t)$, and $(n - m)$-by-$(n - t)$ matrices of zeros only. Then

$$C_1D_1 = (CD, \quad Z_1)$$

so that the bordering preserves the product (as a bordered matrix).

## Exercise 13.1

**1.** Let $F = J/(2)$. Write out the addition and multiplication tables for $DF_2$, the ring of 2-by-2 diagonal matrices over $F$.

**2.** Extend the tables of Problem 1 to the operation tables for $TF_2$, the ring of triangular matrices.

**3.** Prove that $TF_n$, as a vector space over $F$, has dimension $(\frac{1}{2})(n + 1)n$.

**4.** Show that the product of any three strictly triangular elements of $F_3$ is the zero matrix $Z$. Generalize.

**5.** Prove that a triangular matrix is nonsingular if and only if the elements of the main diagonal, $a_{11}, a_{22}, \cdots, a_{nn}$, are all nonzero. (Look at the row space.)

**6.** Write out a nonsingular, triangular, nondiagonal matrix in $R_3$ and find its inverse. What seems to be true about the inverse of a triangular matrix?

**7.** Show that the nonsingular elements of $DF_n$ form a multiplicative group.

**8.** Show that the nonsingular elements of $TF_n$ form a multiplicative group. Compare with the group of Problem 7.

**9.** Let $A$ be an element of $F_n$ which is both idempotent and nonsingular. Prove that $A = I$.

**10.** Prove that a nilpotent matrix $A$ of index $m$ is singular in $F_n$. (Assume $A^{-1}$ exists and show that this leads to a contradiction to the choice of $m$.)

**11.** Show that a singular matrix of $F_n$ need not be nilpotent unless $n = 1$. (Consider $E_{11}$.)

**12.** Write out examples of the elementary matrices in $R_4$, and find their inverses.

**13.** Show that

$$I_{ij} = M_j(-1)A_{ij}(-1)A_{ji}(1)A_{ij}(-1).$$

Illustrate in $R_4$.

**14.** Rewrite the following as bordered matrices in $R_4$, and find their product by using the bordered matrices.

$$A = \begin{pmatrix} 1 & 2 & -3 & -2 \\ 0 & 1 & 3 & -4 \end{pmatrix} \quad \text{and} \quad B = \begin{pmatrix} 1 & 2 & 3 \\ 1 & 1 & 0 \\ 1 & -1 & 1 \\ 1 & 2 & 2 \end{pmatrix}.$$

**15.** Form an element $A$ of $R_3$ by using the first nine digits. Compute the products $I_{13}A$, $AI_{13}$, $M_2(-4)A$, $AM_2(-4)$, $A_{12}(3)A$, and $AA_{12}(3)$. Describe the effects on $A$ in each case.

**16.** An element $A$ of $F_n$ is *symmetric* if and only if $A = A^T$ and *skew* if and only if $A^T = -A$. Show that, if the characteristic of $F$ is not 2, then each $A$ in $F_n$ is expressible uniquely as the sum of a symmetric and a skew matrix. (Note that $(2A = (A + A^T) + (A - A^T)$.)

**17.** Show that, for each $A$ in $F_n$, the products $AA^T$ and $A^TA$ are symmetric matrices.

**18.** Prove that, if $A$ and $B$ are symmetric elements of $F_n$, then: (1) $A + B$ is symmetric; (2) $AB$ is symmetric if and only if $AB = BA$. (Note that $(AB)^T = B^TA^T$.)

## 13.2 A Factorization

Consider the product $C = AB$ when $A$ and $B$ are elements of $F_n$. The first row of $C$ is obtained by using the first row of $A$ and all of the columns of $B$. Thus

$$\begin{aligned} c_{11} &= a_{11}b_{11} + a_{12}b_{12} + \cdots + a_{1n}b_{n1}, \\ c_{12} &= a_{11}b_{12} + a_{12}b_{22} + \cdots + a_{1n}b_{n2}, \\ &\vdots \\ c_{1n} &= a_{11}a_{1n} + a_{12}b_{2n} + \cdots + a_{1n}b_{nn}. \end{aligned}$$

Now look at the $n$ vectors $\mathbf{v}_1, \cdots, \mathbf{v}_n$ of $C_n(F)$ where

$$\mathbf{v}_i = (b_{i1}, b_{i2}, \cdots, b_{in}), \qquad i = 1, \cdots, n.$$

These are clearly the row vectors of $B$. Form the linear combination

$$\mathbf{v} = a_{11}\mathbf{v}_1 + a_{12}\mathbf{v}_2 + \cdots + a_{1n}\mathbf{v}_n$$

and look at the $n$ components of $\mathbf{v}$; they are precisely the scalars

$$c_{11}, c_{12}, \cdots, c_{1n}.$$

In other words, the vector $\mathbf{v}$ from the row space of $B$ is precisely the first row of $AB$.

THEOREM 13.2. *The row space of $AB$ is a subspace of the row space of $B$, and the column space of $AB$ is a subspace of the column space of $A$.*

The argument above for row 1 extends easily to row $i$ to prove the first part of the theorem. The same argument applied to the rows of $C^T = B^T A^T$ takes care of the second statement, which can also be proved directly by considering an arbitrary column of $C$ and showing that it is a linear combination of columns of $A$.

*Corollary* 13.2.1. The rank of $AB$ does not exceed the rank of either factor.

From the theorem above, the rank of $AB$ (i.e., the dimension of the row space of $AB$) is no larger than the rank of $B$ since the row space of $AB$ is a subspace of the row space of $B$. Considering column spaces we see that the rank of $AB$ (i.e., the dimension of the column space of $AB$) is no larger than the rank of $A$. This proves the corollary.

*Corollary* 13.2.2. The product $AB$ is nonsingular if and only if $A$ and $B$ are both nonsingular.

If $A$ and $B$ are nonsingular, then so is $AB$ since $(AB)^{-1} = B^{-1}A^{-1}$. Consider the converse. If $AB$ is nonsingular, then $AB$ has rank $n$, so that by the preceding result $A$ and $B$ both have rank $n$ and are nonsingular.

Now consider the matrix $A$. Forming $n$ linear combinations of the rows of $A$ corresponds to multiplying $A$ on the left by an appropriate $n$-by-$n$ matrix. Since applying an elementary row operation to $A$ consists of replacing the $n$ rows of $A$ by a certain set of $n$ linear combinations of rows of $A$, we see that these operations can be carried out by multiplying $A$ on the left by the appropriate matrices. These appropriate matrices are, as we should expect, the elementary matrices.

(1) The matrix $I_{ij}A$ is the matrix obtained from $A = (a_{rs})$ by interchanging row $i$ and row $j$. For

$$I_{ij}A = A - E_{ii}A - E_{jj}A + E_{ij}A + E_{ji}A,$$

and the matrix

$$A - E_{ii}A - E_{jj}A$$

has only zeros in row $i$ and row $j$, whereas $E_{ij}A$ has row $j$ of $A$ as its row $i$

(all other components are zero) and $E_{ji}A$ has row $i$ of $A$ as its row $j$ (and all other components are zero). Then $I_{ij}A$ has row $j$ of $A$ as its row $i$ and row $i$ of $A$ as its row $j$.

(2) The matrix $M_i(k)A$, $k \neq 0$, is just the matrix obtainable from $A$ by multiplying row $i$ of $A$ by $k$. For

$$M_i(k)A = (I + (k - 1)E_{ii})A = A + (k - 1)E_{ii}A.$$

The matrix $E_{ii}A$ has row $i$ of $A$ as its row $i$ and all other components equal to zero.

(3) The matrix $A_{ij}(k)A$, for $i \neq j$, is obtainable from $A$ by adding $k$ times row $i$ to row $j$. For

$$A_{ij}(k)A = (I + kE_{ji})A$$

and $E_{ji}A$ has row $i$ of $A$ as its row $j$.

(The elementary row operations are, speaking technically, certain elementary automorphisms on the coordinate space $C_n(F)$. The elementary matrices are the matrices of these automorphisms relative to the canonical basis of $C_n(F)$. The matrix $I_{ij}$ is the description, relative to the canonical basis for $C_n(F)$, of the automorphism which interchanges $\mathbf{e}_i$ and $\mathbf{e}_j$ while fixing the other vectors of the canonical basis.)

THEOREM 13.3. *The effect of applying an elementary row operation to an element $A$ of $F_n$ is obtainable by multiplying $A$ on the left by an appropriate elementary matrix.*

This simple result enables us to rewrite all of our results on reduced row echelon form in terms of products of matrices. In particular we obtain the following *unique factorization* theorem.

THEOREM 13.4. *An element $A$ of $F_n$ is expressible in the form*

$$A = BH,$$

*where $B$ is nonsingular and $H$ is in Hermite form. Furthermore this factorization is unique up to a unit of $F_n$.*

DEFINITION 13.1. An element $H = (h_{rs})$ of $F_n$ is in *Hermite form* if and only if:

(1) $H$ is triangular.

(2) All elements of row $i$ are zero if $h_{ii} = 0$.

(3) If $h_{ii} \neq 0$, then $h_{ii} = 1$ and all other elements of column $i$ are equal to 0.

This is just a rearrangement of the reduced row echelon form designed to emphasize the diagonal. A matrix in one form can be changed easily to the other by interchanging the proper rows.

*Example* 1. The matrix

$$C = \begin{pmatrix} 1 & 2 & 0 \\ 0 & 0 & 1 \\ 0 & 0 & 0 \end{pmatrix}$$

is in reduced row echelon form, whereas

$$I_{23}C = \begin{pmatrix} 1 & 2 & 0 \\ 0 & 0 & 0 \\ 0 & 0 & 1 \end{pmatrix}$$

is in Hermite form.

Since a matrix in reduced row echelon form can be changed into Hermite form by interchanging certain rows we conclude that the theorem is just a restatement of our earlier results on arrays and reduced row echelon form. The statement that the factorization

$$A = BH$$

is unique up to a unit means that, if

$$A = B_1 H_1,$$

where $B_1$ is nonsingular and $H_1$ is in Hermite form, then

$$H = H_1.$$

*Example* 2. From the equation

$$A = \begin{pmatrix} 1 & 0 \\ 0 & 1 \end{pmatrix}\begin{pmatrix} 0 & 0 \\ 0 & 1 \end{pmatrix} = \begin{pmatrix} 1 & 0 \\ 1 & 1 \end{pmatrix}\begin{pmatrix} 0 & 0 \\ 0 & 1 \end{pmatrix} = \begin{pmatrix} 0 & 0 \\ 0 & 1 \end{pmatrix}$$

we see that the nonsingular matrix $B$ in the above factorization need not be unique. For here $A = H$ is in Hermite form and $B = I$ and $B_1 = I + E_{21}$ are both nonsingular so that

$$A = BH = B_1 H,$$

yielding two different factorizations. However, $BB_1^{-1}$ is nonsingular so that the factorization is unique up to units (i.e., nonsingular factors).

What are some of the consequences of this factorization (or reduction to Hermite canonical form)?

*Corollary* 13.4.1. A nonsingular matrix is expressible as the product of a finite, ordered set of elementary matrices.

A matrix can be changed to reduced row echelon form by applying in the proper order some finite collection of elementary row operations. Furthermore the (row) rank of the original matrix equals the rank of the final form, so that, if $A$ is nonsingular, then the reduced row echelon form is $I$. Then

$$I = E_k \cdots E_2 E_1 A,$$

where the $E_i$ are the elementary matrices corresponding to the elementary row operations, so that

$$A = E_1^{-1} E_2^{-1} \cdots E_k^{-1} I.$$

Since the inverses of elementary matrices are also elementary matrices we see that $A$ is expressible as the product of a finite, ordered set of elementary matrices. (The ordering is significant since multiplication is not commutative.)

*Corollary* 13.4.2. An automorphism on $V_n(F)$ can be effected by a finite succession of elementary automorphisms.

An *elementary automorphism* is one which corresponds to an elementary matrix relative to some basis for $V_n(F)$.

*Corollary* 13.4.3. If $A$ is a nonsingular element of $F_n$, then the rank of $AB$ equals the rank of $B$.

Multiplying $B$ on the left by $A$ is the same as applying a finite succession of elementary row operations to $B$. Since such row operations have no effect on the dimension of the row space of $B$, the conclusion of the corollary follows.

Now this theory enables us to find the rank of a matrix $A$ in a finite number of steps by reducing $A$ to row echelon or Hermite form, as we saw previously. It also provides us with a simple routine for finding the inverse of $A$ (when it exists) at the same time. This routine involves nothing more than multiplying together the elementary matrices which correspond to the elementary row operations being applied, although no such multiplication ever needs to be carried out. The method is as follows.

Write $A$ and $I$ side by side to form an $n$-by-$2n$ matrix,

$$C = (A, I).$$

Then we reduce $A$ by means of elementary row operations to canonical form, and carry out each operation on the rows of $C$. In finitely many steps we arrive at the $n$-by-$2n$ matrix

$$(H, B^{-1})$$

such that

$$A = BH.$$

How does this happen? Well, each step of the reduction of $A$ to $H$ corresponds to left multiplication by an elementary matrix. Thus $H$ is arrived at after multiplying $A$ by certain elementary matrices on the left,

$$H = E_k \cdots E_2 E_1 A,$$

so that

$$A = E_1{}^{-1} E_2{}^{-2} \cdots E_k{}^{-1} H = BH.$$

But we were applying these row operations to the rows of $C$, yielding

$$\begin{aligned} E_k \cdots E_2 E_1 C &= (E_k \cdots E_2 E_1 A, E_k \cdots E_2 E_1 I), \\ &= (H, B^{-1}). \end{aligned}$$

In particular, if $H = I$, then $B = A$ and $B^{-1} = A^{-1}$, and the next theorem is proved.

THEOREM 13.5. *If elementary row operations reducing A to Hermite form H are applied to the n-by-2n matrix $C = (A, I)$ the resulting matrix is $(H, B^{-1})$ where*

$$A = BH.$$

*Example* 3. Find the inverse of the following element of $R_3$:

$$A = \begin{pmatrix} 1 & 1 & 1 \\ 1 & 2 & 3 \\ 1 & 1 & 2 \end{pmatrix}.$$

Form $C = \begin{pmatrix} 1 & 1 & 1 & 1 & 0 & 0 \\ 1 & 2 & 3 & 0 & 1 & 0 \\ 1 & 1 & 2 & 0 & 0 & 1 \end{pmatrix}$.

Then

$$A_{21}(-1)A_{31}(-1)A_{32}(-2)A_{12}(-1)A_{13}(-1)C = (I, A^{-1})$$

so that

$$A^{-1} = A_{21}(-1)A_{31}(-1)A_{32}(-2)A_{12}(-1)A_{13}(-1)$$

and

$$A^{-1} = \begin{pmatrix} 1 & -1 & 0 \\ 0 & 1 & 0 \\ 0 & 0 & 1 \end{pmatrix}\begin{pmatrix} 1 & 0 & -1 \\ 0 & 1 & 0 \\ 0 & 0 & 1 \end{pmatrix}\begin{pmatrix} 1 & 0 & 0 \\ 0 & 1 & -2 \\ 0 & 0 & 1 \end{pmatrix}\begin{pmatrix} 1 & 0 & 0 \\ -1 & 1 & 0 \\ 0 & 0 & 1 \end{pmatrix}\begin{pmatrix} 1 & 0 & 0 \\ 0 & 1 & 0 \\ -1 & 0 & 1 \end{pmatrix}$$
$$= \begin{pmatrix} 1 & -1 & 1 \\ 1 & 1 & -2 \\ -1 & 0 & 1 \end{pmatrix}.$$

$A^{-1}$ can be expressed as the product of other elementary matrices; e.g.,

$$A^{-1} = A_{21}(-1)A_{31}(-1)A_{13}(-1)A_{32}(-1).$$

We note again that in finding $A^{-1}$ by using the $n$-by-$2n$ matrix $C$ it is unnecessary to write down the elementary matrices as we have here. It is only necessary to apply the corresponding row operations to $C$.

## Exercise 13.2

**1.** Let

$$A = \begin{pmatrix} 1 & -1 & 2 \\ 2 & 3 & 7 \\ -1 & 2 & 3 \end{pmatrix} \quad \text{and} \quad B = \begin{pmatrix} 2 & 7 & 1 \\ 4 & -1 & 2 \\ 4 & -31 & 2 \end{pmatrix}$$

be two elements of $R_3$. Express the rows of $AB$ as linear combinations of the row vectors $\mathbf{v}_1$, $\mathbf{v}_2$, and $\mathbf{v}_3$ of $B$. Express the columns of $AB$ as linear combinations of the column vectors of $A$.

**2.** Find the Hermite factorizations (Theorem 13.4) of the two matrices of Problem 1.

**3.** For the matrix $A$ of Problem 1 write out the products $E_{11}A$, $E_{21}A$, $E_{13}A$, $AE_{13}$, $AE_{22}$, $AE_{12}$. Describe the results.

**4.** What can you say about (*a*) row $i$ of $(I - E_{ii})A$? (*b*) row $i$ of $E_{ij}A$?

**5.** Prove that, if $A$ is nonsingular, then the rank of $AB$ equals the rank of $B$. (Consider the row space of $AB$ and of $B = A^{-1}(AB)$.)

**6.** Give geometrical descriptions of the effects of the elementary matrices $I_{12}$, $M_1(k)$, $M_2(k)$, $A_{12}(k)$, and $A_{21}(k)$ on $C_2(Re)$.

**7.** Discuss the elementary matrices as representations of elementary automorphisms on $V_n(F)$. (See Problem 6.)

**8.** Show that every nonsingular element of $F_2$ is expressible as a product of matrices $I_{12}$, $M_1(k)$, and $A_{12}(1)$. What does this mean, geometrically? (See Problem 6. Note that

$$M_2(k) = I_{12}M_1(k)I_{12}, \qquad A_{12}(k) = M_1(k^{-1})A_{12}(1)M_1(k),$$

etc.)

**9.** Find the inverse in $R_3$ of

$$A = \begin{pmatrix} 2 & -1 & 0 \\ 1 & 2 & 1 \\ -1 & 0 & 3 \end{pmatrix}.$$

Also find two different expressions for $A$ as the product of elementary matrices.

**10.** Use the result of Problem 9 to solve the following linear system:

$$\begin{aligned} 2x_1 - x_2 &= 3, \\ x_1 + 2x_2 + x_3 &= 2, \\ -x_1 + 3x_3 &= 1. \end{aligned}$$

(Rewrite this set of equations as

$$A\mathbf{u} = \mathbf{v}^T$$

where $\mathbf{u} = (x_1, x_2, x_3)$ and $\mathbf{v} = (3, 2, 1)$, and consider $A^{-1}(A\mathbf{u}^T) = A^{-1}\mathbf{v}^T$.)

**11.** Consider the homogeneous linear system

$$A\mathbf{u}^T = \mathbf{z}^T$$

where $A$ is in $F_n$ and $u = (x_1, \cdots, x_n)$ and $\mathbf{z} = (0, \cdots, 0)$ are in $C_n(F)$. Show that the set of such vectors $\mathbf{u}$ form a subspace of $C_n(F)$, the *solution subspace*, whose dimension is $n$ minus the rank of $A$. (Consider $BA\mathbf{u}^T = B\mathbf{z}^T$ when $B$ is a nonsingular matrix such that $BA$ is in Hermite or reduced row echelon form.)

**12.** Consider the linear system

$$A\mathbf{u}^T = \mathbf{v}^T$$

where $A$ is in $F_n$ and $\mathbf{u} = (x_1, \cdots, x_n)$ and $\mathbf{v} = (b_1, \cdots, b_n)$ are in $C_n(F)$. Show that, for given $A$ and $\mathbf{v}$, there exists a solution vector $\mathbf{u}$ if and only if $A$ and the $n$-by-$(n + 1)$ *augmented matrix* $C = (A, \mathbf{v}^T)$ have the same rank. (Consider $PA\mathbf{u}^T = P\mathbf{v}^T$, where $P$ is nonsingular and $PA$ is in Hermite or reduced row echelon form.)

**13.** Take $A$ and $B$ to be the matrices of Problem 1, and discuss the solution vectors of the following systems:

(*a*) $A\mathbf{u}^T = \mathbf{z}^T$;

(*b*) $B\mathbf{u}^T = \mathbf{z}^T$;

(*c*) $A\mathbf{u}^T = \mathbf{v}^T$, where $\mathbf{v} = (1, 2, 3)$;

(*d*) $B\mathbf{u}^T = \mathbf{v}^T$, where $\mathbf{v} = (1, 2, 3)$.

## 13.3 On the Right Side

As we noted previously the column vectors of the product $AB$ are linear combinations of the column vectors of $A$. This means that an elementary column operation on $A$ can be effected by multiplying $A$ on the right by the appropriate elementary matrix. Furthermore multiplying $A$ on the right by an elementary matrix yields a matrix obtainable from $A$ by an elementary column transformation. Now it is possible to go through a discussion of such matters without utilizing the material on elementary row operations and their relations with the elementary matrices, but this repetition can be avoided (as we saw earlier) by using the concept of the transpose of a matrix.

We recall that the matrix $B = (b_{rs})$ is the *transpose* of $A = (a_{rs})$ if and only if

$$b_{rs} = a_{sr}, \qquad r = 1, \cdots, n \quad \text{and} \quad s = 1, \cdots, n.$$

$B$ is denoted by $A^T$.

THEOREM 13.6. *The mapping* $\boldsymbol{T}$,

$$\boldsymbol{T}\colon A \to A^T, \quad \textit{all } A \textit{ in } F_n,$$

*is an anti-isomorphism of the complete matric algebra* $F_n$ *onto itself.*

(An *anti-isomorphism* preserves the addition but reverses the order of multiplication.)

It is very easy to show that $(A + B)^T = A^T + B^T$ so we shall consider only the multiplication here. Let

$$A = (a_{rs}), \quad B = (b_{rs}), \quad A^T = (c_{rs}), \quad \text{and} \quad B^T = (d_{rs});$$

then

$$a_{rs} = c_{sr} \qquad \text{and} \qquad b_{rs} = d_{sr}.$$

Now the $(i, j)$-element of $AB$ is

$$a_{i1}b_{1j} + a_{i2}b_{2j} + \cdots + a_{in}b_{nj}$$

so that the $(i, j)$-element of $(AB)^T$ is

$$a_{j1}b_{1i} + a_{j2}b_{2i} + \cdots + a_{jn}b_{ni}.$$

Also the $(i, j)$-element of $B^TA^T$ is

$$h_{ij} = d_{i1}c_{1j} + d_{i2}c_{2j} + \cdots + d_{in}c_{nj}$$

so that, substituting for the $c$'s and $d$'s, we have

$$h_{ij} = b_{1i}a_{j1} + b_{2i}a_{j2} + \cdots + b_{ni}a_{jn}.$$

This shows that

$$(AB)^T = B^TA^T.$$

When we look at the elementary matrices we see that their transposes are also elementary matrices.

THEOREM 13.7. *The transpose of an elementary matrix is again an elementary matrix.*

This depends upon the rather obvious fact that

$$E_{ij}{}^T = E_{ji}.$$

Then

$$(1) \qquad I_{ij}{}^T = (I - E_{ii} - E_{jj} + E_{ij} + E_{ji})^T,$$
$$= I - E_{ii} - E_{jj} + E_{ji} + E_{ij} = I_{ij};$$
$$(2) \qquad (M_i(k))^T = (I + (k-1)E_{ii})^T = M_i(k);$$

and

$$(3) \qquad (A_{ij}(k))^T = (I + kE_{ij})^T = I + kE_{ij} = A_{ji}(k).$$

*Corollary* 13.7.1. The matrix $A$ of $F_n$ is nonsingular if and only if $A^T$ is nonsingular.

$A$ is nonsingular if and only if it is expressible as the product of a finite set of elementary matrices, and similarly for $A^T$. Such an expression for one ($A$ or $A^T$) is obtainable from such an expression for the other by taking transposes.

*Corollary* 13.7.2. The effect of performing an elementary column operation on $A$ is obtainable by multiplying $A$ on the right by some elementary matrix. Conversely the product $AE$, $E$ an elementary matrix, can be obtained by performing an elementary column operation on $A$.

The result of applying an elementary column operation to $A$ is obtained by performing an elementary row operation of $A^T$, yielding $EA^T$, and taking the transpose of this. The result is

$$(EA^T)^T = (A^T)^T E^T = AE^T,$$

and $E^T$ is an elementary matrix.

Conversely, if $E$ is elementary then the transpose of $AE$ is $E^T A^T$, and $E^T$ is elementary. Since $E^T A^T$ is obtainable by applying an elementary row operation to $A^T$ we see that $AE$ is obtainable by applying an elementary column operation to $A$.

THEOREM 13.8. *An element $A$ of $F_n$ can be expressed in the form*

$$A = HB$$

*where $B$ is nonsingular and $H^T$ is in Hermite form. Furthermore this factorization is unique up to a unit of $F_n$.*

This is just a restatement of Theorem 13.4, as applied to $A^T$. By that theorem $A^T$ is uniquely expressible as

$$A^T = CD$$

where $C$ is nonsingular and $D$ is in Hermite form. Then taking transposes we have

$$A = HB$$

where $H = D^T$ and $B = C^T$.

*Example* 1. Find the unique $H$ of the above theorem for the following element of $R_3$:

$$A = \begin{pmatrix} 1 & 0 & 1 \\ 2 & 2 & 2 \\ -1 & 7 & -1 \end{pmatrix}.$$

We form $A^T$ and apply elementary row transformations:

$$A_1 = A^T = \begin{pmatrix} 1 & 2 & -1 \\ 0 & 2 & 7 \\ 1 & 2 & -1 \end{pmatrix}$$

$$A_2 = A_{13}(-1)A_1 = \begin{pmatrix} 1 & 2 & -1 \\ 0 & 2 & 7 \\ 0 & 0 & 0 \end{pmatrix},$$

$$A_3 = A_{21}(-1)A_2 = \begin{pmatrix} 1 & 0 & -8 \\ 0 & 2 & 7 \\ 0 & 0 & 0 \end{pmatrix},$$

$$A_4 = M_2(\tfrac{1}{2})A_3 = \begin{pmatrix} 1 & 0 & -8 \\ 0 & 1 & \frac{7}{2} \\ 0 & 0 & 0 \end{pmatrix}.$$

Thus

$$H = A_4{}^T = \begin{pmatrix} 1 & 0 & 0 \\ 0 & 1 & 0 \\ -8 & \frac{7}{2} & 0 \end{pmatrix}.$$

Furthermore,

$$H = AA_{31}(-1)A_{12}(-1)M_2(\tfrac{1}{2}).$$

The Hermite factorization of Theorems 13.4 and 13.8 can be considered in another light.

DEFINITION 13.2. Let $A$ and $B$ be two elements of $F_n$. Then $B$ is *right equivalent* with $A$ if and only if $F_n$ contains a nonsingular matrix $C$ such that

$$A = BC.$$

Since the nonsingular matrix $C$ is a product of a finite collection of elementary matrices we see that $B$ is right equivalent with $A$ if and only if $B$ is obtainable from $A$ by means of a finite number of elementary column operations.

THEOREM 13.9. *Right equivalence is an equivalence relation on $F_n$.*

(1) $A = AI$ and $I$ is certainly nonsingular, so that each element of $F_n$ is right equivalent with itself.

(2) If $A = BC$, $C$ nonsingular, then

$$B = AC^{-1},$$

$C^{-1}$ nonsingular, so that the relation is symmetric.

(3) If $A = BC$ and $B = DE$, $C$ and $E$ nonsingular, then $A = D(EC)$ and $EC$ is nonsingular.

This proves the theorem.

Therefore the relation of right equivalence partitions $F_n$ into nonempty, overlapping equivalence classes. Each of these equivalence classes contains *exactly one* matrix whose transpose is in Hermite form. For by Theorem 13.8 each element of $F_n$ is right equivalent with exactly one matrix whose transpose is in Hermite form.

Another such relation was mentioned briefly in Chapter 12 when the subject of changing bases in vector spaces was discussed.

DEFINITION 13.3. Two elements $A$ and $B$ of $F_n$ are *equivalent* if and only if $F_n$ contains nonsingular matrices $C$ and $D$ such that $A = CBD$.

This relation on $F_n$ utilizes both the elementary row operations and the elementary column operations.

THEOREM 13.10. *Equivalence of matrices is an equivalence relation on $F_n$.*

The proof is almost identical with the proof of Theorem 13.9.

Now we ask, what is the simplest matrix that $A$ can be reduced to by using both row and column operations? Certainly we can reduce $A$ to a matrix $H$ such that *both* $H$ and $H^T$ are in Hermite form, and this means that $H$ is a diagonal matrix with only 1's and 0's on the diagonal. By interchanging rows and interchanging columns (if necessary) the 1's can be listed first in the main diagonal, running down from top left to bottom right. Since all of this is accomplished through multiplication (left and right) by nonsingular matrices we see that the rank of the original matrix $A$ equals the rank of the final matrix, and this is clearly the number of 1's on the main diagonal.

This discussion leads to our next theorem.

THEOREM 13.11. *A matrix $A$ of $F_n$ of rank $r$ is equivalent with the matrix*

$$I_r = E_{11} + \cdots + E_{rr}.$$

First we reduce $A$ to Hermite form,

$$H = CA, \qquad C \text{ nonsingular},$$

which is triangular with only 1's and 0's on the main diagonal. Moreover, if $h_{ii}$ of $H = (h_{rs})$ is 1, then all other elements in column $i$ equal zero, and all elements of row $i$ are zero if $h_{ii} = 0$. This means that the only nonzero elements of $H$ not on the main diagonal must lie in rows which have 1 on the main diagonal. For example, in

$$H = \begin{pmatrix} 1 & h & 0 \\ 0 & 0 & 0 \\ 0 & 0 & 1 \end{pmatrix}$$

the element $h$ is unrestricted. Now we apply elementary column operations, using the columns having 1 in the main diagonal, to reduce all elements off the main diagonal to zero. In the above example we multiply $H$ by $A_{21}(-h)$, getting

$$H_1 = HA_{21}(-h) = \begin{pmatrix} 1 & h & 0 \\ 0 & 0 & 0 \\ 0 & 0 & 1 \end{pmatrix}\begin{pmatrix} 1 & -h & 0 \\ 0 & 1 & 0 \\ 0 & 0 & 1 \end{pmatrix} = \begin{pmatrix} 1 & 0 & 0 \\ 0 & 0 & 0 \\ 0 & 0 & 1 \end{pmatrix}.$$

Finally, to obtain the form described in the theorem we do some interchanging of rows and columns. In the example above we interchange rows 2 and 3, getting

$$H_2 = I_{23}H_1 = \begin{pmatrix} 1 & 0 & 0 \\ 0 & 0 & 1 \\ 0 & 0 & 0 \end{pmatrix},$$

and then interchange columns 2 and 3 in $H_2$, for

$$I_2 = \begin{pmatrix} 1 & 0 & 0 \\ 0 & 1 & 0 \\ 0 & 0 & 0 \end{pmatrix} = H_2I_{23}.$$

*Corollary* 13.11.1. Two elements of $F_n$ are equivalent if and only if they are of the same rank.

If $A$ and $B$ are of rank $r$, then by the above theorem there exist nonsingular matrices $C$, $D$, $H$, and $K$ such that

$$CAD = HBK = I_r.$$

Then

$$A = (C^{-1}H)B(KD^{-1})$$

so that $A$ and $B$ are equivalent.

The converse follows from the fact that matrix $CBD$ has the rank of $B$ when $C$ and $D$ are nonsingular.

*Corollary* 13.11.2. If $\boldsymbol{A}$ is a linear transformation from $V_n(F)$ to $W_n(F)$ of rank $r$ and if $A$ is an element of $F_n$ of rank $r$, then bases can be selected for $V_n$ and $W_n$ so that $A$ is the matrix of $\boldsymbol{A}$ relative to these bases.

Let $B$ be the matrix of $A$ relative to bases $\{\mathbf{v}_1, \cdots, \mathbf{v}_n\}$ for $V_n$ and $\{\mathbf{w}_1, \cdots, \mathbf{w}_n\}$ for $W_n$. Then $B$ has rank $r$, since $A$ does, so that $B$ and $A$ are equivalent. Hence there exist nonsingular matrices $C$ and $D$ such that

$$A = CBD.$$

These nonsingular matrices correspond to changes of bases in $V_n$ and $W_n$, and relative to the new bases $A$ is the matrix of $A$.

The canonical form of the theorem above can be used in solving linear systems. The matric equation

$$A\mathbf{u}^T = \mathbf{v}^T,$$

$A$ in $F_n$ and $\mathbf{u}$ and $\mathbf{v}$ in $C_n(F)$, can be rewritten

$$(CAD)D^{-1}\mathbf{u}^T = C\mathbf{v}^T$$

or

$$I_r\mathbf{w}^T = \mathbf{v}_1{}^T$$

with

$$CAD = I_r, \qquad C \text{ and } D \text{ nonsingular},$$
$$\mathbf{w}^T = D^{-1}\mathbf{u}^T,$$

and

$$\mathbf{v}_1{}^T = C\mathbf{v}^T.$$

## Exercise 13.3

1. Write out the transposes of $I_{41}$, $M_2(7)$, $A_{42}(3)$, and $A_{24}(-3)$ in $R_4$.
2. Prove that $E_{ij}{}^T = E_{ji}$.
3. Prove that $(A + B)^T = A^T + B^T$ and that $(A^T)^T = A$.
4. Let $A$ be nonsingular. Show that $(A^T)^{-1} = (A^{-1})^T$.
5. Let

$$A = \begin{pmatrix} 1 & -1 & 2 \\ 2 & 3 & 7 \\ -1 & 2 & 3 \end{pmatrix} \quad \text{and} \quad B = \begin{pmatrix} 2 & 7 & 1 \\ 4 & -1 & 2 \\ 4 & -31 & 2 \end{pmatrix}$$

be elements of $R_3$. Find the Hermite factor (Theorem 13.8) of each.

6. Find the inverse of

$$A = \begin{pmatrix} 2 & -1 & 0 \\ 1 & 2 & 1 \\ -1 & 0 & 3 \end{pmatrix}$$

in $R_3$ by performing elementary column operations on the 6-by-3 matrix

$$C = \begin{pmatrix} A \\ I \end{pmatrix}$$

in such a way as to reduce $A$ to $I$.

7. State a condition which is both necessary and sufficient for two elements of $F_n$ to be right equivalent.

**8.** Define left equivalence on $F_n$, and prove that it is an equivalence relation. Describe a unique representative of each equivalence class in $F_n$.

**9.** Prove Theorem 13.10.

**10.** Reduce the matrices of Problem 5 to the canonical form described in Theorem 13.11.

**11.** Reduce the following element of $R_4$ to the canonical form of Theorem 13.11:

$$A = \begin{pmatrix} 10 & 2 & -2 & 2 \\ 7 & 2 & -1 & 1 \\ -4 & 4 & 4 & -4 \\ -9 & -3 & 1 & -1 \end{pmatrix}.$$

**12.** Let $A$ of $F_n$ have rank $r$. Prove that, if $s$ is an arbitrary integer between $r$ and $n$, then $F_n$ contains an element $B$ of rank $s$ such that $BA = A$. (Write $CAD = I_r$; then $I_sI_r = I_r$ and $C^{-1}I_sC = B$.)

**13.** If $A$ of $F_n$ has rank $r$, then $n - r$ is called the *nullity* of $A$. Sylvester's *Law of Nullity* states that the nullity of $AB$ is no larger than the sum of the nullities of $A$ and $B$ and no smaller than the nullity of either $A$ or $B$. Prove the first part of this theorem by showing that the rank of $AB$ is never less than $r + s - n = s - (n - r)$, where $r$ and $s$ are the ranks of $A$ and $B$. (The rank of $AB$ equals the rank of $(CAD)(D^{-1}B)$ where $C$ and $D$ are nonsingular matrices such that $CAD = I_r$.)

**14.** Let $A$ be an element of $L(V_n(F);\ W_n(F))$. Show that bases can be selected so that $A$ is represented by $I_r$, where $r$ is the rank of $A$.

**15.** If $A = CBD = C_1BD_1$ where $C$, $C_1$, $D$, and $D_1$ are nonsingular elements of $F_n$, is it necessary that $C = C_1$ and $D = D_1$? Explain and illustrate.

**16.** Let $A$ be an element of $F_n$. Form the $2n$-by-$2n$ matrix

$$C = \begin{pmatrix} I & A \\ Z & I \end{pmatrix}$$

where $Z$ and $I$ are the additive and multiplicative identities, respectively, of $F_n$. Show that, if elementary row operations are applied to the first $n$ rows of $C$ and elementary column operations are applied to the last $n$ columns in such a way that $A$ is reduced to $I_r$ and $C$ to

$$\begin{pmatrix} B & I_r \\ Z & D \end{pmatrix},$$

then $BAD = I_r$.

**17.** Solve

$$A\mathbf{u}^T = \mathbf{v}^T$$

for $\mathbf{u} = (x_1, x_2, x_3)$, $\mathbf{v} = (3, 2, 1)$, and

$$A = \begin{pmatrix} 2 & -1 & 0 \\ 1 & 2 & 1 \\ -1 & 0 & 3 \end{pmatrix}$$

by finding nonsingular $C$ and $D$ such that

$$CAD = I.$$

Describe the system of linear equations which can be solved using these results.

## 13.4 Over a Polynomial Domain

It is possible to extend the results of the preceding sections on matrices over a field to matrices over certain rings with only minor changes. In this section we develop the factorization theorem of Section 13.2 for matrices of $S_n$, where $S$ is the polynomial domain of a field $F$. Then a matrix $A$ from this ring $S_n$ is expressible in the form

$$A = BH,$$

where $B$ is a unit of $S_n$ and $H$ is in Hermite form, and the factor $H$ is unique.

Here there are still three types of elementary matrices:

(1) The matrix $I_{ij}$ obtained by interchanging row $i$ and row $j$ of $I$.

(2) The matrix $M_i(k)$ obtained by multiplying row $i$ of $I$ by the nonzero element $k$ of $F$. (Note that $k$ is in $F$!)

(3) The matrix $A_{ij}(m)$ obtained by adding $m$ times row $i$ to row $j$, where $m$ is any element of $S = F[\lambda]$ and $i \neq j$.

The restriction that $k$ in $M_i(k)$ be a nonzero element of $F$ is made so that these elementary matrices of $S_n$ have inverses in $S_n$. (Naturally $B$ is the inverse of $A$ in $S_n$ if and only if $AB = BA = I$.)

These elementary matrices correspond to elementary row operations just as in our discussion of $F_n$. For $A$ in $S_n$:

(1) The matrix $I_{ij}A$ is obtainable by interchanging row $i$ and row $j$ of $A$.

(2) The matrix $M_i(k)A$ is obtainable by multiplying row $i$ of $A$ by the nonzero element $k$ of $F$.

(3) The matrix $A_{ij}(m)A$ is obtainable by adding $m$ times row $i$ to row $j$ of $A$, $m$ in $S = F[\lambda]$ and $i \neq j$.

Using these elementary row operations we can reduce $A$ to a matrix $H$ in $S_n$ of the following form:

(i) $H$ is triangular.

(ii) The diagonal elements $h_{11}, \cdots, h_{nn}$ of $H = (h_{rs})$ are either zero or monic polynomials.

(iii) If $h_{ii} = 0$, then all components in row $i$ equal zero.

(iv) If $h_{ii} \neq 0$, then every nonzero element of column $i$ has degree less than deg $(h_{ii})$.

This is the *Hermite form* of a matrix in $S_n$, $S = F[\lambda]$.

The reduction of a matrix $A$ in $S_n$ to this form is quite like the corresponding reduction in $F_n$. Consequently we shall skip the general discussion, which is just a repetition of the discussion of the reduction of an array to echelon form, and consider an example.

*Example* 1. Reduce the following element to Hermite form over the polynomial domain of $R$:

$$A = \begin{pmatrix} 2\lambda & 0 & 0 \\ 4\lambda^2 & 3 & 3 \\ 0 & 6\lambda & \lambda^2 \end{pmatrix}.$$

$$A_1 = A_{12}(-2\lambda)A = \begin{pmatrix} 2\lambda & 0 & 0 \\ 0 & 3 & 3 \\ 0 & 6\lambda & \lambda^2 \end{pmatrix},$$

$$A_2 = A_{23}(-2\lambda)A_1 = \begin{pmatrix} 2\lambda & 0 & 0 \\ 0 & 3 & 3 \\ 0 & 0 & \lambda^2 - 6\lambda \end{pmatrix},$$

$$H = M_1(\tfrac{1}{2})M_2(\tfrac{1}{3})A_2 = \begin{pmatrix} \lambda & 0 & 0 \\ 0 & 1 & 1 \\ 0 & 0 & \lambda^2 - 6\lambda \end{pmatrix}.$$

We see that $H$ is in Hermite form. Furthermore $A$ can be expressed as

$$A = A_{12}(2\lambda)A_{23}(2\lambda)M_2(3)M_1(2)H = BH,$$

where $B$ is a unit in $S_n$ since it has an inverse.

THEOREM 13.12. *An element $A$ of $S_n$, $S = F[\lambda]$, is expressible in the form*

$$A = BH,$$

*where $B$ is a product of elementary matrices and $H$ is in Hermite form. Moreover the factor $H$ is unique.*

If $H$ were not unique, then we would have

$$A = BH = CK$$

where $C$ is a product of elementary matrices and $K$ is in Hermite form. Then

$$H = B^{-1}CK$$

and we can obtain $H$ from $K$ by performing certain elementary row operations on $K$. Now we treat $H$ and $K$ as 5-by-5 matrices with the same last two rows but different third rows. (This example will illustrate the basic argument without involving excessively clumsy notation.) The rows of $H$ are

$$\begin{aligned} \mathbf{v}_1 &= (h_{11} \;\; h_{12} \;\; h_{13} \;\; h_{14} \;\; h_{15}), \\ \mathbf{v}_2 &= (\;0 \;\; h_{22} \;\; h_{23} \;\; h_{24} \;\; h_{25}), \\ \mathbf{v}_3 &= (\;0 \;\; 0 \;\; h_{33} \;\; h_{34} \;\; h_{35}), \\ \mathbf{v}_4 &= (\;0 \;\; 0 \;\; 0 \;\; h_{44} \;\; h_{45}), \\ \mathbf{v}_5 &= (\;0 \;\; 0 \;\; 0 \;\; 0 \;\; h_{55}), \end{aligned}$$

and the rows of $K$, $\mathbf{u}_1, \cdots, \mathbf{u}_5$, are of the same form, with

$$\mathbf{v}_4 = \mathbf{u}_4 \quad \text{and} \quad \mathbf{v}_5 = \mathbf{u}_5.$$

Now if $\mathbf{v}_3 \neq \mathbf{u}_3$, then both $h_{33}$ and $k_{33}$ cannot be zero, so we will take $h_{33} \neq 0$.

The question is this: Can we obtain $\mathbf{v}_3$ from the rows $\mathbf{u}_1, \mathbf{u}_2, \mathbf{u}_3, \mathbf{u}_4, \mathbf{u}_5$? That is, are there polynomials $a_1, \cdots, a_5$ in $S$ such that

$$\mathbf{v}_3 = a_1\mathbf{u}_1 + \cdots + a_5\mathbf{u}_5 ?$$

Certainly we can rule $\mathbf{u}_1$ and $\mathbf{u}_2$ out of the picture because of the triangular form of $H$ and $K$. So we are left with

$$\mathbf{v}_3 = a_3\mathbf{u}_3 + a_4\mathbf{u}_4 + a_5\mathbf{u}_5.$$

Again we use the zeros below the diagonal to show that

$$k_{33} \neq 0 \qquad \text{and} \qquad a_3 = 1.$$

For otherwise we would have the nonzero polynomial

$$h_{33} = a_3 0 + a_4 0 + a_5 0 = 0.$$

Thus

$$h_{33} = k_{33}.$$

Now consider

$$\mathbf{v}_3 - \mathbf{u}_3 = a_4\mathbf{u}_4 + a_5\mathbf{u}_5$$

and look at the fourth components:

$$h_{34} - k_{34} = a_4 k_{44} + a_5 0.$$

If $k_{44} \neq 0$, $h_{34} \neq k_{34}$, and $a_4 \neq 0$, then we consider degrees (of the polynomials):

$$\deg\,(h_{34} - k_{34}) = \deg\,(a_4 k_{44}).$$

But such an equation is impossible since $h_{34}$ and $k_{34}$ both have degrees *less* than the degree of $k_{44}$ (part (iv) of definition of Hermite form). Hence we see that

$$h_{34} = k_{34},$$

and, similarly, that $h_{35} = k_{35}$. Then $\mathbf{u}_3 = \mathbf{v}_3$, and from this we conclude that $H$ and $K$ cannot be different. So we see that the Hermite factor $H$ is unique.

Theorems very much like this have been proved for matrices over certain other rings (and undoubtedly more such theorems will be proved in the future). We shall not attempt to extend this idea further but will instead sketch a simple application.

*Example* 2. Consider the following system of differential equations:

$$\begin{aligned} DF_1 + DF_2 + F_2 + F_3 &= x^2 + x + 1, \\ D^2F_1 + D^2F_2 + 2DF_2 + DF_3 &= 2x, \\ DF_1 + D^2F_2 + DF_3 + F_3 &= x_2, \end{aligned}$$

where $F_1$, $F_2$, and $F_3$ are functions of the real variable $x$ possessing second derivatives. **Formally** this system can be written as

$$\begin{pmatrix} D & D+1 & 1 \\ D^2 & D^2+2D & D \\ D & D^2 & D+1 \end{pmatrix}\begin{pmatrix} F_1 \\ F_2 \\ F_3 \end{pmatrix} = \begin{pmatrix} x^2+x+1 \\ 2x \\ x^2 \end{pmatrix}$$

or

$$A\mathbf{u}^T = \mathbf{v}^T.$$

We see that

$$A_{23}(-D)M_2(-1)I_{23}A_{23}(1-D)A_{13}(-1)A_{12}(-D)A = \begin{pmatrix} D & D+1 & 1 \\ 0 & 1 & -D \\ 0 & 0 & D^2 \end{pmatrix}.$$

Moreover,

$$A_{23}(-D)M_2(-1)I_{23}A_{23}(1-D)A_{13}(-1)A_{12}(-D)\mathbf{v}^T = \mathbf{w}^T$$

where

$$\mathbf{w} = (x^2+x+1,\ x+2,\ -2)$$

since

$$A_{12}(-D)\mathbf{v}^T = \begin{pmatrix} x^2+x+1 \\ 2x - D(x^2+x+1) \\ x^2 \end{pmatrix} = \begin{pmatrix} x^2+x+1 \\ -1 \\ x^2 \end{pmatrix},$$

and so forth. Here

$$D(x^2+x+1) = 2x+1$$

just as $DF_1$ denotes the derivative of $F_1$. Then the system has been reduced to the simpler system (by reversible reductions so that the systems have the same solutions)

$$\begin{aligned} DF_1 + DF_2 + F_2 + F_3 &= x^2+x+1, \\ F_2 - DF_3 &= x+2, \\ D^2F_3 &= -2. \end{aligned}$$

This system is solved by dealing with the third equation and finding $F_3$, substituting this in equation two and then finding $F_2$, and finally substituting in the first equation and finding $F_1$. These details are omitted here.

Later we shall find that Theorem 13.12 can be used in finding the characteristic polynomial of an element of $F_n$.

## Exercise 13.4

**1.** Find the inverse of each of the following over the polynomial domain of $R$:

$$A = \begin{pmatrix} 1 & \lambda^2 & 0 \\ 0 & 1 & 0 \\ 0 & 0 & 1 \end{pmatrix}; \qquad B = \begin{pmatrix} 10 & \lambda^2+1 \\ 0 & 1 \end{pmatrix};$$

$$C = \begin{pmatrix} 0 & 2 & 0 & 0 \\ 2 & 0 & 0 & 0 \\ 0 & 0 & 1 & 0 \\ 0 & 0 & \lambda^3+1 & 1 \end{pmatrix}.$$

**2.** Write out the following matrices of $S_3$ when $S = R[\lambda]$: $A_{21}(\lambda^3 - \lambda + 1)$; $A_{13}(\lambda)$; $M_2(-1)$; $I_{13}$.

**3.** Find the Hermite factor of

$$A = \begin{pmatrix} 3\lambda + 6 & 0 & \lambda + 2 & 2\lambda \\ 6\lambda & \lambda & 2\lambda & 0 \\ 0 & \lambda - 1 & 0 & 0 \\ \lambda - 1 & 2 - 2\lambda & 0 & 1 \end{pmatrix}.$$

**4.** Let $A$ be the element of $S_n$, $S = F[\lambda]$. Show that, by using *both* elementary row and elementary column operations, $A$ can be changed to a matrix $B = (b_{rs})$ such that $b_{11}$ is the G.C.F. of all the components in $A$. Illustrate with the matrix $A$ of Problem 3.

**5.** Continuing the work of Problem 4 show that a matrix $A$ over $F[\lambda]$ can be reduced by elementary row and column operations to a diagonal matrix $D = (d_{rs})$ where $d_{ii}$ is a factor of $d_{jj}$ if $j$ exceeds $i$ and $d_{ii} \neq 0$. Proceed as follows:

(*a*) Get the G.C.F. of the set of all components of $A$ in the upper left corner.

(*b*) Reduce all other elements in row 1 and in column 1 to zero.

(*c*) Ignore the top row and left column and repeat steps (*a*) and (*b*) on the resulting $(n - 1)$-by-$(n - 1)$ matrix.

(*d*) Continue until a diagonal matrix is obtained. (The nonzero diagonal elements are the *invariant factors* of $A$.)

**6.** Reduce the matrix $A$ of Problem 3 to the diagonal form of Problem 5. What are the invariant factors of $A$?

**7.** Simplify the following system of differential equations:

$$\begin{pmatrix} 0 & 6D & D \\ D - 1 & 0 & D - 1 \\ 3D - 3 & 1 - D & 2D - 2 \end{pmatrix} \begin{pmatrix} F_1 \\ F_2 \\ F_3 \end{pmatrix} = \begin{pmatrix} x + \cos x \\ x^2 + 1 \\ \sin x \end{pmatrix},$$

where $F_1$, $F_2$, and $F_3$ are functions of the real variable $x$. What assumptions need to be made about the $F_i$?

**8.** If the functions $F_1$, $F_2$, $F_3$ of Example 2 are assumed to be polynomial functions, find $F_1$, $F_2$, and $F_3$.

**9.** How would you justify the procedure in Example 2?

**10.** List some rings $S$ which are neither fields nor polynomial domains of fields such that Theorem 13.12 can be extended (in some reasonable form) to $S_n$. (Consider some of the quadratic domains, sfields, etc.)

**11.** What would the Hermite form for matrices with components in $J$ be? For matrices with components in $J/(m)$?

**12.** Describe the elementary matrices in $J_n$.

**13.** Reduce the matrix

$$A = \begin{pmatrix} 4 & 6 & -8 \\ 6 & 4 & 0 \\ 0 & 6 & 10 \end{pmatrix}$$

to Hermite form over $J$ by using appropriate elementary row operations. Is this form unique? Why?

**14.** How would you link left $S$-modules with the matric rings $S_n$?

## 13.5 Determinants

Most students are exposed to some of the simpler facts about determinants in their high school and first-year college algebra courses. There the determinant is commonly introduced as a tool for solving a system of $n$ linear equations in $n$ unknowns. This is a rather unfortunate situation since determinants are not particularly well adapted to such a task, so that students are inclined to regard the subject with no little skepticism. But properly regarded the concept of determinant provides an important and useful link between the elements of $S_n$ and $S$ when $S$ is a commutative ring.

Since the student is expected to have had some slight knowledge of the subject we shall present an inductive definition of determinant without a discussion of the "general" solution of a pair of "indefinite" linear equations in two unknowns. Let $S$ be a commutative ring (which can be thought of, for the most part, as a field $F$ or its polynomial domain). Then the elements of $S$ can be considered as 1-by-1 matrices so that $S_1 = S$, and we define the determinant of such a matrix to be the single component. Thus

$$\mathbf{det}\,(a_{11}) = a_{11}.$$

Stepping up to $S_2$, where the matrices have four components, we define

$$\begin{aligned}\mathbf{det} = \mathbf{det}\begin{pmatrix} a_{11} & a_{12} \\ a_{21} & a_{22} \end{pmatrix}, \\ = (-1)^{1+1}a_{11}\,\mathbf{det}\,(a_{22}) + (-1)^{1+2}a_{12}\,\mathbf{det}\,(a_{21}), \\ = a_{11}a_{22} - a_{12}a_{21}.\end{aligned}$$

Before going on we consider the question of why such an expression should be studied.

*Example* 1. Show that the matrix $A$ of $R_2$ is nonsingular if and only if

$$\mathbf{det}\, A = 0.$$

$A$ is nonsingular if and only if $A$ can be reduced to $I$ by elementary row operations. Taking $a_{11} \neq 0$ (otherwise we can interchange rows) we divide row 1 by $a_{11}$ and *then* add $-a_{21}$ times row 1 to row 2. The resulting row 2 is

$$(0 \quad a_{22} - a_{21}a_{12}/a_{11})$$

and certainly $A$ is nonsingular if and only if the second component

$$a_{22} - a_{21}a_{12}/a_{11} \neq 0.$$

DEFINITION 13.4. If $A$ is an element of $S_n$, where $S$ is a commutative ring, then

(i) $$\mathbf{det}\, A = \mathbf{det}\,(a_{11}) = a_{11} \qquad \text{when } n = 1,$$

and

(ii) $$\mathbf{det}\, A = \sum_{i=1}^{n} (-1)^{1+i} a_{1i}\,\mathbf{det}\, A_{1i}, \qquad n > 1,$$

where $A_{ij}$ denotes the $(n-1)$-by-$(n-1)$ matrix obtained from $A$ by eliminating row $i$ and column $j$.

The matrix $A_{ij}$ is called a *minor* of $A$, and equation (ii), defining the determinant of an element of $S_n$ in terms of determinants of elements in $S_{n-1}$, is called the *expansion of* **det** *A by minors of row* 1. Then the expansion of the determinant of an element of $S_3$ is

$$\mathbf{det}\, A = a_{11}\, \mathbf{det}\, A_{11} - a_{12}\, \mathbf{det}\, A_{12} + a_{13}\, \mathbf{det}\, A_{13}.$$

Because of the inductive nature of the definition we see that the determinant of an element $A$ of $S_n$ is a uniquely determined element **det** $A$ of $S$. Thus we have a mapping from $S_n$ to $S$ defined by

$$A \to \mathbf{det}\, A, \qquad A \text{ in } S_n,$$

and we shall study the properties of this mapping.

*Example* 2. Show that the determinant of an element of $S_2$ can be expressed in terms of the minors of row 2.

From

$$\mathbf{det}\, A = a_{11}a_{22} - a_{12}a_{21}$$

we get

$$\mathbf{det}\, A = (-1)^{2+1}a_{21}\, \mathbf{det}\, A_{21} + (-1)^{2+2}a_{22}\, \mathbf{det}\, A_{22}$$

since

$$\mathbf{det}\, A_{21} = a_{12} \qquad \text{and} \qquad \mathbf{det}\, A_{22} = a_{11}.$$

This suggests that we can release **det** $A$, for $A$ in $S_n$, from its dependence on the first row.

THEOREM 13.13. *If $A$ is in $S_n$, then*

$$\mathbf{det}\, A = (-1)^{i+1}a_{i1}\, \mathbf{det}\, A_{i1} + \cdots + (-1)^{i+n}a_{in}\, \mathbf{det}\, A_{in}$$

*for each i from* 1 *to n.*

Such an expression for **det** $A$ is called the *expansion by minors of row i.*

The proof is by induction on $n$, and we see that the example above serves as a starting point. Then our induction hypothesis states that the determinant of an element of $S_{n-1}$ can be expanded by minors of any row, and we consider the defining expansion of **det** $A$:

$$\mathbf{det}\, A = a_{11}\, \mathbf{det}\, B_1 - a_{12}\, \mathbf{det}\, B_2 + \cdots + (-1)^{1+n}a_{1n}\, \mathbf{det}\, B_n$$

where $B_i = A_{1i}$, for $i = 1, \cdots, n$. Now the matrices $B_i$ are in $S_{n-1}$ so that the determinants of the $B$'s can be expanded by any row desired.

We select as $i$ an arbitrary but fixed element from the integers $2, \cdots, n$. Then we expand each **det** $B_j$ by minors of row $(i - 1)$ of $B_j$ since row $(i - 1)$ of $B_j$ involves the elements of row $i$ in $A$. From the expansions of each **det** $B_j$ in terms of its row $(i - 1)$ we obtain an expansion of **det** $A$ as a sum of $n(n - 1)$ terms. The algebraic signs in this expansion must be watched carefully, for, if $B_j = B = (b_{rs})$, then, expanding by row $(i - 1)$,

$$\mathbf{det}\, B = (-1)^{i-1+1}b_{i-1,1}\, \mathbf{det}\, B_{i-1,1} + \cdots + (-1)^{i-1+n}b_{i-1,n}\, \mathbf{det}\, B_{i-1,n}.$$

But the elements $b_{rs}$ are also elements of $A$ so that for $B = B_1$ we have

$$\textbf{det } B = (-1)^i a_{i2} \textbf{ det } B_{i-1,1} + \cdots + (-1)^{i-1+n} a_{in} \textbf{ det } B_{i-1,n}.$$

Now we can regroup these terms to produce

$$\textbf{det } A = (-1)^{i+1} a_{i1} \textbf{ det } A_{i1} + \cdots + (-1)^{i+n} a_{in} \textbf{ det } A_{in},$$

by selecting the $n - 1$ terms involving the factor $a_{ij}$, for each $j$. The element $a_{ij}$ appears in row $(i - 1)$ of all the $B$'s except $B_j$, and the coefficient of $a_{ij}$ is seen to be $(-1)^{i+j}$ times the expansion of **det** $A_{ij}$ by minors of the first row.

To illustrate we take $n = 4$ and $i = 3$. Then

$$\textbf{det } A = a_{11} \textbf{ det } A_{11} - a_{12} \textbf{ det } A_{12} + a_{13} \textbf{ det } A_{13} - a_{14} \textbf{ det } A_{14}.$$

The matrix $A_{11}$ is

$$B = A_{11} = \begin{pmatrix} a_{22} & a_{23} & a_{24} \\ a_{32} & a_{33} & a_{34} \\ a_{42} & a_{43} & a_{44} \end{pmatrix} = \begin{pmatrix} b_{11} & b_{12} & b_{13} \\ b_{21} & b_{22} & b_{23} \\ b_{31} & b_{32} & b_{33} \end{pmatrix}$$

so that, expanding by row $(i - 1) = 2$, we get

$$\textbf{det } B = (-1)^{2+1} b_{21} \textbf{ det } B_{21} + (-1)^{2+2} b_{22} \textbf{ det } B_{22} + (-1)^{2+3} b_{23} \textbf{ det } B_{23}$$

and

$$\textbf{det } A_{11} = -a_{32} \textbf{ det } B_{21} + a_{33} \textbf{ det } B_{22} - a_{34} \textbf{ det } B_{23}.$$

Similarly

$$\textbf{det } A_{12} = -a_{31} \textbf{ det } C_{21} + a_{33} \textbf{ det } C_{22} - a_{34} \textbf{ det } C_{23}$$

where

$$C = A_{12} = \begin{pmatrix} a_{21} & a_{23} & a_{24} \\ a_{31} & a_{33} & a_{34} \\ a_{41} & a_{43} & a_{44} \end{pmatrix},$$

$$\textbf{det } A_{13} = -a_{31} \textbf{ det } D_{21} + a_{32} \textbf{ det } D_{22} - a_{34} \textbf{ det } D_{23}$$

where

$$D = A_{13},$$

and

$$\textbf{det } A_{14} = -a_{31} \textbf{ det } G_{21} + a_{32} \textbf{ det } G_{22} - a_{33} \textbf{ det } G_{23}$$

where

$$G = A_{14}.$$

Assembling the three terms involving $a_{31}$, we get

$$-a_{31}(-a_{12}\ \mathbf{det}\ C_{21} + a_{13}\ \mathbf{det}\ D_{21} - a_{14}\ \mathbf{det}\ G_{21}),$$

and from

$$C_{21} = \begin{pmatrix} a_{23} & a_{24} \\ a_{43} & a_{44} \end{pmatrix}, \quad D_{21} = \begin{pmatrix} a_{22} & a_{24} \\ a_{42} & a_{44} \end{pmatrix}, \quad \text{and} \quad G_{21} = \begin{pmatrix} a_{22} & a_{23} \\ a_{42} & a_{43} \end{pmatrix}$$

we conclude that the coefficient of $a_{31}$ is the determinant of $A_{31}$ since

$$A_{31} = \begin{pmatrix} a_{12} & a_{13} & a_{14} \\ a_{22} & a_{23} & a_{24} \\ a_{42} & a_{43} & a_{44} \end{pmatrix}.$$

In the same way we show that the coefficient of $a_{32}$ is $-\mathbf{det}\ A_{32}$, of $a_{33}$ is $\mathbf{det}\ A_{33}$, and of $a_{34}$ is $-\mathbf{det}\ A_{34}$. Hence

$$\begin{aligned} \mathbf{det}\ A = (-1)^{3+1}a_{31}\ \mathbf{det}\ A_{31} + (-1)^{3+2}a_{32}\ \mathbf{det}\ A_{32} \\ + (-1)^{3+3}a_{33}\ \mathbf{det}\ A_{33} + (-1)^{3+4}a_{34}\ \mathbf{det}\ A_{34}. \end{aligned}$$

This theorem allows a choice of rows to be made in evaluating a determinant, and this is quite useful.

*Example* 3. Evaluate the determinant of the following element of $R_3$:

$$A = \begin{pmatrix} 1 & 2 & 3 \\ 0 & 4 & 5 \\ 0 & 0 & 6 \end{pmatrix}.$$

We expand about row 3 so that

$$\mathbf{det}\ A = 6\ \mathbf{det}\ A_{33},$$

and $\mathbf{det}\ A_{33}$ can be expanded about row 2 so that

$$\mathbf{det}\ A = 6(4)1 = 24.$$

*Corollary* 13.13.1. If $A$ is a triangular matrix then

$$\mathbf{det}\ A = a_{11}a_{22}\cdots a_{nn}.$$

We proceed, as in the example, to expand $\mathbf{det}\ A$ by row $n$ which conveniently contains $n - 1$ zeros. Then

$$\mathbf{det}\ A = a_{nn}\ \mathbf{det}\ A_{nn}.$$

Since $A_{nn}$ is a triangular element of $S_{n-1}$ we conclude (from the induction hypothesis) that

$$\mathbf{det}\ A = a_{11}a_{22}\cdots a_{nn}.$$

*Corollary* 13.13.2. If the matrix $A$ contains a row of zeros, then $\mathbf{det}\ A = 0$.

Expand about the row of zeros.

*Corollary* 13.13.3. $\mathbf{det}\,(M_i(k)A) = k\,\mathbf{det}\,A$.

Here $M_i(k)$ is the elementary matrix of $S_n$ formed by adding $(k - 1)E_{ii}$ to $I$. As in $F_n$ the matrix $M_i(k)A$ is the matrix obtainable by multiplying the elements of row $i$ by $k$. Then expanding about row $i$ yields

$$\mathbf{det}\,(M_i(k)A) = k\,\mathbf{det}\,A.$$

*Note*: Since $\mathbf{det}\,M_i(k) = k$, by Corollary 13.13.1, we can write

$$\mathbf{det}\,(M_i(k)A) = (\mathbf{det}\,M_i(k))(\mathbf{det}\,A).$$

This last result suggests that we should determine what effect the elementary row operations on $A$ have on $\mathbf{det}\,A$.

THEOREM 13.14. $\mathbf{det}\,(A_{ij}(k)A) = \mathbf{det}\,A$, $\quad i \neq j$ *and* $k$ *in* $S$.

In other words we wish to show that, if matric $B$ is obtained from $A$ by adding $k$ times row $i$ to row $j$, then $A$ and $B$ have equal determinants. Since this is easy to verify in $S_2$ we proceed by induction on $n$. For $A$ and $B$ in $S_n$ we express $\mathbf{det}\,B$ in terms of row $m$ where $m$ differs from both $i$ and $j$. (Naturally we need only consider the case for $n$ larger than 2.) Then the minors of row $m$ in $B$ are obtainable from the corresponding minors of row $m$ in $A$ by adding $k$ times one row to another. Therefore, by the induction hypothesis,

$$\mathbf{det}\,B_{m1} = \mathbf{det}\,A_{m1}, \cdots, \mathbf{det}\,B_{mn} = \mathbf{det}\,A_{mn},$$

so that

$$\mathbf{det}\,B = \mathbf{det}\,A.$$

*Corollary* 13.14.1. $\mathbf{det}\,(A_{ij}(k)A) = (\mathbf{det}\,A_{ij}(k))(\mathbf{det}\,A)$ when $i \neq j$ and $k$ is in $S$.

By Corollary 13.13.1 the determinant of $A_{ij}(k)$ is 1 since that matrix is triangular (upper or lower).

*Corollary* 13.14.2. If row $j$ of $A$ equals $k$ times row $i$ of $A$, $i \neq j$, then $\mathbf{det}\,A = 0$.

For the matrix $B = A_{ij}(-k)A$ has a row of zeros.

*Corollary* 13.14.3. The determinant of the elementary matrix $I_{ij}$, $i \neq j$, is $-1$.

We can write

$$I_{ij} = M_i(-1)A_{ij}(1)A_{ji}(-1)A_{ij}(1).$$

From the corollaries above we have

$$\begin{aligned}\mathbf{det}\,I_{ij} &= (\mathbf{det}\,M_i(-1))(\mathbf{det}\,A_{ij}(1))(\mathbf{det}\,A_{ji}(-1))(\mathbf{det}\,A_{ij}(1)),\\ &= (-1)(1)(1)(1) = -1.\end{aligned}$$

*Corollary* 13.14.4. $\mathbf{det}\,(I_{ij}A) = -\mathbf{det}\,A$ when $i \neq j$.

We see from the preceding proof that

$$I_{ij}A = M_i(-1)A_{ij}(1)A_{ji}(-1)A_{ij}(1)A,$$

so that by using the properties set forth in Corollaries 13.13.3 and 13.14.1 we have

$$\mathbf{det}\,(I_{ij}A) = -\mathbf{det}\,A.$$

Looking back through these simple corollaries we see that

$$\mathbf{det}\,(EA) = (\mathbf{det}\,E)(\mathbf{det}\,A)$$

whenever $E$ is an elementary matrix of $S_n$ and $A$ is arbitrary in $S_n$. In the next section we shall extend this very important multiplicative property to any two matrices whose components are in a field $F$ or a polynomial domain $F[\lambda]$.

These corollaries can be used to simplify the problem of calculating the determinant of a matrix $A$ by permitting us to calculate the determinant of a "simpler" matrix, viz., one with lots of zeros in it.

*Example* 4. Evaluate **det** $A$ for the following element of $R_3$:

$$A = \begin{pmatrix} 2 & 3 & 5 \\ 7 & 8 & 9 \\ 9 & 8 & 6 \end{pmatrix}.$$

We see that

$$A_{23}((-17)/5)A_{13}(-9)A_{12}(-2)A_{21}(-3)I_{12}A = \begin{pmatrix} 1 & -1 & -6 \\ 0 & 5 & 17 \\ 0 & 0 & (11)/5 \end{pmatrix} = B.$$

Then

$$\mathbf{det}\,B = 11$$

and

$$\mathbf{det}\,A = -11$$

since

$$\mathbf{det}\,I_{12} = -1$$

and

$$\mathbf{det}\,A_{ij}(k) = 1.$$

We can prove quite easily by induction that **det** $A$ is linear in each component of the matrix $A$. In fact **det** $A$ consists of the sums and differences of the $n!$ products formed from all possible selections of $n$ components of $A$ with exactly *one* from each row and each column.

*Example* 5. Write out the complete expansion of **det** $A$ when $A = (a_{rs})$ is an element of $S_3$.

$$\begin{aligned} \mathbf{det}\,A &= a_{11}\,\mathbf{det}\,A_{11} - a_{12}\,\mathbf{det}\,A_{12} + a_{13}\,\mathbf{det}\,A_{13}, \\ &= a_{11}(a_{22}a_{33} - a_{23}a_{32}) - a_{12}(a_{21}a_{33} - a_{23}a_{32}) + a_{13}(a_{21}a_{32} - a_{22}a_{31}). \end{aligned}$$

## Exercise 13.5

**1.** Evaluate the determinant of $A$ in Example 4 through repeated application of Definition 13.4.

**2.** Display the minor expansions of **det** $A$ for rows 2 and 3 when $A$ is the matrix of Example 4.

**3.** Let $A = (a_{rs})$ be an element of $S_4$. Write out the minors $A_{24}$ and $A_{41}$.

**4.** Find the determinants of the following matrices over $R$:

(*a*) $$A = \begin{pmatrix} 4 & 5 & -6 \\ 6 & 5 & -3 \\ 1 & -3 & -2 \end{pmatrix};$$

(*b*) $$B = \begin{pmatrix} 2 & 4 & 0 & 3 \\ 2 & 2 & 1 & 4 \\ 2 & 6 & -2 & 8 \\ 3 & 1 & 2 & 6 \end{pmatrix};$$

(*c*) $$C = \begin{pmatrix} 3 & -1 & -1 & 0 \\ -2 & 4 & 1 & 1 \\ 4 & 5 & 3 & 3 \\ 3 & 2 & 7 & 12 \end{pmatrix};$$

(*d*) $$D = \begin{pmatrix} 1 & 2 & 3 & 4 & 5 \\ 2 & 3 & 4 & 5 & 6 \\ 3 & 4 & 5 & 6 & 7 \\ 4 & 5 & 6 & 7 & 8 \\ 5 & 6 & 7 & 8 & 9 \end{pmatrix}.$$

**5.** Find the determinant of each of the matrices of Problem 4 when the components lie in $J/(7)$.

**6.** Let $a$, $b$, and $c$ be arbitrary elements of $S$ and show that the following element of $S_3$,

$$A = \begin{pmatrix} 1 & 1 & 1 \\ a & b & c \\ a^2 & b^2 & c^2 \end{pmatrix},$$

has **det** $A = (a - b)(b - c)(c - a)$. (This is the Vandermonde determinant. What would the statement be in $S_n$?)

**7.** A *monomial matrix* in $F_n$ is one in which exactly one nonzero element appears in each row and in each column (e.g., $I$ and $I_{ij}$). Show that the product of two monomial matrices is again monomial. Prove by induction that the determinant of a monomial matrix is either the product of the nonnegative components or the negative of that product. (Compare with Corollary 13.14.4.)

**8.** Extend the definitions of elementary matrices and elementary row operations in $F_n$ to $S_n$, where $S$ is a commutative ring with identity 1. Note that the matrix $M_i(k)$ does not have an inverse unless $k$ of $S$ has a multiplicative inverse.

**9.** Determine the complete expansion of the determinant of $A$ over $S = R[\lambda]$ for

$$A = \begin{pmatrix} \lambda & \lambda - 1 & \lambda - 2 \\ 3 & 2 & 1 \\ 1 & 2 & 1 \end{pmatrix}.$$

What are the zeros of the resulting polynomial? What is noticeable about the matrix of $R_n$ which is obtained by replacing $\lambda$ by a zero of **det** $A$?

**10.** Verify that **det** $I_{12} = -1$ for $I_{12}$ in $S_2$.

**11.** Prove by induction that the complete expansion of **det** $A$ for $A = (a_{rs})$ in $S_n$ consists of the sums of the $n!$ products of the form

$$ea(1, i_1)a(2, i_2) \cdots a(n, i_n)$$

where

$$a(i, j) = a_{ij},$$

the components of $A$, where $(i_1, i_2, \cdots, i_n)$ is a permutation of the integers $1, 2, \cdots, n$ and where $e$ is 1 or $-1$.

**12.** The permutation $(i_1, i_2, \cdots, i_n)$ is *even* if and only if the product

$$m = ((i_1 - i_2)(i_1 - i_3)\cdots(i_1 - i_n))((i_2 - i_3)\cdots(i_2 - i_n))\cdots((i_{n-1} - i_n))$$

equals $((1 - 2)(1 - 3)\cdots(1 - n))((2 - 3)\cdots(2 - n))\cdots((n - 1 - n))$. (So the permutation $i_1 = 2$, $i_2 = 3$, $i_3 = 1$ is an even permutation of (1, 2, 3) since $((2 - 3)(2 - 1))(3 - 1) = -2 = ((1 - 2)(1 - 3))(2 - 3)$. But the permutation $i_1 = 1$, $i_2 = 3$, $i_3 = 2$ is *odd* or not even since $((i_1 - i_2)(i_1 - i_3))(i_2 - i_3) = +2$ in this case.) Show that the sign affixed to the product

$$a(1, i_1)a(2, i_2)a(3, i_3)$$

of **det** $A$, $A$ in $S_3$, is plus if $(i_1, i_2, i_3)$ is an even permutation and is minus otherwise.

**13.** From Problems 11 and 12 how would you characterize **det** $A$?

**14.** What is the degree of the polynomial

$$\mathbf{det}\,(A - \lambda I)$$

of $F[\lambda]$ when $A$ and $I$ are in $F_n$?

**15.** Let $A$ be an element of $S_n$ where $S = F[\lambda]$. Show that **det** $A$ equals **det** $H$ or $-$**det** $H$ where $H$ is the Hermite factor of $A$,

$$A = BH.$$

**16.** Find the expansion of the determinant of $A$ over $R[\lambda]$ for

$$A = \begin{pmatrix} 4 - \lambda & 2 & 3 \\ 1 & 5 - \lambda & 0 \\ 3 & 0 & -2 - \lambda \end{pmatrix}$$

by finding the Hermite factor of $A$.

## 13.6 Determinant of a Product

In this section we restrict our attention to determinants of matrices from $S_n$ where $S$ is either a field $F$ or the polynomial domain of a field. For these we can prove that

$$\mathbf{det}\,AB = \mathbf{det}\,A \cdot \mathbf{det}\,B$$

when $A$ and $B$ are in $S_n$. The proofs are quite simple.

THEOREM 13.15. *Let $S$ be a field or the polynomial domain of a field. Then for $A$ and $B$ in $S_n$ we have*

$$\det AB = \det A \cdot \det B.$$

The proof is based on the Hermite factorization of an element in $S_n$, and this accounts for the particular rings $S$ which we have specified here.

(1) If $S$ is a field $F$ we can write

$$AB = (CH)B, \qquad H \text{ in Hermite form,}$$

where $C$ is a product of finitely many elementary matrices of $F_n$. Then by Corollaries 13.13.1, 13.13.3, and 13.14.4 we have

$$\det AB = \det C \cdot \det HB.$$

If $A$ has rank $n$, then

$$H = I;$$

otherwise $H$ contains a row of zeros. So if $A$ has rank $n$, then

$$AB = CIB,$$
$$A = C;$$

and

$$\det AB = \det C \cdot \det IB$$

so that

$$\det AB = \det A \cdot \det B.$$

If $A$ has rank less than $n$, then $H$ has a row of zeros. Therefore $HB$ has a row of zeros, so, by Corollary 13.13.2,

$$\det H = \det HB = 0.$$

Then

$$\det AB = \det C \cdot \det HB = 0.$$

But

$$\det A = \det C \cdot \det H = 0$$

so that

$$\det AB = 0 = \det A \cdot \det B.$$

This completes the argument when $S$ is a field.

(2) If $S$ is the polynomial domain of a field, then the above argument has to be altered somewhat (although the following argument actually takes care of Case (1) also). Now the Hermite factor $H$ of $A$ can be reduced to diagonal form (see Exercise 5, page 567) through multiplication on the *right* by the appropriate elementary matrices, and we can write

$$A = CDE,$$

where $C$ and $E$ are products of elementary matrices and $D$ is a diagonal matrix. If the diagonal elements of $D$ are denoted by $d_{ii}$, $i = 1, 2, \cdots, n$, then $D$ can be factored as

$$D = M_1(d_{11})M_2(d_{22}) \cdots M_n(d_{nn}).$$

Therefore Corollaries 13.13.3, 13.14.1, 13.14.3, and 13.14.4 can be applied a finite number of times to justify the following equations:

$$\begin{aligned}&\mathbf{det}\, AB = \mathbf{det}\, C(DEB) = \mathbf{det}\, C \cdot \mathbf{det}\, DEB,\\ &\mathbf{det}\, D(EB) = \mathbf{det}\, D \cdot \mathbf{det}\, EB,\\ &\mathbf{det}\, EB = \mathbf{det}\, E \cdot \mathbf{det}\, B,\\ &\mathbf{det}\, A = \mathbf{det}\, C(DE) = \mathbf{det}\, C \cdot \mathbf{det}\, DE,\end{aligned}$$

and

$$\mathbf{det}\, DE = \mathbf{det}\, D \cdot \mathbf{det}\, E.$$

Thus we see that

$$\mathbf{det}\, AB = \mathbf{det}\, A \cdot \mathbf{det}\, B.$$

This theorem tells us that, when $S$ is a field or the polynomial domain of a field, then the mapping from $S_n$ to $S$ given by

$$\boldsymbol{F}: A \to \mathbf{det}\, A$$

is compatible with the binary operations of multiplication in $S_n$ and $S$.

*Corollary* 13.15.1. The determinantal mapping $\boldsymbol{F}$ from $S_n$ to $S$ is a homomorphism from the multiplicative semigroup $S_n$ onto the multiplicative semigroup $S$. Moreover $A$ of $S_n$ is mapped onto 0 of $S$ if and only if the Hermite factor of $A$ contains a row of zeros.

This corollary is immediate from the above proof.

The potential usefulness of such a mapping is rather apparent when we compare the features of $S$ and $S_n$. Here $S$ is an integral domain, and $S_n$ (for $n$ larger than 1) possesses divisors of zero and has noncommutative multiplication. We shall have occasion to use this mapping in the next section when we encounter the topics of characteristic value, characteristic polynomial and characteristic vector.

THEOREM 13.16. *The matrix $A$ of $F_n$ is nonsingular if and only if*

$$\mathbf{det}\, A \neq 0.$$

Since the determinant of an elementary matrix of $F_n$ is nonzero we see that **det** $A$ is different from zero if and only if the Hermite factor of $A$ has rank $n$. Since the rank of the Hermite factor of $A$ equals the rank of $A$ we see that **det** $A \neq 0$ if and only if $A$ has rank $n$ (i.e., $A$ is nonsingular).

From this we should suspect that **det** $A$ can be used in finding the matrix $A^{-1}$ when it exists. The method of cofactors for finding $A^{-1}$ depends on determinants.

DEFINITION 13.5. The element

$$a'_{ij} = (-1)^{i+j}\, \mathbf{det}\, A_{ij},$$

where $A_{ij}$ is the $(n-1)$-by-$(n-1)$ minor of $A$ of $S_n$ obtained by eliminating row $i$ and column $j$ of $A$, is the *cofactor* of $A_{ij}$ in $A = (a_{rs})$. The transpose of the matrix $(a'_{rs})$ is the *adjoint* of $A$, denoted by **adj** $A$.

*Example* 1. Find **adj** $A$ in $R_3$ when

$$A = \begin{pmatrix} 1 & 2 & 1 \\ 2 & 1 & 1 \\ 0 & 0 & 1 \end{pmatrix}.$$

$$a'_{11} = (-1)^{1+1} \mathbf{det} \begin{pmatrix} 1 & 1 \\ 0 & 1 \end{pmatrix} = 1;$$

$$a'_{12} = (-1)^{1+2} \mathbf{det} \begin{pmatrix} 2 & 1 \\ 0 & 1 \end{pmatrix} = -2;$$

and

$$a'_{13} = (-1)^{1+3} \mathbf{det} \begin{pmatrix} 2 & 1 \\ 0 & 0 \end{pmatrix} = 0.$$

Thus *column* 1 of **adj** $A$ is

$$\begin{pmatrix} 1 \\ -2 \\ 0 \end{pmatrix},$$

and further computation yields

$$\mathbf{adj}\, A = \begin{pmatrix} 1 & -2 & 1 \\ -2 & 1 & 1 \\ 0 & 0 & -3 \end{pmatrix}.$$

Note that

$$A(\mathbf{adj}\, A) = -3I,$$

and

$$\mathbf{det}\, A = -3.$$

This illustrates the next theorem.

THEOREM 13.17. *If $A$ is in $S_n$, then*

$$A(\mathbf{adj}\, A) = (\mathbf{det}\, A)I.$$

This is a consequence of the minor expansion for **det** $A$:

$$\mathbf{det}\, A = a_{i1}a'_{i1} + a_{i2}a'_{i2} + \cdots + a_{in}a'_{in}$$

for each $i = 1, \cdots, n$. On the other hand when $i \neq j$ the element

$$a_{i1}a'_{j1} + a_{i2}a'_{j2} + \cdots + a_{in}a'_{jn}$$

is nothing but the determinant, expanded by minors of row $i$, of a matrix having row $i$ and row $j$ equal. Since such a matrix has determinant zero we see that the product $A(\mathbf{adj}\, A)$ is the scalar **det** $A$ times the identity matrix $I$.

*Example* 2. Illustrate the above argument in $R_3$.

The element

$$a_{11}a'_{21} + a_{12}a'_{22} + a_{13}a'_{23}$$

is the expansion by minors of row 1 of the determinant of

$$B = \begin{pmatrix} a_{11} & a_{12} & a_{13} \\ a_{11} & a_{12} & a_{13} \\ a_{31} & a_{32} & a_{33} \end{pmatrix}.$$

For

$$a'_{21} = (-1)^{2+1} \mathbf{det} \begin{pmatrix} a_{12} & a_{13} \\ a_{32} & a_{33} \end{pmatrix}$$

and so forth. Certainly

$$\mathbf{det}\, B = 0.$$

*Corollary* 13.17.1. If $A$ is in $F_n$ and $\mathbf{det}\, A \neq 0$, then $A^{-1} = (b_{rs})$ where

$$b_{rs} = a'_{sr}/\mathbf{det}\, A.$$

This follows from the theorem when the equation is divided by $\mathbf{det}\, A$, leaving

$$A(\mathbf{adj}\, A)(1/\mathbf{det}\, A) = I.$$

Hence

$$A^{-1} = (1/\mathbf{det}\, A)\, \mathbf{adj}\, A.$$

*Example* 3. Find $A^{-1}$ for the matrix $A$ of Example 1.

There we found

$$A(\mathbf{adj}\, A) = -3I.$$

$$A^{-1} = \begin{pmatrix} -\frac{1}{3} & \frac{2}{3} & -\frac{1}{3} \\ \frac{2}{3} & -\frac{1}{3} & -\frac{1}{3} \\ 0 & 0 & 1 \end{pmatrix}.$$

Note that the method of cofactors involves the evaluation of $n^2$ determinants of matrices in $S_{n-1}$ as well as the evaluation of $\mathbf{det}\, A$. This sharply restricts the usefulness of the method except for small values of $n$ or for very special matrices.

From this corollary we have a fairly useless method for solving certain linear systems over $F$. If a system of $n$ linear equations in $n$ unknowns $x_1, \cdots, x_n$ is written as

$$A\mathbf{u}^T = \mathbf{v}^T,$$

where $A = (a_{rs})$, $\mathbf{u} = (x_1, \cdots, x_n)$, and $\mathbf{v} = (b_1, \cdots, b_n)$, then the system has a unique solution if and only if $A^{-1}$ exists, and we can write

$$A^{-1}A\mathbf{u}^T = \mathbf{u}^T = A^{-1}\mathbf{v}^T.$$

Then

$$x_i = (a'_{1i}b_1 + a'_{2i}b_2 + \cdots + a'_{ni}b_n)/\mathbf{det}\, A,$$

where $a'_{ij}$ is the cofactor of $a_{ij}$ in $A$. This is known as *Cramer's Rule*, and it is frequently written as

$$x_i = \mathbf{det}\, B_i/\mathbf{det}\, A, \qquad i = 1, \cdots, n,$$

where $B_i$ is the matrix obtained by replacing column $i$ of $A$ with the column vector $\mathbf{v}^T$. Then the expansion of **det** $B$ by minors of column $i$ is

$$b_1a'_{1i} + b_2a'_{2i} + \cdots + b_na'_{ni}.$$

Expansion by minors of a *column* has not been discussed up to now, but the validity of such an expansion for the determinant of an element in $F_n$ is easily proved by considering the transpose of a matrix as we now show.

THEOREM 13.18. *Let $A$ be an element of $S_n$ where $S = F$ or $F[\lambda]$. Then* **det** $A$ = **det** $A^T$.

Since $A$ can be expressed in the form

$$A = E_m \cdots E_2E_1H,$$

where the $E_i$ are elementary matrices and $H$ is in Hermite form, we have

$$\mathbf{det}\, A = \mathbf{det}\, E_m \cdots \mathbf{det}\, E_2\, \mathbf{det}\, E_1\, \mathbf{det}\, H$$

and

$$\mathbf{det}\, A^T = \mathbf{det}\, H^T\, \mathbf{det}\, E_1{}^T\, \mathbf{det}\, E_2{}^T \cdots \mathbf{det}\, E_m{}^T.$$

Now $H$ and $H^T$ are both triangular (one upper and the other lower) so that

$$\mathbf{det}\, H = \mathbf{det}\, H^T,$$

so consider the elementary matrices. The matrices $I_{ij}$ and $M_i(k)$ are symmetric,

$$\mathbf{det}\, A_{ij}(k) = 1,$$

and the transpose of $A_{ij}(k)$ is $A_{ji}(k)$. Hence the factors of **det** $A$ and **det** $A^T$ are equal so that

$$\mathbf{det}\, A = \mathbf{det}\, A^T.$$

*Corollary* 13.18.1. The determinant of $A$ in $S_n$, $S = F$ or $F[\lambda]$, can be expanded by minors of any column of $A$.

For this is just the expansion of **det** $A^T$ (= **det** $A$) by minors of a row of $A^T$.

## Exercise 13.6

**1.** Let $A$ and $B$ be elements of $S_2$. Prove by direct computation that **det** $AB$ = **det** $A \cdot$ **det** $B$.

**2.** Let $N$ be the set of all elements $A$ of $F_n$ such that **det** $A = 0$. Show that $N$ is a subsemigroup of the multiplicative semigroup $F_n$ with the property that $AB$ is in $N$ if and only if $A$ and/or $B$ is in $N$. Show also that $F_n = N \cup G$, where $G$ is the full linear group.

**3.** Compute the adjoint of an element $A$ of $S_2$, and find the product $A(\mathbf{adj}\ A)$.

**4.** Explain why the row-column method of multiplying matrices leads to the definition of **adj** $A$ as the transpose of $(a'_{rs})$.

**5.** Compute the inverse of matrix $A$ in Problem 4, Section 13.5, by the method of cofactors.

**6.** Solve the linear system

$$\begin{aligned} x_1 + 2x_2 + 3x_3 &= 4, \\ 2x_1 + 3x_2 - 4x_3 &= 5, \\ 2x_1 - 3x_2 + 4x_3 &= 6, \end{aligned}$$

over $R$ by using Cramer's Rule. Solve by elimination also and compare methods.

**7.** Let $A$ be in $F_n$. Show that $\mathbf{det}\ (\mathbf{adj}\ A) = (\mathbf{det}\ A)^{n-1}$.

**8.** For $A$ and $B$ in $F_n$ show that

$$\mathbf{det}\ AB = \mathbf{det}\ AB^T.$$

What does this say about row-by-row multiplication of matrices?

**9.** How are **det** $A$ and **det** $A^{-1}$ related?

**10.** An element $A$ of $S_n$, $S = F[\lambda]$, is *unimodular* if and only if **det** $A$ is a unit of $S$.

(*a*) Prove that $A$ is unimodular if and only if its Hermite factor $H$ is $I$.

(*b*) Prove that $A$ is unimodular if and only if it is expressible as the product of a finite collection of elementary matrices from $S_n$.

(*c*) Prove that $A$ is unimodular if and only if $S_n$ contains $B$ such that $AB = BA = I$.

**11.** Let $A$ be an element of $R_3$ of rank 2. Show that $A$ possesses a nonzero cofactor.

**12.** An $m$-by-$m$ minor of $A$ of $F_n$ is obtained by eliminating $n - m$ rows and columns from $A$. Show that $A$ has $m$ linearly independent row vectors if it has an $m$-by-$m$ minor whose determinant is nonzero.

**13.** Show that, if the determinants of the three matrices

$$A = \begin{pmatrix} a_1 & b_1 \\ a_2 & b_2 \end{pmatrix}, \quad B = \begin{pmatrix} a_1 & c_1 \\ a_2 & c_2 \end{pmatrix}, \quad C = \begin{pmatrix} b_1 & c_1 \\ b_2 & c_2 \end{pmatrix}$$

are all zero, then the two vectors $(a_1, b_1, c_1)$ and $(a_2, b_2, c_2)$ of $C_3(F)$ are linearly dependent.

**14.** Generalize Problem 13 and show that, if the matrix $A$ of $F_n$ contains $m$ linearly independent row vectors, then $A$ must contain an $m$-by-$m$ minor whose determinant is different from zero. (Show that the elementary row operations on $m$ linearly independent rows of $A$ do not affect the ranks of the $m$-by-$m$ minors which can be obtained from these rows.)

**15.** The *determinantal rank* of $A$ in $F_n$ is defined to be the largest $m$ such that $A$ has an $m$-by-$m$ minor with nonzero determinant. Conclude from Problems 12 and 14 that the determinantal rank of $A$ equals the rank of $A$.

**16.** The matrix $A$ of $F_n$ is *orthogonal* if and only if $A^T = A^{-1}$. What is the value of **det** $A$ when $A$ is orthogonal? Give two examples of orthogonal matrices in $R_3$.

**17.** Show that the matrix of a rotation of $C_2(Re)$ about the origin is orthogonal.

**18.** Show that the orthogonal matrices of $F_n$ form a multiplicative group.

**19.** A matrix $A$ of $J_n$ is unimodular if and only if **det** $A = 1$ or $-1$ (see Problem 10). Show that the unimodular matrices of $J_n$ form a multiplicative group (the *unimodular group*).

## 13.7 Characteristic Polynomial

In Chapter 12 we saw that matrices $A$ and $B$ of $F_n$ correspond to the same linear transformation in $\boldsymbol{L}(V_n(F))$ relative to some bases for $V_n(F)$ if and only if $F_n$ contained a nonsingular matrix $C$ such that

$$B = CAC^{-1}.$$

This is clearly a special case of the relation of equivalence for matrices in $F_n$ since $C^{-1}$ is nonsingular also, so we naturally ask if $C$ can be selected in such a way that $B$ is particularly simple. (Remember that a matrix $A$ of $F_n$ is equivalent with a diagonal matrix $I_r$.) That is, in the language of vector spaces, can a basis be selected for $V_n(F)$ in such a way that the matrix of a specified element of $\boldsymbol{L}(V_n(F))$ is in a particular form? We will investigate this question in the remaining sections of this chapter.

DEFINITION 13.6. The element $B$ of $F_n$ is *similar* to $A$ if and only if there exists a nonsingular matrix $C$ such that

$$B = CAC^{-1}.$$

In other words, two matrices are similar if and only if each corresponds to the same linear transformation relative to the appropriate bases for $V_n(F)$.

THEOREM 13.19. *Similarity is an equivalence relation on* $F_n$.

The proof is like that of Theorem 13.9.

Now what special type of matrix should we select as a possible representative of each equivalence class in the resulting partition? Because of the canonical form (viz., $I_r$) relative to the equivalence relation of equivalence of matrices we might hope that each element of $F_n$ is similar to a diagonal matrix.

*Example* 1. In $F_2$ show that $A = I + E_{12}$ is *not* similar to a diagonal matrix.

Assume that $C$ is a nonsingular matrix such that $CAC^{-1}$ is diagonal. Then

$$CA = DC$$

where

$$C = \begin{pmatrix} a & b \\ c & d \end{pmatrix} \quad \text{and} \quad D = \begin{pmatrix} f & 0 \\ 0 & g \end{pmatrix},$$

so that

$$\begin{pmatrix} a & a + b \\ c & c + d \end{pmatrix} = \begin{pmatrix} fa & fb \\ gc & gd \end{pmatrix}.$$

Hence $a = fa$, $a + b = fb$, $c = gc$, and $c + d = gd$. Now $a$ and $c$ cannot both be zero, but, if $a \neq 0$, then

$$a = fa$$

implies

$$f = 1,$$

which with $a + b = fb$ implies $a = 0$, an impossibility. Also $c \neq 0$ and $c = gc$ imply that $g = 1$ so that

$$c + d = gd = d$$

and $c = 0$. Thus we see that the matrix $C$ does not exist.

This example shows that we cannot expect an element of $F_n$ to be similar in general to a diagonal matrix. So we step down a notch and ask if each matrix over $F$ is similar to a triangular matrix.

*Example* 2. If $A$ is an element of $F_2$, when is it similar to a triangular matrix?

To answer this question we utilize the connection between matrices and linear transformations (we will use this connection a great many times in the next few pages). There exists a nonsingular $C$ such that

$$CAC^{-1} = \begin{pmatrix} a & b \\ 0 & c \end{pmatrix}$$

if and only if $V_2(F)$ has a basis of vectors $\mathbf{v}_1$ and $\mathbf{v}_2$ such that

$$\mathbf{v}_1 A = a\mathbf{v}_1 + b\mathbf{v}_2$$

and

$$\mathbf{v}_2 A = 0\mathbf{v}_1 + c\mathbf{v}_2$$

where $A$ is the linear transformation on $V_2$ defined by the matrix $A$ and a basis for $V_2$, say $\mathbf{u}_1$ and $\mathbf{u}_2$. This is equivalent to the conditions that $V_2$ contains a one-dimensional subspace $(\mathbf{v}_2)$ which is in the nullspace of the linear transformation $A - cI$ since

$$\mathbf{v}_2(A - cI) = c\mathbf{v}_2 - c\mathbf{v}_2 = \mathbf{z}.$$

And this is equivalent to saying that the matrix of $A - cI$ relative to the basis of vectors $\mathbf{u}_1$ and $\mathbf{u}_2$, namely

$$A - cI,$$

is a singular matrix. Thus we see that the matrix $A$ is similar to a triangular matrix if and only if $F$ contains an element $c$ such that

$$\det(A - cI) = 0.$$

That is, $A$ is similar to a triangular matrix in $F_2$ if and only if the polynomial

$$\det(A - \lambda I)$$

of $F[\lambda]$ has a zero in $F$. From this we conclude that a 2-by-2 matrix over the complex field is similar to a triangular matrix.

The results for $F_2$ are quite typical of the general situation, and we shall prove that $A$ of $F_n$ is similar in $F_n$ to a triangular matrix if and only if the polynomial $\mathbf{det}\,(A - \lambda I)$ is decomposable into linear factors in $F[\lambda]$.

DEFINITION 13.7. The polynomial $\mathbf{det}\,(A - \lambda I)$ in $F[\lambda]$ is the *characteristic polynomial* of $A$, and its zeros are the *characteristic values* of $A$.

*Example* 3. The characteristic polynomial in $R[\lambda]$ of

$$A = \begin{pmatrix} 1 & 1 \\ 1 & 2 \end{pmatrix}$$

is $\mathbf{det}\,(A - \lambda I) = \lambda^2 - 3\lambda + 1$. Since this polynomial is irreducible over $R$ we conclude that $A$ is *not* similar to a triangular matrix in $R_2$.

THEOREM 13.20. *If $A$ and $B$ are similar matrices in $F_n$, then $A$ and $B$ have the same characteristic polynomials (and characteristic values).*

If $A$ and $B$ are similar in $F_n$, then a nonsingular $C$ exists such that

$$B = CAC^{-1}.$$

Then

$$B - \lambda I = CAC^{-1} - \lambda I = C(A - \lambda I)C^{-1}$$

so that

$$\mathbf{det}\,(B - \lambda I) = \mathbf{det}\,C \cdot \mathbf{det}\,(A - \lambda I) \cdot \mathbf{det}\,C^{-1}.$$

Since

$$\mathbf{det}\,C \cdot \mathbf{det}\,C^{-1} = \mathbf{det}\,I = 1$$

we have

$$\mathbf{det}\,(B - \lambda I) = \mathbf{det}\,(A - \lambda I).$$

*Corollary* 13.20.1. Each element of $\boldsymbol{L}(V_n(F))$ has a characteristic polynomial in $F[\lambda]$, namely, the characteristic polynomial of the matrix corresponding to the linear transformation relative to any basis for $V_n(F)$.

Relative to different bases for $V_n(F)$ a particular linear transformation has similar describing matrices. Hence there is a unique characteristic polynomial associated with each element of $\boldsymbol{L}(V_n(F))$, and this is called the characteristic polynomial of the linear transformation. Naturally the zeros of this polynomial are the characteristic values of the linear transformation.

So consider the **triangularization problem:** For a given linear transformation $A$ (described by a matrix, say) on $V_n(F)$ find basis vectors $\mathbf{v}_1, \cdots, \mathbf{v}_n$ for $V_n$ such that

$$\begin{aligned}
\mathbf{v}_1 A &= a_{11}\mathbf{v}_1 + a_{12}\mathbf{v}_2 + \cdots + a_{1n}\mathbf{v}_n, \\
\mathbf{v}_2 A &= \qquad\quad\;\; a_{22}\mathbf{v}_2 + \cdots + a_{2n}\mathbf{v}_n, \\
&\;\;\vdots \\
\mathbf{v}_n A &= \qquad\qquad\qquad\qquad\qquad\; a_{nn}\mathbf{v}_n.
\end{aligned}$$

Then the matrix $(a_{rs})$ is triangular,

$$\det\big((a_{rs}) - \lambda I\big) = (a_{11} - \lambda)(a_{22} - \lambda)\cdots(a_{nn} - \lambda),$$

and we see that the diagonal elements of the triangular matrix $(a_{rs})$ of $A$ are precisely the characteristic values of $A$. In other words, if an element $B$ of $F_n$ is similar to a triangular matrix $A$ of $F_n$, $A = (a_{rs})$, then

$$\begin{aligned}\det(B - \lambda I) &= \det(A - \lambda I)\\ &= (a_{11} - \lambda)(a_{22} - \lambda)\cdots(a_{nn} - \lambda).\end{aligned}$$

Thus the complete factorization of the characteristic polynomial of a matrix is a necessary condition for the matrix to be similar to a triangular matrix.

THEOREM 13.21. *An element $A$ of $\mathbf{L}(V_n(F))$ is representable by a triangular matrix from $F_n$ only if the characteristic polynomial of $A$ factors completely in $F[\lambda]$.*

In the next section we shall see that this necessary condition for the triangularization of a matrix is also sufficient. Now for some examples.

*Example* 4. Show that the following element of $R_3$ is not similar in $R_3$ to a triangular matrix:

$$A = \begin{pmatrix} 1 & 1 & 5 \\ -1 & 1 & -2 \\ -1 & 0 & -1 \end{pmatrix}.$$

To find the characteristic polynomial of $A$ we reduce the matrix $A - \lambda I$ to a convenient form over $F[\lambda]$ by means of elementary row transformations:

$$A_1 = A_{31}(1 - \lambda)A_{32}(-1)(A - \lambda I) = \begin{pmatrix} 0 & 1 & \lambda^2 - 4 \\ 0 & 1 - \lambda & \lambda - 1 \\ -1 & 0 & -1 - \lambda \end{pmatrix}.$$

Then

$$\det A_1 = \det(A - \lambda I) = -1(\det B)$$

where $B$ is the minor obtained from $A_1$ by eliminating row 3 and column 1. Hence

$$\det(A - \lambda I) = -(\lambda - 1)(\lambda^2 - 3),$$

and since $\lambda^2 - 3$ is irreducible over $R$ we conclude that $A$ cannot be triangularized.

Relative to the characteristic value 1 we can however make an alteration in the appearance of $A$. Interpret $A$ as the matrix of a linear transformation $\mathbf{A}$ on $C_3(R)$ relative to the canonical basis, so that

$$\begin{aligned}\mathbf{e}_1\mathbf{A} &= \mathbf{e}_1 + \mathbf{e}_2 + 5\mathbf{e}_3,\\ \mathbf{e}_2\mathbf{A} &= -\mathbf{e}_1 + \mathbf{e}_2 - 2\mathbf{e}_3,\\ \mathbf{e}_3\mathbf{A} &= -\mathbf{e}_1 \phantom{+ \mathbf{e}_2} - \mathbf{e}_3.\end{aligned}$$

Then the linear transformation $\mathbf{A} - 1\mathbf{I} = \mathbf{A} - \mathbf{I}$ has a nontrivial nullspace $U$, and from equations

$$\mathbf{e}_1(\mathbf{A} - \mathbf{I}) = \mathbf{e}_2 + 5\mathbf{e}_3,$$
$$\mathbf{e}_2(\mathbf{A} - \mathbf{I}) = -\mathbf{e}_1 - 2\mathbf{e}_3,$$

and

$$\mathbf{e}_3(\mathbf{A} - \mathbf{I}) = -\mathbf{e}_1 - 2\mathbf{e}_3,$$

we see that $\mathbf{u} = \mathbf{e}_2 - \mathbf{e}_3$ is in $U$. Selecting the basis $\mathbf{e}_1$, $\mathbf{e}_2$, and $\mathbf{u}$ for $C_3(R)$ we get a somewhat simpler matrix for $\mathbf{A}$:

$$\begin{aligned} \mathbf{e}_1\mathbf{A} &= \mathbf{e}_1 + \mathbf{e}_2 + 5\mathbf{e}_3 = \mathbf{e}_1 + 6\mathbf{e}_2 - 5\mathbf{u}, \\ \mathbf{e}_2\mathbf{A} &= -\mathbf{e}_1 + \mathbf{e}_2 - 2\mathbf{e}_3 = -\mathbf{e}_1 - \mathbf{e}_2 + 2\mathbf{u}, \\ \mathbf{u}\mathbf{A} &= \mathbf{e}_2\mathbf{A} - \mathbf{e}_3\mathbf{A} = \mathbf{e}_2 - \mathbf{e}_3 = \mathbf{u}. \end{aligned}$$

The change of basis is effected by the linear transformation $\mathbf{C}$ defined by

$$\mathbf{e}_1\mathbf{C} = \mathbf{e}_1, \quad \mathbf{e}_2\mathbf{C} = \mathbf{e}_2, \quad \text{and} \quad \mathbf{e}_3\mathbf{C} = \mathbf{u} = \mathbf{e}_2 - \mathbf{e}_3,$$

so that the matrix $C$ of $\mathbf{C}$ relative to the canonical basis is

$$C = \begin{pmatrix} 1 & 0 & 0 \\ 0 & 1 & 0 \\ 0 & 1 & -1 \end{pmatrix}.$$

Then

$$CAC^{-1} = \begin{pmatrix} 1 & 6 & -5 \\ -1 & -1 & 2 \\ 0 & 0 & 1 \end{pmatrix}$$

is precisely the matrix of $\mathbf{A}$ relative to the new basis made up from $\mathbf{e}_1$, $\mathbf{e}_2$, and $\mathbf{u}$.

DEFINITION 13.8. The vector $\mathbf{v} \neq \mathbf{z}$ in $V_n(F)$ is a *characteristic vector* of the element $\mathbf{A}$ of $L(V_n(F))$ if and only if $\mathbf{v}$ lies in the nullspace of $\mathbf{A} - c\mathbf{I}$ for some scalar $c$.

Obviously the scalar $c$ must be a characteristic value of $\mathbf{A}$ since the existence of $\mathbf{v} \neq \mathbf{z}$ in the nullspace of $\mathbf{A} - c\mathbf{I}$ depends completely upon the rank of $\mathbf{A} - c\mathbf{I}$ being less than $n$. And the rank of $\mathbf{A} - c\mathbf{I}$ is less then $n$ if and only if $c$ is a zero of the characteristic polynomial of $\mathbf{A}$. Thus to each characteristic value of $\mathbf{A}$ there corresponds at least one characteristic vector in $V_n(F)$.

*Example* 5. Show that several linearly independent vectors of $V_n(F)$ can correspond to the same characteristic value for some linear transformations.

The linear transformation $\mathbf{I}$ on $V_n(F)$ has exactly one characteristic value, viz., $c = 1$. At the same time every nonzero vector of $V_n$ is a characteristic vector of $\mathbf{I}$.

It is possible to speak of the characteristic vectors of a matrix $A$ of $F_n$ through the usual association between the elements of $L(V_n(F))$ and $F_n$ relative to a basis for $V_n(F)$. The linear transformation $\mathbf{A}$ associated with $A$ has certain characteristic vectors and these can be considered as characteristic vectors of $A$ *relative to the given basis for* $V_n(F)$. However, other linear transformations, possibly operating on other vector spaces, can also be associated with $A$ so that one must be careful in speaking of characteristic vectors of a matrix $A$ to specify the space $V_n$ and its basis.

## Exercise 13.7

**1.** Write out the proof of Theorem 13.19.

**2.** Show that the two matrices $A = I + E_{12}$ and $I$ of $R_2$ have the same characteristic polynomial and characteristic values. What do you conclude from this?

**3.** Let $A$ be the following element of $R_2$,

$$A = \begin{pmatrix} 1 & 1 \\ -2 & 2 \end{pmatrix}.$$

(i) Find the characteristic polynomial of $A$.

(ii) Find the characteristic values of $A$.

(iii) Relative to the canonical basis for $C_2(R)$, find a characteristic vector for $A$.

(iv) Find $C$ in $R_2$ such that $CAC^{-1}$ is triangular.

**4.** Find the characteristic polynomial of the following matrices over the complex field:

$$A = \begin{pmatrix} 3 & 2 & -1 \\ -2 & 5 & 3 \\ 1 & 7 & 2 \end{pmatrix}; \quad B = \begin{pmatrix} 1 & 0 & 1 \\ -2 & 11 & 9 \\ -3 & 7 & 4 \end{pmatrix}; \quad C = \begin{pmatrix} 1 & 3 & 2 \\ 1 & 4 & 2 \\ -1 & 2 & -1 \end{pmatrix}.$$

**5.** Find the characteristic values of the matrices in Problem 4.

**6.** The matrices of Problem 4 define linear transformations of $C_3(F)$ relative to the canonical basis. Find the characteristic vectors of these. (Consider the system of linear equations in unknowns $x_1$, $x_2$, and $x_3$ of $F$, given by

$$\mathbf{v}(A - cI) = (0, 0, 0)$$

where $\mathbf{v} = (x_1, x_2, x_3)$.)

**7.** Show that different elements of $L(V_n(F))$ can have the same characteristic polynomial.

**8.** Reduce the matrix

$$A = \begin{pmatrix} 1 & 2 \\ 5 & 4 \end{pmatrix}$$

to diagonal form over $R$ by finding $C$ such that $CAC^{-1}$ is diagonal.

**9.** Show that $A$ and $A^T$ have the same characteristic polynomial.

**10.** Prove that the characteristic polynomial of the matrix $A$ of $F_n$ is a polynomial of degree $n$ with leading coefficient $(-1)^n$.

**11.** Let $p(\lambda) = (-1)^n\lambda^n + c_{n-1}\lambda^{n-1} + \cdots + c_1\lambda + c_0$ be the characteristic polynomial of $A = (a_{rs})$ of $F_n$. Prove that

(i) $$c_{n-1} = e(a_{11} + a_{22} + \cdots + a_{nn}),$$

where $e = 1$ or $-1$. (The element $a_{11} + a_{22} + \cdots + a_{nn}$ is the *trace* of $A$.)

(ii) $$c_0 = \mathbf{det}\, A.$$

**12.** Illustrate Problem 11 using the results of Problem 4.

**13.** A mapping $K$ from $F_n$ to some set $S$ is a *similarity invariant* if $K(A) = K(B)$ whenever $A$ and $B$ are similar. Prove that the following mappings are invariants of similarity:

(*a*) $K_1(A) = \mathbf{det}\,(A - \lambda I)$, all $A$ in $F_n$.
(*b*) $K_2(A) = \mathbf{det}\,A$, all $A$ in $F_n$.
(*c*) $K_3(A) = \text{trace}\,A$, all $A$ in $F_n$.
(*d*) $K_4(A) = m$, where $m$ is the dimension of the subspace of $F_n$ (as a vector space over $F$) spanned by the matrices $I, A, A^2, \cdots$.

**14.** Show that nonsimilar matrices sometimes have the same trace, the same determinant, and the same characteristic polynomial.

**15.** Show that a matrix $A$ from $R_2$ with trace $A = 3$ and $\mathbf{det}\,A = 2$ is similar to the diagonal matrix $2E_{11} + E_{22}$ by considering the characteristic polynomial of $A$.

**16.** Prove the converse of Problem 15.

**17.** Show that the vector $\mathbf{v}$ of $C_n(F)$ is a characteristic vector, relative to the canonical basis of $C_n$, of the matrix $A$ of $F_n$ if and only if

$$\mathbf{v}A = c\mathbf{v}, \qquad c \text{ in } F.$$

**18.** Show that, if $A$ has $n$ linearly independent characteristic vectors $\mathbf{v}_1, \cdots, \mathbf{v}_n$ in $C_n(F)$, then the matrix $P$ formed by stacking these $n$ row vectors is a nonsingular matrix of $F_n$ such that $PAP^{-1}$ is diagonal.

## 13.8 Triangularization and Diagonalization

Now we are able to develop necessary and sufficient conditions for a matrix $A$ of $F_n$ to be similar to a triangular matrix or to a diagonal matrix. First we prove the converse of Theorem 13.21.

DEFINITION 13.9. The subspace $U$ of $V_n(F)$ is *A-invariant* (i.e., invariant under the linear transformation $A$) if and only if $\mathbf{u}A$ is in $U$ when $\mathbf{u}$ is a vector of $U$.

We see in the triangularization described earlier that the subspace $(\mathbf{v}_n)$ of dimension 1 is necessarily $A$-invariant since

$$a\mathbf{v}_nA = aa_{11}\mathbf{v}_n$$

is certainly in $(\mathbf{v}_n)$ for each $a$ in $F$.

THEOREM 13.2. *If $U = (\mathbf{u})$ is a nonzero $A$-invariant subspace of $V_n$, then $A$ induces a linear transformation $A_1$ on the quotient space $V_n/U$ and the characteristic polynomial of $A$ is $(c - \lambda)m(\lambda)$ where $m(\lambda)$ is the characteristic polynomial of $A_1$ and $\mathbf{u}A = c\mathbf{u}$.*

Since $\mathbf{u} \neq \mathbf{z}$ we can choose $n - 1$ other vectors of $V_n(F)$ such that

$$\mathbf{v}_1, \mathbf{v}_2, \cdots, \mathbf{v}_n = \mathbf{u}$$

form a basis for $V_n(F)$. Then the $n - 1$ cosets

$$\mathbf{v}_1' = \mathbf{v}_1 + U, \mathbf{v}_2' = \mathbf{v}_2 + U, \cdots, \mathbf{v}_{n-1}' = \mathbf{v}_{n-1} + U$$

form a basis for the $(n - 1)$-dimensional vector space $V_n/U$ which consists of the cosets

$$\mathbf{v}' = \mathbf{v} + U.$$

Addition and scalar multiplication in $V_n/U$ are defined in the obvious way:

$$\mathbf{v}' + \mathbf{w}' = \mathbf{v} + U + \mathbf{w} + U = \mathbf{v} + \mathbf{w} + U$$

and

$$a\mathbf{v}' = a(\mathbf{v} + U) = a\mathbf{v} + U.$$

Then the mapping $A_1$ is defined by

$$\mathbf{v}'A_1 = \mathbf{v}A + U,$$

all $\mathbf{v}'$ in $V_n/U$. Of course we must show that this definition is independent of the particular representative $\mathbf{v}$ of the coset $\mathbf{v}' = \mathbf{v} + U$, so choose $\mathbf{w}$ from the coset $\mathbf{v}'$. Then

$$\mathbf{w} = \mathbf{v} + a\mathbf{u}, \qquad a\mathbf{u} \text{ in } U,$$

so that

$$\mathbf{w}A = \mathbf{v}A + a\mathbf{u}A = \mathbf{v}A + ac\mathbf{u}.$$

Since $ac\mathbf{u}$ is in $U$ (and this is why $U$ must be $A$-invariant) we see that $\mathbf{w}A$ is in the coset $\mathbf{v}A + U$. This means that $A_1$ is not dependent on any particular coset representative so that $A_1$ is a genuine mapping from $V_n/U$ to $V_n/U$.

We see that $A_1$ is also linear. Consider

$$(a\mathbf{v}' + b\mathbf{w}')A_1 = (a\mathbf{v} + b\mathbf{w})A + U.$$

Since $(a\mathbf{v} + b\mathbf{w})A = a\mathbf{v}A + b\mathbf{w}A$ in $V_n$ we get

$$(a\mathbf{v}' + b\mathbf{w}')A_1 = a\mathbf{v}'A_1 + b\mathbf{w}'A_1$$

so that $A_1$ is linear.

A look at the matrix of $A$ relative to the basis vectors $\mathbf{v}_1, \cdots, \mathbf{v}_n$ is quite revealing:

$$\begin{aligned}
\mathbf{v}_1A &= a_{11}\mathbf{v}_1 + \cdots + a_{1n}\mathbf{v}_n,\\
\mathbf{v}_2A &= a_{21}\mathbf{v}_1 + \cdots + a_{2n}\mathbf{v}_n,\\
&\ \ \vdots\\
\mathbf{v}_nA &= \mathbf{u}A = c\mathbf{u} = c\mathbf{v}_n.
\end{aligned}$$

Thus the bottom row of the resulting matrix $(a_{rs})$ is $(0, 0, \cdots, 0, c)$. Moreover, from

$$\begin{aligned}
\mathbf{v}'_1A_1 &= a_{11}\mathbf{v}'_1 + \cdots + a_{1,\,n-1}\mathbf{v}'_{n-1},\\
&\ \ \vdots\\
v'_{n-1}A_1 &= a_{n-1,\,1}\mathbf{v}'_1 + \cdots + a_{n-1,\,n-1}\mathbf{v}'_{n-1},
\end{aligned}$$

in $V_n/U$ we see that the resulting matrix of $A_1$ is precisely the $(n-1)$-by-$(n-1)$ minor $A_{nn}$ of $(a_{rs})$ which is obtainable by slicing row $n$ and column $n$ from $(a_{rs})$. From this we conclude that

$$\mathbf{det}\,\big((a_{rs}) - \lambda I\big) = (c - \lambda)\,\mathbf{det}\,(A_{nn} - \lambda I)$$

by expanding by minors of row $n$.

*Example* 1. Let the linear transformation $A$ on $C_3(R)$ be defined by the matrix

$$\begin{pmatrix} 2 & 2 & 1 \\ 2 & 4 & 2 \\ 0 & 1 & 1 \end{pmatrix}$$

relative to the canonical basis of $C_3(R)$. Find an $A$-invariant subspace of $C_3(R)$.

Form the determinant $p(\lambda)$ of

$$\begin{pmatrix} 2-\lambda & 2 & 1 \\ 2 & 4-\lambda & 2 \\ 0 & 1 & 1-\lambda \end{pmatrix};$$

$$p(\lambda) = (1-\lambda)(\lambda^2 - 6\lambda + 2).$$

Obviously 1 is a characteristic value of $A$;

$$\begin{aligned} \mathbf{e}_1(A - I) &= \mathbf{e}_1 + 2\mathbf{e}_2 + \mathbf{e}_3, \\ \mathbf{e}_2(A - I) &= 2\mathbf{e}_1 + 3\mathbf{e}_2 + 2\mathbf{e}_3, \\ \mathbf{e}_3(A - I) &= \mathbf{e}_2, \end{aligned}$$

so that, by inspection, we have

$$(2\mathbf{e}_1 - \mathbf{e}_2 - \mathbf{e}_3)(A - I) = \mathbf{z}.$$

Hence for

$$\mathbf{u} = 2\mathbf{e}_1 - \mathbf{e}_2 - \mathbf{e}_3$$

we have

$$\mathbf{u}A = 1\mathbf{u}.$$

Taking $\{\mathbf{e}_1, \mathbf{e}_2, \mathbf{u}\}$ as a basis for $C_3(R)$ we get the following matrix for $A$:

$$B = \begin{pmatrix} 4 & 1 & -1 \\ 6 & 2 & -2 \\ 0 & 0 & 1 \end{pmatrix}.$$

The linear transformation $A_1$ induced on the quotient space $C_3(R)/U$, $U = (\mathbf{u})$, by $A$ has the basis

$$\mathbf{e}'_1 = \mathbf{e}_1 + U, \qquad \mathbf{e}'_2 = \mathbf{e}_2 + U;$$

then

$$\mathbf{e}'_1 A_1 = 4\mathbf{e}'_1 + \mathbf{e}'_2$$

and

$$\mathbf{e}'_2 A_1 = 6\mathbf{e}'_1 + 2\mathbf{e}'_2.$$

The resulting matrix for $A_1$ is the minor

$$B_{33} = \begin{pmatrix} 4 & 1 \\ 6 & 2 \end{pmatrix}.$$

Computing the determinant of $B - \lambda I$ yields

$$\begin{aligned}\mathbf{det}\,(B - \lambda I) &= (1 - \lambda)\,\mathbf{det}\,(B_{33} - \lambda I)\\ &= (1 - \lambda)(\lambda^2 - 6\lambda + 2) = p(\lambda).\end{aligned}$$

Using Theorem 13.22 we obtain the converse of Theorem 13.21 quite easily.

THEOREM 13.23. *If the characteristic polynomial $p(\lambda)$ of the linear transformation $\boldsymbol{A}$ on $V_n(F)$ reduces completely in $F[\lambda]$, then a basis can be selected for $V_n(F)$ so that the resulting matrix $A$ corresponding to $\boldsymbol{A}$ is triangular.*

For the characteristic value $c_n$ of $\boldsymbol{A}$ the linear transformation $\boldsymbol{A} - c_n\boldsymbol{I}$ has a nontrivial nullspace (for a matrix of this mapping is singular). Choose $\mathbf{v}_n \neq \mathbf{z}$ in this nullspace. Then

$$\mathbf{v}_n\boldsymbol{A} = c_n\mathbf{v}_n$$

so that $U = (\mathbf{v}_n)$ is $\boldsymbol{A}$-invariant. Now consider the quotient space $V_n/U$ and its induced linear transformation $\boldsymbol{A}_1$. The dimension of $V_n/U$ is $n - 1$ and the characteristic polynomial of $\boldsymbol{A}_1$ is $p(\lambda)/(c_n - \lambda)$. Therefore the induction hypothesis applied to $V_n/U$ and $\boldsymbol{A}_1$ yields a matrix representing $\boldsymbol{A}$ which is indeed triangular. That is, $V_n/U$ has a basis of $n - 1$ vectors $\mathbf{v}'_i$, $i = 1, \cdots, n - 1$, such that $\boldsymbol{A}_1$ is triangularly represented. Then selecting an arbitrary vector $\mathbf{v}_i$ in the coset $\mathbf{v}'_i$ we obtain a basis $\{\mathbf{v}_1, \cdots, \mathbf{v}_{n-1}, \mathbf{v}_n\}$ such that $\boldsymbol{A}$ is represented by a matrix $A$ in triangular form. Moreover, if $A = (a_{rs})$, then the minor $A_{nn}$ is the matrix describing $\boldsymbol{A}_1$ relative to the above basis for $V_n/U$.

*Example* 2. Reduce the following element of $R_3$ to triangular form by similarity transformations,

$$A = \begin{pmatrix} 1 & 1 & 0 \\ 2 & 3 & -3 \\ 0 & 1 & 1 \end{pmatrix}.$$

The characteristic polynomial is

$$p(\lambda) = (1 - \lambda)(\lambda - 2)^2.$$

When we consider the space $C_3(R)$ and its canonical basis we get the linear transformation $\boldsymbol{A}$:

$$\begin{aligned}\mathbf{e}_1\boldsymbol{A} &= \mathbf{e}_1 + \mathbf{e}_2,\\ \mathbf{e}_2\boldsymbol{A} &= 2\mathbf{e}_1 + 3\mathbf{e}_2 - 3\mathbf{e}_3,\\ \mathbf{e}_3\boldsymbol{A} &= \mathbf{e}_2 + \mathbf{e}_3.\end{aligned}$$

The linear transformation $\boldsymbol{A} - \boldsymbol{I}$ has the nullspace $U$ spanned by $\mathbf{u} = \mathbf{e}_1 - \mathbf{e}_3$ since the matrix

$$A - I = \begin{pmatrix} 0 & 1 & 0 \\ 2 & 2 & -3 \\ 0 & 1 & 0 \end{pmatrix}$$

tells us that $(\mathbf{e}_1\boldsymbol{A} - \mathbf{e}_1) - (\mathbf{e}_3\boldsymbol{A} - \mathbf{e}_3) = \mathbf{z}$, and that no other such relation exists.

Then $\mathbf{e}_1$, $\mathbf{e}_2$, and $\mathbf{u}$ form a basis for $C_3$ such that $A$ is represented by

$$B = \begin{pmatrix} 1 & 1 & 0 \\ -1 & 3 & 3 \\ 0 & 0 & 1 \end{pmatrix}.$$

The change of basis is given by the linear transformation $C$,

$$\mathbf{e}_1 C = \mathbf{e}_1, \qquad \mathbf{e}_2 C = \mathbf{e}_2, \qquad \text{and} \qquad \mathbf{e}_3 C = \mathbf{u} = \mathbf{e}_1 - \mathbf{e}_3,$$

and its matrix $C$ relative to the canonical basis has the property

$$CAC^{-1} = B.$$

Now we consider the minor

$$A_1 = \begin{pmatrix} 1 & 1 \\ -1 & 3 \end{pmatrix}.$$

which is the matrix of the linear transformation $A_1$ induced on $C_3/U$ by $A$, relative to the basis vectors $\mathbf{e}'_1$ and $\mathbf{e}'_2$. The characteristic polynomial of $A_1$ is

$$\mathbf{det}\,(A_1 - \lambda I) = \lambda^2 - 4\lambda + 4 = (\lambda - 2)^2.$$

The matrix

$$A_1 - 2I = \begin{pmatrix} -1 & 1 \\ -1 & 1 \end{pmatrix},$$

has rank 1 so that $C_3/U$ contains the vector $\mathbf{v}' = \mathbf{e}'_1 - \mathbf{e}'_2$ such that

$$\mathbf{v}'A_1 = 2\mathbf{v}'.$$

Then back in $C_3$ we select the basis $\mathbf{e}_1$, $\{\mathbf{v} = \mathbf{e}_1 - \mathbf{e}_2$, and $\mathbf{u} = \mathbf{e}_1 - \mathbf{e}_3\}$:

$$\begin{aligned} \mathbf{e}_1 A &= \mathbf{e}_1 + \mathbf{e}_2 = 2\mathbf{e}_1 - \mathbf{v}, \\ \mathbf{v}A &= (\mathbf{e}_1 + \mathbf{e}_2) - (-\mathbf{e}_1 + 3\mathbf{e}_2 + 3\mathbf{u}) = 2\mathbf{v} - 3\mathbf{u}, \\ \mathbf{u}A &= \mathbf{u}, \end{aligned}$$

so that relative to this basis $A$ is described by the triangular matrix

$$D = \begin{pmatrix} 2 & -1 & 0 \\ 0 & 2 & -3 \\ 0 & 0 & 1 \end{pmatrix}.$$

Moreover, from the equations

$$\mathbf{e}_1 = \mathbf{e}_1, \qquad \mathbf{v} = \mathbf{e}_1 - \mathbf{e}_2, \qquad \text{and} \qquad \mathbf{u} = \mathbf{e}_1 - \mathbf{e}_3$$

we get a nonsingular matrix $K$,

$$K = \begin{pmatrix} 1 & 0 & 0 \\ 1 & -1 & 0 \\ 1 & 0 & -1 \end{pmatrix}.$$

such that

$$D = KAK^{-1}.$$

So we see that for the triangularization problem the concept of characteristic vector is quite important since it enables us to prove the existence of a chain of invariant subspaces.

*Corollary* 13.23.1. If the characteristic polynomial of the element $A$ of $\mathbf{L}(V_n(F))$ factors completely in $F[\lambda]$, then $V_n(F)$ contains $n$ $A$-invariant subspaces $U_1, U_2, \cdots, U_n$ such that

(1) $U_1 \subset U_2 \subset \cdots \subset U_n$.

(2) $U_i$ is of dimension $i$.

This is just another way of stating the theorem.

The concept of characteristic vector is also useful in deciding whether a matrix is similar to a diagonal matrix.

THEOREM 13.24. *The element $A$ of $\mathbf{L}(V_n(F))$ is representable by a diagonal matrix if and only if $A$ has $n$ linearly independent characteristic vectors in $V_n(F)$.*

If $A$ has $n$ linearly independent characteristic vectors $\mathbf{v}_1, \cdots, \mathbf{v}_n$, then

$$\mathbf{v}_i A = c_i \mathbf{v}_i, \qquad c_i \text{ in } F,$$

and relative to the basis for $V_n$ provided by these vectors, $A$ is represented by

$$A = c_1 E_{11} + c_2 E_{22} + \cdots + c_n E_{nn}.$$

Conversely, if the vectors $\mathbf{u}_1, \cdots, \mathbf{u}_n$ form a basis for $V_n(F)$ with the property that $A$ corresponds to the diagonal matrix

$$A = a_1 E_{11} + \cdots + a_n E_{nn}$$

relative to this basis, then certainly these vectors are characteristic vectors of $A$.

*Corollary* 13.24.1. If the linear transformation $A$ of $\mathbf{L}(V_n(F))$ can be represented by a diagonal matrix of $F_n$, then the characteristic polynomial of $A$ factors completely in $F[\lambda]$.

A diagonal matrix is a special type of triangular matrix.

Now we know from Example 1 of the previous section that even though the characteristic polynomial of the matrix $A$ does factor completely in $F[\lambda]$, it is possible that $A$ is *not* similar to a diagonal matrix. But, if $A$ has $n$ distinct characteristic values in $F$, then $A$ is similar to a diagonal matrix.

*Corollary* 13.24.2. If the matrix $A$ of $F_n$ has $n$ distinct characteristic values in $F$, then $A$ is similar to the diagonal matrix having these values on the main diagonal.

Now $A$ corresponds to the element $A$ of $\mathbf{L}(V_n(F))$, and for each of the characteristic values $c_1, \cdots, c_n$ we know that $A$ has a characteristic vector $\mathbf{v}_i$,

$$\mathbf{v}_i A = c_i \mathbf{v}_i, \qquad i = 1, \cdots, n,$$

since $A - c_i I$ is a singular matrix. Then these $n$ vectors $\mathbf{v}_1, \cdots, \mathbf{v}_n$ are linearly independent as we shall show.

(1) $\mathbf{v}_1$ and $\mathbf{v}_2$ are linearly independent, for, if $\mathbf{v}_1 = a\mathbf{v}_2$, then

$$\mathbf{v}_1 A = c_1\mathbf{v}_1 = a\mathbf{v}_2 A = ac_2\mathbf{v}_2 = c_2\mathbf{v}_1,$$

so that

$$c_1\mathbf{v}_1 - c_2\mathbf{v}_1 = (c_1 - c_2)\mathbf{v}_1 = \mathbf{z}.$$

But this is impossible since

$$c_1 \neq c_2 \qquad \text{and} \qquad \mathbf{v}_1 \neq \mathbf{z}.$$

(2) Suppose $\mathbf{v}_1, \cdots, \mathbf{v}_k$ are linearly independent and consider $\mathbf{v}_{k+1} = \mathbf{v}$. If

$$\mathbf{v} = a_1\mathbf{v}_1 + \cdots + a_k\mathbf{v}_k,$$

then

$$\mathbf{v}A = c\mathbf{v} = a_1c_1\mathbf{v}_1 + \cdots + a_kc_k\mathbf{v}_k.$$

Now $c = 0$ implies that the vectors $\mathbf{v}_1, \cdots, \mathbf{v}_k$ are dependent, whereas $c \neq 0$ permits $\mathbf{v}$ to be eliminated, yielding

$$a_1(c - c_1)\mathbf{v}_1 + a_2(c - c_2)\mathbf{v}_2 + \cdots + a_k(c - c_k)\mathbf{v}_k = \mathbf{z}.$$

Since $c - c_i \neq 0$, $i = 1, \cdots, n$, this last equation contradicts the independence of $\mathbf{v}_1, \cdots, \mathbf{v}_k$. So we conclude that the characteristic vector $\mathbf{v}$ is independent of $\mathbf{v}_1, \cdots, \mathbf{v}_k$.

Then by induction we have $\mathbf{v}_1, \cdots, \mathbf{v}_n$ linearly independent so that they form a basis for $V_n(F)$.

*Example* 3. Find a nonsingular matrix $C$ such that $CAC^{-1}$ is diagonal when

$$A = \begin{pmatrix} 1 & 2 & 0 \\ 2 & 2 & 2 \\ 0 & 1 & 1 \end{pmatrix}.$$

The characteristic polynomial of $A$ is $-(\lambda - 1)(\lambda + 1)(\lambda - 4)$. Switching to $C_3(R)$ and using its canonical basis we get the following characteristic vectors:

(1) For $c_1 = 1$, $\mathbf{v}_1 = (1, 0, -2) = \mathbf{e}_1 - 2\mathbf{e}_3$.
(2) For $c_2 = -1$, $\mathbf{v}_2 = (1, -1, 1) = \mathbf{e}_1 - \mathbf{e}_2 + \mathbf{e}_3$.
(3) For $c_3 = 4$, $\mathbf{v}_3 = (2, 3, 2) = 2\mathbf{e}_1 + 3\mathbf{e}_2 + 2\mathbf{e}_3$.

Then

$$\begin{pmatrix} 1 & 0 & -2 \\ 1 & -1 & 1 \\ 2 & 3 & 2 \end{pmatrix}\begin{pmatrix} 1 & 2 & 0 \\ 2 & 2 & 2 \\ 0 & 1 & 1 \end{pmatrix} = \begin{pmatrix} 1 & 0 & 0 \\ 0 & -1 & 0 \\ 0 & 0 & 4 \end{pmatrix}\begin{pmatrix} 1 & 0 & -2 \\ 1 & -1 & 1 \\ 2 & 3 & 2 \end{pmatrix}.$$

## Exercise 13.8

**1.** Let $A$ be the matrix $A$ of Problem 4 in the previous set of exercises. Find a matrix $D$ such that $DAD^{-1}$ is triangular. Do the same for matrices $B$ and $C$ of Problem 4.

**2.** Show that the matrix

$$A = \begin{pmatrix} 0 & 0 & 0 & -4 \\ 1 & 0 & 0 & 0 \\ 0 & 1 & 0 & 5 \\ 0 & 0 & 1 & 0 \end{pmatrix}$$

of $R_4$ is similar to a diagonal matrix.

**3.** Let the linear transformation $A$ be a rotation of 3-space $C_3(Re)$ about the $x_3$-axis. Describe the $A$-invariant subspaces of $C_3(Re)$. Is a subspace of an $A$-invariant subspace always $A$-invariant?

**4.** Write a matric description of the linear transformation $A$ of Problem 3.

**5.** Prove that the intersection of two $A$-invariant subspaces of $V(F)$ is also $A$-invariant.

**6.** Let $U$ be a nonzero subspace of $V_n(F)$, and let the $m$ vectors $\mathbf{v}_1, \cdots, \mathbf{v}_m$ lie in $m$ linearly independent cosets of $U$ in $V_n/U$. Show that the $m$ vectors are linearly independent in $V_n(F)$. (From $a_1\mathbf{v}_1 + \cdots + a_m\mathbf{v}_m = \mathbf{z}$ we get $a_1(\mathbf{v}_1 + U) + \cdots + a_m(\mathbf{v}_m + U) = \mathbf{z} + U$)

**7.** Find a matrix $C$ in $R_4$ such that $CAC^{-1}$ is diagonal, for the matrix $A$ of Problem 2. (See Example 3.)

**8.** Show that the matrices

$$A = \begin{pmatrix} 0 & 5 & 0 \\ 4 & 4 & 1 \\ 3 & 2 & 0 \end{pmatrix} \quad \text{and} \quad B = \begin{pmatrix} 0 & 2 & 0 \\ 1 & 0 & 4 \\ 0 & 0 & 3 \end{pmatrix}$$

and similar over $F = J/(7)$.

**9.** Compute $CAC^{-1}$ over $R$ when

$$C = \begin{pmatrix} 1 & 1 & 1 \\ 1 & 2 & 4 \\ 1 & 3 & 9 \end{pmatrix} \quad \text{and} \quad A = \begin{pmatrix} 0 & 0 & 6 \\ 1 & 0 & -11 \\ 0 & 1 & 6 \end{pmatrix}.$$

**10.** Consider the system of differential equations

$$DF_i = a_{i1}F_1 + \cdots + a_{in}F_n, \qquad i = 1, 2, \cdots, n,$$

where the $F_i$ are differentiable functions of the real variable $x$. Show that this system can be written formally as

$$\begin{pmatrix} D & 0 & \cdots & 0 \\ 0 & D & \cdots & 0 \\ \vdots & & & \\ 0 & & \cdots & D \end{pmatrix} \begin{pmatrix} F_1 \\ F_2 \\ \vdots \\ F_n \end{pmatrix} = \begin{pmatrix} a_{11} & \cdots & a_{1n} \\ \vdots & & \\ a_{n1} & \cdots & a_{nn} \end{pmatrix} \begin{pmatrix} F_1 \\ \vdots \\ F_n \end{pmatrix}$$

or

$$B\mathbf{v}^T = A\mathbf{v}^T$$

where $\mathbf{v} = (F_1, \cdots, F_n)$ and $B$ is the operator matrix having $D$'s on the main diagonal. Let $C$ be a real matrix such that $CAC^{-1}$ is diagonal, and discuss the system

$$CBC^{-1}C\mathbf{v}^T = CAC^{-1}C\mathbf{v}^T.$$

Illustrate for $n = 2$.

**11.** Let $p(\lambda) = \lambda^4 + a_3\lambda^3 + a_2\lambda^2 + a_1\lambda + a_0$ be an element of $F[\lambda]$. Show that $p(\lambda)$ is the characteristic polynomial of the matrix

$$A = \begin{pmatrix} 0 & 0 & 0 & -a_0 \\ 1 & 0 & 0 & -a_1 \\ 0 & 1 & 0 & -a_2 \\ 0 & 0 & 1 & -a_3 \end{pmatrix}$$

by reducing the matrix $A - \lambda I$ to the form

$$A_1 = \begin{pmatrix} 0 & 0 & 0 & -p(\lambda) \\ 1 & 0 & 0 & -a_1 - a_2\lambda - a_3\lambda^2 - \lambda^3 \\ 0 & 1 & 0 & -a_2 - a_3\lambda - \lambda^2 \\ 0 & 0 & 1 & -a_3 - \lambda \end{pmatrix}$$

with $A_1 = A_{21}(\lambda)A_{32}(\lambda)A_{43}(\lambda)(A - \lambda I)$. Generalize. (The matrix $A$ is the *companion matrix of* $p(\lambda)$.)

**12.** Using the results of Problem 11 list three matrices in $F_4$, $F = J/(11)$, which are similar to diagonal matrices.

**13.** Let $p(\lambda) = (\lambda - c_1)(\lambda - c_2)\cdots(\lambda - c_n)$ be the characteristic polynomial of $A$ from $F_n$. Show that, if the characteristic values are all distinct, then

$$p(A) = (A - c_1I)(A - c_2I)\cdots(A - c_nI) = Z.$$

**14.** Let $(A; F)$ be the subring of $F_n$ generated by the powers of $A$ and the scalar matrices. Compare the polynomial ring of $F$ with the polynomial ring of $(A; F)$. How does this permit the substitution (i.e., specialization) of $A$ for $\lambda$?

## 13.9 Nilpotent Matrices and Transformations

We know that a matrix $A$ of $F_n$ whose characteristic polynomial decomposes into a product of linear factors over $F$ is similar to a matrix $B$ having the properties:

(1) The elements below the main diagonal of $B$ are all zeros.

(2) The elements on the main diagonal of $B$ are the characteristic values of $A$.

In this section we work with the elements *above* the main diagonal of $B$ in order to obtain a unique representative of the equivalence class to which $A$ and $B$ belong.

First we note from Corollary 13.24.2 that we need only to consider the case when $A$ has fewer than $n$ distinct characteristic values. For, if there are $n$ distinct characteristic values, then $A$ is similar to a diagonal matrix which is clearly unique up to the arrangement of the diagonal elements.

If $(\lambda - c)^e$ is a factor of $p(\lambda) = \mathbf{det}\,(A - \lambda I)$ but $(\lambda - c)^{e+1}$ is not, then $c$ is a characteristic value of $A$ of *multiplicity* $e$, where $e$ is a positive integer. Then by a very slight adjustment of the proof of Theorem 13.23 we can prove that $A$ is similar to a triangular matrix $B$ in which the like characteristic values of $A$ are clustered together on the main diagonal.

THEOREM 13.25. *If $c_1, \cdots, c_m$ are the distinct characteristic values of $A$, $c_i$ of multiplicity $e_i$, then $A$ is similar to a triangular matrix $B$ with the last $e_m$ elements on its main diagonal equal to $c_m$, the next $e_{m-1}$ elements equal to $c_{m-1}$, etc.*

The proof is almost identical with the proof of Theorem 13.23.

So let $A$ be similar to a triangular matrix $B$ having the last $e = e_m$ elements of its main diagonal equal to $c = c_m$, a characteristic value of $A$ of multiplicity $e$. Then $B$ corresponds to a linear transformation $A$ on $V_n(F)$ relative to a basis $\{\mathbf{v}_1, \cdots, \mathbf{v}_n\}$ of $V_n(F)$, and if we denote the last $e$ vectors of this basis, viz., $\mathbf{v}_{n-e+1}, \cdots, \mathbf{v}_n$, as $\mathbf{u}_1, \cdots,$ and $\mathbf{u}_e$, respectively, then these vectors form a basis for an $A$-invariant subspace $U = U_m$ of $V_n(F)$. Moreover,

$$\begin{aligned}
\mathbf{u}_1 A &= c\mathbf{u}_1 + c_{12}\mathbf{u}_2 + \cdots + c_{1e}\mathbf{u}_e,\\
\mathbf{u}_2 A &= \phantom{c\mathbf{u}_1 + {}} c\mathbf{u}_2 + \cdots + c_{2e}\mathbf{u}_e,\\
&\ \vdots\\
\mathbf{u}_e A &= \phantom{c\mathbf{u}_1 + c\mathbf{u}_2 + \cdots + {}} c\mathbf{u}_e,
\end{aligned}$$

and $A$ induces a linear transformation $A_m$ on $U$ whose matrix $B_m$ is the lower left corner of the matrix $B$. Now we come to the reason for this arrangement:

*Lemma* 13.1. $A_m - cI$ is a nilpotent linear transformation on $U_m$ of index $e$ or less.

For the matrix $B_m - cI$ is a strictly triangular $e$-by-$e$ matrix. Hence

$$(B_m - cI)^e = Z.$$

*Example* 1. If

$$B_m = \begin{pmatrix} 2 & 3 & 4 \\ 0 & 2 & 1 \\ 0 & 0 & 2 \end{pmatrix},$$

then

$$C = B_m - 2I = \begin{pmatrix} 0 & 3 & 4 \\ 0 & 0 & 1 \\ 0 & 0 & 0 \end{pmatrix},$$

$$C^2 = \begin{pmatrix} 0 & 0 & 3 \\ 0 & 0 & 0 \\ 0 & 0 & 0 \end{pmatrix},$$

and $C^3 = Z$.

But what is especially nice about a nilpotent linear transformation? The following results will answer that question.

*Lemma* 13.2. If $\boldsymbol{H}$ is a nilpotent linear transformation on $V_n(F)$, then $V_n(F)$ contains nonzero vectors $\mathbf{v}_1, \cdots, \mathbf{v}_k$ such that the nonzero vectors of the form $\mathbf{v}_i\boldsymbol{H}^r$ form a basis for $V_n(F)$.

(It is understood that

$$\mathbf{v}_i = \mathbf{v}_i\boldsymbol{I} = \mathbf{v}_i\boldsymbol{H}^0$$

is of the prescribed form also.)

The proof is by induction on $n$, the dimension of the space $V_n(F)$. Since the only nilpotent linear transformation on $V_1(F)$ is the zero mapping, the lemma is obviously true when we use any $\mathbf{v}_1 \neq \mathbf{z}$ in $V_1(F)$. So we assume as our induction hypothesis the statement of the lemma for a vector space of dimension less than $n$.

Now consider the subspace $V_n\boldsymbol{H}$ of all vectors $\mathbf{v}\boldsymbol{H}$, $\mathbf{v}$ in $V_n$. Since $\boldsymbol{H}^m = \boldsymbol{Z}$ for some $m$, it is obvious that $V_n\boldsymbol{H}$ has dimension less than $n$. For $V_n\boldsymbol{H} = V_n$ implies that

$$V_n = V_n\boldsymbol{H} = V_n\boldsymbol{H}^2 = \cdots = V_n\boldsymbol{H}^m = V_n\boldsymbol{Z} = (\mathbf{z}).$$

Applying the induction hypothesis to the linear transformation $\boldsymbol{H}$ on $V_n\boldsymbol{H}$ we obtain vectors $\mathbf{u}_1, \cdots, \mathbf{u}_s$ different from $\mathbf{z}$ such that the collection of nonzero vectors of the form $\mathbf{u}_i\boldsymbol{H}^r$ is a basis for $V_n\boldsymbol{H}$. Now since $\mathbf{u}_i$ is in $V_n\boldsymbol{H}$ we know that $V_n$ contains a vector $\mathbf{v}_i$ such that

$$\mathbf{u}_i = \mathbf{v}_i\boldsymbol{H}, \qquad i = 1, \cdots, s.$$

Then the nonzero vectors of the form $\mathbf{v}_i\boldsymbol{H}^r$ are linearly independent in $V_n$. To show this we take a special case (which serves merely to simplify the notation). Let $\mathbf{u}_1$, $\mathbf{u}_1\boldsymbol{H}$, $\mathbf{u}_2$, $\mathbf{u}_2\boldsymbol{H}$, and $\mathbf{u}_3$ form a basis for $V_n\boldsymbol{H}$. If

$$a_1\mathbf{v}_1 + a_2\mathbf{v}_1\boldsymbol{H} + a_3\mathbf{v}_1\boldsymbol{H}^2 + a_4\mathbf{v}_2 + a_5\mathbf{v}_2\boldsymbol{H} + a_6\mathbf{v}_2\boldsymbol{H}^2 + a_7\mathbf{v}_3 + a_8\mathbf{v}_3\boldsymbol{H} = \mathbf{z},$$

$a_i$ in $F$, then operating on this by $H$ yields

$$a_1\mathbf{v}_1\boldsymbol{H} + a_2\mathbf{v}_1\boldsymbol{H}^2 + a_4\mathbf{v}_2\boldsymbol{H} + a_5\mathbf{v}_2\boldsymbol{H}^2 + a_7\mathbf{v}_3\boldsymbol{H} = \mathbf{z}\boldsymbol{H} = \mathbf{z},$$

since

$$\mathbf{v}_1\boldsymbol{H}^3 = \mathbf{u}_1\boldsymbol{H}^2 = \mathbf{v}_2\boldsymbol{H}^3 = \mathbf{u}_2\boldsymbol{H}^2 = \mathbf{v}_3\boldsymbol{H}^2 = \mathbf{u}_3\boldsymbol{H} = \mathbf{z}.$$

Therefore

$$a_1\mathbf{u}_1 + a_2\mathbf{u}_1\boldsymbol{H} + a_4\mathbf{u}_2 + a_5\mathbf{u}_2\boldsymbol{H} + a_7\mathbf{u}_3 = \mathbf{z},$$

implying that

$$a_1 = a_2 = a_4 = a_5 = a_7 = 0$$

since the elements of a basis are linearly independent. Then the first equation above becomes

$$a_3\mathbf{v}_1\boldsymbol{H}^2 + a_6\mathbf{v}_2\boldsymbol{H}^2 + a_8\mathbf{v}_3\boldsymbol{H} = \mathbf{z}$$

or

$$a_3\mathbf{u}_1\boldsymbol{H} + a_6\mathbf{u}_2\boldsymbol{H} + a_8\mathbf{u}_3 = \mathbf{z},$$

so that

$$a_3 = a_6 = a_8 = 0$$

for the same reason.

This example is sufficiently general to justify the conclusion that the collection of nonzero vectors of the form $\mathbf{v}_i\boldsymbol{H}^r$ in $V_n$ is linearly independent and spans an $\boldsymbol{H}$-invariant subspace $W$.

Now let $\mathbf{v}$ be an arbitrary element of $V_n$; we claim $\mathbf{v}$ is expressible as the sum $\mathbf{u} + \mathbf{w}$ where $\mathbf{u}$ is in the nullspace $N_H$ of $\boldsymbol{H}$ and $\mathbf{w}$ is in $W$. To show this we exhibit the general method as applied to the special example above.

Since $\mathbf{v}\boldsymbol{H}$ is in $V_n\boldsymbol{H}$ there are scalars $b_i$ such that

$$\mathbf{v} = b_1\mathbf{u}_1 + b_2\mathbf{u}_1\boldsymbol{H} + b_3\mathbf{u}_2 + b_4\mathbf{u}_2\boldsymbol{H} + b_5\mathbf{u}_5.$$

Now consider

$$\mathbf{u} = \mathbf{v} - b_1\mathbf{v}_1 - b_2\mathbf{v}_1\boldsymbol{H} - b_3\mathbf{v}_2 - b_4\mathbf{v}_2\boldsymbol{H} - b_5\mathbf{v}_5;$$

certainly

$$\mathbf{u}\boldsymbol{H} = \mathbf{z} \quad \text{and} \quad \mathbf{w} = \mathbf{v} - \mathbf{u}$$

is in $W$. Hence $V_n(F) = W + N_H$ so that $\mathbf{v}_{s+1}, \cdots, \mathbf{v}_k$ can be selected from $N_H$ to extend the basis for $W$ to the desired basis for $V_n(F)$.

DEFINITION 13.10. The components $a_{i,\,i+1}$ of $A = (a_{rs})$ make up the *second diagonal* of $A$. $A$ is in *second diagonal echelon form* if and only if $A$ has only zero components off the second diagonal and 0's and 1's on the second diagonal. A maximal string of 1's, $a_{i,\,i+1} = 1$ for $i = j + 1, \cdots, j + k$, on the second diagonal is called an *echelon* of length $k$.

THEOREM 13.26. *If* $\boldsymbol{H}$ *is a nilpotent linear transformation on* $V_n(F)$, *then a basis can be selected for* $V_n(F)$ *so that the matrix describing* $\boldsymbol{H}$ *is in second diagonal echelon form.*

This is a consequence of Lemma 13.2.

*Example* 2. The following matrices are in second diagonal echelon form:

$$A = \begin{pmatrix} 0 & 1 & 0 & 0 & 0 \\ 0 & 0 & 1 & 0 & 0 \\ 0 & 0 & 0 & 1 & 0 \\ 0 & 0 & 0 & 0 & 0 \\ 0 & 0 & 0 & 0 & 0 \end{pmatrix}, \qquad B = \begin{pmatrix} 0 & 0 & 0 & 0 & 0 \\ 0 & 0 & 1 & 0 & 0 \\ 0 & 0 & 0 & 1 & 0 \\ 0 & 0 & 0 & 0 & 1 \\ 0 & 0 & 0 & 0 & 0 \end{pmatrix}.$$

Actually $A$ and $B$ are similar since $A = CBC^{-1}$ with $C = E_{12} + E_{23} + E_{34} + E_{45} + E_{51}$. Furthermore

$$A^2 = \begin{pmatrix} 0 & 0 & 1 & 0 & 0 \\ 0 & 0 & 0 & 1 & 0 \\ 0 & 0 & 0 & 0 & 0 \\ 0 & 0 & 0 & 0 & 0 \\ 0 & 0 & 0 & 0 & 0 \end{pmatrix}$$

so that $A^2$ has an echelon of length 2 in its third diagonal, and $A^3$ has an echelon of length 1 in its fourth diagonal.

*Lemma* 13.3. The nilpotent linear transformation $\boldsymbol{H}$ on $V_n(F)$ has a unique (up to permutations of the echelons) describing matrix in second diagonal echelon form.

The proof is again an induction argument. Each echelon of length $k$ in the second diagonal of the matrix $A$ representing $\boldsymbol{H}$ over $V_n$ corresponds to an echelon of length $k - 1$ (if $k$ exceeds 1) in the second diagonal of the matrix $A_1$ representing $\boldsymbol{H}$ over $V_n\boldsymbol{H}$. For we worked backward from the matrix $A_1$ in Lemma 13.2. Furthermore the number of echelons of length 1 in $A$ equals the dimension of the nullspace of $\boldsymbol{H}$ in $V_n\boldsymbol{H}$. Since the echelons of $A_1$ and the nullspace of $\boldsymbol{H}$ in $V_n\boldsymbol{H}$ are uniquely determined, the uniqueness of the second diagonal echelon form of $A$ follows.

Note that an echelon of length $k$ in the second diagonal of $A$ comes from the basis elements $\mathbf{v}, \mathbf{v}\boldsymbol{H}, \mathbf{v}\boldsymbol{H}^2, \cdots, \mathbf{v}\boldsymbol{H}^k$ of $V_n(F)$. For

$$\mathbf{v}\boldsymbol{H} = 0\mathbf{v} + 1\mathbf{v}\boldsymbol{H} + 0\mathbf{v}\boldsymbol{H}^2 + \cdots,$$
$$(\mathbf{v}\boldsymbol{H})\boldsymbol{H} = 0\mathbf{v} + 0\mathbf{v}\boldsymbol{H} + 1\mathbf{v}\boldsymbol{H}^2 + \cdots,$$

etc.; the key is provided by the essential fact,

$$\mathbf{v}\boldsymbol{H}^{k+1} = \mathbf{z}.$$

This echelon can be easily shifted to another position in the second diagonal by interchanging the cluster

$$\mathbf{v}, \mathbf{v}\boldsymbol{H}, \cdots, \mathbf{v}\boldsymbol{H}^k$$

(defined by $\mathbf{v}\boldsymbol{H}^{k+1} = \mathbf{z}$) with another cluster

$$\mathbf{u}, \mathbf{u}\boldsymbol{H}, \cdots, \mathbf{u}\boldsymbol{H}^q$$

(defined by $\mathbf{u}\boldsymbol{H}^{q+1} = \mathbf{z}$) in the basis for $V_n$ obtained in Lemma 13.2.

Thus we conclude that a nilpotent matrix of $F_n$ is similar to a matrix $B$ in second diagonal echelon which is unique up to a rearrangement of the echelons in the second diagonal of $B$. Therefore the similarity class to which $A$ (and $B$) belong is identified completely by the echelons in the second diagonal of $B$.

*Example* 3. Determine all equivalence classes (relative to similarity) of nilpotent matrices in $\boldsymbol{R}_4$.

The second diagonal of a 4-by-4 matrix contains three elements, $a_{12}$, $a_{23}$, and $a_{34}$. Then the equivalence classes are identified by the following ordered triples:

(1) $(a_{12}, a_{23}, a_{34}) = (a, b, c) = (1, 1, 1)$.
(2) $(a, b, c) = (1, 1, 0)$.
(3) $(a, b, c) = (1, 0, 0)$.
(4) $(a, b, c) = (0, 0, 0)$.
(5) $(a, b, c) = (1, 0, 1)$.

In (1) there is one echelon of length 3, in (2) one echelon of length 2, in (3) one echelon of length 1, and in (5) two echelons of length 1. There are no other possibilities *since echelons are separated by one or more zeros.*

*Example* 4. In $R_8$ there is an equivalence class of similar nilpotent matrices represented by the matrix in second diagonal echelon form with second diagonal

$$(a_{12}, \cdots, a_{78}) = (1, 0, 1, 1, 1, 0, 1).$$

Here we have *three* echelons, two of length 1 and one of length 3.

THEOREM 13.27. *If $A$ is a nilpotent matrix of $F_n$, then $p(\lambda) = (-\lambda)^n$ is the characteristic polynomial of $A$, and the index of $A$ is $r + 1$ where $r$ is the maximum of the lengths of the echelons in the canonical representative of $A$.*

This follows immediately from an inspection of the unique second diagonal echelon form matrix $B$ to which $A$ is similar.

## Exercise 13.9

**1.** Let

$$A = \begin{pmatrix} 0 & 1 & 2 \\ 0 & 0 & 3 \\ 0 & 0 & 0 \end{pmatrix}$$

be the matrix of a linear transformation $H$ on $C_3(R)$ relative to the canonical basis.

(*a*) Show that $H$ is nilpotent of index 3.

(*b*) Find $\mathbf{w} \neq \mathbf{z}$ in $VH^2$, $V = C_3(R)$, and find $\mathbf{u}$ in $VH$ such that $\mathbf{u}H = \mathbf{w}$.

(*c*) Find $\mathbf{v}$ in $C_3(R)$ such that $\mathbf{v}H = \mathbf{u}$ and $\mathbf{v}H^2 = \mathbf{w}$. Show that $\mathbf{v}$, $\mathbf{u}$, and $\mathbf{w}$ form a basis for $C_3(R)$.

(*d*) Find a nonsingular matrix $C$ such that $CAC^{-1}$ is in second diagonal echelon form. (Note: $\mathbf{v} = \mathbf{e}_1$ and $C = E_{11} + E_{22} + 2E_{23} + 3E_{33}$ are possible answers.)

**2.** Prove that a nilpotent element of $F_n$ has index no larger than $n$.

**3.** Prove that a matrix $B$ which is similar to a matrix $A$ that is nilpotent of index $m$, is itself nilpotent of index $m$.

**4.** Let the space $V_9H$ have the basis $\{\mathbf{u}_1, \mathbf{u}_1H, \mathbf{u}_2, \mathbf{u}_2H, \mathbf{u}_3\}$, where

$$\mathbf{u}_1H^2 = \mathbf{u}_2H^2 = \mathbf{u}_3H = \mathbf{z}.$$

Write out the second diagonal echelon matrix $A$ of $H$ over $V_9$.

**5.** Describe all of the equivalence classes (relative to similarity) of nilpotent matrices of $F_8$.

**6.** Write out $B^2$ and $A^3$ for the matrices of Example 2.

**7.** Let the matrix $A$ of $R_4$ have the characteristic polynomial $(\lambda - c)^4$. Show that $A$ is similar to exactly one matrix of the form $cI + B$, where $B$ is one of the five matrices in second diagonal echelon form described in Example 3. (Note that $A - cI$ is nilpotent.)

**8.** Determine the number of nonsimilar matrices of $R_3$ having the same characteristic polynomial $-(\lambda - 2)^3$. Write out the canonical representative of each.

**9.** Let $A$ be a matrix of class (3) of Example 3 and $B$ be a matrix of class (5) of that example. Denote by $\boldsymbol{A}$ and $\boldsymbol{B}$ the linear transformations on $V_4(R)$ corresponding to these matrices relative to the basis $\{\mathbf{v}_1, \mathbf{v}_2, \mathbf{v}_3, \mathbf{v}_4\}$. Show that $V_4\boldsymbol{A}$ has dimension 1 and $V_4\boldsymbol{B}$ has dimension 2. Show also that $A^2 = B^2 = Z$.

**10.** Let $\boldsymbol{A}$ and $\boldsymbol{B}$ be the linear transformations on $V(R) = C_5(R)$ described by the matrices of Example 2 relative to the canonical basis for $V$. Describe $V\boldsymbol{A}$ and $V\boldsymbol{B}$; $V\boldsymbol{A}^2$ and $V\boldsymbol{B}^2$; $V\boldsymbol{A}^3$ and $V\boldsymbol{B}^3$. How are the transformations $\boldsymbol{A}$ and $\boldsymbol{B}$ related?

## 13.10 Jordan Form

Now that we have some additional knowledge about nilpotent transformations we consider again the linear transformation $\boldsymbol{A}$ on $V_n(F)$ which has the characteristic value $c = c_m$ of multiplicity $e = e_m$. Then $V_n$ has a basis $\{\mathbf{v}_1, \cdots, \mathbf{v}_n\}$ with the properties:

(1) $\boldsymbol{A}$ is represented by a triangular matrix relative to this basis.

(2) $\mathbf{u}_1 = \mathbf{v}_{n-e+1}, \cdots,$ and $\mathbf{u}_e = \mathbf{v}_n$ form a basis for an $\boldsymbol{A}$-invariant subspace $U = U_m$ on which $\boldsymbol{A}$ induces a linear transformation $\boldsymbol{A}_m$ whose characteristic polynomial is $(c - \lambda)^e$.

(3) $\boldsymbol{A}_m - c\boldsymbol{I}$ is nilpotent.

(4) A basis can be selected for $U_m$ so that $\boldsymbol{A}_m - c\boldsymbol{I}$ is represented by a matrix $B_m$ in second diagonal echelon form.

(5) $\boldsymbol{A}_m$ is represented by $cI + B_m$ relative to this new basis.

So we now have a matrix for $\boldsymbol{A}$ of the form

$$\begin{pmatrix} C & D \\ Z_1 & B_m \end{pmatrix}$$

where $C$ is a triangular $(n - e)$-by-$(n - e)$ matrix, $Z_1$ is an $e$-by-$(n - e)$ zero matrix, and $D$ is an $(n - e)$-by-$e$ matrix which we shall shortly replace by a zero matrix. This is done by means of the following lemma.

*Lemma* 13.4. Let $\{\mathbf{v}_1, \cdots, \mathbf{v}_m, \mathbf{u}, \mathbf{u}\boldsymbol{H}, \cdots, \mathbf{u}\boldsymbol{H}^{r-1}\}$ be a basis for the space $U(F)$, and suppose

$$\mathbf{u}\boldsymbol{H}^r = \mathbf{z}$$

and

$$\mathbf{v}_1\boldsymbol{H} = a_1\mathbf{v}_1 + \cdots + a_m\mathbf{v}_m + b_1\mathbf{u} + \cdots + b_r\mathbf{u}\boldsymbol{H}^{r-1}$$

with $a_1 \neq 0$ in $F$. Then $\mathbf{v}_1$ can be replaced by $\mathbf{w}_1$ such that

$$\mathbf{w}_1 H = a_1\mathbf{w}_1 + a_2\mathbf{v}_2 + \cdots + a_m\mathbf{v}_m,$$

and

$$\mathbf{w}_1, \mathbf{v}_2, \cdots, \mathbf{v}_m, \mathbf{u}, \mathbf{u}H, \cdots, \mathbf{u}H^{r-1}$$

form a basis for $U$.

We shall find scalars $c_i$ in $F$ such that

$$\mathbf{w}_1 = \mathbf{v}_1 + c_1\mathbf{u} + c_2\mathbf{u}H + \cdots + c_r\mathbf{u}H^{r-1}$$

has the desired properties. Then

$$\mathbf{w}_1 H = \mathbf{v}_1 H + c_1\mathbf{u}H + c_2\mathbf{u}H^2 + \cdots + c_{r-1}\mathbf{u}H^{r-1}$$

since

$$c_r\mathbf{u}H^r = \mathbf{z},$$

and we must have

$$\begin{aligned} a_1\mathbf{v}_1 + b_1\mathbf{u} + \cdots + b_r\mathbf{u}H^{r-1} + c_1\mathbf{u}H + \cdots + c_{r-1}\mathbf{u}H^{r-1} \\ = a_1(\mathbf{v}_1 + c_1\mathbf{u} + c_2\mathbf{u}H + \cdots + c_r\mathbf{u}H^{r-1}). \end{aligned}$$

So we select the $c_i$, starting with $c_1$:

$$a_1c_1 = b_1,\ a_1c_2 = b_2 + c_1,\ a_1c_3 = b_3 + c_2, \cdots, a_1c_r = b_r + c_{r-1}.$$

Thus we can select the desired values for $c_i$ by solving for $c_1$, then for $c_2$, then for $c_3$, etc. Since $\mathbf{v}_1 = \mathbf{w}_1 - c_1\mathbf{u} - \cdots - c_r\mathbf{u}H^{r-1}$ it is obvious that $\mathbf{v}_1$ can be replaced by $\mathbf{w}_1$ in the basis.

THEOREM 13.28. *If the linear transformation $A$ on $V_n(F)$ has a characteristic polynomial which factors completely over $F$, and if $c$ is a characteristic value of $A$ of multiplicity $e$, then $V_n$ contains two $A$-invariant subspaces $U$ and $W$ such that*

(i) $$U + W = V_n,$$

*and*

(ii) $$U \cap W = (\mathbf{z}).$$

This is just another way of saying that the basis vectors $\mathbf{v}_1, \cdots, \mathbf{v}_{n-e}$ described at the beginning of this section can be replaced by vectors $\mathbf{w}_1, \cdots, \mathbf{w}_{n-e}$ (using the lemma just proved) so that the matrix representing $A$ has the form

$$\begin{pmatrix} C_1 & Z_2 \\ Z_1 & B_m \end{pmatrix}$$

where $Z_2$ is an $(n - e)$-by-$e$ matrix of zeros. Then $W$ is the subspace spanned by the $n - e$ vectors $\mathbf{w}_1, \cdots, \mathbf{w}_{n-e}$ and $U$ is the subspace $U_m$ described earlier.

Now, how do we use the lemma to get these new basis vectors? First we form the linear transformation $\boldsymbol{H} = A - c\boldsymbol{I}$. Then the basis for $U = U_m$ consists of clusters of vectors of the form

$$\mathbf{u}, \mathbf{u}\boldsymbol{H}, \cdots, \mathbf{u}\boldsymbol{H}^{r-1},$$

and

$$\mathbf{v}_1\boldsymbol{H} = (c_1 - c)\mathbf{v}_1 + \cdots + a_{n-e}\mathbf{v}_{n-e} + b_1\mathbf{u} + \cdots.$$

Since $a_1 = (c_1 - c) \neq 0$ in $F$, as $c_1$ and $c_m = c$ are different characteristic values of $A$, we can apply the lemma, once for each cluster of vectors $\mathbf{u}, \mathbf{u}\boldsymbol{H}, \cdots, \mathbf{u}\boldsymbol{H}^{r-1}$ in the basis for $U$, to obtain $\mathbf{w}_1$ such that

$$\mathbf{w}_1\boldsymbol{H} = (c_1 - c)\mathbf{w}_1 + a_2\mathbf{v}_2 + \cdots + a_{n-e}\mathbf{v}_{n-e}.$$

Exactly $n - e$ such steps yield linearly independent vectors $\mathbf{w}_1, \cdots, \mathbf{w}_{n-e}$ such that

$$\mathbf{w}_i\boldsymbol{H} = c_{ii}\mathbf{w}_i + \cdots + c_{i,\ n-e}\mathbf{w}_{n-e}, \qquad i = 1, \cdots, n - e,$$

with

$$c_{ii} = c_j - c$$

for some characteristic value $c_j$ of $A$. Therefore

$$\mathbf{w}_i = c_j\mathbf{w}_i + \cdots + c_{i,\ n-e}\mathbf{w}_{n-e}$$

for each $i = 1, \cdots, n - e$, and $A$ is represented over $W$ by the $(n - e)$-by-$(n - e)$ triangular matrix $C_1$.

THEOREM 13.29. *Let*

$$p(\lambda) = (c_1 - \lambda)^{e_1}(c_2 - \lambda)^{e_2}\cdots(c_m - \lambda)^{e_m}, \qquad c_i \text{ in } F,$$

*be the characteristic polynomial of the element $A$ of $\mathbf{L}(V_n(F))$. Then a basis can be selected for $V_n(F)$ so that the resulting matrix of $A$ has the block form*

$$A = \begin{pmatrix} B_1 & Z_2 & \cdots & \\ & & & \\ Z_1 & B_2 & & \\ \cdot & & \cdot & \\ \cdot & & & \cdot \\ \cdot & & & B_m \end{pmatrix}$$

*where each $B_i = c_iI + H_i$, $H_i$ an $e_i$-by-$e_i$ matrix in second diagonal echelon form, and the matrices $Z_1, Z_2$, etc., are matrices of zeros.*

The matrix $A$ is in *Jordan canonical form.*

THEOREM 13.28 enables us to proceed by induction on the order of the space. By that theorem a basis $\{\mathbf{w}_1, \cdots, \mathbf{w}_{n-e}, \mathbf{u}_1, \cdots, \mathbf{u}_e\}$ exists for $V_n$ such that

$$W = (\mathbf{w}_1, \cdots, \mathbf{w}_{n-e}) \qquad \text{and} \qquad U_m = (\mathbf{u}_1, \cdots, \mathbf{u}_e)$$

are $A$-invariant subspaces of dimensions $n - e$ and $e$, respectively. The matrix representing $A$ over $U_m$ is $B_m$. We consider $A$ over the space $W(F)$ and apply the induction hypothesis. The result is a basis for $V_n = W + U_m$ relative to which $A$ is represented by the matrix $A$ in Jordan canonical form, and the theorem is proved.

*Corollary* 13.29.1. If the characteristic polynomial of $A$ in $F_n$ factors completely over $F$, then $A$ factors in $F_n$ as

$$A = CBC^{-1},$$

where $B$ is in Jordan canonical form. This factorization is unique (up to a unit multiple of $C$).

The matrix $A$ defines a linear transformation $A$ on $V_n(F)$ relative to an arbitrary basis of $V_n$. Choosing a new basis for $V_n(F)$ in such a way that $A$ is represented by a matrix $B$ in Jordan form, we have

$$A = CBC^{-1},$$

where $C$ is the nonsingular matrix corresponding to the change of basis. The uniqueness of $B$ comes from two things:

(1) The characteristic values of $A$ and all matrices similar to $A$ are the same.

(2) The second diagonal echelon form $H_i$ is unique up to a permutation of the echelons.

Then the diagonal blocks

$$B_i = c_i I + H_i, \qquad i = 1, \cdots, m,$$

can be interchanged, and the echelons within each $H_i$ can be permuted, but these changes in $B$ correspond to changes of basis in $V_n(F)$, which correspond to multiplying the matrix $C$ by nonsingular matrices. Hence the basic features of $B$ are unique, and $B$ is called the *Jordan canonical factor* of $A$.

*Example* 1. Find the Jordan canonical factor $B$ in $R_4$ of

$$A = \begin{pmatrix} 1 & 2 & 3 & 14 \\ 0 & 1 & 5 & 7 \\ 0 & 0 & 2 & 7 \\ 0 & 0 & 0 & 2 \end{pmatrix}.$$

Let $\mathbf{e}_1, \mathbf{e}_2, \mathbf{e}_3, \mathbf{e}_4$ be the canonical basis elements of $V = C_4(R)$ and $A$ be the linear transformation corresponding to $A$ relative to this basis. In $U = (\mathbf{e}_3, \mathbf{e}_4)$ we have for $H = A - 2I$,

$$\mathbf{e}_3 H = 7\mathbf{e}_4 \neq \mathbf{z}.$$

Thus $\mathbf{v}_3 = \mathbf{e}_3$ and $\mathbf{v}_4 = \mathbf{e}_3 H$ can replace $\mathbf{e}_3$ and $\mathbf{e}_4$ in the basis for $U$ (and for $V$):

$$\begin{aligned} \mathbf{v}_3 A &= \mathbf{e}_3(2I + H) = 2\mathbf{e}_3 + \mathbf{e}_3 H = 2\mathbf{v}_3 + \mathbf{v}_4, \\ \mathbf{v}_4 H &= \mathbf{e}_3 H(2I + H) = 2\mathbf{e}_3 H \quad = 0\mathbf{v}_3 + 2\mathbf{v}_4, \end{aligned}$$

so that over $U$, $A$ is represented now by

$$B_2 = \begin{pmatrix} 2 & 1 \\ 0 & 2 \end{pmatrix}.$$

In $V$ we have

$$\mathbf{e}_1 A = \mathbf{e}_1 + 2\mathbf{e}_2 + 3\mathbf{v}_3 + 2\mathbf{v}_4$$

and

$$\mathbf{e}_1 H = -1\mathbf{e}_1 + 2\mathbf{e}_2 + 3\mathbf{v}_3 + 2\mathbf{v}_3 H,$$

so we select $a$ and $b$ in $R$ and form

$$\mathbf{v}_1 = \mathbf{e}_1 + a\mathbf{v}_3 + b\mathbf{v}_3 H,$$

so that

$$\mathbf{v}_1 H = -\mathbf{v}_1 + 2\mathbf{e}_2.$$

From

$$\mathbf{v}_1 H = -\mathbf{e}_1 + 2\mathbf{e}_2 + 3\mathbf{v}_3 + 2\mathbf{v}_3 H + \mathrm{a}\mathbf{v}_3 H$$

we see that

$$a = -3 \qquad \text{and} \qquad b = 1,$$

and

$$\mathbf{v}_1 = \mathbf{e}_1 - 3\mathbf{v}_3 + \mathbf{v}_4.$$

In the same way we consider

$$\mathbf{e}_2 H = -\mathbf{e}_2 + 5\mathbf{v}_3 + \mathbf{v}_4$$

and find that

$$\mathbf{v}_2 = \mathbf{e}_2 - 5\mathbf{v}_3 + 4\mathbf{v}_4$$

is a vector such that

$$\mathbf{v}_2 H = -\mathbf{v}_2.$$

Thus relative to the new basis for $V = C_4$, $\{\mathbf{v}_1, \mathbf{v}_2, \mathbf{v}_3, \mathbf{v}_4\}$, $A$ is represented by the matrix

$$\begin{pmatrix} 1 & 2 & 0 & 0 \\ 0 & 1 & 0 & 0 \\ 0 & 0 & 2 & 1 \\ 0 & 0 & 0 & 2 \end{pmatrix},$$

and $V$ is split into two $A$-invariant subspaces, $W = (\mathbf{v}_1, \mathbf{v}_2)$ and $U = (\mathbf{v}_3, \mathbf{v}_4)$.

Working in $W$ now we select $\mathbf{w}_1 = \mathbf{v}_1$ and $\mathbf{w}_2 = \mathbf{v}_1(A - I) = 2\mathbf{v}_2$. Then

$$\mathbf{w}_1 A = 1\mathbf{w}_1 + 1\mathbf{w}_2,$$

and

$$\mathbf{w}_2 A = 0\mathbf{w}_1 + 1\mathbf{w}_2,$$

so that $A$ is represented, relative to the basis $\{\mathbf{w}_1, \mathbf{w}_2, \mathbf{v}_3, \mathbf{v}_4\}$ for $V$, by

$$B = \begin{pmatrix} 1 & 1 & 0 & 0 \\ 0 & 1 & 0 & 0 \\ 0 & 0 & 2 & 1 \\ 0 & 0 & 0 & 2 \end{pmatrix} = \begin{pmatrix} B_1 & Z_1 \\ Z_2 & B_2 \end{pmatrix}$$

where $B_1 = 1I + H_1$ and $B_2 = 2I + H_2$.

*Example* 2. Determine the number of classes of matrices in $R_5$ which have the characteristic polynomial $(5 - \lambda)^3(2 - \lambda)^2$.

To solve this we determine the number of nonsimilar matrices $B_1 = 5I + H_1$ in $R_3$ and $B_2 = 2I + H_2$ in $R_2$, where $H_1$ and $H_2$ are in second diagonal echelon form:

$$H_1 = \begin{pmatrix} 0 & a & 0 \\ 0 & 0 & b \\ 0 & 0 & 0 \end{pmatrix} \quad \text{and} \quad H_2 = \begin{pmatrix} 0 & c \\ 0 & 0 \end{pmatrix},$$

$a$, $b$, and $c$ being 1 or 0.

(1) $(a, b) = (1, 1)$, $(a, b) = (1, 0)$, and $(a, b) = (0, 0)$ are the only possibilities for $H_2$ since $(a, b) = (0, 1)$ and $(a, b) = (1, 0)$ yield similar $H$'s and $B$'s.

(2) $c = 0$ or 1.

Thus there are $3 \cdot 2 = 6$ equivalence classes of similar matrices having the given characteristic polynomial.

Now we use the properties of the Jordan canonical form to prove that the subspace of the vector space $F_n$ which is spanned by $I, A, A^2, \cdots$, for a given $A$ in $F_n$ has dimension no larger than $n$.

THEOREM 13.30 (HAMILTON-CAYLEY THEOREM). *If*

$$p(\lambda) = a_0 + a_1\lambda + \cdots + (-1)^n\lambda^n$$

*is the characteristic polynomial of the matrix $A$ of $F_n$, then*

$$p(A) = a_0I + a_1A + \cdots + (-1)A^n = Z.$$

Here we are really dealing with the polynomial ring $S[\lambda]$ of the ring $S = S_A$ generated by the scalar matrices of $F_n$ and the matrix $A$. These rings are commutative rings with multiplicative identities, and we wish to show that the element $A$ of $S$ is a zero of the polynomial

$$a_0I + a_1I\lambda + \cdots + (-1)I\lambda^n,$$

where $\lambda$ is the indeterminate of $S[\lambda]$.

First we assume that $p(\lambda)$ factors completely over $F$. Then

$$p(\lambda) = (c_1 - \lambda)^{e_1} \cdots (c_m - \lambda)^{e_m},$$

so that since $S$ is Abelian (making substitution of $A$, or specialization for $A$, a homomorphism from $S[\lambda]$ onto $S$) we have

$$p(A) = (c_1I - A)^{e_1} \cdots (c_mI - A)^{e_m}.$$

Now $A$ is similar to the matrix $B$ in Jordan form,

$$CAC^{-1} = B,$$

so that

$$Cp(A)C^{-1} = (c_1I - B)^{e_1} \cdots (c_mI - B)^{e_m}.$$

(Note that $CAAC^{-1} = CAC^{-1}CAC^{-1} = (CAC^{-1})^2$, etc.)

But $B$ is made up of $e_i$-by-$e_i$ blocks

$$B_i = c_i I + H_i, \qquad i = 1, \cdots, m,$$

on its main diagonal and zeros off, so that $(c_i I - B)^{e_i}$ has the $e_i$-by-$e_i$ matrix

$$(c_i I - B_i)^{e_i} = (-H_i)^{e_i} = Z$$

on its main diagonal. To illustrate we use the matrix $B$ of Example 1:

$$(c_1 I - B)^2 = (I - B)^2 = \left(\begin{array}{cc:cc} 0 & -1 & 0 & 0 \\ 0 & 0 & 0 & 0 \\ \hdashline 0 & 0 & -1 & -1 \\ 0 & 0 & 0 & -1 \end{array}\right)^2 = \left(\begin{array}{cc:cc} 0 & 0 & 0 & 0 \\ 0 & 0 & 0 & 0 \\ \hdashline 0 & 0 & 1 & 2 \\ 0 & 0 & 0 & 1 \end{array}\right)$$

and

$$(c_2 I - B)^2 = (2I - B)^2 = \left(\begin{array}{cc:cc} 1 & 0 & 0 & 0 \\ 0 & 1 & 0 & 0 \\ \hdashline 0 & 0 & 0 & 0 \\ 0 & 0 & 0 & 0 \end{array}\right).$$

Clearly

$$(I - B)^2(2I - B)^2 = Z,$$

and this leads us to conclude that

$$Cp(A)C^{-1} = p(B) = Z,$$

so that

$$p(A) = a_0 I + a_1 A + \cdots + (-1)A^n = C^{-1}ZC = Z.$$

If $p(\lambda)$ does not factor completely over $F$, then we extend $F$ to a root field $F^*$ of $F$ and work as above in $F^*$. Then

$$p(A) = a_0 I + a_1 A + \cdots + (-1)A^n = Z$$

in $F^*$, and since all of the components of these matrices lie in $F$ we see that the result holds in $F$ also.

*Example* 3. The matrix

$$A = \begin{pmatrix} 1 & 1 \\ -1 & 1 \end{pmatrix}$$

of $R_2$ has characteristic polynomial $p(\lambda) = \lambda^2 - 2\lambda + 2$ (which is irreducible over $R$). From

$$A^2 = \begin{pmatrix} 0 & 2 \\ -2 & 0 \end{pmatrix}$$

we see that

$$p(A) = \begin{pmatrix} 2 & 0 \\ 0 & 2 \end{pmatrix} - \begin{pmatrix} 2 & 2 \\ -2 & 2 \end{pmatrix} + \begin{pmatrix} 0 & 2 \\ -2 & 0 \end{pmatrix} = \begin{pmatrix} 0 & 0 \\ 0 & 0 \end{pmatrix}.$$

The Hamilton-Cayley Theorem illustrates one use of the Jordan canonical form (or Jordan factorization) in the study of polynomial rings and functions of matrices.

## Exercise 13.10

**1.** Let the linear transformation $A$ on $C_4(R) = V$ have the matrix $A$ relative to the canonical basis for $C_4$:

$$A = \begin{pmatrix} 2 & 1 & 3 & 5 \\ 0 & 2 & -1 & 2 \\ 0 & 0 & -1 & 0 \\ 0 & 0 & 0 & -1 \end{pmatrix}.$$

Find a basis for $V$ so that $A$ is represented by a matrix in Jordan form.

**2.** Find the Jordan factor $B$ of

$$A = \begin{pmatrix} 0 & 0 & -1 \\ 1 & 0 & 1 \\ 0 & 1 & 1 \end{pmatrix}$$

over the complex field.

**3.** Find the inverse of

$$A = \begin{pmatrix} 1 & 1 \\ 0 & 1 \end{pmatrix}$$

in $R_2$. What do you conclude about the inverse of a matrix in Jordan canonical form? Generalize.

**4.** The characteristic polynomial of $A$ is $(1 - \lambda)^3$ when

$$A = \begin{pmatrix} 0 & 0 & 1 \\ 1 & 0 & -3 \\ 0 & 1 & 3 \end{pmatrix}.$$

Show that $(I - A)^2 \neq Z$. From this fact determine that $B = I + (E_{12} + E_{23})$ is the Jordan factor of $A$.

**5.** By inspecting the matrix

$$B = \begin{pmatrix} 2 & 1 & 0 & 0 \\ 0 & 2 & 0 & 0 \\ 0 & 0 & 2 & 0 \\ 0 & 0 & 0 & 3 \end{pmatrix}$$

of $R_4$ determine a polynomial $m(\lambda)$ of degree 3 such that $m(B) = Z$. Compare $m(\lambda)$ with the characteristic polynomial of $B$.

**6.** Write out all possible Jordan matrices having the characteristic polynomial

(*a*) $(-1 - \lambda)^2(1 - \lambda)(2 - \lambda)$.
(*b*) $(1 - \lambda)^4$.
(*c*) $(1 - \lambda)^2(2 - \lambda)^3(4 - \lambda)^2$.

**7.** The monic polynomial $q(\lambda)$ of $F[\lambda]$,

$$q(\lambda) = c_0 + c_1\lambda + \cdots + \lambda^r$$

is *satisfied by* $A$ of $F_n$ if and only if

$$q(A) = c_0 I + c_1 A + \cdots + A^r = Z.$$

Discuss the relation between $F$, the ring $FI$ of scalar multiples of $I$ in $F_n$, $S = S_A$, $F[\lambda]$, and $S[\lambda]$.

**8.** The monic polynomial $m(\lambda)$ of least degree among the $q(\lambda)$ satisfied by $A$ is called the *minimal polynomial* of $A$.

(*a*) Prove that $m(\lambda)$ is unique for $A$.

(*b*) Prove that $m(\lambda)$ is a factor of $p(\lambda) = \mathbf{det}\,(A - \lambda I)$. (Use the G.C.F.)

**9.** If $A$ of $F_6$ has characteristic polynomial $(3 - \lambda)^6$ and minimal polynomial $m(\lambda) = (\lambda - 3)^3$, what are the possible Jordan factors of $A$? (There are three nonsimilar answers.)

**10.** If $p(\lambda) = (c_1 - \lambda)^{e_1} \cdots (c_m - \lambda)^{e_m}$ and $m(\lambda) = (\lambda - c_1) \cdots (\lambda - c_m)$ are the characteristic and minimal polynomials of $A$ of $F_n$, show that the Jordan factor of $A$ is a diagonal matrix.

**11.** The vector space $V_n(F)$ is the *direct sum* of subspaces $U$ and $W$ if and only if $U + W = V_n$ and $U \cap W = (z)$. Show that a nonnilpotent linear transformation $\mathbf{A}$ of rank less than $n$ in $\mathbf{L}(V_n(F))$ splits $V_n$ into a direct sum by the following steps:

(i) Show that there is an $m$ such that

$$V_n\mathbf{A}^m = V_n\mathbf{A}^{m+1} \neq (\mathbf{z}).$$

(ii) Show that $\mathbf{A}$ induces a nilpotent linear transformation $\mathbf{H}$ on the null-space $U$ of $\mathbf{A}^m$.

(iii) Show that $\mathbf{A}$ induces a nonsingular linear transformation $\mathbf{C}$ on the quotient space $V_n/U$.

(iv) Show that $V_n$ has a basis relative to which $\mathbf{A}$ is represented by a matrix of the form

$$\begin{pmatrix} C & D \\ Z & H \end{pmatrix}$$

where $C$ is a nonsingular, triangular matrix representing $\mathbf{C}$ over $V_n/U$ and $H$ is a matrix in second diagonal echelon form representing $\mathbf{H}$ over $U$.

(v) Use the method of Lemma 13.4 to show that $V_n$ contains an $\mathbf{A}$-invariant subspace $W$ such that

$$V_n = W + U, \qquad W \cap U = (\mathbf{z}).$$

**12.** Show that similar matrices satisfy the same polynomials.

**13.** Show that, if $c_0 I + c_1 A + \cdots + A^m = Z$, then

$$A^{-1} = -c_0^{-1}(c_1 I + \cdots + A^{m-1}).$$

Find $A^{-1}$ for $A$ in Problem 2 by this method.

**14.** Let $\mathbf{det}\,(A - \lambda I) = (-1)^n(\lambda^n + b_1\lambda^{n-1} + \cdots + b_{n-1}\lambda + b_n)$, and let the trace of $A = (a_{rs})$ be

$$\mathbf{tr}\, A = a_{11} + a_{22} + \cdots + a_{nn}.$$

Show that, over a field of characteristic zero:

$$\begin{aligned} b_1 &= -\mathbf{tr}\, A; \\ b_2 &= -(\tfrac{1}{2})(b_1\, \mathbf{tr}\, A + \mathbf{tr} A^2); \\ b_3 &= -(\tfrac{1}{3})(b_2\, \mathbf{tr}\, A + b_1\, \mathbf{tr}\, A^2 + \mathbf{tr}\, A^3) \\ &\vdots \\ b_n &= -(1/n)(b_{n-1}\, \mathbf{tr}\, A + b_{n-2}\, \mathbf{tr}\, A^2 + \cdots + \mathbf{tr}\, A^n). \end{aligned}$$

Combine these results with the Hamilton-Cayley Theorem and the statement of Problem 13 to devise a method (due to J. S. Frame) for finding $A^{-1}$ and the characteristic polynomial of $A$.

**15.** A subspace $U$ of the $n^2$-dimensional space $F_n$ is *nonsingular* if and only if every nonzero matrix in $U$ is nonsingular. (The subspace of scalar matrices is one such subspace.) Determine maximal subspaces of this type.

**16.** Prove that a matrix $A$ in $F_n$, $F$ of characteristic zero, can be expressed as the sum $A = B + C$ where $\mathbf{tr}\, B = 0$ and $C$ is a scalar matrix. Is this decomposition unique? Why is the restriction on the characteristic of $F$ needed (or is it)?

## 13.11 Remarks

Let $\mathbf{M}$ be an equivalence relation in $F_n$; we write $A\mathbf{M}B$ if $(A, B)$ belongs to $\mathbf{M}$ and $A\not\mathbf{M}B$ otherwise. A collection $C(\mathbf{M})$ of matrices from $F_n$ is a *canonical set for* $\mathbf{M}$ if exactly one element $C$ of $C(\mathbf{M})$ is in each equivalence class $[A]_{\mathbf{M}}$ of $F_n$, and if $C$ is in the class of $A$, so that $A\mathbf{M}C$, we say that $C$ is the *canonical form* of $A$ relative to $\mathbf{M}$. In other words, the canonical form $C$ is a uniquely specified $\mathbf{M}$-equivalence class representative. Ideally $C$ should exhibit in as simple a fashion as possible the outstanding features of the matrices in the $\mathbf{M}$-equivalence class it represents. Since this is sometimes a difficult criterion to meet, there are often several different canonical sets for one relation $M$, each designed to show up certain important features of an equivalence class. Then we can study these features for all of the matrices in the class by treating the particular canonical representative.

The equivalence relations on $F_n$ of row-equivalence, column-equivalence, two-sided equivalence, and similarity are just a few of the many equivalence relations which are treated in the theory of matrices. These arose in connection with our investigations of subspaces of $V_n(F)$ and of different bases for $V_n(F)$. Other topics involving $V_n(F)$, $\boldsymbol{L}(V_n(F))$, and $F_n$ naturally lead to other equivalence relations and canonical forms.

## 13.12 Suggested Reading

*Articles*

Brenner, J. L., "Characteristic roots," *Amer. Math. Monthly* **60** (1953), 112–113.

Cater, S., "An elementary development of Jordan canonical form," *Amer. Math. Monthly* **69** (1962), 391–393.

Flanders, H., "Methods of proof in linear algebra," *Amer. Math. Monthly* **63** (1956), 1–15.

Greenspan, Donald, "Methods of matrix inversion," *Amer. Math. Monthly* **62** (1955), 303–318.

MacDuffee, C. C., "Some application of matrices to the theory of equations," *Amer. Math. Monthly* **57** (1950), 154–161.

Price, G. B., "Some identities in the theory of determinants," *Amer. Math. Monthly* **54** (1947), 75–90.

Ryser, H. J., "Geometries and incidence matrices," Slaught Memorial Paper 4, pp. 25–31, Buffalo, Mathematical Association of America, 1955.

*Books*

Albert, A. A., *Introduction to Algebraic Theories*, University of Chicago Press, Chicago, 1941.

Beaumont, R. A., and R. W. Ball, *Introduction to Modern Algebra and Matrix Theory*, Rinehart & Co., New York, 1954.

Finkbeiner, D. T., *Introduction to Matrices and Linear Transformations*, W. H. Freeman & Company, San Francisco, 1960.

Frazer, R. A., W. J. Duncan, and A. R. Collar, *Elementary Matrices and Some Applications to Dynamics and Differential Equations*, 3rd ed., The University Press, Cambridge, Eng. 1946.

Higman, B., *Applied Group-Theoretic and Matrix Methods*, Oxford University Press, London, 1955.

Hohn, F. E., *Elementary Matrix Algebra*, 2nd ed., The Macmillan Co., New York, 1964.

Kemeny, J. G., J. L. Snell, and G. L. Thompson, *Finite Mathematics*, Prentice-Hall, Inc., Englewood Cliffs, N.J., 1957.

MacDuffee, C. C., *Vectors and Matrices*, Carus Monograph 7, Mathematical Association of America, Menasha, Wis., 1943.

Murdoch, D. C., *Linear Algebra for the Undergraduate*, John Wiley & Sons, New York, 1957.

Perlis, S., *The Theory of Matrices*, Addison-Wesley Publishing Co., Cambridge, Mass., 1952.

Stoll, R. R., *Linear Algebra and Matrix Theory*, McGraw-Hill Book Co., New York, 1952.

Thrall, R. M., and L. Tornheim, *Vector Spaces and Matrices*, John Wiley & Sons, New York, 1957.

# General References

Albert, A. A., *Modern Higher Algebra*, University of Chicago Press, Chicago, 1937.

Birkhoff, G., and S. MacLane, *A Survey of Modern Algebra*, rev. ed., The Macmillan Co., New York, 1953.

Jacobson, N., *Lectures in Abstract Algebra*, D. Van Nostrand Co., New York, vol. I, 1951; vol. II, 1952.

Johnson, R. E., *First Course in Abstract Algebra*, Prentice-Hall, Inc., Englewood Cliffs, N.J., 1953.

MacDuffee, C. C., *An Introduction to Abstract Algebra*, John Wiley & Sons, New York, 1940.

McCoy, N., *Introduction to Modern Algebra*, Allyn and Bacon, Boston, Mass., 1960.

Moore, J. T., *Elements of Abstract Algebra*, The Macmillan Co., New York, 1962.

# Index


Abelian group, 192
Absolute value, 66
Absorption property, 388
Abstract system, 24
Addition
 of fractions, 68
 of linear transformations, 505
 of matrices, 508
 of polynomials, 302
 of vectors, 449
Additive coset, 175
Additive group, 269
Additive inverse, 56, 258
Additive number theory, 152
Adjoint matrix, 578
$A$-invariant subspace, 588
Algebra
 linear, 537
 semisimple, 540
Algebraic
 domain, 413
 extension, 330
 integer, 413
 system, 24
Algebraically closed field, 330
Algorithm, Euclidean, 97, 316
Alternating group, $A_4$, 245
Annihilator, 260, 266
Anti-isomorphism, 556
Arithmetic, Fundamental Theorem of, 93
Arrays, 473
 equivalent, 492
 of systems, 485
Associate, 370
Association, 77
Associative law, 35
 generalized, 77
Associative operation, 22
Associativity, 38
Augmented matrix, 555
Automorphism group of a field, 341, 442
Automorphism
 elementary, 553
 of a field, 339, 340, 442
 of a group, 240
 inner, 240
 of a ring, 278
Axiom
 of extent, 2
 of induction, 34
 of pair equality, 9
Axioms
 for natural numbers, 33
 of a system, 24

Base of notation, 84, 87
Basis
 canonical, 470, 483, 510
 change of, 530
 $J$, 380
 minimal, 381
 of a vector space, 465
Binary operation, 21
Binary relation, 10
Binomial expansion, 265
Boolean ring, 25
Bordered matrix, 548
Bound, upper, 45

Cancellation
 law, 41, 56, 201
 left, 23
 semigroup, 391
Canonical basis, 470, 483, 510
Canonical factor, Jordan, 604

Canonical form, 611
  Jordan, 605
Canonical set, 611
Cardinal, 46
Cartesian product, 10
Cayley-Hamilton Theorem, 607
Cayley's Theorem, 203
Center of a group, 214, 239, 241
Centralizer, 241, 525
Change of basis, 530
Characteristic
  of a domain, 273
  of a field, 274
  polynomial, 584
  of a ring, 269, 270
  value, 584, 597
  vector, 586
Chinese Remainder Theorem, 140
Class
  congruence, 88
  conjugate, 241
  equation of a group, 243
  equivalence, 11
  residue, 162
Classification, 11
Closed, algebraically, 330
Coefficient field, 337, 343
Coefficients, method of undetermined, 357
Cofactor, 578
Column echelon form, reduced, 489
Column
  operation, 489
  rank, 489
  subscript, 473
Combination, linear, 455
Common factor, 96
  greatest, 97, 314
  of ideals, 397
Common multiple, least, 107
Commutative
  group, 192
  law, 35, 80
  operation, 22
  ring, 250
Commutativity, 37
Companion matrix, 596
Compatible mappings, 64, 168
Complement, orthogonal, 487
Complete matric ring, 521
Complex conjugate, 342
Component; *see* Coordinate
Composite
  function, 20
  ideal, 395
  integer, 92
  mapping, 20
  quadratic integer, 368
Composition factor, 247
Composition series, 247
Concrete system, 24
Congruence
  class, 88, 143
  of integers, 88
  linear, 134
  in rings, 288
Conjugate
  class, 241
  complex, 342
  element, 240
  ideal, 389
  of quadratic integer, 366
  subgroup, 240
Constant function, 290
Continuity, 76
Contradiction, proof by, 41
Converse, 20
Coordinate *n*-space, 452
Coset, 215
  additive, 175
  decomposition, 217
  of a subgroup, 215
Count, 46
Countably infinite, 162
Counting, 46
Counting functions, 111
Cramer's Rule, 580
Cube, doubling of, 347
Cut, Dedekind, 75
Cyclic
  group, 211
  subgroup, 211

Decomposition
  coset, 217
  partial fraction, 354
Dedekind cut, 75
Definition, recursive, 264
Degree of a polynomial, 305
DeMorgan's Theorem, 6
Density, 74
Denumerable set, 50
Dependent vectors, linearly, 461
Derivative, formal, 327, 339, 424
Descent, Fermat's method of, 149
Determinant, 568
Determinantal rank, 581
Diagonal
  echelon form, 599
  matrix, 544
  second, 599
Diagram, 420
  Venn, 5
  nodal, 14
Difference ring, 285

Difference, set, 4
Dimension of vector space, 467
Dimension of algebra, 538
Diophantine equation, 123
Diophantine problems, 121
Direct product, 219, 223
  outer, 219
Discriminant, quadratic, 363
Distributive law, 37
  generalized, 80, 263
Distributive operation, 23
Division, 70
  ring, 250
  synthetic, 312
Divisor Theorem, 82, 307, 373
Divisors of zero, 166, 250
Domain
  algebraic, 413
  of function, 16
  Gaussian, 373
  integral, 250
  principal ideal, 409
  sub—, 269
Doubly ordered set, 473
Dual space, 511
Duality, principle of, 27

Echelon, 599
Echelon form
  reduced column, 489
  reduced row, 477
  second diagonal, 599
Element
  characteristic of, 269
  conjugate, 240
  generating, 206
  idempotent, 199, 267
  identity, 23, 55, 193
  inverse, 55, 69, 193
  smallest, 43
Element of a set, 2
Elementary
  automorphism, 553
  column operations, 489
  matrix, 546
  row operations, 474
Empty set, 3
Equality
  of functions, 18
  of pairs, 9
  of sets, 2
Equations
  class, 243
  Diophantine, 123
  system of linear, 485
Equivalence class, 11, 111
Equivalence relation, 10, 52, 67, 89
Equivalence right, 558
Equivalent
  arrays, 492
  matrices, 536, 559
  sets, 18
Eratosthenes, sieve of, 96
Euclidean algorithm
  for integers, 97
  for polynomials, 316
Euler-Fermat Theorem, 116
Euler phi-function, $\phi(n)$, 111
Even permutation, 575
Expansion by minors, 569, 586
Expansion, Taylor's, 425
Exponentiation, 79, 210, 264
Extension
  algebraic, 330
  binomial, 265
  quadratic, 360
  radical, 350
  of rings, 276
  of systems, 65
  transcendental, 351
Extent, axiom of, 2

Factor
  common, 96, 397
  composition, 247
  greatest common, 97, 314, 397
  Hermite, 564
  ideal, 187, 393
  integral, 89
  invariant, 567
  Jordan canonical, 605
  polynomial, 310
  of quadratic integer, 368
Factorization, 92
  unique, 93, 318
Fermat's
  Little Theorem, 118
  method of descent, 149
  Theorem, 151
Field, 250
  algebraic extension, 330
  algebraically closed, 330
  automorphism group of a, 341
  coefficient, 337, 343
  Galois, 436
  prime, 276
  root, 335
  skew, 250
  splitting, 335
Finite
  group, 193
  induction, 34
  ordered set, 298
  set, 49

Form
  canonical, 611
  Hermite, 551, 563
  Jordan canonical, 604
  radix, 84
  rational, 352
  reduced column echelon, 489
  reduced row echelon, 477
  second diagonal echelon, 599
Formal derivative, 327, 339, 424
Formula
  Lagrange's interpolation, 294, 326
  quadratic, 362
Fraction, 67
  partial — decomposition, 354
Function, 15
  composite, 20
  counting, 111
  negative, 63
  notation, 16, 494
  polynomial, 291
  ring, 289
Functional, linear, 511
Fundamental Theorem of Arithmetic, 93

Galois field, $GF(p^n)$, 436
  automorphisms of, 442
Galois group, 343
Galois theory, 331
  Gauss' Lemma, 323
Gaussian
  domain, 373
  integer, 373
  prime, 377
Generalized
  associative law, 77
  commutative law, 80
  distributive law, 80, 263
  trichotomy law, 80
Generating set, 456
Generator
  of group, 206, 211
  of ideal, 371, 409
  of vector space, 461
Greater than, 39, 73
G.C.F. (greatest common factor), 97, 314, 397
Group, 192
  Abelian, 192
  alternating, 245
  center of, 239, 241
  cyclic, 211
  exponentiation, 210
  finite, 193
  Galois, 343
  general linear, 546
  isomorphic, 203
  order of, 193
  permutation, 203
  quotient, 234
  representation, 197, 203
  solvable, 248
  sub—, 207
  Sylow subgroup of, 245
  symmetric, 195, 198, 207
  unimodular, 582

Hamilton-Cayley Theorem, 607
Hermite factor, 564
Hermite form, 551, 563
Homomorphic image, 168
Homomorphism
  of a group, 234
  of $J$, 168
  kernel of, 235, 281, 496
  of a ring, 280
  of a vector space, 494

Ideal
  conjugate, 389
  factor, 187, 393
  of $J$, 174
  of $J/(m)$, 179
  maximal, 184, 297, 395
  numbers, 151, 360
  prime, 413
  principal, 371, 409
  relatively prime, 399
  of ring, 282
  semigroup, 387
  torsion, 287
Idempotent, 23, 199, 267
Idempotent matrix, 546
Identity
  element, 23, 55, 193
  function, 20
  mapping, 20
  matrix, 544
  ring with, 250
  transformation, 518
Image, 16
  homomorphic, 168
  space, 496
  of vector, 494
Inconsistent system, 487
Independence of vectors, 461
Independent set of vectors, 461
Indeterminate, 303
Index of subgroup, 218
Induced operation, 63
Induced partition, 13
Induction
  axiom of, 34

hypothesis, 34
mathematical, 33
principle of mathematical, 34
second principle of, 44
set, 276
third principle of, 45
Inequality, 39
Infinite set, 49
countably, 162
Inner automorphism, 240
Inner product, 487, 515
Integers
algebraic, 413
composite, 92
Gaussian, 373
negative, 61
positive, 61
prime, 92
rational, 70
relatively prime, 104
ring of, $J$, 53
system of, 54
zero, 61
Integral domain, 250
Interpolation formula of Lagrange, 294, 326
Intersection, set, 4
Into mapping, 18
Invariant
factors, 567
similarity, 588
subspace, 588
Inverse
element, 55, 69, 193
mapping, 18
of matrix, 527
Invertible operation, 23
Irrational number, 76
Irreducible polynomial, 313
Isomorphic
groups, 203
rings, 272
vector spaces, 470
Isomorphism, 64, 70, 272, 470
anti—, 556
natural, 416

$J$, ring of integers, 53
basis, 380
ideal of, 174, 184
quotient system of, 176
$J/(m)$, integers mod $m$, 163
ideal of, 179
quotient system of, 180
Jordan canonical form, 604
Jordan factor, 605
Jordan-Hoelder Theorem, 247

Kernel
of homomorphism, 235, 280
of linear transformation, 496

Lagrange's
interpolation formula, 294, 326
Theorem, 217
Larger than, 39, 58
Law
associative, 35, 38, 77
cancellation, 41, 201
commutative, 35, 37, 80
distributive, 37, 80, 263
of signs, 72
trichotomy, 39, 59, 80
Leading coefficient, 305
L.C.M. (least common multiple), 107
Least residue, 90
Left
coset, 215
ideal, 538
identity, 23
module, 450
regular representation, 539
$S$-module, 450
vector space, 451
zero, 23
Legendre symbol, 405
Less than, 39
Linear
algebra, 537
combination, 455
congruence, 134
dependence, 461
equations, 123, 485
independence, 461
order, 13, 40
Linear transformations, 494
matrix of, 500
product of, 511
ring of, 518
sum of, 505
Loop, 196, 207

Mapping, 16
compatible, 64
composite, 20
identity, 20
inverse, 18
natural, 284
successor, 49
Matric
addition, 508
multiplication, 514
ring, 521
units, 510, 545
Matrices
equivalent, 536, 559

Matrices (*cont.*)
  partitioned, 515
  similar, 534, 582
Matrix, 500
  augmented, 555
  bordered, 548
  companion, 596
  diagonal, 544
  elementary, 546
  Hermite, 564
  idempotent, 546
  identity, 544
  inverse of, 527, 546
  Jordan, 604
  monomial, 574
  nilpotent, 546
  nonsingular, 527, 546
  orthogonal, 581
  rectangular, 500
  scalar, 523, 544
  singular, 546
  skew, 549
  strictly triangular, 546
  symmetric, 549
  of transformation, 500
  triangular, 545
  unimodular, 581
  zero, $Z$, 509
Maximal
  ideal, 184, 297, 395
  normal subgroup, 247
  subgroup, 227
Membership, set, 2
Method
  of descent (Fermat), 149
  of Frame, 611
  of undetermined coefficients, 357
Minimal
  basis, 381
  polynomial, 610
  subspace, 460
Minor of matrix, 569, 581
Minors, expansion by, 569, 580
Modular systems, 415
Module, 450
Modulus, 88
Monic polynomial, 307
Monomial matrix, 574
Multiple, 89, 368
  common, 107
  least common (L.C.M.), 107
  scalar, 79, 261, 506, 509
Multiplication; *see* Product, 37, 68
  of functions, 20
  of matrices, 514
  scalar, 450
  table, 22
  of transformations, 511
Multiplicity
  of characteristic value, 597
  of zero, 327

Natural
  isomorphism, 416
  mapping, 284
  number, 33
  number system, 33
Near-ring, 525
Negative function, 63
Negative integer, 61
Negative rational, 70, 72
New mathematics, 415
Nilpotent algebra, 540
Nilpotent matrix, 546
Nonsingular matrix, 527, 546
Nonsingular subspace, 611
Nonsingular transformation, 527
Norm, 366, 389
Normal subgroup, 233
Normalizer of subgroup, 246
Notation
  base of, 84, 87
  function, 15
  position, 86
  right hand function, 494
Nullity, Sylvester's Law, 562
Nullspace, 496
Numbers
  algebraic, 330, 413
  complex, 342
  ideal, 151, 360
  irrational, 76
  natural, 33
  rational, 67
  real, 76
  transcendental, 359

Odd permutation, 575
One-to-one mapping, 18
Onto mapping, 18
Operation
  associative, 22
  binary, 21
  commutative, 22
  distributive, 22
  elementary column, 489
  elementary row, 474
  induced, 63
  invertible, 23
  table, 22
  ternary, 23
  well-defined, 54, 56, 57, 163
Order
  of group, 193
  of group element, 206

linear, 13, 40
partial, 13
Ordered
m-tuple, 298
pair, 9
set, 79, 298
triple, 9
Orthogonal
complement, 487
matrix, 581
subspace, 458
Outer direct product, 219

Pair equality, 9
Partial fractions, 354
Partial order, 13
Partition, 11, 13
Partitioned matrices, 515
Permutation, 20, 195
Permutation representation, regular, 203
Phi-function, $\phi(n)$, 111
Polynomial, 300
characteristic, 584
domain, $S[\lambda]$, 307
extension, 302
function, 291
irreducible, 313
minimal, 610
monic, 307
prime, 318
ring, 302
zero of, 305
Position notation, 86
Positive integers, 61
Positive rationals, 72
Power set, 11
Pre-image, 497
problem, 50, 66
Prime
field, 276
Gaussian, 377
ideal, 184, 395, 413
integer, 92, 95
quadratic, 368
relatively, 104
Primitive root of unity, 403
Primitive triple, 144
Principal ideal, 371, 409
Principle of duality, 27
Principle of mathematical induction, 34, 44, 45
Product; *see* Multiplication
Cartesian, 10
of cosets, 222, 233
direct, 219, 223
of functions, 20
of ideals, 187
inner, 487, 515
of mappings, 20, 195
of matrices, 514
scalar, 253, 261
of transformations, 511
Projection, 495
Proof by contradiction, 41
Proper
ideal, 282
subgroup, 207
subring, 267
subset, 3
subspace, 457
Proposition, 34
Pythagorean triple, 144

Quadratic
discriminant, 363
domain, 364
extension, 360
formula, 362
integer, 364
pure, 403
Reciprocity Law, 406
residue, 403
Quaternion group, 256
Quaternions, 252
Quotient, 82, 308
group, 222, 234
ring, 285
space, 588
system, 176, 180

Radical extension, 350
Radicals, solvable by, 350
Radix form, 84
Range of function, 16
Range of mapping, 16
Range of transformation, 496
Rank
of array, 491
column, 489
determinantal, 581
of matrix, 527
of transformation, 501
row, 474
Rational
cut, 76
form, 352
integer, 70
number, 67
number system, *R*, 68
quaternions, 253
*Re*, real number system, 76
Reciprocal, 67
Reciprocity, Quadratic, 406

Recursive definition, 264
Reduction Theorem, 100, 109, 130
Reflexive property, 10
Regular representation, 203, 539
Relation, 10, 14
  equivalence, 52, 67, 89
Relatively prime
  ideals, 399
  integers, 104
  polynomials, 318
Remainder, 82, 308
  Theorem, 309
  Chinese — Theorem, 140
Representation, group, 197, 203
Residue
  class, 162
  least, 90
  quadratic, 403
Right
  coset, 215
  equivalence, 558
  hand function notation, 494
  ideal, 537
  identity, 23
  module, 451
  regular representation, 539
  zero, 23
Ring, 249
  automorphism of, 278
  Boolean, 25
  characteristic of, 270
  commutative, 250
  congruence, 288
  difference, 285
  division, 250
  extension of, 273
  of functions, 289
  homomorphism of, 280
  with identity, 250
  of integers, *J*, 54
  isomorphism of, 272
  matric, 521
  polynomial, 302
Root field, 335
Rotation about origin, 495
Row
  echelon form, 477
  operation, 474
  rank, 474
  space, 474
  subscript, 473
  vectors, 474

$S[\lambda]$, polynomial ring of *S*, 307
Scalar, 451
  matrix, 544
  multiplication, 79, 451, 506, 509
  product, 79, 210, 253, 261, 451
  transformation, 495
Second induction principle, 44
Semigroup, 77
  cancellation, 391
  ideal, 387
Semisimple algebra, 540
Series, composition, 247
Set, 2
  denumerable, 50
  difference, 4
  doubly ordered, 473
  empty, 3
  finite, 49
  induction, 276
  infinite, 49
  intersection, 4
  membership, 2
  ordered, 79
  power, 11
  union, 4
  void, 3
Sfield, 250
*S*-homomorphism, 498
Sieve of Eratosthenes, 96
Signs, law of, 72
Similar matrices, 534, 582
Similarity invariant, 588
Singular matrix, 546
Skew field, 250
Skew matrix, 549
Smaller than, 39, 58
Smallest element, 43
*S*-module, 450
Solution subspace, 555
Solvable group, 248
Solvable by radicals, 350
Span a space, 456
Spanning set, 456
Specialization, 296, 304
Splitting field, 335
Squares, sum of two, 158
Step-up theorem, 427
Straight-edge-and-compass, 347
Strictly triangular matrix, 546
Structure Theory, Wedderburn, 540
Subdomain, 269
Subfield, 269
Subgroup, 207
  conjugate, 240
  cosets of, 215
  cyclic, 211
  index, 218
  normal, 233, 247
  proper, 207
  Sylow, 245
  trivial, 208
Submodule, 454

Subring, 267
Subscript
  column, 473
  row, 473
Subset, 3
Subspace, 455
  *A*-invariant, 588
  minimal, 460
  nonsingular, 611
  orthogonal, 458
  proper, 457
  solution, 555
  spanned by, 456
  trivial, 457
Subsystem, 63, 174
Substitution, 296, 304
Subtraction, 56, 258
Successor mapping, 49
Sum; *see* Addition
  of subspaces, 457
  of two squares, 158
Sylvester's Law, 562
Sylow subgroup, 245
Sylow Theorem, 245
Symmetric
  group, 195
  matrices, 549
  property, 10
Symmetries, 198
Symmetry group, 198, 207
Synthetic division, 312
System
  abstract, 24
  algebraic, 24
  array of, 485
  concrete, 24
  inconsistent, 487
  of integers, 54
  of linear equations, 485
  mathematical, 24
  modular, 415
  natural number, 33
  quotient, 176, 180
  rational number, 68
  real number, 76
  of residue classes, 163
  theory of, 24

Table
  multiplication, 22
  operation, 22
Taylor's expansion, 425
Ternary operation, 23
Ternary relation, 14
Third induction principle, 45
Torsion ideal, 287
Total matric ring, 521
Trace of matrix, 587
Transcendental extension, 351
Transcendental number, 359
Transformations, linear, 494
  addition of, 505
  matrix of, 500
  multiplication of, 511
  rank of, 501
  ring of, 518
  scalar, 495
  scalar multiple of, 506
Transitive property, 10
Transitivity, 59
Transpose, 489, 556
Triangular matrix, 545
Triangularization problem, 584
Trichotomy, 39, 59, 80
Triple, ordered, 9
Triple, primitive, 144
Triple, Pythagorean, 144
Trisection of angle, 347
Trivial subgroup, 208
Trivial subspace, 457
Two-sided ideal, 537
Two-sided module, 451

Undetermined coefficients, 357
Unimodular group, 582
Unimodular matrix, 581
Union of sets, 4
Unique factorization
  of Gaussian integers, 373
  of ideals, 399
  of integers, 93
  of matrices, 543, 551, 605
  of polynomials, 318
  of quadratic integers, 409
  restored, 187
  Theorem, 93, 318
Uniqueness, 83
Unit, 368
Unit ideal, 395
Units, matric, 510, 545
Upper bound, 45

Value, absolute, 66
Value, characteristic, 584
Variable, 303
Vectors, 449
  characteristic, 584
  coordinate, 452
  dependent, 461
  linearly independent, 461
  row, 474
Vector space, 451
  basis of, 465

Vector space (*cont.*)
  dimension of, 467
  homomorphism, 494
  isomorphism, 470
  left, 451
Venn diagram, 5
Void set, 3

Wedderburn Structure Theory, 540
Well-defined operation, 54, 56, 57, 163
Well-ordering Theorem, 43

Wilson's Theorem, 153

Zero (left and right), 23
  divisors of, 166, 250
  ideal, 282
  integer, 61
  matrix, 521
  multiplicity of, 327
  of polynomial, 305
  rational, 72
  vector, 450, 451